SAFETY SYMBOLS

SAFETY SYMBOLS	HAZARD	PRECAUTION	REMEDY
Disposal	Special disposal required	Dispose of wastes as directed by your teacher.	Ask your teacher how to dispose of laboratory materials.
Biological	Organisms that can harm humans	Avoid breathing in or skin contact with organisms. Wear dust mask or gloves. Wash hands thoroughly.	Notify your teacher if you suspect contact.
Extreme Temperature	Objects that can burn skin by being too cold or too hot	Use proper protection when handling.	Go to your teacher for first aid.
Sharp Object	Use of tools or glassware that can easily puncture or slice skin	Practice common sense behavior and follow guidelines for use of the tool.	Go to your teacher for first aid.
Fumes	Potential danger from smelling fumes	Must have good ventilation and never smell fumes directly.	Leave foul area and notify your teacher immediately.
Electrical	Possible danger from electrical shock or burn	Double-check setup with instructor. Check condition of wires and apparatus.	Do not attempt to fix electrical problems. Notify your teacher immediately.
Irritant	Substances that can irritate your skin or mucous membranes	Wear dust mask or gloves. Practice extra care when handling these materials.	Go to your teacher for first aid.
Chemical	Substances (acids and bases) that can react with and destroy tissue and other materials	Wear goggles and an apron.	Immediately flush with water and notify your teacher.
Toxic	Poisonous substance	Follow your teacher's instructions. Always wash hands thoroughly after use.	Go to your teacher for first aid.
Fire	Flammable and combustible materials may burn if exposed to an open flame or spark	Avoid flames and heat sources. Be aware of locations of fire safety equipment.	Notify your teacher immediately. Use fire safety equipment if necessary.

Eye Safety
This symbol appears when a danger to eyes exists.

Clothing Protection
This symbol appears when substances could stain or burn clothing.

Animal Safety
This symbol appears whenever live animals are studied and the safety of the animals and students must be ensured.

Glencoe McGraw-Hill

New York, New York Columbus, Ohio Woodland Hills, California Peoria, Illinois

A Glencoe Program

California Edition

Glencoe Science Voyages

California Student Edition
California Teacher Wraparound Edition
Assessment
- Chapter Review
- California Science Content Standards Practice Questions
- Performance Assessment
- Assessment—Chapter and Unit Tests
- ExamView Test Bank Software
- Performance Assessment in the Science Classroom
- Alternate Assessment in the Science Classroom

Study Guide for Content Mastery, SE and TE
Chapter Overview Study Guide, SE and TE
Reinforcement
Enrichment
Critical Thinking/Problem Solving
Multicultural Connections
Activity Worksheets
Laboratory Manual, SE and TE
Science Inquiry Activities, SE and TE
California Home Involvement
Teaching Transparencies
Section Focus Transparencies
Science Integration Transparencies
Spanish Resources
California Lesson Plans
Lab and Safety Skills in the Science Classroom
Cooperative Learning in the Science Classroom
Exploring Environmental Issues
MindJogger Videoquizzes and Teacher Guide
English/Spanish Audiocassettes
Interactive Lesson Planner CD-ROM
Interactive CD-ROM
Internet Site
Using the Internet in the Science Classroom

The "Test-Taking Tip" and "Test Practice" features in this book were written by The Princeton Review, the nation's leader in test preparation. Through its association with McGraw-Hill, The Princeton Review offers the best way to help students excel on standardized assessments.

The Princeton Review is not affiliated with Princeton University or Educational Testing Service.

Glencoe/McGraw-Hill
A Division of The ***McGraw-Hill*** *Companies*

Send all inquiries to:
Glencoe/McGraw-Hill
8787 Orion Place
Columbus, OH 43240

ISBN 0-07-823987-7
Printed in the United States of America.
1 2 3 4 5 6 7 8 9 10 071/055 06 05 04 03 02 01 00

Series Authors

Alton Biggs
Biology Instructor
Allen High School
Allen, Texas

John Eric Burns
Science Teacher
Ramona Jr. High School
Chino, California

Lucy Daniel, Ph.D.
Teacher, Consultant
Rutherford County Schools
Rutherfordton, North Carolina

Cathy Ezrailson
Science Department Head
Oak Ridge High School
Conroe, Texas

Ralph Feather, Jr., Ph.D.
Science Department Chair
Derry Area School District
Derry, Pennsylvania

Patricia Horton
Math and Science Teacher
Summit Intermediate School
Etiwanda, California

Thomas McCarthy, Ph.D.
Science Department Chair
St. Edwards School
Vero Beach, Florida

Ed Ortleb
Science Consultant
St. Louis Public Schools
St. Louis, Missouri

Susan Leach Snyder
Science Department Chair
Jones Middle School
Upper Arlington, Ohio

Eric Werwa, Ph.D.
Department of Physics and Astronomy
Otterbein College
Westerville, Ohio

National Geographic Society
Educational Division
Washington D.C.

Contributing Authors

Al Janulaw
Science Teacher
Creekside Middle School
Rohnert Park, California

Penny Parsekian
Science Writer for
The National Geographic Society
New London, Connecticut

Gerry Madrazo, Ph.D.
Mathematics and Science Education Network
University of North Carolina, Chapel Hill
Chapel Hill, North Carolina

Series Consultants

Chemistry

Douglas Martin, Ph.D.
Chemistry Department
Sonoma State University
Rohnert Park, California

Cheryl Wistrom, Ph.D.
Associate Professor of Chemistry
Saint Joseph's College
Rensselaer, Indiana

Earth Science

Maureen Allen
Science Resource Specialist
Irvine Unified School District
Laguna Hills, California

Tomasz K. Baumiller, Ph.D.
Museum of Paleontology
University of Michigan
Ann Arbor, Michigan

Connie Sutton, Ph.D.
Department of Geoscience
Indiana University
Indiana, Pennsylvania

Physics

Thomas Barrett, Ph.D.
Department of Physics
The Ohio State University
Columbus, Ohio

David Haase, Ph.D.
Professor of Physics
North Carolina State University
Raleigh, North Carolina

Life Science

William Ausich, Ph.D.
Department of Geological Sciences
The Ohio State University
Columbus, Ohio

Dennis Stockdale
Asheville High School
Asheville, North Carolina

Daniel Zeigler, Ph.D.
Director
Bacillus Genetic Stock Center
The Ohio State University
Columbus, Ohio

Reading

Nancy Farnan, Ph.D.
School of Teacher Education
San Diego State University
San Diego, California

Gary Kroesch
Mount Carmel High School
San Diego, California

Safety

Mark Vinciguerra
Lab Safety Instructor
Department of Physics
The Ohio State University
Columbus, Ohio

Curriculum

Tom Custer, Ph.D.
Maryland State Department of Education
Challenge/Reconstructed Schools
Baltimore, Maryland

Series Reviewers

Jhina Alvarado
Potrero Hill Middle School for the Arts
San Francisco, California

Richard Cheeseman
Bert Lynn Middle School
Torrance, California

Linda Cook
Rider High School
Wichita Falls, Texas

John B. Davis
Niagara-Wheatfield Central School
Sanborn, New York

Shirley Ann DeFilippo
Timothy Edwards Middle School
South Windsor, Connecticut

Janet Doughty
H J McDonald Middle School
New Bern, North Carolina

Jason Druten
Jefferson Middle School
Torrance, California

Lin Harp
Magellan Middle School
Raleigh, North Carolina

Doris Holland
West Cary Middle School
Raleigh, North Carolina

Deborah Huffine
Noblesville Intermediate School
Noblesville, Indiana

Paul Osborne
DeValls Bluff High School
DeValls Bluff, Arkansas

Erik Resnick
Robert E. Peary Middle School
Gardena, California

Robert Sirbu
Lowell Junior High School
Oakland, California

Michael Tally
Wake County Public Schools
Raleigh, North Carolina

Cindy Williamson
Whiteville City Schools
Whiteville, North Carolina

Maurice Yaggi
Middlebrook School
Wilton, Connecticut

Donna York
Anchorage School District
Anchorage, Alaska

Activity Testers

Clayton Millage
Science Teacher
Lynden Middle School
Lynden, Washington

Science Kit and Boreal Laboratories
Tonawanda, New York

Contents in Brief

State of California Science Content Standards

GRADE SIX: FOCUS ON EARTH SCIENCE

What are science content standards and why does California have them? Standards are guidelines for schools, students, and parents that describe the essential science concepts and skills for understanding the world in which we live. In 1999, The California State Board of Education established science content standards, and these standards will be the basis for state assessments that measure student achievement in science.

ADDITIONAL CONTENT STANDARDS FOR GRADE 6

- California Science Standards and Case Studies, found at the back of the book
- California Science Content Standards Assessment Practice booklets
- Chapter Assessments at the end of each chapter
- Science Voyages Website at www.glencoe.com/sec/science/ca

Plate Tectonics and Earth's Structure

1. Plate tectonics explains important features of the Earth's surface and major geologic events. As the basis for understanding this concept, students know:
   - **a.** the fit of the continents, location of earthquakes, volcanoes, and midocean ridges, and the distribution of fossils, rock types, and ancient climatic zones provide evidence
     Sections 9-1, 9-2, 9-3, 10-1, 11-1, pages 616-617
   - **b.** the solid Earth is layered with cold, brittle lithosphere; hot convecting mantle; and dense, metallic core.
     Sections 9-2, 9-3, 10-2, pages 617, 633
   - **c.** lithospheric plates that are the size of continents and oceans move at rates of centimeters per year in response to movements in the mantle.
     Sections 9-2, 9-3, 11-1, pages 617, 620
   - **d.** earthquakes are sudden motions along breaks in the crust called faults, and volcanoes/fissures are locations where magma reaches the surface.
     Sections 5-1, 9-2, 9-3, 10-1, 10-2, 11-1, 11-2, 11-3, pages 627, 635
   - **e.** major geologic events, such as earthquakes, volcanic eruptions, and mountain building result from plate motions.
     Sections 5-1, 9-3, 10-1, 11-1, 11-2, 11-3, pages 628, 620-621
   - **f.** how to explain major features of California geology in terms of plate tectonics (including mountains, faults, volcanoes).
     Sections 9-3, 10-1, pages 618, 620-621, 635-636
   - **g.** how to determine the epicenter of an earthquake and that the effects of an earthquake vary with its size, distance from the epicenter, local geology, and the type of construction involved.
     Sections 9-3, 10-2, 10-3, pages 618-619

Shaping the Earth's Surface

2. Topography is reshaped by weathering of rock and soil and by the transportation and deposition of sediment. As the basis for understanding this concept, students know:
   - **a.** water running downhill is the dominant process in shaping the landscape, including California's landscape.
     Sections 6-2, 7-1, 7-2, 8-1, 8-2, pages 622-625
   - **b.** rivers and streams are dynamic systems that erode and transport sediment, change course, and flood their banks in natural and recurring patterns.
     Sections 5-1, 7-1, 7-2, 8-1, 8-2, 24-3, page 623
   - **c.** beaches are dynamic systems in which sand is supplied by rivers and moved along the coast by wave action.
     Sections 7-3, 8-1, 8-3, 9-3, 17-3, 24-3, pages 623-624
   - **d.** earthquakes, volcanic eruptions, landslides, and floods change human and wildlife habitats.
     Sections 7-1, 8-1, 9-3, 10-1, 10-2, 10-3, 11-1, 11-2, 11-3, pages 623-626

Heat (Thermal Energy) (Physical Science)

3. Heat moves in a predictable flow from warmer objects to cooler objects until all objects are at the same temperature. As a basis for understanding this concept, students know:
   - **a.** energy can be carried from one place to another by heat flow, or by waves including water waves, light and sound, or by moving objects.
     Sections 8-3, 14-1, 14-2, 17-3, 23-3, 26-1, 26-2, 26-3, pages 622-625
   - **b.** when fuel is consumed, most of the energy released becomes heat energy.
     Sections 4-1, 4-2, 26-3, page 628
   - **c.** heat flows in solids by conduction (which involves no flow of matter) and in fluids by conduction and also by convection (which involves flow of matter).
     Sections 9-3, 14-1, 14-2, 14-3, 26-2, pages 628-629
   - **d.** heat energy is also transferred between objects by radiation; radiation can travel through space.
     Sections 14-1, 14-2, 16-3, 26-2, page 629

Energy in the Earth System

4. Many phenomena on the Earth's surface are affected by the transfer of energy hrough radiation and convection currents. As a basis for understanding this concept, students know:
   - **a.** the sun is the major source of energy for phenomena on the Earth's surface, powering winds, ocean currents, and the water cycle.
     Sections 4-2, 14-1, 14-2, 14-3, 16-1, 16-3, 17-2, pages 632, 637
   - **b.** solar energy reaches Earth through radiation, mostly in the form of visible light.
     Sections 14-1, 14-2, 16-1, 16-3, 26-2, 570-571, 602-603, pages 632-633
   - **c.** heat from Earth's interior reaches the surface primarily through convection.
     Sections 9-3, 11-1, pages 630-631, 633, 635
   - **d.** convection currents distribute heat in the atmosphere and oceans.
     Sections 14-2, 14-3, 16-3, 17-2, pages 633-634
   - **e.** differences in pressure, heat, air movement, and humidity result in changes of weather.
     Sections 14-1, 14-3, 15-1, 15-2, 15-3, 16-1, 16-3, page 634

Ecology (Life Science)

5. Organisms in ecosystems exchange energy and nutrients among themselves and with the environment. As a basis for understanding this concept, students know:
   - **a.** energy entering ecosystems as sunlight is transferred by producers into chemical energy through photosynthesis, and then from organism to organism in food webs.
     Sections 23-1, 23-3, 26-3, page 635
   - **b.** over time, matter is transferred from one organism to others in the food web, and between organisms and the physical environment.
     Sections 23-3, 26-3, pages 637-638
   - **c.** populations of organisms can be categorized by the functions they serve in an ecosystem.
     Sections 23-1, 23-2, 23-3, pages 638-639
   - **d.** different kinds of organisms may play similar ecological roles in similar biomes.
     Sections 22-1, 23-2, 23-3, 24-2, 24-3, page 639
   - **e.** the number and types of organisms an ecosystem can support depends on the resources available and abiotic factors, such as quantity of light and water, range of temperatures, and soil composition.
     Sections 22-3, 23-1, 23-2, 24-1, 24-2, 24-3, page 639

Resources

6. Sources of energy and materials differ in amounts, distribution, usefulness, and the time required for their formation. As a basis for understanding this concept, students know:
   - **a.** the utility of energy sources is determined by factors that are involved in converting these sources to useful forms and the consequences of the conversion process.
     Sections 4-1, 4-2, 16-3, pages 630-633, 642-643, 645-646
   - **b.** different natural energy and material resources, including air, soil, rocks, minerals, petroleum, fresh water, wildlife, and forests, and classify them as renewable or nonrenewable.
     Sections 4-1, 4-2, 4-3, 4-4, 6-2, 14-2, 23-1, page 643
   - **c.** natural origin of the materials used to make common objects.
     Sections 4-1, 4-4, 6-2, pages 643-644

Investigation and Experimentation

7. Scientific progress is made by asking meaningful questions and conducting careful investigations. As a basis for understanding this concept, and to address the content the other three strands, students should develop their own questions and perform investigations. Students will:
   - **a.** develop a hypothesis.
     Sections 1-1, 1-2, 9-3, 14-1, 14-2, 15-3, 16-1, 23-2, 25-3, 27-3, pages 623, 643-646, 674-675
   - **b.** select and use appropriate tools and technology (including calculators, computers, balances, spring scales, microscopes, and binoculars) to perform tests, collect data, and display data.
     Sections 2-2, 2-3, 6-1, 6-2, 7-1, 8-3, 9-3, 10-1, 14-1, 16-1, 22-3, 23-1, 23-2, 24-2, 25-3, 26-2, 27-2, 27-3
   - **c.** construct appropriate graphs from data and develop qualitative statements about the relationships between variables.
     Sections 1-2, 2-3, 6-1, 6-2, 8-1, 9-3, 10-2, 10-3, 14-1, 14-2, 15-1, 16-3, 17-1, 21-3, 25-2, 27-3, pages 631, 633, 641
   - **d.** communicate the steps and results from an investigation in written reports and verbal presentations.
     Sections 1-2, 1-2, 4-1, 4-3, 6-1, 6-2, 14-2, 15-1, 16-3, 21-1, 21-2, 22-2, 25-1, 25-3, 27-3, pages 621, 626, 637, 644, 646
   - **e.** recognize whether evidence is consistent with a proposed explanation.
     Sections 1-2, 6-1, 7-3, 8-1, 9-1, 9-2, 9-3, 10-2, 10-3, 17-3, 23-3, 25-3, 27-3, pages 622, 627, 632
   - **f.** read a topographic map and a geologic map for evidence provided on the maps, and construct and interpret a simple scale map.
     Sections 1-1, 4-4, 5-1, 5-2, 5-3, 9-2, 9-3, 11-1, pages 618, 636, 638, 643, 698
   - **g.** interpret events by sequence and time from natural phenomena (e.g., relative ages of rocks and intrusions).
     Sections 4-1, 5-1, 6-2, 8-1, 8-2, 9-2, 9-3, 10-1, 11-1, 11-2, 11-3, 14-2, 16-3, pages 622-624, 632
   - **h.** identify changes in natural phenomena over time without manipulating the phenomena (e.g., a tree limb, a grove of trees, a stream, a hillslope).
     Sections 6-1, 6-2, 9-3, 15-3, 16-1, 16-3, 21-3, 23-1, 24-2, 24-3, pages 622-623, 632, 641

Contents

Contents

UNIT 2 Earth's Changing Surface 152

UNIT 3 Earth's Interior 244

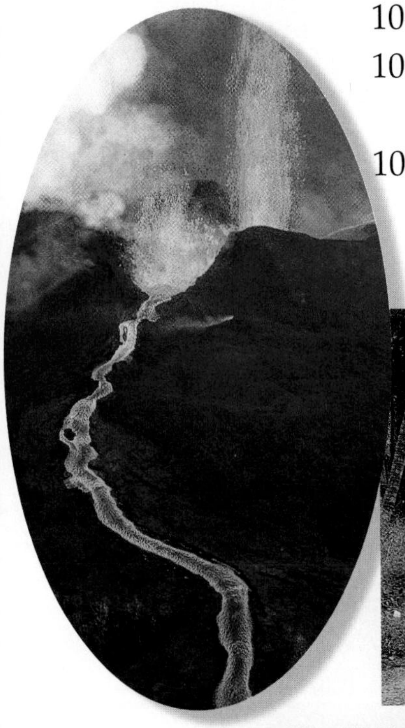

Contents

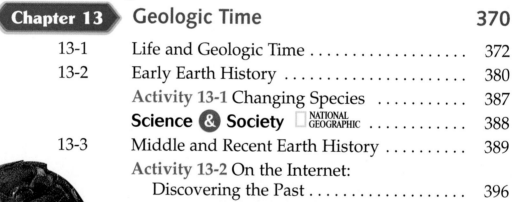

UNIT 5 Earth's Air and Water 402

Contents

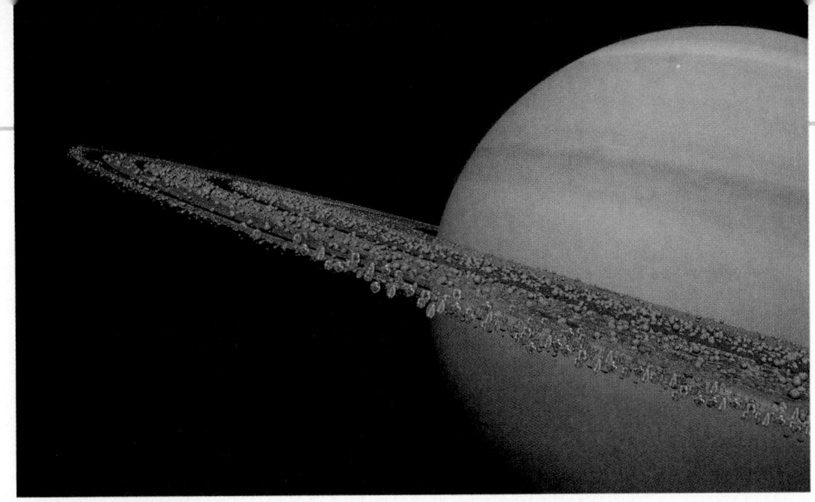

Contents

Contents

Science Connections

NATIONAL GEOGRAPHIC

Reading & Writing in Science

Science & Math

Science & Society

History of Science

How it Works

Activities

Activities

MiniLab

Try at Home MiniLab

Explore Activities

Problem Solving

Skill Builders

Skill Activities

UNIT 1

The Nature of Science

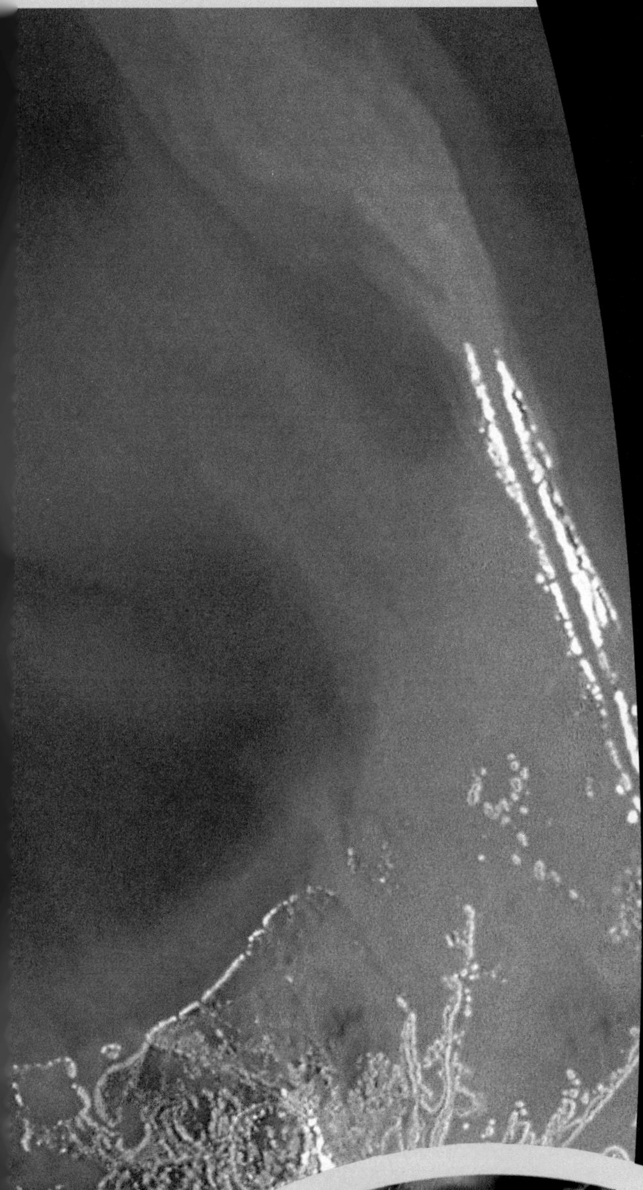

NATIONAL GEOGRAPHIC

What's Happening Here?

A girl dangles her fingers in the cool, clear waters of Minnesota's Lake Itasca (below), source of the mighty Mississippi River. Does she realize that the water she touches will pass by great cities of America's heartland and form the borders of ten states? Hundreds of miles south of the lake, the river loses speed as it enters the Gulf of Mexico, drops its sediment, and creates a bird-foot delta (left) as its grand finale. Like the girl on the lake, we don't see what lies beyond our immediate surroundings. Science can help us explore the unknown and discover patterns that organize and guide our curiosity. Today, with the help of scientific tools such as the infrared survey camera that captured this image of the delta, we can see farther and more clearly into the world beyond our senses.

interNET CONNECTION

Explore the Glencoe Science Web Site at **www.glencoe.com/sec/science/ca** to find out more about topics found in this unit.

CHAPTER

1 The Nature of Science

Chapter Preview

Skills Preview

Skill Builders
- Compare and Contrast
- Separate and Control Variables

Activities
- Model
- Observe and Infer

MiniLabs
- Observe and Infer

Reading Check

As you read about the nature of science, think about the role of fact and opinion in this field. Is there a place for opinion in science? Why or why not?

Explore Activity

The scientist in the photograph is excavating, or digging up, the remains of an ancient, elephant-like mammal called a mastodon in South Dakota. Excavations to unearth bones or other evidence of past life are often slow processes that involve a lot of careful work. Care must be taken so that the remains are not broken or destroyed as they are removed from the soil. Try your hand at excavating an oatmeal cookie without destroying the treasures within.

Model an Excavation

CAUTION: *Never eat or drink in the science lab and never use lab glassware as food or drink containers.*

1. Obtain an oatmeal cookie with raisins and walnuts from your teacher.
2. Place the cookie on a piece of waxed paper.
3. Use a biology probe to carefully remove the raisins and walnuts from the cookie without damaging either.
4. Wash your hands with soap and water when you have finished.
5. Give all pieces of the excavated cookie to your teacher for disposal.

Science Journal

In your Science Journal, write a paragraph that explains how probing the cookie might be similar to removing bones, tools, or other evidence of ancient life from Earth's crust.

1·1 How Science Works

What You'll Learn

- Archaeology is the study of the cultural remains of ancient people
- Science is a process of understanding the world
- Technology is the use of scientific knowledge

Vocabulary
science
technology

Why It's Important

- Science and technology are important parts of your everyday world.

Groundbreaking News!

It was Friday morning and the students in Ms. Garcia's science lab were anxiously waiting for class to start. Unlike most days in science class at York Middle School, this class would be a field trip to the north end of the school. Students were eager to observe work that would result in the long-awaited gymnasium. The students in group 4— Ben, Emily, Maria, and Juan— peered out the windows. They saw bulldozers and other construction equipment much like the one shown in **Figure 1-1** pull up to the school. With pencils and notebooks in hand, the interested students hiked out to the site. They watched as massive shovels moved hundreds of kilograms of dirt from one spot to another.

Buried Treasure?

All of a sudden, the power-shovel operator stopped the giant scoop in midair. He looked curiously into the hole he was making as he climbed from his seat high above the ground. He called some of the other workers over. They all stared into the pit. One of the workers motioned for Ms. Garcia and her students to come a little closer. Everyone was surprised at what they saw. A piece of broken pottery was sticking out from the loose soil.

Figure 1-1 Construction efforts sometimes unearth prehistoric sites.

Science in Action

One worker suggested that the pottery might be only one of thousands of pieces of trash that were buried long before the school was built. Another worker, however, wasn't so sure. He thought that the pottery could perhaps be an ancient piece of art, such as the one shown in **Figure 1-2A.** Nonetheless, a decision was made to stop the excavation, at least for the moment.

Back in the classroom, the students talked excitedly about the find. This, they all agreed, was real science. **Science,** they knew, is the process of trying to understand the world.

Calling in the Experts

While not wanting to dampen their enthusiasm, Ms. Garcia reminded the students that the piece of pottery might be something that was thrown out only decades ago. To be sure, however, the school's principal called an archaeologist at the local college. An *archaeologist,* such as the two shown in **Figure 1-2B,** is a scientist who studies the cultural remains of ancient peoples. Cultural remains might be tools, weapons, rock drawings, buildings, or pottery, such as that found at the school. Dr. Lum, the students were told, would be at the school on Monday to examine the pottery.

Ms. Garcia suggested that her students go to the library to research more about the history of their area. Ben and the others in his group quickly began their research. Maria thought that it would be a good idea to take notes on their findings. That way, they could compare what they found with what Dr. Lum told them on Monday. The others in the group agreed and put their science notebooks into their backpacks before heading to the library.

Figure 1-2

A Archaeologists study pottery and other items found at sites to learn more about ancient peoples.

B Archaeologists work in the field to gather data.

Researching the Past

Once at the library, Juan used an encyclopedia to begin his research. He found out that archaeology is a branch of science that studies the tools and other cultural remains of humans. There are two major branches of archaeology, as shown in **Figure 1-3.** One branch focuses on groups of people who lived before history was written. The other branch studies civilizations that developed since people began writing things down. To his surprise, Juan also discovered that archaeology covers a time span of more than 3 million years. About 3.5 million years ago, he read, our first ancestors appeared on Earth.

Reading Check

What is archaeology?

The other students took turns finding out about the history of their area. Ben found out that many scientists hypothesize that the first people came to North America from Asia about 12 000 years ago. Over thousands of years, these people migrated to different parts of the country. Emily and Maria discovered that the area around their city was settled about 2000 years ago. After locating a few more sources, the students took notes on all the information they had gathered. Emily suggested that they also should write down any questions they had about the pottery or the science of archaeology. Juan, Ben, and Maria agreed and each wrote down a few questions. The group left the library anxious to hear how its findings would compare with what Dr. Lum would have to say on Monday.

Figure 1-3

A One branch of archaeology studies the cultural remains of people who lived before history was written.

Dr. Lum's Visit

Dr. Lum arrived a few minutes before nine o'clock. The students could hardly contain their excitement. When the bell rang, Emily's hand shot up. She was hoping to be the first to ask the scientist about the pottery. But, before calling on her, Dr. Lum explained that she wanted to give the students a little background information and then she would answer questions.

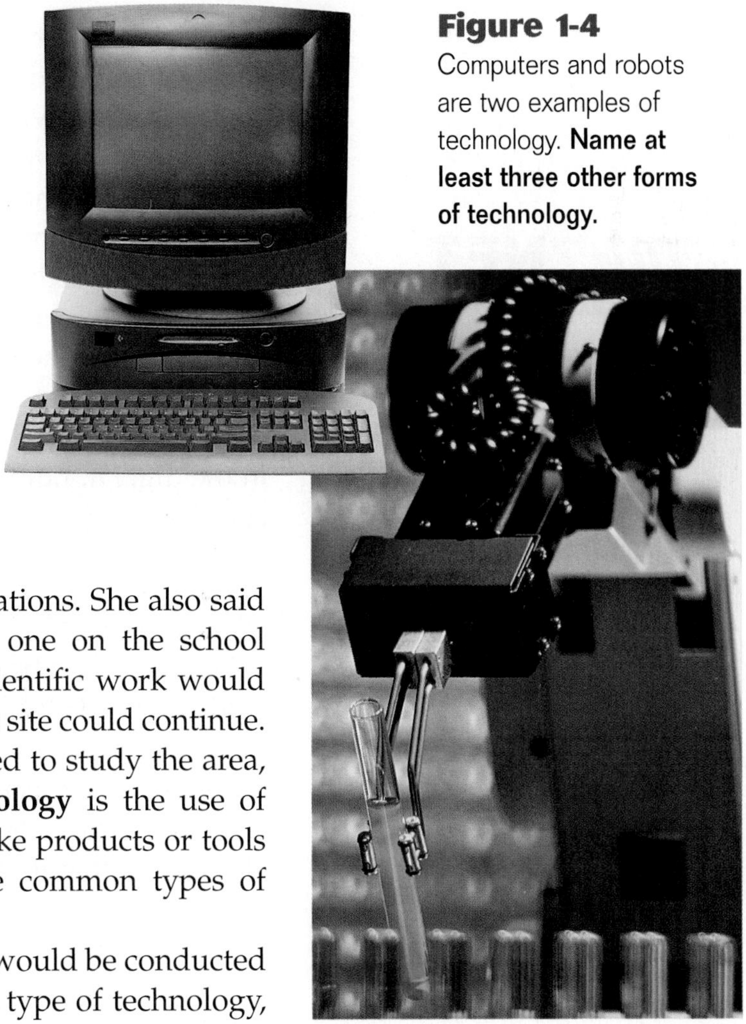

Figure 1-4
Computers and robots are two examples of technology. **Name at least three other forms of technology.**

Dr. Lum began by saying that it is important to preserve prehistoric sites and remains for present and future generations. She also said that many archaeological sites, like the one on the school grounds, are found by accident. More scientific work would have to be done before construction on the site could continue. Several kinds of technology would be used to study the area, such as computers and cameras. **Technology** is the use of knowledge gained through science to make products or tools people can use. **Figure 1-4** shows some common types of technology.

Dr. Lum explained that a radar survey would be conducted to help study the find at the school. This type of technology, Dr. Lum explained, helps scientists "see" what's beneath the ground without disturbing the site. Experts from other fields of science probably would be called upon to help evaluate the site. For instance, geologists, scientists who study Earth processes, might be contacted to help with soil studies.

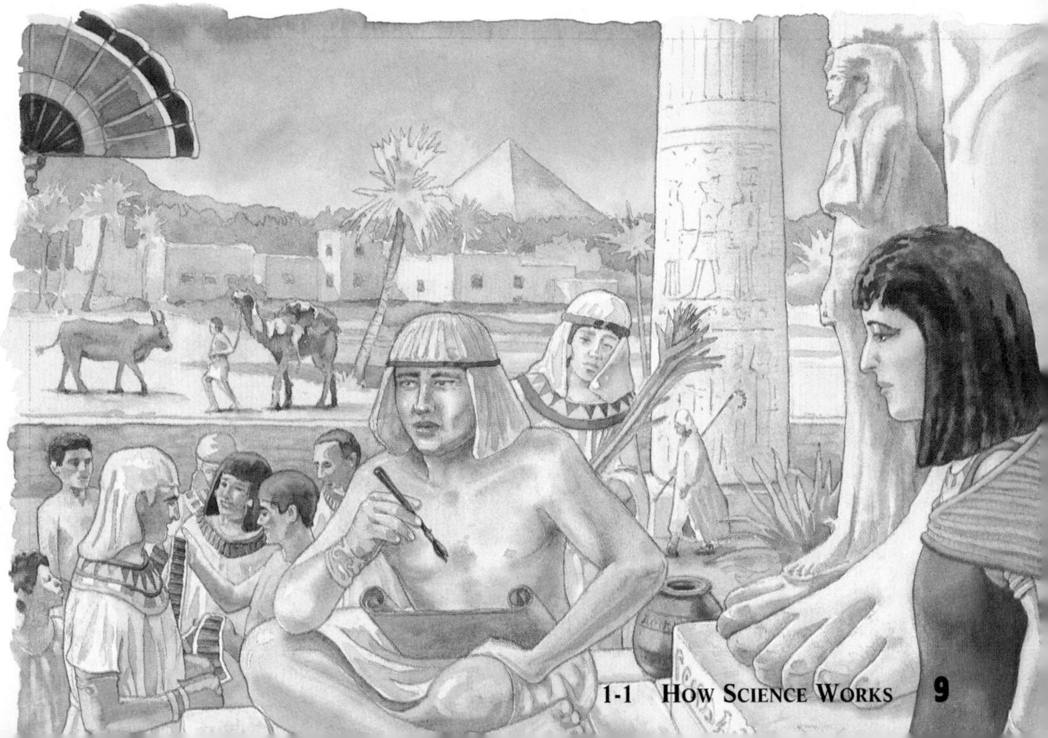

B Archaeologists also study civilizations that have developed since people began recording history. **The two branches of archaeology cover a time span of how many years?**

Working Together

Dr. Lum ended her talk by suggesting that the students go back to the site with her. There, she would examine what had been found. She also would try to answer any questions the students might have about the find.

Maria and Emily led the group of curious students back toward the north end of the school yard. Dr. Lum used her hand lens to examine the piece of pottery carefully. After a few minutes, she announced that she was sure the pottery was old and that an archaeological dig, or excavation of the site, was in order. The students asked if they could participate in the dig. Dr. Lum said she would welcome all the help they could give.

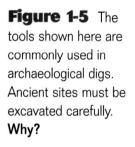

*inter***NET**
CONNECTION

Visit the Glencoe Science Web Site at **www.glencoe.com/sec/science/ca** for more information about archaeology.

Digging In

Weeks passed before the radar surveys were complete. The students in Ms. Garcia's class spent most of their time learning about how an archaeological excavation is done. Maria reported to the class that the holes and ditches being dug around the site would help determine the size of the site. She also added that it was important that the site be disturbed as little as possible. By keeping the site intact, much of the history of the site could be retold.

Finally, the day came when the students could participate in the dig. Each was given a small hand shovel, a soft paintbrush, and a pair of gardening gloves, such as those shown in **Figure 1-5.** Each student was paired with an amateur archaeologist. All of those involved were instructed to work slowly and carefully in order to excavate this important piece of their city's past.

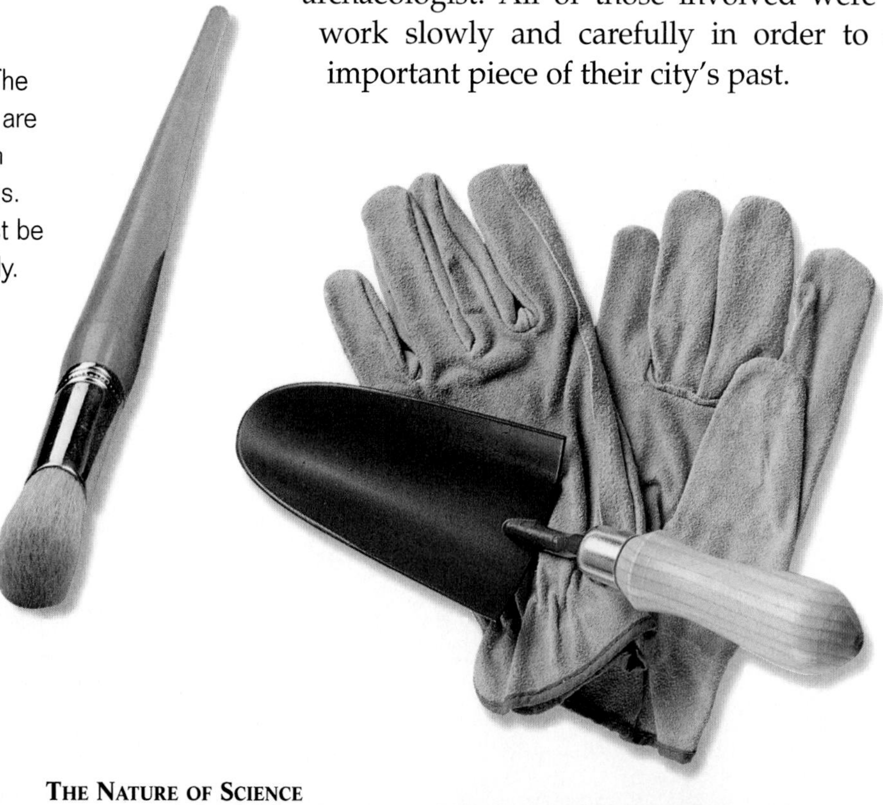

Figure 1-5 The tools shown here are commonly used in archaeological digs. Ancient sites must be excavated carefully. **Why?**

Clues to the Past

Many pieces of pottery, along with some tools, were found at the site. Before the artifacts were removed from the soil, college students working with Dr. Lum took pictures or made drawings of the pieces. These were used to make maps showing the exact location of each artifact before it was excavated. The maps also would be used to show differences in the site both vertically and horizontally.

Lab Work

Each piece was given a number that described its location and its orientation in the soil. After the artifacts were registered and cataloged, they were removed from the site. Dr. Lum told the students that she would take the finds back to her lab. There, they would be cleaned, studied, and stored, as shown in **Figure 1-6.**

Figure 1-6 After artifacts are excavated, they're cleaned and tagged for further study.

Dr. Lum explained that chemical analyses of the pottery and tools would be used to determine the exact age of each piece. Based on her knowledge of the area, Dr. Lum thought that the site was at least several thousand years old.

Section Assessment

1. What is archaeology?
2. Describe some common forms of technology.
3. Why do scientists conduct radar surveys of archaeological sites?
4. **Think Critically:** Why are maps of prehistoric sites often made before removing the artifacts?
5. **Skill Builder**
   Comparing and Contrasting
   Compare and contrast science and technology. If you need help, refer to Comparing and Contrasting in the **Skill Handbook** on page 672.

Using Computers

Word Processing Use some local reference books to find out about the prehistoric history of your state or the area around your town. Write a creative yet factual story based on what you find. If you need help, refer to page 684.

Design Your Own Experiment

Activity 1 • 1

Model an Archaeological Dig

Possible Materials

- Small stones and pebbles
- Craft sticks
- Bits of black tissue paper
- Toothpicks
- Sand
- Small plastic, interlocking building blocks
- Small paintbrushes
- Plastic shovels
- Large plastic dishwashing tub or clear storage box
- Ruler, pencil, and paper

Have you ever put together a model airplane? If so, your model was a small version of a large object. Scientists often use models to study objects that are too large or too small to observe directly. In this activity, your group will construct a model of a prehistoric site. You'll cover the site with sand and give it to another group to unearth. As amateur archaeologists, each of you will attempt to reconstruct the site based on what you find.

Recognize the Problem

What can be learned from an archaeological excavation?

Form a Hypothesis

Think about some of the things you use every day. Based on your basic needs, make a hypothesis as to what you might find at a prehistoric site once inhabited by humans.

Goals

- **Make a model** of a prehistoric site.
- **Design an experiment** to show how the prehistoric site might be excavated.
- **Make a map** of the site you construct.

Safety Precautions

Test Your Hypothesis

Plan

1. Based on the basic needs generated by your group, **make a model** of an ancient site where people once lived. You might want to include a hearth used for cooking, a trash pit, some sort of shelter, a protective wall, a burial site, a water source, and some tools.
2. **Decide** which of the possible materials listed would be best for each item you include in your site. Remember that others will be trying to determine what is contained at your site.
3. How will you cover your site so that other groups can **excavate** the artifacts?
4. Using the ruler, **determine** a way to make a map of your site.

Do

1. Make sure your teacher approves your plan before you proceed. Make any suggested changes in your plan before you start.
2. **Make the model** in the plastic dish-washing tub or storage box.
3. **Make a map** of your site.
4. **Exchange** your model with another group. Carefully **excavate** the site your group is given using the brushes and shovels.
5. **Make a map** that shows where you found each item in the model you are excavating.
6. While doing the experiment, **record** your observations in your Science Journal.

Analyze Your Data

1. Were any of the items in the site similar to the items you use or see around your community every day? Were any of the items unfamiliar? **Explain.**
2. Why did you make maps of your site and the site you excavated?
3. Did any of the excavating tools damage or disturb the site?
4. **Write** a report explaining what you found and what it might have been used for.

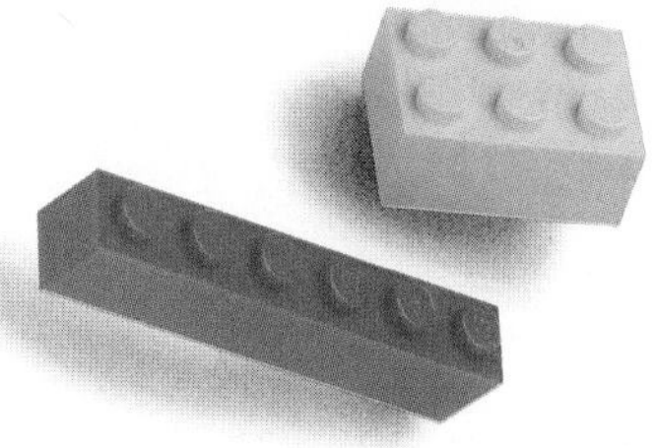

Draw Conclusions

1. How did your map of the site you excavated **compare** with that produced by the group that made the site?
2. Radar surveys that penetrate the ground are often conducted over possible archaeological sites. Why?

1-2 Scientific Problem Solving

What You'll Learn

- Scientific methods include several steps that are taken to try to solve a problem
- Many scientific experiments test variables
- A control can be used to make comparisons during an experiment

Vocabulary
scientific methods
observation
inference
hypothesis
independent variable
dependent variable
constant
control

Why It's Important

- Scientific methods can help you solve problems.

Scientific Methods

Several steps were taken to solve the pottery problem at York Middle School. When the pottery was found, a decision was made to stop construction. One adult guessed that the pottery was fairly old. An expert was called to verify the guess made about the pottery. Based on prior knowledge and further testing, it was concluded that the pottery was from a prehistoric culture.

Step-by-step procedures of scientific problem solving are called **scientific methods.** Any scientific method involves several steps. These steps can vary from situation to situation and aren't necessarily done in a specific order. The basic steps in a commonly used scientific method are shown in **Figure 1-7.** Let's take a look at each step in turn.

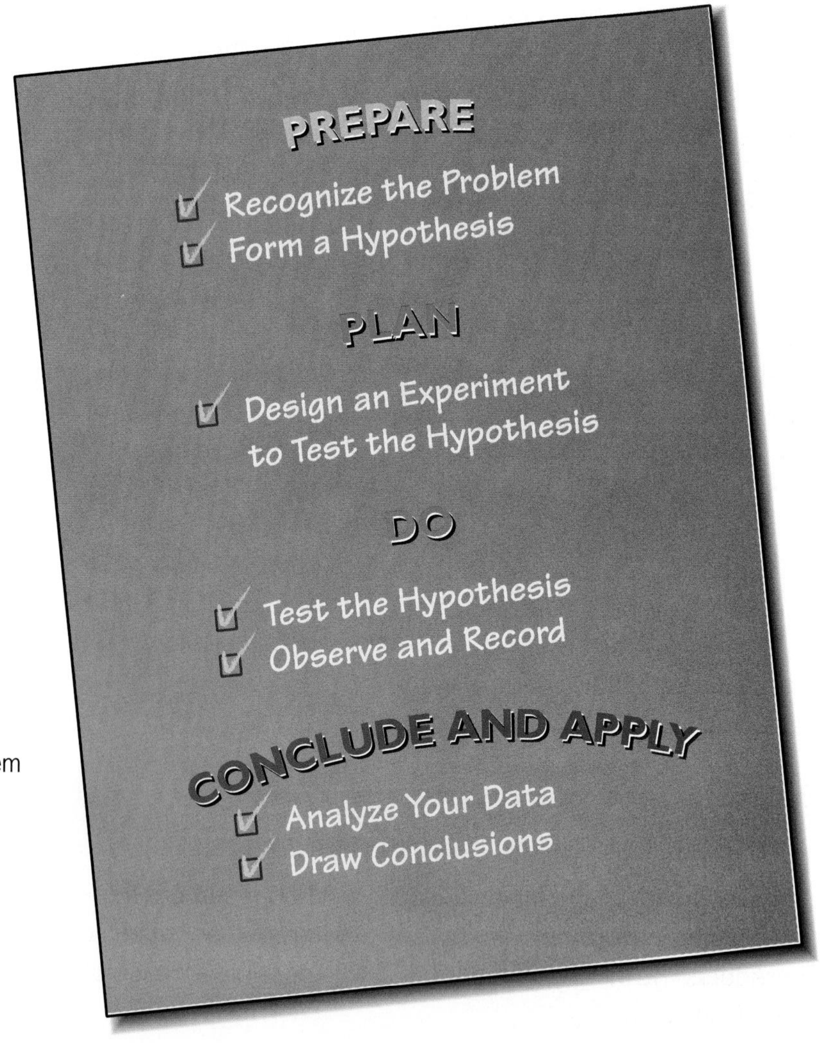

Figure 1-7 This illustration shows one way to solve a problem or find an answer to a question. **What are scientific methods used for?**

Figure 1-8 Gathering information in the library or on the Internet can make your problem-solving tasks easier. **Besides books and computers, what other resources can you use to help you gather information?**

Recognize the Problem

Ben thought about all the science he had learned over the past few months. He was eager to find out more about the world around him. What can I explore, he thought to himself as he looked around his bedroom. It was then that Ben noticed that the plant on his window sill was droopy. He quickly watered the wilting plant. Later in the day, Ben observed that the droopy plant had perked up. He concluded that he should remember to water the plant on a regular basis. So, every day after school, he watered the plant in his room.

After a few weeks, Ben noticed that the leaves on his plant had turned yellow and brown. He knew from science class that plants need water, so why was this plant not doing well? He talked to his teacher about the plant. She suggested that Ben use what he learned in science class to solve his problem. She pointed out that this problem might make a good project for the upcoming science fair.

Ben has already completed the first step in a scientific approach to solving a problem—he recognizes a problem. A scientific problem is simply a question you don't know the answer to. In order to solve his problem, Ben must do research about his plant. Using reference materials such as those shown in **Figure 1-8,** Ben identified his plant as a fig. In his Science Journal, he drew a picture of a plant and listed some facts about it. ☑

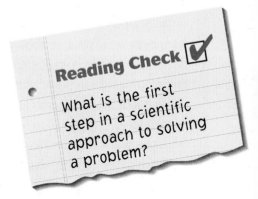

Reading Check ☑

What is the first step in a scientific approach to solving a problem?

Flex Your Brain

If you are faced with a scientific problem like Ben's, you can use the *Flex Your Brain* activity on the next page to help you solve the problem. *Flex Your Brain* is a way to keep your thinking on track when you are investigating a topic or a problem. It helps you explore what you already know and can lead you to new conclusions and awareness about a topic. Lastly, *Flex Your Brain* encourages you to review and talk about the steps you took. Communicating the results of your research is an important part of doing science. Scientists share their results so that other scientists can analyze the results or conduct new tests based on previously learned knowledge. Scientists may communicate by writing papers for science journals, speaking before large groups, or talking with other scientists directly. **Figure 1-9** shows some scientists sharing lab results. To learn more about communicating and other science skills, refer to the **Skill Handbook** at the back of this book.

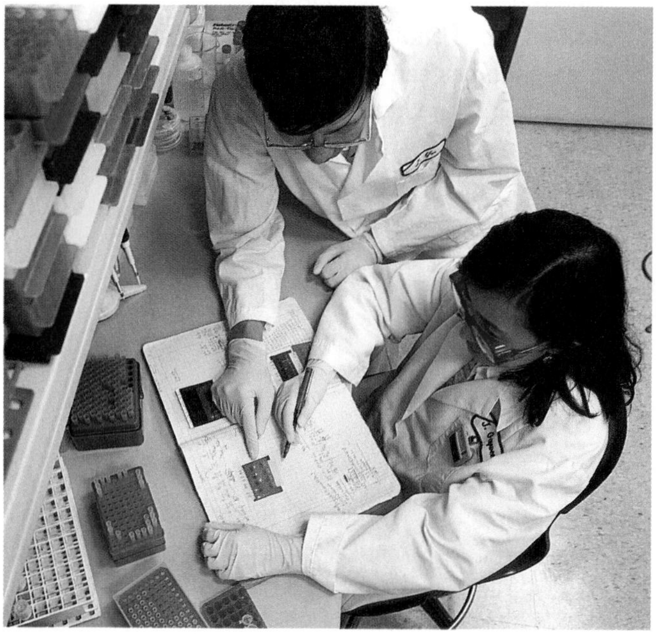

Figure 1-9 These scientists are sharing the results of an experiment with one another.

Problem Solving

Flex Your Brain

Solving problems requires a plan. This plan may be a simple thing that you do in your head, or it may be something more complicated that you actually write down. Use the *Flex Your Brain* activity on the next page to help you organize a plan for solving a problem. You may want to learn more about plants or about archaeological digs. Record your results in your Science Journal. The photograph on the right shows a Science Journal entry. You can use your Science Journal to record observations, express ideas, and draw sketches. Your Science Journal helps you practice communicating your thoughts and ideas, which you can then share with your classmates.

Think Critically: Why does *Flex Your Brain* ask you to share what you learned?

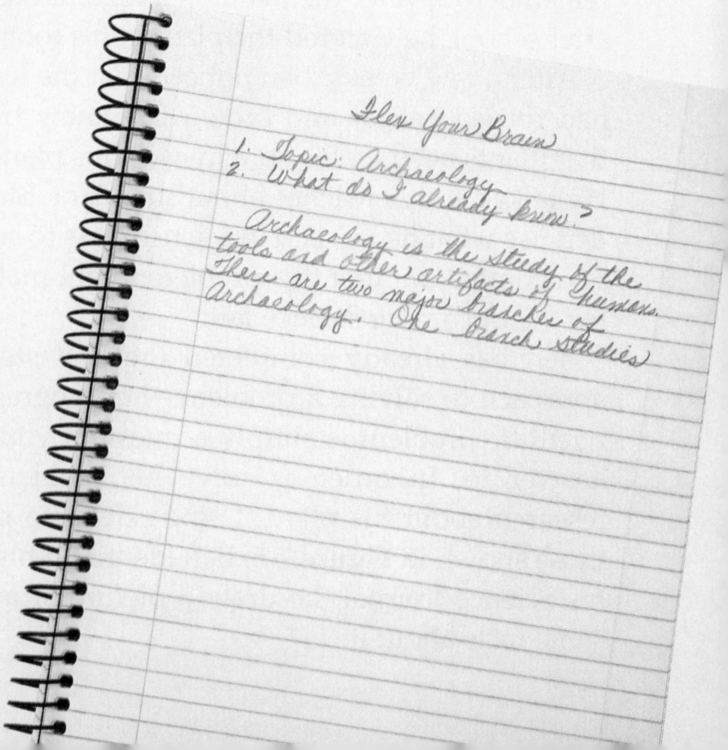

VISUALIZING Problem Solving

Flex Your Brain

1 **Topic:** ______________________

2 **What do I already know?**
1. ______
2. ______
3. ______
4. ______
5. ______

3 **Q:** Ask a question

____

4 **A:** Guess an answer

____

5 **How sure am I? (circle one)**

Not sure				Very sure
1	2	3	4	5

6 **How can I find out?**
1. ______
2. ______
3. ______
4. ______
5. ______

7 **EXPLORE**

8 **Do I think differently?** yes / no

9 **What do I know now?**
1. ______
2. ______
3. ______
4. ______
5. ______

10 **SHARE**
1. ______
2. ______
3. ______

1 Fill in the topic.

2 Jot down what you already know about the topic.

3 Using what you already know (step 2), form a question about the topic. Are you unsure about one of the items you listed? Do you want to know more? Do you want to know what, how, or why? Write down your question.

4 Guess an answer to your question. In the next few steps, you will be exploring the reasonableness of your answer. Write down your guess.

5 Circle the number in the box that matches how sure you are of your answer in step 4. This is your chance to rate your confidence in what you've done so far and, later, to see how your level of sureness affects your thinking.

6 How can you find out more about your topic? You might want to read a book, ask an expert, or do an experiment. Write down ways you can find out more.

7 Make a plan to explore your answer. Use the resources you listed in step 6. Then, carry out your plan.

8 Now that you've explored, go back to your answer in step 4. Would you answer differently?

9 Considering what you learned in your exploration, answer your question again, adding new things you've learned. You may completely change your answer.

10 It's important to be able to talk about thinking. Choose three people to tell about how you arrived at your response in every step. For example, don't just read what you wrote down in step 2. Try to share how you thought of those things.

LIFE SCIENCE INTEGRATION

Conserving Water

Deserts are regions of Earth that receive less than 25 cm of precipitation annually. Most of the plants in these natural habitats are cacti. Cacti have thin leaves called spines. Research how the spines and the roots of the cacti help these plants survive in desert areas.

Observe and Infer

Before Ben could communicate his results, he had to plan and carry out his experiment. First, he made and recorded careful observations about his plant. **Observations** can be bits of information you gather with your senses. Most scientific observations are made with your eyes and ears. But, you also can observe with your senses of touch, taste, and smell. Ben observed that many of the leaves had fallen off his plant. The stem, in places, was peeling. Ben also noticed that some white, powdery, smelly stuff was covering the soil in the pot. He stuck his finger into the soil. It was very wet.

Observations like Ben's often lead to inferences. An **inference** is a conclusion about an observation. Ben inferred that he was perhaps watering his plant too often. Can you make any other inferences about why Ben's plant wasn't thriving?

Form a Hypothesis

After a problem has been identified, a scientist may make a hypothesis. A **hypothesis** is a statement that can be tested. Hypotheses are based on observations, research, and prior knowledge of a problem. **Table 1-1** compares and contrasts hypotheses with two other scientific statements—scientific theories and scientific laws. Ben decided to use his inference about watering too often as his hypothesis. His hypothesis was: Fig plants grow best when they are watered only once a week.

Table 1-1

Scientific Statements

Hypothesis	Theory	Law
A hypothesis is a statement that can be tested. Hypotheses that are supported by repeated tests are used to form theories.	A theory is an explanation supported by results obtained from repeated experiments. Theories attempt to explain why something happens.	A scientific law describes the behavior of something in nature. Generally, laws predict or describe what will happen in a given situation but don't explain why. **What is the difference between a scientific theory and a scientific law?**

Figure 1-10 The amount of water added to the plants is the variable in this experiment.

A At the beginning of the experiment, similar sized plants received the same amount of sunlight and were planted in the same type of soil. The plant on the right received no water at all. It was the control.

B Three weeks later, by controlling other factors and changing only one variable—how frequently the plant was watered—the results of the experiment clearly show the effect of water on plants.

Test Your Hypothesis

In order to test his hypothesis, Ben will carry out an experiment using three plants. An experiment, as you probably already know, is a series of carefully planned steps used to test a hypothesis. In any experiment, it's important to keep everything the same except for the item or variable you are testing so that you'll know which variable caused the results. The one factor that you change in an experiment is called the **independent variable.**

In Ben's proposed experiment, the independent variable will be the number of times he waters each plant in a week. He will then observe how well each plant grows based on the amount of water the plants receive. The growth of the plants is the dependent variable in Ben's experiment. A **dependent variable** is the factor being measured in an experiment. **Figure 1-10** shows an experiment that tests the effects of water on plants.

Plan the Experiment

In order to truly test only one variable at a time, scientists often use constants. **Constants** are factors in an experiment that stay the same. In his experiment, Ben will use the same size plants, which will be potted with the same kinds and amounts of soil. His teacher pointed out that Ben also must put his plants into identical containers. Other constants in Ben's experiment will be the amount of water he'll use to water each plant and the amount of light each plant will get.

Some experiments also have a control. A **control** is a standard used for comparison. Ben knows that all plants, even cacti, need water. He's just not sure how often a fig plant needs to be watered. His control might be a plant that receives no water during the experiment.

*inter***NET**
CONNECTION

Visit the Glencoe Science Web Site at **www.glencoe.com/sec/science/ca** for more information about doing scientific experiments.

Try at Home

MiniLab

Observing and Inferring

Procedure

1. Look at the illustration in **Figure 1-11.** It is part of a larger illustration.
2. Record in your Science Journal everything you can observe about the illustration.
3. Use your list of observations to make inferences about what might be happening in the illustration.

Analysis

1. What do you think is happening in the illustration?
2. Compare your inference with the entire illustration on the Reviewing Main Ideas page under Section 1-2. How close was your inference to the illustration?

Do the Experiment

Ben gathered all the materials he would need to test his experiment. Before he starts, Ben knows from Ms. Garcia's labs that he must write down a plan to follow. In his Science Journal, he wrote that he would use three different plants. One (Plant A) would not be watered. This would be his control. A second plant (Plant B) would get watered every day during the week. The third plant (Plant C) would get watered only once a week. His experiment would last one month.

Ben then made a table in which to record his observations. He listed each plant and the number of times it was to get watered. Ben made room in the table for his measurements. He also made a plan to record his observations, which would include the height of each plant, the color of its leaves, and the number of leaves it dropped, if any. To learn more about observing, study **Figure 1-11** and do the MiniLab on this page.

Figure 1-11 Study this illustration. Then do the MiniLab above to practice observing and inferring—two important science skills.

Analyze Your Data

Data are collected during any scientific study. Some data are numeric values such as the length of an object or the temperature of a liquid. Other data include observations that use adjectives and phrases such as *faster than, smaller, not as well as,* and *greener.* An experimenter must record and study the data collected before he or she can draw conclusions about an experiment.

By the end of the month, Ben observed that the few leaves still left on the plant that received no water were brown and shriveled. It had lost most of its leaves. The plant that was watered every day had a few leaves left on its branches, but these leaves didn't look too healthy. Some white, smelly stuff covered the soil. Ben noticed that the plant that was watered once a week had grown the tallest. Many healthy green and white leaves hung from its branches.

Draw Conclusions

After studying his data, Ben was ready to draw some conclusions. A conclusion is a statement based on what has been observed. Ben concluded that not watering a plant caused the leaves to dry out and die. Watering a plant too much also caused the leaves to die. Watering the plant once a week seemed to be the best schedule for a fig plant.

Ben told his teacher about his results. She reminded him that in order to make sure his conclusions were valid, he should repeat his experiment. Ben agreed and did the same experiment again. Based on the results of his second experiment, Ben was able to conclude confidently that watering a plant once a week made it grow well in the temperature and light conditions he used. His hypothesis was supported, and he entered his project in his school's science fair, much like the students shown in **Figure 1-12.**

Figure 1-12

A These students are preparing for their school's science fair.

Plant Observations

Week	Plant A	Plant B	Plant C
1	10.5 cm	10.3 cm	10.8 cm
2	10.7 cm	11.2 cm	12.6 cm
3	10.9 cm	12.0 cm	14.6 cm
4	11.1 cm	12.4 cm	15.5 cm

B This table shows the results of an experiment similar to Ben's.

Section Assessment

1. Name the steps followed in a commonly used scientific method.
2. How are observations different from inferences?
3. Why should experiments be repeated more than once?
4. **Think Critically:** Why is it important to test only one variable at a time?
5.  **Skill Builder**
   Separating and Controlling Variables Separating and controlling variables is an important part of conducting an experiment. Do the **Chapter 1 Skill Activity** on page 694 to practice this science skill.

Using Math

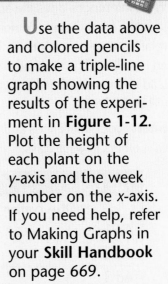

Use the data above and colored pencils to make a triple-line graph showing the results of the experiment in **Figure 1-12.** Plot the height of each plant on the *y*-axis and the week number on the *x*-axis. If you need help, refer to Making Graphs in your **Skill Handbook** on page 669.

Materials
- Magazine advertisements
- Paper (one sheet)
- Colored pencils or markers

Advertising Inferences

Imagine you're flipping through your favorite magazine and you see an ad showing a skateboard with wings. Would you infer that the skateboard could fly? In this activity, you'll use advertisements to practice the science skills of observing and inferring. Do the products really do what the ads lead you to infer?

What You'll Investigate

What observations and inferences can you make from advertisements?

Goals
- **Make inferences** based on observations.
- **Recognize** the limits of observations.

Procedure
1. **Select** three ads from those supplied by your teacher. In your Science Journal, **make a table** like the one shown below.
2. For each ad, **list** your observations. For example, you may **observe** that there are athletic people pictured in a soda ad.
3. What inferences does the advertiser want you to make from the ad? **Make inferences** that relate your observations to the product that the ad is selling. The soda ad, for example, may lead you to infer that if you drink that soda, you will be athletic.
4. **Share** your inferences and advertisements with others in your class.

Ad Data

	Observation	Inference
Ad 1		
Ad 2		
Ad 3		

Conclude and Apply
1. **Compare** and **contrast** your classmates' inferences with your own. Are there other explanations for the things you observed in the ads?
2. **Create** your own ad to sell a product. Think about what people will observe in the ad and what you want them to infer from it.
3. Have a classmate make inferences about your ad. What did your classmate infer about the ad you created? Is this what you wanted the classmate to infer? **Explain.**

Radar

Radar is an electronic system used to locate and identify distant objects. Police officers (top left) use radar to detect drivers who go over the speed limit. Meteorologists use radar to keep tabs on weather systems (bottom left). Air-traffic controllers rely on radar for tracking airplanes. People who fish use radar to locate schools of fish.

How Radar Works

The term *radar* stands for **RA**dio **D**etecting **A**nd **R**anging system. A radar system is made of several parts. The transmitter generates electromagnetic waves, which are produced by the motion of electrically charged particles. Light, radio waves, and microwaves are all examples of electromagnetic waves. In a radar system, these waves leave the transmitter through one or more antennae. When the waves encounter an object, the radio waves scatter. These scattered waves, often called echoes, are received by other antennae in the radar system. An amplifier increases the signals of these echoes. A computer then processes the signals and displays them on a screen. The distance to the target object, its altitude or depth, and the object's position relative to the radar source also can be displayed on the screen.

Ground Penetrating Radar

A type of radar called ground penetrating radar (GPR) can be used to explore archaeological sites. The system can be used to identify important underground features before a site is excavated. This step helps scientists decide which parts of the site are safe to explore and which should be avoided to prevent damaging the site. Computers process the data gathered by radar and use the information to create three-dimensional maps of the site.

Radar Development in World War II

Even before the United States entered World War II, the first Army radar was patented in May of 1937. By 1941, early warning radars could detect an approaching plane, though not its altitude or size. Radar was one of the most important communication developments of World War II.

interNET CONNECTION

Visit the Glencoe Science Web Site at **www.glencoe.com/sec/science/ca** for more information about the uses of GPR. How is GPR used in environmental cleanups or in efforts to locate abandoned mines?

Chapter 1 Reviewing Main Ideas

For a **preview** of this chapter, study this Reviewing Main Ideas before you read the chapter. After you have studied this chapter, you can use the Reviewing Main Ideas to **review** the chapter.

The Glencoe MindJogger, Audiocassettes, and CD-ROM provide additional opportunities for review.

Section 1-1 HOW SCIENCE WORKS

Science is a process of understanding the world around you. **Technology** is the use of the knowledge gained through scientific thinking and problem solving. Archaeologists, scientists who study the artifacts of ancient people, use both science and technology in their work. Many archaeological sites and the artifacts they contain are found by accident. The excavation of an archaeological find is done slowly and carefully so that the artifacts and the site itself are not damaged or destroyed. Artifacts such as tools and pottery can be dated using chemical analyses. During an archaeological dig, maps are often made to show the location of each artifact with respect to the site. ***Describe the two branches of archaeology.***

Reading Check ✓

The suffix *-logy* means "science" or "study of." Identify and define a dozen other branches of science with names that end in *-logy*.

Section 1-2 SCIENTIFIC PROBLEM SOLVING

Scientific methods are step-by-step approaches to solving problems. Steps that can be used in scientific problem solving include identifying the problem, forming and testing a **hypothesis,** analyzing the results of the test, and drawing conclusions. Many scientific experiments involve two variables, or factors, that change. An **independent variable** is a factor that the experimenter changes. The **dependent variable** is the factor that changes as a result of the independent variable. **Constants** are factors in an experiment that don't change. A **control,** when one is included, is a standard used for comparison. ***Why should you test only one variable at a time?***

Career CONNECTION

Amanda Shaw, International Science Fair Contestant

Amanda Shaw is an example of how young people can become involved in science. Her science fair project studied the effects of carbon dioxide and plants on global warming. After winning first place in a regional competition, Amanda went on to compete against hundreds of other young scientists at the International Science and Engineering Fair (ISEF). Many scientists first become interested in environmental issues by participating in science fair projects. ***What does it take to make a good science fair project?***

Chapter 1 Assessment

Using Vocabulary

a. constant
b. control
c. dependent variable
d. hypothesis
e. independent variable
f. inference
g. observation
h. science
i. scientific methods
j. technology

Each phrase below describes a science term from the list. Write the term that matches the phrase describing it.

1. variable changed by the person doing the experiment
2. a statement that can be tested
3. step-by-step approach to solving problems
4. information you gather with your senses
5. the process of understanding the world around you

Checking Concepts

Choose the word or phrase that best answers the question.

6. A scientist publishes the results of her experiments. Which science skill is she practicing?
   A) observing
   B) inferring
   C) communicating
   D) hypothesizing
7. What technology helps archaeologists to "see" a buried site before they begin excavating it?
   A) mapmaking
   B) digging
   C) radar
   D) experimenting
8. What is the first step in a commonly used scientific method?
   A) forming a hypothesis
   B) recognizing a problem
   C) drawing conclusions
   D) analyzing data
9. Why do scientists make maps of archaeological sites?
   A) to photograph artifacts
   B) to calculate the exact age of artifacts
   C) to record where the artifacts were found
   D) to discover artifacts
10. What is a standard used for comparison in an experiment called?
    A) a constant
    B) an independent variable
    C) a dependent variable
    D) a control
11. What is a conclusion based on an observation?
    A) a control
    B) a hypothesis
    C) an inference
    D) a variable
12. What is a series of carefully planned steps used to test a hypothesis?
    A) a constant
    B) an observation
    C) an experiment
    D) a conclusion
13. Why should an experiment be repeated?
    A) to form a hypothesis
    B) to reduce the chance of error
    C) to change controls
    D) to identify the problem
14. What should an experimenter do after analyzing test results?
    A) identify the problem
    B) draw conclusions
    C) carry out the experiment
    D) form a hypothesis
15. A computer is an example of which of the following?
    A) an experiment
    B) a control
    C) an excavation
    D) technology

Thinking Critically

16. An archaeologist finds a site that contains many different layers of artifacts. What might she conclude about the people who lived at the site?

17. Is every scientific problem solved using the same steps? Explain.

18. Explain why the following statement is false. Scientists do all their work in laboratories.

19. Describe how you might test which laundry soap cleans the best. Be sure to include variables, constants, and a control.

20. Why is it important to accurately record and measure data during an experiment?

Developing Skills

If you need help, refer to the Skill Handbook.

21. Concept Map: Use the following terms to complete the concept map of a commonly used scientific method shown on this page: *analyze data, form a hypothesis, design an experiment to test the hypothesis,* and *observe and record.*

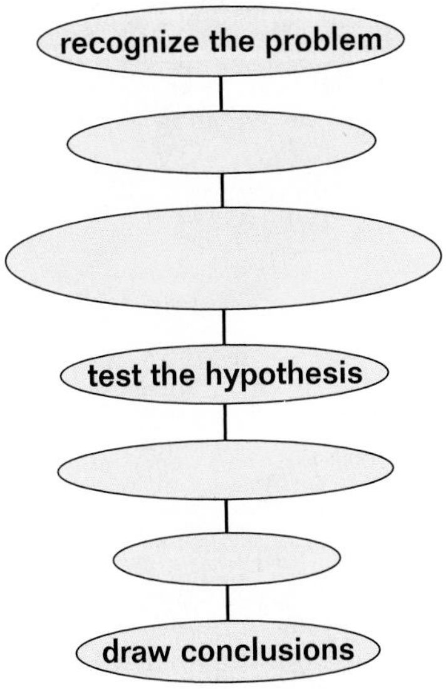

22. Separating and Controlling Variables: Give an example of how Ben controlled variables in his fig plant experiment.

THE PRINCETON REVIEW

Test-Taking Tip

Don't Guess When answering questions about a topic, do not guess. Always return to the original material to reread and get the details from there.

Test Practice

Use these questions to test your Science Proficiency.

1. Min observed that a plant in a shady corner of her bedroom was not growing as well as a plant on the windowsill. She guessed that plants need sunlight to grow and decided to conduct an experiment to test her hypothesis. She put one plant in the cool dark basement of her house and another in the warm bright kitchen. What is wrong with Min's experiment?

A) She did not form a hypothesis.
B) She did not control variables.
C) She did not carry out the experiment.
D) She did not identify the problem.

2. You see a flock of geese flying south and think that the geese must be migrating to a warmer climate for the winter. Which of the following **BEST** describes how you reached this explanation?

A) You made an observation, then an inference.
B) You made an inference, then an observation.
C) You made an inference, then a conclusion.
D) You made a conclusion, then a hypothesis.

CHAPTER

2 Measurement

Chapter Preview

Skills Preview

Skill Builders

- Use Numbers
- Make a Graph

Activities

- Make a Model
- Design an Experiment

MiniLabs

- Measure in SI

Reading Check

Look up words that begin with the prefixes listed in **Table 2-2.** Explain why the words have these prefixes.

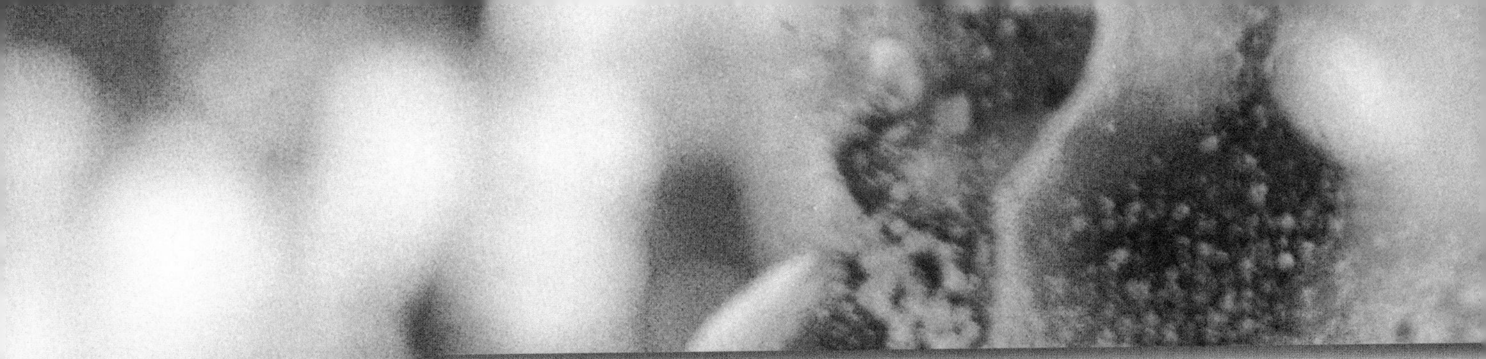

Explore Activity

Carl Lewis goes the distance in both the long jump shown here and in other Olympic events. He won a total of nine gold medals at the Olympic Games in 1984, 1988, 1992, and 1996. Four of his gold medals are in the long jump. His winning jump at the 1996 Olympics was a distance of 8.5 m. Carl Lewis and other athletes depend on accurate and precise measurement in competitions. A fraction of a centimeter can separate the gold and silver medalists in the long jump.

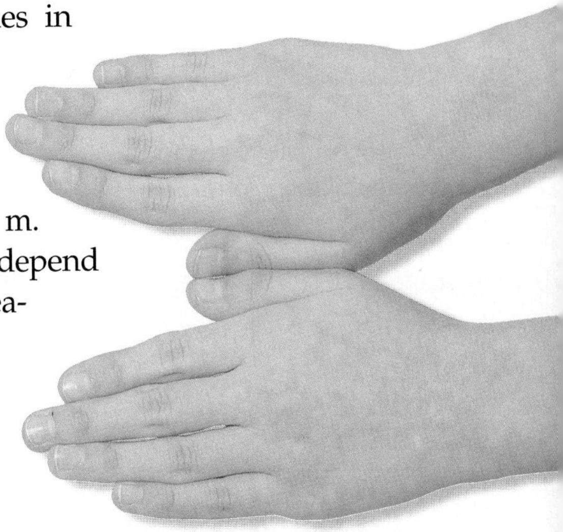

Measuring Length

1. Horses are measured in a unit called *hands.* One hand is about 10 cm. Measure several items using the width of your own hand as *1 hand.*
2. About how many hands long is your arm from shoulder to fingertip? How wide is this book?
3. Now, measure two other objects in the classroom using your hand.

Science Journal

Why switch from hands to meters and centimeters as units of length?

2·1 Description and Measurement

What You'll Learn

- Different methods of measurement
- How exact a measurement is

Vocabulary
measurement
estimation

Why It's Important

- Measurement helps you communicate information and ideas.

Measurement

If someone asked you to describe what you are wearing today, what would you say? You'd probably start by describing colors and styles. Then, you might mention sizes: size 7 shoes, size 13 shirt. Every day, you are surrounded by numbers. **Measurement** is a way to describe the world with numbers. It answers questions such as how much, how long, or how far. Measurement can describe the amount of milk in a carton, the cost of a new compact disc, or the distance between your home and your school. It also can describe the volume of water in the oceans, the mass of an atom, or how fast a penguin's heart pumps blood.

Figure 2-1 shows a fossilized *Knightia* fish. This fossil is about 50 million years old. An average *Knightia* was about 10 cm long. About 60 percent of the fish in the Green River shale quarries, from which this fossil comes, are *Knightia.* Scientists use these measurements to describe and understand fossils. Information described with numbers, such as length and age, is a measurement.

CHEMISTRY INTEGRATION

Descriptions of Matter
A description of matter that does not involve measurement is qualitative. For example, water is composed of hydrogen and oxygen. A quantitative description uses measurement. For example, one water molecule is composed of one oxygen atom and two hydrogen atoms. Give a qualitative and quantitative description of your hand.

Figure 2-1 This *Knightia* fossil fish is from the Green River shale formation in western Wyoming. **Does this photo show the actual size of the fossil? Explain.**

Figure 2-2 Accurate measurement of distance and time is important for competitive sports such as swimming. **Would a clock that only measured in minutes be accurate enough for this race?**

Measurement also can describe events such as the one shown in **Figure 2-2.** In the 1968 summer Olympics, swimmer Debbie Meyer of the United States came in first in the women's 200-m freestyle. She swam the race in 130.5 s. Claudia Poli of Costa Rica won first place in 1996. She swam the 200 meters in 118.16 s. In this example, measurement conveys information about the year of the race, the length, the finishing order, and the time. Information about who competed and in what sport are not measurements but are needed to describe the event completely.

Estimation

You have probably used a ruler, meterstick, or tape measure to find an object's length. What happens when you want to describe a tree's height but you can't measure it with a meterstick? You can use your knowledge about the height of a familiar object to estimate the height of the tree.

Estimation can help you make a rough measurement of an object by guessing. Estimation is based on experience, as shown in **Figure 2-3.** It is useful when you are in a hurry and exact data are not required. Estimation is a valuable skill that improves with experience, practice, and understanding.

Figure 2-3 This student is about 1.5 m tall. **Estimate the size of the tree in the photo.**

MiniLab

Measuring Accurately

Procedure

Use the equipment in your classroom to practice measuring. You can use a graduated cylinder to measure water volume, a balance to measure the mass of a small object, a meterstick to measure the door, and a clock to measure pulse rate. For hints on making measurements, use the **Field Guide to Laboratory Equipment** at the end of this chapter.

Analysis

1. What measurements could you easily make at home?
2. What limitations does each piece of equipment have?
3. Before standardized instruments were widely available, a scientist might have used a pulse or the swing of a pendulum to measure time. What are some of the limitations of these measures?

Using Estimation

You can compare an object whose length you do not know with familiar objects to estimate its length. When you estimate, you often use the word *about.* One meter is about the height of a doorknob above the floor. One centimeter is about the width of the tip of your smallest finger. One millimeter is about the thickness of a dime. To estimate your height, would you use meters, centimeters, or millimeters? What unit would you use to estimate the size of the point of your pencil?

Estimation also is used to check that an answer is reasonable. Suppose you calculate your friend's running speed as 47 m/s. You are familiar with how long a second is and how long a meter is. Can you picture your friend running a 50-m dash in 1 s? Estimation tells you that 47 m/s is too high a speed, and you should check your work.

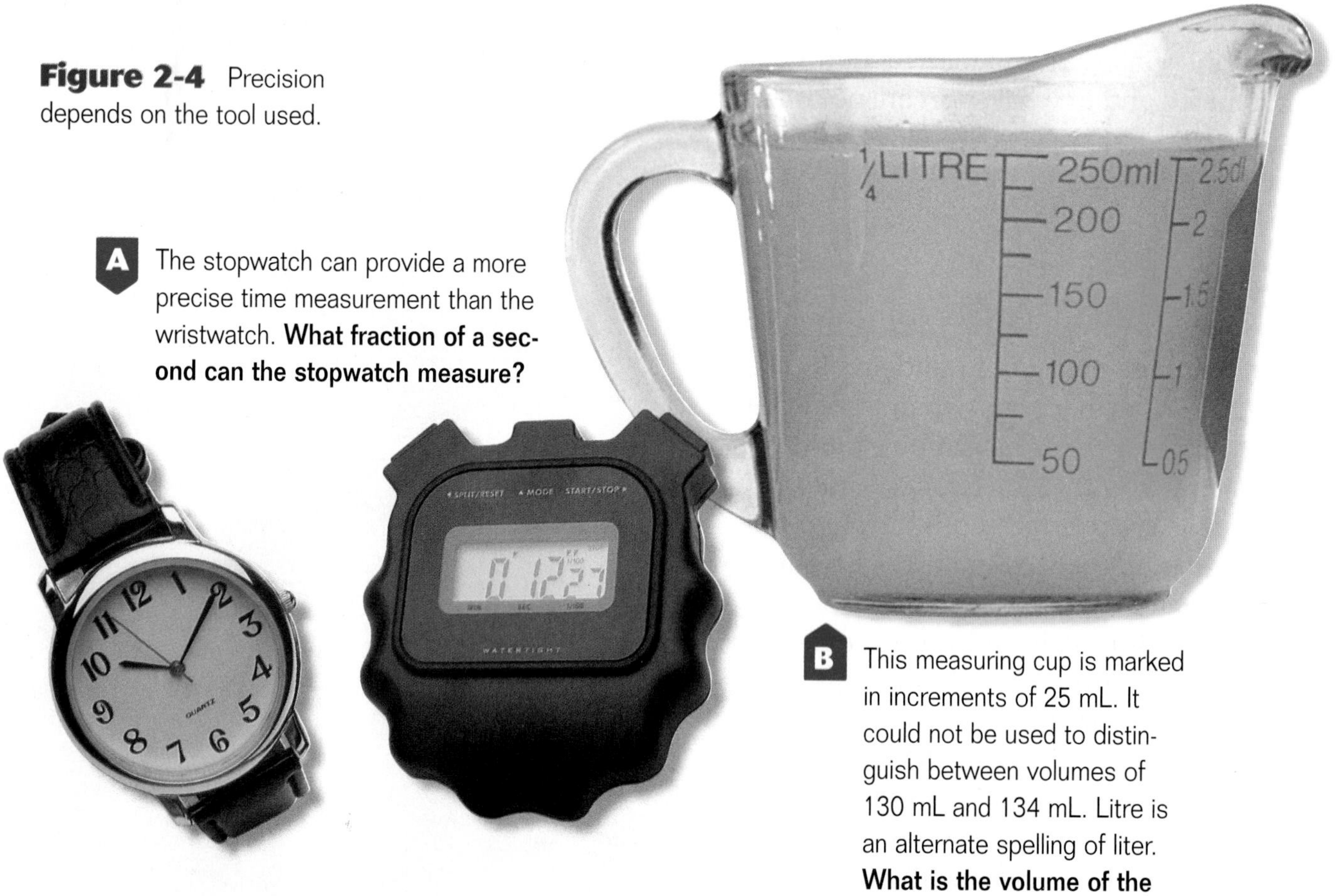

Figure 2-4 Precision depends on the tool used.

A The stopwatch can provide a more precise time measurement than the wristwatch. **What fraction of a second can the stopwatch measure?**

B This measuring cup is marked in increments of 25 mL. It could not be used to distinguish between volumes of 130 mL and 134 mL. Litre is an alternate spelling of liter. **What is the volume of the liquid in the cup?**

VISUALIZING Precision and Accuracy

Figure 2-5 Shooting baskets illustrates accuracy and precision.

A When your shots hit all over, they are not accurate or precise.

B When your shots consistently hit a point well to the left of the basket, they are precise but not accurate.

C When your shots are consistently in the basket, they are precise and accurate.

Precision and Accuracy

Precision describes how carefully you make your measurement. The precision of the tool used determines the precision of the measurement, as shown in **Figure 2-4.** If you measure the width of this book with a ruler marked to millimeters, you can determine the precise width of the book only to the nearest millimeter. A precise measurement can be reproduced. For example, if you measure your desk to be precisely 85 cm high, the person next to you will also measure 85 cm.

Look at an almanac that lists Olympic winners of the past. Winning measurements for some events are given with more precision over time. Times from the 1896 Olympics might be given to the nearest second. Times for later Olympics are given to the nearest tenth of a second, then the nearest hundredth of a second. This is an example of how improved tools make more precise measurements.

Accuracy compares a measurement to the real value. A clock that does not work well could give precise measurements that are inaccurate. **Figure 2-5** illustrates the difference between precision and accuracy. ☑

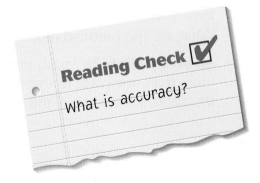

Reading Check ☑

What is accuracy?

Figure 2-6 This laboratory scale can measure to the nearest hundredth of a gram. **What is the mass of the object rounded to the nearest tenth of a gram?**

Rounding a Measure

Sometimes, you have more precision than you need, as shown in **Figure 2-6.** Not all measurements must be made with instruments that measure with great precision. For example, you could measure the length of the sidewalk outside your school to the nearest millimeter. However, you would probably need to know the length only to the nearest meter or tenth of a meter. If your teacher told you the length was 135.841 m, you could round the distance to 135.8 m or 136 m. To round a given value, follow these steps.

1. Look at the digit to the right of the place being rounded.
   - The digit remains the same if the digit to the right is 0, 1, 2, 3, or 4.
   - Round up if the digit to the right is 5, 6, 7, 8, or 9.
2. The remaining digits to the right of the rounding place are eliminated from the rounded answer.

Using Math

Rounding

Example Problem

Refer to the periodic table inside the back cover of this book. The atomic mass of lithium is 6.941 atomic mass units. The atomic mass of neon is 20.180 atomic mass units. You decide that you need to know these values only to the nearest unit to solve a problem. What are the rounded values?

Problem-Solving Steps

1. What number is to the right of the ones place? lithium: 9 neon: 1
2. Do you round the ones place up or down? lithium: up; neon: down
3. **Solution:** lithium: 6.941 rounds to 7 atomic mass units
   neon: 20.180 rounds to 20 atomic mass units

Practice Problem

What are the rounded atomic masses to the nearest tenth of a unit?

Strategy Hint: To round to a certain place, remember to ignore all the numbers more than one place to the right. For example, to round 31 498.89 to the nearest thousand, look at the 4 and round down. Ignore the 8s and 9s that follow the 4.

Precision and Number of Digits

Suppose you want to divide a 2-L bottle of soda equally among seven people. You find $2 \div 7$ on your calculator: 0.285 714 285 7. Will you measure exactly 0.285 714 285 7 L of soda for each person? (Even this number is inexact. Your calculator rounds or cuts off the answer when its display is out of room.) In this case, you need to know that each person gets about 0.3 L. You don't have to copy every digit that appears on your calculator.

A good way to determine the number of digits in the answer when you multiply or divide is to look at the number of digits in each piece of information. In this case, 2 L has one digit and seven people has one digit. The answer should probably have only one or two digits.

Suppose you measure a folder to be 0.008 m thick. You place it on a desk that is 1 m off the ground. Is the top of the folder exactly 1.008 m off the ground? Probably not. The desk might be 1.05 m, or 0.937 m, or any other measure that rounds to 1 m. Because you know the height of the desk only to the ones digit and the height of the folder to the thousandths digit, trying to add them exactly does not make sense. If you round to the ones, the least precise digit in the problem, you get 1 m as the height.

interNET CONNECTION

Visit the Glencoe Science Web Site at **www.glencoe.com/sec/science/ca** for more information about measurement.

Section Assessment

1. Estimate the distance between your desk and your teacher's desk. Explain the method you used.
2. Measure the height of your desk to the nearest half-centimeter.
3. Sarah measured her father's garden. It is 11.72 m long. Round the measure to the nearest tenth of a meter.
4. **Think Critically:** You are given two metric rulers, one marked in half-centimeters and one marked in millimeters. Which would be most helpful in measuring small items such as the width of a wire?
5. **Skill Builder**
   Using Numbers Numbers are used to make measurements. Do the **Chapter 2 Skill Activity** on page 695 to use numbers to describe familiar objects.

Science Journal

In your Science Journal, describe your backpack. Include one set of qualities that have no measurements, such as color and texture, and one set of measurements, such as width and mass.

Global Positioning System

In the early days of flight, pilots flew relatively close to the ground and navigated by landmarks and natural features such as rivers and mountains. In darkness or bad weather, pilots were out of luck. The invention of radar made it possible to navigate without seeing the ground. Today, pilots can determine their position with even greater precision using the Global Positioning System (GPS). The GPS can determine the position, speed, and direction of movement of a pilot or any other person using the system anywhere on Earth.

How GPS Works

Twenty-four GPS satellites orbit in a circular path 17 500 km above Earth. The satellites, powered by solar cells (see inset), send signals to receivers on Earth. Each receiver measures the distance between itself and every satellite within range. Three satellite readings are enough for people using a GPS receiver to determine their position on Earth's surface. To ensure accuracy, receivers use information from four satellites. The woman at right holds an antenna that is receiving position data from the GPS satellite system.

The GPS measures the time it takes for the receiver to communicate with each satellite. This measurement is used to calculate latitude, longitude, and elevation. If the receiver is moving, its velocity also can be determined. Receivers at ground-based stations with fixed positions are used to check accuracy and to make corrections for errors.

A variety of GPS receiving units are available, with different levels of precision. Small receivers, used by boaters and hikers, are precise to within a few hundred meters. GPS receivers used for making topographic maps and construction layouts measure position to within several centimeters, while those used for measuring difficult terrain such as mountains and rivers can measure accurately to within less than 1 cm.

interNET CONNECTION

To research how scientists use GPS to help them in their studies, visit the Glencoe Science Web Site at **www.glencoe.com/sec/science/ca.**

SI Units

2·2

The International System

Can you imagine how confusing it would be if scientists in every country used different measuring systems? Sharing data and ideas would be complicated. To avoid confusion, scientists need a common language. The International System of Units, or **SI,** was established in 1960 as the general system for measurement. It was designed to provide a worldwide standard of physical measurement for science, industry, and commerce. SI uses units such as meter, cubic meter, kilogram, and kelvin, as shown in **Table 2-1.**

The SI units are related by multiples of ten. A unit, such as the meter, can be converted to a smaller or larger unit by multiplying by a power of 10. The new unit is renamed by adding a prefix, shown in **Table 2-2.** For example, one millionth of a meter is one *micro*meter. One thousand grams is one *kilo*gram.

To convert between units, multiply by the appropriate power of ten. For example, to rewrite a kilogram measurement as a gram measurement, multiply by 1000.

What You'll Learn

- SI is the international system of measurement
- The SI units of length, volume, mass, temperature, time, and rate

Vocabulary

SI	**kilogram**
meter	**Kelvin**
mass	**rate**

Why It's Important

- The SI system is used throughout the world.

Table 2-1

SI Units

Quantity	Unit	Symbol
length	meter	m
volume	cubic meter	m^3
mass	kilogram	kg
temperature	kelvin	K
time	second	s

Table 2-2

Prefixes Used with SI Units

Prefix	Multiplier
tera-	1 000 000 000 000
giga-	1 000 000 000
mega-	1 000 000
kilo-	1000
hecto-	100
deca-	10
[unit]	1
deci-	0.1
centi-	0.01
milli-	0.001
micro-	0.000 001
nano-	0.000 000 001

Using Math

Using Unit Analysis

Example Problem

Rafael measured his classroom to be 468 cm long. Find the length in meters.

Problem-Solving Steps

1. Write the number you want to convert. 468 cm
2. Determine what unit you want the answer to be in. meters
3. Write the number of centimeters in a meter as a fraction. In this case, there are 100 cm in 1 m.

   Use $\frac{100\ \text{cm}}{1\ \text{m}}$ or $\frac{1\ \text{m}}{100\ \text{cm}}$.
4. Write the expression, including the units. Check that the units cancel correctly so the answer will be in meters.
5. **Solution:** $468\ \text{cm} \times \frac{1\ \text{m}}{100\ \text{cm}} = 4.68\ \text{m}$

Practice Problem

How many milliseconds are in 23.6 s?

Strategy Hint: Check that the units cancel appropriately before making calculations. For example, if your expression for speed will produce an answer in square meters, you can see that you have made an error before doing any calculations.

Figure 2-7 The actual size of these red blood cells is about 15 micrometers across. **How many meters is this?**

Length

Length is defined as the distance between two points. Length can describe the distance from Earth to Mars or the distance across a cell under a microscope, as shown in **Figure 2-7.** In your science lab, you will usually measure length with a metric ruler or meterstick.

The **meter** (m) is the SI unit of length. One meter is about the length of a baseball bat. The size of a room would be measured in meters.

Smaller objects can be measured in centimeters (cm) or millimeters (mm). The length of your textbook or pencil would be measured in centimeters. Millimeters might be used to measure the width of the letters on this page. To measure the length of small things such as blood cells, bacteria, or viruses, scientists use micrometers (millionths of a meter) and nanometers (billionths of a meter).

Sometimes scientists need to measure long distances, such as the distance a migrating bird travels. To measure such lengths they use kilometers. Kilometers may be most familiar to you as the measure of a race or the distance traveled in a car, as shown in **Figure 2-8.**

Figure 2-8 Long distances are measured in kilometers. This sign warns drivers in Australia about animals crossing the road. **About how many kilometers is the distance between your home and your school?**

Volume

The amount of space an object occupies is its volume. The cubic meter (m^3), shown in **Figure 2-9,** is the SI unit of volume. You can measure smaller volumes with the cubic centimeter (cm^3 or cc). To find the volume of a square or rectangular object, such as a brick or your textbook, measure its length, width, and height, and multiply them. What is the volume of a compact disc case?

You are probably familiar with a 2-liter bottle. A liter is a measurement of liquid volume. A cube 10 cm on a side (1000 cm^3) holds one liter of water. A cube 1 cm on a side (1 cm^3) holds one milliliter of water.

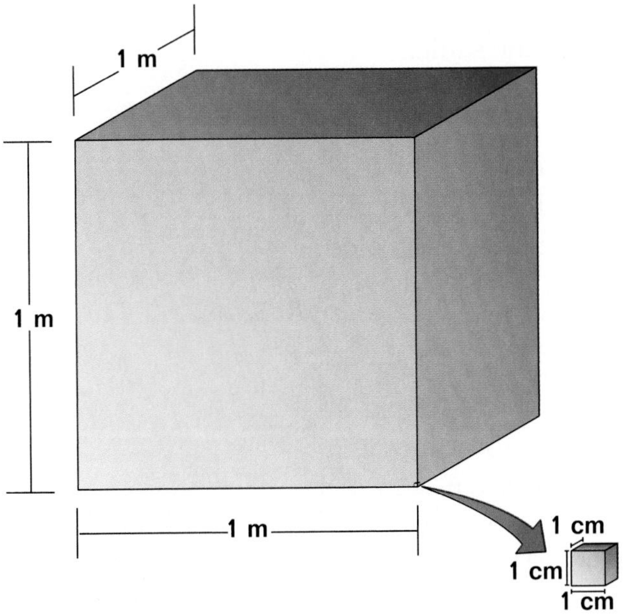

Figure 2-9 A cubic meter equals the volume of a cube 1 meter by 1 meter by 1 meter. **How many cubic centimeters are in a cubic meter?**

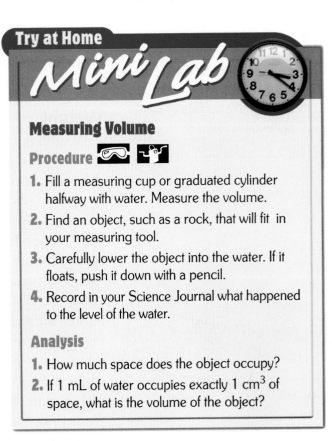

Try at Home

MiniLab

Measuring Volume

Procedure

1. Fill a measuring cup or graduated cylinder halfway with water. Measure the volume.
2. Find an object, such as a rock, that will fit in your measuring tool.
3. Carefully lower the object into the water. If it floats, push it down with a pencil.
4. Record in your Science Journal what happened to the level of the water.

Analysis

1. How much space does the object occupy?
2. If 1 mL of water occupies exactly 1 cm^3 of space, what is the volume of the object?

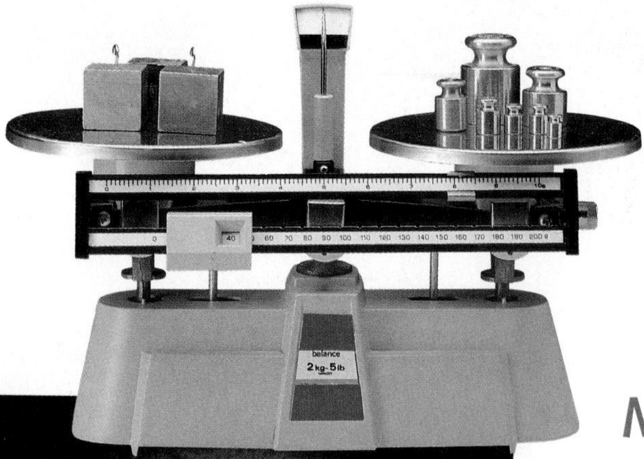

Figure 2-10 Mass is not the same as weight.

A A pan balance compares an unknown mass to known masses.

B Jupiter has a mass of 1.90×10^{27} kg. It does not make sense to talk about the weight of Jupite because it is not on the surface of Earth or another planet.

Mass

The **mass** of an object measures the amount of matter in the object. The **kilogram** (kg) is the SI unit for mass. One liter of water has a mass of about 1 kg. Smaller masses are measured in grams (g). One gram is about the mass of a large paper clip. You can measure mass with a pan balance, shown in **Figure 2-10A.** The pan balance compares an object to a known mass. It is balanced when the masses on both sides are equal.

Why use the word *mass* instead of weight? Weight and mass are not the same. Mass depends on the amount of matter in an object. Mass never changes, as shown in **Figure 2-10B.** When you ride in an elevator or on the space shuttle, your mass stays the same.

Weight

Weight is a measurement of force. It depends on gravity, which can change depending on where the object is located. A spring scale, shown in **Figure 2-11,** measures weight. The reading on the scale depends on the force pulling the spring. When you start riding up in an elevator, you feel heavier for a moment. When the elevator starts down, you feel lighter for a moment. If you were standing in the elevator on a bathroom scale, which uses a spring, you would see a slight change in your weight. But, if you had a pan balance in the elevator, it would not suddenly tip. The masses in the pans would not change, and it would remain balanced.

Reading Check

What does weight measure?

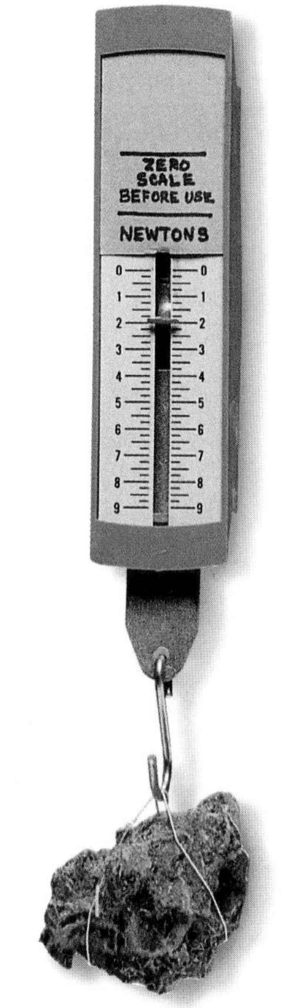

Figure 2-11 A spring scale measures an object's weight by how much it stretches a spring. **What is the weight of the rock?**

Temperature

The physical property of temperature is used to measure how hot or cold an object is. You may know about the Fahrenheit or Celsius temperature scale on a thermometer. Temperature is measured in SI with the **Kelvin** scale. A 1 K difference in temperature is the same as a 1°C difference in temperature, as shown in **Figure 2-12.** However, the two scales start at different points. Zero degrees Celsius is the freezing point of water at sea level. Water boils at 100°C. Zero kelvin is the coldest temperature possible in nature.

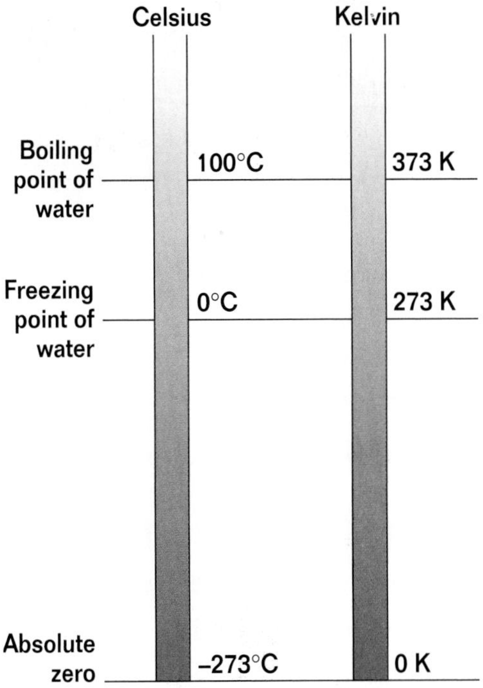

Figure 2-12 The Kelvin scale starts at 0 K.

Time and Rates

Time is the interval between two events. The SI unit of time is the second (s). Time is sometimes measured in hours (h). Though this is not an SI unit, it is easier to use when you discuss long periods.

A **rate** is a ratio of two measurements with different units. One rate you are familiar with is speed, the distance traveled in a given time. Speeds are often measured in kilometers per hour (km/h).

PHYSICS INTEGRATION

Rates are combinations of SI units. Rates are most often seen with units of time, but any measures with different units can be combined in a rate. Other rates might be

$$\frac{\text{grains}}{\text{liter}},\ \frac{\text{insects}}{\text{square meter}},\ \text{or}\ \frac{°\text{C}}{\text{hour}}.$$

Section Assessment

1. What property of an object does the cubic meter measure?
2. How would you change a measure in centimeters to kilometers?
3. **Think Critically:** You are given a small metal cube and told to find its mass. What tool(s) will you need, and how will you use the tool(s) to determine its mass?
4. **Skill Builder**
   Forming Operational Definitions
   Give an operational definition of a spring scale. If you need help, refer to Forming Operational Definitions in the **Skill Handbook** on page 674.

Using Math

A block of wood is 0.2 m by 0.1 m by 0.5 m. Find its dimensions in centimeters. Use these to find its volume in cubic centimeters.

Activity 2•1

Using Scientific Methods

Scale Drawing

Materials

- Graph paper (1 cm)
- Pencil
- Metric ruler
- Meterstick

A scale drawing is used to represent something that is too large or too small to be drawn at its actual size. Blueprints for a house are a good example of a scale drawing.

What You'll Investigate

How can you represent your classroom accurately in a scale drawing?

Goals

- **Measure** using SI.
- **Make** a data table.
- **Calculate** new measurements.
- **Draw** an accurate scale drawing.

Procedure

1. Use your meterstick to **measure** the length and width of your classroom. Note the locations and sizes of doors and windows.
2. **Record** the lengths of each item in a data table.
3. Use a scale of 2 cm = 1 m to calculate the lengths to be used in the drawing. **Record** them in your data table.
4. **Draw** the floor plan. Include the scale.

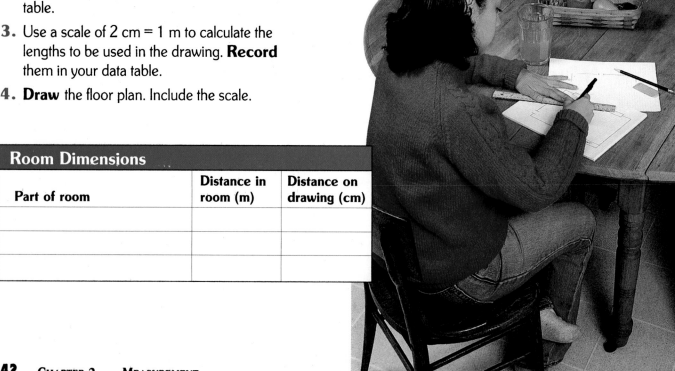

Room Dimensions

Part of room	Distance in room (m)	Distance on drawing (cm)

Conclude and Apply

1. How did you **calculate** the lengths to be used on your drawing?
2. What would your scale drawing look like if you choose a different scale?
3. Sketch your room at home, estimating the distances. **Compare** this to your scale drawing of the classroom. When would you use each type of illustration?

Communicating Data

2·3

Scientific Illustrations

Most science books include some pictures. Photographs and drawings illustrate the ideas in the book. They also can give new information. For example, a drawing of an airplane engine can show how all the parts fit together.

Photographs

A photograph can show an object exactly as it is. A movie can show how an object moves. A movie can be slowed down or speeded up to show interesting features, as shown in **Figure 2-13.** In your schoolwork, you might use photographs in a report. For example, you could show the different types of trees in your neighborhood for a report on ecology.

What You'll Learn

- How to use pictures and tables to give information
- How to identify and use three types of graphs
- How to distinguish the correct use of each type of graph

Vocabulary

table
graph
line graph
bar graph
circle graph

Why It's Important

- Illustrations, tables, and graphs help communicate data.

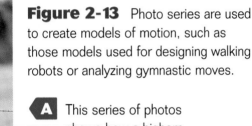

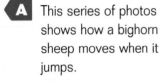

Figure 2-13 Photo series are used to create models of motion, such as those models used for designing walking robots or analyzing gymnastic moves.

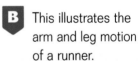

A This series of photos shows how a bighorn sheep moves when it jumps.

B This illustrates the arm and leg motion of a runner.

interNET CONNECTION

Visit the Glencoe Science Web Site at **www.glencoe.com/sec/science/ca** for more information about scientific illustration.

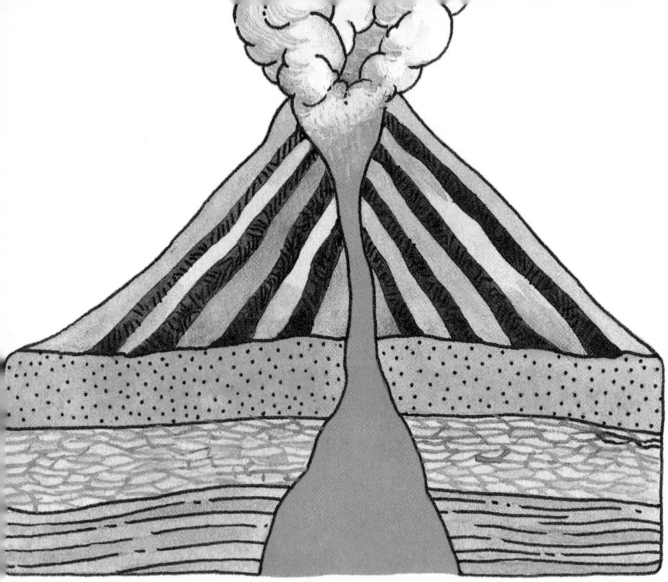

Figure 2-14 This drawing shows the layers of rock around a volcano. It also shows the volcano's interior.

Drawings

Sometimes a photograph is not the best kind of illustration to use. For example, a canyon cut through red rock reveals many rock layers. If the layers are all shades of red, a drawing can show where the line between two layers lies. The drawing can show important things, like the size of each layer, and can leave out unimportant details, like the patterns of dust on the rock.

In your studies, you might use a drawing of the Earth-moon-sun system to explain an eclipse. A drawing also can show things we can't photograph. We do not have photographs of our solar system from far away, but from drawings you know what it looks like. You also will make quick sketches to help model problems. For example, you could sketch the outline of two continents to show how they might have fit together.

A drawing can show hidden things. Geologists can use a drawing to show the inside of a volcano, as in **Figure 2-14.** Architects use drawings to show what the inside of a building will look like. Biologists use drawings to show where the nerves in your arm are found. ☑

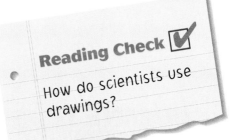

Reading Check ☑

How do scientists use drawings?

Problem Solving

Communicate with Art and Words

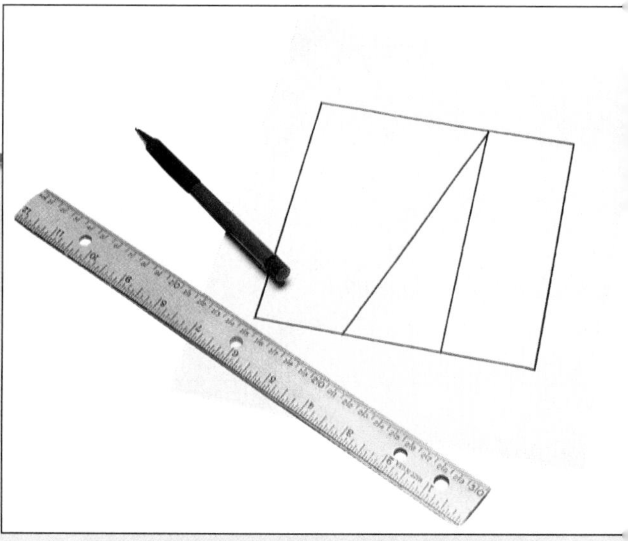

Imagine you are an engineer. You have a clever idea for improving a machine. Or, you are a botanist with a new idea about a plant's structure. How do you explain your idea?

To explain your ideas, you must communicate them clearly. One way is with a picture. How hard is it to describe something using only words?

Use a ruler and pencil to sketch a simple design, such as a triangle inside a square. Write a description that would explain how to make the design without actually seeing it. For example, it might start: "Draw a square 15 cm on a side. Mark a point 5 cm to the right of the lower-left corner . . ."

Trade your description with another student and try to draw the design based on the directions. Compare your design with the original.

Think Critically: Explain how this exercise relates to the problem of describing a new invention for people who cannot see it.

Tables and Graphs

Scientists and mathematicians need an organized way to collect and display data. A **table** displays information in rows and columns so that it is easier to read and understand, as seen in **Figure 2-15.** The data in the table could be presented in a paragraph, but it would be harder to pick out the facts or make comparisons.

A graph can show the relationships between the data. A **graph** is used to collect, organize, and summarize data in a visual way. A graph can display one set of data or more. Three common types of graphs are line graphs, bar graphs, and circle graphs.

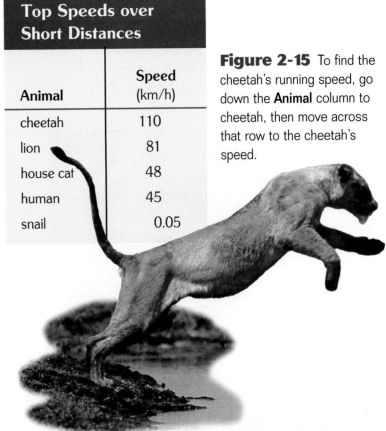

Top Speeds over Short Distances

Animal	Speed (km/h)
cheetah	110
lion	81
house cat	48
human	45
snail	0.05

Figure 2-15 To find the cheetah's running speed, go down the **Animal** column to cheetah, then move across that row to the cheetah's speed.

Line Graph

The table in **Figure 2-15** has two variables, type of animal and speed. A variable is something that can change, or vary. A **line graph** is used to show the relationship between two variables. An example is shown in **Figure 2-16.** Both variables must be numbers. Age and height will work, but age and favorite sport will not. One variable is shown on the bottom line, or axis, of the graph. The other variable is placed along the vertical axis. A line shows the relationship between the two variables.

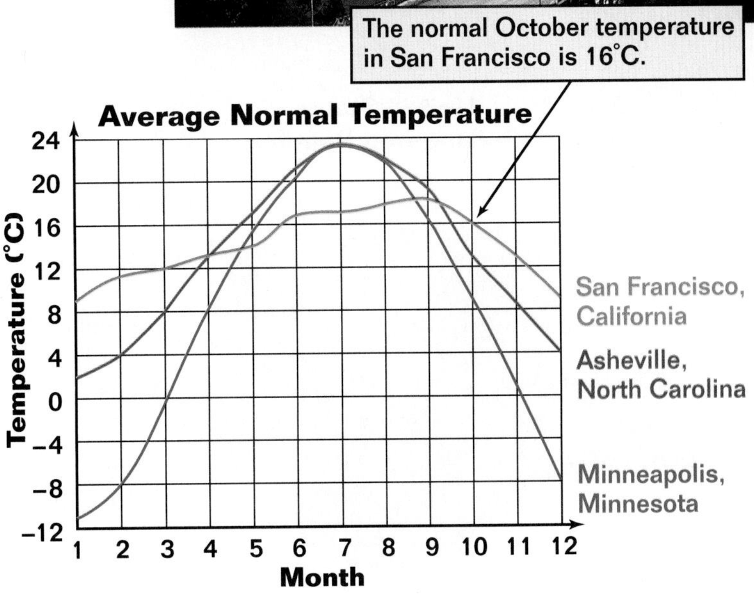

Figure 2-16 The line graph has a horizontal axis and a vertical axis. This graph shows that Minneapolis and Asheville reach the same summer temperature, but Minneapolis has a much greater variation in temperature. The normal temperature in San Francisco peaks later than the temperature in the other two cities. It also has less variation.

Figure 2-17

A This bar graph has categories on the horizontal axis and numbers on the vertical axis. You can see that about 53 percent of junior high schools have modems. **What percentage of senior high schools have modems?**

B The bar graph below has numbers on both axes. Bar graphs can be horizontal or vertical. They can display any numerical data, not just percents. **Based on the bar graph, how did the percentage of homes with computers change between 1991 and 1997?**

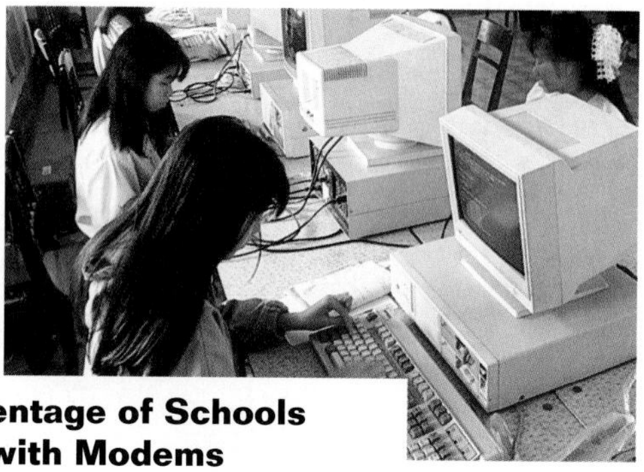

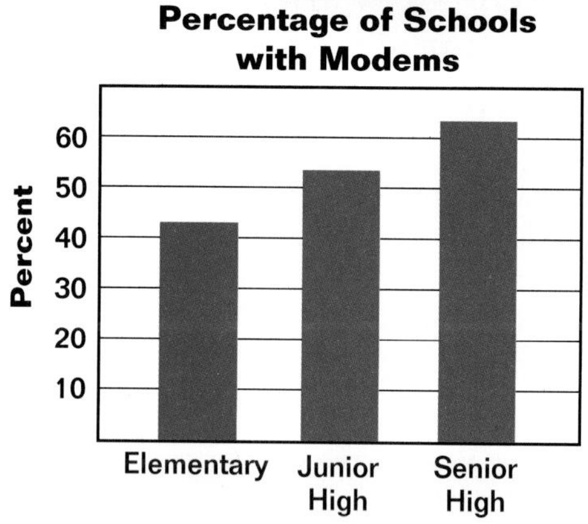

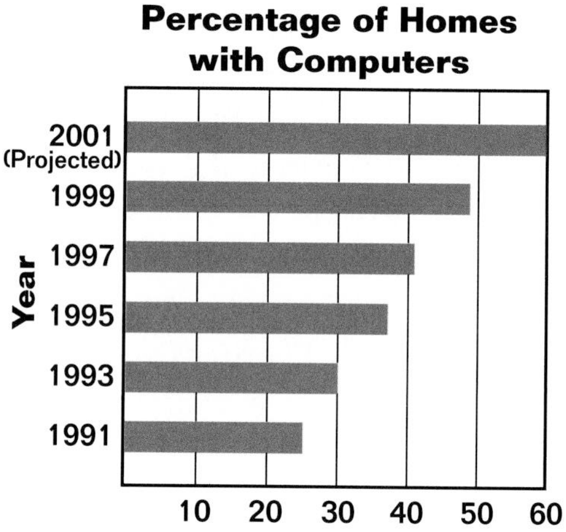

Bar Graph

A **bar graph** uses bars to show the relationships between variables. A bar graph is similar to a line graph. One variable is divided into parts. It can be numbers, such as the time of day, or a category, such as an animal. The second variable must be a number. The bars show the size of the second variable. For example, if you made a graph of the running speed data, the bar for the lion would represent 81 km/h. Examples of bar graphs are shown in **Figure 2-17.**

Figure 2-18 This graph uses a circle divided into sections. All the sections together equal 100 percent. **What category has the greatest number of endangered species?**

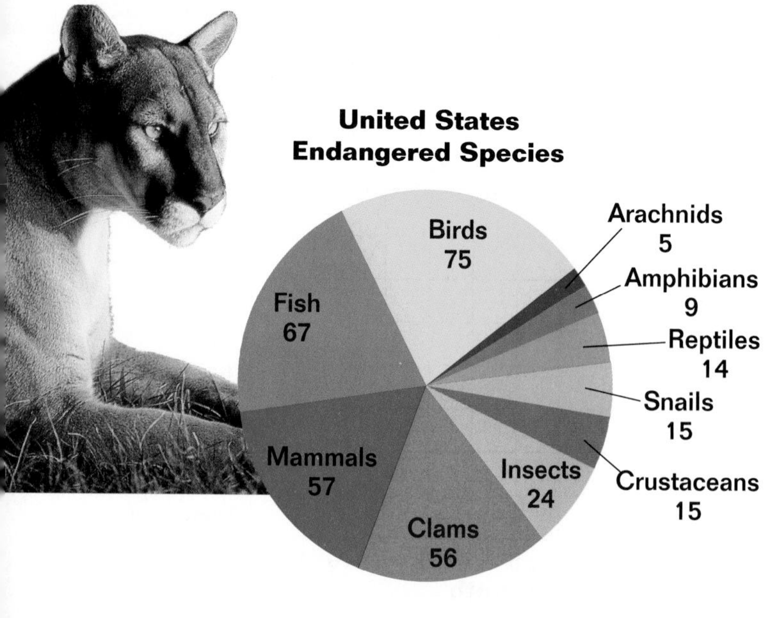

Circle Graph

Suppose you want to show how many people in your class play soccer. A **circle graph** shows the parts of a whole. The circle represents the whole. The sections of the circle represent the parts of the whole, as shown in **Figure 2-18.**

To make a circle graph, find the percent for each part. Multiply the percent by 360° to find the angle measure of that part. For example, there are 337 endangered species in **Figure 2-18** and 57 are mammals. Mammals account for 17 percent of endangered species. Multiply 360° by 0.17. A 62° section represents the mammals.

Misleading Graphs

When using or making graphs to display data, be careful. The scale of a graph can be misleading. The way you mark the scale on a graph can create the wrong impression, as seen in **Figure 2-19A.**

A broken scale is used for small but significant changes. Examples include a climate warming by 0.01°C a year or the finishing times for the top runners in a marathon, as shown in **Figure 2-19B.**

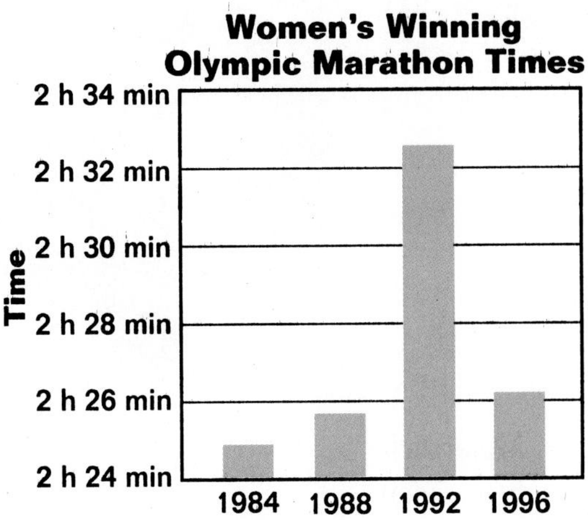

Figure 2-19 An axis that does not start at zero can be misleading. However, it is sometimes necessary.

A The vacation-time graph uses a broken vertical axis (not starting at zero) to make it appear that vacation time has doubled since 1996. The actual increase is about 15 percent.

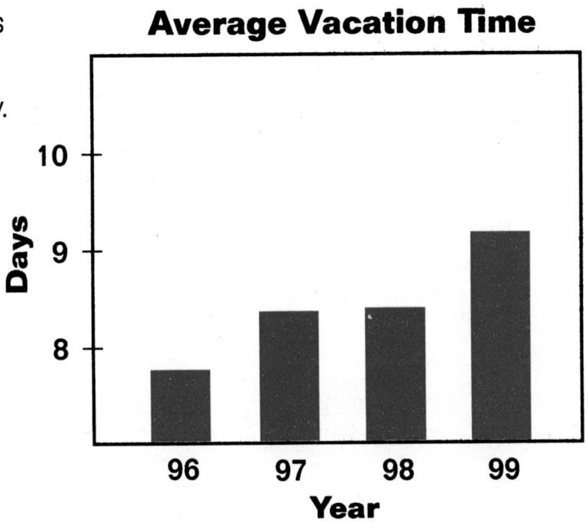

B The difference between the winning times is small. Without the broken axis, all the bars would appear to be the same height because the vertical axis would be divided into hours.

Section Assessment

1. Suppose your class surveys the students in your school about their favorite after-school activities. What type of graph would you use to display your data? Explain your choice.
2. Explain how to use **Figure 2-19B** to find the running time of the 1988 women's Olympic marathon winner.
3. **Think Critically:** How are line, bar, and circle graphs the same? How are they different?
4. **Skill Builder**
   Making and Using Graphs Graph the amount of time you spent reading each day for the past week. What type of graph will you use? If you need help, refer to Making and Using Graphs in the **Skill Handbook** on page 669.

Using Computers

Spreadsheet Use a spreadsheet table to display the total mass of a 500-kg elevator as passengers of 50 kg each are added. If you need help, refer to page 690.

Design Your Own Experiment

Activity 2·2

Pace Yourself

Possible Materials

- Meterstick
- Stopwatch
  **watch with a second hand*

**Alternate Materials*

In a track meet, you run a distance. The distance you are to run has been precisely measured. Officials watch the start to be sure all of the runners begin the race at the same time. The finish line is carefully observed so the timer is stopped at the moment you cross the line. The officials measure your time as precisely as possible. The runner with the shortest time to cover that distance wins. The results are then communicated using tables or other data displays.

Recognize the Problem

Measure running speed for each person in your group and display these data.

Form a Hypothesis

Think about the information you have learned about precision, measurement, and graphing. In your group, make a hypothesis about a technique that will provide you with the most precise measurement of each person's walking and running pace.

Goals

- **Design an experiment** that allows you to accurately measure speed for each member of your group.
- **Display data** in a table and a graph.

Safety Precautions

- Work in an area where it is safe to run.
- Participate only if you are physically able to exercise safely.

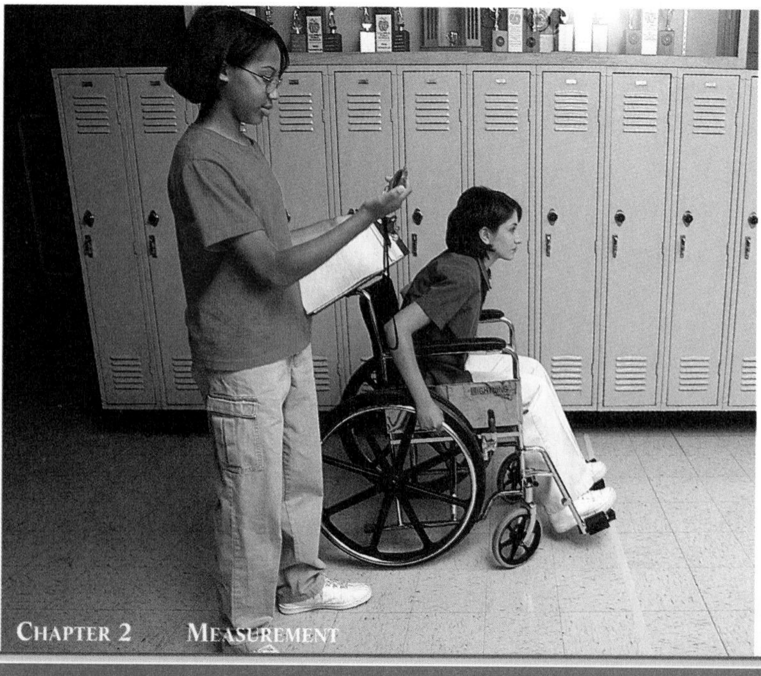

Test Your Hypothesis

Plan

1. As a group, decide what materials you will need.
2. How far will you walk? How far will you run? How will you **measure** that distance? How precise can you be?
3. How will you **measure** time? How precise can you be?
4. List the steps and materials you will use to **test your hypothesis.** Be specific. Will you repeat any part of your test?
5. Before you begin, **create a data table.** Your group must decide on its design. Be sure to leave room to record the results for each person's walking and running time. If more than one trial is to be run for each measurement, include room for the additional data.

Do

1. Make sure that your teacher approves your plan and data table before you begin.
2. **Carry out the experiment** as planned and approved.
3. Be sure to **record your data** in the data table as you proceed with the measurements.

Analyze Your Data

1. **Graph** your data. What type of graph would be best?
2. Are your data table and graph easy to understand? Explain.
3. How do you know that your measurements are precise?

Draw Conclusions

1. How is it possible for different members of a group to find different times while **measuring** the same event?
2. What tools would help you collect more precise **data?**
3. What other data displays could you use? What are the advantages and disadvantages of each?

FIELD GUIDE to Laboratory Equipment

FIELD ACTIVITY

Look around your science classroom. Use this field guide to identify the pieces of equipment available in your classroom or in a laboratory. Practice using the equipment provided by your teacher.

Scientists make observations, form hypotheses, plan and do experiments, collect and analyze their data, and draw conclusions. You will do activities in which you also will use scientific methods while you study science. The quality of the information that you gather during the activities will depend upon correct use of laboratory equipment.

Each set of instructions will tell you what materials and equipment you will need to do the activity. Some of the items will be found around your classroom or at home. Others will be the same types of equipment used by scientists in laboratories and out in the field. Safety symbols guide you in how to use them safely. To find out more about safety symbols, refer to the chart inside the front cover of this book.

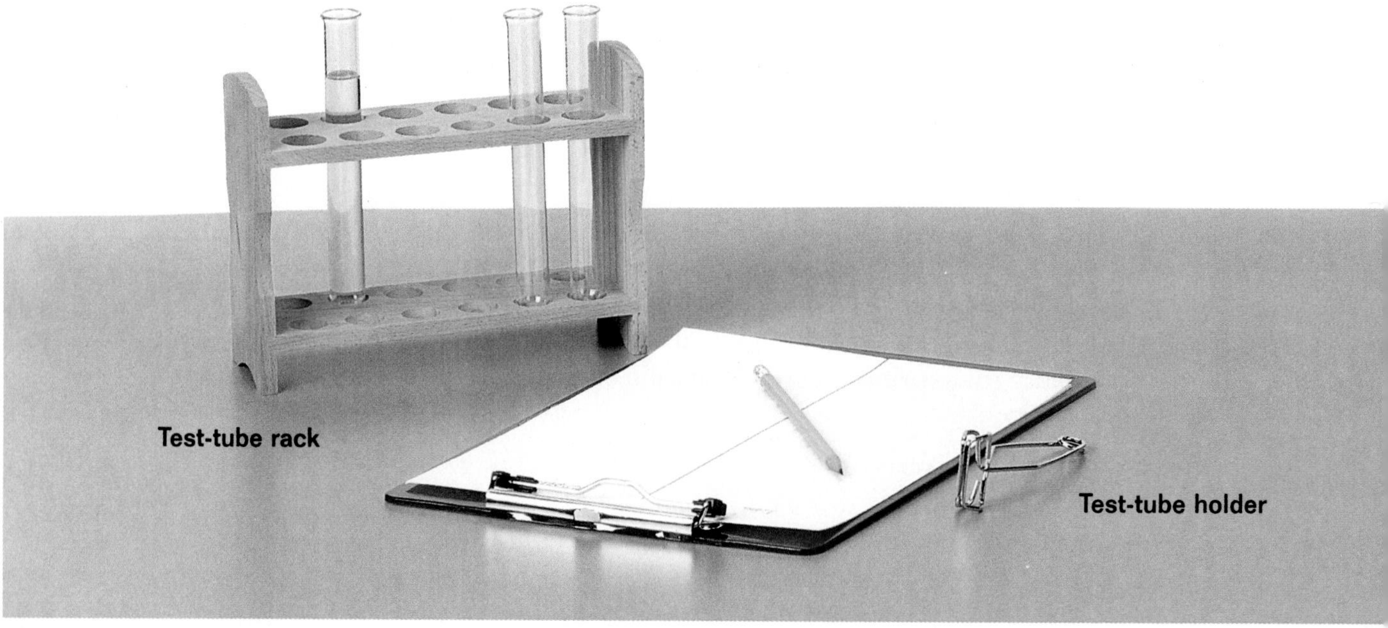
Test-tube rack

Test-tube holder

Laboratory Safety

In the science classroom or laboratory, you are responsible for your own safety and for the safety of your teacher and your classmates. To prevent accidents, be sure to use the following steps.

- Do not perform an activity without your teacher's permission.
- Tie back long hair. Do not wear loose, dangling clothing or jewelry that could catch fire or get caught in something.
- Read through the entire activity before you begin. If you do not understand any part of it, ask your teacher for help.
- Look at the safety symbols. Always wear your goggles, apron, and gloves whenever you are told. Read the safety precautions at the beginning of the procedure.
- Never taste any of the substances you use or make in an activity.
- Immediately report any accident, injury, or damaged equipment to your teacher.

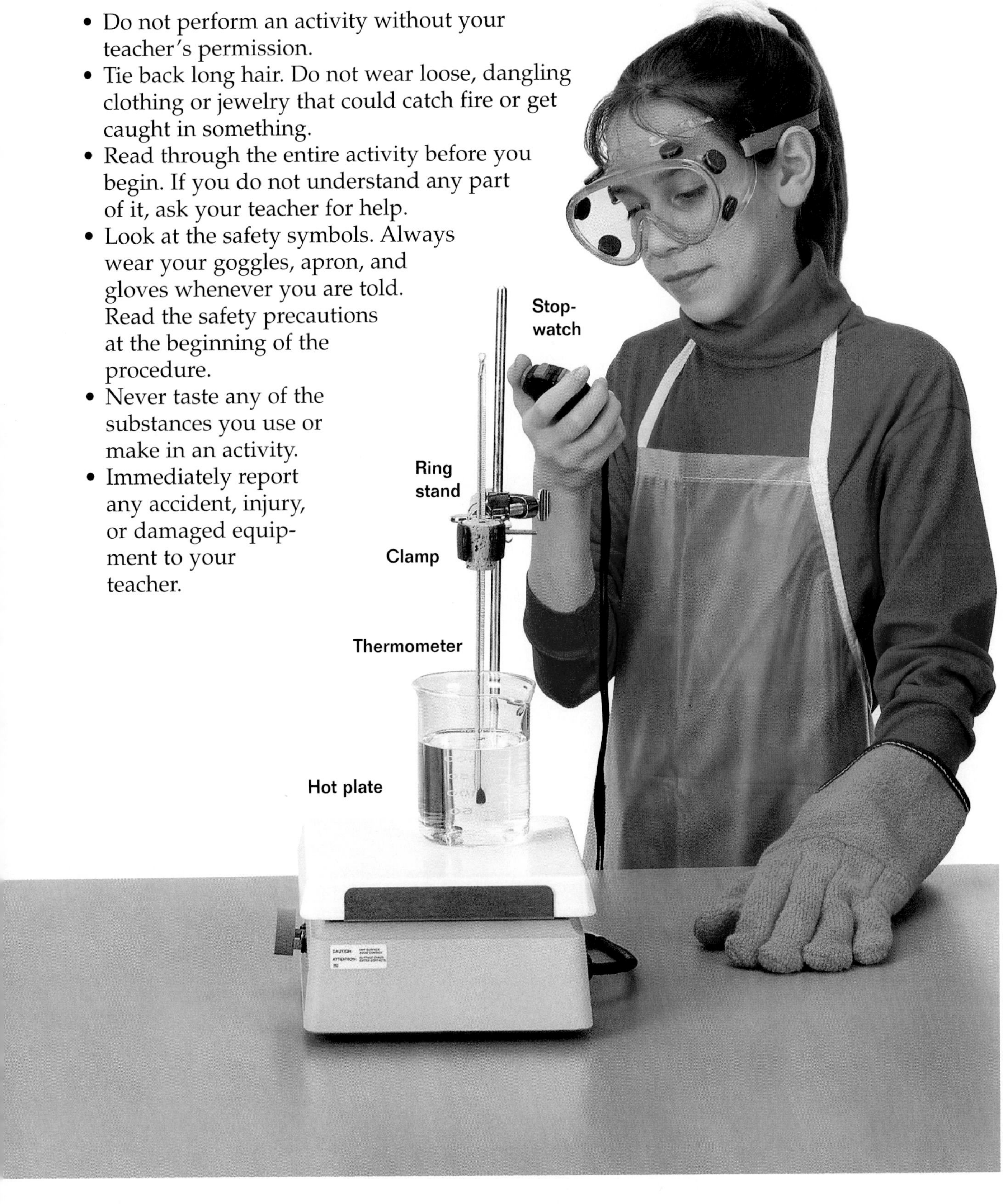

Guide to Labware

Many of your activities will tell you to use the laboratory glassware below. Identify which of the pieces would be most useful for measuring. Explain.

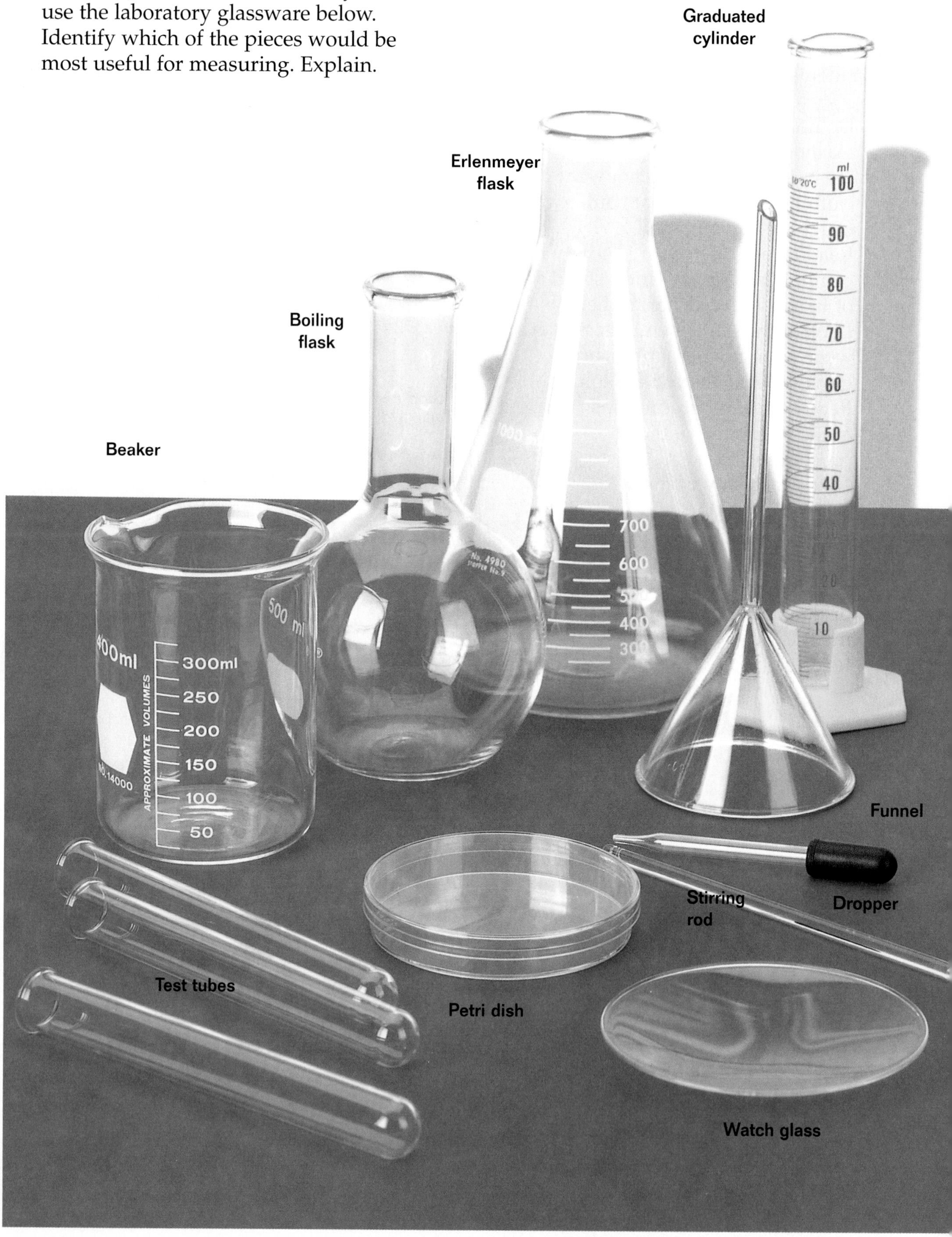

How to Take Good Measurements

To be sure that your measurements are accurate and precise, laboratory instruments must be used correctly.

Measuring Length

- Never measure from the end of a meterstick (or metric ruler). Place the meterstick next to the object and read the metric scale at each end of the object. Subtract your readings to find the length of the object.
- A meterstick should be read while you are looking straight at the mark. You will have to look directly in front or overhead, not at an angle.

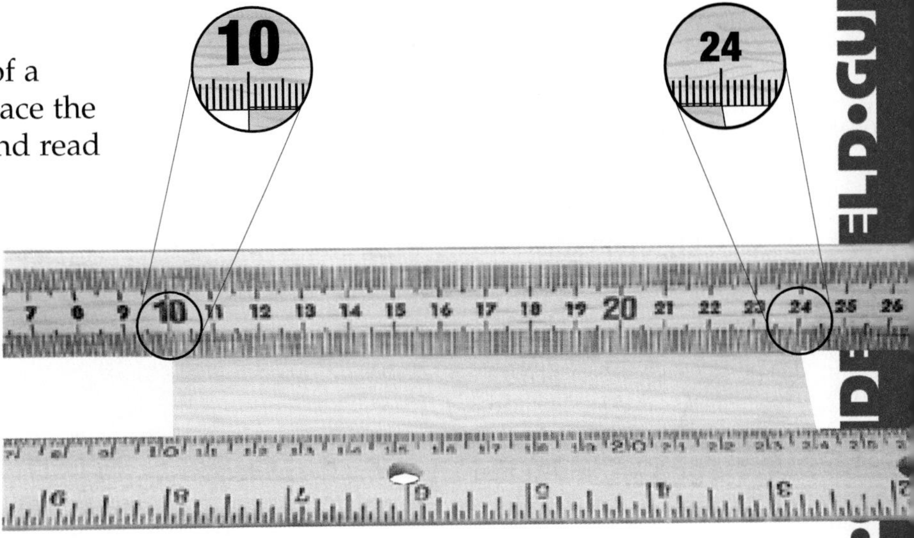

Measuring Liquid Volume and Temperature

- The meniscus is the curve at the top of a liquid. It can curve downward or upward. Look straight at the meniscus when you make your measurement, not above or below.
- A graduated cylinder is used to measure liquid volume. It is often marked in 1-mL segments. To get an accurate measurement, you should read the marking at the bottom of the meniscus.
- Thermometers use liquid volume to measure temperature. The curve of the meniscus will vary due to the type of liquid in the thermometer.

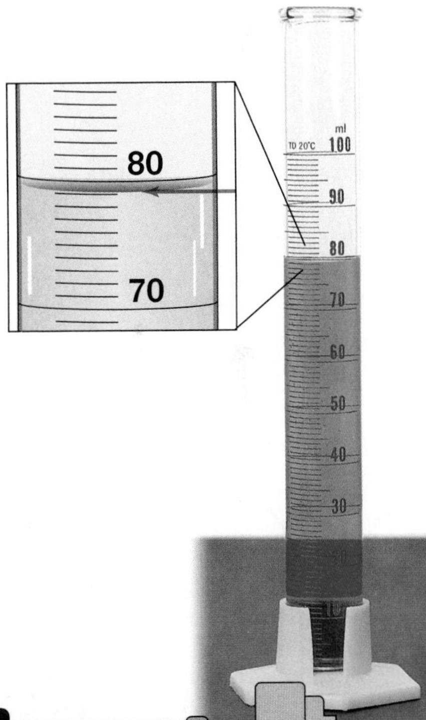

Measuring Mass

- Place the item to be measured in the pan.
- Slide the rider with the largest mass along the balance arm until the pointer drops below zero. Back that rider off one notch.
- Repeat the process with the other two riders. The pointer will swing an equal distance above and below the zero point when the mass of the object is balanced. You do not have to wait for the pointer to stop moving.
- Add the values of the masses on each beam to find the object's mass.

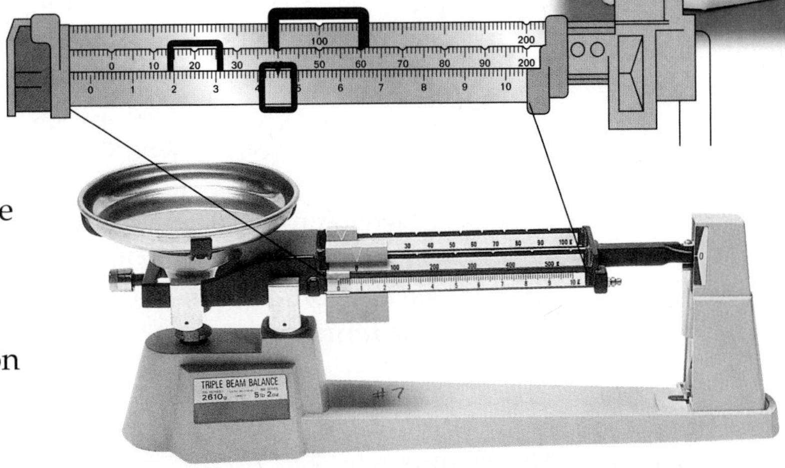

Chapter 2 Reviewing Main Ideas

For a **preview** of this chapter, study this Reviewing Main Ideas before you read the chapter. After you have studied this chapter, you can use the Reviewing Main Ideas to **review** the chapter.

GLENCOE TECHNOLOGY The Glencoe MindJogger, Audiocassettes, and CD-ROM provide additional opportunities for review.

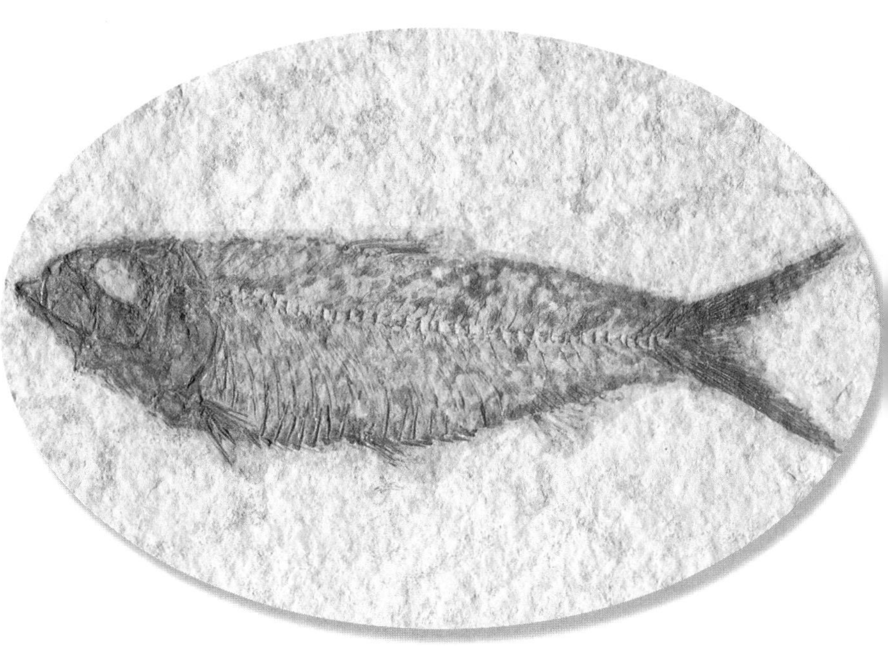

Section

2-1 MEASUREMENT

Measurement is a way to describe the world. Measurements such as length, volume, mass, temperature, and rates are used to describe objects and events. ***Name three quantities that could be used to describe your pen.***

ESTIMATION, ACCURACY, AND PRECISION

Estimation is used to make an educated guess at a measurement. It also is used when determining which point on a ruler or other scale is closest to the correct value. Accuracy describes how close a measurement is to the true value. Precision describes the exactness of a measurement. A mass of 55 kg is known to the nearest kilogram. A mass of 55.040 kg is known to the nearest thousandth of a kilogram. ***If the digital readout on a scale is 48.049 g, what is the mass to the nearest tenth of a gram?***

Reading Check

Find a graph or other illustration in a newspaper or magazine. Explain its purpose.

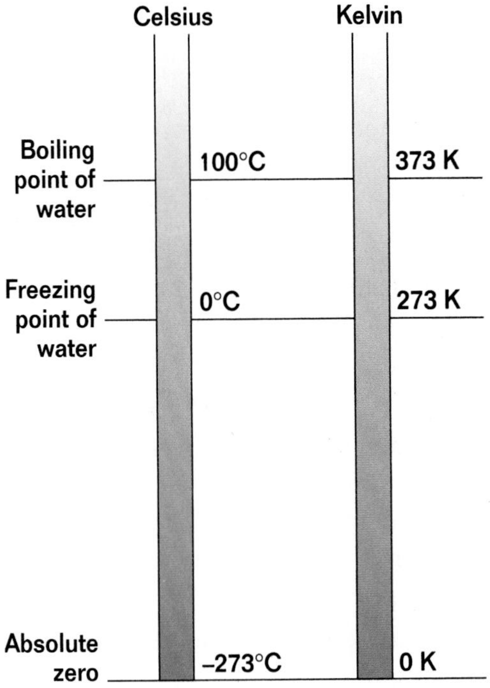

Section 2-2 SI UNITS

The international system of measurement is called **SI.** It is used throughout the world for communicating data in trade, commerce, and science. ***Why do scientists need to use the same measurement system?***

The SI unit of length is the **meter.** Volume, the amount of space an object occupies, can be measured in cubic meters. The **mass** of an object is measured in **kilograms.** Temperature can be measured on different scales. The SI unit of temperature is the **Kelvin.** ***What units would you use to describe the speed of a paper airplane?***

Section 2-3 COMMUNICATING DATA

Tables, illustrations, and **graphs** can present data more clearly than explaining everything in words. They help scientists collect, organize, summarize, and display data in a way that is easy to use and understand. ***Why is the graph shown here a better choice for the data than a circle graph?***

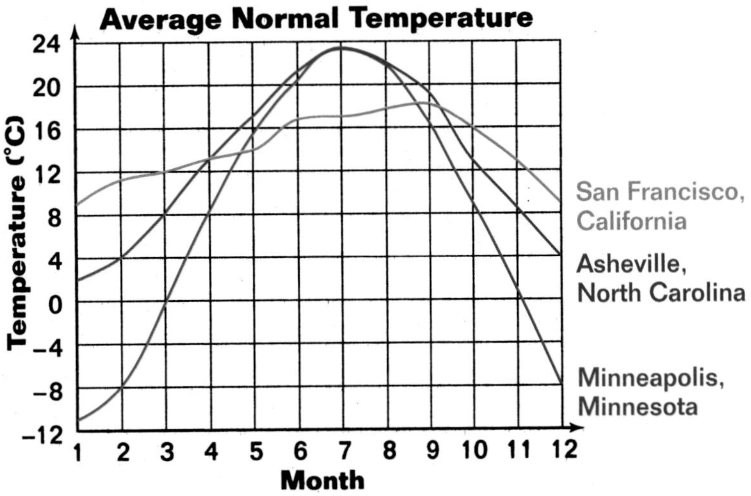

Chapter 2 Assessment

Using Vocabulary

a. bar graph
b. circle graph
c. estimation
d. graph
e. Kelvin
f. kilogram
g. line graph
h. mass
i. measurement
j. meter
k. rate
l. SI
m. table

Each phrase below describes a science term from the list. Write the term that matches the phrase describing it.

1. the SI unit for length
2. a description with numbers
3. a method of making a rough measurement
4. the amount of matter in an object
5. a graph that shows parts of a whole

Checking Concepts

Choose the word or phrase that best answers the question.

6. The measurement 25.81 g is precise to the nearest what?
   A) gram
   B) kilogram
   C) tenth of a gram
   D) hundredth of a gram
7. What is the SI unit of mass?
   A) kilometer
   B) meter
   C) liter
   D) kilogram
8. What would you use to measure the length of an object?
   A) graduated cylinder
   B) balance
   C) meterstick
   D) spring scale
9. The cubic meter is the SI unit of what?
   A) volume
   B) weight
   C) mass
   D) distance
10. Which of the following can improve with practice?
   A) length
   B) estimation
   C) precision
   D) mass
11. Thermometers measure temperature with what scale?
   A) volume
   B) mass
   C) Celsius
   D) mercury
12. Which is used to organize data?
   A) table
   B) rate
   C) precision
   D) graduated cylinder
13. To show the number of wins for each football team in your district, use which of the following?
   A) circle graph
   B) line graph
   C) bar graph
   D) SI
14. What organizes data in rows and columns?
   A) bar graph
   B) circle graph
   C) line graph
   D) table
15. To show 25 percent on a circle graph, the section must measure what angle?
   A) 25 degrees
   B) 90 degrees
   C) 180 degrees
   D) 360 degrees

Thinking Critically

16. How would you estimate the volume your backpack could hold?
17. Why do scientists in the United States use SI rather than the English system (feet, pounds, pints, etc.) of measurement?
18. List the following lengths in order from smallest to largest: 1 m, 1 mm, 10 km, 100 mm.
19. When would you use a line graph? Can you use a bar graph for the same purpose?
20. This chapter has treated color as a quality that is not measured. However, computer artists can specify a color by using numbers to describe the amount of each

color of ink to be used at each point in a picture. Why do you think this method of describing color was invented?

Developing Skills

If you need help, refer to the Skill Handbook.

21. **Measuring in SI:** Make a fist. Use a centimeter ruler to measure the height, width, and depth of your fist.
22. **Comparing and Contrasting:** How are volume, length, and mass similar? How are they different? What units are used to measure each?
23. **Making and Using Graphs:** The table gives the area of several bodies of water. Make a bar graph of the data.

Areas of Bodies of Water

Body of Water	Area (km^2)
Currituck Sound (North Carolina)	301
Pocomoke Sound (Maryland/Virginia)	286
Chincoteague Bay (Maryland/Virginia)	272
Core Sound (North Carolina)	229

24. **Interpreting Scientific Illustrations:** What does the figure show? How has it been simplified?

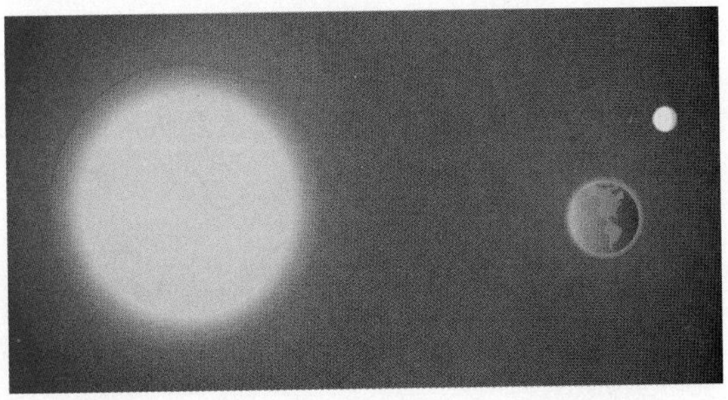

25. **Forming Operational Definitions:** Give an operational definition of a pan balance.

THE PRINCETON REVIEW

Test-Taking Tip

Survey the Surroundings Find out what the conditions will be for taking the test. Will the test be timed? Will you be allowed a break? Know these things in advance so that you can practice taking tests under the same conditions.

Test Practice

Use these questions to test your Science Proficiency.

1. Estimate the percentage of hydrogen in the human body.

Elements in the Human Body

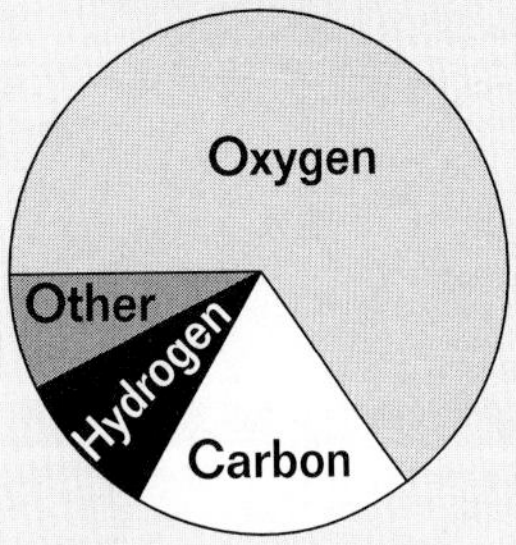

A) 50 percent
B) 25 percent
C) 10 percent
D) 1 percent

2. What are commonly used units for SI?
A) meter, cubic meter, kilogram, second
B) length, volume, mass, time
C) kilo, deci, centi, milli
D) inch, mile, foot, pound

CHAPTER

3 Rocks

Chapter Preview

Skills Preview

Skill Builders

- Interpret Scientific Illustrations
- Interpret Data

Activities

- Draw Conclusions

MiniLabs

- Observe and Infer

Reading Check

List the chapter vocabulary terms in a column. Beside each one, write what you think the word means. As you read, revise your definitions whenever necessary.

Explore Activity

These columns of rock stand like sentinels in the desert sun of Monument Valley, Utah. Though they look large and imposing, they are made of tiny particles of sand and other materials tightly pressed together. Other rocks form from molten lava ejected from volcanoes or from the remains of once-living plants and animals. If you examine rocks closely, you can sometimes tell what they are made of.

Determine What Rocks Are Made Of

1. Collect three or four different rock fragments from around your home.
2. Draw a picture of the details you see in each rock.
3. Look for different types of materials within the same rock. If these different materials could be separated by physical means, then the rock would be considered a mixture.

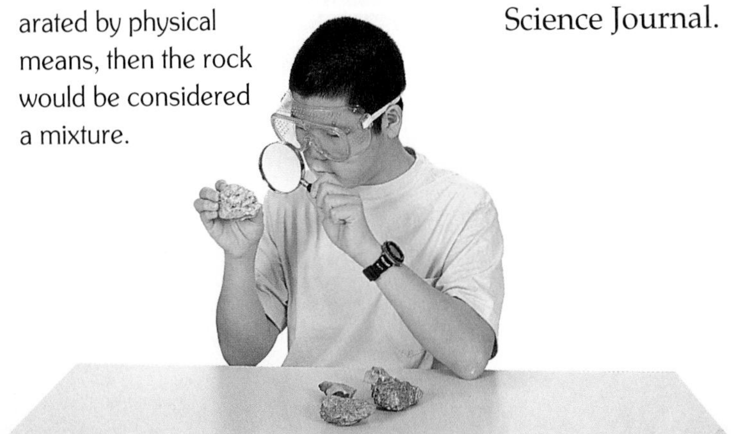

Science Journal

What do you notice about each rock? Are your rocks mixtures? If so, what might they be mixtures of? Write your observations in your Science Journal.

3-1 The Rock Cycle

What You'll Learn

- How to differentiate between a rock and a mineral
- The rock cycle and some changes that a rock may undergo

Vocabulary
rock
rock cycle

Why It's Important

- Rocks are materials that change as their environment changes.

What is a rock?

Imagine that you're on your way home from a friend's house when you notice an unusual rock in a driveway. You pick it up, wondering why it looks different from other rocks nearby. The other rocks are flat and dull, but this one is rounded and has shiny crystals in it. You decide to stick the interesting rock in your pocket and ask your Earth science teacher about it tomorrow.

What exactly should you ask your teacher? You might begin by asking, "What is a rock?" and "Why are rocks so different from one another?"

Forming Rocks

A **rock** is a mixture of minerals, mineraloids, glass, or organic matter. Quartz is a common mineral found in rocks. Other common rock-forming minerals include feldspar, hornblende, and mica. **Figure 3-1** shows all these minerals mixed together to form the rock granite.

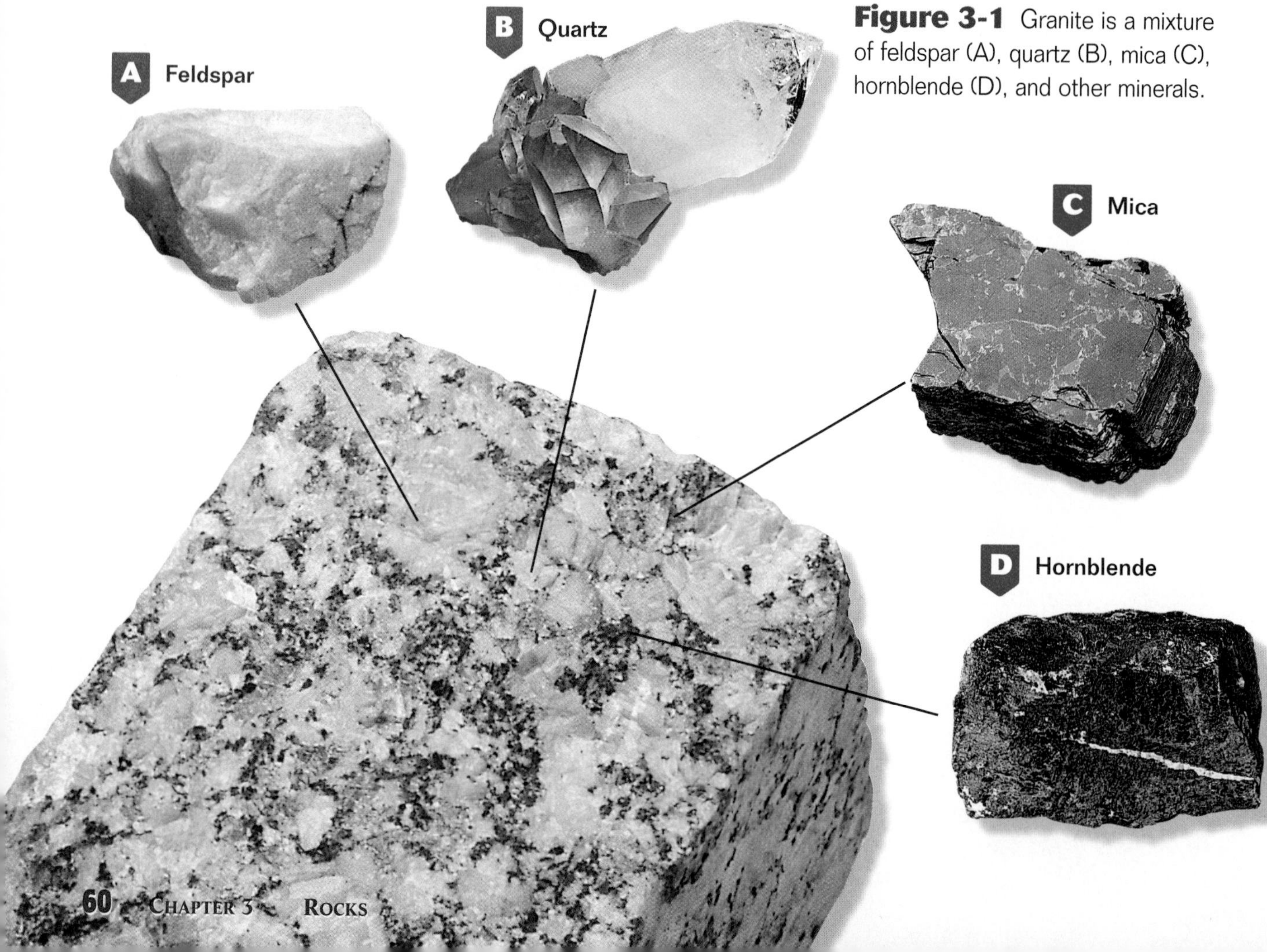

Figure 3-1 Granite is a mixture of feldspar (A), quartz (B), mica (C), hornblende (D), and other minerals.

VISUALIZING
The Rock Cycle

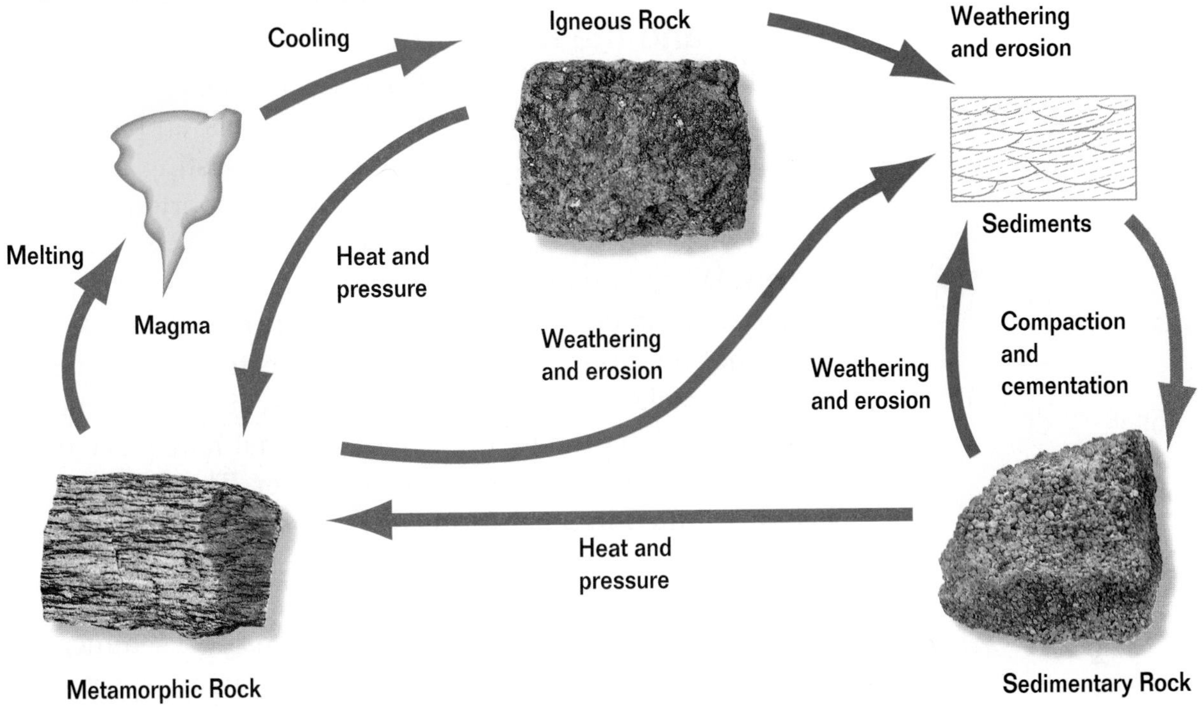

Figure 3-2 This model of the rock cycle shows how rocks are constantly changed from one form to another. **How are rocks different from minerals?**

How do these minerals mix together? And, once they've formed a rock, do they stay in that same rock forever?

The Rock Cycle

Rocks are constantly changing from one type to another. Scientists have created a model called the **rock cycle,** shown in **Figure 3-2,** to illustrate the process. The rock cycle shows the three types of rock and the processes that form them. Look at the rock cycle and notice that rocks are changed by processes such as weathering, erosion, compaction, cementation, melting, and cooling. For example, a sedimentary rock can be changed by heat and pressure to form a metamorphic rock. The metamorphic rock can then melt and later cool to form an igneous rock. The igneous rock

MiniLab

Changing Rocks

Procedure

1. Obtain samples of fine-grained sand and glitter from your teacher.
2. Place the sand and gitter into a flat pan.
3. Mix a solution of water and white glue.
4. Pour the solution into the pan and mix thoroughly with the sand and glitter.
5. Place a layer of waxed paper over the mixture, then place a heavy weight on top of the waxed paper.

Analysis

1. After several days, remove the weight and examine the mixture.
2. How is the process used to make the model mixture similar to one part of the rock cycle?
3. Describe other processes that might be used to model other parts of the rock cycle.

may then weather and erode, and the fragments from it might form another sedimentary rock. Heat and pressure can also change igneous rocks into metamorphic rocks.

Matter and the Rock Cycle

Notice from three of the green arrows in the rock cycle diagram in **Figure 3-2** that grains of minerals and rocks are weathered and eroded from any type of existing rock. This sediment is taken off and then may be transported by wind, water, or ice for tens, hundreds, or even thousands of kilometers. When you think of rock removal, it may seem that the material is somehow destroyed and lost from the cycle. But, this is not the case. The chemical elements that make up minerals and rocks are not destroyed. This fact illustrates the law of conservation of matter. The changes that take place in the rock cycle never destroy or create matter. The elements are just distributed in other forms. ☑

Reading Check ☑

What is the law of conservation of matter?

Weathering and the Rock Cycle

Weathering is part of the cycle that forms new sedimentary rocks. Weathering processes can wear away spectacular mountains like the ones shown in **Figure 3-3.** Some of the mineral matter in mountains is broken off by wind, water, or ice, but otherwise remains the same. This is an example of matter that has undergone a physical change. Some of this mineral matter is carried away in streams as individual particles that we cannot see. These particles are free to react with other particles to produce new minerals. This is an example of a chemical change. The new minerals that form when particles bond together may be totally different from the original rocks and minerals from which they

Figure 3-3 These mountains are part of the Himalaya in Nepal, which include the highest peak on Earth. **What processes cause the uneven surfaces of these majestic mountains?**

were dissolved. The next time you see water flowing down a river channel, think about all the particles that are in solution there. They may have come from a mountain high above you.

In the following sections, you will explore weathering, erosion, deposition, and other processes involved in the rock cycle. The rock cycle shows how all of these processes interact to form and change the rocks around you. Like the geologists in **Figure 3-4,** let's now investigate how igneous, metamorphic, and sedimentary rocks fit into the rock cycle.

Figure 3-4 Geologists working in the field gather information about the rock cycle. Later, they analyze the data in a laboratory, often using a computer.

Section Assessment

1. What materials mix together to form a rock?
2. What is the rock cycle?
3. Describe one way that the rock cycle can illustrate the law of conservation of matter.
4. **Think Critically:** Look at the model of the rock cycle. How would you define *magma* based on **Figure 3-2?** How would you define *sediments* and *sedimentary rock?*
5. **Skill Builder**
   Concept Mapping Make a concept map that explains how igneous rocks can become sedimentary, then metamorphic, and finally, other igneous rocks. If you need help, refer to Concept Mapping in the **Skill Handbook** on page 666.

Science Journal

Review the model of the rock cycle in **Figure 3-2.** In your Science Journal, write a story or poem that explains what can happen to a sedimentary rock as it changes through the rock cycle.

Activity 3•1

Materials

- Igneous rock samples (5)
- Hand lens
- **Table 3-1**
- Appendices F and G

Igneous Rocks

One way that rocks can form is from melted rock material, called magma. Some rocks formed in this way cool quickly from lava at or near Earth's surface. Others cool slowly from magma deep inside Earth. You can determine how igneous rocks form by observing their mineral content and how big the mineral grains are.

What You'll Investigate

Goals

- **Observe** and **classify** igneous rocks based on texture and color.
- **Recognize** that the texture of igneous rocks is determined by how fast they cool.
- **Recognize** that the color of igneous rocks is an indication of mineral content and chemical composition.

Safety Precautions

Procedure

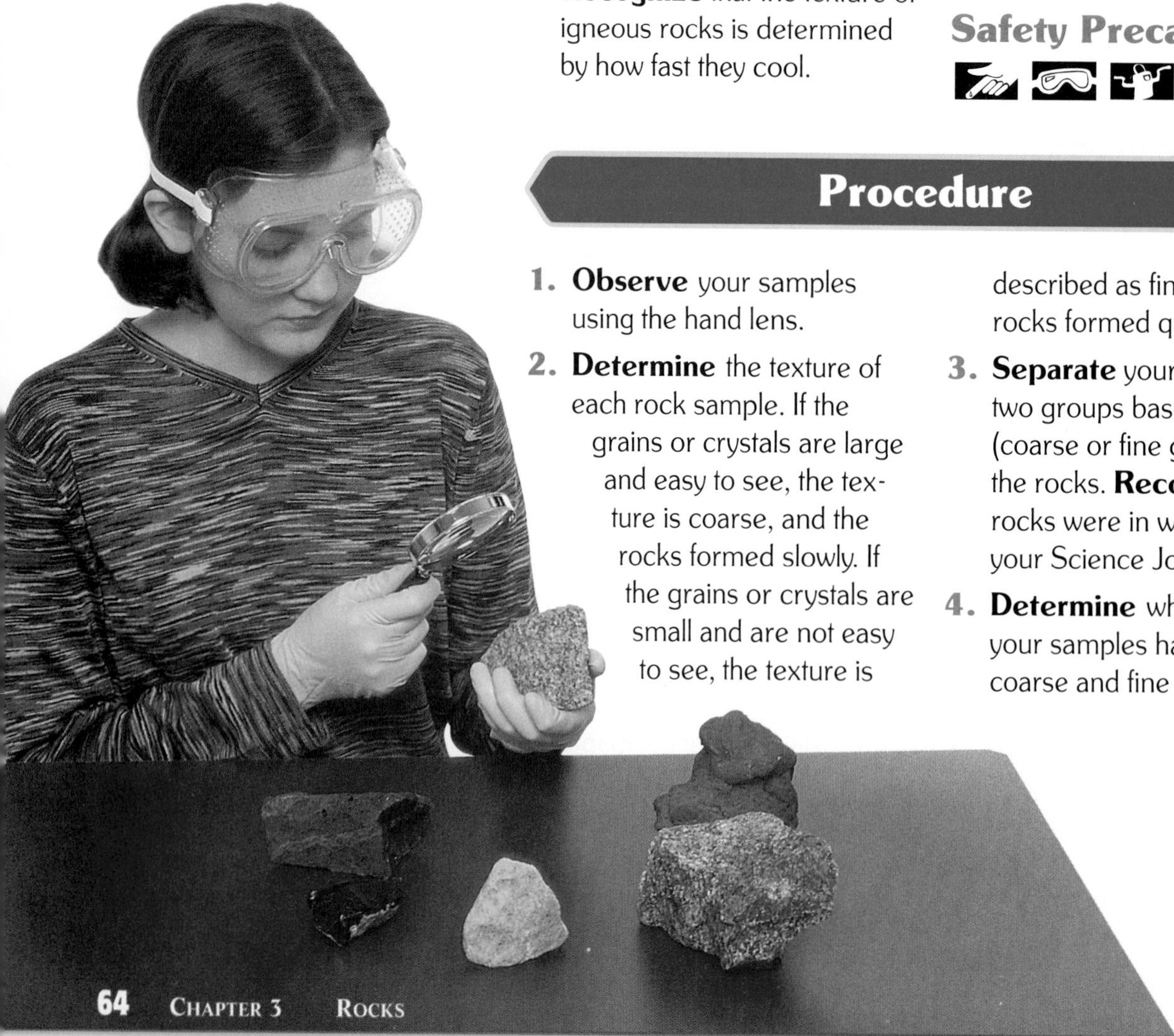

1. **Observe** your samples using the hand lens.
2. **Determine** the texture of each rock sample. If the grains or crystals are large and easy to see, the texture is coarse, and the rocks formed slowly. If the grains or crystals are small and are not easy to see, the texture is described as fine, and the rocks formed quickly.
3. **Separate** your samples into two groups based on texture (coarse or fine grained) of the rocks. **Record** which rocks were in which group in your Science Journal.
4. **Determine** whether any of your samples has both coarse and fine crystals in it.

5. **Classify** your rocks based on chemical composition. Igneous rocks that are dark colored generally have a higher percentage of iron and magnesium in them. Igneous rocks that are light colored generally have a higher percentage of the compound silica (SiO_2) in them. Rocks that are intermediate in color are also intermediate in composition. Record your data in your Science Journal.
6. Using Appendix F, can you **infer** what minerals have formed in the light-colored rocks? What about the dark-colored or intermediate-colored rocks? Record your inferences in your Science Journal.
7. Using **Table 3-1,** Appendices F and G, and the information you have entered in your Science Journal, **fill** in the data table.

Igneous Rock Data

Texture*	Color	Minerals Present	Rock Name
glassy		none visible	
		feldspar** augite olivine	
glassy, with abundant holes	usually light-colored		
fine, with abundant holes	dark colored		

*Glassy and fine-textured rocks may not have visible minerals.

**May not be distinguished without a microscope.

Conclude and Apply

1. Dark-colored igneous rocks are classified as basaltic, light-colored ones as granitic, and intermediate-colored ones as andesitic. Based on this, how would yours be **classified?**
2. What minerals might be causing the varying colors found in your rocks?
3. Place your pumice sample in a container of water. What happens? **Explain** the cause of what you observe.
4. What process could form a rock that has large crystals surrounded by small crystals?

3•2 Igneous Rocks

What You'll Learn

- How to recognize magma and lava as the materials that cool to form igneous rocks
- How to contrast the formation of intrusive and extrusive igneous rocks
- How to contrast granitic and basaltic igneous rocks

Vocabulary

igneous rock **lava** **intrusive** **extrusive** **basaltic** **granitic**

Why It's Important

- Igneous rocks are the most abundant kind of rock on Earth. They contain many valuable resources.

Origin of Igneous Rocks

In July 3, 1998, the Soufrière Hills volcano on the island of Montserrat in the Caribbean erupted. Perhaps you've heard of other recent volcanic eruptions. When most volcanoes erupt, they eject a thick, gooey flow of molten material. Molten material flows when it is hot and becomes solid when it cools. When the molten material, called magma, from a volcano or from deep inside Earth cools, it forms **igneous rocks.** But why do volcanoes, such as the ones in **Figure 3-5,** erupt, and where does the molten material come from?

VISUALIZING
Igneous Activity

Figure 3-5 Magma trapped below Earth's surface is insulated by the rocks surrounding it. This holds in the heat and causes the magma to cool slowly. The atoms have time to arrange into large crystals called mineral grains.

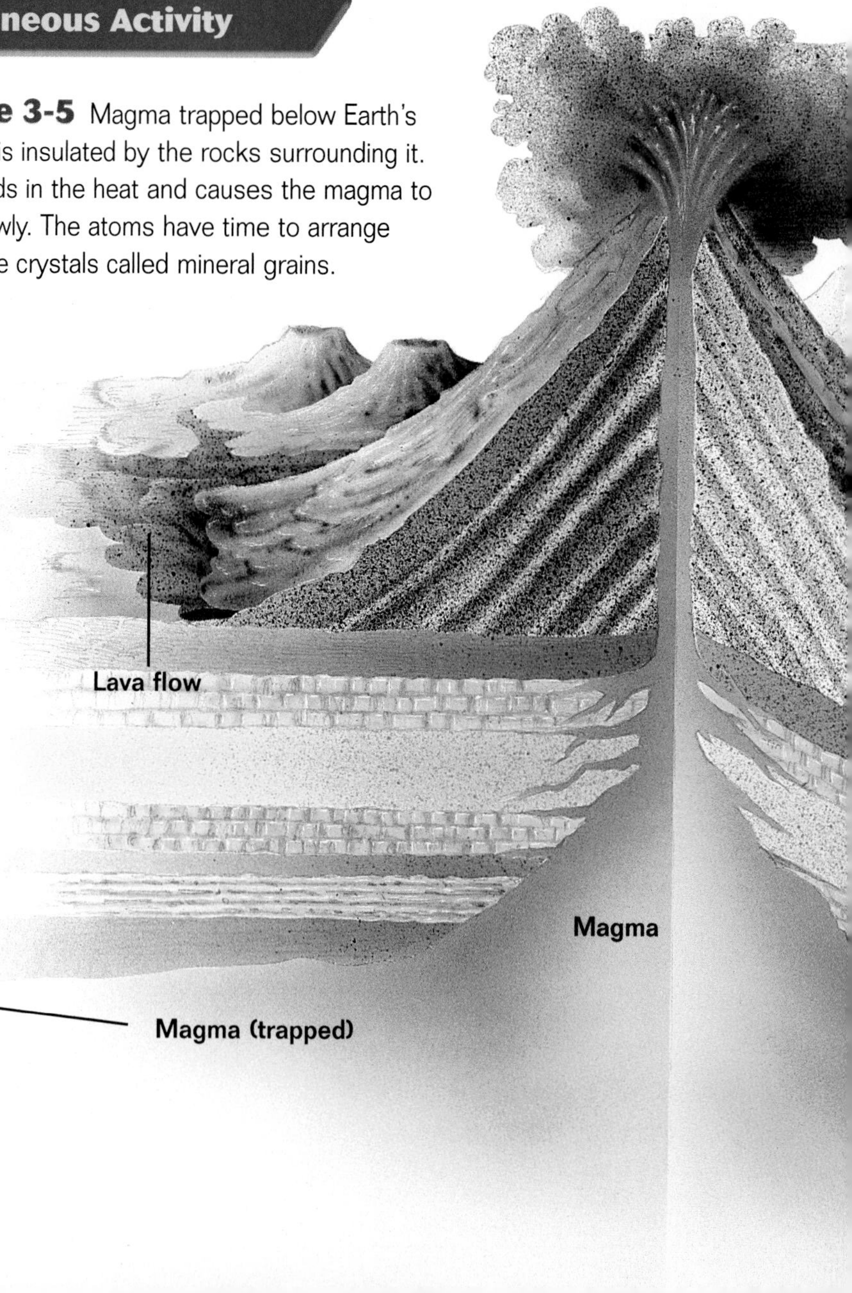

A Intrusive rocks such as diorite have large crystal grains. **In your Science Journal, explain how diorite forms.**

Diorite

Magma

Most magmas come from regions deep below Earth's surface. They exist at depths ranging from near Earth's surface to about 150 km below the surface. Temperatures of magmas range from about 650°C to 1200°C, depending on the chemical composition and pressure of the magma. Radioactive elements in Earth materials deep below Earth's surface generate heat. Earth's interior also retains heat from its original formation. In certain places within Earth, the temperature and pressure are just right to melt rocks and form magma.

Magma is less dense than surrounding solid rock, so it is forced upward toward Earth's surface. The magma that eventually reaches Earth's surface and flows from volcanoes is called **lava.**

interNET CONNECTION

Visit the Glencoe Science Web Site at **www.glencoe.com/sec/science/ca** for more information about how the lives of people have been affected by volcanic eruptions.

B Extrusive rocks such as andesite form from fast-cooling lava. Magma is forced upward toward Earth's surface, where it cools to form extrusive igneous rocks.

Figure 3-6 Obsidian (A), pumice (B), and scoria (C) are actually glass but are classified as extrusive igneous rocks. **Did the lava that formed these rocks cool quickly or slowly? Explain your answer.**

Intrusive Rocks

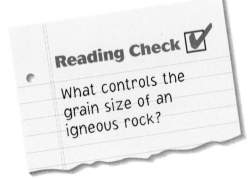

Magma is made up of atoms of melted minerals. As magma cools, the atoms rearrange themselves into new crystals called mineral grains. Rocks form as these mineral grains grow together. Rocks that form below Earth's surface are **intrusive** igneous rocks. Generally, intrusive igneous rocks have large mineral grains. Intrusive rocks are found at Earth's surface when the kilometers of rock and soil that once covered them have been removed, or when they are pushed up by forces in Earth.

Reading Check

What controls the grain size of an igneous rock?

Extrusive Rocks

Extrusive igneous rocks are formed as lava cools on or near Earth's surface. When lava flows on Earth's surface, it is exposed to air and moisture. Lava cools quickly under these conditions. The quick cooling rate keeps large mineral grains from growing. The atoms don't have time to arrange into large crystals. Extrusive igneous rocks have a fine-grained texture.

Figure 3-6 shows pumice, obsidian, and scoria. These rocks cooled so quickly that no visible mineral grains formed. Most of the atoms in these rocks are not arranged into orderly patterns. Because of their lack of atomic order, obsidian, scoria, and pumice are examples of natural glass.

In the case of pumice and scoria, air and other gases become trapped in the gooey molten material as it cools. These gases eventually escape, but holes are left behind where the rock formed around the pockets of gas.

Classification of Igneous Rocks

Igneous rocks are called intrusive or extrusive depending on where they formed. A way to further classify these rocks is by magma type. As shown in **Table 3-1,** an igneous rock can form from basaltic, granitic, or andesitic magma.

Table 3-1

Common Igneous Rocks		
Type of Magma or Lava	**Intrusive**	**Extrusive**
Basaltic	Gabbro	Basalt
		Scoria
Andesitic	Diorite	Andesite
Granitic	Granite	Rhyolite
		Pumice
		Obsidian

Basaltic Rocks

Basaltic igneous rocks are dense, heavy, dark-colored rocks that form from basaltic magma. Basaltic magma is rich in iron and magnesium. Basaltic lava is fluid and flows freely from the volcanoes in Hawaii, as shown in **Figure 3-7.** How does this explain the black beach sand common in Hawaii?

Granitic and Andesitic Rocks

CHEMISTRY INTEGRATION

Granitic igneous rocks are light-colored rocks of a lower density than basaltic rocks. Granitic magma is thick and stiff and contains a lot of silica, which is the compound SiO_2. Granitic magma can build up a great deal of gas pressure, which is released explosively during violent volcanic eruptions.

Andesitic rocks have mineral compositions between those of granitic and basaltic rocks. Many volcanoes in the Pacific Ocean are andesitic. These volcanoes also can erupt violently.

Figure 3-7 Basalt is the most common extrusive rock. Sediments from weathered and eroded basalt form the black-sand beaches of the Hawaiian Islands. In this photo, basaltic lava is flowing into the ocean, producing steam.

Figure 3-8 The eruption of Soufrière Hills volcano affected two-thirds of the Caribbean island of Montserrat. The gray material that covers everything in the photo is ash that has fallen from the eruption.

CHEMISTRY INTEGRATION

Melting Minerals
As heat increases inside Earth, materials contained in rocks begin to melt. In your Science Journal, describe what is happening to the atoms and molecules to cause this change of state.

The classification of an igneous rock tells a lot about its origin, formation, and composition. Basalt is an extrusive, basaltic igneous rock. This means that it formed on Earth's surface, where cooling was fast, giving the rock a fine-grained texture. Basalt has a high concentration of iron and magnesium because it forms from basaltic lava.

Igneous rocks are the most abundant type of rock on Earth. Igneous rocks form when lava or magma solidifies. Later, you will learn more about volcanoes and their effects on people. **Figure 3-8** shows one way erupting volcanoes impact people's lives and property.

Section Assessment

1. Why do some types of magma and lava form igneous rocks that are dark colored and dense?
2. How do intrusive and extrusive igneous rocks differ?
3. Why does magma rise toward Earth's surface?
4. **Think Critically:** How are granite and rhyolite similar? How are they different?
5. **Skill Builder**
   Interpreting Scientific Illustrations
   Suppose you are given a photograph of two igneous rocks. You are told one is an intrusive rock and one is extrusive. By looking only at the photographs, how could you know which is which? If you need help, refer to Interpreting Scientific Illustrations in the **Skill Handbook** on page 678.

Using Math

Four elements make up more than 87 percent of all the rocks in Earth's crust.
Oxygen—46.6 percent
Silicon—27.7 percent
Aluminum—8.1 percent
Iron—5.0 percent

Make a bar graph of these data. If you need help, see page 670.

Metamorphic Rocks

3-3

Origin of Metamorphic Rocks

Imagine that you wake up, go into the kitchen, and pack a lunch for school. You place a sandwich and a cream-filled cake in the bag. As you leave for school, you decide to throw in an apple. At lunchtime, you open your lunch bag and notice that things have changed. Your cream-filled cake doesn't look good anymore. The apple rested on the cake all morning. The heat in your locker and the pressure from the apple have changed the form of your lunch. Rocks like those in **Figure 3-9** also can be affected by temperature changes and pressure.

Metamorphic Rocks

Rocks that have changed because of changes in temperature and pressure or the presence of hot, watery fluids are called **metamorphic rocks.** Sometimes the composition of a new metamorphic rock is different from the preexisting rock. Metamorphic rocks can form from changes in igneous, sedimentary, or other metamorphic rocks. What Earth processes can change these rocks?

What You'll Learn

- The conditions in Earth that cause metamorphic rocks to form
- How to classify metamorphic rocks as foliated or nonfoliated

Vocabulary

metamorphic rock
foliated
nonfoliated

Why It's Important

- Metamorphic rocks can help you understand the rock cycle. They form under conditions that are in between those of igneous and sedimentary rocks.

Figure 3-9 The mineral grains in granite (A) are flattened and aligned when pressure is applied to them. As a result, gneiss (B) is formed. **What other conditions can cause metamorphic rocks to form?**

Heat and Pressure

Rocks beneath Earth's surface are under great pressure from rock layers above them. Once the heat and pressure reach a certain point, the rocks melt and magma forms. But, what happens if the heat isn't high enough or the pressure isn't enough to cause the rocks to melt?

In areas where melting doesn't occur, some mineral grains are flattened like the cake in the lunch bag. Sometimes, minerals exchange atoms with surrounding minerals and new, bigger minerals form.

An igneous rock can be transformed into a metamorphic rock. For example, the igneous rock granite can be changed into the metamorphic rock gneiss (NISE).

Depending upon the amount of pressure and temperature applied, one type of rock can change into several different metamorphic rocks. Shale, for example, will change into slate. As more and more pressure and temperature are applied, the slate can change into phyllite, then schist, and eventually gneiss. Schist also forms when basalt is metamorphosed.

Fluids

Did you know that fluids can move through solid rock? These fluids, which are mostly water with dissolved particles of elements, can chemically react with a rock and change its composition, especially when the fluids are hot. That's what happens when basalt changes to hornblende schist. **Figure 3-10A** shows basalt, a rock that is extrusive igneous. Compare the grain size of this basalt with the hornblende schist shown in **Figure 3-10B.** In the process of transforming from basalt, the schist changed in mineral composition and the grains

Figure 3-10 When it metamorphoses in the presence of water-rich fluids, basalt (A) changes into hornblende schist (B).

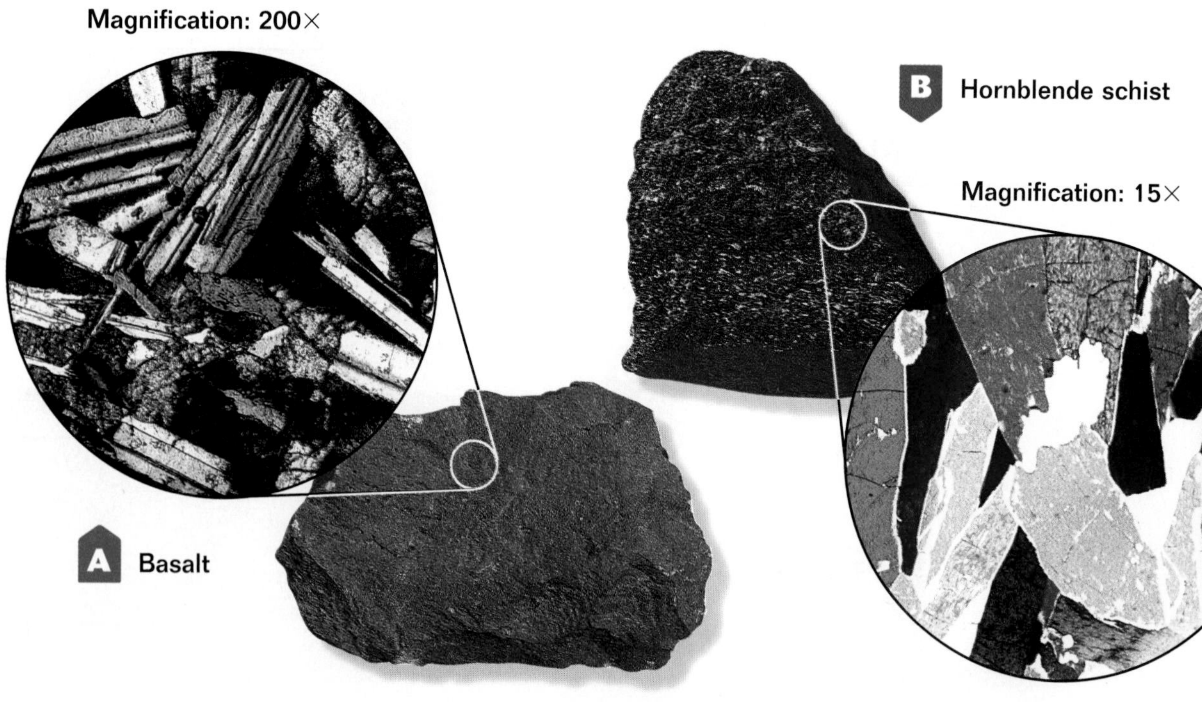

enlarged. The mineral hornblende in the schist contains hydrogen and oxygen in a form that shows that water is present in this mineral. This water was not present in the basalt before metamorphism. Most fluids that transform rocks during metamorphism are hot and are composed of water and carbon dioxide.

Classification of Metamorphic Rocks

Metamorphic rocks form from changes in igneous, sedimentary, or other metamorphic rocks. Heat, pressure, and fluids trigger the changes. The resulting rocks can be classified according to their texture.

Figure 3-11 The different minerals in shale result in the many different colors of slate. **Explain why slate is used for patio and stepping stones and roofing shingles.**

Foliated Rocks

When mineral grains flatten and line up in parallel layers, the metamorphic rock has a **foliated** texture. Two examples of foliated rocks are slate and gneiss. Slate forms from the sedimentary rock shale. The minerals in shale are arranged into layers when they're exposed to heat and pressure. As **Figure 3-11** shows, slate is easily separated along these foliation layers. The minerals in slate are so tightly pressed together that water can't pass between them easily.

Gneiss, another foliated rock, forms when granite and other rocks are changed. Quartz, feldspar, mica, and other minerals in granite aren't changed much, but they are rearranged into alternating layers.

Nonfoliated Rocks

In some metamorphic rocks, no layering occurs. The mineral grains grow and rearrange, but they don't form layers. This process produces a **nonfoliated** texture.

Sandstone is a sedimentary rock that's often composed mostly of quartz grains. When its mineral grains are changed by heat and pressure, the nonfoliated metamorphic rock called quartzite is formed. The change that occurs is in the size of the mineral grains.

Another nonfoliated metamorphic rock is marble. Marble forms from the sedimentary rock limestone, which is composed of the mineral calcite. Look at **Figure 3-12.** The calcite crystals give marble the glassy, shiny luster that makes it a popular material for sculpturing. Usually, marble contains several other minerals besides calcite. For example, hornblende and serpentine give marble a black or greenish tone, whereas hematite makes it red.

So far, we've traveled through only a portion of the rock cycle. We still haven't observed how sedimentary rocks are formed and how igneous and metamorphic rocks evolve from them. The next section will complete our investigation of the rock cycle.

Figure 3-12 This marble sculpture is located in Tokyo, Japan. Sculptors often work with marble because it is soft and easy to shape. Its calcite crystals give it a glassy, shiny luster.

Section Assessment

1. How is the formation of metamorphic rock different from that of igneous rock?
2. How are metamorphic rocks classified? What are the characteristics of rocks in each of these classifications?
3. **Think Critically:** Marble is used to make sculptures. What properties of marble make it useful for this purpose?
4. **Skill Builder**
   Sequencing Put the following events in a sequence that could explain how a metamorphic rock might form from an igneous rock. (HINT: Start with igneous rock forms.) Use each event just once. If you need help, refer to Sequencing in the **Skill Handbook** on page 666.

   Events: *sedimentary rock forms, weathering occurs, heat and pressure are applied, igneous rock forms, metamorphic rock forms, erosion occurs, sediments are formed, deposition occurs*

Using Computers

Using Graphics Software With **Figure 3-9** as a model, use a computer to illustrate the portion of the rock cycle that shows how metamorphic rocks form. Be sure your model illustrates how directed pressure causes alignment of mineral grains. If you need help, refer to page 686.

Sedimentary Rocks

3-4

Origin of Sedimentary Rocks

Igneous rocks are the most common rocks on Earth, but most of them exist well below the surface. Chances are, you've seen more sedimentary rocks than igneous rocks. That's because 75 percent of the rocks at Earth's surface are sedimentary rocks.

Sedimentary rocks form when sediments become pressed or cemented together, or when minerals come out of mineral-rich solutions, or are left behind by evaporation. **Sediments** are loose materials such as rock fragments, mineral grains, and bits of plant and animal remains that have been moved by wind, water, ice, or gravity. Minerals that are dissolved in water also are sediments. But, where do sediments come from? If you look at the model of the rock cycle, you will see that they come from already-existing rocks that are weathered and eroded.

What You'll Learn

- How sedimentary rocks form from sediments
- How to classify sedimentary rocks as detrital, chemical, or biochemical in origin

Vocabulary

sedimentary rock
sediment
compaction
cementation

Why It's Important

- Some sedimentary rocks, like coal, are important sources of energy.

Sedimentary Rock Layers

Sedimentary rocks often form as layers, like those shown in **Figure 3-13.** The older layers are on the bottom because they were deposited first. Then, more sediments pile up and the lower layers become squeezed together to form solid rock.

Sedimentary rock layers are a lot like the papers in your locker. The oldest papers are on the bottom, and the ones you get back today will be deposited on top of them. However, if you disturb the papers by searching through them for a pencil at the bottom of the pile, the older ones may come to the top. Sometimes, forces within Earth disturb layers of rock. The layers are overturned, and the oldest are no longer on the bottom.

Figure 3-13 These sedimentary rock layers in Arizona formed as piles of sediment were deposited on top of one another. **How can these rock layers be used to sequence events in time, provided that the layers are not disturbed?**

MiniLab

Classifying Sediments

Procedure

CAUTION: *Use care when handling sharp objects.*

1. Spread different samples of sediment on a sheet of paper.
2. Use **Table 3-2** to determine the size range of gravel-sized sediment.
3. Use tweezers or a dissecting probe and a magnifying lens to separate the gravel-sized sediments.
4. Separate the gravel pile into two piles based on shape—rounded or angular.

Analyze

1. Describe the grains in both piles.
2. Use **Table 3-2** to determine what rock is probably made from each type of sediment that you have.

Classification of Sedimentary Rocks

Sedimentary rocks can be composed of just about anything. Sediments come from weathered and eroded igneous, metamorphic, and sedimentary rocks. Sediments also come from the remains of plants and animals. The composition of a sedimentary rock depends upon the composition of the rocks and the living things that its sediments came from.

Like igneous and metamorphic rocks, sedimentary rocks are classified by their composition and by the way they formed. Sedimentary rocks are usually classified as detrital, chemical, or biochemical.

Detrital Sedimentary Rocks

The word *detrital* comes from the Latin word *detritus*, which means "to wear away." Detrital sedimentary rocks are made from the broken fragments of other rocks. These sediments are compacted and cemented together.

Table 3-2

Sediment Sizes

Sediment	Clay	Silt	Sand	Gravel
Size range	< 0.004 mm	0.004–0.06 mm	0.06–2 mm	>2 mm
Example	Shale	Siltstone	Sandstone	Conglomerate (shown) or Breccia (angular)

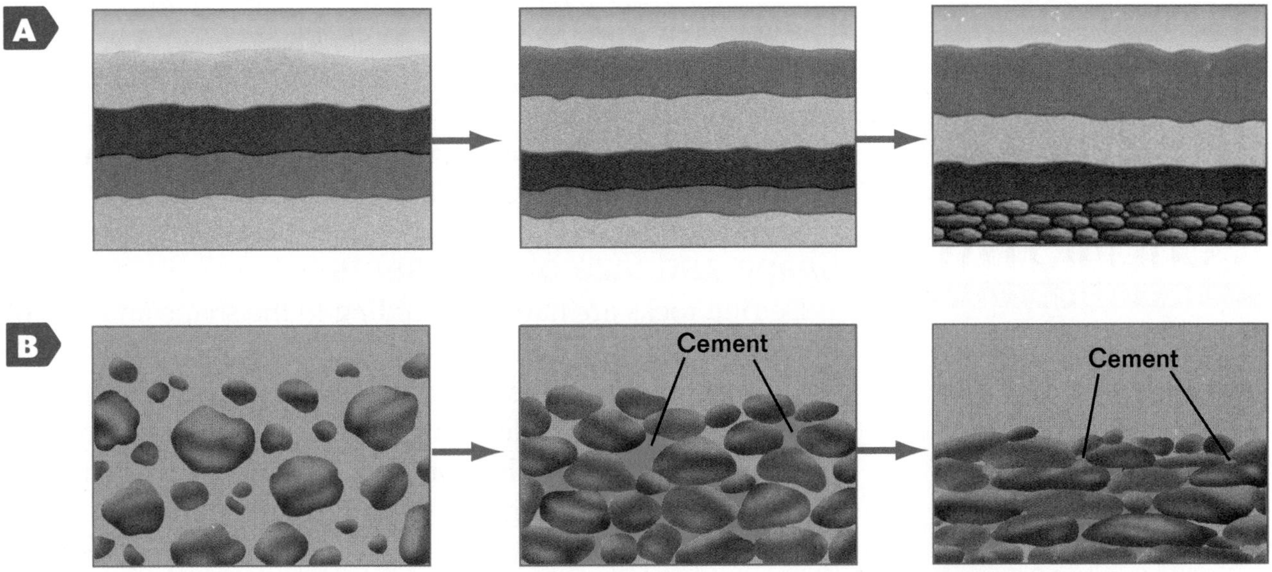

Figure 3-14 Two processes that form sedimentary rocks are compaction (A) and cementation (B).

Weathering and Erosion

When rock is exposed to air, water, or ice, it is unstable and breaks down chemically and mechanically. This process, which breaks rocks into smaller pieces, is called weathering. **Table 3-2** shows how these pieces are classified by size. The movement of weathered material is called erosion.

Compaction

Erosion moves sediments to a new location, where they are then deposited. Here, layer upon layer of sediment builds up. Pressure from the upper layers pushes down on the lower layers. If the sediments are small, they can stick together and form solid rock. This process, shown in **Figure 3-14A,** is called **compaction.**

You've compacted sediments if you've ever made mud pies. Mud is made of small, clay-sized sediments. They easily stick together under the pressure applied by your hands.

Cementation

If sediments are large, like sand and pebbles, pressure alone can't make them stick together. Large sediments have to be cemented together. **Cementation,** which is shown in **Figure 3-14B,** occurs when water soaks through soil and rock. As it moves, it dissolves minerals in the rock such as quartz, calcite, hematite, and limonite. These minerals are natural cements. The resulting solution of water and dissolved minerals moves through open spaces between sediments. The natural cements are deposited around the pieces of sediment and they stick together. A group of sediments cemented together in this way forms a detrital sedimentary rock.

Clastic Texture

Detrital sedimentary rocks often are referred to as clastic rocks because of their texture. The word *clastic* comes from the Greek word *klastos*, meaning "broken." Detrital sedimentary rocks have a clastic texture, but so do some biochemical rocks.

CHEMISTRY INTEGRATION

Cave Formation
You may know of large caves or caverns that have formed underground in limestone deposits. Research the chemical reactions that form caves in Carlsbad Caverns, New Mexico, or Mammoth Cave, Kentucky.

Shape and Size of Sediments

Detrital rocks are named according to the shape and size of the sediments. For example, conglomerate and breccia both form from large sediments. If the sediments have been well rounded, the rock is called conglomerate. If the sediments are not rounded and have sharp angles, the rock is called breccia.

The gravel-sized sediments in both conglomerate and breccia may consist of any type of rock or mineral. Often, they are chunks of the minerals quartz or feldspar. They also can be pieces of rocks such as gneiss, granite, or limestone. The cement holding them all together is usually quartz or calcite.

Have you ever looked at the concrete in sidewalks and driveways? Look at **Figure 3-15.** Concrete is made of gravel and sand grains that have been cemented together. The structure is similar to that of naturally occurring conglomerate, but is it considered a rock?

Figure 3-16 shows the sedimentary rock sandstone. Sandstone is formed from smaller particles than conglomerates and breccias. Its sand-sized sediments are usually grains of the minerals quartz and feldspar that are compacted and cemented together but can be just about any mineral. Siltstone is similar to sandstone except it is composed of smaller, silt-sized particles. Shale is a detrital sedimentary rock that is composed mainly of clay minerals and quartz, with

Conglomerate

Figure 3-15 The concrete making up the steps is similar to naturally occurring conglomerate.

lesser feldspar and other minerals. Its sediments are clay-sized particles. Clay-sized sediments are compacted together by pressure from overlying layers.

Figure 3-16 This rock formed from sand deposited in layers by desert winds. **Why does this sandstone look like desert sand dunes?**

Chemical Sedimentary Rocks

Chemical sedimentary rocks form when dissolved minerals come out of a solution or are left behind when a solution evaporates. You can show that salt is deposited in the bottom of a glass or pan when saltwater solution evaporates. In a similar way, minerals collect when seas or lakes evaporate. The deposits of minerals that come out of solution, or remain after evaporation, form rocks. ☑

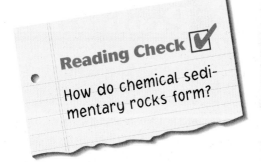

Reading Check ☑

How do chemical sedimentary rocks form?

Limestone

Calcium carbonate is carried in solution in ocean water. When calcium carbonate comes out of solution as calcite and its many crystals grow together, limestone is formed. Limestone also may contain other minerals and sediments, but it's at least 50 percent calcite. Limestone is usually deposited on sea or ocean floors. Large areas of the United States have limestone bedrock because oceans once covered much of the country for millions of years.

Rock Salt

When lakes and seas evaporate, they often deposit the mineral halite. Halite, mixed with a few other minerals, forms rock salt. Rock salt deposits range in thickness from a few meters to more than 400 m. People mine these deposits because rock salt is an important resource. It's used in the manufacturing of glass, paper, soap, and dairy products. The halite in rock salt is used as table salt.

Biochemical Sedimentary Rocks

When rocks form from the remains of once-living things, they are biochemical sedimentary rocks. One of the most common biochemical sedimentary rocks is fossil-rich limestone. Like chemical limestone, fossil-rich limestone is made of the mineral calcite ($CaCO_3$). But, fossil-rich limestone also contains remains of once-living ocean animals instead of only calcite that has come out of ocean water.

Animals such as mussels, corals, and snails make their shells from $CaCO_3$ that eventually becomes calcite. When they die, their shells accumulate on the ocean floor. These shells are cemented together, and fossil-rich limestone is formed. If the shell fragments are relatively large, the rock is called coquina (koh KEE nuh). Chalk is made of microscopic shells. An example of chalk is shown in **Figure 3-18.** When you use naturally occurring chalk to write with, you're actually crushing and smearing the calcite shells of once-living ocean organisms.

Another useful biochemical sedimentary rock is coal. Coal forms when pieces of dead plants are buried under other sediments in swamps. These plant materials are chemically

Problem Solving

Observing Changes in Rocks

We see rocks all around us, but most of the time we are not aware that they are constantly changing. When rocks are exposed to air and water at Earth's surface, they are not stable, and they begin to disintegrate. This process is called weathering. Most of the time, we can't observe weathering directly, mainly because it happens so slowly.

Part of Cleopatra's Needle, located in Central Park, New York, is shown here. It is an ancient granite obelisk, which is a tall stone monument, that was moved from Egypt to New York City in 1880. The surface of the obelisk was carved with hieroglyphics that had remained mostly unchanged for 35 centuries in Egypt. After it was moved, it took less than 75 years for the surface of the stone to change.

Think Critically: Observe the surfaces of Cleopatra's Needle shown above. Infer why one side of the granite obelisk is worn down more than the other side. Why do you think the surface of the obelisk remained unchanged in Egypt for tens of centuries but changed in less than a single century in Central Park?

changed by microorganisms. The resulting sediments are compacted over millions of years to form coal. Coal is used as an important source of energy.

Coal has been and still is economically important to the technological advancement of the United States. It supplies fuel for electricity. Although mines of today are technologically advanced and the companies involved work within regulations to minimize the effects of mining on the environment, this has not always been so. The effects of old mining can be seen in many places in the United States. **Figure 3-17** shows a typical coal seam, or layer, that formed between layers of other sedimentary rocks.

Figure 3-17 This black coal in Healy, Alaska, was formed by compaction of once-living organisms. **What types of organisms died and were buried to form this coal?**

Using Math

Calculating Thickness

Example Problem:

It took 300 million years for a layer of plant matter about 0.9 to 2.1 m thick to produce a bed of bituminous coal 0.3 m thick. At this rate, estimate the thickness of plant matter that produced a bed of coal 0.15 m thick.

Problem-Solving Steps:

1. What is known?
   It took 300 million years for a layer of plant matter 0.9 to 2.1 m thick to produce a bed of coal 0.3 m thick. Another bed of coal is 0.15 m thick.
2. What is unknown? the thickness of plant matter needed to form 0.15 m of coal
3. Set up the proportion: $\frac{(0.9 \text{ m plant matter})}{(0.3 \text{ m coal})} = \frac{(? \text{ m plant matter})}{(0.15 \text{ m coal})}$

   Thickness of plant matter = (new coal thickness × original thickness of plant matter) ÷ original coal thickness
4. **Solution:** A) Thickness = (0.15 m × 0.9 m) ÷ 0.3 m = 0.45 m
   B) Thickness = (0.15 m × 2.1 m) ÷ 0.3 m = 1.05 m

Plant matter with a thickness of 0.45 m to 1.05 m will form 0.15 m of coal.

Practice Problem

At the same rate, estimate the thickness of plant matter that produced a bed of coal 0.6 m thick.

Figure 3-18 The White Cliffs of Dover England are composed mostly of chalk. **What is chalk made of?**

Magnification: 25×

Another Look at the Rock Cycle

You have seen that the rock cycle has no beginning and no end. Rocks are continually changing from one form to another. Sediments come from rocks and other objects that have been broken apart. Even the magma that forms igneous rocks comes from the melting of rocks that already exist.

All of the rocks that you've learned about in this chapter formed through the processes of the rock cycle. And, all of the rocks around you, including those used to build houses and monuments, are part of the rock cycle. They are all changing. The rock cycle is a continuous, dynamic process.

Section Assessment

1. Where do sediments come from?
2. List chemical sedimentary rocks that are essential to your health or that are used to make life more convenient. How is each used?
3. **Think Critically:** Use the rock cycle to explain how pieces of granite and slate could be found in the same piece of conglomerate.
4. **Skill Builder**
   Making and Using Tables You are told to determine the compositions and other properties of a group of rocks. How would you organize these properties so that the rocks could be identified easily? To learn how, do the **Chapter 3 Skill Activity** on page 696.

Using Math

Sediment sizes are presented in **Table 3-2.** How many times larger than clay are the largest grains of silt and sand?

Energy from Waste Coal

Waste Coal—Problem and Solution

Waste coal is a by-product of coal mining. It is poor-quality coal that cannot be used at the time it is mined.

Piles of waste coal (inset) are unsightly and unsafe. Because it is high in sulfur, waste coal generates acid runoff when soaked by rain. This runoff pollutes nearby waterways and land. Until recently, waste coal was also unsafe to burn. Its sulfur content caused too much air pollution.

Today, new processes make it possible to burn waste coal without polluting the air. The coal is trucked to a burning facility where it is pulverized and mixed with crushed limestone. As the mixture burns, the limestone removes more than 92 percent of the sulfur dioxide emissions. Air-quality levels are monitored carefully to make sure the facility complies with pollution-control laws.

Cogeneration

Some power companies burn waste coal to produce electricity and use the low-pressure steam from the process to meet community heating needs. Generating both thermal and electrical energy in this way is called cogeneration. By using cogeneration, power companies help correct an environmental problem (acid runoff from waste coal) while generating useful energy. One such company, the Colver Power Project in Cambria County, Pennsylvania, is shown in the large photo at left. This plant was awarded *Power* magazine's 1996 Powerplant Award, the 1997 Pennsylvania Governor's Award for Environmental Excellence, and the 1997 Three Rivers Environmental Award for Business Stewardship. The Colver plant shows how an industry can help solve an environmental problem.

interNET CONNECTION

Scientists are looking into other ways to solve problems associated with the mining and burning of coal. Visit the Glencoe Science Web Site at **www.glencoe.com/sec/science/ca** for more information about current research projects. Outline one or two of these projects in your Science Journal.

Activity 3-2

Sedimentary Rocks

Materials

- Unknown sedimentary rock samples
- Marking pen
- 5 percent hydrochloric acid (HCl)
  **vinegar*
- Dropper
- Hand lens
- Paper towels
- Water
- Magnifying lens
- Metric ruler

**Alternate Materials*

Sedimentary rocks are formed by compaction and cementation of sediment. Because sediment is found in all shapes and sizes, do you think these characteristics could be used to classify detrital sedimentary rocks? Sedimentary rocks also can be classified as chemical or biochemical.

What You'll Investigate

You will observe how rock characteristics are used to classify sedimentary rocks as detrital, chemical, or biochemical.

Goals

- **Observe** sedimentary rock characteristics.
- **Compare** and **contrast** clastic and nonclastic textures.
- **Classify** sedimentary rocks as detrital, chemical, or biochemical.

Safety Precautions

CAUTION: *Use care when handling sharp objects.*

Procedure

1. In your Science Journal, make a Sedimentary Rock Samples chart similar to the one shown on the next page.
2. **Determine,** using a magnifying lens and a metric ruler, the sizes of sediments in each sample. Using **Table 3-2, classify** the sediments in the detrital rocks as gravel, sand, silt, or clay. Hint: silt- and clay-sized sediments are so small that they are difficult to measure. In general, the sediment is silt if it is gritty and just barely visible, and clay if it is smooth and individual grains are not visible.

3. Put a few drops of HCl or vinegar on each rock sample. Bubbling on a rock indicates the presence of calcite. **CAUTION:** *HCl is an acid and can cause burns. Wear goggles. Rinse spills with water and wash hands afterwards.*
4. Look for fossils and **describe** them if any are present.
5. **Determine** whether each sample has a clastic or nonclastic texture.
6. **Classify** your samples as detrital, chemical, or biochemical. Identify each rock sample.

Sandstone

Shale

Conclude and Apply

1. Why did you test the rocks with acid? What minerals react with acid?
2. The mineral halite forms by evaporation. Would you **classify** halite as a detrital, a chemical, or a biochemical rock?
3. **Compare** and **contrast** sedimentary rocks with a clastic texture with sedimentary rocks with a nonclastic texture.
4. **Explain** how you can classify sedimentary rocks.

Fossil-rich limestone

Conglomerate

Sedimentary Rock Samples

Sample	Observations	Minerals or Fossils Present	Sediment Size	Detrital, Chemical, or Biochemical	Rock Name
A					
B					
C					
D					
E					

Chapter 3 Reviewing Main Ideas

For a **preview** of this chapter, study this Reviewing Main Ideas before you read the chapter. After you have studied this chapter, you can use the Reviewing Main Ideas to **review** the chapter.

GLENCOE TECHNOLOGY The Glencoe MindJogger, Audiocassettes, and CD-ROM provide additional opportunities for review.

Section 3-1 THE ROCK CYCLE

A **rock** is a mixture of one or more minerals, mineraloids, glass, or organic matter. The **rock cycle** includes all processes by which rocks form. Any type of rock can change into any other type of rock through the rock cycle. ***What type of rock forms when heat, pressure, and hot-water solutions are applied?***

Section 3-2 IGNEOUS ROCKS

Magma is molten material that hardens to form **igneous rocks. Intrusive** igneous rocks form when magma cools below Earth's surface. **Extrusive** igneous rocks form when lava cools at or near Earth's surface. **Basaltic** rocks are dense, heavy, dark-colored rocks. **Granitic** rocks are light-colored and less dense than basaltic rocks. Andesitic rocks are intermediate between basaltic rocks and granitic rocks. ***Why would basaltic rocks be darkest in color and have the highest density?***

Reading Check

Suggest one or two additional illustrations for this chapter and explain why they would be valuable.

Section

3-3 METAMORPHIC ROCKS

Changes in heat, pressure, and fluid activity can cause **metamorphic** rocks to form. Slate and gneiss are examples of **foliated** metamorphic rocks. When foliation, or layering, of crystals is not visible, as in quartzite and marble, metamorphic rocks are called **nonfoliated.** ***Mica schist is a rock that forms at pressures and temperatures intermediate between slate and gneiss. Would it most likely be foliated or nonfoliated?***

Section

3-4 SEDIMENTARY ROCKS

Detrital **sedimentary** rocks form when fragments of rocks and minerals are compacted and cemented together. Detrital rocks always have a clastic texture because of the presence of rock fragments and mineral grains. Chemical sedimentary rocks come out of solution or are left behind by evaporation. Chemical rocks usually have a nonclastic, crystalline texture. Biochemical sedimentary rocks are made mostly of remains of once-living organisms. ***Classify each of the following rocks as detrital, chemical, or biochemical: shale, fossil-rich limestone, chemical limestone, coal, sandstone, and rock salt.***

Chapter 3 Assessment

Using Vocabulary

a. basaltic
b. cementation
c. compaction
d. extrusive
e. foliated
f. granitic
g. igneous rock
h. intrusive
i. lava
j. metamorphic rock
k. nonfoliated
l. rock
m. rock cycle
n. sediment
o. sedimentary rock

Explain the differences between the terms in each of the following pairs.

1. foliated, nonfoliated
2. cementation, compaction
3. sediment, lava
4. extrusive, intrusive
5. basaltic, granitic

Checking Concepts

Choose the word or phrase that best answers the question.

6. Why does magma tend to rise toward Earth's surface?
   A) It is more dense than surrounding rocks.
   B) It is more massive than surrounding rocks.
   C) It is cooler than surrounding rocks.
   D) It is less dense than surrounding rocks.
7. During metamorphism of granite into gneiss, what happens to minerals?
   A) They partly melt.
   B) They become new sediments.
   C) They grow smaller.
   D) They align into layers.
8. Which rock has large mineral grains?
   A) intrusive C) obsidian
   B) extrusive D) basaltic
9. What do igneous rocks form from?
   A) sediments C) gravel
   B) mud D) magma
10. What kind of rock is marble?
    A) foliated C) intrusive
    B) nonfoliated D) extrusive
11. What sedimentary rock is made of large, angular pieces of sediments?
    A) conglomerate C) limestone
    B) breccia D) chalk
12. Which of the following is an example of a detrital sedimentary rock?
    A) limestone C) breccia
    B) evaporite D) chalk
13. During what process are sediments pressed together?
    A) cooling C) melting
    B) weathering D) compaction
14. What is molten material at Earth's surface called?
    A) limestone C) breccia
    B) lava D) granite
15. Which of these is **NOT** a biochemical rock?
    A) conglomerate C) chalk
    B) coal D) coquina

Thinking Critically

16. Granite, pumice, and scoria are igneous rocks. Why doesn't granite have airholes like the other two?
17. Why are only a few fossils found in marble?
18. Explain why coquina is classified as a biochemical rock with a clastic texture.
19. What is true about the texture of all detrital sedimentary rocks?
20. Why are granitic igneous rocks light in color?

Developing Skills

If you need help, refer to the Skill Handbook.

21. **Concept Mapping:** Copy and complete the concept map shown below. Add ovals and connecting lines so you can include examples of each classification of rock.

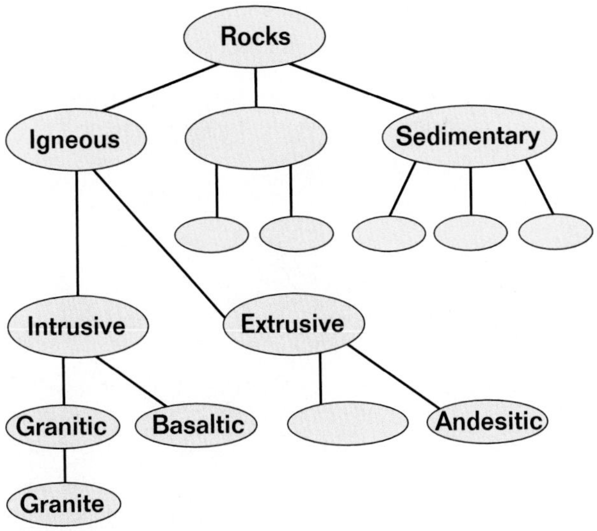

22. **Comparing and Contrasting:** Compare and contrast basaltic and granitic magmas.
23. **Hypothesizing:** A geologist found a sequence of rocks in which 200-million-year-old shales were lying on top of 100-million-year-old sandstones. Hypothesize how this could happen.
24. **Recognizing Cause and Effect:** Explain the causes and effects of pressure and temperature on shale.
25. **Measuring in SI:** Assume that the conglomerate shown on the second page of **Activity 3-2** is one-half of its actual size. Determine the average length of the gravel shown in the rock.

THE PRINCETON REVIEW

Test-Taking Tip

Dress Comfortably Loose, layered clothing is best. Whatever the temperature, you're prepared. Those who look at important test scores do not take climate into consideration.

Test Practice

Use these questions to test your Science Proficiency.

1. There is no end or beginning to the rock cycle. Which of the following statements **BEST** explains why this is true?
   A) There is no set course for the rock cycle. Any rock in the rock cycle can change into any other rock.
   B) The cycle begins with the melting of Earth materials.
   C) Weathering and erosion happen to all rocks before they melt.
   D) New crystals grow in magma, eventually producing igneous rock.
2. Detrital rocks have a clastic texture, but not all rocks with a clastic texture are detrital. Which of the following statements **BEST** explains how this can be?
   A) Clastic texture means rocks are made of broken pieces.
   B) Chemical rocks have nonclastic texture.
   C) Coquina, a biochemical rock, is made of broken shells and is therefore said to have a clastic texture.
   D) Detrital rocks are often called clastic rocks.

CHAPTER

4 Resources

Chapter Preview

Section 4-1
Energy Resources

Section 4-2
Alternative Energy Resources

Section 4-3
Water

Section 4-4
Land

Skills Preview

Skill Builders

- Make and Use a Graph

Activities

- Design an Experiment
- Interpret Data

MiniLabs

- Model

Reading Check

List the chapter vocabulary in a column. Next to each word, write what you think the word means. As you read, change your definitions whenever needed.

Explore Activity

Do you know that you use resources 24 hours a day? Even when you are asleep, resources are used to light streetlights and heat your home. Resources also were used to make your pajamas, your sheets, and the bed you sleep in. Where do these resources come from? Look no farther than the nearest farm or forest for the resources that provide you with countless products. Where do we get the resources to meet our energy needs? Coal, oil, and natural gas provide much of our energy, but we also harness energy from wind, water, and the sun. In fact, the greatest source of energy on Earth is the sun.

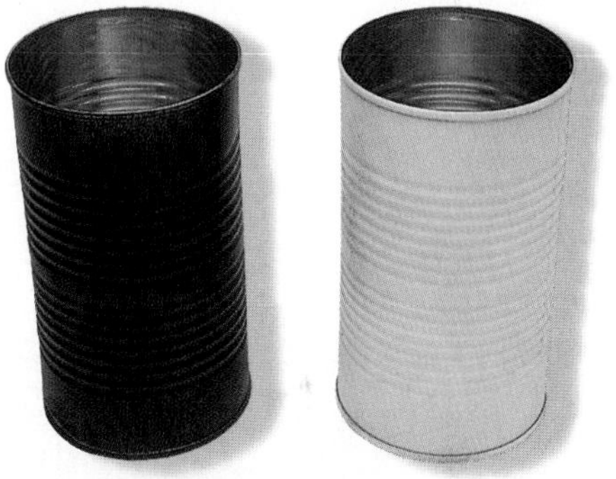

Observe Sun Energy

1. Get two empty tin cans from your teacher. Paint the outside of one can black or wrap it in black construction paper. Paint the outside of the other can white or wrap it in white construction paper.
2. Fill both cans with cool tap water. Record the temperature of the water in each can.
3. Tape a piece of black construction paper over the top of the black can. Tape a piece of white construction paper over the top of the white can. Place both cans in direct sunlight.
4. After an hour, record the temperature of the water in both cans.

Science Journal

Which had the greater increase in temperature—the water in the black can or the water in the white can? How does the color of an object affect its ability to absorb energy from the sun? Which color of clothing would be best for summer?

4-1 Energy Resources

What You'll Learn

- Advantages and disadvantages of using fossil fuels
- Nonrenewable resources

Vocabulary
fossil fuel
pollution
acid rain
nonrenewable

Why It's Important

- Energy resources provide the electricity you use.

Generating Energy

Does your day start like this? You wake up to the BEEP-BEEP of the alarm clock. You switch on the light and stumble toward the bathroom. You take a hot shower, then head back to your bedroom to dress. You flip on the radio to hear the weather report so you know what to wear. Your day has hardly begun and already you've used electricity at least four times. Have you ever wondered where your electricity comes from?

Fossil Fuels

In the United States, electrical power plants are the main sources of energy for homes and factories. Energy is the ability to change things, such as the temperature, speed, or direction of an object. When energy is used to change things, energy itself often changes from one form to another. Wood, for instance, contains chemical energy. As wood is burned, its chemical energy is changed into heat and light energy. Most power plants produce electricity by burning fossil fuels. **Fossil fuels** are energy resources formed from the decaying remains of ancient plants and animals. Coal, oil, and natural gas are examples of fossil fuels. Let's take a closer look at how these important energy resources are formed.

VISUALIZING Coal Formation

Figure 4-1 Coal is formed from the remains of ancient swamp vegetation.

A As the plants died and fell into the swamp, they were covered by layers of sediment. Over time, heat and pressure caused the decayed plants to form into a solid layer of lignite.

Coal

The coal we use today began to form millions of years ago in swampy regions where huge, fernlike plants grew in abundance. When the plants died and fell into the swamp, they were covered by sediments such as mud, sand, and other dead plants. Layer upon layer of sediments piled up. The weight of these sediments pressed down on the decayed matter. The intense pressure generated heat. The combination of heat and pressure changed the decayed material into a soft, brown coal called lignite. Over time, more and more layers of sediments piled on top of the lignite, and further changes occurred in the coal, as shown in **Figure 4-1.**

Oil and Natural Gas

Most geologists agree that oil and natural gas form over millions of years from the decay of algae and tiny ocean animals that are called plankton. The process begins when these organisms die and sink to the seafloor. Over centuries, these decaying organisms pile up on the ocean floor. Thick layers of sand and mud are deposited over the decayed organisms. The combination of pressure and heat causes chemical reactions to occur. The decayed material eventually forms the liquid we call oil and the gases we call natural gas.

LIFE SCIENCE INTEGRATION

Fossilized Shells

Through experience, geologists have found that when they drill into Earth's crust and find certain types of fossil shells, oil is probably nearby. These fossil shells are often the remains of tiny ocean organisms called foraminifera (fuh ram uh NIHF ra). Find out more about foraminifera. In your Science Journal, write a brief paragraph explaining why foraminifera are commonly found near oil deposits.

B More layers of sediment piled on top of the lignite and compressed it even further. With the deeper layers, temperatures also increased and lignite became bituminous coal.

C When layers of bituminous coal were severely compressed and heated by forces within Earth, the layers changed into anthracite coal, the hardest of all coals.

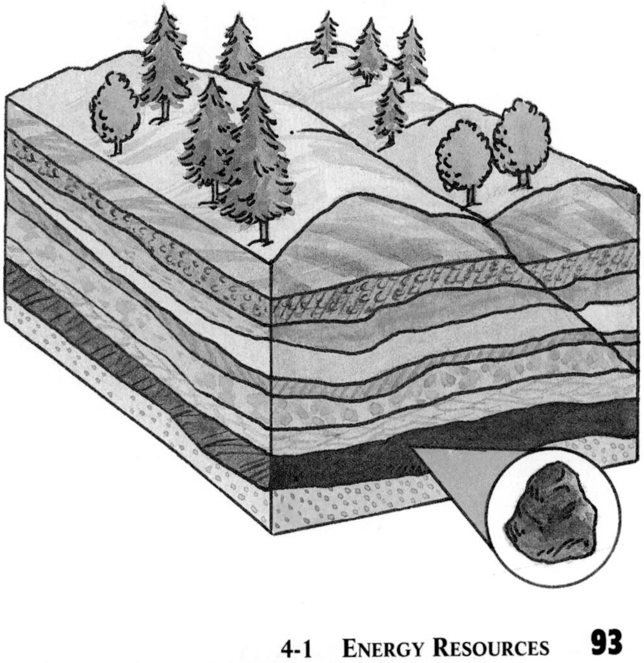

Figure 4-2 Engineers drill through layers of rock to reach underground deposits of oil and natural gas.

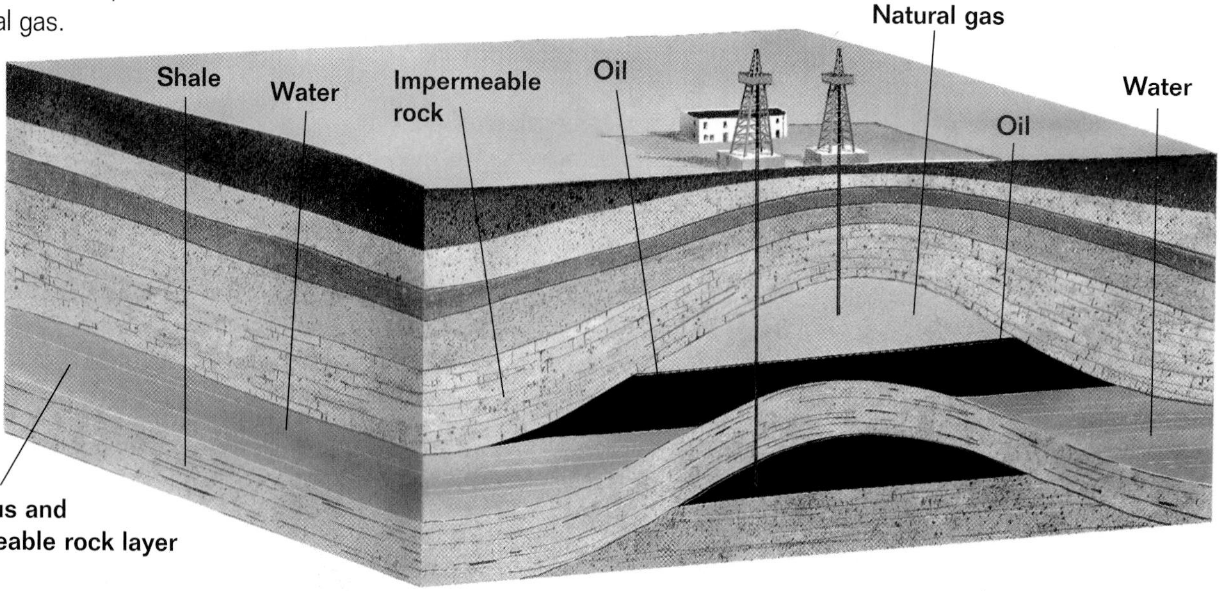

Figure 4-2 shows how engineers reach the oil and natural gas stored in Earth. Once pumped out of Earth, oil and natural gas are used for many things. We refine oil to produce gasoline and other fuels. Oil also is used to lubricate machines and to make plastics and other items such as shingles for your home. Natural gas is also used to heat homes and cook food. Natural gas is also an important source of sulfur, which is used to make many chemicals.

Pollution and Fossil Fuels

Reading Check

What is pollution?

Think again of all the ways you use electricity each morning. Your life would be very different if we didn't have fossil fuels to generate energy. Fossil fuels are important resources. However, when they are burned to produce energy, environmental problems can occur. When fossil fuels are burned in cars, power plants, homes, and factories, gases such as nitrogen oxide and sulfur oxide and tiny bits of soot and dust are released into the air. These substances cause pollution. **Pollution** is the introduction of harmful waste products, chemicals, and substances into the environment.

Air pollution can make your throat feel dry or your eyes sting. Many people have trouble breathing when air pollution levels are high. For the elderly and people with lung or heart problems, air pollution can be deadly. Air pollution can also lead to acid rain. **Acid rain** is produced when gases released by burning oil and coal mix with water in the air.

Spare the Air

The best solution for air pollution is prevention. Reducing the number of pollutants released into the air is easier to do than cleaning up the pollutants already in the air. As shown in **Figure 4-3,** new cars are made today that release fewer harmful gases and use less fuel than older models. Governments around the world also are working together to find ways to reduce the amount of air pollutants that are released into the atmosphere by factories.

Figure 4-3 Modern cars use catalytic converters and unleaded gasoline. Both features help reduce the amount of pollutants released into the air. The streamlined shape and tires of modern cars help increase gas mileage, which in turn helps reduce use of fossil fuels.

Nonrenewable Resources

Problems with fossil fuels aren't limited to pollution alone. We may find ourselves running out of these energy resources if we use up our supply of fossil fuels. Can this happen? Many people think so. Remember that the process of fossil fuel formation can take millions of years. Plants and animals that die today won't become fossil fuels for many centuries. What impact does this factor have on our use of fossil fuels? Are we using them faster than they are being replaced?

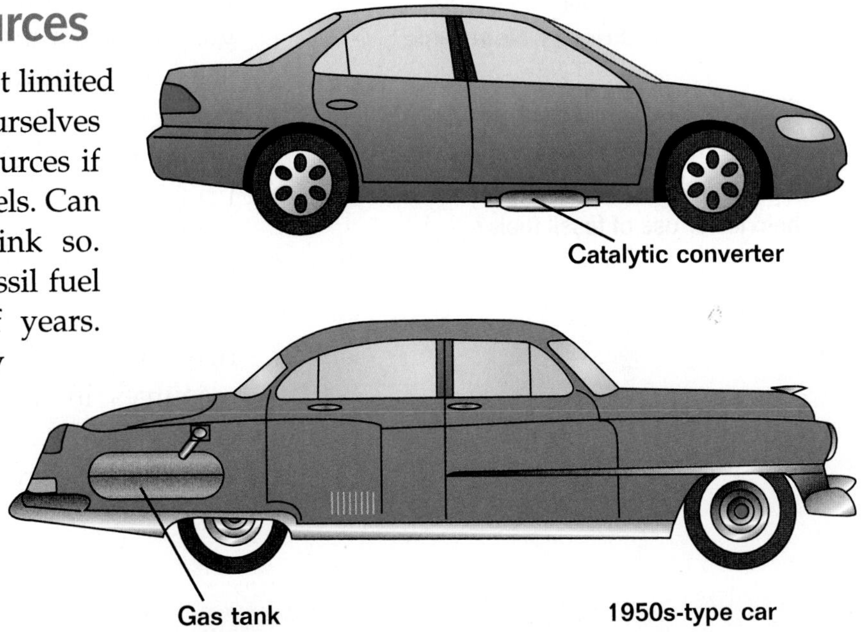

Problem Solving

Estimate Car Pooling Benefits

Sally, Fred, Jose, and Tania live in the same neighborhood and work in the same city. Each drives 60 km round-trip to work, five days a week, 50 weeks a year. Each pays 4 dollars per workday to park his or her car. It costs each 20 cents per kilometer for gasoline and car maintenance. Tania has suggested that they start a car pool to save money.

Think Critically: How much money could each driver save if they participate equally in the car pool? Assume that the four drivers take their two-week vacations at the same time and that their four cars get similar gas mileage. In your Science Journal, show the steps you took to calculate your answer.

mileage = 60 km for 5 days a week
50 weeks/year

parking costs = $4/day
gasoline and maintenance = 20 cents/km

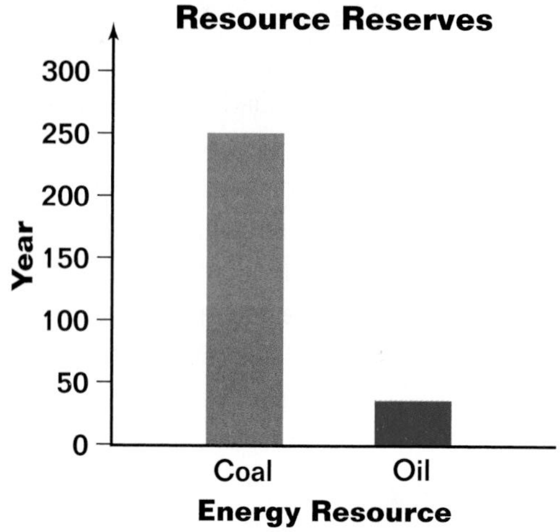

Figure 4-4 This graph shows available reserves of coal and oil. **What might you do at home to help lower use of fossil fuels?**

If you answered yes, you're right. Some energy resources are being used faster than natural processes can replace them. Resources that cannot be replaced by natural processes in less than 100 years are **nonrenewable.** Fossil fuels are nonrenewable. This means that we may run out of these important sources of energy someday. The question is, when?

How much is left?

At current rates of use, coal provides about 29 percent of the world's energy needs, and oil and natural gas provide almost 61 percent. As **Figure 4-4** shows, scientists estimate that we have enough coal reserves to last 200 to 300 years at present rates of usage. But, our available reserves of oil may be used up within 30 to 40 years.

How can we solve this problem? Conserving electricity helps reduce pollution. It also helps lower the use of fossil fuels. Can you think of other ways to help? How about this—we can use other energy resources in addition to fossil fuels to meet our energy needs. In the next section, you'll learn about alternative sources of energy that can be used again and again.

Section Assessment

1. Why is coal considered a nonrenewable resource?
2. Describe two problems with the use of fossil fuels.
3. Explain how acid rain forms.
4. Why are coal, oil, and natural gas called fossil fuels?
5. **Think Critically:** Why are you likely to find natural gas and oil deposits together, but less likely to find coal deposits at the same location?
6. **Skill Builder**
   Recognizing Cause and Effect
   Explain how keeping a television on overnight has an impact on the environment. Relate your answer to use of fossil fuels. If you need help, refer to Recognizing Cause and Effect in the **Skill Handbook** on page 673.

Using Math

In the United States, there are 5630 cars for every 10 000 people. In Cambodia, a country in Southeast Asia, there is only one car for every 10 000 people. The population of the United States is about 263 million; the population of Cambodia is nearly 10 million. How many cars are in each country?

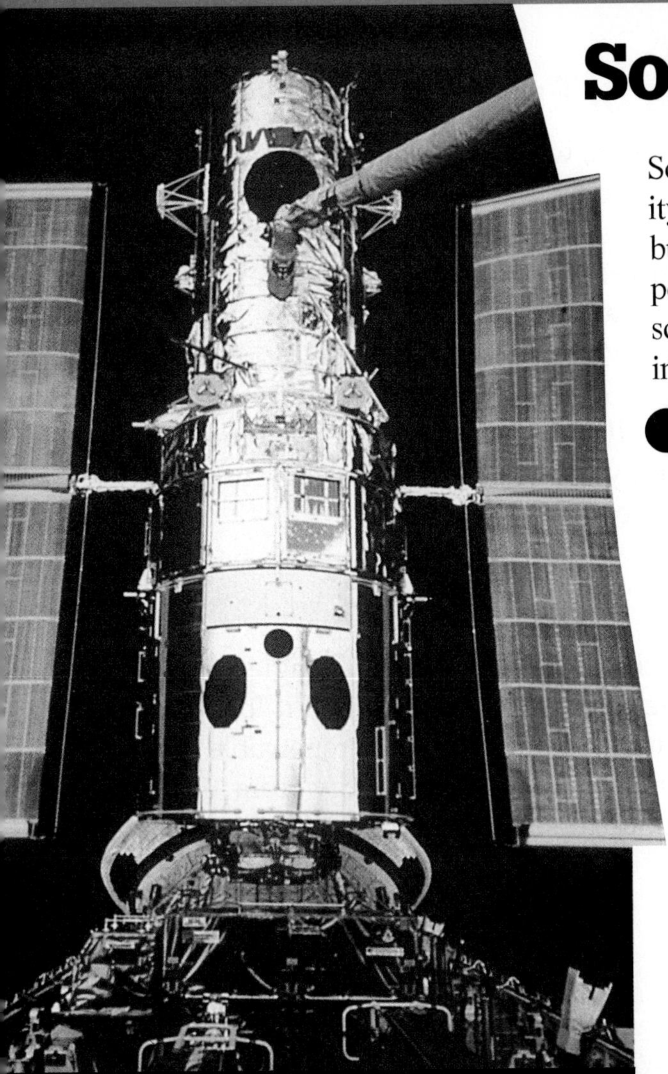

Solar Cells

Solar cells are devices that use sunlight to produce electricity. They can be used to warm and light houses and other buildings as well as to run appliances, pump water, and power a car. Some watches, calculators, and toys run on solar energy, and solar cells also provide power for objects in space, such as the *Hubble Space Telescope* shown at left.

HOW A SOLAR CELL WORKS

1. The central part of a solar cell is made of two thin layers of substances called semiconductors. A semiconductor is an element that conducts an electric current better than a nonmetal but not as well as a metal.
2. These layers are sandwiched between metal contacts that connect the solar cell with an electric circuit.
3. The entire solar cell is enclosed in glass or some other transparent material.
4. When sunlight strikes the cell, some electrons gain enough energy to break free from the atoms in the semiconductors.
5. This electron flow creates an electric current through the electric circuit.

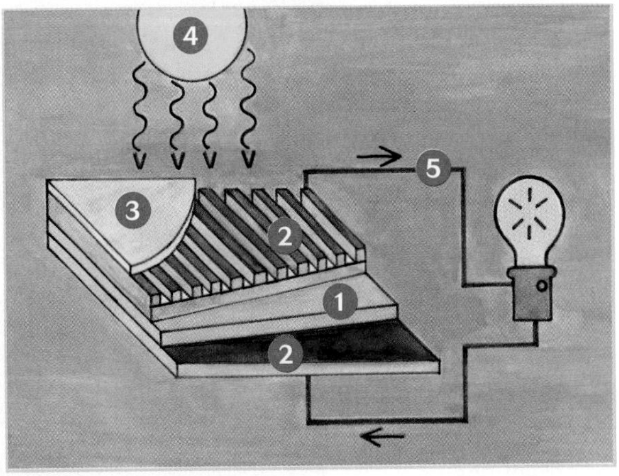

Career CONNECTION

Currently, more than 200 000 homes around the world use solar cell systems to provide all their electricity. Such systems, however, are still expensive to produce. Solar engineers are working to improve the efficiency of these systems. A solar engineer must have a degree in electrical engineering and a good knowledge of math, physics, and graphic design. Find out more about the jobs done by these engineers. Then, make a list of the kinds of companies and agencies that might employ solar engineers.

Think Critically

1. What do you think is the purpose of the outer-glass shell of a solar cell?
2. Solar cells can be linked to form solar panels. Solar panels can be used to heat houses. Do you think such a heating system would be more efficient in Nome, Alaska, or Houston, Texas? Explain.

4-2 Alternative Energy Resources

What You'll Learn

- Different kinds of renewable resources
- Advantages and disadvantages of using alternative energy resources

Vocabulary
renewable
solar energy
hydroelectric power
geothermal energy
nuclear energy

Why It's Important

- Many alternative sources of energy are renewable.

Other Sources of Energy

When you sit in the sun, walk in the wind, or swim against an ocean current, you are feeling the power of resources that can be used to meet our energy needs. But unlike fossil fuels, sun, wind, and water are energy resources that can be used again and again. They are constant—the sun has shone for millions of years and will shine for millions more. Energy resources that can be recycled or replaced by natural processes in less than 100 years are considered **renewable.** Some renewable energy resources include the sun, wind, water, and geothermal energy.

Solar Energy

Suppose you're a scientist trying to find a single source of energy to meet all the world's needs. You might look to the sun for a solution. Energy from the sun is renewable and it doesn't cause pollution. Plus, enough energy from the sun reaches Earth in an hour to supply all the energy the world

Figure 4-5 The mirrors on this tower in France collect energy from the sun. **Describe one advantage of solar-energy use.**

uses in one year. Currently, we do not have the technology to harness all of the sun's energy. But we do use energy from the sun, called **solar energy,** for many things. One example is shown in **Figure 4-5.** This towering structure of flat mirrors is located outside the town of Odeillo, France. The mirrors are positioned to focus energy from the sun on one part of the tower. The heat is used to run a laboratory inside the tower, where temperatures can reach as high as 3300°C.

Figure 4-6 The model train and the calculator shown here receive their power from the sun.
What are solar cells?

Solar Cells

Other types of solar-energy technology are much simpler than the example shown in **Figure 4-5.** For instance, you may have used a solar calculator to complete your homework assignments. Solar calculators, such as the one shown in **Figure 4-6,** are powered by solar cells, which collect light and change it into electricity. In a solar cell, thin layers of silicon—a hard, dark-colored element—are sandwiched together and attached to tiny wires. As light strikes the different layers, it produces an electrical current.

Is solar energy the answer?

Nonpolluting, renewable, and abundant—solar energy sounds like a wonderful way to generate energy, doesn't it? So why don't we rely on solar energy to meet all of our energy needs?

Solar energy has some serious drawbacks. It's available only when the sun is shining, so solar cells can't work at night. In addition, different parts of Earth receive different amounts of solar energy. If you live in an area that is cloudy much of the time, it's doubtful that solar energy can meet all of your energy needs because solar cells work less efficiently during cloudy days. At this point, we don't have the technology to harness and store effectively all the sun's vast energy. Until we do, some scientists think that the best solution to energy problems may be to use fossil fuels and solar energy, in combination with other energy sources. You'll read about these next. ☑

Reading Check ☑

Describe one problem with solar energy use.

Figure 4-7 This windmill in California uses energy from the wind to pump water.

Energy from Wind

Imagine this. Outside, the sky is a clear shade of blue and the wind scatters fallen leaves across the street. Inside, a kite hangs in your closet. Can you think of a good way to spend the day?

A windy day is perfect for flying a kite. A strong wind can lift a kite high in the sky and whip it all around. When you fly a kite, you use energy from the wind. Energy from wind was and still is used to send sailboats skimming across the ocean. In the past, windmills, such as the one shown in **Figure 4-7,** used wind energy to grind corn and pump water. Today, windmills also are used to generate electricity. When a large number of windmills are placed in one area for the purpose of generating electricity, the area is called a wind farm.

Like all forms of energy, energy from the wind has advantages and disadvantages. Wind is nonpolluting; it produces no environmental harm or waste. However, only a few regions of the world have winds strong enough to generate electricity on a large scale. Also, wind isn't steady. Sometimes it blows too hard; sometimes it stops altogether.

Hydroelectric Power

If you've ever watched a river flow, you've seen a form of energy in action. Energy from moving water can also generate electricity. The production of electricity by water is called **hydroelectric power.** People in southern Canada and the eastern United States use the power of the water in the Niagara Falls to generate hydroelectric power for a number of large cities. In other places where there are no natural waterfalls, people have built concrete dams to produce hydroelectricity. The Shasta Dam, on northern California's Sacramento River, is the tallest structure of its type in the world. What happens to the water of the Sacramento River behind the dam?

Figure 4-8 Water in the reservoir is released through gateways into pipes near the base of the dam.

A The pipes lead to the turbines. Because of the weight of the water in the reservoir above, the water in the pipes is under great pressure as it falls to the turbines.

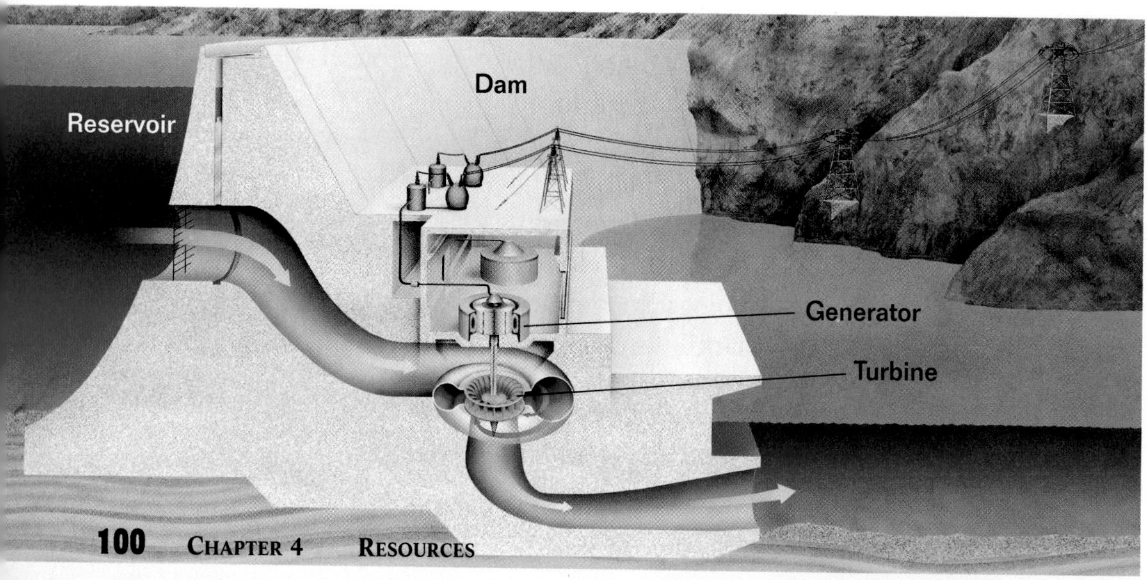

B The pressure of the water turns the turbines that drive the electrical generators in the plant.

The river water that backs up behind a dam creates a reservoir or large reserve of water. Many reservoirs are big enough to be considered lakes. Lake Shasta, the reservoir created by the dam on the Sacramento River, is 56 km wide. Look at **Figure 4-8** to see how a dam and a hydroelectric power plant work to generate electricity.

Hydroelectric Power Problems

Like solar power and energy from the wind, hydroelectric power doesn't cause pollution and it's renewable. But this energy resource has its problems. When dams are built, the reservoir located behind the dam can fill with sediment, and increased erosion can occur downstream. Land above the dam is flooded and wildlife habitats are disturbed. In addition, dams and power plants have already been built near most rivers suitable for generating hydroelectricity. Other places can't use hydroelectric power because they're not located near fast-flowing water.

MiniLab

Modeling the Effects of Heat

Procedure

1. Fill a glass beaker with cold water.
2. Fill a small, clear plastic bottle nearly full of cold water. Add several drops of food coloring to the bottle.
3. Carefully lower the small bottle into the beaker so that the bottle is upright underwater. Hold the bottle in place, if necessary. Observe what happens to the colored liquid inside the bottle.
4. Repeat the experiment, but this time fill the bottle with hot water. Observe what happens to the colored liquid inside the bottle.

Analysis

1. How did heat affect the movement of the colored liquid inside the bottle?
2. Changes in heat and pressure force hot water under Earth's surface to rise. How is the movement of the colored liquid in the bottle similar to the movement of hot water under Earth?

Energy from Earth

Another renewable energy resource can be found under Earth's surface near beds of hot molten rock called magma. The heated rocks that surround the magma produce **geothermal energy,** or heat energy from Earth, which can be used to generate electricity. **Figure 4-9** shows a geyser in New Zealand that produces geothermal energy. A geyser forms when water reaches the heated rocks and turns to steam. Heat and pressure from surrounding layers of rock produce steam and force it up in powerful spurts through openings in Earth's crust. This is an example of geothermal energy that occurs when magma is located close to Earth's surface. People in Iceland and California use the hot water and steam from the geysers to heat their homes.

Sometimes magma is not found close to Earth's surface, so engineers have to drill wells to reach the heated rock that surrounds the magma.

Figure 4-9 Geothermal energy is generated by geysers such as this one in New Zealand.

Heat and pressure then force the steam to rise to Earth's surface. There, it can be used to turn mechanical energy into electrical energy, much like the energy of moving water can be used to produce electricity.

Geothermal Energy Problems

As you've been learning, the use of each type of energy resource has advantages and disadvantages. Geothermal energy is no exception. Like fossil fuels, geothermal energy can release gases into the atmosphere that pollute the air. In addition, only a few places have magma near Earth's surface. To generate geothermal power elsewhere, deep wells must be drilled. This process is expensive and can disrupt natural habitats near the well.

*inter***NET** CONNECTION

Visit the Glencoe Science Web Site at **www.glencoe.com/sec/science/ca** for more information about nuclear energy.

Nuclear Energy

Atoms are the basic units of matter, and each atom contains a nucleus. All nuclei (singular *nucleus*) store energy. Scientists have found a way to generate energy from atoms. This is called nuclear energy. **Nuclear energy** is produced by splitting the nuclei of certain elements. In this process, known as fission, neutrons inside the nuclei are released. This produces heat energy that is used to change water into steam. The steam is then used to change mechanical energy into electrical energy, as shown in **Figure 4-10.**

The most commonly used fuel in nuclear power plants is the ore uranium. Uranium has a nucleus that can be split easily. Once the ore is mined, it's refined and placed in long, metal pipes called fuel rods. The fuel rods sit in a pool of cooling water within a nuclear reactor, shown in **Figure 4-11.** Energy is released when neutrons given off by the uranium split the nuclei of other uranium atoms, which in turn release more neutrons and more energy. This process, known as a chain reaction, happens very fast.

Figure 4-10 Heat energy is generated by fission within the nuclear reactor. This heat is used to change water into steam. The steam moves the turbine, which is connected to a generator that produces electrical energy.

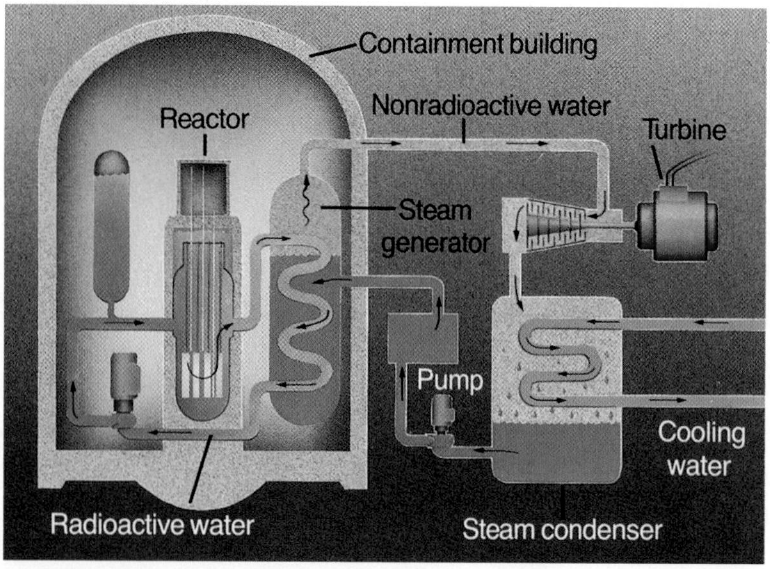

Nuclear Energy Problems

Nuclear energy produces more than electricity; it also produces nuclear waste. This waste material is highly radioactive. This means that the waste contains materials that can cause cancer or have other harmful effects on living things. Some of the waste will remain radioactive for more than 10 000 years. Nuclear waste must be handled and stored carefully to keep it from harming living things or from entering the environment. As you may have guessed, this is a major drawback in using nuclear power.

Figure 4-11 Fuel rods are placed in a nuclear reactor. Most of the high-level radioactive waste in the United States comes from used fuel rods.

Nuclear Energy Use

Because of potential problems in storing nuclear waste, nuclear energy has seen limited use in the United States. Electricity generated from nuclear power makes up only eight percent of the total energy used in the United States. Worldwide, about 25 countries use nuclear energy to generate electricity. France leads the world in production of nuclear energy—more than 80 percent of France's energy needs are met by nuclear power.

Currently, the use of nuclear energy and renewable energy resources is limited. But improvements in technology may enable these resources, particularly the sun, to be major sources of energy in the future.

Section Assessment

1. What is a renewable resource?
2. What are some advantages and disadvantages of solar energy, wind energy, and hydroelectric energy?
3. Compare and contrast nuclear energy use in the United States and France.
4. **Think Critically:** A well is drilled near a body of magma to produce electricity. Explain how energy changes form during this process.
5. **Skill Builder**
   Using Numbers Wind farms and solar power plants take up a good deal of land. Do the **Chapter 4 Skill Activity** on page 697 to interpret how much land is required for these alternative energy sources.

Science Journal

In your Science Journal, develop a plan to meet your town's energy needs using at least three different energy resources. Describe the energy sources that will provide electricity to buildings and homes. Explain why you chose each resource.

4•3 Water

What You'll Learn

- How important water is to living things
- Different sources of water
- How the location of water affects where humans live

Vocabulary
groundwater
point source
nonpoint source

Why It's Important

- You'll learn how water becomes polluted and what you can do to help keep it clean.

Water—A Vital Resource

Have you ever seen a picture of Earth from space, such as the one shown in **Figure 4-12A?** What strikes you most about the photograph? Earth has lots of water, doesn't it? In fact, about 70 percent of Earth is covered by water. This water continually moves through the water cycle, which is shown in **Figure 4-12B.** Water helps shape Earth's surface through the processes of erosion and deposition. Most importantly, water keeps all living things alive. Without water, living things could not carry out important life processes, such as growth and waste removal. Do you know that the bodies of most organisms are made up mostly of water? Scientists estimate that two-thirds of the weight of the human body is water. Water may be our most valuable resource. That's why it's important to know as much as we can about water, including how much is available and where it comes from.

Usable Water

Of the vast amount of water on Earth, only a small portion is available for use by humans. Approximately 97 percent of the world's total water supply is salt water in the oceans. That leaves only three percent as freshwater, and more than three-fourths of that is frozen in glaciers and ice caps. Thus, less than one percent of Earth's total

Figure 4-12
All living things need clean water to survive.

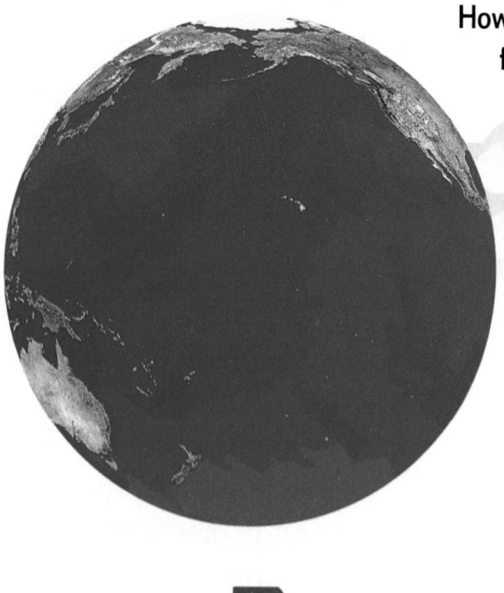

A About 70 percent of Earth is covered by water. **How much is available for use by humans?**

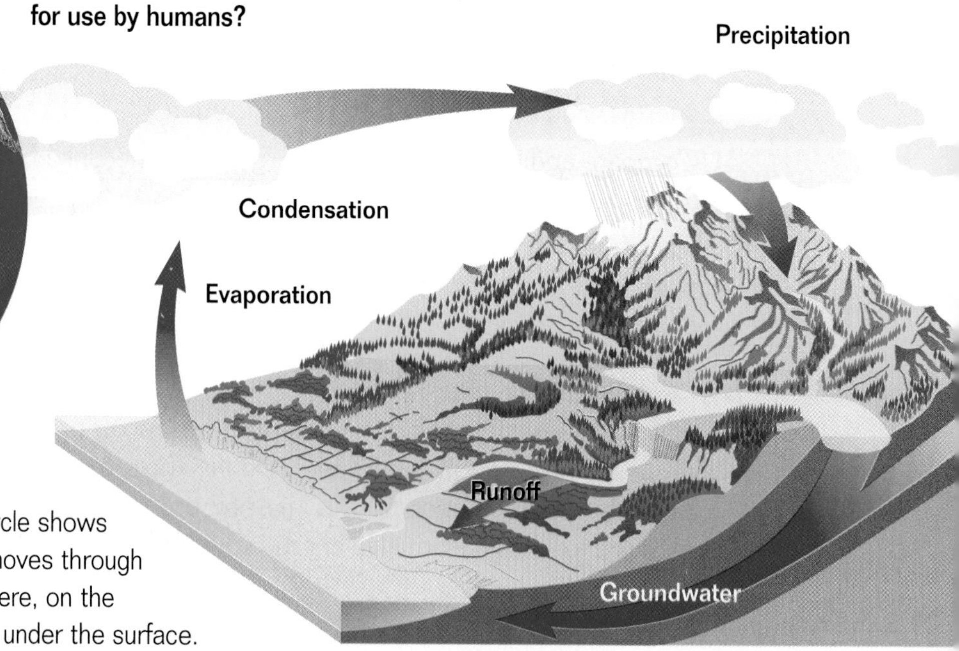

B The water cycle shows how water moves through the atmosphere, on the surface, and under the surface.

Figure 4-13 Groundwater is found under Earth's surface in small spaces between bits of soil and rock. **How do people reach groundwater?**

water supply is available for us to use for drinking, cooking, and other purposes. This one percent is found either underground or in lakes, streams, and rivers.

Groundwater

When you turn on a faucet, water flows out. Where does this water come from? One plentiful source of fresh water is groundwater that lies under Earth's surface. **Groundwater** is water that soaks into the ground and collects in small spaces between bits of soil and rock, as shown in **Figure 4-13.** If the small spaces are connected, the water can flow through layers of rock and soil. People drill down into these layers to make wells. They then pump the water to the surface for use as drinking water, for factories, or for watering crops and animals. ☑

Reading Check ☑

What is groundwater?

In the United States, groundwater provides 40 percent of public water supplies. Industries and farms also use groundwater. In many agricultural areas, groundwater is the only source of water available. Is this important resource renewable or nonrenewable? Some people consider groundwater renewable because it is part of the water cycle, which recycles water constantly. But, it takes a long time for groundwater to move through rock layers. Therefore, it can take a long time to clean up groundwater if it becomes polluted. Because of this, clean, usable groundwater should be considered a nonrenewable resource.

Surface Water

Not all places get their water from underground. If you live in a city or town, you may be using surface water. Surface water comes from streams, rivers, ponds, lakes, and reservoirs—it's the water we can see easily on Earth's surface. Do you use surface water or groundwater to meet your water needs? If you don't know, find out. Ask your teacher or parents, or check with your city water department.

Water Use

Nothing is as refreshing as a glass of cold water on a hot summer day—except maybe a cool dip in a city pool. Our bodies need water to survive, but we also depend on water for recreational uses such as swimming, boating, and fishing. We need water to bathe, wash clothes, cook food, and water plants, and these are just a few of the ways we use water.

Water is also used by industries to manufacture products and to transport some of those products on boats to stores and factories. Boats also are used to transport people across oceans or along rivers. Farmers use water to irrigate crops and water animals. Can you think of any other uses for water? Many plants and animals live in oceans, lakes, or rivers. They spend their entire lives in water. Water is their home. What do you think might happen to these living things if the water they live in were polluted?

Figure 4-14 shows the impact polluted water can have on fish. Not a pretty sight, is it? Keep in mind that the same pollutants that can kill fish in rivers also can make their way into a city's water supply. That's why it's important to clean water before we use it and to clean it again after we use it. Before we examine some methods used to make sure that water supplies are clean and safe, let's take a look at how water can become polluted.

Try at Home

MiniLab

Observing How Water Is Cleaned

Procedure

1. Fill a clean, empty mayonnaise jar two-thirds full of water.
2. Add a cup of potting soil to the jar.
3. Put the lid on the jar, close it tightly, then shake the jar until the water becomes muddy.
4. Put the jar aside and let it stand for two days.

Analysis

1. What happened to the soil in the jar? What happened to the water?
2. Look at **Figure 4-16.** Which part of the water-purification process did you model? Explain.
3. Which types of impurities would not be removed by the processes modeled in this activity?

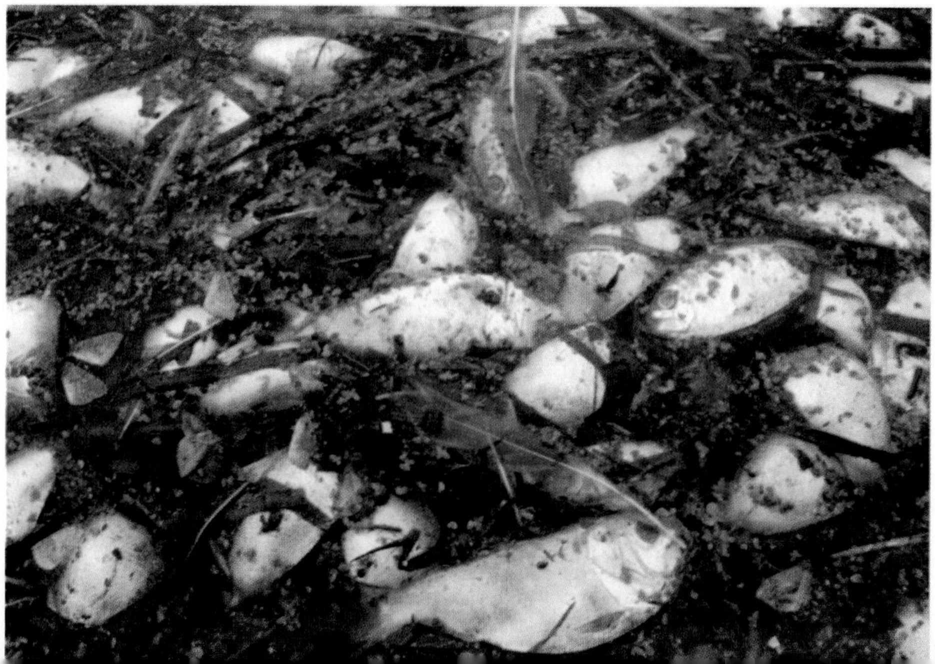

Figure 4-14 This fish kill occurred on the lower Neuse River in North Carolina in 1995.

Figure 4-15 Water pollution can cause serious problems.

A This stream in Spain was polluted by industrial wastes.

B This oil spill, the dark color leaking from the tanker, may threaten marine organisms and nearby beaches.

Water Pollution

Have you ever seen a stream such as the one shown in **Figure 4-15A?** The chemicals found in the stream are an example of water pollution. Water pollution occurs when debris, chemicals, or biological materials are added to water. These pollutants lower its quality. Some pollution comes from a single, identifiable source called a **point source.** If an oil tanker such as the one shown in **Figure 4-15B** begins leaking, a skim of oil is released into the sea and directly pollutes the water. You can see the pollution occurring. Have you ever seen examples of this type of pollution near your home or school?

Most types of pollution are hard to trace to a single source. The pollution comes from many different sources, called **nonpoint sources,** such as industries, homes, and farms. How can a farm pollute water? Chemical fertilizers are used to increase crop yields. These fertilizers can be carried away by runoff and deposited in streams, lakes, and wetlands. Some of these chemicals seep into the ground and can pollute groundwater supplies. Can you think of any way that you might cause water pollution? If you spill gasoline in your driveway, the gasoline will be carried away by runoff. It can enter the city sewage system or a stream and eventually make its way into a drinking water supply.

Using Math

If all the world's water were represented by 100 mL in a graduated cylinder, how much of the water in the cylinder would be available to use as freshwater?

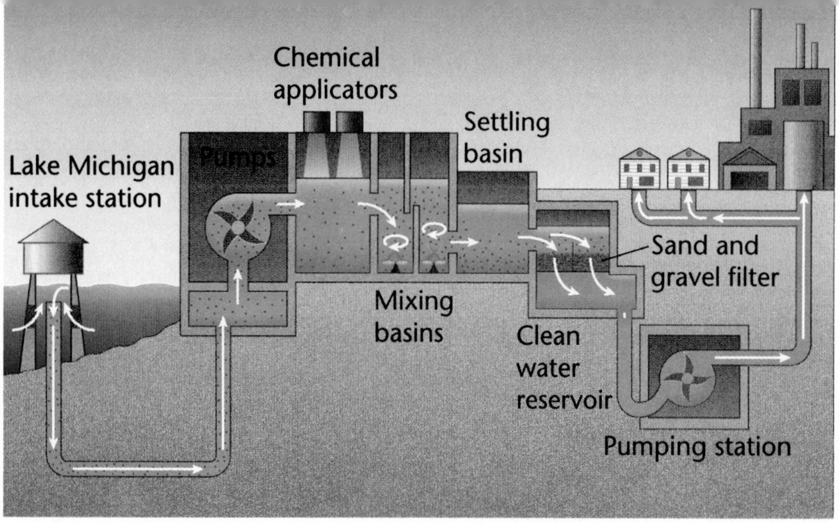

Figure 4-16 In this water-purification plant, water is pumped into a tank, where chemicals are added to kill microorganisms. The water is then mixed and run through a settling basin. Large particles of matter settle out. Smaller particles are filtered by sand and gravel. Clean water is then pumped to consumers.

Cleaning Up Water

Many countries are working together to reduce the amount of water pollution. For example, the United States and Canada have agreed to clean up the pollution in Lake Erie, which borders both countries. The U.S. government also has passed several laws to keep water supplies clean. The Safe Drinking Water Act is a set of government standards designed to ensure safe drinking water. The Clean Water Act gives money to states to build water-treatment plants, such as the one shown in **Figure 4-16.** Water is cleaned at such plants before being used for drinking and other purposes.

Is there anything you can do to help reduce water pollution? Sure, there is. Keep pet wastes, leaves, oil, and other debris from entering storm drains, which often lead directly to streams or lakes. Properly dispose of hazardous substances, such as used oil, antifreeze, and paint; *do not* pour them down a storm drain.

***inter*NET CONNECTION**

Visit the Glencoe Science Web Site at **www.glencoe.com/sec/science/ca** for more information about ways to reduce water pollution.

Water Distribution

As you have learned, water is vital to the survival of all living things. Take a look at the map shown in **Figure 4-17.** Do you see a relationship between the location of major centers of population and major bodies of water? People usually build cities near shorelines and along large rivers. As you can see from the map, desert areas don't have many cities or towns.

Living near large bodies of water has its problems. Sometimes there are floods. Sometimes the water is too polluted to use. That's why so many countries have passed laws to reduce water pollution and to monitor the quality of the water supply. Water is a valuable resource—every bit as valuable as the energy resources you studied earlier. As you continue with the discovery of the many resources around you, you will gain an understanding of other natural resources.

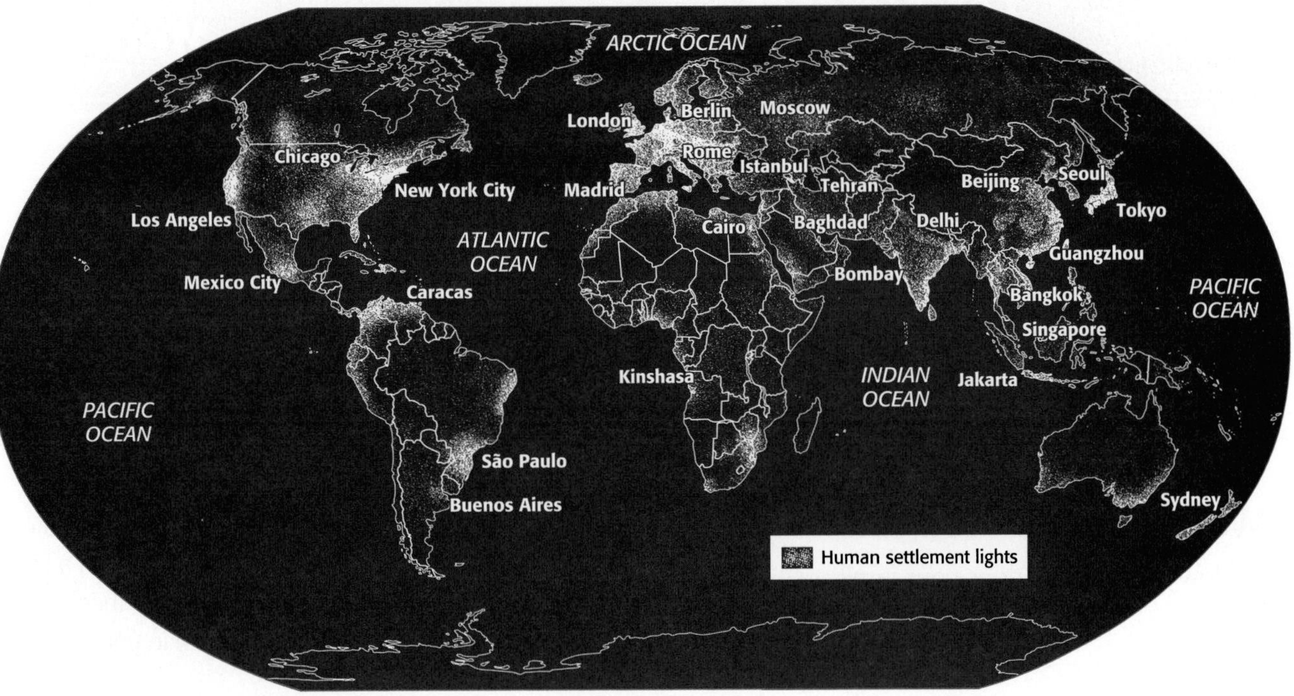

Figure 4-17 This map shows that most of the world's population is centered around large bodies of water. The lighter, white areas indicate human settlement. The lighter the area, the more dense the population.

Section Assessment

1. Why is water considered one of our most valuable resources?
2. List three ways that humans use water. Describe where the water comes from for each of these uses.
3. **Think Critically:** Some cities are located near desert areas. How do you think they might meet their demands for water?
4. **Skill Builder**
   Concept Mapping Make an events chain concept map that shows how soap chemicals in a bucket of water might end up as pollution in a local stream. If you need help, refer to Concept Mapping in the **Skill Handbook** on page 666.

interNET CONNECTION

Visit the Glencoe Science Web Site at **www.glencoe.com/sec/science/ca** for more information about the Clean Water Act. Then write a brief summary of how this legislation encourages water-quality standards in the United States.

Using Water

Materials

- Calculator

Water is an important resource that we use every day. You wash dishes and clothes and you wash yourself and brush your teeth. All of these activities require water. The average person in the United States uses about 397 L of water each day. Do this activity to see how much water you use.

What You'll Investigate

How much water does your family use in three days?

Goals

- **Calculate** how much water the people in your household use in three days.
- **Make a plan** to reduce the amount of water used by your family.
- **Describe** how people use water.

Procedure

1. Use the table on this page to **calculate** how much water your family uses.
2. For three days, have the people who live in your house **keep a record** of when they do the activities listed in the table. If your family members forget to mark down their water usage, complete the activity using your own water-usage record.
3. The numbers in the table describe approximately how many liters an average person uses in a single day for the activity listed. **Multiply** these numbers by the number of people in your household who did these activities.
4. **Add up** the totals for each day. The final sum will be the total amount of water used for these activities in three days.

Conclude and Apply

1. How much water did your family use in three days?
2. **Study** the activities listed in the table. Do you see any ways to reduce the amount of water used?
3. **Develop** a detailed plan to reduce the amount of water your family used.
4. **Study** the table again. It lists only a few ways in which your family uses water. **Describe** at least three other activities not listed in the table.

Activity	Conditions	Amount of Water Used
Washing dishes by hand	Water is running all the time	113 L/person/day
Washing dishes by hand	Sink is filled with water	19 L/person/day
Washing clothes in machine	Small load with high water setting	68 L/person/day
Washing clothes in machine	Full load with high water setting	45 L/person/day
Taking a shower	10 minutes long	150 L/person/day
Taking a bath	Bathtub is full of water	113 L/person/day
Flushing the toilet	Water-saving toilet	23 L/person/day
Brushing teeth	Water is running all the time	17 L/person/day

Land

4•4

Land as a Resource

Has your neighborhood changed lately? How about the outskirts of your town? Perhaps a grassy field has been turned into a parking lot, or some nearby farmland has become a place where new homes were built. These changes, shown in **Figure 4-18,** are examples of the different ways we use land as a resource. How else do we use land?

Land Use

Think about where your food comes from. We need land to raise the crops and animals we use for food. A simple peanut butter-and-jelly sandwich requires land to grow the wheat needed to make bread, land to grow peanuts for the peanut butter, and land to grow the sugarcane and fruit for the jelly. A hamburger? Land is needed to raise cattle and to grow the grain the cattle eat.

Think about your home, your school, and other places you go, like a park or a shopping mall. The things that you buy in the shopping mall come from factories. All these buildings take up space. This means that every time we build a house, a mall, or a factory, we use more land. Land is a renewable resource because in most cases, it can be used over and over again. But one look at a globe will show you that the amount of land is limited. Therefore, we have to make wise choices when it comes to land use.

What You'll Learn

- Land is a renewable resource
- Why trees are renewable resources, but forests are not
- How we use mineral resources

Vocabulary

conservation
ore

Why It's Important

- You'll know what resources are used to make some of the things you use every day.

Figure 4-18 This farmland will soon be a new housing development. **What are some other ways that we use land?**

Figure 4-19 People are working to protect natural habitats in many areas, such as this tropical rain forest in Costa Rica.

Using Land Wisely

People need food, clothing, jobs, and a place to live, and each of these things takes space. But, preserving natural habitats, such as the one shown in **Figure 4-19,** is also important. Remember, a habitat is the place where organisms live. Ponds, wetlands, and forests are examples of natural habitats. If we fill in a wetland to construct an apartment building, an important natural habitat is lost.

Laws help to protect against habitat loss and help us use land wisely. Before major construction can take place in a new area, the land must be studied to determine the impact construction will have on the living things, the soil, and the water in the area. If endangered plants or animals live in the area, construction may not be allowed.

Problems can also arise when we use land for farming or grazing animals. If these activities are not done properly, soil can become eroded from overuse. **Figure 4-20** shows how farmers and ranchers work to reduce soil erosion problems.

Resources from Land

We use land to grow crops, raise animals, and to live on. In addition to meeting our needs for food and shelter, land provides us with two other important resources: forests and minerals.

Figure 4-20

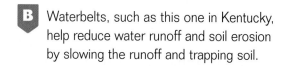

A Improper use of rangeland can cause soil erosion, as seen in this photo from Brazil.

B Waterbelts, such as this one in Kentucky, help reduce water runoff and soil erosion by slowing the runoff and trapping soil.

Figure 4-21

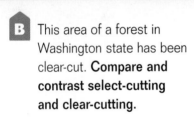

A Certain trees in this forest were cut down and new trees planted in their place. This is an example of select-cutting.

B This area of a forest in Washington state has been clear-cut. **Compare and contrast select-cutting and clear-cutting.**

Forests

Look around your classroom. Do you see books, paper, desks, and pencils? All these products are made of wood. They come from trees in a forest that were cut down and taken to a lumberyard to be processed into boards and other wooden products.

In addition to providing us with much-needed wood, forests play an important role in keeping Earth's atmosphere in balance. How? Remember what you learned about photosynthesis. In this process, trees and other plants use carbon dioxide, water, and sunlight to make oxygen and carbohydrates. As forests grow, they take in carbon dioxide. If an entire forest is cut down, it doesn't take in carbon dioxide, and more of this gas is left in the atmosphere. Increases in atmospheric carbon dioxide may cause global warming, which is a rise in temperatures around the world. Global warming may lead to changes in climate that could impact natural habitats all over Earth.

Forest Conservation

LIFE SCIENCE INTEGRATION

Because forests are such a valuable resource, they must be used with care. That's why many states now have forest conservation laws. **Conservation** is the careful use of resources with the goal of reducing damage to the environment. In **Figure 4-21,** some methods of forest conservation are shown.

In select-cutting, shown in **Figure 4-21A,** a limited number of trees are cut, and new trees are planted in their place. The young saplings grow among the older trees. By the time all of the original trees are cut, a new forest has gradually grown.

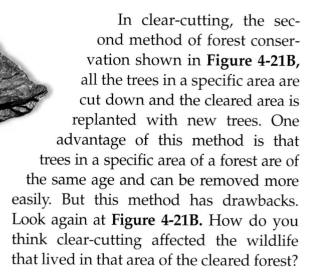

Figure 4-22 Motorcycle parts and saw blades are two of many products made from the iron ore hematite.

In clear-cutting, the second method of forest conservation shown in **Figure 4-21B,** all the trees in a specific area are cut down and the cleared area is replanted with new trees. One advantage of this method is that trees in a specific area of a forest are of the same age and can be removed more easily. But this method has drawbacks. Look again at **Figure 4-21B.** How do you think clear-cutting affected the wildlife that lived in that area of the cleared forest?

Renewable or Nonrenewable?

If you've ever planted a tree, you know that it takes time for a tree to grow. Some trees take many years to mature. Still, trees can be viewed as a renewable resource because as one tree is cut, another can be planted in its place.

Forests, on the other hand, are nonrenewable. Why? Individual trees can be replanted. But, forests are complex ecosystems that support countless living things. A forest ecosystem takes more than 100 years to develop. If many or all of the trees are removed from one forest, it could take centuries for the forest ecosystem to develop again.

Mineral Resources

Take a moment to look around the classroom again. List three or four items that you use every day. Now, try to decide what resources they were made from. It's easy if the item is made of wood. But what about the metal in your desk, in the door handle, or surrounding the windows? Metal objects come from mineral resources, which are found in rocks. So minerals are another type of resource that we get from land.

No matter which type of rock you pick up, it's likely made up of a number of valuable minerals. Generally, it costs more to get those minerals out of the rock than the minerals are worth. But, sometimes we find large deposits of minerals in one place. These minerals can be classified as ores. An **ore** is a mineral resource that can be mined at a profit. **Figure 4-22** shows common uses for iron ore. ☑

Reading Check ☑

What is an ore?

Do we have enough ore?

What would life be like if we did not have enough of some of the metals that we use every day? We already have used up many of the world's richest ore deposits, and we are currently using more mineral resources than ever before.

Ore deposits are nonrenewable resources. They take millions of years to form but can be mined out only in decades. There is a concern that we may run out of some types of ore deposits in the future.

How can we solve this problem? Some people have suggested that we may be able to mine some low-grade ore deposits, but mining these deposits would be expensive, and they eventually would be depleted too. The best way to make sure a continued supply of important metals exists is to recycle.

Figure 4-23 Industrial plants, such as the one shown here in Ohio, can create air pollution when they burn fossil fuels to generate electricity or to manufacture products.

Problems with Using Ores

Ores, like fossil fuels, are resources found under Earth's surface. To get to ores, large quantities of soil and rock often must be moved. This process is called mining. Mines can look unsightly and the waste rock produced by mines can pollute surface water. Air pollution also is produced when large industrial plants such as the one shown in **Figure 4-23** process the ores, generating dust and soot particles. Thus, the use of ores, like fossil fuels, affects the environment. Care must be taken to mine and use the ores in ways that do not harm water resources, living things, and natural habitats.

Section Assessment

1. We have only a limited amount of land, yet land is a renewable resource. Why?
2. Trees are renewable resources, but forests are not. Why?
3. Compare and contrast minerals and ores.
4. **Think Critically:** About 117 000 km^2 of tropical rain forests are cut down each year. Why should people everywhere be concerned about the loss of forests located in the tropics?
5. **Skill Builder**
   Using a Word Processor Using a word processor, compile a list of do's and don'ts for forest conservation. If you need help, refer to Using a Word Processor in the **Technology Skill Handbook** on page 684.

Science Journal

Research one of the resources discussed in this section. Describe an environmental problem associated with its use. In your Science Journal, write a report that explains possible solutions to this problem.

Design Your Own Experiment

Activity 4-2

Using Land

Possible Materials

- Grid paper (10 squares by 10 squares)
- Colored pencils

Imagine planning a small town. Your job in this activity is to draw up a master plan to decide how 100 square units of land can be turned into a town.

Recognize the Problem

How should land resources be used?

Form a Hypothesis

People need homes in which to live, places to work, and stores from which to buy things. Children need to attend schools and have parks in which to play. How can all of these needs be met when planning a small town?

Goals

- **Design** a plan in which 100 square units of land can be turned into a town.

Parts of Your Town	Number of Blocks Needed
Office buildings	6 blocks in one group
Industrial plant	6 blocks in one group
School	1 block
Landfill for garbage	4 blocks in one group
Houses and apartments	44 blocks—can be broken up
Stores and businesses	19 blocks—can be broken up
Park	20 blocks—can be broken up

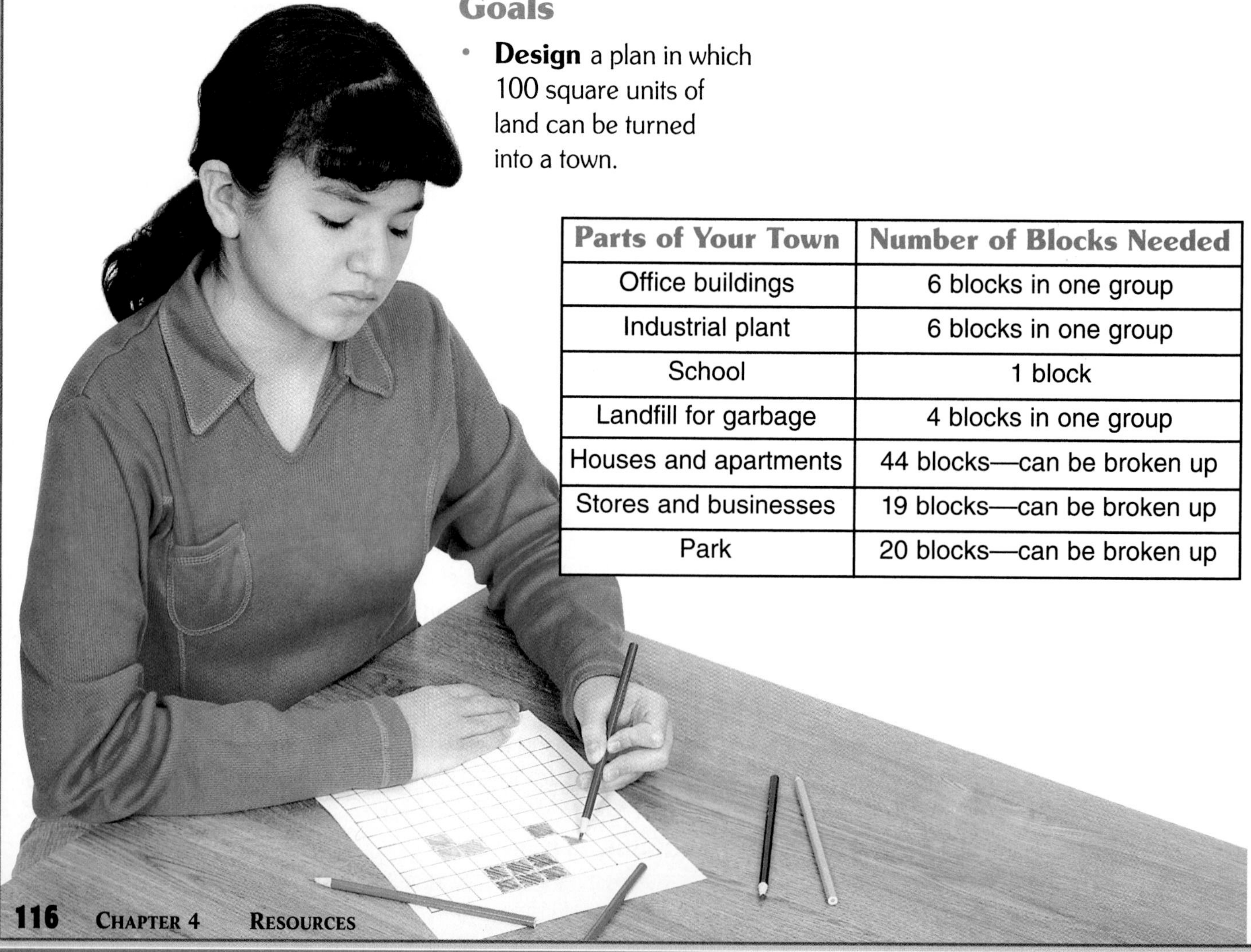

Test Your Hypothesis

Plan

1. **Make** a square graph 10 blocks across and 10 blocks down. The graph represents a 100-square-unit piece of land.
2. The table on the previous page shows the different parts of a town that need to be included in your plan. The office buildings and industrial plant are places where the people of the town will work. They are each 6 blocks in size. These blocks must be treated as one group—they cannot be divided. The landfill is 4 blocks in size. It, too, cannot be broken up.
3. All other town parts can be broken up as needed. Stores and businesses are areas in which shops are located, as well as medical offices, restaurants, churches, and cemeteries.
4. As a group, **discuss** how the different parts of the town might be put together. Should the park be in the center of town or near the edge of town? Should the school be near the offices or near the houses? Where should the landfill go?
5. How will you show the different town parts on your grid paper?

Do

1. Make sure your teacher approves your plan before you proceed.
2. As a group, **plan** your town. Check over your plan to make sure that all town parts are accounted for.

Analyze Your Data

1. Where did you place the office buildings and the industrial plant? Why were they placed there? Where did you place the houses, school, and businesses? **Explain** why you placed each one as you did.
2. Did you make one park or many parks? What are the advantages of your park(s) plan?

Draw Conclusions

1. Where did you place the landfill? Will any of the townspeople be upset by its location? To answer this question, it may help to know what direction the wind usually blows from in your town.
2. Where would you put an airport in this town? Keep in mind safety issues, noise levels, and transportation needs.

Chapter 4 Reviewing Main Ideas

For a **preview** of this chapter, study this Reviewing Main Ideas before you read the chapter. After you have studied this chapter, you can use the Reviewing Main Ideas to **review** the chapter.

The Glencoe MindJogger, Audiocassettes, and CD-ROM provide additional opportunities for review.

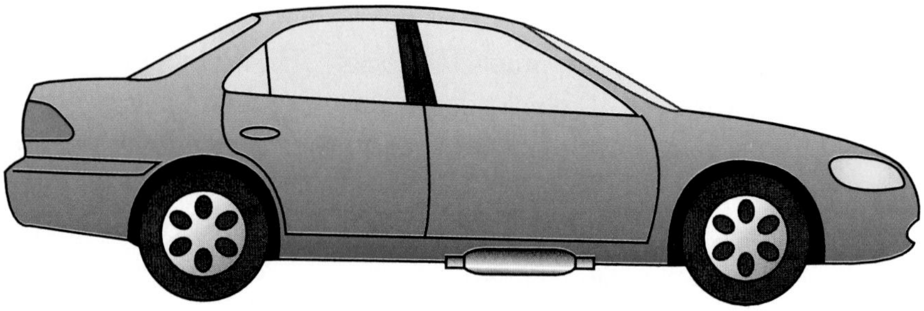

Section 4-1 ENERGY RESOURCES

Fossil fuels such as coal, oil, and gas are **nonrenewable** energy resources. They are being used faster than Earth can replace them. Fossil fuels provide us with much-needed energy, but certain problems are associated with their use. ***What is acid rain?***

Section 4-2 ALTERNATIVE ENERGY RESOURCES

Alternative energy resources, such as **solar energy,** energy from the wind, **hydroelectric power,** and **geothermal energy** are constant and will not run out. For this reason, they are considered **renewable.** Though some of these resources do not cause pollution, certain drawbacks are associated with their use. ***Why can't wind energy be used to meet all of the world's energy needs?***

Reading Check

What words beginning with the prefix *non-* could you use to describe solar energy? To describe fossil fuels?

Section
4-3 WATER

Less than one percent of Earth's total water supply is in a form that people can readily use. We use water to meet our basic needs, and we use it for industry, agriculture, and recreation. Clean water can become a nonrenewable resource if water supplies are overused or polluted. ***Why is most water on Earth unusable as drinking water or for agriculture and industry?***

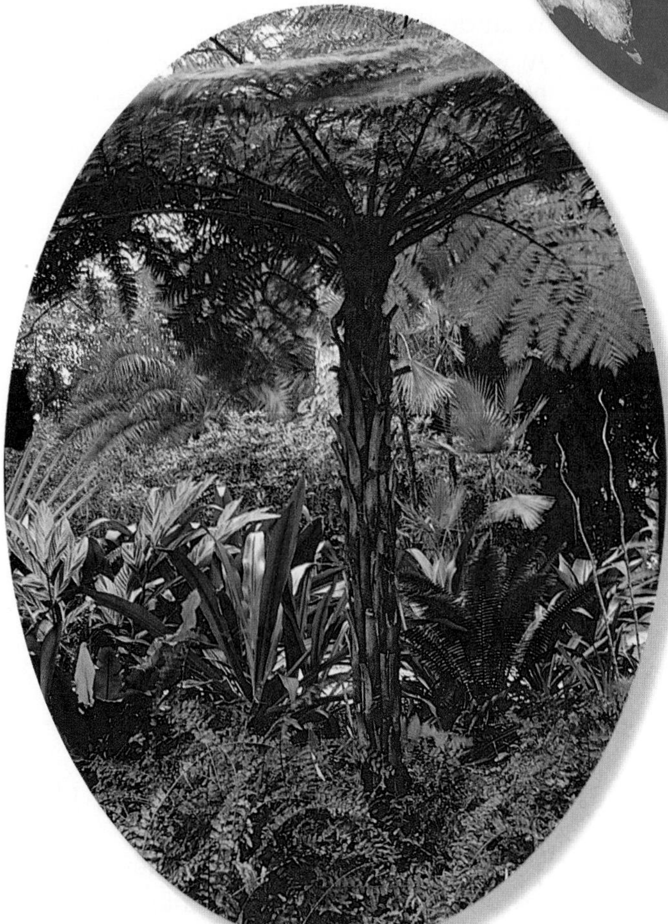

Section
4-4 LAND

Land is a valuable resource used for food, shelter, and other needs. Land also provides us with two other important resources: wood and minerals. All of Earth's resources must be managed wisely. If one resource is polluted or overused, other resources can be affected as well. ***Give an example of a way to harvest trees that conserves forests.***

Chapter 4 Assessment

Using Vocabulary

a. acid rain
b. conservation
c. fossil fuel
d. geothermal energy
e. groundwater
f. hydroelectric power
g. nonpoint source
h. nonrenewable
i. nuclear energy
j. ore
k. point source
l. pollution
m. renewable
n. solar energy

Each of the following sentences is false. Make the sentence true by replacing the italicized word with a word from the list above.

1. Solar energy is an example of a *non-renewable* resource.
2. Careful use of resources with the goal of reducing damage to the environment is called *pollution.*
3. *Nuclear energy* forms from the remains of dead plants and animals.
4. Water that soaks into the ground and collects in the small spaces between bits of rock and soil is called *acid rain.*
5. The introduction of harmful waste products, chemicals, and substances into the environment is called *conservation.*

Checking Concepts

Choose the word or phrase that best answers the question.

6. What does nuclear energy produce?
   A) solar energy
   B) radioactive waste
   C) conservation
   D) nonrenewable resources
7. What is water in rivers, streams, lakes, and reservoirs called?
   A) peat
   B) surface water
   C) groundwater
   D) natural gas
8. Which of the following is an example of a fossil fuel?
   A) wind
   B) water
   C) natural gas
   D) uranium
9. Approximately what percent of the energy used in the United States comes from coal?
   A) 12
   B) 22
   C) 32
   D) 52
10. What kind of resource can be mined for a profit?
    A) solar cell
    B) wind
    C) dam
    D) ore
11. What kind of energy is generated by large dams built on rivers?
    A) wind
    B) nuclear
    C) hydroelectric
    D) solar
12. When many windmills are located in one place in order to generate electricity, what do they form?
    A) wind farm
    B) dam
    C) oil well
    D) nuclear reactor
13. Where does the heat energy from geothermal energy come from?
    A) water
    B) atoms
    C) heated rocks
    D) wind
14. When gases released by burning coal or oil mix with water in the air, what can they form?
    A) acid rain
    B) fission
    C) conservation
    D) groundwater
15. A nonrenewable resource can't be replaced in less than how many years?
    A) 5
    B) 10
    C) 50
    D) 100

Thinking Critically

16. With all of the paper products that we use every day, why don't we run out of trees?
17. Some heavily populated countries cause less environmental damage than countries with far fewer people. Why?

18. A shark that lives at sea is found dead. It has traces of chemicals in its body that, in turn, can be traced to pesticides used on farms. How can this happen?
19. Why shouldn't nuclear wastes be stored near an area prone to earthquakes?
20. Once a mineral resource is classified as an ore, will it always remain an ore? Explain your answer.

Developing Skills

If you need help, refer to the Skill Handbook.

21. **Sequencing:** If a well were drilled into a rock layer that contains oil, natural gas, and water, which substance would be encountered first? Explain.
22. **Comparing and Contrasting:** Compare and contrast solar energy and wind energy.
23. **Interpreting Scientific Illustrations:** The figure below shows a water-purification plant. In your own words, describe the path water takes from a stream to your faucet.

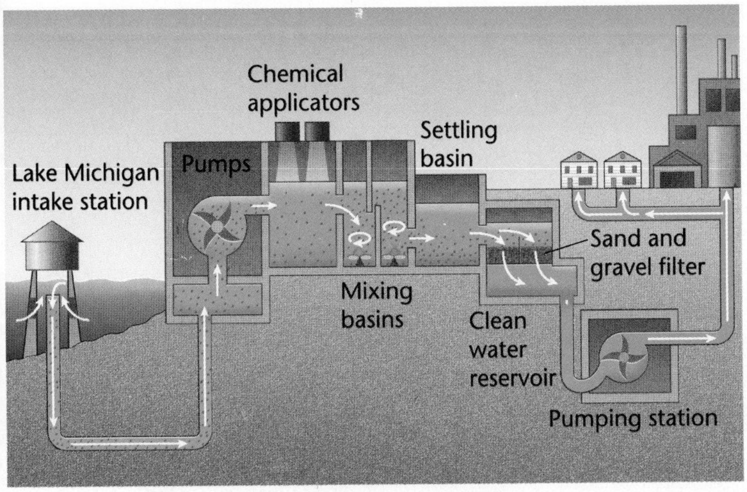

24. **Making and Using Tables:** Make a table that shows the advantages and disadvantages of each energy resource discussed in this chapter.

THE PRINCETON REVIEW

Test-Taking Tip

Use Roots to Learn The roots of words can help you group words together as you learn them. If you learn that *trans-* means "across," as in *transfer,* you might then remember the meaning of words like *transplant, transform,* and *transverse.*

Test Practice

Use these questions to test your Science Proficiency.

1. Trees are considered renewable resources, but forests are not. Which of the following statements **BEST** explains why?
   A) Forests are complex ecosystems that take longer than 100 years to develop.
   B) Forest conservation methods haven't been developed yet.
   C) Forests are not classified as resources.
   D) Forests can never grow back.
2. The use of nuclear energy is limited in the United States. Which of the following statements **BEST** explains why?
   A) There are no nuclear power plants in the United States.
   B) The use of nuclear energy releases too much carbon dioxide into Earth's atmosphere.
   C) Used fuel rods contain radioactive waste that must be handled carefully and stored in a place where they can't harm the environment.
   D) Nuclear power plants are inefficient in generating electricity.

CHAPTER 5

Views of Earth

Chapter Preview

Skills Preview

Skill Builders

- Map Concepts
- Measure in SI

Activities

- Compare and Contrast
- Interpret Data

MiniLabs

- Interpret Scientific Illustrations
- Make a Model

Reading Check

Locate a legend, myth, or folktale from another culture that explains the creation of mountains, plains, or other landforms. Share it with the class.

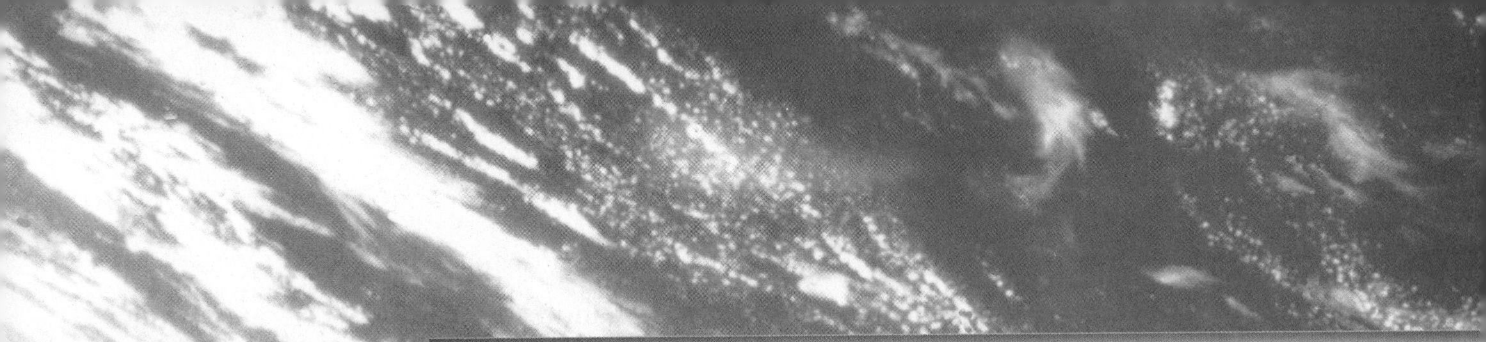

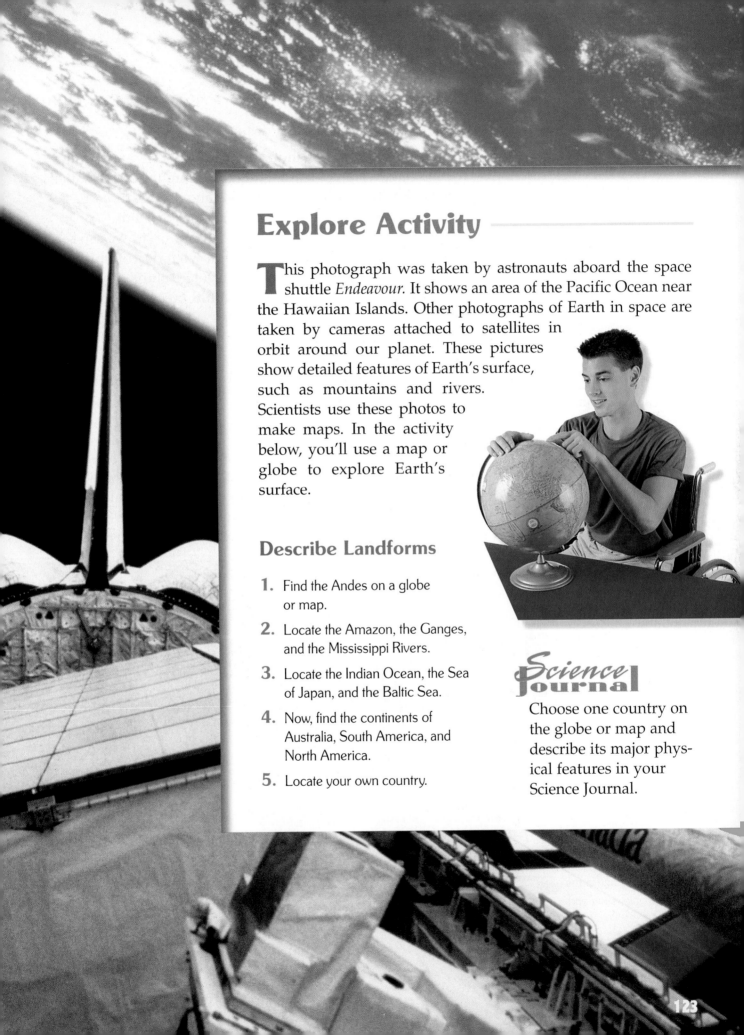

Explore Activity

This photograph was taken by astronauts aboard the space shuttle *Endeavour.* It shows an area of the Pacific Ocean near the Hawaiian Islands. Other photographs of Earth in space are taken by cameras attached to satellites in orbit around our planet. These pictures show detailed features of Earth's surface, such as mountains and rivers. Scientists use these photos to make maps. In the activity below, you'll use a map or globe to explore Earth's surface.

Describe Landforms

1. Find the Andes on a globe or map.
2. Locate the Amazon, the Ganges, and the Mississippi Rivers.
3. Locate the Indian Ocean, the Sea of Japan, and the Baltic Sea.
4. Now, find the continents of Australia, South America, and North America.
5. Locate your own country.

Science Journal

Choose one country on the globe or map and describe its major physical features in your Science Journal.

5•1 Landforms

What You'll Learn

- Differences between plains and plateaus
- Describe folded, upwarped, fault-block, and volcanic mountains

Vocabulary
plain
plateau
folded mountain
upwarped mountain
fault-block mountain
volcanic mountain

Why It's Important

- You'll learn how the land around you formed.

Plains

A lot of interesting landforms can be seen around the world. A landform is a feature that makes up the shape of the land on Earth's surface. **Figure 5-1** shows the three basic types of landforms: plains, plateaus, and mountains.

We all know what mountains are. In our minds, we can see tall peaks reaching toward the sky. But what do you think of when you hear the word *plains?* You might think of endless flat fields of wheat or grass. That would be correct, because many plains are used to grow crops. **Plains** are large, flat areas. Most plains are found in the interior regions of continents. Those found near the ocean are called coastal plains. Together, interior plains and coastal plains make up one-half of all the land in the United States.

Coastal Plains

Coastal plains are broad areas along the ocean's shore. They are often called lowlands because of their low elevations. Elevation refers to distance above or below sea level. As you might guess, sea level has zero elevation. The Atlantic Coastal Plain is a good example of this type of landform.

Figure 5-1 Three basic types of landforms are plains, plateaus, and mountains.

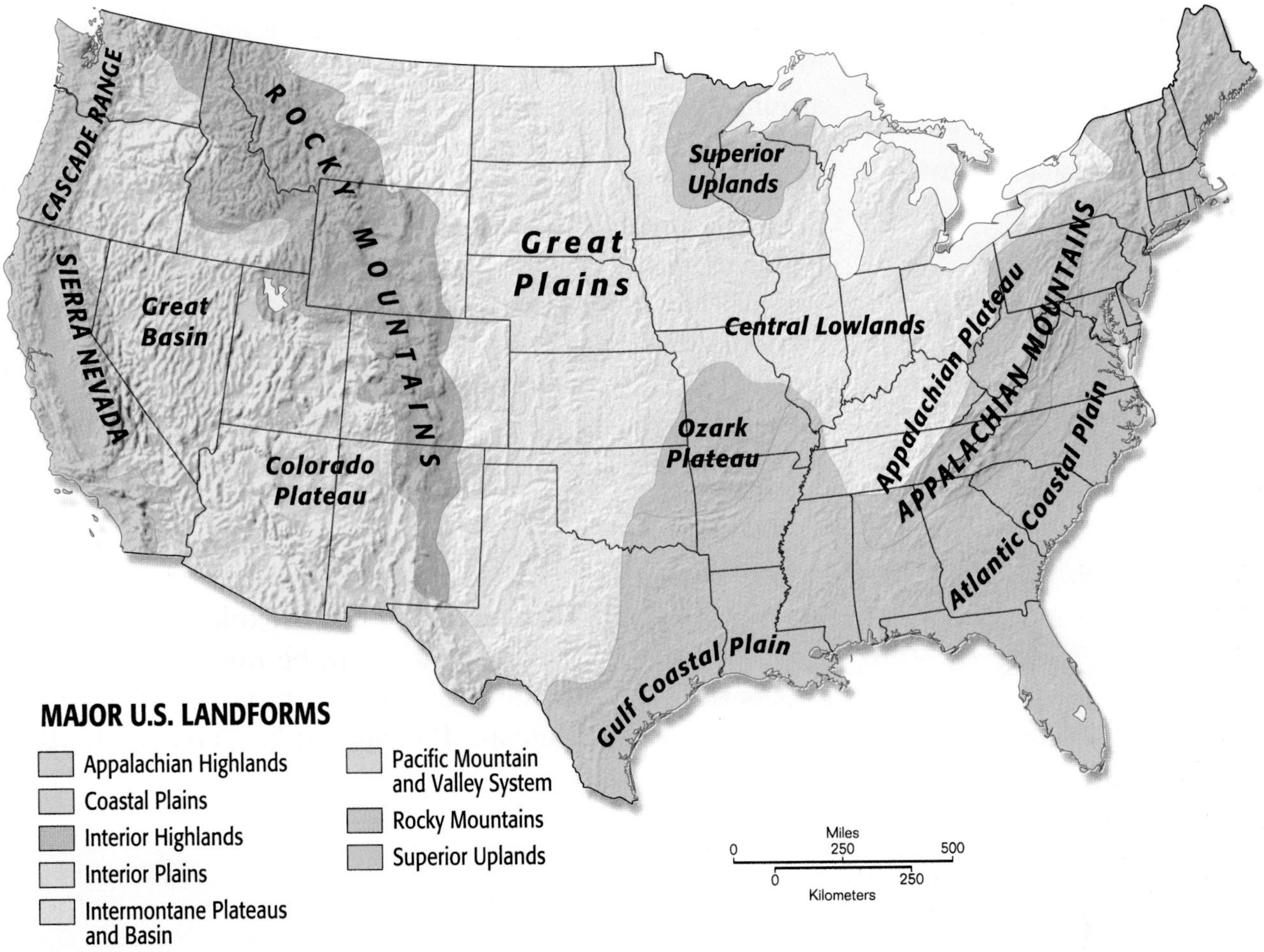

Figure 5-2 The plains, plateaus, and mountains of the United States are divided into eight major regions. **Based upon the information in this map, describe the region that you live in.**

It stretches along the east coast of the United States. This area has low rolling hills, swamps, and marshes. A marsh is grassy wetland, usually flooded with water.

If you hiked along the Atlantic Coastal Plain, you would know it isn't perfectly flat. Many low hills and valleys have been carved by rivers. What do you suppose caused the Atlantic Coastal Plain to form? It actually began forming under water about 70 million years ago from sediments made of marine organisms that fell to the ancient ocean floor. When sea level dropped, the plain was exposed.

Another example of this landform is the Gulf Coastal Plain shown in **Figure 5-2.** It includes the lowlands in the southern United States that surround the Gulf of Mexico. Much of this plain was formed from sediments deposited by the Mississippi River as it entered the Gulf of Mexico.

Using Math

The elevation of Denver, Colorado, is about 1624.5 m above sea level. The elevation of New Orleans, Louisiana, is 1626 m lower than Denver's. Find the elevation of New Orleans.

Interior Plains

A large part of the center of the United States is called the interior plains. The interior plains of the United States are also shown in **Figure 5-2.** They stretch from the Appalachian Mountains in the east, to the Rocky Mountains in the west, to the Gulf Coastal Plain in the south. They include the rolling hills of the Great Lakes area and the Central Lowlands around the Missouri and Mississippi Rivers.

A large part of the interior plains is known as the Great Plains. They lie between the Mississippi lowlands and the Rocky Mountains. The Great Plains are flat, grassy, dry areas with few trees. They are called high plains because of their elevation. They range from 350 m above sea level at their eastern border to 1500 m above sea level at their western boundary. The Great Plains are covered with nearly horizontal layers of loose materials eroded from the Rocky Mountains. Streams deposited these sediments over the last 28 million years.

Try at Home

Mini Lab

Profiling the United States

Procedure

1. Place the bottom edge of a piece of paper across the middle of **Figure 5-2,** extending from the west coast to the east coast.
2. Mark where different landforms are located along this edge.
3. Use a map of the United States and the descriptions of the landforms in Section 5-1 to help you draw a profile, or side view, of the United States. Use steep, jagged lines to represent mountains. Low, flat lines can represent plains.

Analysis

1. Describe how your profile changed shape as you moved from west to east.
2. Describe how the shape of your profile would be different if you moved from north to south.

Plateaus

If you would like to explore some higher regions, you might be interested in going to the second basic type of landform—a plateau. **Plateaus** (pla TOHZ) are flat,

raised areas of land. They are areas made up of nearly horizontal rocks that have been uplifted by forces within Earth. Plateaus are different from plains in that they rise steeply from the land around them. An example of a plateau in the United States is the Colorado Plateau, which lies just west of the Rocky Mountains. The Colorado River, as shown in **Figure 5-3,** has cut deeply into the rock layers of the plateau, forming the Grand Canyon. Because the Colorado Plateau is located in what is now a dry region, only a few rivers have developed on its surface. If you hiked around on this plateau, you would see a desert landscape.

Mountains

Plains and plateaus are mostly flat. If you want to see a steep rock face, you must go to the third basic type of landform—a mountain. Mountains rise high above the surrounding land, often showing a spectacular view from the top. The world's highest mountain peak is Mount Everest in the Himalayas. It is more than 8800 m above sea level. By contrast, mountain peaks in the United States reach just over 6000 m. Mountains vary greatly in size and in how they are formed. The four main types of mountains are folded, upwarped, fault-block, and volcanic.

Reading Check

What are the four main types of mountains?

Figure 5-3 Rivers cut deep into the Colorado Plateau, as shown by the Colorado River near Moab, Utah. **How are plateaus different from plains?**

Figure 5-4 Folded mountains form when rock layers are squeezed from opposite sides. **When did the Appalachian Mountains form?**

Folded Mountains

The first mountains we will investigate are folded mountains. If you travel through a road cut in the Appalachian Mountains, you'll see rock layers that are folded like the ones in **Figure 5-4.** Folded rock layers look like a rug that has been pushed up against a wall. What do you think caused this to happen?

PHYSICS INTEGRATION

Tremendous forces inside Earth force horizontal rock layers together. When rock layers are squeezed from opposite sides, they buckle and fold into **folded mountains.** The Appalachian Mountains are folded mountains that formed 250 to 350 million years ago. They are some of the oldest and longest mountain ranges in North America, stretching from Newfoundland, Canada, all the way south to Alabama. At one time, the Appalachians were higher than the Rocky Mountains. Weathering and erosion have worn them down to less than 2000 m above sea level.

Figure 5-5
The southern Rocky Mountains are upwarped mountains that formed when crust was pushed up by forces inside Earth.

Upwarped Mountains

The southern Rocky Mountains in Colorado and New Mexico, the Black Hills in South Dakota, and the Adirondack Mountains in New York are upwarped mountains. **Figure 5-5** shows a mountain range in Colorado. What do you notice about the shape of the mountains? The sharp peaks and ridges are characteristic of upwarped mountains. **Upwarped mountains** are formed when crust is pushed up by forces inside Earth. Over time, the soil and other materials on top of Earth's crust erode, leaving the rock underneath exposed. These rocks then erode to form peaks and ridges.

Figure 5-6 Fault-block mountains such as the Grand Tetons are formed when faults occur. Some rock blocks move up, while others move down. **What types of peaks are characteristic of these mountains?**

CHEMISTRY INTEGRATION

Violent Eruptions
The composition of erupting materials helps determine a volcano's shape. High amounts of water and the compound silica (SiO_2) create violently erupting volcanoes with steep sides. Find a picture of Mauna Loa in Hawaii and observe its shape. Do its eruptions contain high amounts of water and silica? Explain.

Fault-Block Mountains

The Grand Teton Mountains of Wyoming, shown in **Figure 5-6,** and the Sierra Nevada in California formed in yet another way. **Fault-block mountains** are made of huge, tilted blocks of rocks that are separated from surrounding rock by faults. A fault is a large crack in rocks along which there is movement. As **Figure 5-6** shows, when these mountains formed, one block was tilted and pushed up. The other block was pushed down. If you ever go to the Tetons or to the Sierra Nevada, you'll see the sharp, jagged peaks that are characteristic of fault-block mountains.

Volcanic Mountains

Mount St. Helens in Washington and Mauna Loa in Hawaii are two of many volcanic mountains in the United States. **Volcanic mountains** like the one shown in **Figure 5-7** begin to form when molten material reaches the surface through a

weak area of the crust. The materials pile up, one layer on top of another, until a cone-shaped structure forms. The Hawaiian Islands are huge volcanoes that sit on the ocean floor. Only their peaks stick out above the water.

Plains, plateaus, and mountains offer different kinds of landforms to explore. They range from low coastal plains and high desert plateaus to mountain ranges thousands of meters high.

Figure 5-7
The volcanic mountains of Hawaii are made of molten material that oozed from Earth's crust and formed cone-shaped structures.

Section Assessment

1. Describe the eight major landform regions in the United States.
2. What causes some mountains to be folded and others to be upwarped?
3. **Think Critically:** If you wanted to know whether a particular mountain was formed by a fault, what would you look for?
4. **Skill Builder**
   Concept Mapping Make an events-chain concept map to explain how upwarped mountains form. If you need help, refer to Concept Mapping in the **Skill Handbook** on page 666.

Using Computers

Spreadsheet Design a spreadsheet that compares the origin and features of folded, upwarped, fault-block, and volcanic mountains. Label the columns and rows. Explain an advantage of using a spreadsheet to compare different types of mountains. If you need help, refer to page 690.

5•2 Viewpoints

What You'll Learn

- The difference between latitude and longitude
- How latitude and longitude are used to identify locations
- How to calculate the time and date in different time zones

Vocabulary
equator
latitude
prime meridian
longitude
International Date Line

Why It's Important

- You'll learn how to locate places on Earth.

Latitude and Longitude

To explore landforms, you'll want to learn how to find locations on Earth. If you wanted to go to the Hawaiian Islands, how would you describe their location? You might say that they are located in the Pacific Ocean. That's correct, but there is a more exact way to locate places on Earth—lines of latitude and longitude. These lines form an imaginary grid system that shows exactly where places on Earth are located.

Latitude

Look at **Figure 5-8.** The **equator** is an imaginary line that circles Earth exactly halfway between the north and south poles. The equator separates Earth into two equal halves, called the northern hemisphere and the southern hemisphere. The lines running parallel to the equator are called lines of latitude, or parallels. **Latitude** is the distance in degrees either north or south of the equator. Because parallel lines do not intersect, lines of latitude do not intersect.

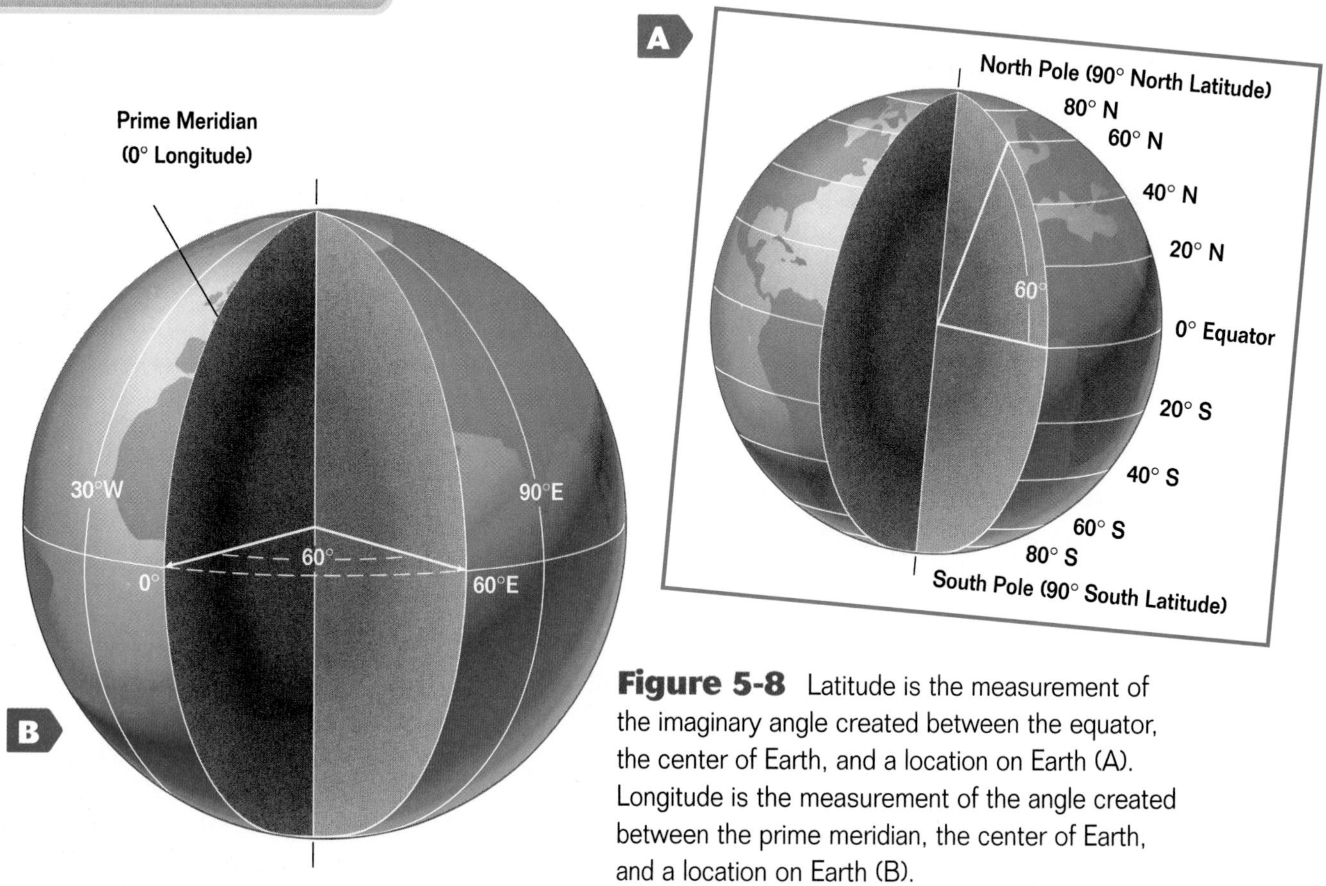

Figure 5-8 Latitude is the measurement of the imaginary angle created between the equator, the center of Earth, and a location on Earth (A). Longitude is the measurement of the angle created between the prime meridian, the center of Earth, and a location on Earth (B).

The equator is numbered 0° latitude. The poles are each numbered 90°. Therefore, latitude is measured from 0° at the equator to 90° at the poles. Locations north of the equator are referred to by degrees north latitude. Locations south of the equator are referred to by degrees south latitude.

Longitude

Latitude lines are used for locations north and south of the equator, but what about locations in east and west directions? These vertical lines, seen in **Figure 5-8B,** have two names—meridians and lines of longitude. Just as the equator is used as a reference point for north/south grid lines, there's a reference point for east/west grid lines—the **prime meridian.** This imaginary line represents 0° longitude. In 1884, astronomers decided the prime meridian should go through the Greenwich (GREN itch) Observatory near London, England.

Longitude refers to distances in degrees east or west of the prime meridian. Points west of the prime meridian have west longitude measured from 0° to 180°, while points east of the prime meridian have east longitude, also measured from 0° to 180°.

The prime meridian does not circle Earth as the equator does. Rather, it runs from the north pole through Greenwich, England, to the south pole. The line of longitude on the opposite side of Earth from the prime meridian is the 180° meridian. East lines of longitude meet west lines of longitude at the 180° meridian.

Using latitude and longitude, you can locate Hawaii more accurately, as shown in **Figure 5-9.** Hawaii is located at 20° north latitude and about 155° west longitude, or 20°N, 155°W. Note that latitude comes first when the latitude and longitude of a particular location are given.

Mini Lab

Interpreting Latitude and Longitude

Procedure

1. Find the equator and prime meridian on a world map.
2. Move your finger to latitudes north of the equator, then south of the equator. Move your finger to longitudes west of the prime meridian, then east of the prime meridian.

Analysis

1. Identify the cities that have the following coordinates:
   - **a.** 56°N, 38°E
   - **b.** 34°S, 18°E
   - **c.** 23°N, 82°W
2. Determine the latitude and longitude of the following cities:
   - **a.** London, England
   - **b.** Melbourne, Australia
   - **c.** Buenos Aires, Argentina

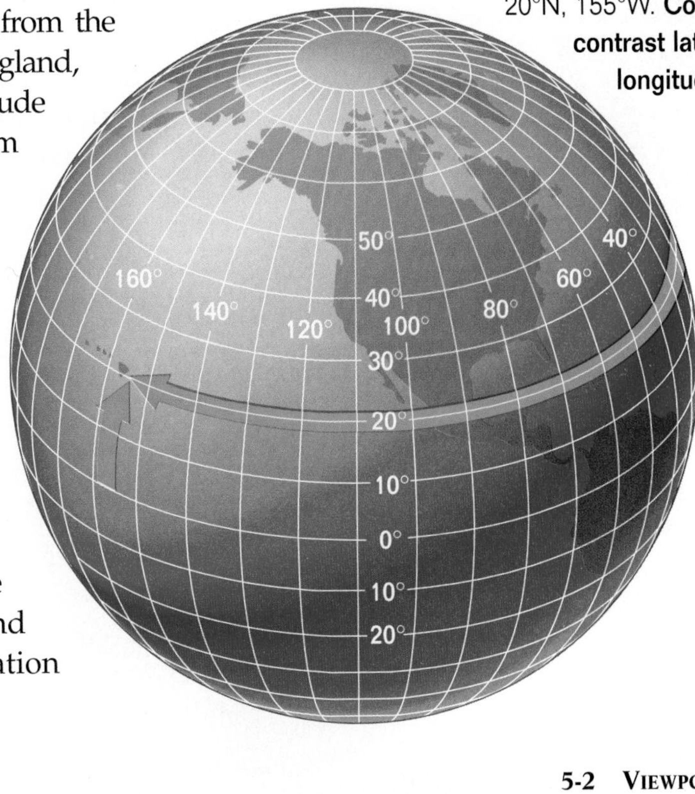

Figure 5-9 The large island of Hawaii is located at about 20°N, 155°W. **Compare and contrast latitude and longitude.**

Earth Time

What time is it right now? That depends on where you are on Earth. Time is measured by tracking Earth's movement in relation to the sun. Earth rotates once every 24 hours. When one half of Earth is facing the sun, the other half is facing away from it. For the half facing the sunlight, it is day. For the half in darkness, it is night.

Time Zones

How can you know what time it is at different places on Earth? Earth is divided into time zones. Because Earth takes 24 hours to rotate, it is divided into 24 time zones, each one hour different. Each time zone is 15 degrees wide on a globe or map. The United States has six different time zones. Look at **Figure 5-10.** Because Earth is rotating, the eastern United States starts a new day while the western part of the country is still in darkness. ☑

Reading Check ☑

How many degrees wide is each time zone?

As you can see in **Figure 5-11,** time zones do not strictly follow lines of longitude. Time zone boundaries have been adjusted in local areas. For example, if a city were split by a time zone boundary, the results could be confusing. In such a situation, the time zone boundary is moved outside of the city.

Calendar Dates

One day ends and the next day begins at midnight. If it is 11:59 P.M. Tuesday, two minutes later it is 12:01 A.M. Wednesday. The calendar moves forward to the next day in each time zone at midnight.

You gain or lose time each time you travel through a time zone. If you travel far enough, you gain or lose a whole day. The **International Date Line** is the transition line for calendar days. If you were traveling west across the International Date Line, located at the 180° meridian, you would move your calendar forward one day. If you were traveling east, you would move your calendar back one day.

Figure 5-10 There are six time zones in the United States.

A Atlanta, Georgia, lies in the eastern time zone. Students there would be on their way to school at 7:00 A.M.

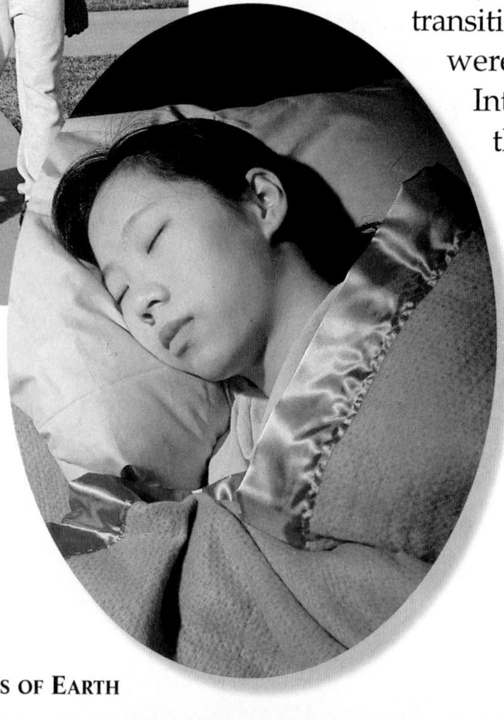

B But, a student in Los Angeles, California, which lies in the Pacific time zone three hours earlier, would still be fast asleep. **What time would it be in Los Angeles when the students in Atlanta returned home at 3:00 P.M.?**

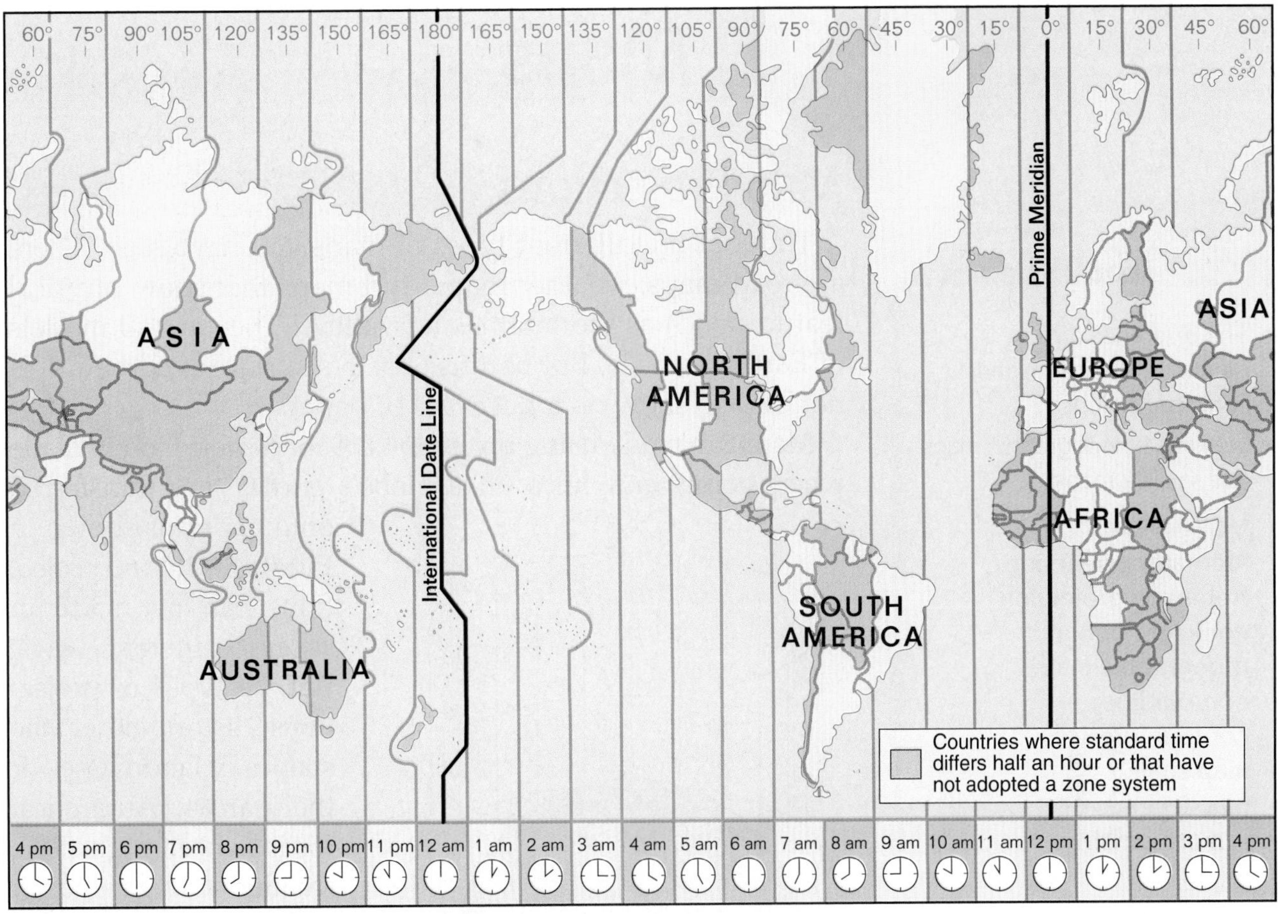

Figure 5-11 Lines of longitude roughly determine the locations of time zone boundaries. These boundaries are adjusted locally to avoid splitting cities and other political subdivisions (such as counties) into different time zones.

Section Assessment

1. How do lines of latitude and longitude help us find locations on Earth?
2. What are the latitude and longitude of New Orleans?
3. **Think Critically:** How could you leave home on Monday to go sailing, sail for an hour on Sunday, and return home on Monday?
4. **Skill Builder**
   Interpreting Scientific Illustrations
   Use a world map to find the approximate latitude and longitude of the following locations: Sri Lanka; Tokyo, Japan; and the Falkland Islands. If you need help, refer to Interpreting Scientific Illustrations in the **Skill Handbook** on page 678.

Using Math

If you left London on the Concorde jet airplane at 8 A.M. London time, you would arrive in New York at 6 A.M. New York time. You would have crossed five time zones during your flight. How long would your trip have taken?

5•3 Maps

What You'll Learn

- The difference among Mercator, Robinson, and conic projections
- Features of topographic maps and satellite maps

Vocabulary

Mercator projection
Robinson projection
conic projection
topographic map
contour line
contour interval
map scale
map legend
remote sensing

Why It's Important

- Different kinds of maps work better for different purposes.

Map Projections

Think of the different types of maps you have seen. There are road maps, weather maps, and maps that show physical features such as mountains and valleys. They are all models of Earth's surface. But because Earth's surface is curved, it is not easy to show on a flat piece of paper.

Maps are made using projections. A map projection is made when points and lines on a globe's surface are transferred onto paper, as shown in **Figure 5-12.** Map projections can be made in several different ways. But, all types of projections distort either the shapes of landmasses or their areas. Antarctica, for instance, might look smaller or larger than it really is.

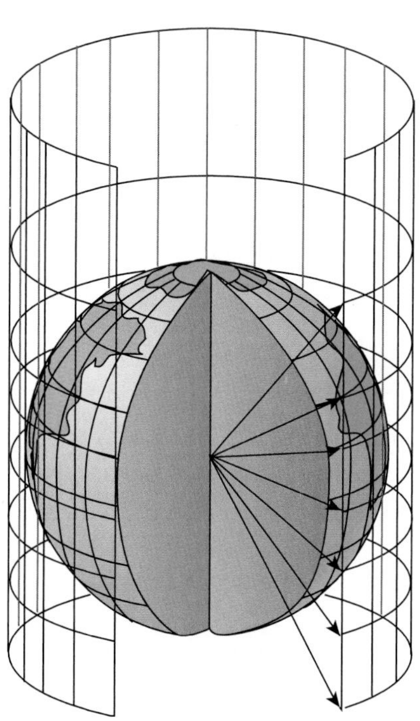

A In a Mercator projection, lines of longitude are drawn parallel to each other. **What does this do to areas near the poles?**

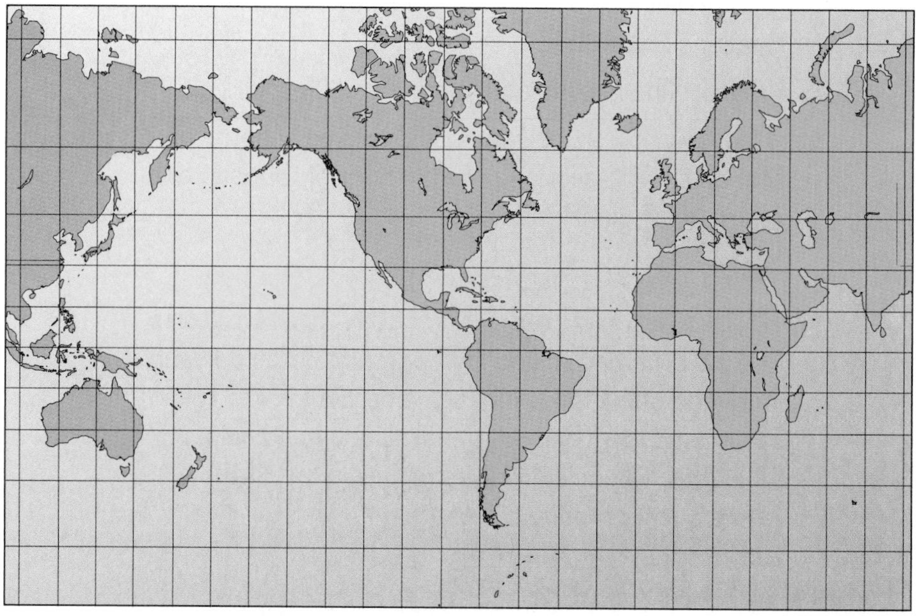

Figure 5-12 Because Earth's surface is curved, all types of map projections distort either the shapes of landmasses or their areas.

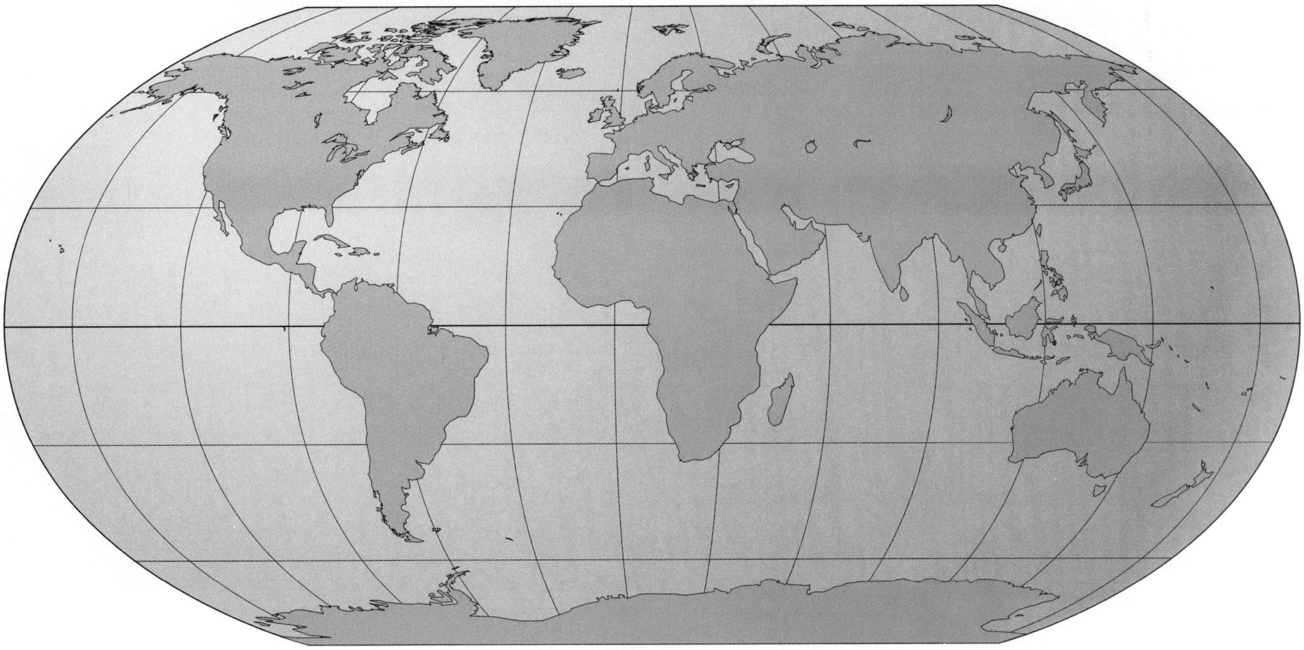

B A Robinson projection shows less distortion near the poles than a Mercator projection.

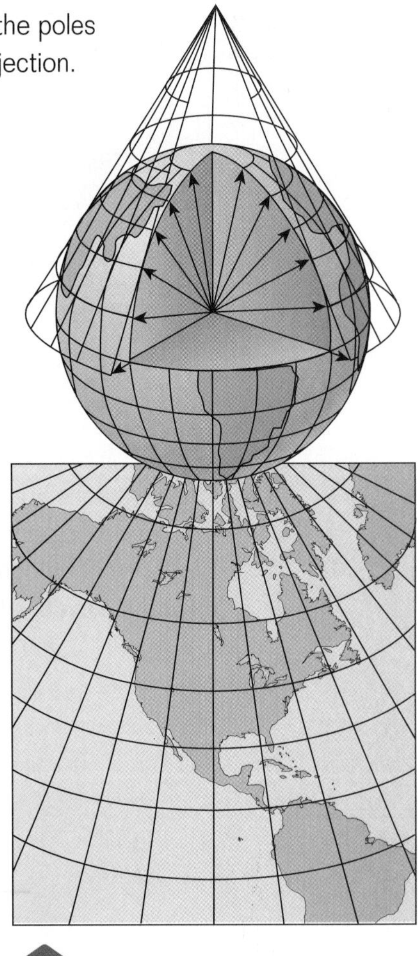

C A conic projection is accurate for small areas of Earth. **What could you use this type of map for?**

Mercator Projection

A **Mercator projection** has correct shapes of continents, but their areas are distorted. Lines of longitude are projected onto the map parallel to each other. As you learned earlier, only latitude lines are parallel. Longitude lines meet at the poles. When longitude lines are projected as parallel, areas near the poles appear bigger than they should. Look at Greenland in the Mercator projection in **Figure 5-12A.** It appears to be larger than South America. Greenland is actually much smaller than South America. Mercator projections are mainly used on ships.

Robinson Projection

A **Robinson projection** has accurate continent shapes and shows accurate land areas. As shown in **Figure 5-12B,** lines of latitude remain parallel, and lines of longitude are curved as they would be on a globe. This results in more correct continent shapes.

Conic Projection

A third type of projection is a conic projection. You use this type of projection, shown in **Figure 5-12C,** whenever you look at a road map or a weather map. **Conic projections** are used to produce maps of small areas. They are made by projecting points and lines from a globe onto a cone.

VISUALIZING
Topographic Maps

Figure 5-13 A topographic map shows changes in the elevation of Earth's surface.

A Wizard Island is a volcanic cinder-cone that forms an island in Crater Lake, Oregon.

B Different points of elevation are projected onto paper.

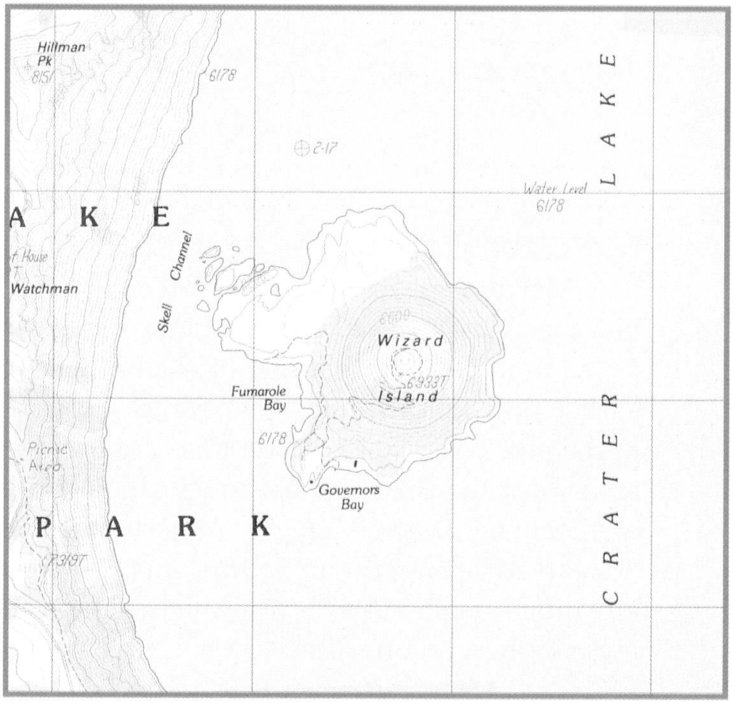

C The points of elevation are connected to form a topographic map of the island. **What do contour intervals tell us about elevation?**

Topographic Maps

If you wanted to go hiking, a conic map projection would get you to the mountain. Next, you would need a detailed map showing the hills and valleys of that specific area. A **topographic map** shows the changes in elevation of Earth's surface. With a topographic map, you could tell how steep the mountain trail is. It would also show natural features such as mountains, hills, plains, lakes, and rivers, and cultural features such as roads, cities, dams, and other structures built by people.

Contour Lines

Before starting your hike up the mountain, you would look at the contour lines on your topographic map to see the trail's changes in elevation. A **contour line** is a line on a map that connects points of equal elevation. Elevation refers to the distance of a location above or below sea level. The difference in elevation between two side-by-side contour lines is called the **contour interval.** If the contour interval were 10 m, then when you walked between those two lines on the trail, you would have climbed or walked down 10 m.

As **Figure 5-13C** shows, the elevation of the contour interval can vary. For mountains, the contour lines might be close and the contour interval might be as great as 100 m. This would tell you that the land is steep because there is a large change in elevation between lines. However, if there isn't a great change in elevation and the contour lines are far apart, your map might have a contour interval of 5 m. **Table 5-1** gives additional tips for examining contour lines.

Index Contours

Some contour lines, called index contours, are marked with their elevation. If the contour interval is 5 m, you can tell the elevation of other lines around the index contour. You would add or subtract 5 m from the elevation shown on the index contour.

interNET CONNECTION

Visit the Glencoe Science Web Site at **www.glencoe.com/sec/science/ca** for more information about maps.

Table 5-1

Contour Rules

Here are some rules to remember when examining contour lines.

1. **Contour lines close around hills and basins or depressions.** To decide whether you're looking at a hill or basin, you can read the elevation numbers or look for hachures. Hachures are short lines at right angles to the contour line that are used to show depressions. These lines point toward lower elevations. See **Figure 5-14.**

2. **Contour lines never cross.** If they did, it would mean that the spot where they cross would have two different elevations.

3. **Contour lines form Vs that point upstream whenever they cross streams.** This is because streams flow in depressions that are beneath the elevation of the surrounding land surface. When the contour lines follow the depression, they appear as Vs pointing upstream on the map.

Reading Check ☑

What is a map scale?

Map Scale

Another thing you would want to know before you set out on your hike is, "How far is it to the top of the mountain?" Because maps are small models of Earth's surface, distances and sizes of things on a map are proportional to the real thing on Earth. This is done by using scale distances.

The **map scale** is the relationship between the distances on the map and actual distances on Earth's surface. Scale is often represented as a ratio. For example, a topographic map of the Grand Canyon may have a scale that reads "1:80 000." This means that one unit on the map represents 80 000 units on land. If the unit you wanted to use was a centimeter, then 1 cm on the map would equal 80 000 cm on land. The unit of distance may be in feet or millimeters or any other measure of distance. However, the units of measure on each side of the ratio must always be the same. A map scale may also be in the form of a small bar that is divided into units. The units are scaled down to match real distances on Earth. ☑

Map Legend

Topographic maps and most other maps have a legend. A **map legend** explains what the symbols used on the map mean. Some frequently used symbols for topographic maps are shown in **Figure 5-14.**

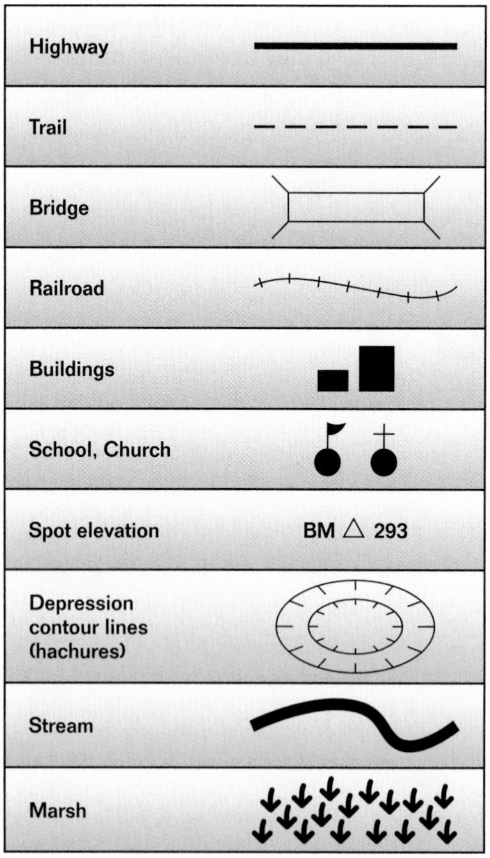

Figure 5-14 Here are some typical symbols used on topographic maps.

Three-Dimensional Maps

Topographic maps are two-dimensional models used to study features on Earth's surface. To unravel Earth's complex structure, however, scientists need to know what Earth looks like inside. With computers, topographic maps are digitized to get a three-dimensional or 3-D view of features such as rock beds or river systems. Digitizing is a process by which points are located on a coordinate grid.

Map Uses

As you have learned, there are many different ways to view Earth. The map you choose to use will depend upon your need. For instance, if you wanted to determine New Zealand's location relative to Canada, you would probably examine a Mercator projection. In your search, you would use lines of latitude and longitude, and a map scale. If you

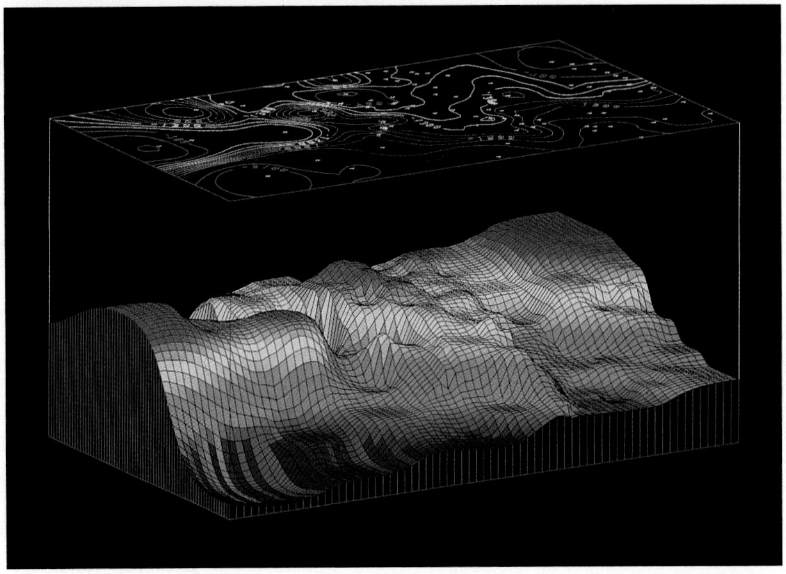

Figure 5-15 This computer-generated map shows a river system in Montana. **How does this map differ from a topographic map?**

wanted to travel across the country, you would rely on a conic projection. You would also use a map legend to help you locate features along your trip. And, if you wanted to scale the highest peak in your county, you would take along a topographic map.

As **Figure 5-15** shows, mapmaking, also called cartography, has experienced a technological revolution in the past few decades. Remote sensing and computers have changed the way maps are made. Read on to learn more about remote sensing.

Problem Solving

Interpreting a Topographic Map

The map at right is a topographic map of an area in California. One sunny day, two hikers started from the point marked with the + on the map. One hiker climbed the peak of Cedar Mountain, while the other climbed the peak of Orr Mountain.

Both traveled at the same rate on flat or gentle slopes. Their climbs slowed as the ground grew steeper. Study the map, then answer the questions below.

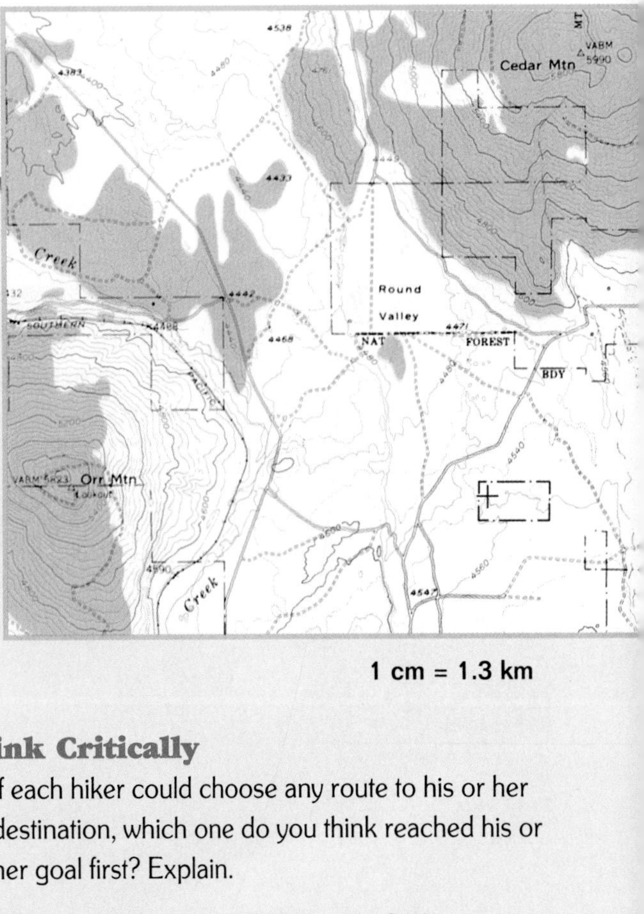

1 cm = 1.3 km

Solve the Problem

1. Which peak is higher?
2. Which hiker had the steeper climb? Explain using contour lines.
3. Name three items found in a map legend that the hiker heading for Orr Mountain crossed before reaching his or her goal.

Think Critically

1. If each hiker could choose any route to his or her destination, which one do you think reached his or her goal first? Explain.
2. Once at the top, could the hiker on Cedar Mountain see the hiker on Orr Mountain? Why or why not?

Remote Sensing

Scientists use remote-sensing techniques to collect much of the data used for making maps. **Remote sensing** is a way of collecting information about Earth from a distance. Satellites and sonar are two remote-sensing devices.

*inter***NET**
CONNECTION

Visit the Glencoe Science Web Site at **www.glencoe.com/sec/science/ca** to find out more about the Global Positioning System.

Topex-Poseidon Satellite

The Topex-Poseidon Satellite (*Topex* stands for "topographic experiment") uses radar to compute the distance to the ocean's surface. Radar waves are high-frequency radio signals that are beamed from the satellite to the ocean. As **Figure 5-16** illustrates, a receiving device then picks up the returning echo as it bounces off the water. The distance to the water's surface is calculated using the radar speed and the time it takes for the signal to be reflected. Using satellite-to-sea measurements, computers can draw maps of ocean features.

Global Positioning System

The Global Positioning System, or GPS, is a satellite-based, radio-navigation system that allows users to determine their exact position anywhere on Earth. Twenty-four satellites orbit 20 200 km above the planet. Each satellite sends an accurate position and time signal. The satellites are arranged in their orbits so that signals from at least six can be picked up at any given moment by someone using a GPS receiver. By processing the signals coming from multiple satellites, the receiver calculates the user's exact location. GPS technology is a valuable navigational tool. It is also used to create detailed maps and to track wildlife.

Figure 5-16 Using high-frequency radio waves, the Topex-Poseidon Satellite can map ocean floor features.

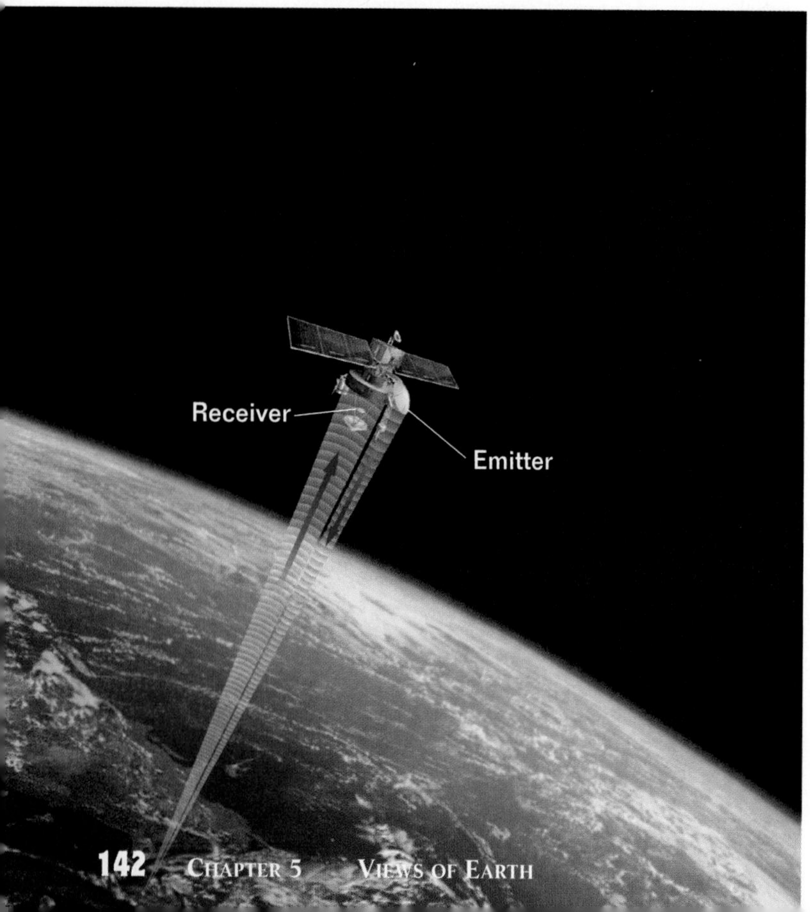

Sea Beam

Sonar refers to the use of sound waves to detect ocean-bottom features. First, a sound wave is sent from a ship toward the ocean floor. A receiving device then picks up the returning echo when it bounces off the bottom. Shipboard computers measure the distance to the bottom using the speed of sound in water and the time it takes for the sound to be reflected.

Using a technology called Sea Beam, scientists make accurate maps of the ocean floor. A ship equipped with Sea Beam, shown in **Figure 5-17,** has more than a dozen sonar devices, each aimed at different parts of the sea. Computers assemble these sonar data into detailed, continuous maps of the ocean floor.

Figure 5-17 This underwater formation was mapped using data from Sea Beam.

Section Assessment

1. Why does Greenland appear to be larger on a Mercator projection than it does on a Robinson projection?
2. Why can't contour lines ever cross?
3. Name two remote-sensing devices.
4. **Think Critically:** Suppose you have a topographic map with a contour interval of 50 m. According to the map scale, 1 cm on the map equals 1 km. The distance between points A and B on the map is 8 cm. Four contour lines lie between them. How far apart are the points, and what is the change in elevation?
5. **Skill Builder**
   Making Models Architects use detailed maps called scale drawings to help them plan their work. Do the **Chapter 5 Skill Activity** on page 698 to make a scale drawing of your classroom.

Science Journal

Draw a map in your Science Journal that your friends could use to get from school to your home. Include symbols and a map scale.

Design Your Own Experiment

Activity 5 • 1

Modeling Earth

Possible Materials

- Fine-point, transparency marker
- Blank transparency
- Overhead projector
- Sheet of white paper
- Pencil
- Tape
- Corrugated cardboard sheets
  * foam board sheets
- Scissors
- Glue
- Metric ruler

** Alternate Materials*

Have you ever built a model plane, train, or car? Modeling is more than just fun. Models are used to help engineers and designers build actual planes, trains, and cars. A topographic map is a two-dimensional model—on flat paper. How can you build a three-dimensional model of a landform?

Recognize the Problem

How can a 3-D model be made of an area shown on a topographic map?

Form a Hypothesis

Based on the drawing below, state a hypothesis about how you can make a large model of Blackberry Hill, such that its base is the length of a piece of notebook paper.

Goals

- **Design and make a 3-D model** that shows the relationship between topographic maps and landforms.
- **Interpret** data from your model.

Safety Precautions

Be careful while working near the overhead projector light. It can get hot. While using scissors, be careful not to cut yourself.

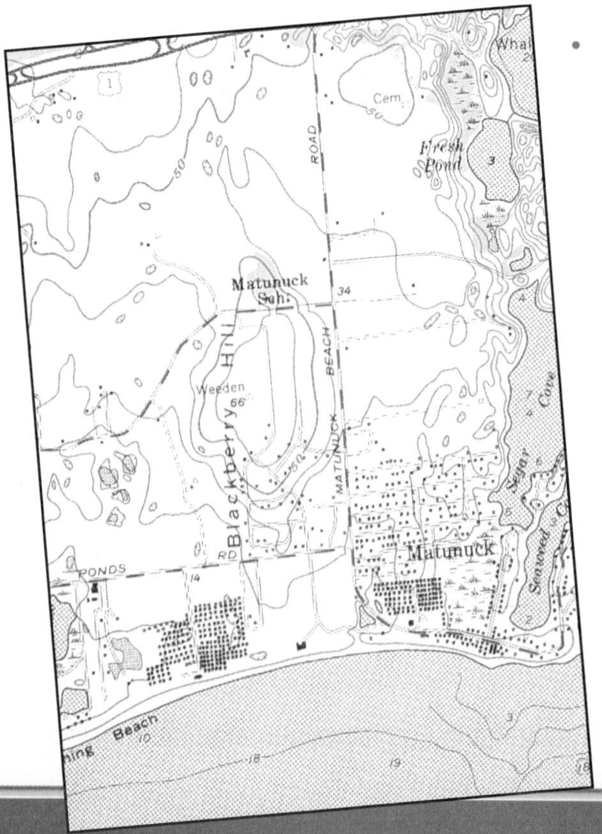

Test Your Hypothesis

Plan

1. With your partner, **design** a way that you can make an enlarged **copy** of the topographical features of Blackberry Hill using a transparency marker, overhead projector, pencil, sheet of white paper, and tape. **Write down** the steps you will take.
2. **Explain** how you can use the contour lines on your white paper as patterns for making the different layers of your model.
3. **Describe** a way to make your 3-D model using stacked sheets of cardboard or foam board.

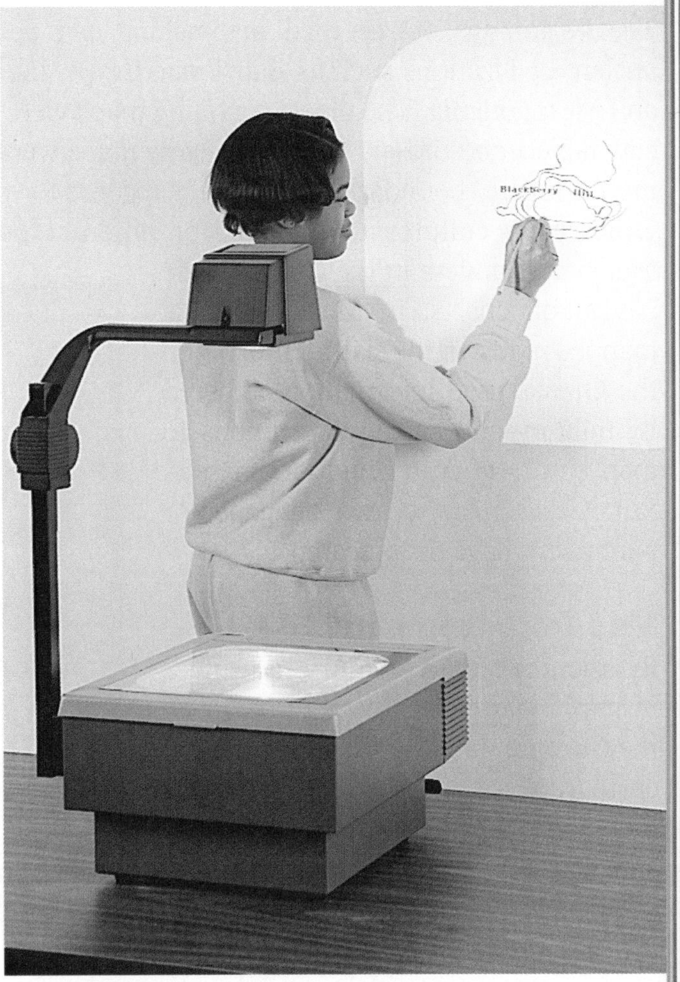

Do

1. Make sure your teacher approves your plan before you proceed.
2. Read over your entire plan to make sure that all steps are in a logical order.
3. **Build** your model as planned.
4. While the activity is going on, **record** observations in your Science Journal.

Analyze Your Data

1. **Compare** your model with other students' models. How are they similar? How are they different?
2. **Determine** the horizontal scale of your model.

Draw Conclusions

1. **Infer** what the height of each sheet in your model represents.
2. **Describe** the most difficult part of making your model.

Mapmaking

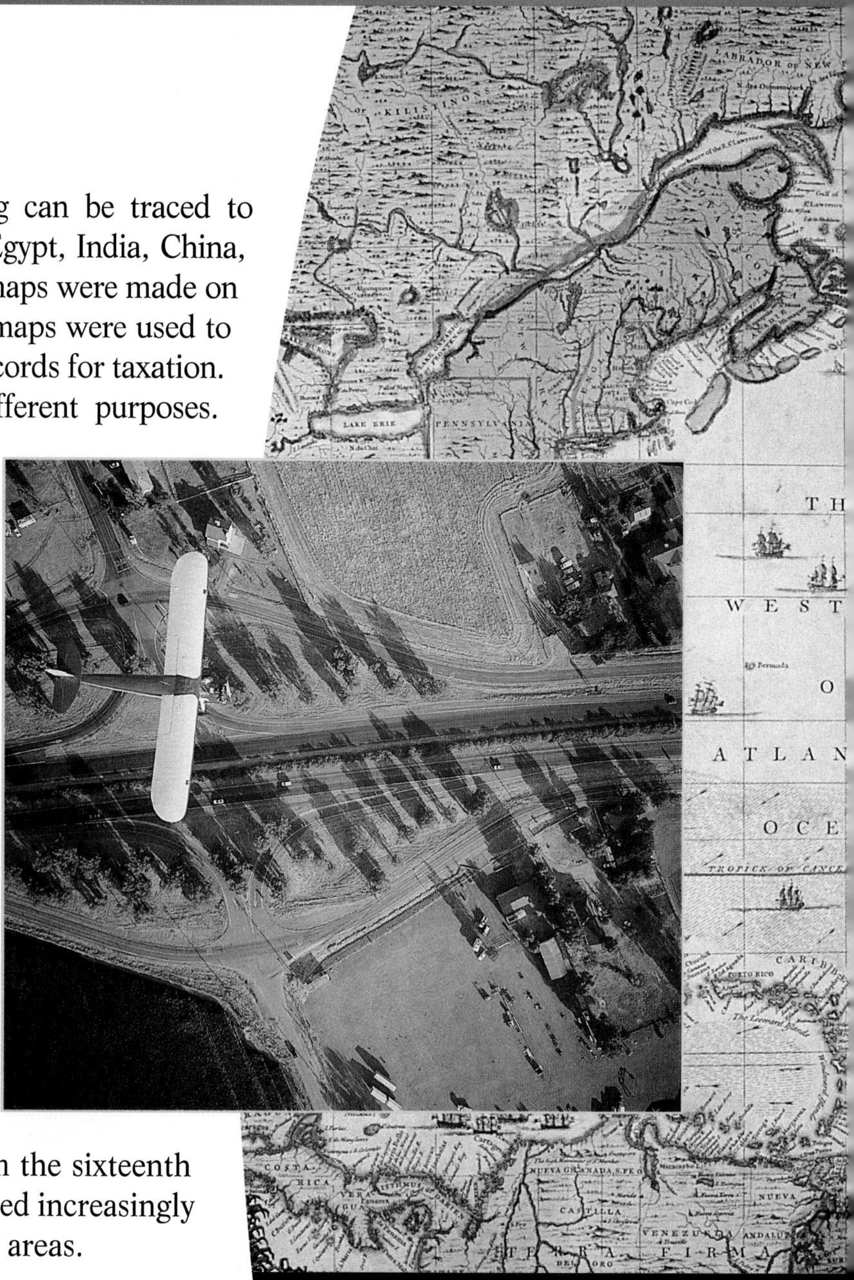

Ancient Maps

The beginnings of recorded mapmaking can be traced to ancient civilizations such as Babylonia, Egypt, India, China, and Mesopotamia. The oldest surviving maps were made on clay tablets and mosaic tile. Those early maps were used to mark property boundaries and to keep records for taxation. Other early cultures used maps for different purposes. Marshall Islanders in the Pacific made navigation charts. In Mexico, people mapped roads. In the sixth century B.C., the Greeks used information gathered by military and sailing expeditions to map bodies of water and landmasses. But, Greek maps drawn on paper or parchment have disappeared.

Map Improvements

By the thirteenth century, advances in mathematics led to more accurate measurements. Mapmakers, called cartographers, used these measurements and their observations of physical features to create more detailed maps. The development of the printing press and engraving techniques made maps more widely available. From the sixteenth to nineteenth centuries, explorers provided increasingly accurate maps of coastlines and interior areas.

View from Above

Aerial photography (inset) revolutionized mapmaking through photogrammetry—making measurements from photographs. Today, photographs from space satellites give cartographers even greater details of Earth. In addition, modern cartographers use computers to make and update maps. When they enter data on a computer, the computer draws the map. Digital map data can be used in many ways. For instance, computer programs in cars can inform drivers where they are and how to reach their destinations.

Science JOURNAL

Pretend you have hidden a treasure. In your Science Journal, draw a map that would lead a friend to the treasure.

Making a Topographic Map

Materials

- Plastic model landform
- Water tinted with food coloring
- Transparency
- Clear, plastic storage box with lid
- Beaker
- Metric ruler
- Tape
- Transparency marker

Have you ever wondered how topographic maps are made? Today, radar and remote-sensing devices aboard satellites collect data, and computers and graphic systems make the maps. In the past, surveyors and aerial photographers collected data. Then, maps were hand drawn by cartographers, or map-makers. In this activity, you can try your hand at cartography.

What You'll Investigate

How is a topographic map made?

Goals

- **Make** a topographic map.
- **Compare and contrast** contour intervals.

Procedure

1. Using the ruler and the transparency marker, make marks up the side of the storage box 2 cm apart.
2. **Secure** the transparency to the outside of the box lid with tape.
3. Place the plastic model in the box. The bottom of the box will be zero elevation.
4. Using the beaker, **pour** water into the box to a height of 2 cm. Place the lid on the box.
5. Use the transparency marker to **trace** the top of the water line on the transparency.
6. Using the scale 2 cm = 10 m, **mark** the elevation on the line.
7. Remove the lid and **add** water until a depth of 4 cm is reached.
8. **Map** this level on the storage box lid and **record** the elevation.
9. Repeat the process of **adding** water and **tracing** until you have the hill **mapped.**
10. **Transfer** the tracing of the hill onto a sheet of white paper.

Conclude and Apply

1. What is the contour interval of this topographic map?
2. How does the distance between contour lines on the map show the steepness of the slope on the landform model?
3. **Determine** the total elevation of the hill.
4. How was elevation represented on your map?
5. How are elevations shown on topographic maps?
6. Must all topographic maps have a 0-m elevation contour line? **Explain.**
7. **Compare** the contour interval of an area of high relief with one of low relief on a topographic map.

Chapter 5 Reviewing Main Ideas

For a **preview** of this chapter, study this Reviewing Main Ideas before you read the chapter. After you have studied this chapter, you can use the Reviewing Main Ideas to **review** the chapter.

GLENCOE TECHNOLOGY

The Glencoe MindJogger, Audiocassettes, and CD-ROM provide additional opportunities for review.

Section

5-1 LANDFORMS

The three main types of landforms are plains, plateaus, and mountains. **Plains** are large, flat areas. **Plateaus** are relatively flat, raised areas of land made up of nearly horizontal rocks that have been uplifted by forces within Earth. **Mountains** rise high above the surrounding land. They vary greatly in size and how they are formed. *Which type of mountain is shown here?*

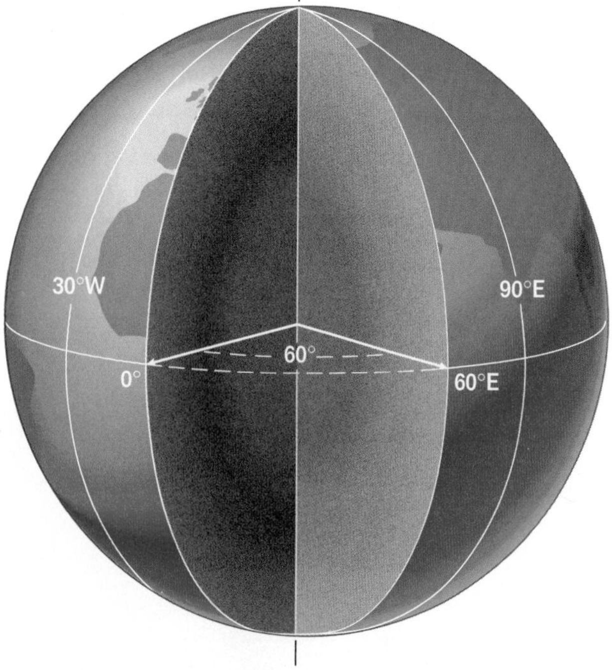

Section

5-2 VIEWPOINTS

Latitude and **longitude** form an imaginary grid system that enables points on Earth to be located exactly. **Latitude** is the distance in degrees north or south of the equator. Lines of latitude are parallel to the equator. **Longitude** is the distance in degrees east or west of the prime meridian. The prime meridian runs through Greenwich, England. *What line of longitude is located on the side of Earth opposite to the prime meridian?*

Reading Check

Locate three or four words that are not on the vocabulary list but were unfamiliar to you before you read this chapter. Define these words.

Section

5-3 MAPS

Topographic maps show the changes in elevation of Earth's surface. **Mercator, Robinson,** and **conic projections** are made by transferring points and lines on a globe's surface onto paper. ***Why are all map projections distorted in either the shapes of landmasses or the areas of landmasses?***

REMOTE SENSING

Remote Sensing is a way of collecting information about Earth from a distance. Satellites and sonar are two remote-sensing devices. Using sonar, for instance, scientists can make detailed maps of the ocean floor. Other remote-sensing devices are used to navigate or track wildlife. ***What is the Global Positioning System?***

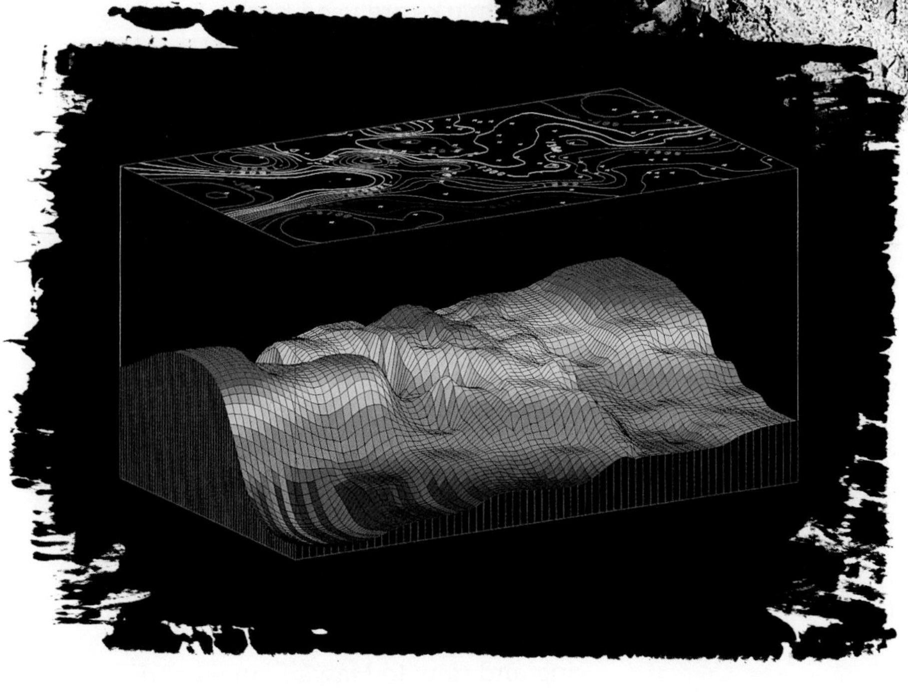

Chapter 5 Assessment

Using Vocabulary

a. conic projection
b. contour interval
c. contour line
d. equator
e. fault-block mountain
f. folded mountain
g. International Date Line
h. latitude
i. longitude
j. map legend
k. map scale
l. Mercator projection
m. plain
n. plateau
o. prime meridian
p. remote sensing
q. Robinson projection
r. topographic map
s. upwarped mountain
t. volcanic mountain

For each set of terms below, choose the one term that does not belong and explain why it does not belong.

1. contour interval, contour line, conic projection
2. map scale, latitude, longitude
3. upwarped mountain, equator, volcanic mountain
4. plain, plateau, prime meridian
5. Mercator projection, Robinson projection, remote sensing

Checking Concepts

Choose the word or phrase that best answers the question.

6. What makes up about 50 percent of all land areas in the United States?
   A) plateaus C) mountains
   B) plains D) volcanoes
7. Where is the north pole located?
   A) 0°N C) 50°N
   B) 180°N D) 90°N
8. What kind of mountains are the Hawaiian Islands?
   A) fault-block C) upwarped
   B) volcanic D) folded
9. What do we call lines parallel to the equator?
   A) lines of latitude C) lines of longitude
   B) prime meridians D) contour lines
10. How many degrees apart are the 24 time zones?
   A) 10 C) 15
   B) 34 D) 25
11. Which type of map is distorted at the poles?
   A) conic C) Robinson
   B) topographic D) Mercator
12. Which type of map shows changes in elevation at Earth's surface?
   A) conic C) Robinson
   B) topographic D) Mercator
13. What is measured with respect to sea level?
   A) contour interval C) conic projection
   B) elevation D) sonar
14. What marks are used to show depressions on topographic maps?
   A) degrees C) hachures
   B) scales D) legends
15. Which major U.S. landform includes the Grand Canyon?
   A) Great Plains
   B) Colorado Plateau
   C) Gulf Coastal Plain
   D) Appalachian Mountains

Thinking Critically

16. How would a topographic map of the Atlantic Coastal Plain differ from a topographic map of the Rocky Mountains?
17. If you left Korea early Wednesday morning and flew to Hawaii, on what day of the week would you arrive?

18. If you were flying directly south from the north pole and reached 70° north latitude, how many more degrees of latitude would be left to pass over before reaching the south pole?

19. Using a map, arrange these cities in order from the city with the earliest time to that with the latest time on a given day: Anchorage, Alaska; San Francisco, California; Bangor, Maine; Columbus, Ohio; Houston, Texas.

20. What does a map scale of 1:50 000 mean?

Developing Skills

If you need help, refer to the Skill Handbook.

21. **Measuring in SI:** What is the area in square kilometers of the topographic map in the Problem Solving feature in Section 5-3?

22. **Comparing and Contrasting:** Compare and contrast Mercator, Robinson, and conic map projections.

23. **Concept Mapping:** Make a network tree concept map that explains how topographic maps are used. Use the following terms: *topographic maps, mountains, rivers, natural features, contour lines, changes in elevation, equal elevation, hills,* and *plains.*

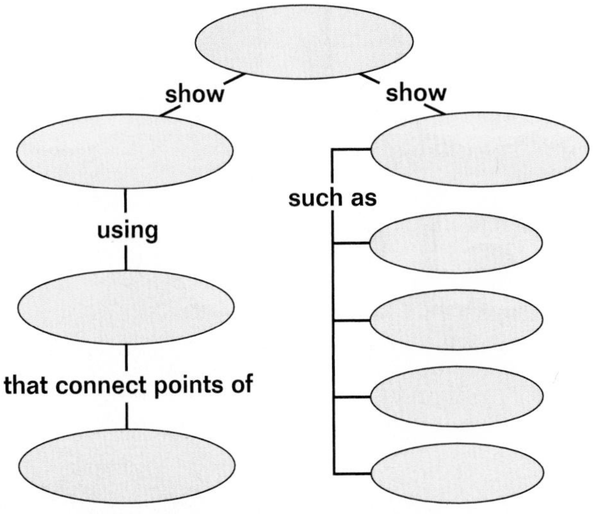

THE PRINCETON REVIEW

Test-Taking Tip

Stock Up on Supplies Be sure to supply yourself with the test-taking essentials: number two pencils, pens, erasers, a ruler, and a pencil sharpener. If the room doesn't have a pencil sharpener, a broken pencil can be a problem.

Test Practice

Use these questions to test your Science Proficiency.

1. The Adirondack Mountains are upwarped mountains. Today, the rock material that was once present on the tops of these mountains is gone. Why?
   A) The rock material was pushed inside Earth.
   B) Sharp peaks and ridges formed over the rock material.
   C) The rock material became magma.
   D) The rock material was eroded.

2. Ships use sonar to detect and map ocean-bottom features. Which of the following events occurs first in the map-making process?
   A) Computers transform sonar data into detailed maps.
   B) A sound wave is sent from the ship to the ocean floor.
   C) Computers calculate the distance from the ship to the ocean floor.
   D) A receiving device picks up the echo of sonar bouncing off the ocean floor.

UNIT 2

Earth's Changing Surface

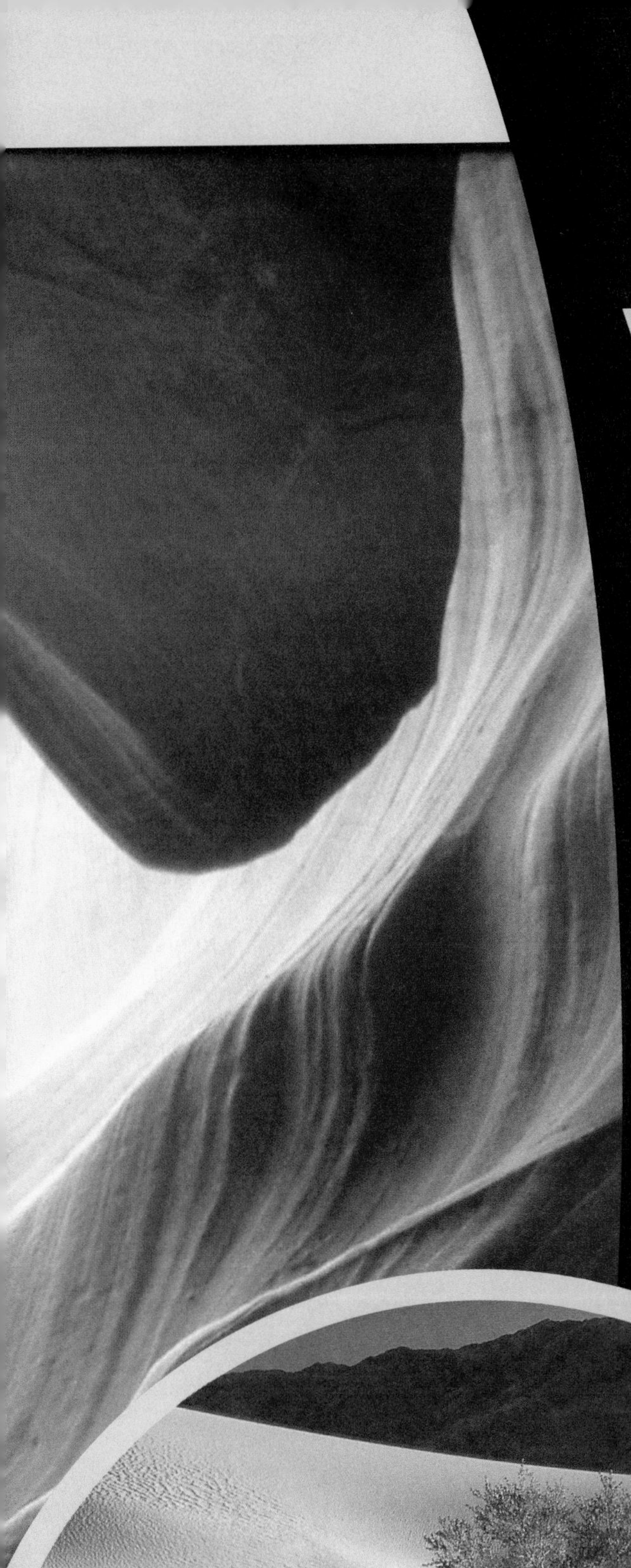

NATIONAL GEOGRAPHIC

What's Happening Here?

Dip your hand into water, and it feels soft to the touch—yet water is also nature's most powerful sculptor. Take Arizona's Antelope Canyon (left). About 190 million years ago, sand dunes formed in this area. Over time, these dunes were turned into rock, forming sandstone. Later, a stream gradually wore a wide canyon through the dunes. Later, the climate became so dry that the canyon filled in with sand. Flash floods carved out this chasm and water-borne grit polished the stone sides. What gives the rock its glowing red color? Iron in the rock is rusting from exposure to the water and the oxygen in the air. Other elements also shape Earth's contours. In California's Death Valley (below), the dry climate enables the wind to mound the sandy soil into dunes. In this unit, you will learn about forces and processes that rearrange the surface of Earth—sometimes slowly as with rusting, drying, and cracking, or rapidly as with floods and storms.

interNET CONNECTION

Explore the Glencoe Science Web Site at **www.glencoe.com/sec/science/ca** to find out more about topics found in this unit.

CHAPTER

6 Weathering and Soil

Chapter Preview

Section 6-1
- Weathering

Section 6-2
- Soil

Skills Preview

Skill Builders

- Recognize Cause and Effect
- Map Concepts

Activities

- Hypothesize
- Interpret Data

MiniLabs

- Observe
- Compare and Contrast

Reading Check

As you read, identify and define forms of the word *weather.* Then use a dictionary to find and define additional forms of this word.

Explore Activity

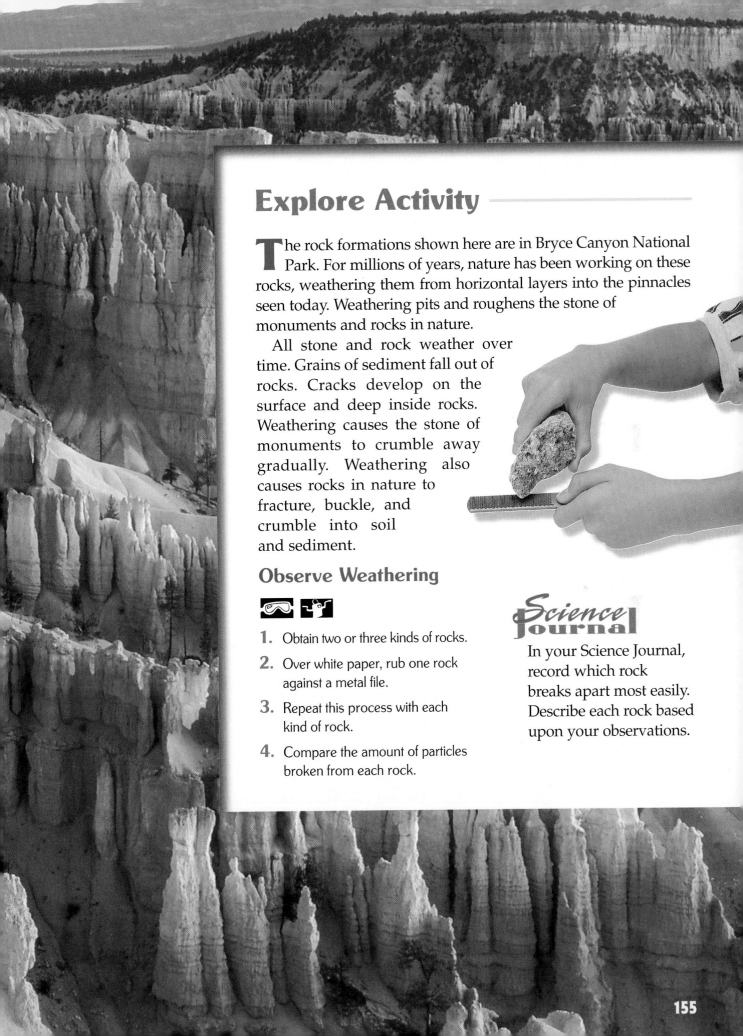

The rock formations shown here are in Bryce Canyon National Park. For millions of years, nature has been working on these rocks, weathering them from horizontal layers into the pinnacles seen today. Weathering pits and roughens the stone of monuments and rocks in nature.

All stone and rock weather over time. Grains of sediment fall out of rocks. Cracks develop on the surface and deep inside rocks. Weathering causes the stone of monuments to crumble away gradually. Weathering also causes rocks in nature to fracture, buckle, and crumble into soil and sediment.

Observe Weathering

1. Obtain two or three kinds of rocks.
2. Over white paper, rub one rock against a metal file.
3. Repeat this process with each kind of rock.
4. Compare the amount of particles broken from each rock.

Science Journal

In your Science Journal, record which rock breaks apart most easily. Describe each rock based upon your observations.

6•1 Weathering

Evidence of Weathering

***What* You'll Learn**

- The difference between mechanical weathering and chemical weathering
- The effects of climate on weathering

Vocabulary
weathering
mechanical weathering
ice wedging
chemical weathering
oxidation
climate

***Why* It's Important**

- Weathering causes rocks to crumble and landforms to change shape over time.

The next time you take a walk or a drive, notice the sand and grit along the sidewalk and curb. Much of the gritty sediment you see comes from small particles that break loose from concrete curbs and from rocks exposed to the natural elements. These sediments are evidence that weathering is taking place.

Weathering is the process that breaks down rocks into smaller and smaller fragments. Conditions and processes in the environment cause the weathering of rock and concrete. Rocks break down into small pieces called sediment. These sediments also can form soil. Soil formation is dependent upon the process of weathering.

Over millions of years, the process of weathering has helped change Earth's surface. It continues today. **Figure 6-1** illustrates how weathering wears down mountains to hills. Weathering makes it difficult to read the writing on tombstones and slowly breaks down statues. Weathering also can cause potholes in streets. The two types of weathering are mechanical and chemical. They work together to break down rock.

Figure 6-1 Over long periods of time, weathering helps change sharp, jagged mountains into smooth, rolling mountains and hills.

A The Grand Tetons in Wyoming (A) have not been exposed to agents of weathering as long as the mountains of Mount Washington Valley, New Hampshire, (B) have been.

B

Figure 6-2 Pavements such as driveways and sidewalks can be broken up by tree roots.

A As trees grow, their roots spread throughout the soil.

B As roots grow under a sidewalk, their increased size forces the concrete to crack.

C Over time, the sidewalk buckles and breaks apart.

Mechanical Weathering

Mechanical weathering breaks apart rocks without changing their chemical composition. Each fragment and particle weathered away by a mechanical process keeps the same characteristics as the original rock. Mechanical weathering can be caused by growing plants, expanding ice, mineral crystal growth, lightning, and expansion and contraction when an area heats and cools. These physical processes produce enough force to break rocks into smaller pieces. ☑

Reading Check ☑

What is mechanical weathering?

Plants

Plant roots grow into cracks of rocks where they find water and nutrients. As roots grow, they wedge rocks apart. If you've skated on a sidewalk and tripped over a crack near a tree, you have experienced the results of mechanical weathering. The sidewalk near the tree in **Figure 6-2C** shows signs of weathering. How could cracks in rocks occur in the same way? **Figure 6-3** might give you some ideas.

Figure 6-3 Tree roots cause mechanical weathering of rocks as shown by this tree in Glacier National Park, Montana.

Lichen plants also cause mechanical weathering. Parts of the plant expand and shrink with the amount of available water. This is similar to the process of ice wedging described below.

Ice Wedging

The mechanical weathering process known as **ice wedging** is illustrated in **Figure 6-4.** In cold areas, low temperatures freeze water. Warmer temperatures thaw the ice. Ice wedging is noticeable in the mountains. It is one factor that wears down sharp mountain peaks to rounded hills—a process pictured in **Figure 6-1.** This cycle of freezing and thawing not only breaks up rocks but also breaks up roads and highways. When water enters cracks in road pavement and freezes, it forces the pavement apart. This can cause potholes to form in roads. Weathering by both roots and ice wedging rapidly can reduce rocks to smaller pieces. Breaking up rocks through mechanical weathering exposes a greater surface area to additional weathering. As the amount of surface area increases, the rate of weathering increases.

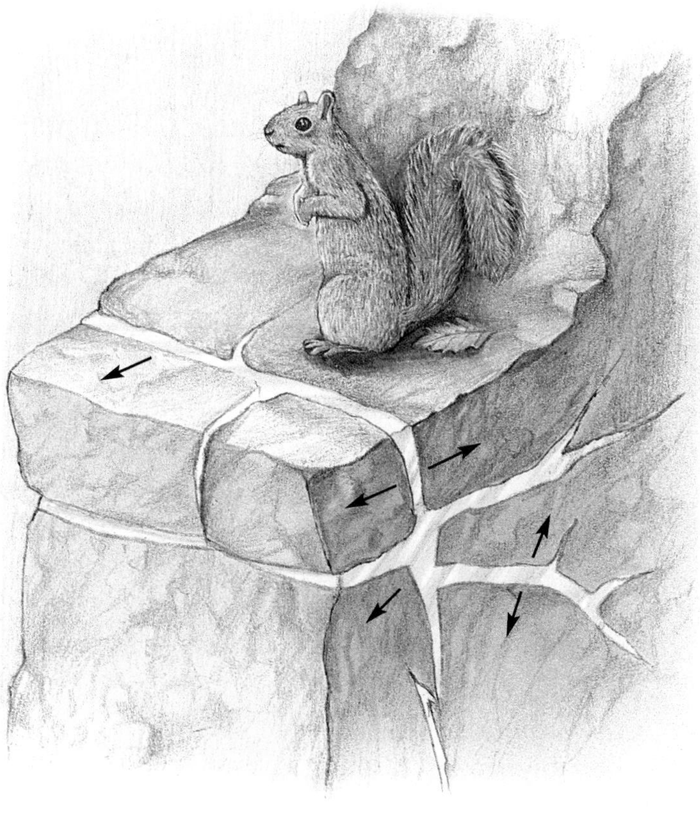

Figure 6-4 When water freezes in cracks of rocks, it expands. Pressure builds and breaks apart the rock. As the ice thaws and then the water refreezes, this process occurs again.

Chemical Weathering

CHEMISTRY INTEGRATION

The second type of weathering occurs when water, air, and other substances react with the minerals in rocks. This type of weathering is called **chemical weathering** because the chemical composition of the rock changes. Let's see how chemical weathering happens.

Water

Water is an important agent of chemical weathering. When the hydrogen and oxygen atoms in water react with the chemicals in some rocks, new substances form. These substances are much different from those of the original rock.

Acids

Naturally formed acids can weather rocks chemically. When water mixes with carbon dioxide from the air, a weak acid, called carbonic acid, forms. Carbonic acid is the same weak acid that makes soft drinks fizzy. Carbonic acid reacts with minerals such as calcite, the main mineral in limestone. The product of this reaction then dissolves and can be carried away with the acid. Over thousands of years, carbonic acid has weathered so much limestone that caves have formed, such as the one shown in **Figure 6-5.**

Figure 6-5 Lehman Cave in Great Basin National Park, Nevada, is a product of chemical weathering. **How did water help form this cave?**

Chemical weathering also occurs when carbonic acid comes in contact with granite rock. Over a long time, the mineral feldspar in granite is broken down into the clay mineral kaolinite. Kaolinite clay makes up most of the material in some soils. Clay is an end product of weathering.

Some roots and decaying plants give off acids that can dissolve minerals in rock. Removing these minerals weakens the rock. Eventually, the rock will break into smaller pieces. The next time you find a moss-covered rock, peel back the moss and look at the small pits underneath. Acids from the rootlike structures of the moss caused the pits.

CHEMISTRY INTEGRATION

Cave Beauty

Some cave formations are made of calcite. The chemical formula for calcite, a common rock-forming mineral, is $CaCO_3$. Use the periodic table in the back of the book to identify the elements in this formula.

Oxygen

Oxygen helps cause chemical weathering. You've seen rusty swing sets and cars. Rust is caused by oxidation. **Oxidation** (ahk sih DAY shun) occurs when a material such as iron is exposed to oxygen and water. When rocks containing iron are exposed to water and the oxygen in the air, the iron in the rock rusts and turns reddish, as seen in **Figure 6-6.**

Climate and Weathering

Mechanical and chemical weathering occur everywhere. However, climate affects the rate and type of weathering. **Climate** is the pattern of weather that occurs in a particular area over many years. In cold climates, where freezing and thawing are frequent, mechanical weathering breaks down rocks rapidly through the process of ice wedging.

Chemical weathering is more rapid in warm, wet climates. Thus, chemical weathering occurs quickly in tropical areas such as the Amazon River region of South America. Lack of moisture in deserts and low temperatures in polar regions slow down chemical weathering. How weathering affects rock depends on the type of rock, as illustrated in **Figure 6-7.**

Mechanical and chemical weathering work together. For example, when rocks break apart because of mechanical weathering, more surface area is exposed, and the rate of chemical weathering increases.

Try at Home

MiniLab

Observing the Formation of Rust

Procedure

1. Place some steel wool in a glass dish with 1 cm of water.
2. Observe for several days.

Analysis

1. What changes occurred?
2. What caused the changes?
3. How are these changes related to weathering?

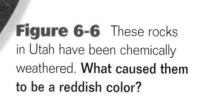

Figure 6-6 These rocks in Utah have been chemically weathered. **What caused them to be a reddish color?**

Figure 6-7 These old tombstones are about the same age, but they have weathered differently. The type of rock also influences how fast a surface weathers. **Why?**

Now you can understand how weathering affects roads, buildings, streets, cemeteries, sidewalks, rocks, caves, and mountains. When weathering breaks down rocks, it contributes to the rock cycle by making sediment that can form sedimentary rocks. Weathering also begins the process of breaking down rock into soil. These steps are discussed in the next section.

Section Assessment

1. What is the difference between mechanical and chemical weathering?
2. How is mechanical weathering affected by climate?
3. **Think Critically:** How can water be a factor in both mechanical and chemical weathering?
4. **Skill Builder**
   Observing and Inferring Do the **Chapter 6 Skill Activity** on page 699 to learn more about mechanical weathering.

Using Computers

Spreadsheet Make a spreadsheet that identifies examples of weathering that you see around your neighborhood and school and classifies each example as the result of mechanical weathering, chemical weathering, or both. If you need help, refer to page 690.

Design Your Own Experiment

Activity 6 • 1

Weathering Chalk

Possible Materials

- Equal-sized pieces of chalk (6)
- Small beakers or clear plastic cups (2)
- Metric ruler
- Water
- White vinegar (100 mL)
- Hot plate
- Graduated cylinder (250 mL)

Chalk is a type of limestone made of the shells of tiny organisms. When you write your name on the chalkboard or draw a picture on the driveway with a piece of chalk, what happens to the chalk? It is mechanically weathered. This experiment will help you understand how chalk can be chemically weathered.

Recognize the Problem

How can chalk be chemically weathered? What variables affect the rate of chemical weathering?

Form a Hypothesis

How do you think acidity, surface area, and temperature affect the rate of chemical weathering of chalk? What happens to chalk in water or acid (vinegar)? How will the size of the chalk pieces affect the rate of weathering? What will happen if you heat the acid? **Make hypotheses** to support your ideas.

Goals

- **Design** experiments to compare the effects of acidity, surface area, and temperature on the rate of chemical weathering of chalk.
- **Describe** factors that affect chemical weathering.

Safety Precautions

Wear safety goggles when pouring acids.

CAUTION: *If mixing liquids, always add acid to water.* Be careful when using a hot plate and heated solutions.

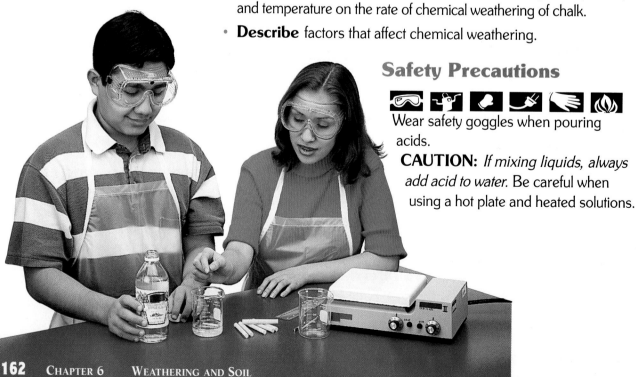

Test Your Hypothesis

Plan

1. **Develop** hypotheses about the effects of acidity, surface area, and temperature on the rate of chemical weathering.
2. Decide how to test your first hypothesis. **List** the steps needed to test the hypothesis.
3. Repeat step 2 for your other two hypotheses.
4. **Design** data tables in your Science Journal. Make one for acidity, one for surface area, and one for temperature.
5. **Identify** what remains constant in your experiment and what varies. Each test should have only one variable. Have you allowed for a control in each experiment?
6. **Summarize** your data in a graph. Decide from reading the **Skill Handbook** which type of graph to use.

Do

1. Make sure your teacher approves your plan before you start the experiment.
2. Carry out the three experiments as planned.
3. While the experiments are going on, **write** your observations and **complete** the data tables in your Science Journal.

Analyze Your Data

1. **Analyze** your graph to find out which substance—water or acid—weathered the chalk more quickly. Was your hypothesis supported by your data?
2. **Infer** from your data obtained in the surface-area experiment whether the amount of surface area makes a difference in the rate of chemical weathering. Explain why this occurs.

Draw Conclusions

1. **Explain** how the chalk was chemically weathered.
2. How does heat affect the rate of chemical weathering?
3. What does this imply about weathering in the tropics?

6•2 Soil

Formation of Soil

What You'll Learn

- How soil develops from rock
- How to describe soil by comparing the A, B, and C soil horizons
- How environmental conditions affect the development of soils
- Ways to reduce soil erosion

Vocabulary

soil
horizon
humus
litter
soil profile
leaching

Why It's Important

- Some regions of Earth are more fertile than others because soil forms in different ways.

How often have you been told "Take off those dirty shoes before you come into this house"? Ever since you were a child, you've had experience with what many people call dirt, which is actually soil. Soil is found in lots of places: empty lots, farm fields, gardens, and forests.

What is soil and where does it come from? The surface of Earth is covered by a layer of rock and mineral fragments produced by weathering. As you learned in Section 6-1, weathering gradually breaks rocks into smaller and smaller fragments. But, these fragments are not soil until plants and animals live in them. Plants and animals add organic matter such as leaves, twigs, and dead worms and insects to the rock fragments. Then, soil begins to develop. **Soil** is a mixture of weathered rock, organic matter, mineral fragments, water, and air. **Figure 6-8** illustrates the process of soil development. Soil is a material that supports vegetation. Climate, types of rock, slope, amount of moisture, and length of time rock has been weathering affect the formation of soil.

VISUALIZING Soil Development

Figure 6-8 Soil is constantly developing from rock.

A Rock at the surface begins to fracture and break down.

B As rock weathers into smaller fragments, plants begin to grow in the weathered rock.

Composition of Soil

Soil may contain small rodents, insects, worms, algae, fungi, bacteria, and decaying organic matter. As soil develops, organic material, such as plants, decays until the original form of the matter has disappeared. The material turns into dark-colored matter called **humus** (HYEW mus). Humus serves as a source of nutrients for plants, providing nitrogen, phosphorus, potassium, and sulfur. Humus also promotes good soil structure and helps soil hold water. As worms, insects, and rodents burrow throughout soil, they mix the humus with the fragments of rock. In good-quality surface soil, about half of the volume is humus and half is broken-down rock. ☑

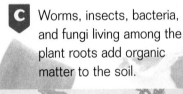

Soil can take thousands of years to form and can range in thickness from 60 m in some areas to just a few centimeters in others. A fertile soil is one that supplies nutrients for plant growth. Soils that develop near rivers often are fertile. Other soils, such as those that develop on steep slopes, may be poor in nutrients and have low fertility.

Soils have small spaces in them. These spaces fill with air or water. In swampy areas, water may fill these spaces year-round. In other areas, soil may fill up with water after rains or during floods.

Reading Check ☑

Why is humus important?

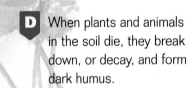

C Worms, insects, bacteria, and fungi living among the plant roots add organic matter to the soil.

D When plants and animals in the soil die, they break down, or decay, and form dark humus.

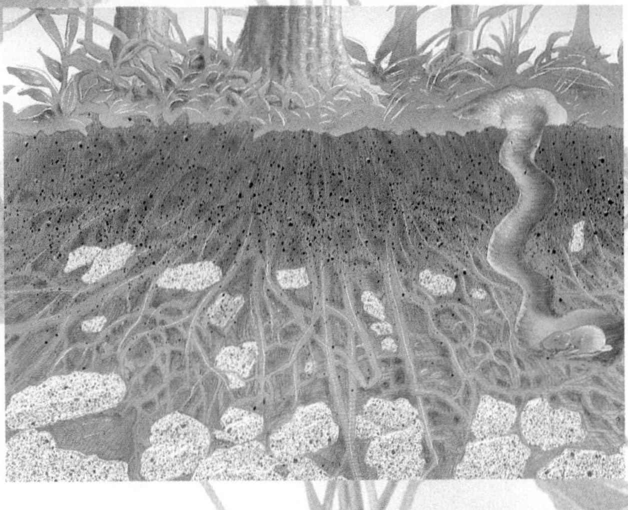

Mini Lab

Comparing Components of Soil

Procedure

1. Collect a sample of soil.
2. Observe it closely with a magnifying glass or a microscope.

Analysis

1. Describe the different particles found in your sample. Did you find any remains of once-living organisms?
2. Compare and contrast your sample with those other students have collected. How are the samples the same? How are they different?

Soil Profile

You may have seen layers of soil if you've ever dug a deep hole or driven by a steep slope such as a road cut where the soil and rock are exposed. You might have observed that plants grow in the top layer of soil. The top layer of soil is darker than the soil layers below it. These different layers of soil make up what is called a **soil profile.** Each layer in the soil profile is called a **horizon.** There are generally three horizons. They are labeled A, B, and C, as in the diagram in **Figure 6-9.**

Figure 6-9 Under this meadow is soil with a specific profile.

A The soil profile of this meadow has three main horizons.

B The horizons in this soil profile reflect the climatic conditions under which it formed. The A horizon contains humus and small grains of rocks. The dark color reflects the organic material it contains. The B horizon contains minerals that have been dissolved and moved from the A horizon plus some clay. The C horizon consists mainly of original rock that has not been changed and that has no organic material.

The photo in **Figure 6-10** shows soil horizons in an eroded hillside. You might also see soil profiles in streambeds, at construction sites, or even in your own garden.

Horizon A

The A horizon is the top layer of soil. In a forest or unplowed area, it may be covered with litter. **Litter** is composed of leaves, twigs, and other organic material that changes to humus when it is exposed to decomposing organisms. Litter helps prevent erosion and hold water. The A horizon is also known as topsoil. Topsoil has more humus and smaller rock and mineral particles than the other layers in a soil profile. A scoop of topsoil will show dark-colored soil, grains of rocks and minerals, decayed leaves, plant roots, insects, and worms. The A horizon is the key to successful plant growth and development.

Figure 6-10 Each soil horizon is unique due to the amount of mineral and organic material. **In which direction are minerals moved?**

Horizon B

The layer below the A horizon is the B horizon. It contrasts sharply with the A horizon. Because litter does not add to this horizon, it is lighter in color than the A horizon and contains less humus. The B horizon also contains elements washed down from the A horizon by the process of leaching.

Leaching is the removal of minerals that have been dissolved in water. The process of leaching resembles making coffee in a drip coffeemaker. In a coffeemaker, water drips into ground coffee. In the soil, water seeps into the A horizon. In a coffeemaker, the water absorbs the flavor and color from the coffee and flows down into a coffeepot. In the soil, the water reacts with humus to form an acid. This acid dissolves some of the elements from the minerals in the A horizon and carries them into the B horizon. Some leaching also occurs in the B horizon and moves minerals into the C horizon.

Horizon C

The C horizon is below the B horizon. It is the bottom of the soil profile and consists mostly of partially weathered parent rock. Leaching from the B horizon also may provide other minerals. What would you find if you dug all the way to the bottom of the C horizon? As you might have guessed, there would be solid rock. This is the rock that gave rise to the soil horizons above it.

In many places on Earth, the land is covered by material that was deposited by glaciers. This unsorted mass of ground-up rock, broken rock, and boulders has filled in the low spots in many places, creating, for example, the flat landscapes of the Midwest. The soils that developed on this glacial material are extremely fertile. The rich soils are an important part of the Midwest's agricultural industry. How does this soil profile differ from the one described above? If you were to dig down through the C horizon, you would find solid bedrock as before, but it would not be the rock that the soil formed from. What is the material that formed this soil profile?

Problem Solving

Interpret Crop Data

Good soil is necessary for crop production. Fertilizers and good farming practices help improve soil quality. Today's increasing world population requires that more food be produced to curb starvation. The chart below shows how world agricultural yield and population increased from 1950 to 1996.

Think Critically: Analyze the chart. Is the increase in agricultural production keeping up with human population growth? What do you think is the reason?

Food and Population Data

Time Span	Percent increase in world agricultural production	Average percent growth rate in population
1960s	3.0	1.95
1970s	2.4	1.83
1980s	2.2	1.78
1990–1996	1.6	1.61

Types of Soil

The texture of soil depends on the amounts of sand, silt, and clay that are in it. In turn, the texture of soil affects how water runs through it. That is not all you'll discover from examining soil profiles.

If you examine a soil profile in one place, it will not look exactly like a soil profile from another location. Different locations affect the way a profile looks. Deserts are dry. Prairies are semidry. The temperate zone profile represents a soil from an area with a moderate amount of rain and moderate temperatures. Crops like the wheat in **Figure 6-11** grow well in temperate zone soils.

interNET CONNECTION

Visit the Glencoe Science Web Site at **www.glencoe.com/sec/science/ca** for more information about soil and climate.

Soil Types Reflect Climate

The thickness of the soil horizons and the soil composition of the profiles also depend on a number of conditions, including climate. Examples of three soil profiles from different climates are shown in **Figure 6-12.**

Chemical weathering is much slower in areas where there is little rainfall, and soils in desert climates contain little organic material. The soil horizons in drier areas also are thinner than soil horizons in wetter climates. The amount of precipitation affects how much leaching of minerals occurs in the soil. Soils that have been leached are light in color. Some can be almost white.

Time also affects soil development, changing the characteristics of soil. If the weathering of the rock has been going on for a short time, the parent rock of the soil determines the soil characteristics. As the weathering continues for a longer time, the soil resembles the parent rock less and less.

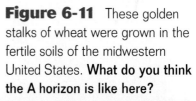

Figure 6-11 These golden stalks of wheat were grown in the fertile soils of the midwestern United States. **What do you think the A horizon is like here?**

Slope also affects soil profiles. On steep slopes, soil horizons are often poorly developed. In bottomlands, where there is a lot of water, soils are often thick, dark, and full of organic material. A south-facing slope receives more sunlight and consequently has different soil development than a north-facing slope. The amount of humus in the soil also affects soil profiles. In the United States, nine groups of soils are recognized, as well as many subgroups. The map in **Figure 6-13** shows the nine main soil groups.

interNET CONNECTION

Visit the Glencoe Science Web Site at **www.glencoe.com/sec/science/ca** for more information about soil types and agriculture.

Soil—An Important Resource

Soil is important. Many of the things we take for granted—food, paper, and cotton—have a direct connection to the soil. Vegetables, grains, and cotton come from plants. Livestock such as cattle and pigs feed on grasses. Paper comes from

VISUALIZING Soil Profiles

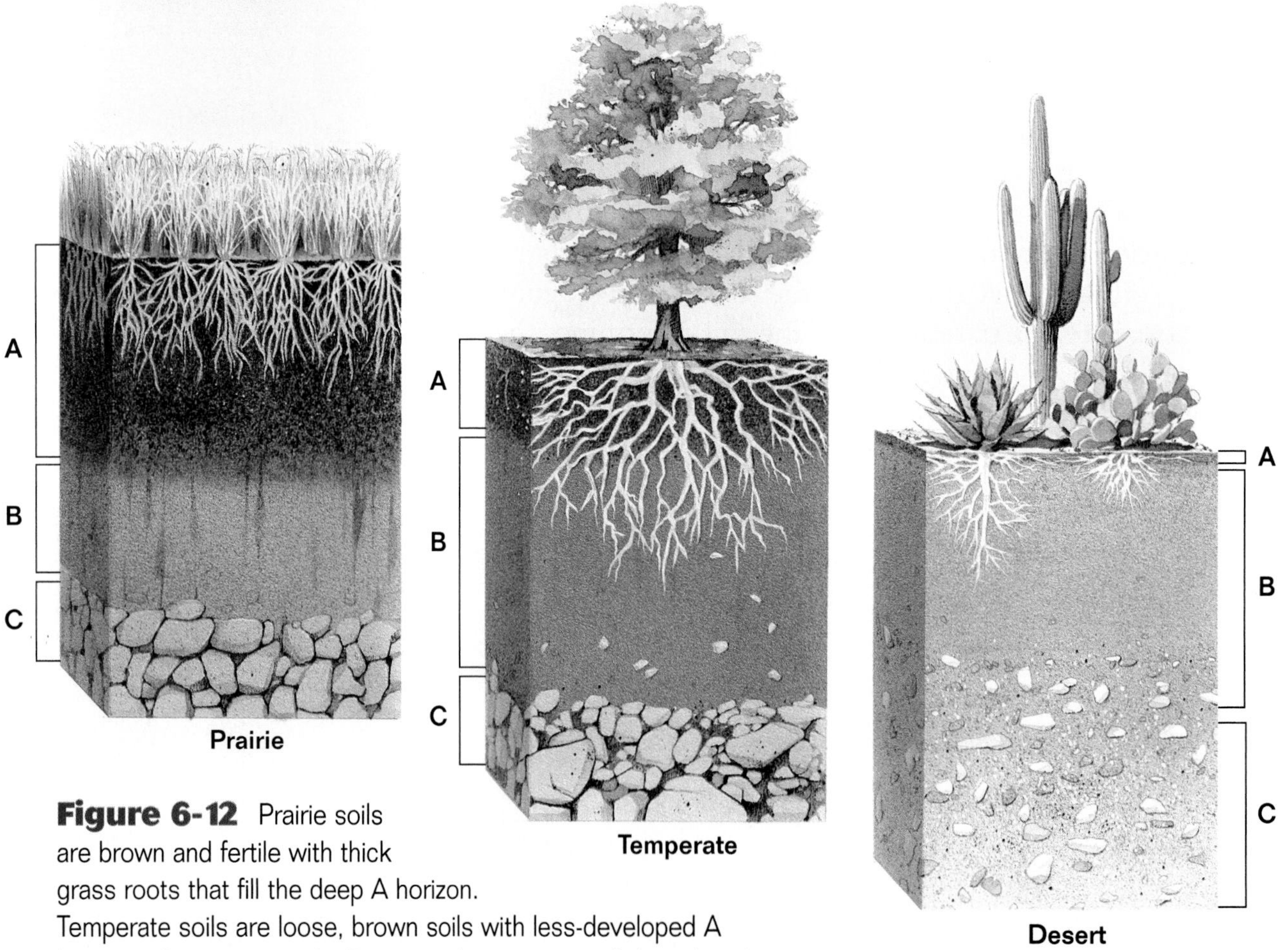

Figure 6-12 Prairie soils are brown and fertile with thick grass roots that fill the deep A horizon. Temperate soils are loose, brown soils with less-developed A horizons than prairie soils. Desert soils are coarse, light-colored, and contain a lot of minerals. Of the three soil types shown here, desert soils have the least-developed A horizon.

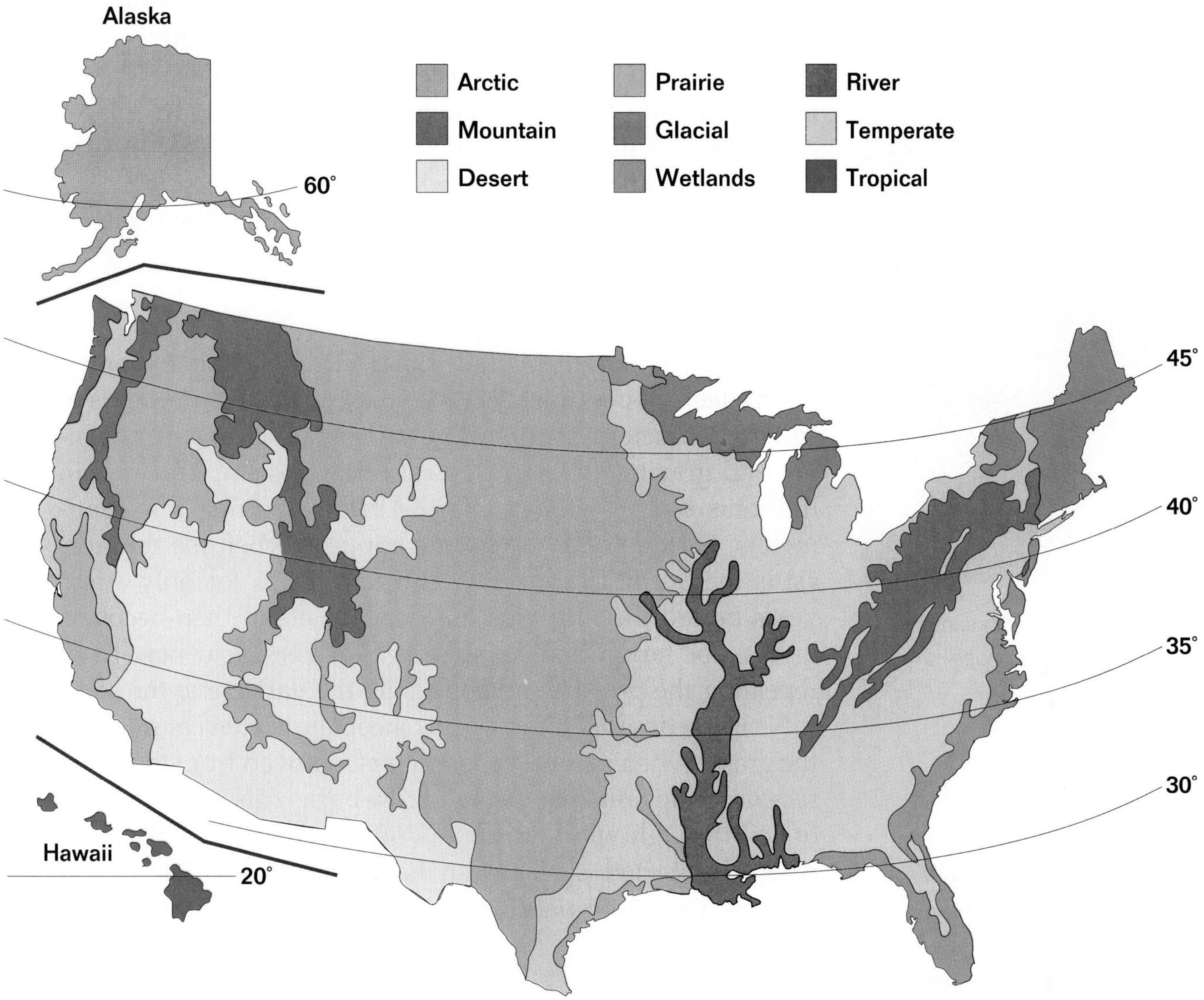

Figure 6-13 The United States has nine different soil types. They vary in color, depth of horizons, soil moisture, texture, and fertility.

trees. Plants, grasses, and trees all grow in soil. Without soil, we cannot grow food, raise livestock, or produce paper or other products we need.

When vegetation is removed from soil, the soil is exposed to the direct action of rain and wind. Rain and wind can erode the topsoil and carry it away, destroying the soil's structure. Also, without plants, soil development slows and sometimes stops because humus is no longer being produced.

Plowing and Soil Loss

Every year, the population of Earth increases by nearly 95 million people. More people means a need for more food. Farmers plow more fields to raise more food for the increasing population. This increases the use of our soil resources.

It is difficult to manage soils effectively. Plowing soil mechanically turns and loosens the soil, improving it for crops. However, plowing soil removes the plant cover that

Figure 6-14 With some farming practices, soil loss can occur.

holds soil particles in place, leaving soils open to wind and water erosion. Wind is harmful when the soil is dry. Sometimes, as shown in **Figure 6-14,** the wind blows soil from a newly plowed field. Soil erosion in many places occurs at a much faster rate than the natural processes of weathering can replace it. Under these conditions, soil is a nonrenewable resource because lost soil cannot be replaced in a short amount of time.

Soil Erosion in the Tropics

Soil loss is severe in the tropics. Tropical rains running down steep slopes quickly erode soil. Each year, thousands of square kilometers of tropical rain forest are cleared for farming and grazing. Soils in tropical rain forests appear rich in nutrients but are almost infertile below the first few centimeters. **Figure 6-15** shows what happens when the rain forest is removed. The soil is useful to farmers for only a few years before the nutrients are gone. The soil then becomes useless for farming or for grazing. Farmers clear new land, repeating the process and increasing the damage to the soil.

Near the deserts of the world, sheep and cattle eat much of the grass. When natural vegetation is removed from land that receives little rain, plants don't grow back. This leads to a loss of soil through wind erosion. Groundwater evaporates. The dry, unprotected surface can be blown away. The desert spreads. Desert formation happens on every continent.

Figure 6-15 Soil in tropical rain forests weathers quickly when trees are cut down. **What type of weathering is occurring here?**

A In the Cuyabeno Wildlife Reserve in Ecuador, portions of the rain forest have been cut down for use in settlements.

B Harsh results of deforestation can be seen in the Tobago Rain Forest in the Caribbean.

Farmers Work to Minimize Soil Loss

All over the world, farmers take steps to slow down soil erosion. They plant shelter belts of trees to break the force of the wind. They cover bare soils with decaying plants to hold soil particles in place. In dry areas, instead of plowing under the natural vegetation to plant crops, farmers graze animals on the vegetation. Proper grazing management can keep plants in place and reduce soil erosion.

Steep slopes, prone to erosion, can be taken out of cultivation or terraced. In the tropics, planting trees to block the force of rain falling on open ground reduces erosion. On gentle slopes, plowing along the natural contours of the land or planting crops in strips helps reduce water erosion. In strip cropping, a crop that covers the ground is alternated with a crop such as corn that leaves a considerable amount of land exposed. In recent years, many farmers have begun to practice no-till farming. Normally, farmers till or plow their fields three or more times a year. In no-till farming, seen in **Figure 6-16,** plant stalks are left in the field. At the next planting, farmers seed crops without destroying these stalks and without plowing the soil. No-till farming provides cover for the soil all year-round and reduces erosion.

Figure 6-16 In no-till farming, the soil is not plowed before planting. **How does this conserve soil?**

Section Assessment

1. How do organisms help soils develop?
2. Why do soil profiles contain layers or horizons?
3. Why does horizon B contain minerals from horizon A?
4. **Think Critically:** Why is the soil profile in a rain forest different from one in a desert?
5. **Skill Builder**
   Concept Mapping Make an events chain map that explains how soil develops. Use the following terms and phrases: *soil is formed, humus develops, rock is weathered, plants grow, worms and insects move in,* and *humus mixes with weathered rock.* If you need help, refer to Concept Mapping in the **Skill Handbook** on page 666.

Using Math

Soil texture depends on the percentages of three different types of particles: clay, silt, and sand. The best texture for growing most crops is a mixture of at least two of these. If a 400-g sand sample has 150 g of clay, 200 g of silt, and 50 g of sand, what is the percentage of each type of particle?

Activity 6•2

Using Scientific Methods

Soil Characteristics

Materials

- Soil sample
- Cheesecloth squares
- Sand
- Graduated cylinder (100 mL)
- Gravel
- Plastic coffee-can lids (3)
- Clay
- Rubber bands (3)
- Water
- Beakers (250 mL) (3)
- Watch
- Large polystyrene or plastic cups (3)
- Pie pans
- Hand lens
- Scissors
- Thumbtack

There are thousands of soils around the world. In your area, you've probably noticed that there are a number of different soils. Collect samples of soil to compare from around your neighborhood and from designated areas of your school grounds.

What You'll Investigate

What are the characteristics of soils?

Goals

- Analyze permeability of different soils.

Procedure

1. **Spread** your soil sample in a pie pan.
2. **Describe** the color of the soil and **examine** the soil with a hand lens. Describe the different particles.
3. **Rub** a small amount of soil between your fingers. **Describe** how it feels. Also, press the soil sample together. Does it stick together? Wet the sample and try this again. Record all your observations.
4. **Test** the soil for how water moves through it. **Label** the three cups A, B, and C. Using a thumbtack, punch ten holes in and around the bottom of each cup.
5. **Cover** the area of holes with a square of cheesecloth and **secure** with a rubber band.
6. To hold the cups over the beakers, **cut** the three coffee-can lids so that the cups will just fit inside the hole (see photo). **Place** a cup and lid over each beaker.
7. Fill cup A halfway with dry sand and cup B with clay. Fill cup C halfway with a mixture of equal parts of sand, gravel, and clay.
8. Use the graduated cylinder to pour 100 mL of water into each cup. **Record** the time when the water is first poured into each cup and when the water first drips from each cup.
9. Allow the water to drip for 25 minutes, then **measure and record** the amount of water in each beaker.

Conclude and Apply

1. How does the addition of gravel and sand affect the permeability of clay?
2. **Describe** three characteristics of soil. Which characteristics affect permeability?
3. Use your observations to **explain** which soil sample would be best for growing plants.

Compost

A composter allows you to recycle food wastes, grass clippings, and other organic materials and turn them into something useful. By composting, people can reduce the amount of garbage to be picked up, save precious landfill space, and make a soil conditioner at the same time.

THE COMPOST PROCESS

1

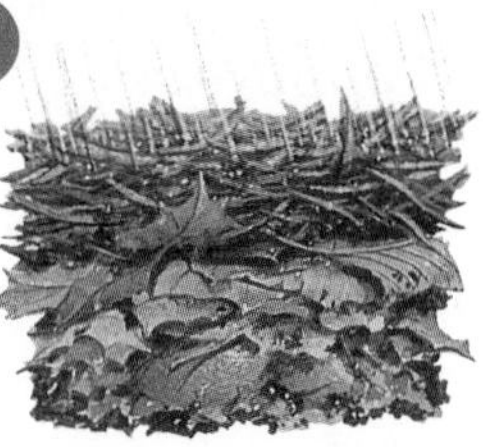

Composting begins when plant materials such as grass clippings, organic garbage, and weeds are piled up, usually layered with soil or manure, and allowed to decay. At left, a compost heap has been prepared.

2

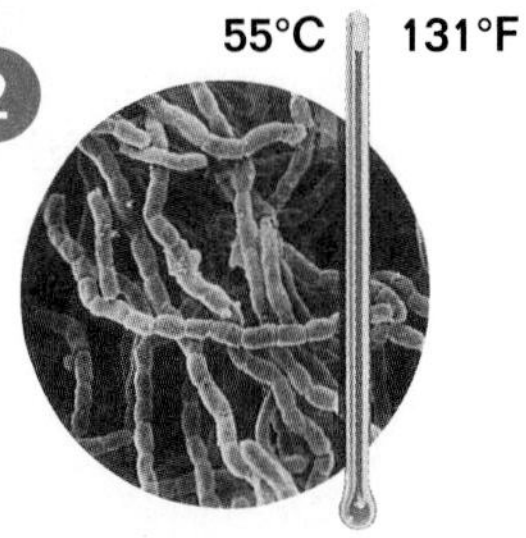

The activity of bacteria heats the interior of the compost heap. Fungi and actinomycetes (in circle), a form of bacteria, break down tough debris, enabling bacteria to decompose it more quickly.

3

Invertebrates (animals without backbones) such as insect larvae and worms eat decaying vegetation. Their droppings are added to the mix. As these organisms tunnel, they create more surface area for fungi and bacteria to work on.

4

The completed compost is a rich, crumbly, dark, soil-like substance used to fertilize soil and improve its structure. Compost also can be used as mulch on the soil surface to help retain soil moisture and prevent the growth of weeds.

Career CONNECTION

Horticulturists are people who work with plants and soil. Most horticulturists have a bachelor's degree, but this degree is not required for all horticulture-related jobs. Write a letter to your local nursery asking about the education and experience required to work there.

Think Critically

1. How does compost help plants?
2. Why does food waste decompose better in a compost pile than in a landfill?

Chapter 6 Reviewing Main Ideas

For a **preview** of this chapter, study this Reviewing Main Ideas before you read the chapter. After you have studied this chapter, you can use the Reviewing Main Ideas to **review** the chapter.

The Glencoe MindJogger, Audiocassettes, and CD-ROM provide additional opportunities for review.

Section

6-1 MECHANICAL WEATHERING

Mechanical weathering breaks apart rocks without changing their chemical composition. Water, by expanding and contracting through freeze-and-thaw cycles, is a major agent of mechanical weathering. Plant and tree roots also weather rocks. Mechanical weathering is not limited to rocks. Roads and sidewalks also are affected by freeze-and-thaw cycles or growing roots. ***Compare and contrast the different agents of mechanical weathering.***

CHEMICAL WEATHERING

Chemical weathering changes the mineral composition of rocks. Water that is acidic may dissolve rock or simply dissolve certain minerals within a rock. Exposure to oxygen causes some rocks to turn red, or rust. Some plants even cause chemical weathering by secreting acids. ***Describe how water can become an agent of chemical weathering.***

Reading Check

After reviewing the illustrations on soil development, describe the steps in your own words. Be sure to number the steps.

Section

6-2 SOIL

Soil develops when rock is weathered and organic matter is added. Soil has **horizons** that differ in their color and composition. Climate, parent rock, slope, amount of **humus,** and time affect the development of soil and give soil its characteristics. ***Explain why some soils take more time to develop than others.***

Career CONNECTION

Susan Colclazer, Naturalist A naturalist is a person who studies the life sciences in the field more than in a laboratory. Many types of scientists who are interested in Bryce Canyon. Naturalists, geologists, archaeologists, sociologists, and botanists have made studies there, as well. Make a list of things these types of scientists might study in the canyon, and tell how their findings would add to the overall picture of the canyon's history.

Chapter 6 Assessment

Using Vocabulary

a. chemical weathering
b. climate
c. horizon
d. humus
e. ice wedging
f. leaching
g. litter
h. mechanical weathering
i. oxidation
j. soil
k. soil profile
l. weathering

The sentences below include italicized terms that have been used incorrectly. Change the incorrect terms so that the sentence reads correctly. Underline your change.

1. When rocks break down without changing in chemical composition, *oxidation* occurs.
2. *Mechanical weathering* results in a change in a rock's composition.
3. *Desert* formation occurs when weathered rock and organic matter are mixed together.
4. *Litter* is composed of decayed organic matter.
5. The A, B, and C layers of a soil make up the soil *horizon.*

Checking Concepts

Choose the word or phrase that best answers the question.

6. What is caused when plants produce acids?
   A) desert formation
   B) overgrazing
   C) mechanical weathering
   D) chemical weathering
7. What happens to water that allows freezing and thawing to weather rocks?
   A) contracts
   B) gets more dense
   C) expands
   D) percolates
8. What occurs when roots force rocks apart?
   A) mechanical weathering
   B) leaching
   C) ice wedging
   D) chemical weathering
9. What reacts with iron to form rust?
   A) oxygen
   B) carbon dioxide
   C) feldspar
   D) paint
10. What can result when poor farming practices occur in areas that receive little rain?
    A) ice wedging
    B) oxidation
    C) leaching
    D) desert formation
11. In what region is chemical weathering most rapid?
    A) cold, dry
    B) cold, moist
    C) warm, moist
    D) warm, dry
12. What is a mixture of weathered rock and organic matter called?
    A) soil
    B) limestone
    C) carbon dioxide
    D) clay
13. What is another term for decayed organic matter?
    A) leaching
    B) humus
    C) soil
    D) sediment
14. In what horizon is humus found almost exclusively?
    A) A horizon
    B) B horizon
    C) C horizon
    D) D horizon
15. What does no-till farming help prevent?
    A) leaching
    B) crop rotation
    C) overgrazing
    D) soil erosion

Thinking Critically

16. Which type of weathering, mechanical or chemical, would you expect to have more effect in a desert region? Explain.
17. Plants cause mechanical weathering. Explain how animals also can be considered agents of mechanical weathering.
18. Why is soil so important?
19. Why is it difficult to replace lost topsoil?

20. Explain how chemical weathering can form a cavern.

Developing Skills

If you need help, refer to the Skill Handbook.

21. **Sequencing:** Do a sequence chart of soil development.
22. **Concept Mapping:** Complete the events chain concept map that shows two ways in which acids can cause chemical weathering.

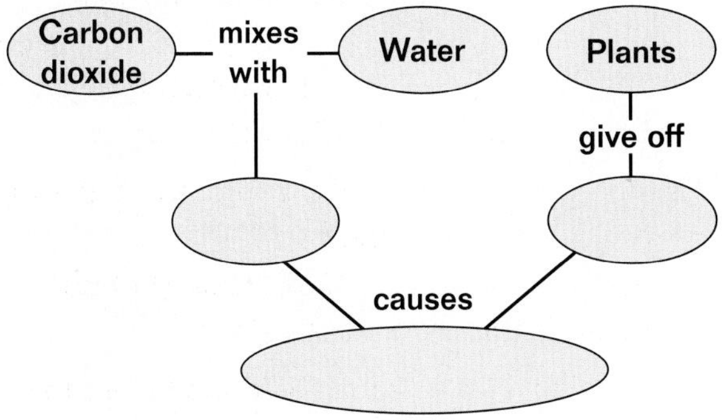

23. **Using Variables, Constants, and Controls:** Juan Carlos wanted to know if planting grass on a slope would prevent soil from being washed away. To find out, he put the same amount and kind of soil in two identical pans. In one of the pans, he planted grass. To create equal slopes for his test, he placed identical wooden wedges under one end of each pan. He was careful to pour the same amount of water at the same rate over the soil in the two pans. What is Juan's control? What factors in his activity are constants? What is the variable he is testing?
24. **Classifying:** Classify the following events as either chemical or mechanical weathering. Rocks that contain iron rust. Freezing and thawing of water cause cracks to form in the street. Acids from mosses leave small pits in rocks. Roots of trees break rocks apart. Water seeping through cracks in limestone dissolves away some of the rock.

THE PRINCETON REVIEW

Test-Taking Tip

Wear a Watch If you are taking a timed test, you should pace yourself. Do not spend too much time on any one question, but don't spend time staring at the clock. When the test begins, place your watch on the desk and check it after each section of the test.

Test Practice

Use these questions to test your Science Proficiency.

1. The curb along a street is crumbling and a big weed is growing from one of the cracks. Which of the following is an inference and not an observation?
   A) Tiny pieces of concrete are found along the base of the curb.
   B) Plant roots are located among the cracks in the curb.
   C) Mechanical and chemical weathering are causing the curb to crumble.
   D) The curb has cracks of varying lengths and widths.
2. Soils have several horizons. Which of the following **BEST** describes the B horizon?
   A) It is made of humus, small rocks, and mineral particles.
   B) It is mostly partly weathered bedrock.
   C) It is full of organisms like insects and worms.
   D) It is light in color and contains soil materials leached from the A horizon.

CHAPTER

7 Erosional Forces

Chapter Preview

Section 7-1
Gravity
Section 7-2
Glaciers
Section 7-3
Wind

Skills Preview

Skill Builders
- Compare and Contrast
- Sequence

Activities
- Design an Experiment
- Analyze Data

MiniLabs
- Observe
- Infer

Reading Check

As you read this chapter, list words that have different meanings when used elsewhere, such as *slump, creep, till,* and *deposition.* Explain the other meanings of these terms.

Explore Activity

The forces of nature are strong enough to wear the jagged peaks of young mountains into the rolling, smooth tops of older mountain ranges. Weathering breaks down rocks into smaller particles. Then forces of nature move these particles and deposit them elsewhere. One of these forces, water, has eroded the canyon to the left in Grand Canyon National Park. Erosional forces constantly change the surface of Earth, making changes in our landscape.

Observe Movement of Sediments

1. Place a small pile of a sand and gravel mixture in one end of a large shoe box lid.
2. Move the pile to the other end of the lid without touching the particles with your hands.
3. Try to move the mixture in a number of different ways.

Science Journal

In your Science Journal, describe the methods you used. Explain how your methods compare with forces of nature that move sediment.

7•1 Gravity

What You'll Learn

- The differences between erosion and deposition
- The similarities and differences of slumps, creep, rockslides, and mudflows
- Why building on steep slopes is a questionable practice

Vocabulary
erosion
deposition
mass movement
slump
creep

Why It's Important

- Landforms change because of erosion, deposition, and mass movements.

Erosion and Deposition

Have you ever been by a river just after a heavy rain? The water may look as muddy as the water in **Figure 7-1.** A river looks muddy when there is a lot of sediment and soil in it. Some of the soil comes from along the riverbank itself. In the upper left part of the photograph, you can see where the bank is being eroded at the curve in the river. The rest of the sediment in the photograph is carried to the river from more distant sources.

Muddy water is a product of erosion. **Erosion** is a process that wears away surface materials and moves them from one place to another. The major causes of erosion are gravity, glaciers, wind, and water. The first three will be discussed in this chapter. Another kind of erosion is shown in **Figure 7-2.**

Figure 7-1 The muddy look of some rivers comes from the load of sediment carried by water.

As you investigate the agents of erosion, you will notice that they have several things in common. Gravity, glaciers, wind, and water all wear away materials and carry them off. But, these agents erode materials only when they have enough energy of motion to do work. For example, air can't erode sediments when the air is still. But, once air begins moving and develops into wind, it carries dust, soil, and even rock along with it.

All agents of erosion deposit the sediments they are carrying when their erosion energy decreases. This dropping of sediments is called **deposition.** Deposition is the final stage of an erosional process. Sediments and rocks are deposited. The surface of Earth is changed. But, next year or a million years from now, those sediments may be eroded again.

Using Math

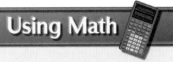

Two rocks fall off a cliff at the same time. One rock weighs 10 N, and the other rock weighs 30 N. They both reach the ground at the same time. Explain why this happened.

Erosion and Deposition by Gravity

Gravity is the force of attraction that exists between all objects. Because Earth has great mass, other objects are attracted to Earth. This makes gravity a force of erosion and deposition. Gravity causes loose materials to move down a slope.

Figure 7-2 This hill has been eroded. **What was the agent of erosion?**

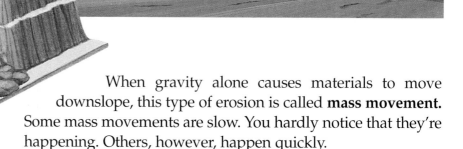

Figure 7-3 Slumps occur when material slips downslope as one large mass. **What might have caused this slump to happen?**

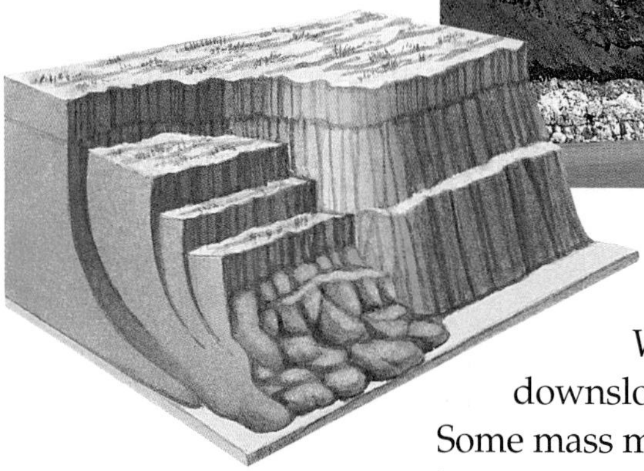

When gravity alone causes materials to move downslope, this type of erosion is called **mass movement.** Some mass movements are slow. You hardly notice that they're happening. Others, however, happen quickly.

Slump

A **slump** is a mass movement that happens when loose materials or rock layers slip down a slope. In a slump, strong rock or sediment lies over weaker materials. The underlying material weakens even more and can no longer support the rock and sediment above. The soil and rock slip downslope in one large mass.

Sometimes, a slump happens when water enters the upper layer on a slope but cannot flow through the lower layers. Water and mud build up. The upper layer of sediments slips along the mud and slides downslope. As shown in **Figure 7-3,** a curved scar is left where the slumped materials originally rested. Slumps happen most often after earthquakes or heavy, continuing rains.

Figure 7-4 Perhaps you can find evidence of soil creep around your home or school. Look for tilted retaining walls and fences and even sod that has stretched apart.

A Several years of creeping downslope can cause objects such as trees and fence posts to lean.

B Below the surface, as the ground freezes, expanding ice in the soil pushes up fine-grained sediment particles. Then, when the soil thaws, the sediment falls downslope, often less than 1 mm at a time.

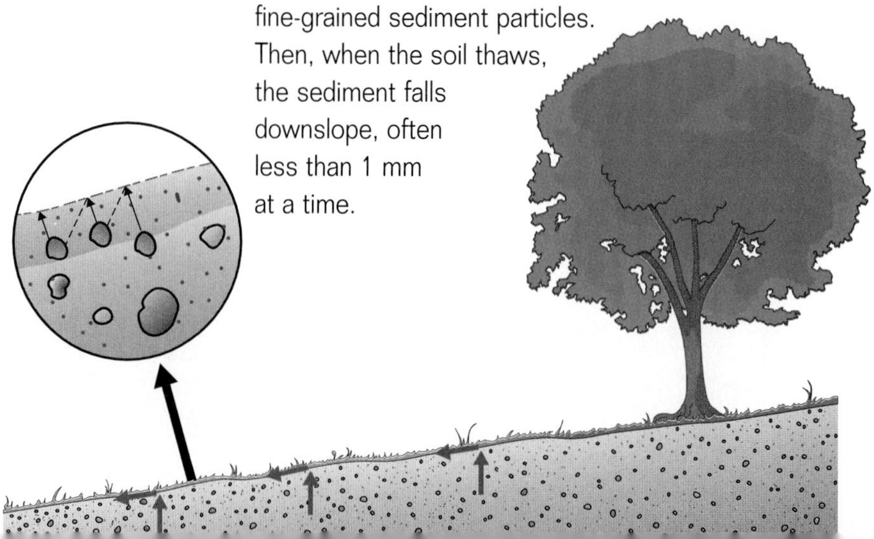

Creep

On your next drive, look along the roadway for slopes where trees, utility poles, and fence posts lean downhill. Leaning poles show another mass movement called creep. **Creep** gets its name from the way sediments slowly inch their way down a hill. As **Figure 7-4** illustrates, creep is common in areas of freezing and thawing.

Rockslides

"Falling Rock" signs warn of another type of mass movement called a rockslide. Rockslides happen when large blocks of rock break loose from a steep slope and start tumbling. As they fall, these rocks crash into other rocks and knock them loose. More and more rocks break loose and tumble to the bottom.

Rockslides are fast and can be destructive in populated mountain areas. They commonly occur in mountainous areas or where there are steep cliffs, as shown in **Figure 7-5.** Rockslides happen most often after heavy rains or during earthquakes, but they can happen on any rocky slope at any time without warning.

The fall of a single, large rock down a steep slope can cause serious damage to structures at the bottom. During the winter, when ice freezes and thaws in the cracks of the rocks, pieces

Figure 7-5 Piles of broken rock at the bottom of a cliff, such as these rockfalls in southwestern Montana, tell you that rockslides have occurred and are likely to happen again.

Figure 7-6 In the Alps, a rock fell from the cliff above and struck this apartment building. **Why did this happen?**

of the rock fracture. In the spring, the pieces of rock break loose and fall down the mountainside. Rockfalls like the one in **Figure 7-6** often occur in mountainous areas.

Mudflows

Imagine traveling along a mountain road during a rainstorm. Suddenly a wall of mud, the thickness of chocolate pudding, slides down a slope and threatens to cover your car. You've been caught in a mudflow, a thick mixture of sediments and water flowing down a slope. The mudflow in **Figure 7-7** caused a lot of destruction.

Mudflows usually occur in normally dry areas where there are thick layers of dry sediments. When heavy rains fall in these areas, water mixes with sediments and becomes thick and pasty. Gravity causes this mass to slide downhill. When a mudflow finally reaches the bottom of a slope, it loses its energy of motion and deposits all the sediments and other things it has been carrying. These deposits usually form a

interNET CONNECTION

Visit the Glencoe Science Web Site at **www.glencoe.com/sec/science/ca** for more information about mudslides throughout history.

mass that spreads out in a fan shape. Why might mudflows cause more damage than floodwaters?

Mudflows, rockslides, creep, and slump are similar in some ways. They are most likely to occur on steep slopes. They all depend on gravity to make them happen. And, no matter what type of mass movement, they occur more often after a heavy rain. The water adds mass and makes the area slippery where different layers of sediment meet.

Figure 7-7 A mudflow, such as this one in Seattle, Washington, has enough energy to move almost anything in its path. **How do mudflows differ from slumps, creep, and rockslides?**

Erosion-Prone Land

Some people like to live in houses and apartments on the sides of hills and mountains. But, when you consider gravity as an agent of erosion, do you think steep slopes are safe places to live?

Building on Steep Slopes

When people build homes on steep slopes, they must constantly battle naturally occurring erosion. Sometimes, when they build, people make a slope steeper or remove vegetation. This speeds up the erosion process and creates additional problems. Some steep slopes are prone to slumps because of weak sediment layers underneath.

Making Steep Slopes Safe

People can have a beautiful view and reduce erosion on steep slopes. One of the best ways is to plant vegetation. Plant roots may not seem strong, but they do hold soil in place. Plants also absorb large amounts of water. A person living on a steep slope might also build terraces or walls to reduce erosion.

MiniLab

Observing Mass Movements

Procedure

1. Put a mixture of dry sand and gravel in a pan. Use these sediments to model how mass movements of sediments occur.
2. After you have modeled slumps and rockslides with dry sediment, add small amounts of water to different parts of your landforms to model mudflows, slumps, and rockslides.

Analysis

1. What factors must be present for mass movements to occur?
2. In what ways are the three mass movements similar? Different?

Reading Check

What can be done to stop erosion on steep slopes?

*inter*NET CONNECTION

Visit the Glencoe Science Web Site at **www.glencoe.com/sec/science/ca** for more information about agriculture in developing countries.

Terraces are broad, steplike cuts made into the side of a slope, as shown in **Figure 7-8.** When water flows into a terrace, it slows down and loses its energy. Terracing slows soil erosion. Walls made of concrete or railroad ties can also reduce erosion by keeping soil and rocks from sliding downhill. However, preventing mass movements on a slope is difficult because rain or earthquakes can cause the upper layers of rock to slip over the lower layers. Not even planting bushes and trees could save the houses in **Figure 7-9.**

People who live in areas with erosion problems spend a lot of time and money trying to preserve their land. Sometimes, they're successful in slowing down erosion, but they can never eliminate it and the danger of mass movement. Eventually, gravity wins. Sediments move from place to place, constantly making slopes less steep and changing the shape of the land.

Figure 7-8 These terraces in Java help conserve soil so vegetables can grow. **How do terraces keep soil from eroding away?**

Figure 7-9 Heavy rains caused by El Niño resulted in this landslide in California. **What type of mass movement occurred here?**

Section Assessment

1. Define *erosion* and name the agents that cause it.
2. How does erosion change the surface of Earth?
3. What characteristics do all types of mass movements have in common?
4. If creep has occurred in an area, what evidence would you see?
5. **Think Critically:** When people build houses and roads, they often pile up dirt or cut into the sides of hills. Predict how these activities affect sediments on a slope.
6. **Skill Builder**
   Concept Mapping Learn more about erosional forces by doing the **Chapter 7 Skill Activity** on page 700.

Using Computers

Spreadsheets Pretend that you live along a beach where the water is 500 m from your front door. Each year, slumping causes about 1.5 m of your beach to cave into the water. Design a spreadsheet that will predict how much property will be left each year for ten years. Use the labels "Years" and "Meters Left." Type a formula that will compute the amount of land left the second year. If you need help, refer to page 690.

7•2 Glaciers

What You'll Learn

- How glaciers move
- Glacial erosion
- Similarities and differences between till and outwash

Vocabulary

glacier
plucking
till
moraine

Why It's Important

- Erosion and deposition by glaciers are responsible for creating many landforms on Earth.

Continental and Valley Glaciers

Does it snow where you live? In some areas of the world, it is so cold that snow remains on the ground year-round. When snow doesn't melt, it begins piling up. As it accumulates, the weight of the snow becomes great enough to compress its bottom layers into ice. Eventually, the snow can pile so high that the pressure on the ice on the bottom causes partial melting. The ice becomes putty-like. The whole mass begins to slide on this putty-like layer, and it moves downhill. This moving mass of ice and snow is a **glacier.**

Glaciers are agents of erosion. As glaciers pass over land, they erode it, changing its features. Glaciers then carry eroded material along and deposit it somewhere else. Glacial erosion and deposition change large areas of Earth. There are two types of glaciers: continental glaciers and valley glaciers.

Continental Glaciers

Continental glaciers are huge masses of ice and snow. In the past, continental glaciers covered up to 28 percent of Earth. **Figure 7-10** shows how much of North America was covered

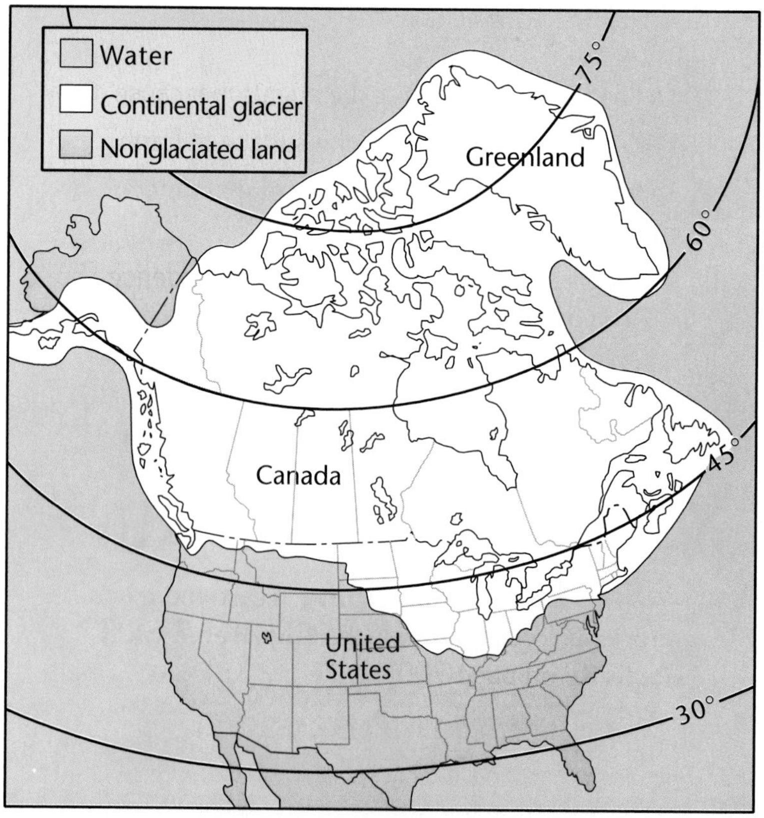

Figure 7-10 This map shows how far the continental glaciers spread in North America about 20 000 years ago. **Was your location covered? If so, what evidence of glaciers does your area show?**

Figure 7-11 Continental glaciers and valley glaciers are both agents of erosion.

A Today, a continental glacier covers Antarctica.

B Glaciers, like this one in Tibet, form between mountain peaks that lie above the snowline, where snow lasts all year.

during the last ice age. Scientists call the periods when glaciers covered much of Earth *ice ages.* The most recent ice age began over a period of 2 to 3 million years ago. During the time when much of North America was covered by ice, the average air temperature on Earth was about 5°C lower than it is today. Then, about 20 000 years ago, the ice sheets began to melt. Today, glaciers like the one in **Figure 7-11A** cover only ten percent of Earth, mostly near the poles in Antarctica and Greenland. Continental glaciers are so thick that they can almost bury mountain ranges on the land they cover. Glaciers make it impossible to see most of the land features in Antarctica.

Valley Glaciers

Valley glaciers occur even in today's warmer global climate. In the high mountains where the average temperature is low enough to prevent snow from melting during the summer, valley glaciers grow and creep along. **Figure 7-11B** shows a valley glacier in Tibet.

How is it possible that something as fragile as snow or ice can become an agent of erosion that pushes aside trees, drags along rocks, and erodes the surface of Earth?

Glacial Erosion

As they move over land, glaciers are like bulldozers, pushing loose materials they encounter. Eroded sediments pile up along its sides, as seen in **Figure 7-12A,** are pushed in front of a glacier, or are carried underneath it. Glaciers also weather and erode rock and soil that isn't loose. When glacial ice melts, water flows into cracks in rocks. Later, the water refreezes in these cracks, expands, and fractures the rock into pieces. These rock pieces are then lifted out by the glacial ice sheet. This process, called **plucking,** results in boulders, gravel, and sand being added to the bottom and sides of a glacier.

As a glacier moves forward, plucked rock fragments and sand at its base scrape the soil and bedrock, eroding even more material than ice alone could. When bedrock is gouged deeply by dragged rock fragments, marks such as those in **Figure 7-12B** are left behind. These marks, called grooves, are

VISUALIZING Glaciers

Figure 7-12 The diagram and photos show landforms characteristic of glacial erosion.

A No agent of erosion is more powerful than an advancing glacier.

B When glaciers melt, striations or grooves may be found on the rocks beneath. These glacial grooves on Kelley's Island, Ohio, are 10 m wide and 5 m deep.

deep, long, parallel scars on rocks. Less-deep marks are called striations (stri AY shuns). These marks indicate the direction the glacier moved.

Evidence of Valley Glaciers

If you visit the mountains, you can see if valley glaciers ever existed there. You might look for striations, then search for evidence of plucking. Glacial plucking often occurs near the top of a mountain where a glacier is in contact with a wall of rock. Valley glaciers erode bowl-shaped basins, called cirques (SURKS), in the sides of the mountains. A cirque is shown in **Figure 7-12C.** If two or more glaciers erode a mountain summit from several directions, a ridge, called an arête (ah RET), or sharpened peak, called a horn, forms. The photo in **Figure 7-12D** shows a mountain horn.

C This cirque, a bowl-shaped basin, was formed by erosion at the start of a valley glacier.

D A horn is a sharpened peak formed by glacial action in three or more cirques.

Valley glaciers flow down mountain slopes and along valleys, eroding as they go. Valleys that have been eroded by glaciers have a different shape from those eroded by streams. Stream-eroded valleys are normally V-shaped. Glacially eroded valleys are U-shaped because a glacier plucks and scrapes soil and rock from the sides as well as from the bottom. A U-shaped valley is illustrated in **Figure 7-12.**

Glacial Deposition

When glaciers begin to melt, they no longer have enough energy to carry much sediment. The sediment drops, or is deposited, on the land.

Figure 7-13 Till has been deposited by the Tasman Glacier in New Zealand.

Till

When the glacier slows down, a jumble of boulders, sand, clay, and silt drops from its base. This mixture of different-sized sediments is called **till. Figure 7-13** shows the unlayered appearance of till. Till deposits can cover huge areas of land. During the last ice age, continental glaciers in the northern United States dropped enough till to completely fill valleys and make these areas appear flat. Till areas include the wide swath of wheat land running northwestward from Iowa to northern Montana; some farmland in parts of Ohio, Indiana, and Illinois; and the rocky pastures of New England.

Till is also deposited in front of a glacier when it stops moving forward. Unlike the till that drops from a glacier's base, this second type of deposit doesn't cover a wide area. Because it's made of the rocks and soil that the glacier has been pushing along, it looks like a big ridge of material left behind by a bulldozer. Such a ridge is called a **moraine. Figure 7-14** shows moraines that were deposited at the end and along the sides of the glacier. A moraine that was deposited at the end of a glacier is shown in **Figure 7-15** and is called a terminal moraine.

Reading Check

What is till?

Outwash

When more snow melts than is accumulated, the glacier starts to melt and retreat. Material deposited by the meltwater from a glacier is called outwash. Outwash is shown in **Figure 7-15.** The meltwater carries sediments and deposits them in layers much as a river does. Heavier sediments drop first so the bigger pieces of rock are deposited closer to the glacier. The outwash from a glacier can also form into a fan-shaped deposit when the stream of meltwater drops sand and gravel in front of the glacier.

Another type of outwash deposit looks like a long, winding ridge. This deposit forms beneath a melting glacier when meltwater forms a river within the ice. This river carries sand and gravel and deposits them within its channel. When the glacier melts, a winding ridge of sand and gravel, called an esker (ES kur), is left behind. An esker is shown in **Figure 7-15.** Meltwater also forms outwash plains of deposited materials in front of a retreating glacier.

Figure 7-14 The Athabaska Glacier in Jasper National Park in Alberta, Canada, is surrounded by many glacial features. **Which ones do you see?**

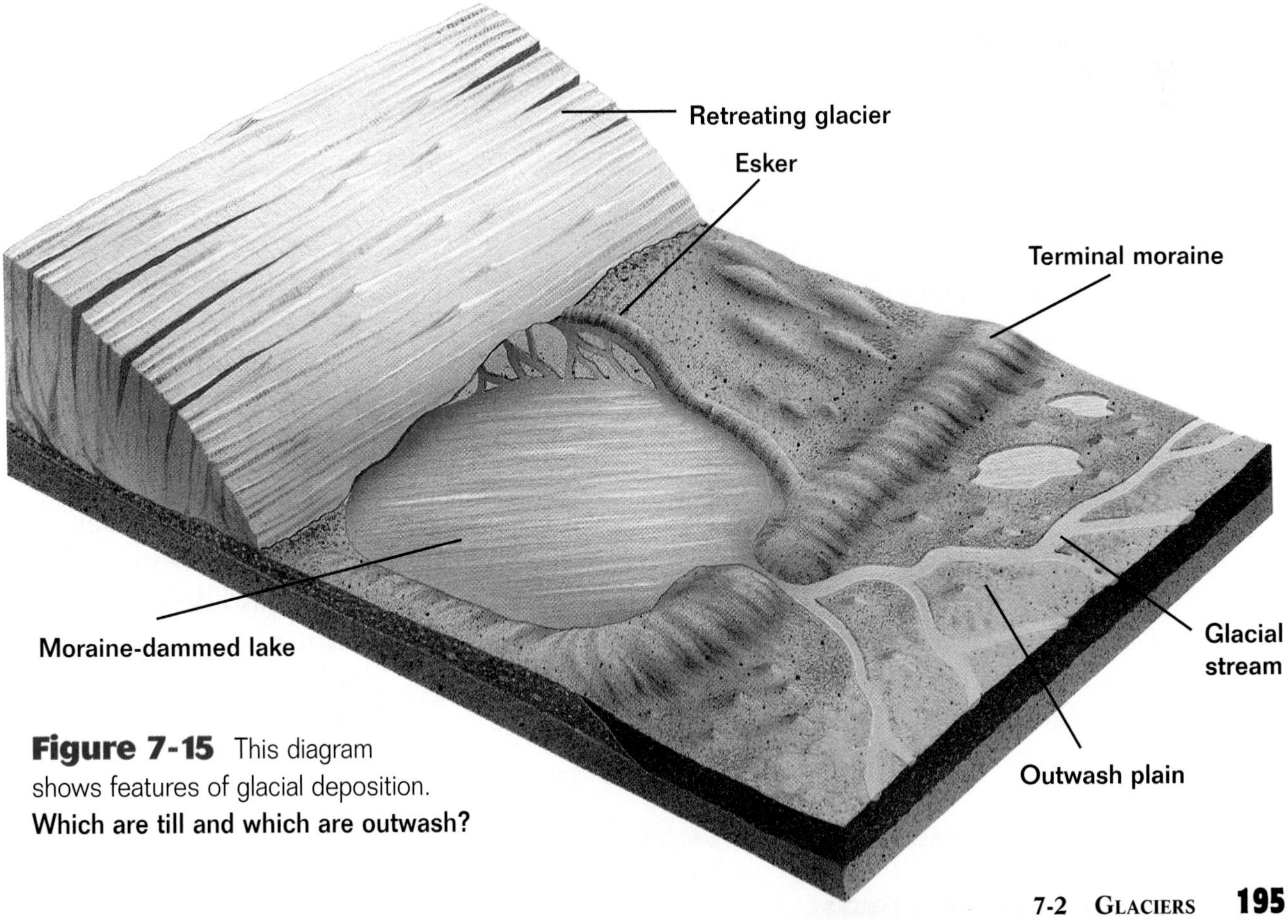

Figure 7-15 This diagram shows features of glacial deposition. **Which are till and which are outwash?**

B This V-shaped valley, cut by the Yellowstone River in what is now Yellowstone National Park, looks different from the U-shaped valley.

Figure 7-16

A This U-shaped valley in Gates of the Arctic National Park in Alaska was carved by a glacier.

Glaciers from the last ice age changed the surface of Earth. Glaciers eroded mountaintops and dug out valleys like the U-shaped one in **Figure 7-16A.** Water erosion forms V-shaped valleys like the one in **Figure 7-16B.** Glaciers also deposited sediments over vast areas of North America and Europe. Today, glaciers in the polar regions and in mountains continue to change the surface features of Earth.

Section Assessment

1. How does a glacier cause erosion?
2. Explain how till and outwash are different.
3. How do moraines form?
4. **Think Critically:** Rivers and lakes that receive water from glacial meltwater often appear milky blue in color. Explain why this occurs.
5. **Skill Builder**
   Recognizing Cause and Effect Since 1900, the Alps have lost 50 percent of their ice caps, and New Zealand's glaciers have shrunk by 26 percent. Describe what you think is causing glaciers to melt around the world. Describe what you think the effects of melting have been. If you need help, refer to Recognizing Cause and Effect in the **Skill Handbook** on page 673.

Science Journal

An erratic is a rock fragment deposited by a glacier. Erratic comes from the Latin word *errare* meaning "to wander." Research how glaciers erode and deposit erratics. In your Science Journal, write a poem about the "life" of an erratic.

Glacial Grooving

Throughout the world's mountainous regions, there are 200 000 valley glaciers moving in response to local freezing and thawing conditions, as well as gravity.

Materials

- Sand
- Large plastic or metal tray
  **stream table*
- Ice block containing sand, clay, and gravel
- Books (2–3)
  **wood block*
- Metric ruler
- Overhead light source with reflector

**Alternate Materials*

What You'll Investigate

What happens when a valley glacier moves? How is the land affected?

Goals

- **Observe** glacial deposits.
- **Compare** stream and glacial valleys.

Procedure

1. Set up the large tray as shown. Place the books under one end of the tray to give it a slope.
2. Cut a narrow channel, like a river, through the sand. **Measure** and **record** its width and depth. **Draw** a sketch that includes these measurements.
3. Position the overhead light source to shine on the channel as shown.
4. Force the ice block into the river channel at the upper end of the stream table.

5. Gently push the "glacier" along the river channel until it's halfway between the top and bottom of the stream table and is positioned directly under the light.
6. Turn on the light and allow the ice to melt. **Record** what happens. Does the meltwater change the original channel?
7. **Record** the width and depth of the glacial channel. **Draw** a sketch of the channel and include these measurements.

Conclude and Apply

1. **Explain** how you can determine the direction a glacier traveled from the location of deposits.
2. **Explain** how you can determine the direction of glacial movement from sediments deposited by meltwater.
3. How do valley glaciers affect the surface over which they move?

Glacier Data

Sample Data	Width	Depth	Observations
Original channel	6 cm	3 cm	stream channel looked V-shaped
Glacier channel			
Meltwater channel			

Music of the Dust Bowl

Blowing in the Wind

In the 1930s, a severe drought struck Texas, Oklahoma, Colorado, Kansas, and New Mexico. Years of overgrazing and overfarming had stripped vast expanses of the land of protective grass. With nothing to hold the parched soil, it blew away, forming towering clouds of dust (right) that traveled hundreds of miles. This dry region of the United States became known as the Dust Bowl.

Songs for the People

Woody Guthrie (inset) wrote and sang folk songs about the hardships faced by the people of the Dust Bowl. His song "The Great Dust Storm" describes a region where, according to Guthrie, "the dust flows and the farmer owes."

The storm took place at sundown
It lasted through the night.
When we looked out next morning
We saw a terrible sight.
We saw outside our window
Where wheat fields they had grown,
Was now a rippling ocean
Of dust the wind had blown.
It covered up our fences,
It covered up our barns,
It covered up our tractors
In this wild and dusty storm. ©

Guthrie's songs also tell of courage and humor. His lyrics in "Dust Pneumonia Blues" describe a girl so unused to water that she faints in the rain. Her boyfriend throws a bucket of dirt on her to revive her.

Science JOURNAL

Research details of Woody Guthrie's life. In your Science Journal, compare his life with the lyrics of his songs. How did his experiences influence his lyrics? Write a song or poem that reflects an event that you or someone you know has experienced.

Wind

7-3

Wind Erosion

When air moves, it can pick up loose material and transport it to other places. Air differs from other erosional forces because it usually cannot pick up heavy sediments. But, unlike rivers and glaciers that move in channels and through valleys, wind can carry and deposit sediments over large areas. Sometimes wind carries dust from fields or volcanoes high into the atmosphere and deposits it far away.

Deflation and Abrasion

Wind erodes Earth's surface by deflation and abrasion. When wind erodes by **deflation,** it blows across loose sediment, removing small particles such as clay, silt, and sand. The heavier, coarser material is left behind. **Figure 7-17** illustrates deflation. When these windblown sediments strike rock, the surface gets scraped and worn away. This type of erosion is called **abrasion.** Both deflation and abrasion happen to all land surfaces but occur mostly in deserts, beaches, and plowed fields. In these areas, there are fewer plants to hold the sediments. When winds blow over them, there is nothing to hold them down.

What You'll Learn

- How wind causes deflation and abrasion
- How loess and dunes form

Vocabulary

deflation
abrasion
loess

Why It's Important

- Wind erosion and deposition help change the landscape.

Figure 7-17 Deflation produces airborne sediments and leaves behind what is called desert pavement.

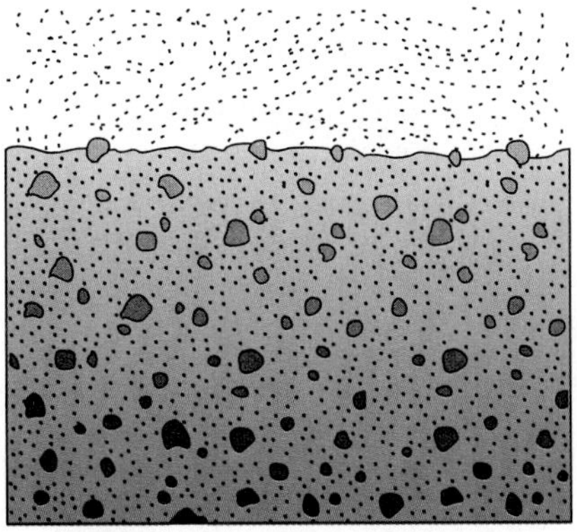

A As deflation begins, wind blows away silt and sand.

C After finer particles are blown away, the larger pebbles and rocks left behind form a pavement that prevents further deflation.

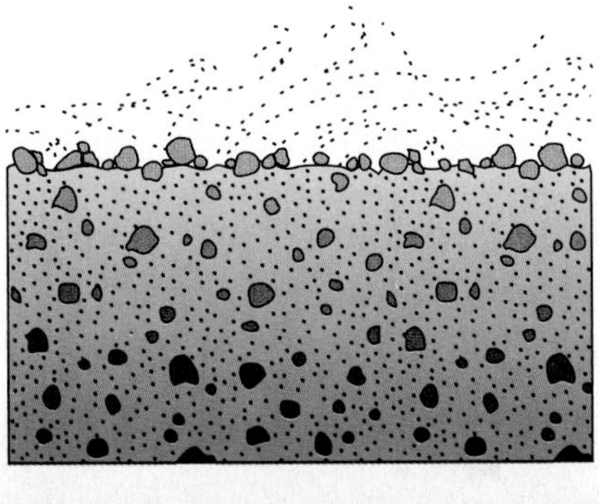

B Deflation continues to remove finer particles. Deflation lowers the surface.

Figure 7-18 Wind erosion can be just like sandblasting.

A When modern archaeologists discovered the Sphinx, it was buried up to its neck in sand. The head shows how abrasive Egypt's desert winds can be.

B This worker is using abrasion to clean and smooth a limestone waterfall.

Abrasion works similar to sandblasting that a crew of restoration workers might do. These workers use machines that spray a mixture of sand and water against a building. The blast of sand wears away dirt from stone, concrete, or brick walls. It also polishes the building walls by breaking away small pieces and leaving an even, smooth finish.

Wind acts like a sandblasting machine rolling and blowing sand grains along. These sand grains strike rocks and break off small fragments. The rocks become pitted or worn down. **Figure 7-18** shows how machine and wind abrasion are similar.

Reading Check

How is wind erosion similar to sandblasting?

Sandstorms

Even when the wind blows strongly, it seldom bounces sand grains higher than one-half meter from the ground. Sand grains are too heavy for wind to lift high in the air. However, sandstorms do occur. When the wind blows forcefully in the sandy parts of deserts, sand grains bounce along and hit other sand grains, causing more and more grains to rise into the air. These wind-blown sand grains form a low cloud, just above the ground. Most sandstorms occur in deserts and sometimes on beaches and in dry riverbeds.

Dust Storms

When soil is moist, it stays packed on the ground. But, when the soil dries out, it can be eroded by wind. Because soil particles weigh less than sand, wind can pick them up and blow them high into the atmosphere. But, because silt and clay particles are small and closely packed, a faster wind is needed to lift these fine particles of soil than is needed to lift grains of sand. Once the wind does lift them, it can hold these particles and carry them long distances. In the 1930s, silt and dust picked up in Kansas fell in New England and in the North Atlantic Ocean. Today, dust blown from the Sahara can be traced as far as the West Indies.

Dust storms play an important part in soil erosion. Where the land is dry, dust storms can cover hundreds of miles. The storms blow topsoil from open fields, overgrazed areas, and places where vegetation has disappeared. A dust storm is shown in **Figure 7-19.**

Figure 7-19 During the 1930s, the southern part of the Great Plains of the United States was known as the Dust Bowl because dust storms swept away the soil. Dust storms still occur around the world in places such as Mongolia, in western India, in northern Africa, and in the United States.

Problem Solving

Deserts

Precipitation, like rainfall and snowfall, and temperature help determine whether or not a region is a desert. Some deserts have such low amounts of precipitation that evaporation from the soil and plants is actually greater than the amount of precipitation. When this happens, plants must get their moisture from underground sources near their deep roots. Deserts also receive a varying amount of precipitation from year to year.

The temperature of deserts can vary a great deal, also. All deserts are not hot. Some deserts in mountain valleys can be quite cold. Because deserts absorb and give up their heat quickly, they can be much warmer during the day than at night.

The graph on the right shows how the amount of precipitation and temperature compare for different kinds of ecological communities (biomes). Study the graph to answer the questions.

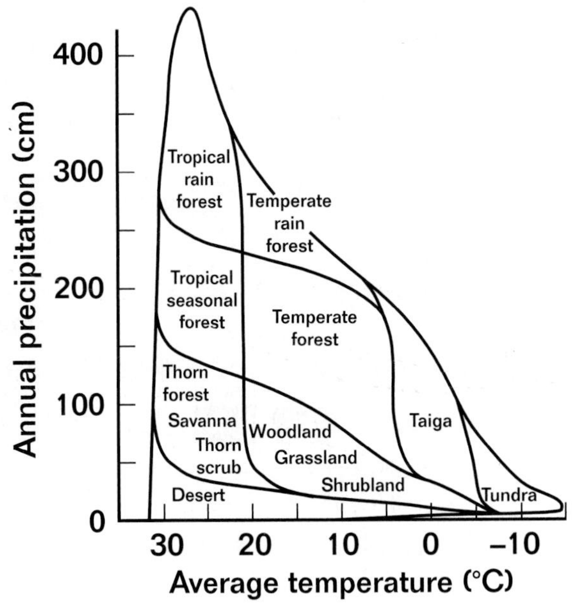

Think Critically: Of all the ecological communities shown in the graph, which shows the greatest range of average temperature? What is the greatest annual precipitation an ecological community can receive and still be classified as a desert? In which ecological community do you live?

Figure 7-20 This marram grass was planted to limit the erosion of sand dunes in Cornwall, England. **How does grass slow erosion?**

Reducing Wind Erosion

LIFE SCIENCE INTEGRATION

As you've learned, wind erosion is most common where plants do not exist to protect the soil. One of the best ways to slow or stop wind erosion is to plant vegetation.

Windbreaks

People in many countries plant vegetation to reduce wind erosion. For centuries, farmers have planted trees along their fields that act as windbreaks and prevent soil erosion. As the wind hits the trees, its energy of motion is reduced and no longer has the energy to lift particles.

In one study, a thin belt of cottonwood trees reduced the effect of a 25 km/h wind to about 66 percent of its normal speed. Tree belts also trap snow and hold it on land, adding to the moisture of the soil, which helps prevent further erosion.

Try at Home

Mini Lab

Observing How Soil Is Held in Place

Procedure

1. Obtain a piece of sod (a chunk of soil about 5 cm thick with grass growing from it).
2. Carefully remove the soil from the sod roots by hand. Examine the roots with a magnifying glass or hand lens.

Analysis

1. Draw several of these roots in your Science Journal.
2. What characteristics of grass roots help hold soil in place and thus help reduce erosion?

Roots

Along many steep slopes, seacoasts, and deserts, vegetation is planted to help reduce erosion. Plants with fibrous root systems, such as grasses, are the best to stop wind erosion. Grass roots are shallow and slender. They also have many fibers. They twist and turn between particles in the soil and hold the soil in place.

Planting vegetation is a good way to reduce the effects of deflation and abrasion. But, if the wind is strong and the soil is dry, nothing can stop it completely. **Figure 7-20** shows a project to stop wind erosion.

Deposition by Wind

Sediments blown away by wind are eventually deposited. These windblown deposits develop into several types of landforms.

Figure 7-21 Scott's Bluff, near Scott's Bluff, Nebraska, is composed partially of windblown loess.

Loess

Some large deposits of windblown sediments are found near the Mississippi River. These wind deposits of fine-grained sediments are known as **loess** (LUSS). Strong winds that blew across glacial outwash areas carried the sediments and deposited them. The sediments settled on hilltops and in valleys. Once there, the particles were packed together, creating a thick, unlayered yellow-brown–colored deposit.

Loess is as fine as talcum powder. Many farmlands of the midwestern United States are on the fertile soils that have developed from loess deposits. The loess pictured in **Figure 7-21** was deposited by winds that blew across the outwash plains of retreating glaciers.

Dunes

What happens when wind blows sediments against an obstacle such as a rock or a clump of vegetation? The sediments settle behind the obstacle. More and more sediments build up, and eventually a dune is formed. A dune is a mound of sand drifted by the wind.

Sand dunes move as wind erodes them and deposits the sand downwind of the dune. On Cape Cod, Massachusetts, and along the Gulf of California, the coast of Oregon, and the eastern shore of Lake Michigan, you can see beach sand dunes. Sand dunes build up where there is sand and prevailing winds or sea breezes that blow daily.

To understand how a dune forms, think of the sand at the back of a beach. That sand is dry because the ocean and lake waves do not reach these areas. The wind blows this dry sand farther inland until something such as a rock or a fence slows the wind. The wind sweeps around or over the rock. Like a river, air drops sediment when its energy decreases.

LIFE SCIENCE INTEGRATION

Plant Roots

Red clover has a taproot system consisting of one main root that grows directly downward. Sea oats have a fibrous root system that branches out in all directions. Infer which type of plant would be better to plant along coastal sand dunes to prevent wind erosion. Explain your answer.

Figure 7-22 Dunes are the most common wind deposits. Sand dunes form in deserts and beaches where sand is abundant. They are constantly changing and moving as wind erodes them. **What is the wind direction in this photo?**

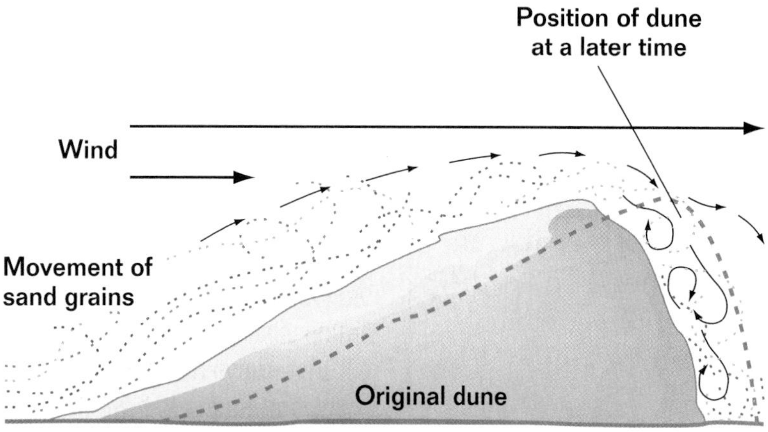

Figure 7-23 As wind blows the sand, the grains jump, roll, and slide up the gentler slope of the dune, accumulate at the top, then slide down the steeper slope on the side away from the wind.

Sand starts to build up behind the rock. As the sand continues to build up, the mound of sand becomes an obstacle itself and traps even more sand. If the wind blows long enough, the mound of sand will become a sand dune, as shown in **Figure 7-22.**

Sand will continue to build up and form a dune until the sand runs out or the obstruction is removed. Some sand dunes may grow to 50 m to 180 m high, but most are much lower.

Dune Movement

A sand dune has two sides. The side facing the wind has a gentler slope. The side away from the wind is steeper. Examining the shape of a dune tells you the direction from which the wind usually blows.

Unless sand dunes are planted with grasses, most dunes don't stay still. They move away or migrate from the direction of the wind. This process is shown in **Figure 7-23.** Some dunes are known as traveling dunes because they move across desert areas as they lose sand on one side and build it up on the other.

Dune Shape

The shape of a dune can also tell you the wind direction. The most commonly known dune shape is a crescent-shaped dune. The open end of a crescent-shaped dune points downwind. When viewed from above, the points are directed downwind. This type of dune forms on hard surfaces where the sand supply is limited. They often occur as single dunes. **Figure 7-24** shows several dune shapes.

When dunes and loess form, the landscape is changed. Wind, like gravity, running water, and glaciers, shapes the land as it erodes sediments. But, the new landforms created by these agents of erosion are themselves being eroded. Erosion and deposition are part of a cycle of change that constantly shapes and reshapes the land.

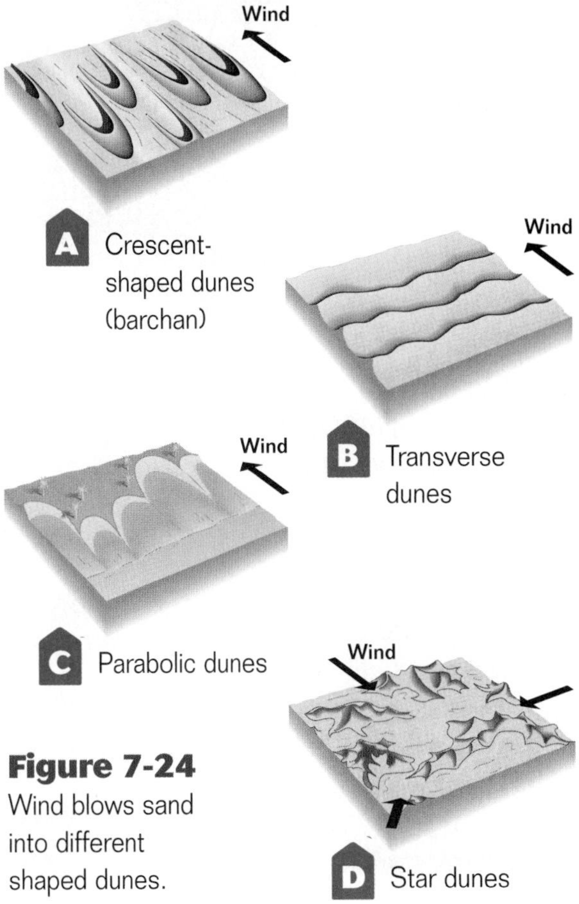

Figure 7-24
Wind blows sand into different shaped dunes.

Section Assessment

1. Compare and contrast abrasion and deflation. How do they affect the surface of Earth?
2. Explain the differences between dust storms and sandstorms. Describe how the energy of motion affects the deposition of sand and dust by these storms.
3. **Think Critically:** You notice that snow is piling up behind a fence outside your apartment building. Why?
4. **Skill Builder**
Sequencing Sequence the following events that describe how a sand dune forms. If you need help, refer to Sequencing in the **Skill Handbook** on page 666.
   - **a.** Grains collect to form a mound.
   - **b.** Wind blows sand grains until they hit an obstacle.
   - **c.** Wind blows over an area and causes deflation.
   - **d.** Vegetation grows on the dune.

Using Math

Between 1972 and 1992, the Sahara Desert in northern Africa increased by nearly 700 km^2 in Mali and the Sudan. Calculate the average number of square kilometers the desert increased each year between 1972 and 1992. At this rate, predict how much additional desert that area will have by 2002.

Design Your Own Experiment

Activity 7•2

Blowing in the Wind

Possible Materials

- Flat pans (4)
- Fine sand (400 mL)
- Gravel (400 mL)
- Hair dryer
- Sprinkling can
- Water
- Cardboard sheets (28 cm × 35 cm) (4)
- Tape
- Mixing bowl
- Metric ruler

Have you ever played a sport outside and suddenly had the wind blow dust into your eyes? What did you do? Turn your back? Cover your eyes? How does wind pick up sediment? Why does wind pick up some sediments and leave others on the ground?

Recognize the Problem

What factors affect wind erosion? Do both sediment moisture and speed of wind affect the rate of wind erosion?

Form a Hypothesis

How does the amount of moisture in the sediment affect the ability of wind to erode the sediments? Does the speed of the wind limit the size of sediments it can transport? Form a hypothesis about how sediment moisture affects wind erosion. Form another hypothesis about how wind speed affects the size of the sediment the wind can transport.

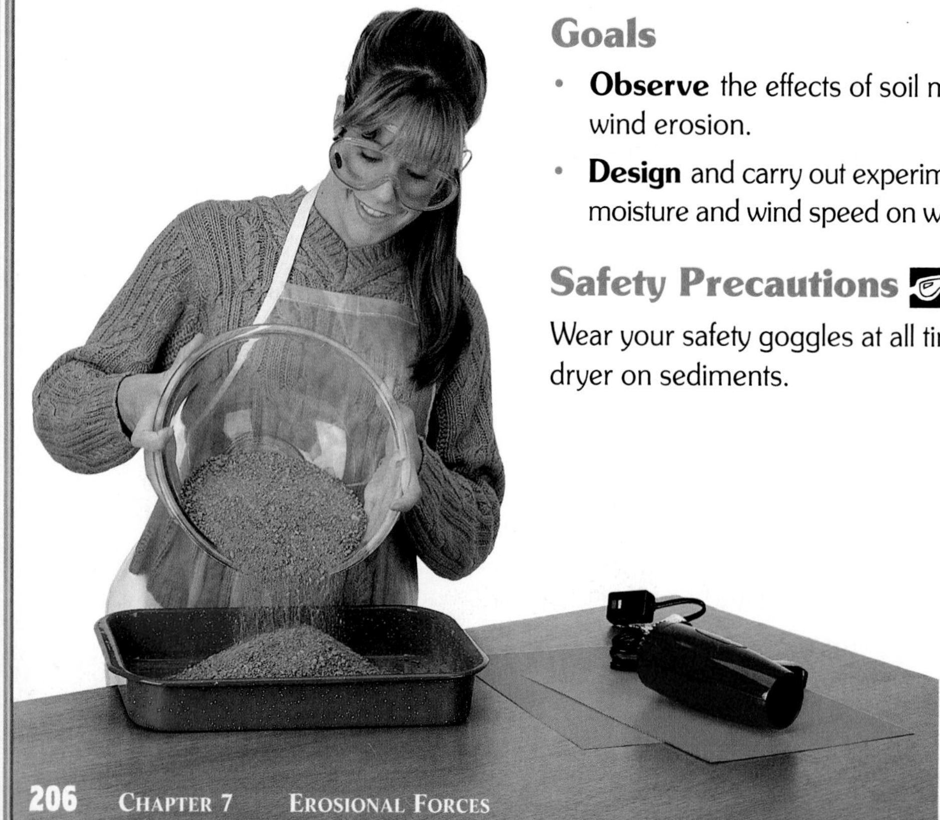

Goals

- **Observe** the effects of soil moisture and wind speed on wind erosion.
- **Design** and carry out experiments that test the effects of soil moisture and wind speed on wind erosion.

Safety Precautions

Wear your safety goggles at all times when using the hair dryer on sediments.

Test Your Hypothesis

Plan

1. As a group, agree upon and write out your hypothesis statements.
2. List the steps needed to test your first hypothesis. Plan specific steps and vary only one factor at a time. Then, list the steps needed to test your second hypothesis. Test only one factor at a time.
3. Mix the sediments in the pans. Plan how you will fold cardboard sheets and attach them to the pans to keep sediments contained.
4. Design data tables in your Science Journal. Use them as your group collects data.

Do

1. Make sure your teacher approves your plan before you proceed.
2. Carry out the experiments as planned.
3. During the experiments, record observations that you make and complete the data tables in your Science Journal.

Analyze Your Data

1. **Compare** your results with those of other groups.
2. **Graph** the relationship that exists between the speed of the wind and the size of the sediments it transports.

Draw Conclusions

1. How does the energy of motion explain the results of your experiment?
2. **Explain** the relationship between the sediment moisture and the amount of sediment eroded.
3. **Based on your graph, explain** the relationship between wind speed and sediment size.

Chapter 7 Reviewing Main Ideas

For a **preview** of this chapter, study this Reviewing Main Ideas before you read the chapter. After you have studied this chapter, you can use the Reviewing Main Ideas to **review** the chapter.

The Glencoe MindJogger, Audiocassettes, and CD-ROM provide additional opportunities for review.

Section

7-1 GRAVITY

Erosion is the process that wears down and transports sediments. **Deposition** occurs when an agent of erosion loses its energy of motion and can no longer carry its load. **Slump, creep,** rockslides, and mudflows are all mass movements related to gravity. ***What characteristics do slump and creep have in common?***

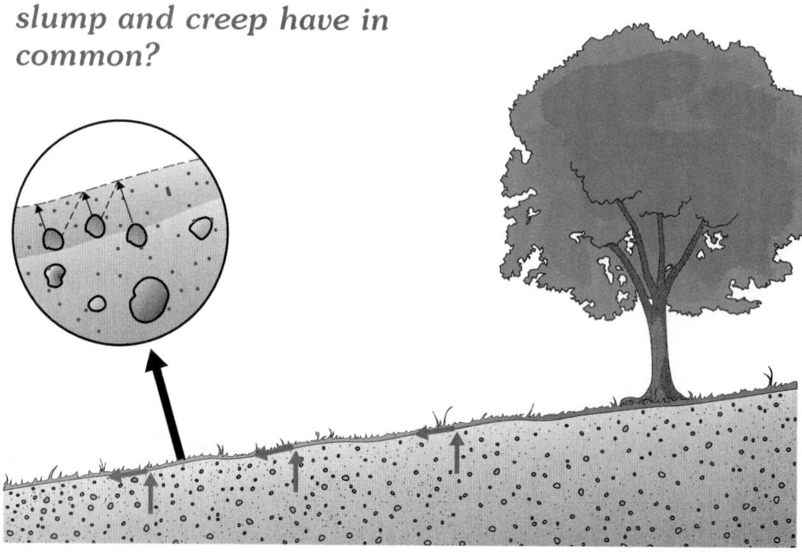

EROSION-PRONE LAND

Vegetation, terraces, and retaining walls can reduce erosion on slopes. Removing vegetation from and building on steep slopes increases erosion. The roots that help hold the soil together and the plants that block wind and rain on the surface are no longer there to do their job. ***What do you think happened in this picture?***

Reading Check ☑

Choose a section of this chapter and rewrite the main headings as questions. Then, answer each question.

Section

7-2 GLACIERS

Glaciers are powerful agents of erosion. **Plucking** adds rock and soil to a glacier's sides and bottom as water freezes and thaws and breaks off pieces of surrounding rocks. Glaciers deposit two kinds of material, **till** (sediments dropped directly from glacial ice and snow) and outwash (debris deposited by its meltwater). ***Which of these two sediments is a jumbled pile of rocks?***

Section

7-3 WIND

Deflation occurs when wind erodes only fine-grained sediments, leaving coarse sediments behind. The pitting and polishing of rocks and sediments by windblown sediments is called **abrasion.** Wind deposits include loess and dunes. **Loess** consists of fine-grained particles that are tightly packed. Dunes form when windblown sediments pile up behind an obstacle. ***What determines how far dust and sand are blown by the wind?***

Chapter 7 Assessment

Using Vocabulary

a. abrasion	g. loess
b. creep	h. mass movement
c. deflation	i. moraine
d. deposition	j. plucking
e. erosion	k. slump
f. glacier	l. till

Explain the difference in the terms given below. Then, explain how the terms are related.

1. abrasion, plucking
2. creep, mass movement
3. deflation, loess
4. erosion, slump
5. glacier, till

Checking Concepts

Choose the word or phrase that best answers the question.

6. Which of the following is the slowest type of mass movement?
   A) abrasion
   B) creep
   C) slump
   D) mudflow
7. The best vegetation to plant to reduce erosion has what kind of root system?
   A) taproot system
   B) striated root system
   C) fibrous root system
   D) sheet root system
8. What does a valley glacier create at the point where it starts?
   A) esker
   B) moraine
   C) till
   D) cirque
9. What happens when glacial erosion occurs?
   A) Eskers form.
   B) Landforms such as arêtes and grooves are formed.
   C) Moraines are deposited.
   D) The climate gets warmer.
10. What term describes a mass of snow and ice in motion?
   A) loess deposit
   B) glacier
   C) outwash
   D) abrasion
11. What shape do glacier-created valleys have?
   A) V shaped
   B) L shaped
   C) U shaped
   D) S shaped
12. Which term is an example of a structure created by deposition?
   A) cirque
   B) abrasion
   C) striation
   D) dune
13. Which characteristic is common to all agents of erosion?
   A) They carry sediments when they have enough energy of motion.
   B) They are most likely to erode when sediments are moist.
   C) They create deposits called dunes.
   D) They erode large sediments before they erode small ones.
14. What type of wind erosion leaves pebbles and boulders behind?
   A) deflation
   B) loess
   C) abrasion
   D) sandblasting
15. What is a ridge formed by deposition of till called?
   A) striation
   B) esker
   C) cirque
   D) moraine

Thinking Critically

16. How can striations give information about the direction a glacier moved?
17. How effective would a retaining wall made of fine wire mesh be against erosion?
18. Sand dunes often migrate. What can be done to prevent the migration of beach dunes?
19. Scientists have found evidence of movement of ice within a glacier. Explain how this could occur. (HINT: Recall

how putty-like ice forms at the base of a glacier.)

20. The front end of a valley glacier is at a lower elevation than the tail end. How does this explain melting at its front end while snow is still accumulating at its tail end?

Developing Skills

If you need help, refer to the Skill Handbook.

21. **Making Tables:** Make a table to contrast continental and valley glaciers.
22. **Designing an Experiment:** Explain how to test the effect of glacial thickness on a glacier's ability to erode.
23. **Sequencing:** Copy and complete the events chain to show how a sand dune forms. Use the terms *sand rolls, migrating, wind blows, sand accumulates, dune, dry sand, obstruction traps,* and *stabilized.*

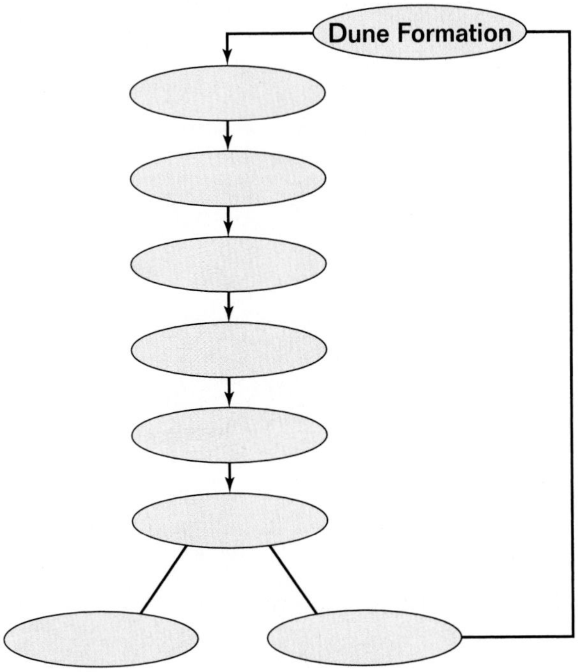

24. **Hypothesizing:** Hypothesize why the materials of loess deposits were transported farther than those of sand dune deposits.

THE PRINCETON REVIEW

Test-Taking Tip

Ignore Everyone While you take a test, pay no attention to anyone else in the room. Don't worry if your friends finish a test before you do. If someone tries to talk to you during a test, don't answer. You run the risk of the teacher thinking you were cheating—even if you weren't.

Test Practice

1. A glacier doesn't develop overnight. Several things must happen before a glacier forms. Of the choices below, which occurs first?
   A) Snow falls in an area. It doesn't melt but instead begins piling up.
   B) The mass of snow and ice moves downhill.
   C) The bottom of the snow layer is compressed into layers of ice.
   D) The bottom of the snow layer partially melts and becomes putty-like.
2. All of the following can be classified as erosional features of a glacier except one. Which one doesn't fit?
   A) striations
   B) U-shaped valley
   C) cirque
   D) till
3. Wind can be a strong erosional force. What determines the amount of erosion that wind can cause in a particular region?
   A) the size of the sediments
   B) the amount of cloud cover
   C) the number of sand dunes
   D) the amount of loess

CHAPTER

8 Water Erosion and Deposition

Chapter Preview

Section 8-1
Surface Water

Section 8-2
Groundwater

Section 8-3
Ocean Shoreline

Skills Preview

Skill Builders

- Compare and Contrast
- Map Concepts

Activities

- Hypothesize
- Classify

MiniLabs

- Make a Model
- Record Observations

Reading Check

Before you read the chapter, it helps to read the Reviewing Main Ideas pages at the end of the chapter. This helps you to know what the most important ideas are.

Explore Activity

Do you know what caused the patterns in this landscape in Canyonlands National Park in Utah? Water! The Green River wears away and moves tons of sediment. Water is the major cause of erosion. It's easy to see why—moving water has great energy. Sometimes, rainwater just soaks into sediments. Other times, it moves down the slope because of gravity's pull. What determines whether rain soaks into the ground or runs off and erodes the surface?

Observe Erosion

1. Place an aluminum pie pan on your desktop.
2. Make a pile of dry soil in the pan.
3. Slowly drip water from a dropper onto the pile and observe what happens.
4. Drip the water more quickly and continue to observe what happens.
5. Repeat steps 1–4, but this time change the slope of the hill. Start again with dry soil.

Science Journal

In your Science Journal, record what effect your rainwater had on the different slopes.

8•1 Surface Water

What You'll Learn

- What causes runoff
- How rill, sheet, gully, and stream erosion compare
- The three different stages of stream development
- How alluvial fans and deltas form

Vocabulary

runoff · **meander** · **rill erosion** · **floodplain** · **gully erosion** · **delta** · **sheet erosion** · **alluvial fan** · **drainage basin**

Why It's Important

- Runoff and streams shape Earth's surface.

Runoff

Water that doesn't soak into the ground or evaporate but instead flows across Earth's surface is called **runoff.** If you've ever spilled milk while pouring it, you've experienced something similar to runoff. You can picture it in your mind. You start pouring a glass of milk, but it overflows, spilling all over the table. Then, before you can grab a towel to clean up the mess, the milk runs off the table and onto the floor. This is similar to what happens to rainwater that doesn't soak into the ground or evaporate. It runs along the ground and eventually enters streams, lakes, or the ocean.

Factors Affecting Runoff

What factors determine whether rain soaks into the ground or runs off? The amount of rain and the length of time it falls are two factors that affect the amount of runoff. Light rain

B

A

Figure 8-1 In areas with gentle slopes and much vegetation, such as the Emerald Hills in New Zealand (A), there is little runoff and erosion. Lack of vegetation has led to severe soil erosion in some areas (B).

Figure 8-2 During floods, the high volume of fast-moving water erodes large amounts of soil.

falling over several hours will probably have time to soak into the ground. Heavy rain falling in less than an hour or so will run off because it doesn't have time to soak in.

Another factor that affects the amount of runoff is the slope of the land. Gentle slopes and flat areas hold water in place, giving it a chance to evaporate or sink into the ground. On steep slopes, however, gravity causes water to run off before either of these things can happen.

As you can see in **Figure 8-1,** the amount of vegetation, such as grass, also affects the amount of runoff. Just like milk running off the table, water will run off smooth surfaces that have little or no vegetation. Plants and their roots act like sponges to soak up and hold water. By slowing down runoff, plants and roots help prevent the erosion of soil. In areas where plants have been cleared, large amounts of soil erosion may occur.

The Effects of Gravity

PHYSICS INTEGRATION

Gravity is the attracting force all objects have for one another. The greater the amount of matter or mass of an object, the greater its force of gravity. Because Earth has a much greater mass than any of the objects on it, Earth's gravitational force pulls objects toward its center. Water falling down a slope is evidence of gravity. As objects drop to Earth's surface, they pick up speed. Thus, when water falls down a slope, it too picks up speed. Its energy of motion is much greater, and, as shown in **Figure 8-2,** it erodes more quickly than slower-moving water.

Water Erosion

Suppose you and several friends walk the same way to school each day through a field or an empty lot. You always walk in the same footsteps as you did the day before. After a few weeks, you've worn a path through the field. Water also wears a path as it travels down a slope time after time.

Figure 8-3 Heavy rains can remove large amounts of soil and sediment, forming a deep gully in the side of a slope.

Figure 8-4 The runoff that causes sheet erosion eventually loses its energy of motion. Note how the running water appears to stop at the bottom center of the photo. The sediments left behind cover the soil like a sheet.

PHYSICS INTEGRATION

Gravity

Erosion is the result of forces that act on rocks and soil to change their shape. One force that drives most types of erosion is gravity. Gravity gives water its potential, or stored, energy. When this energy is changed into kinetic energy, or energy of motion, water becomes a powerful force strong enough to move mountains. Visit the Glencoe Science Web Site at **www.glencoe.com/sec/science/ca** for more information on gravity.

Rill and Gully Erosion

You may have seen a scar or small channel on the side of a slope that was left behind by running water. This is evidence of rill erosion. **Rill erosion** begins when a small stream forms during a heavy rain. As this stream flows along, it has enough energy to carry away plants and soil. There's a scar left on the slope where the water eroded the plants and soil. If a stream frequently flows in the same path, rill erosion may change over time into gully erosion.

In **gully erosion,** a rill channel becomes broader and deeper. Large amounts of soil are removed to form a gully as shown in **Figure 8-3.**

Sheet Erosion

Water often erodes without being in a stream channel. For example, when it rains over a fairly flat area, the rainwater builds until it eventually begins moving down a gentle slope. **Sheet erosion** happens when rainwater flows into lower elevations, carrying sediments with it, as shown in **Figure 8-4.** At these lower elevations, the water loses some of its energy, and it drains into the soil or slowly evaporates.

MiniLab

Observing Stream Erosion

Procedure

1. Fill a paint pan with 3 cm of soil.
2. Use the edge of a ruler or a pencil to level the soil, and use your hands to gently pack it down.
3. With your finger or a pencil, make a stream channel in the soil. Put several bends or turns in the channel so that the water will not be able to flow along a straight path.
4. Slowly pour water from a beaker into the channel from the higher end of the pan.

Analysis

1. Describe where the stream erodes the most sediments.
2. Describe how the path of a stream of running water affects the rate at which erosion takes place.

Stream Erosion

Sometimes, water continues to flow along a low place it has formed. It then becomes a stream like the one shown in **Figure 8-5.** As the water in a stream moves along, it continues to pick up sediments from the bottom and sides of its channel. Water picks up and carries some of the lightweight sediments, while large, heavy particles just roll along the bottom of the stream channel. All of these different-sized materials scrape against the bottom and sides of the channel, where they continue to knock loose more sediments. Because of this, a stream continually cuts a deeper and wider channel.

River System Development

Is there a stream in your neighborhood or town? Maybe you've been fishing in that stream. Each day, thousands of liters of water flow through your neighborhood or town in that stream. Where does all the water come from?

Figure 8-5 This is a cross section of a typical stream channel. **How will the shape of this channel change over time?**

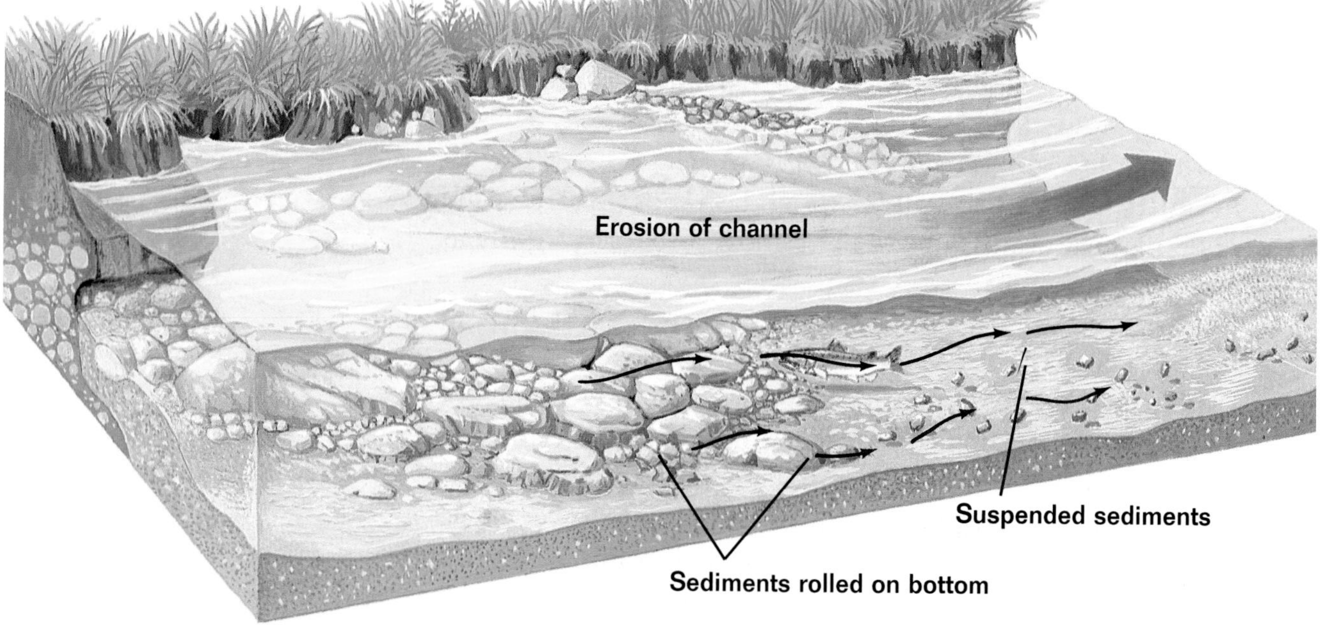

Figure 8-6 River systems can be compared with the structure of a tree.

A A large portion of the streams and rivers in the United States are part of the Mississippi River drainage basin, or watershed. **What river represents the "trunk" of the river system?**

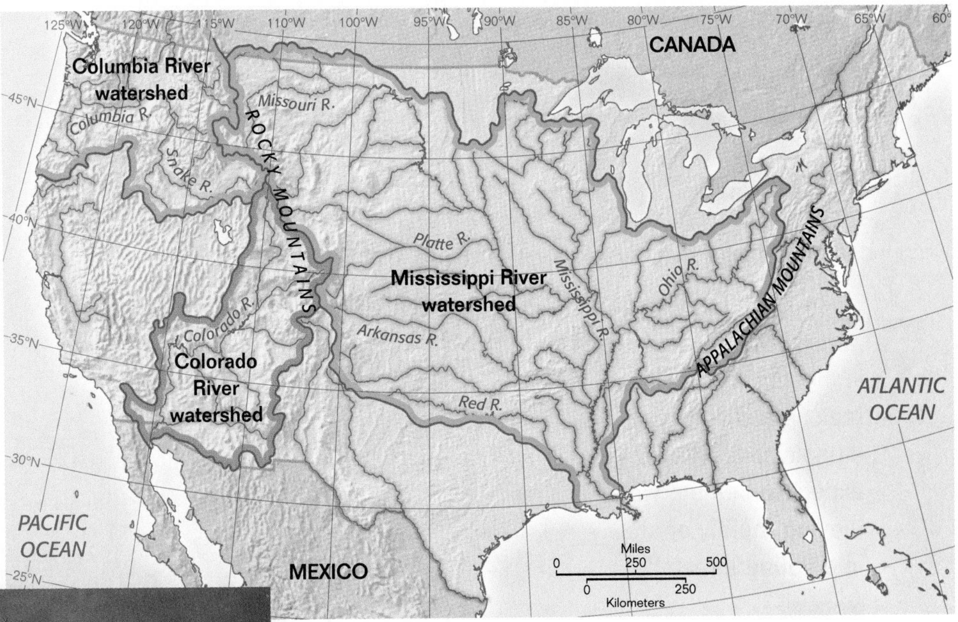

B The system of twigs, branches, and the trunk that make up a tree is similar to the system of streams and rivers that make up a river system.

River Systems

The stream in your neighborhood is really a part of a river system. The water in the stream came from rills, gullies, and smaller streams located upstream. Just as the tree in **Figure 8-6** is a system containing twigs, branches, and a trunk, a river system also has many parts. Water runs off of the ground and enters small streams. Where small streams join, a larger stream forms. Finally, these larger streams join together, forming a larger body of water called a *river.*

Drainage Basins

The land area from which a stream gets its water is called a **drainage basin.** A drainage basin can be compared to a bathtub. Water that collects in a bathtub flows toward one location—the drain. Likewise, all of the water in a river system eventually flows to one location—the main river. The largest drainage basin in the United States is the Mississippi River drainage basin as shown in **Figure 8-6A.**

*inter***NET** CONNECTION

Visit the Glencoe Science Web Site at **www.glencoe.com/sec/science/ca** for more information on rivers.

VISUALIZING Stream Development

Figure 8-7 Streams at all stages of development can be found in most major river systems.

A Young streams are found in mountainous or hilly regions and flow down steep slopes. **Would you expect to see the water moving rapidly or slowly in a young stream?**

B A curving stream that flows down a gradual slope is a mature stream. **Why wouldn't you expect to see many large rapids or waterfalls along a mature stream?**

Stages of Stream Development

There are many different types of streams. Some are narrow and swift moving, and others are wide and slow moving. Streams differ because they are in different stages of development. These stages depend on the slope of the ground over which the stream flows. Streams are classified as young, mature, or old. **Figure 8-7,** on these two pages, describes how each of the stages come together to form a drainage basin.

The stages of development aren't always related to the age of a river. The New River in West Virginia, for example, is one of the oldest rivers in North America. However, it has a steep valley, and flows swiftly through rapids and, as a result, is classified as a *young stream.*

Young Streams

A stream that flows swiftly through a steep valley and has steep sides is a young stream. A young stream may have whitewater rapids and waterfalls. Because the water is flowing rapidly downhill, it has a high level of energy and erodes the stream bottom more than its sides.

Mature Streams

The next stage in the development of a stream is the mature stage. A mature stream flows less swiftly through its valley. Most of the rocks in the streambed that cause waterfalls and rapids have been eroded away.

C Old streams flow slowly through flat, broad floodplains. **What happens to the area surrounding an old-stage stream during floods?**

Figure 8-8 Flooding causes problems for people who live along major rivers. Floodwater broke through a levee during the Mississippi River flooding in 1993 (A). Kansas City, Missouri, experienced severe flooding during this 1993 flood (B).

The ability of a mature stream to erode is no longer concentrated on its bottom. Now, the stream starts to erode more along its sides. Curves develop. These curves form because the speed of the water changes throughout the width of the channel.

Reading Check ✓

What is a meander?

Water in shallow areas of a stream is slowed down by the friction caused by the bottom of the river. In deep areas, less of the water comes in contact with the bottom. This means that deep water has less friction with the bottom of the stream and therefore flows faster. This faster-moving water erodes the side of the stream where the current is strongest, forming curves. A curve that forms in this way is called a **meander** (mee AN dur). **Figure 8-7C** shows what a meandering stream looks like from the air. ✓

The broad, flat valley floor carved by a meandering stream is called a **floodplain.** When a stream floods, it will often cover a part of or the whole floodplain.

Old Streams

The last stage in the development of a stream is the old stage. An old stream flows slowly through a broad, flat floodplain that it has carved. Below St. Louis, Missouri, the lower Mississippi River is in the old stage.

Major river systems usually contain streams in all stages of development. At the outer edges of a river system, you find whitewater streams moving swiftly down mountains and hills. At the bottom of mountains and hills, you find streams that are starting to meander and are in the mature stage of development. These streams meet at the trunk of the drainage basin to form a major river.

Too Much Water

What happens when a river system has too much water in it? The water needs to go somewhere, and out and over the banks is the only choice. A river that overflows its banks can bring disaster. To prevent this type of flooding, dams and levees are built. A dam is built to control the water flow downstream. It may be built of soil or sand, or steel and concrete.

interNET CONNECTION

Visit the Glencoe Science Web Site at **www.glencoe.com/sec/science/ca** for more information on floods.

Problem Solving

Predicting Floods

Each year, floods claim more than 100 lives, drive about 300 000 Americans from their homes, and cause more than $3 billion in property damage. That's why flood prediction is so important. To accurately predict floods, a lot must be known about the drainage basin of a particular stream. One important piece of information is how fast water drains from the basin.

When it rains, it takes a while for runoff to drain a basin and reach the stream channel. Imagine that it rains on a parking lot with a drain near one end. All of the water does not reach the drain at the same time because it takes longer for the water at the far end of the parking lot to travel to the drain. Also, the parking lot is probably not level, so some areas drain more quickly than others. This is similar to runoff from a drainage basin flowing into a stream channel.

The graphs below show runoff of two drainage basins after a 3-cm rainfall. The graphs show the speed of the flow over time. Study the two graphs and interpret the data to explain the differences.

Think Critically: Which of these two drainage basins will most likely flood? What might be different about the two drainage basins that would explain the differences in their flow rates?

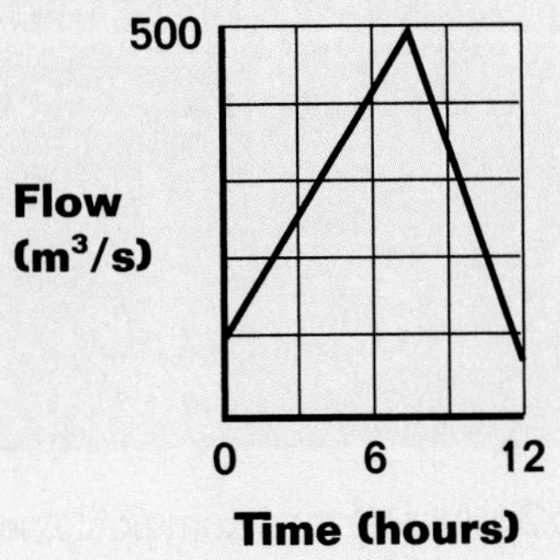

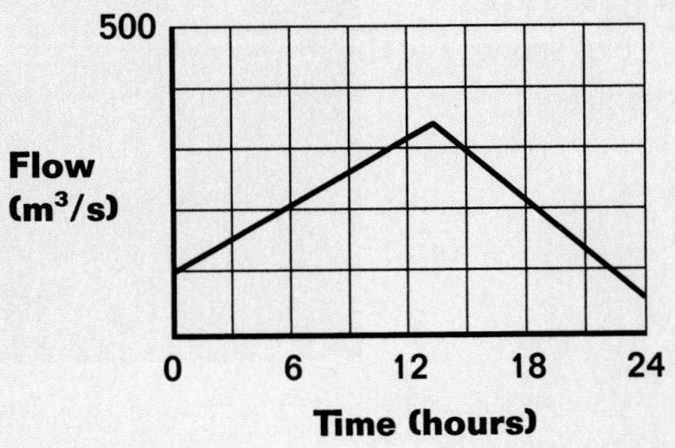

In either case, its function is still the same. Levees are mounds of earth that are built along the sides of a river. They prevent rivers from overflowing their banks. Unfortunately, dams and levees cannot stop the water when flooding is great. This was the case in 1993 when the Mississippi River flooded parts of nine midwestern states. **Figure 8-8** shows some of the damage that resulted from this flood.

Deposition by Surface Water

As water moves throughout a river system, what do you suppose happens as it loses some of its energy of motion? The water can no longer carry some of its sediments, and they are deposited.

Some stream sediments aren't carried far at all before they are deposited. In fact, many sediments are deposited within the stream channel itself. Other stream sediments travel great distances before they are deposited. Sediments picked up when rill and gully erosion occur are examples. Water usually has a lot of energy as it moves down a steep slope. When the water begins flowing on a level surface, it slows down, loses energy, and drops its sediments.

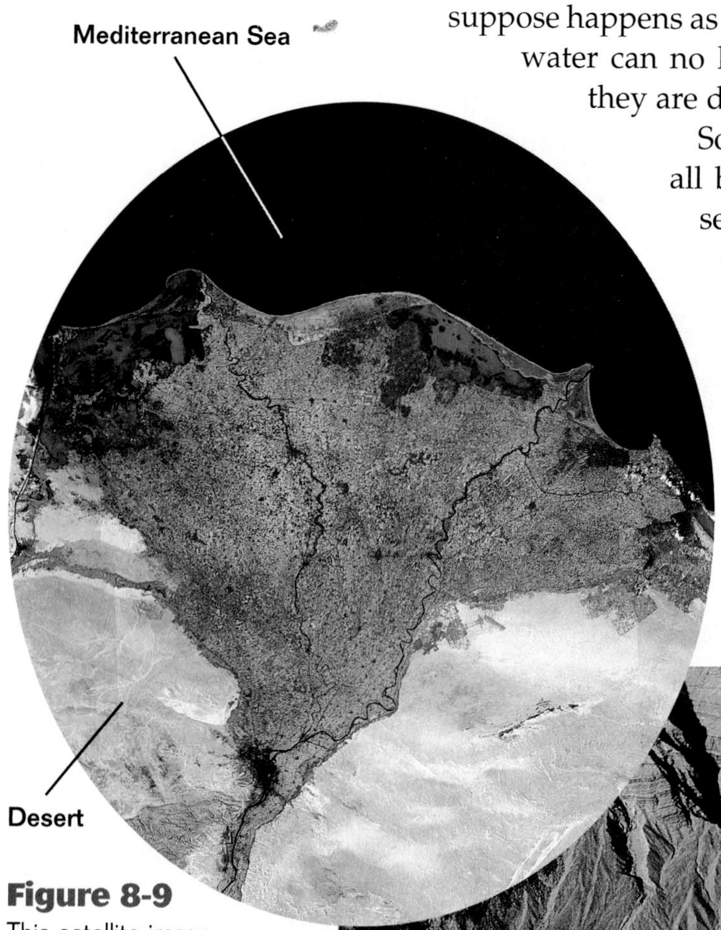

Figure 8-9
This satellite image of the Nile River Delta in Egypt shows the typical triangular shape. The green color shows areas of vegetation.

Figure 8-10 Alluvial fans commonly occur at the base of steep mountain slopes. They form on land. **How might the amount and type of vegetation affect the alluvial fan?**

Sediments that are deposited as the water empties into an ocean, gulf, or lake form a triangular or fan-shaped deposit called a **delta,** as shown in **Figure 8-9.** When the river waters empty from a mountain valley out onto a flat open plain, the deposit is called an **alluvial** (uh LEW vee ul) **fan,** as shown in **Figure 8-10.**

The Mississippi River provides a real-life example of the topics presented in this section. Runoff causes rill and gully erosion as it picks up sediments and carries them into the larger streams that flow into the Mississippi River. The Mississippi is large and has a lot of energy. It can erode a great deal of sediment. As it flows, it cuts into its banks and picks up more sediments. In other places, where the land is flat, the river deposits some of its sediments in its own channel.

Eventually, the Mississippi River reaches the Gulf of Mexico. There it flows into the gulf, loses most of its energy of motion, and dumps its sediments in a large deposit on the Louisiana coast. This deposit, shown in **Figure 8-11,** is the Mississippi Delta.

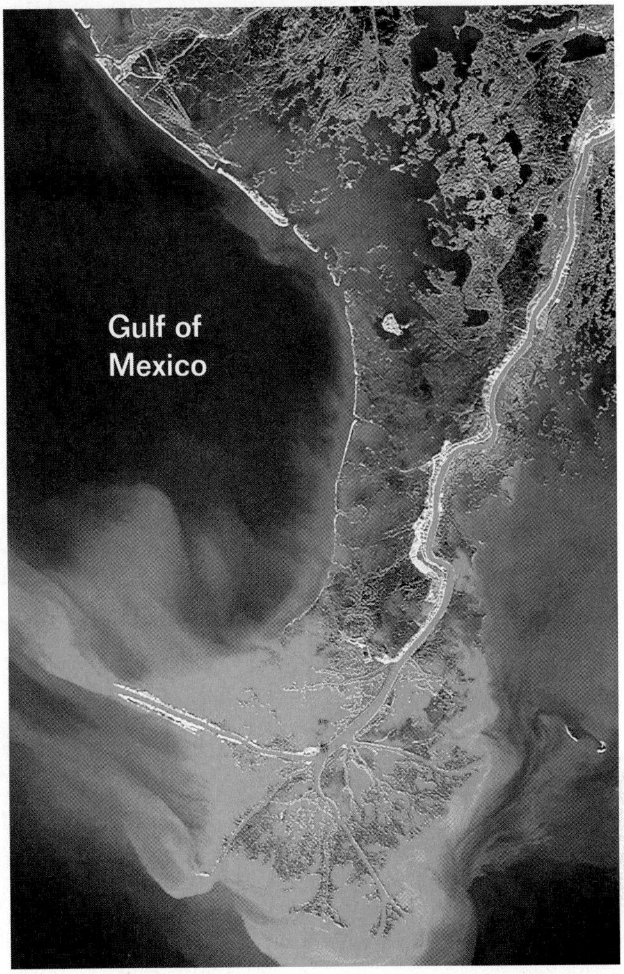

Figure 8-11 This satellite image of the Mississippi Delta shows how sediments accumulate where the Mississippi River empties into the Gulf of Mexico.

Section Assessment

1. How does the slope of an area affect its runoff?
2. Describe the three stages of stream development.
3. What is a delta?
4. **Think Critically:** How is a stream's rate of flow related to the amount of erosion it causes and the size of the sediments it deposits?
5. **Skill Builder**
   Interpreting Scientific Illustrations Do the **Chapter 8 Skill Activity** on page 701 to interpret a scientific illustration on drainage basins.

Using Computers

Spreadsheet Design a table using spreadsheet software to compare and contrast sheet, rill, gully, and stream erosion. For help with spreadsheets see page 690.

Design Your Own Experiment

Activity 8•1

Stream Speed

Possible Materials

- Paint pan
- Sand
- Cups (2)
  **beakers*
- Rubber tubing
- Meterstick
- Small cork
- Water
- Stopwatch
- Funnel
- Clothespin
  **hose clamp*

**Alternate Materials*

Have you ever wondered what it would be like to make a raft and use it to float on a river? Do you think that guiding a raft would be easy? Probably not. You'd be at the mercy of the current. The greater the speed of the river, the stronger the current.

Recognize the Problem

What factors affect a stream's speed? How does the speed of a stream affect the water's ability to erode?

Form a Hypothesis

Think about streams, then consider various factors that may affect how fast a stream flows. Based on your observations, the goals of this experiment, and the possible materials, make a hypothesis about how the speed of a stream affects erosion.

Goals

- **Design** an experiment to show the relationship between the speed of a stream and a stream's ability to erode.
- **Observe** the effects of slope of a stream on speed of the stream.
- **Observe** the effects of speed of a stream on erosion.

Safety Precautions

Wash your hands after you handle the sand.

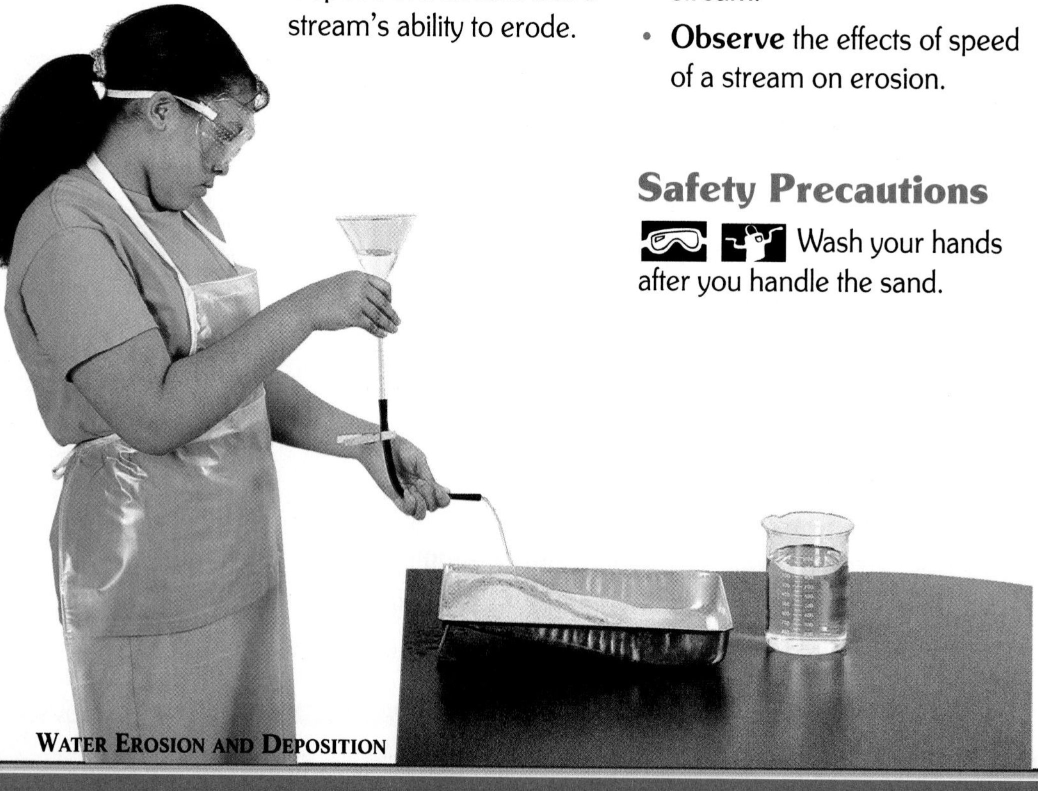

Test Your Hypothesis

Plan

1. Decide how your group will test its hypothesis.
2. List the steps that you need to take to test your hypothesis. Include in your plan how you will (a) make your stream channel, (b) adjust the height of the slope, (c) **measure** the length of the stream channel, (d) use tubing and one of the cups to begin the water flowing down the stream, (e) catch the overflow water at the other end of the pan with your other cup, (f) **determine** the time it takes the cork to flow down the stream channel, and (g) **observe** the amount of erosion that takes place. Make a complete materials list.
3. **Prepare** a data table in your Science Journal so that it is ready to use as your group collects data. Will the data be summarized in graphs? Decide which type of graph to use.
4. **Identify** any constants and the variables of the experiment. Have you allowed for a control in your experiment? Do you have to run any tests more than one time?

Do

1. Make sure your teacher approves your plan and your data table before you proceed.
2. Carry out the experiment as planned.
3. While doing the experiment, record your observations and complete the data table in your Science Journal.

Analyze Your Data

1. **Calculate** the speed of your streams by dividing the distance by the time (speed = distance/time).
2. Were sediments carried along with the water to the end of your stream channels?
3. Did the slope affect the speed of the streams in your experiment?

Draw Conclusions

1. Did the streams with the greatest or least slopes erode the most sediments? Explain.
2. How would your results change if a stronger flow of water was used? How does this compare to flooding?

8•2 Groundwater

What You'll Learn

- The importance of groundwater
- The effect that soil and rock permeability have on groundwater movement
- Ways that groundwater erodes and deposits sediments

Vocabulary

groundwater	water table
permeable	spring
impermeable	geyser
aquifer	cave

Why It's Important

- The groundwater system is one of our important sources of drinking water.

Groundwater System Development

What would have happened if the spilled milk in Section 8-1 had run off the table onto a carpeted floor? It would have quickly soaked into the carpet. Water that falls on Earth can also soak into the ground.

What happens to the water then? Water that soaks into the ground becomes a part of a system, just as water that stays above ground becomes a part of a river system. Soil is made up of many small rock fragments. Weathered rock lies beneath the soil. Between these fragments and pieces of weathered rock are spaces called pores, as shown in **Figure 8-12.** Water that soaks into the ground collects in these pores and becomes part of what is called **groundwater.**

Figure 8-12 Some soils and rocks have connected pores through which water can move.

Permeability

A groundwater system is similar to a river system. However, instead of having channels that connect different parts of the drainage basin, the groundwater system has connecting pores. Soil and rock are **permeable** (PUR mee uh bul) if the pore spaces are connected and water can pass through them. Sandstone is an example of a permeable rock.

Soil or rock that has many large, connected pores is highly permeable. Water can pass through it easily. Soil or rock is less permeable if the connected pore spaces are fewer in number or if the pores themselves are fewer or smaller. Some material, such as clay, has small pore spaces or no pores at all. This material is **impermeable,** which means that water cannot pass through it.

Using Math

In an experiment, you find that 100 mL of gravel can hold 31 mL of water. Calculate the percentage of pore space.

Groundwater Movement

How deep into Earth's crust do you suppose groundwater can go? Groundwater will keep going deeper into Earth until it reaches a layer of impermeable rock. When this happens, the water can't move down any deeper. As a result, water begins filling up the pores in the rocks above the impermeable layer. A layer of permeable rock that lets water move freely is an **aquifer** (AK wuh fur). The area where all of the pores in the rock are filled with water is the zone of saturation. The upper surface of this zone is the **water table,** as seen in **Figure 8-13.**

Figure 8-13 If you want to know where the water table is in a particular area, find a stream. A stream's surface level is the water table. Below that is the zone of saturation.

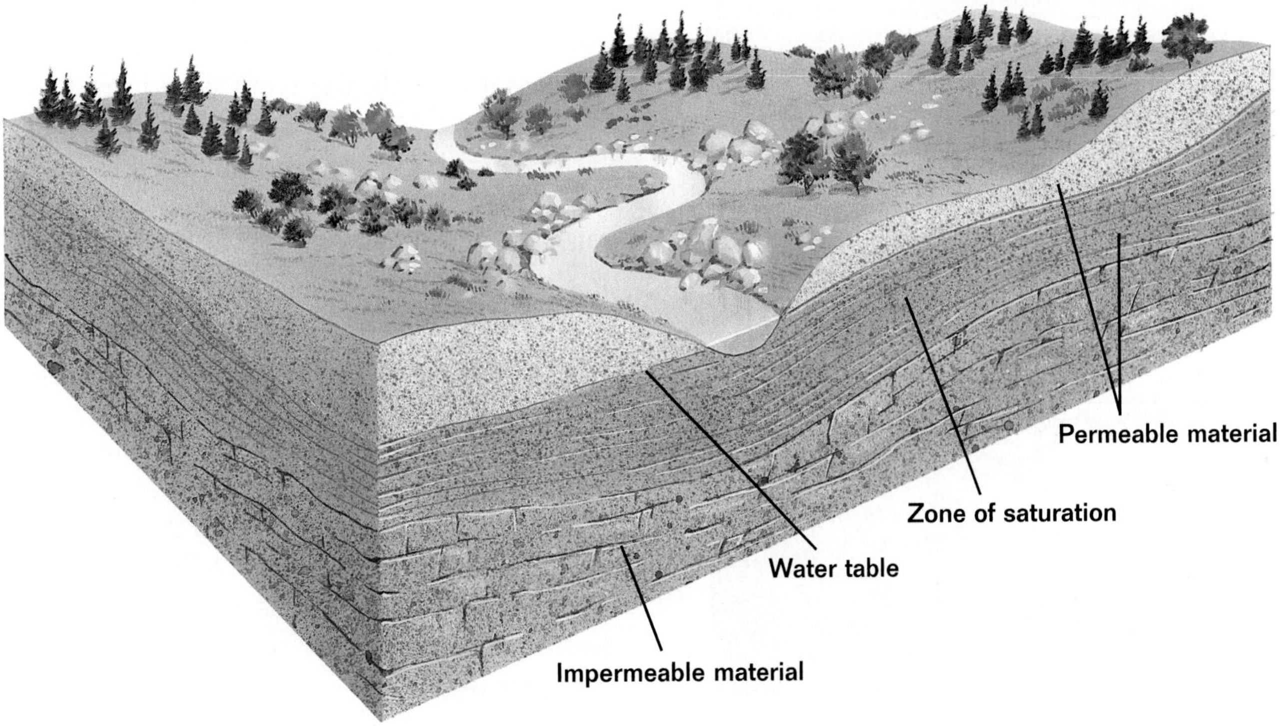

Try at Home

MiniLab

Measuring Pore Space

1. Use two identical clear, plastic containers.
2. Place 3 cm of sand in one container and 3 cm of gravel in the other container.
3. Fill a measuring cup with 200 mL of water.
4. Pour the water slowly into the container with the sand and stop when the water just covers the top of the sand.
5. Record the volume of the water used.
6. Repeat steps 3–5 with the gravel.

Analysis

1. Which substance has more pore space—sand or gravel? How do you know?
2. If you repeated your experiment, but first crushed your gravel into smaller pieces, would the pore space change? How?

Figure 8-14 The years on the pole show how much the ground level dropped in the San Joaquin Valley, California, between 1925 and 1977.

Water Table

What's so important about the zone of saturation and the water table? Think about how much water you use each day. An average person in the United States uses about 397 L every day. That's enough to fill 1138 soft-drink cans. If your water supply comes from a seemingly endless source, such as a large lake, you may never think about limiting your usage. But many people get drinking water from groundwater through wells that have been drilled into the zone of saturation.

Wells

A good well extends deep into the zone of saturation, past the top of the water table. Groundwater flows into the well, and a pump brings it to the surface. Because the water table sometimes drops during dry seasons, even a good well can go dry. Time is needed then for the water table to rise, either by rainfall or from an increase in the amount of groundwater.

In a city or town where groundwater is the main source of drinking water, the number of wells becomes important. Imagine that a large factory is built in such a town. Now the demand on the groundwater supply is even greater. Even in times of normal rainfall, the wells could go dry. This is because more water is taken out of the ground than can be replaced by rain.

If too much water is pumped out, the land level could sink from the weight of the sediments above the now-empty pore spaces. **Figure 8-14** shows what happens when too much groundwater was removed in California.

One type of well doesn't need a pump to bring water to the surface. An artesian well is a well in which water rises to the surface under pressure. Artesian wells are less common than other wells because of the special conditions they require, as shown in **Figure 8-15.**

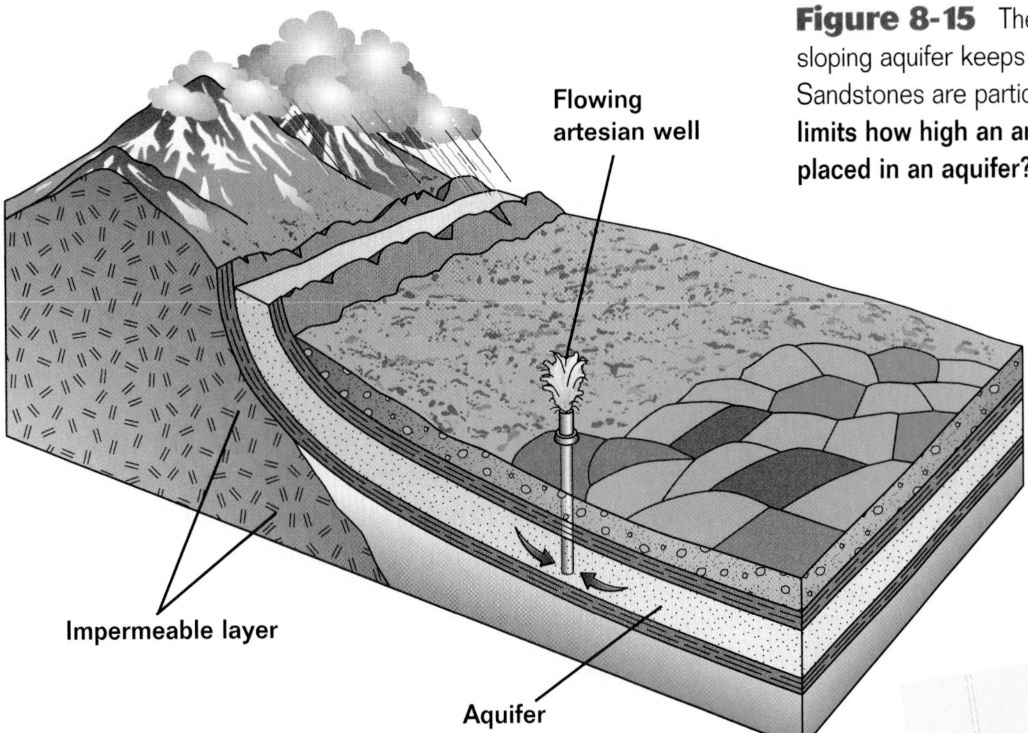

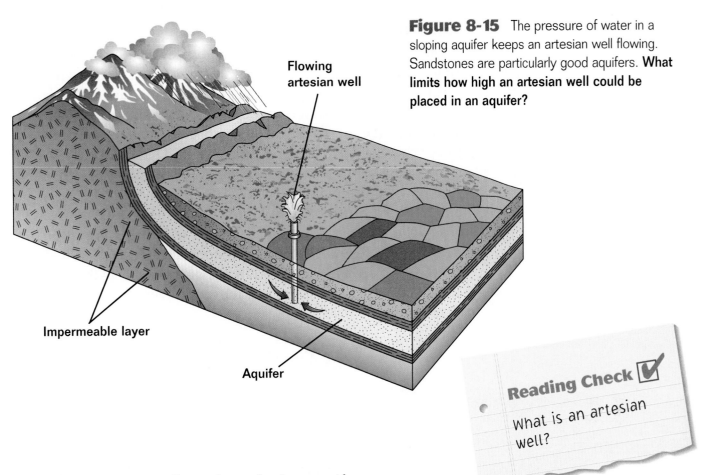

Figure 8-15 The pressure of water in a sloping aquifer keeps an artesian well flowing. Sandstones are particularly good aquifers. **What limits how high an artesian well could be placed in an aquifer?**

Reading Check

What is an artesian well?

An artesian well needs a sloping aquifer located between two impermeable layers. Water will enter at the high part of the sloping aquifer. Water in the higher part of the aquifer puts pressure on the water in the lower part. If a well is drilled into the lower part of the aquifer, the pressurized water will flow to the surface. Sometimes, the pressure is great enough to force the water into the air, forming a fountain.

Springs

In some places, the water table meets Earth's surface. When this happens, water flows out and forms a **spring.** Springs are found on hillsides or in any other place where the water table is exposed at the surface. Springs can often be used as a source of freshwater, as shown in **Figure 8-16.**

The water from most springs is cold. But, in some places, groundwater is heated and comes to the surface as a hot spring. The groundwater is heated by rocks that come in contact with molten material beneath Earth's surface.

Figure 8-16 This natural spring in the Grand Canyon is called Vasey's Paradise.

Geysers

One of the places where groundwater is heated is in Yellowstone National Park in Wyoming. Yellowstone has hot springs and geysers. A **geyser,** like the one in **Figure 8-17A,** is a hot spring that erupts periodically, shooting water and steam into the air. Groundwater is heated to high temperatures, causing it to expand underground. This expansion forces some of the water out of the ground, taking the pressure off of the remaining water. The remaining water boils quickly, with much of it turning to steam. The steam shoots out of the opening like steam out of a teakettle, forcing the remaining water out with it. Yellowstone's famous geyser, Old Faithful, pictured in **Figure 8-17B,** shoots between 14 000 and 32 000 L of water and steam into the air on average once every 80 minutes.

CHEMISTRY INTEGRATION

Acid Rain

Acid rain happens when gases released by burning oil and coal mix with water in the air to form acidic rain or snow. Infer what effect acid rain might have on a statue made of limestone.

Groundwater Erosion and Deposition

Just as water is the most powerful agent of erosion on Earth's surface, it can also have a great effect underground. When water mixes with carbon dioxide in the air, it forms a weak acid. One type of rock that is easily dissolved by this acid is limestone. As acidic groundwater moves through natural cracks in limestone, it dissolves the rock. Gradually, the cracks in the limestone are enlarged until an underground opening called a **cave** is formed.

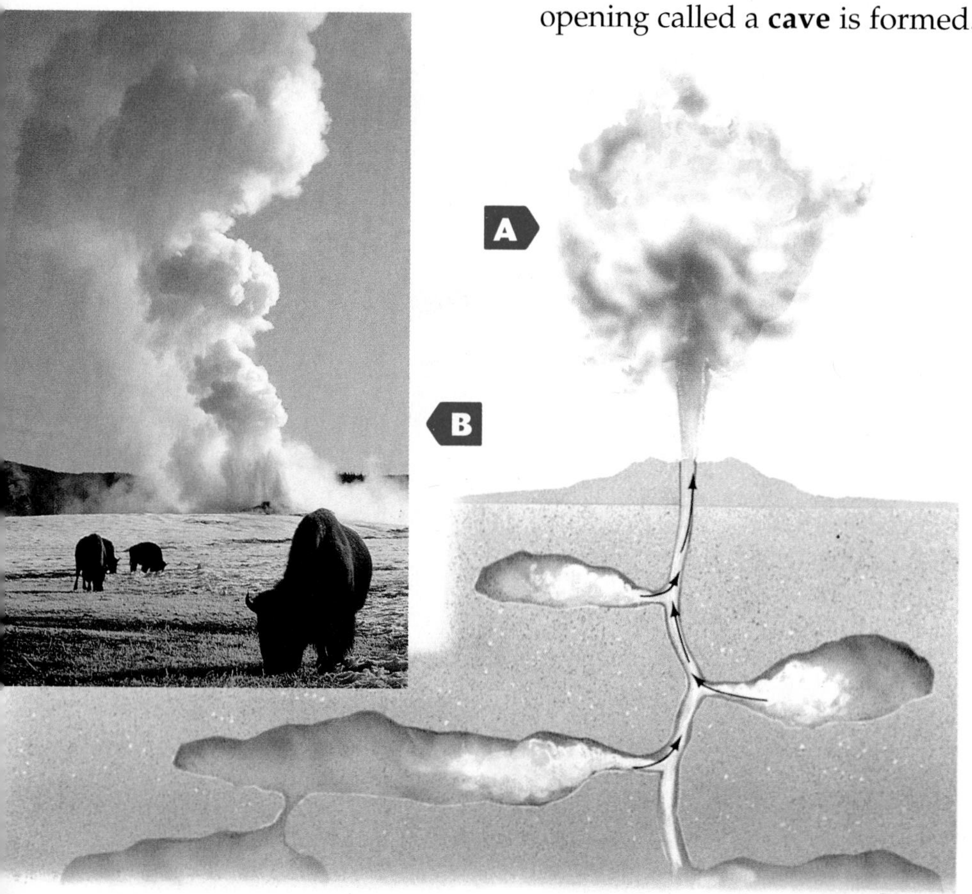

Figure 8-17 After a geyser erupts (A), water runs back into underground openings where it is heated and erupts again. Yellowstone's famous geyser, Old Faithful (B), used to erupt about once each 76 minutes. An earthquake on January 9, 1998, slowed Old Faithful's "clock" down four minutes to an average of one eruption about every 80 minutes. The average height of the geyser's water is 40.5 m.

Cave Formation

You've probably seen a picture of the inside of a cave, or perhaps you've visited one. Groundwater not only dissolves limestone to make caves, but it also can make deposits on the insides of caves, as shown in **Figure 8-18.**

Water often drips slowly from cracks in the cave walls and ceilings. This water contains calcium ions dissolved from the limestone. If this water evaporates while hanging from the ceiling of a cave, a deposit of calcite is left behind. Stalactites form when this happens over and over. Where drops of water fall to the floor of the cave, a stalagmite forms.

Figure 8-18 Water containing dissolved calcium ions forms interesting features in caves. Look at the features in the cave shown above. **How do you think these features formed?**

Sinkholes

If underground rock is dissolved near the surface, a sinkhole may form. A sinkhole is a depression that forms when the roof of a cave collapses.

In summary, when rain falls and becomes groundwater, it might dissolve a cave, erupt from a geyser, or be pumped from a well to be used at your house.

Section Assessment

1. How does water enter the groundwater system?
2. How does the permeability of soil and rocks affect the flow of groundwater?
3. Explain how caves form.
4. **Think Critically:** Would you expect water in wells, geysers, and hot springs to contain eroded materials? Why or why not?
5. **Skill Builder**
   Comparing and Contrasting Compare and contrast wells, geysers, and hot springs. If you need help, refer to Comparing and Contrasting in the **Skill Handbook** on page 672.

Science Journal

Read an article about geothermal energy and draw a diagram in your Science Journal explaining how it works. Also list the limitations of this energy source.

8•3 Ocean Shoreline

What You'll Learn

- ► The forces that cause shoreline erosion
- ► How different types of shorelines compare
- ► Some origins of sand

Vocabulary

longshore current
beach
barrier island

Why It's Important

- ► Shorelines look the way they do because forces shape them.

The Shore

Picture yourself sitting on a beautiful, white-sand beach. Palm trees sway in the breeze above your head, and small children play in the quiet waves lapping at the water's edge. It's hard to imagine a place more peaceful than this shore. Now, picture yourself sitting along another shore. You're on a high cliff, overlooking waves crashing onto huge boulders below. Both of these places are shorelines. A shoreline is where land meets the ocean.

The two shorelines just described are very different. Why are they so different? Both experience surface waves, tides, and currents. These cause both shorelines to change constantly. Sometimes, you can see these changes from hour to hour. We'll look at why these shorelines are different, but first, let's learn about the forces that carve shores.

Shoreline Forces

Along all shorelines, like the one in **Figure 8-19A,** surface waves continue to move sediments back and forth. Waves shape shorelines by eroding and redepositing sediments. The

Figure 8-19

A Waves, tides, and currents cause shorelines to change constantly.

B Waves approaching the shoreline at an angle create a longshore current. When the water built up by waves returns to sea, a rip current forms. **Why is it wise to avoid rip currents when swimming at a beach?**

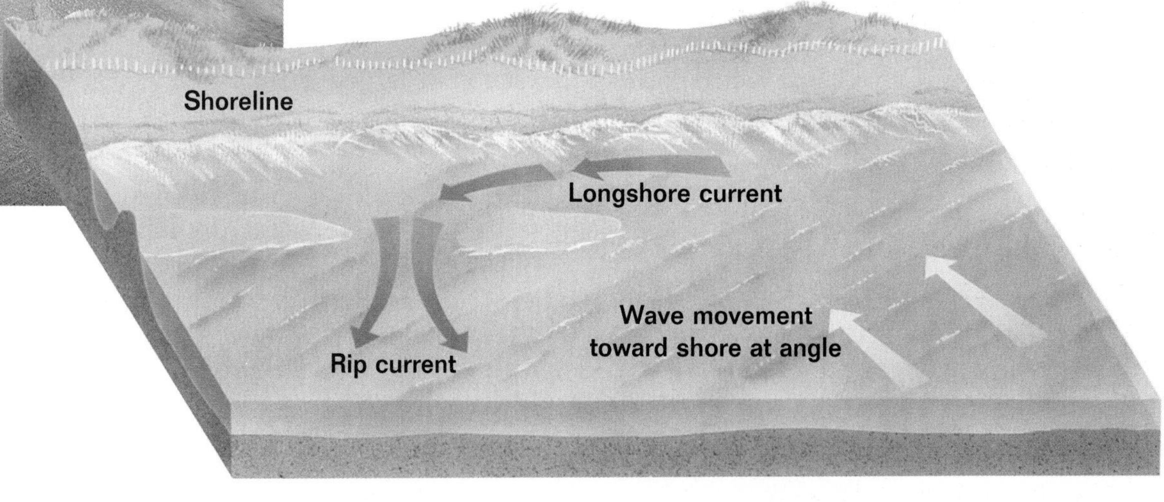

Figure 8-20 Along a rocky shoreline, the force of pounding waves breaks rock fragments loose and grinds them into smaller and smaller sediments.

tides also shape shorelines. Every day, tides raise and lower the place on the shoreline where surface waves erode and deposit sediments.

Waves usually collide with a shore at slight angles. This creates a **longshore current** of water that runs along the shore, as shown in **Figure 8-19B.** Longshore currents carry many metric tons of loose sediments and act like rivers of sand in the ocean. What do you suppose happens if a longshore current isn't carrying all of the sand it has the energy to carry? It will use this extra energy to erode more shoreline sediments. ☑

Reading Check ☑

What is a longshore current?

You've seen the forces that affect all shorelines. Now, we'll look at the differences that make one shore a flat, sandy beach and another shore a steep, rocky cliff.

Rocky Shorelines

Along rocky shorelines like the one in **Figure 8-20,** rocks and cliffs are the most common features. Waves wear away the rocks to form hollows. Over time, these enlarge and become caves. When too much erosion occurs, the overhanging rock may fall off into the ocean. Rock fragments broken from the cliffs are ground up by the endless motion of waves. They are transported as sediment by the longshore current. These fragments act like the sand on sandpaper.

Softer rocks are eroded away before harder rocks, leaving islands of harder rocks. This takes many years, but remember that the ocean never stops. In a single day, about 14 000 waves will crash onto any shore.

The rock fragments produced by eroding waves are sediments. When rocky shorelines are being eroded, where do you think the sediments go? Waves carry them away and deposit them where water is quieter. If you want to relax on a nice wide, sandy beach, you shouldn't go to a rocky shoreline.

Figure 8-21 Sand varies in size, color, and composition. This sand contains shell fragments and tiny grains of quartz.

Sandy Beaches

Smooth, gently sloping shorelines are different from steep, rocky shorelines. Beaches are the main feature here. **Beaches** are deposits of sediment that run parallel to the shore. They stretch inland as far as the tides and waves are able to deposit sediment.

Beaches are made of different materials like the sand shown in **Figure 8-21.** Some are made of rock fragments from the shoreline, and others are made of seashell fragments. These fragments range from pebbles large enough to fill your hand to fine sand. Sand grains are 0.07 mm to 2 mm in diameter. Why do many beaches have this size particles? This is because waves break rocks and seashells down to sand-sized particles. The constant wave motion bumps sand grains together and, in the process, rounds their corners.

What kinds of materials do you think make up most beach sands? Most are made of resistant minerals such as quartz. However, sand in some places is made of other things. For example, Hawaii's black sands are made of basalt, and green sands are made of the mineral olivine. Jamaica's white sands are made of coral and shell fragments.

Figure 8-22 Longshore currents move sediment along shorelines, changing beaches and creating baymouth bars and spits, like those in this aerial photograph of Martha's Vineyard, Massachusetts.

Sand Erosion and Deposition

Sand is carried down beaches by longshore currents to form features such as those seen in **Figure 8-22.** Sand is also moved by storms and the wind. Thus, beaches are fragile, short-term land features that are easily damaged by storms and human activities such as construction.

Barrier Islands

Barrier islands are sand deposits that parallel the shore but are separated from the mainland, as shown in **Figure 8-23.** These islands start as underwater sand ridges formed by breaking waves. Hurricanes and storms add sediment to them, raising some to sea level. Once a barrier island is exposed, the wind blows the loose sand into dunes, keeping the island above sea level. As with all seashore features, barrier islands are short-term, lasting from a few years to a few centuries.

Figure 8-23 Many barrier islands have formed along North America's Atlantic Coast and the Gulf of Mexico. The size and shape of these islands constantly change due to wave action.

Section Assessment

1. What causes shoreline erosion?
2. Contrast the features you'd find along a steep, rocky shoreline with the features you'd find along a gently sloping shoreline.
3. **Think Critically:** Why is there no sand on many of the world's shorelines?
4. **Skill Builder**
   Concept Mapping Make a cycle concept map that discusses how the sand from a barrier island that is currently in place can become a new barrier island 100 years from now. Use these terms: *barrier island, breaking waves, wind, longshore currents,* and *new barrier island.* If you need help, refer to Concept Mapping in the **Skill Handbook** on page 666.

Using Math

If in a single day, about 14 000 waves crash onto a shore, how many waves crash onto a shore in one year? Calculate how many have crashed onto a shore since you were born. Explain how you found your answer.

Materials

- Samples of different sands (3)
- Hand lens
- Magnet
  *stereomicroscope

*Alternate Materials

What's so special about sand?

You know that sand is made of many different kinds of grains, but did you realize that the slope of a beach is actually related to the size of its grains? The coarser the grain size, the steeper the beach. Did you know that many sands are mined because they have economic value?

What You'll Investigate

What characteristics can be used to classify beach sands?

Goals

- **Observe** differences in sand.
- **Classify** characteristics of beach sand.

Procedure

1. **Design** a data table in which to record your data when you **compare** the three sand samples. You will need five columns in your table. One column will be for the samples and the others for the characteristics you will be examining. If you need help in designing your table, refer to the **Skill Handbook.**
2. Use the diagram below to determine the average roundness of each sample.

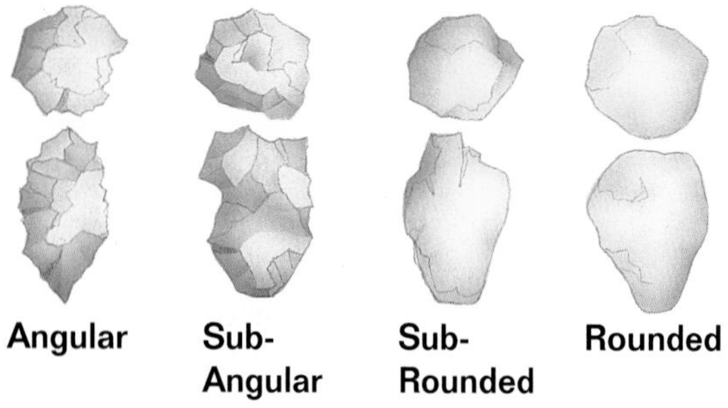

3. **Identify** the grain size of your samples by using the sand gauge on this page. To determine the grain size, place sand grains in the middle of the circle of the sand gauge. Use the upper half of the circle for dark-colored particles and the bottom half of the circle for light-colored particles.
4. Decide on two other characteristics to examine that will help you **classify** your samples.

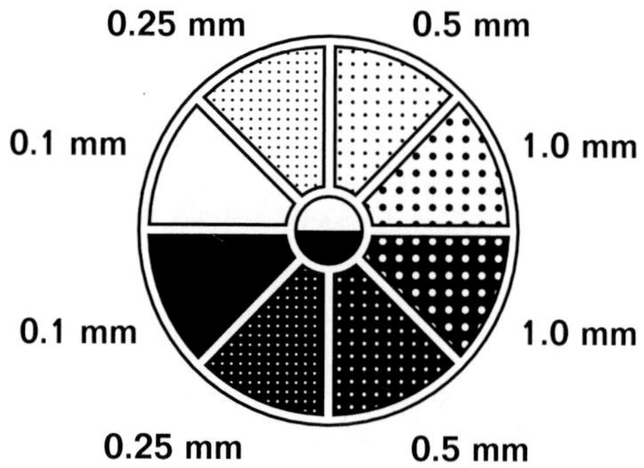

Sand Gauge

Conclude and Apply

1. **Compare and contrast** some characteristics of beach sand.
2. Why are there differences in the characteristics of different sand samples?

Water Wars

Mono Lake

The algae, brine shrimp, alkali flies, and birds of Mono Lake (left) don't know it, but they are living in an 800 000-year-old habitat. Mono Lake, located at the base of the Sierra Nevada mountain range in California, is fed by mountain streams and groundwater. Its drainage basin averages eight inches of rainfall each year. Under natural conditions, the only way that water leaves the lake is through evaporation.

Freshwater springs containing the chemical calcium rise up through the carbon dioxide–rich lake water. This forms calcium carbonate. This solid then forms around the mouth of the springs. Algae grow around these springs and give off additional calcium deposits, which become stiff and thick. These structures, called tufa (inset), can be more than three meters tall and can be 900 years old.

Human Impact

Human activities have been harmful to the lake. Since 1941, water has been pumped from some of the streams that flow into Mono Lake. Without freshwater to refill the lake, in 50 years its level dropped 14 m, its volume decreased by half, and the amount of salt in the lake (salinity) has doubled. Dusts that contained salt, blowing from the area once covered by the lake, caused air pollution. The duck population dropped from millions to just a few thousand by 1995. Some scientists who study the brine shrimp believe that the increase in salinity has caused the reproductive rate of the shrimp to decrease. As the lake level dropped, ghostly tufa structures were exposed and subjected to weathering and erosion.

The Public Takes a Stand

As a result of pressure from people worried about the future of Mono Lake, authorities decided to limit the amount of water pumped from the mountain streams that feed it. This allowed the lake to rise. The required lake level is now about halfway between the 1941 and the 1995 lake levels.

interNET CONNECTION

Visit the Glencoe Science Web Site at **www.glencoe.com/sec/science/ca** for more information about solutions to the water shortage problems in the southwestern United States.

Chapter 8 Reviewing Main Ideas

For a **preview** of this chapter, study this Reviewing Main Ideas before you read the chapter. After you have studied this chapter, you can use the Reviewing Main Ideas to **review** the chapter.

GLENCOE TECHNOLOGY

The Glencoe MindJogger, Audiocassettes, and CD-ROM provide additional opportunities for review.

Section

8-1 SURFACE WATER

When rain falls on a slope, gravity pulls it down the slope. This water is called **runoff.** As the runoff flows along, it carries sediment with it. If enough rain falls and the slope is steep enough, large amounts of sediment can be transported with the runoff. The steeper the slope, the faster the water flows, and the more sediment the runoff can carry. **Rill, gully,** and **sheet erosion** are all types of surface water erosion caused by runoff. Gentle slopes or vegetation enable water to soak into the ground or be taken up by the plants. ***How does water change the landforms that make up Earth's surface? How has it affected the land near you?***

RIVER SYSTEMS

Runoff generally flows into streams that merge with larger and larger rivers until it reaches a lake or ocean. Major river systems usually contain different types of streams. In the mountains, a young stream flows through a steep valley and has rapids and waterfalls. These streams flow down steep hills, and therefore flow quickly and have lots of energy. Mature streams flow through gentler terrain and have less energy. Curves start to develop as the river **meanders** across a broad, flat valley floor. Old streams, which flow slowly, are often wide and snake back and forth across their floodplains. ***Describe how a mountain stream changes over time. How does the speed at which the water flows affect how much sediment it can carry?***

Reading Check

To help you understand the main ideas of this chapter, make a list of the vocabulary words and review their meanings.

Section

8-2 GROUNDWATER

When water soaks into the ground, it becomes part of a vast water system called **groundwater.** Although rock may seem solid, many types are filled with a network of connected spaces called pores. When water fills these spaces, a layer of saturated rock forms, the top of which is called the **water table.** This layer is often the source of water for many homes. As water slowly flows underground, it can carry dissolved minerals away, leaving behind large underground **caves.** ***Why is a spring considered part of the groundwater system? How can groundwater erosion result in the formation of a sinkhole?***

Section

8-3 OCEAN SHORELINE

Ocean shorelines are active systems. Sand is deposited by rivers and moved along the coast by waves and currents. Waves and currents give tremendous amounts of energy to water. Pounding waves break up rocks into tiny fragments called sediment. Over time, the waves and currents move this sediment and redeposit it, constantly changing **beaches,** sandbars, and spits. ***How could a severe storm such as a hurricane change the shape of a beach?***

Chapter 8 Assessment

Using Vocabulary

a. alluvial fan
b. aquifer
c. barrier island
d. beach
e. cave
f. delta
g. drainage basin
h. floodplain
i. geyser
j. groundwater
k. gully erosion
l. impermeable
m. longshore current
n. meander
o. permeable
p. rill erosion
q. runoff
r. sheet erosion
s. spring
t. water table

Each phrase below describes a science term from the list. Write the term that matches the phrase describing it.

1. water that flows over Earth's surface
2. water that flows parallel to the shore
3. a curve in a stream channel
4. a triangular deposit that forms when a river enters a gulf or lake
5. water that soaks into the ground

Checking Concepts

Choose the word or phrase that best answers the question.

6. What is an example of a structure created by deposition?
   A) beach
   B) rill
   C) cave
   D) geyser
7. What is a deposit that forms when a mountain river runs out onto a plain called?
   A) subsidence
   B) an alluvial fan
   C) infiltration
   D) water diversion
8. What is a layer of rock that water flows through?
   A) an aquifer
   B) a pore
   C) a water table
   D) impermeable
9. What is the network formed by a river and all the smaller streams that contribute to it?
   A) groundwater system
   B) zone of saturation
   C) river system
   D) water table
10. Which term describes soils through which fluids can easily flow?
    A) impermeable
    B) meanders
    C) saturated
    D) permeable
11. Which stage of development are mountain streams in?
    A) young
    B) mature
    C) old
    D) meandering
12. What forms when the water table is exposed at the surface?
    A) meander
    B) spring
    C) aquifer
    D) stalactite
13. What contains heated groundwater that reaches Earth's surface?
    A) water table
    B) cave
    C) aquifer
    D) hot spring
14. Where are beaches most common?
    A) rocky shorelines
    B) flat shorelines
    C) aquifers
    D) young streams
15. Why does water rise in an artesian well?
    A) a pump
    B) erosion
    C) heat
    D) pressure

Thinking Critically

16. Explain why the Mississippi River has meanders.
17. What determines whether a stream, erodes its bottom or its sides?
18. Why would you be concerned if developers of a new housing project started drilling wells near your well?
19. A stack is an island of rock along certain shorelines. Along what kind of shoreline would you find stacks? Explain.

20. Explain why beach sands collected from different locations will differ in composition, color, and texture.

Developing Skills

If you need help, refer to the Skill Handbook.

21. **Concept Mapping:** Complete the concept map below using the following terms: *developed meanders, gentle curves, gentle gradient, old, rapids, steep gradient, wide floodplain, young.*

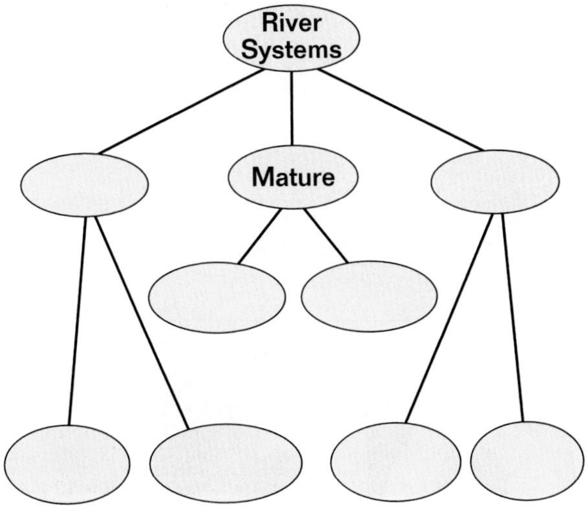

22. **Interpreting Data:** If the Brahmaputra River in India flows at a rate of 19 800 m^3/s and the La Plata River in South America flows at 79 300 m^3/s, infer which river erodes more sediments.

23. **Hypothesizing:** Hypothesize why most of the silt in the Mississippi Delta is found farther out to sea than the sand-sized particles.

24. **Outlining:** Make an outline that explains the three stages of stream development.

25. **Using Variables, Constants, and Controls:** Explain how you could test the effect of slope on the amount of runoff produced.

THE PRINCETON REVIEW

Test-Taking Tip

Use the Buddy System Study in a group. A small group of people works well because together the group can share each others' knowledge and skills. Keep it small and keep on target.

Test Practice

Use these questions to test your Science Proficiency.

1. If you wanted to have an exciting white-water raft ride, where would you go?
   A) to a meandering river
   B) to a delta
   C) to a place where there is sheet erosion
   D) to a young stream

2. It is believed that our planet is getting warmer. Which statement best supports this theory?
   A) Most sand is made of quartz.
   B) Ice caps are melting and shoreline erosion is increasing.
   C) Deltas are forming at the mouths of rivers.
   D) Old streams are developing meanders.

3. Read the table below and determine which river will likely cause more erosion.

River	Length of River (km)	Average Width of River (m)	Flow Rate (km/hr)
Bowman	400	75	4
Canadys	400	75	3.5
St. George	400	75	4.65
Snyder	400	75	5

   A) Bowman
   B) Canadys
   C) St. George
   D) Snyder

UNIT 3

Earth's Interior

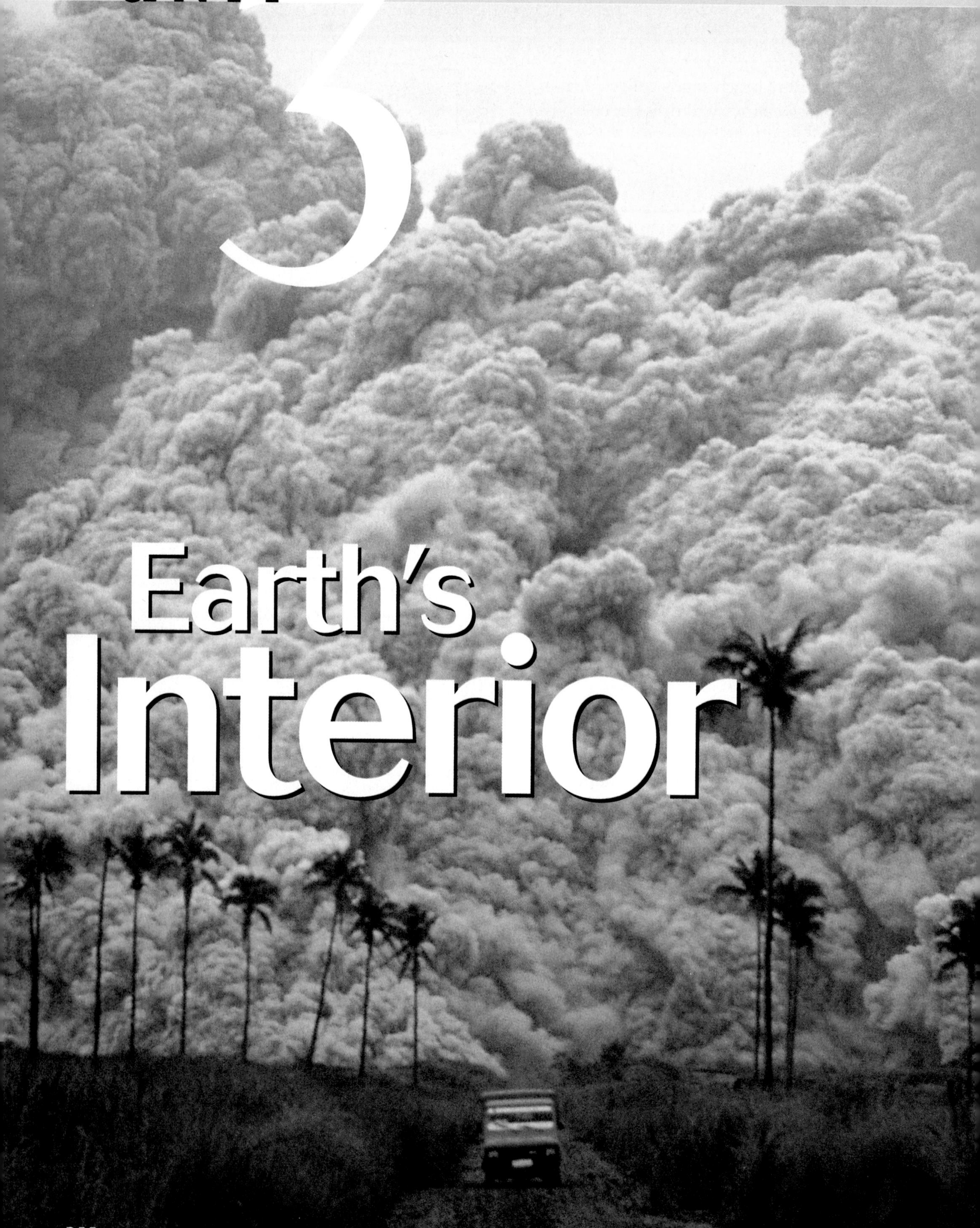

NATIONAL GEOGRAPHIC

What's Happening Here?

The earth beneath your feet is not as solid as it feels. Earth's surface is, in fact, broken into massive, shifting plates. Along the edges of these plates, molten rock finds its way to the surface, creating volcanoes that can erupt with tremendous force. The people in this truck (left) narrowly escaped the explosion of Mount Pinatubo on the Philippine island of Luzon in 1991. Some 800 inhabitants of Luzon did not escape. When Mount Pinatubo awoke from its 600-year slumber, it spewed out more gas and debris than any other volcanic eruption of this century. Earth's internal processes also cause earthquakes. The twisted wreckage of a train in Kobe, Japan (below), illustrates the terrible destructive power unleashed by the quake of 1995. In this unit, you will learn how understanding the forces that originate deep within Earth helps us to predict the destruction they can cause.

interNET CONNECTION

Explore the Glencoe Science Web Site at **www.glencoe.com/sec/science/ca** to find out more about topics found in this unit.

CHAPTER

9

Plate Tectonics

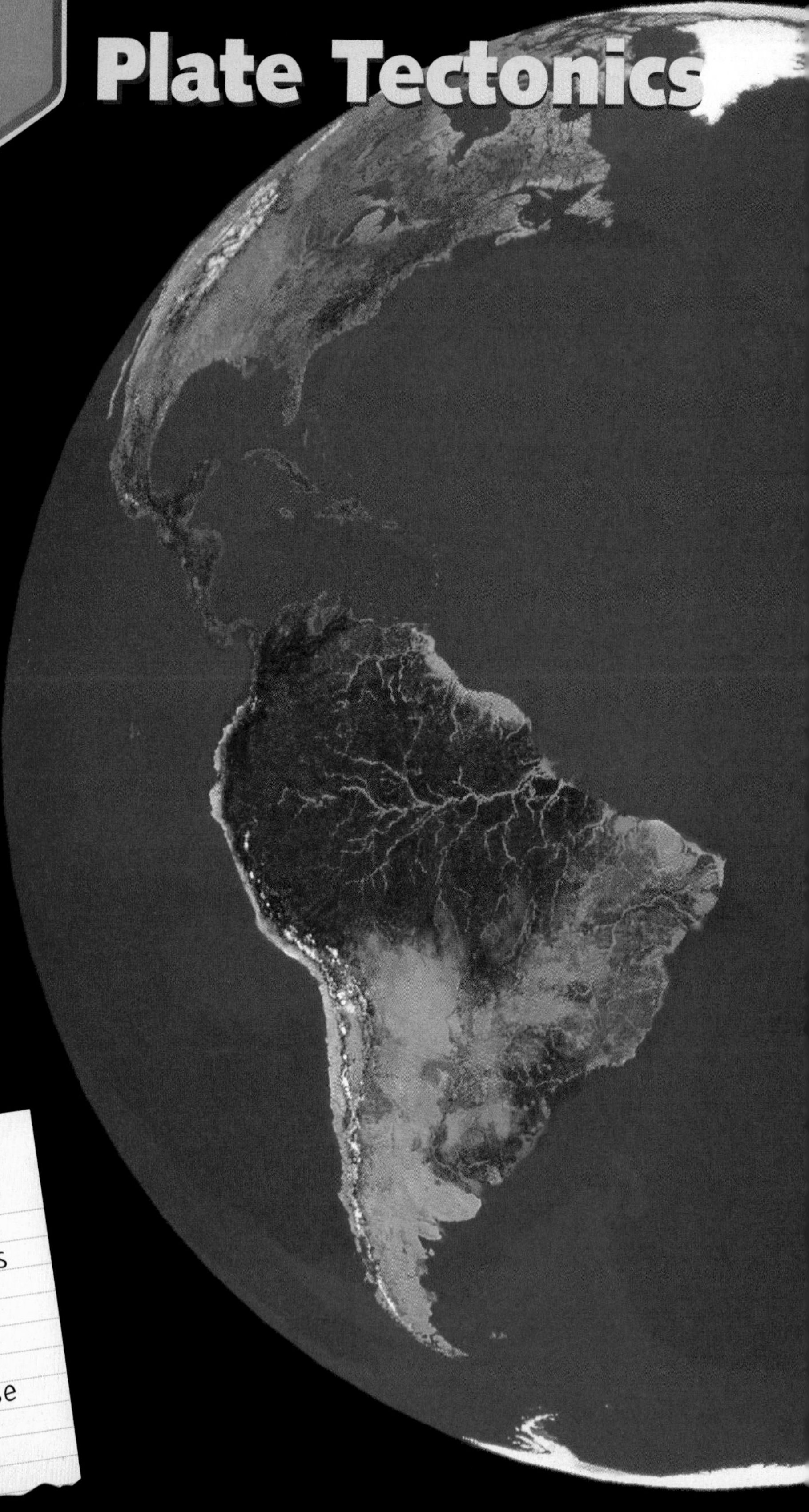

Chapter Preview

Skills Preview

Skill Builders

- Compare and Contrast
- Interpret a Scientific Diagram

Activities

- Interpret Data
- Make a Prediction

MiniLabs

- Interpret Data
- Make a Model

Reading Check

As you read, list the prefixes you encounter such as *con-* or *sub-* and look up their meanings. Identify other words that begin with these prefixes.

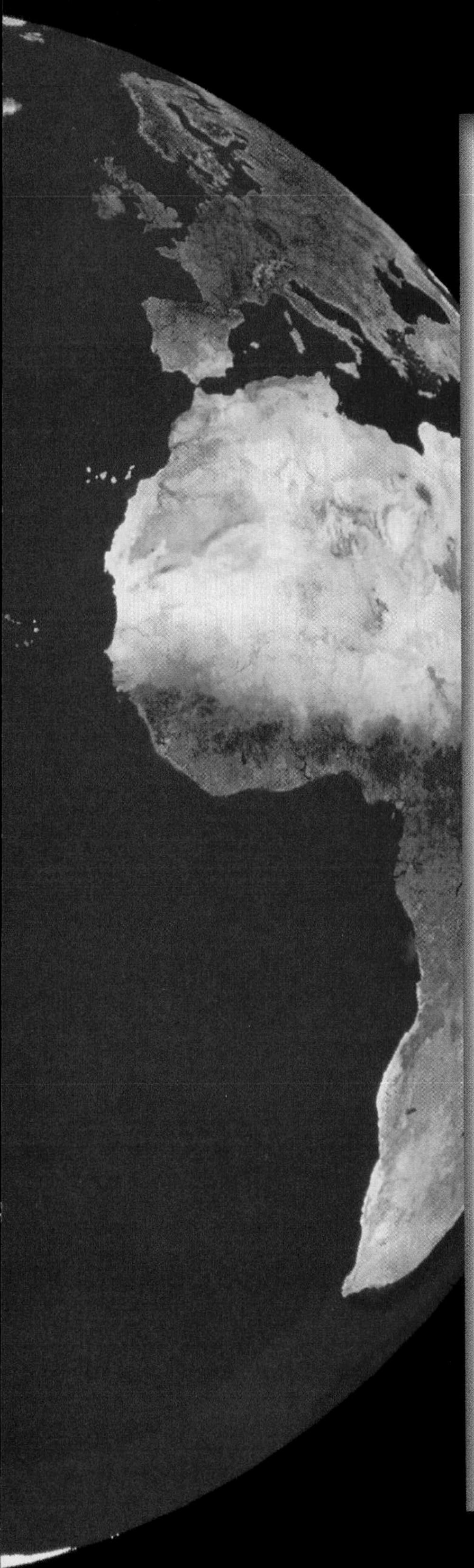

Explore Activity

This photograph of Earth is unique because the clouds have been removed using a computer. You can see the shapes of the continents just like on a map. Look closely at the general shapes of the continents. Do you see any relationship between continents? If this photograph of Earth were cut into pieces, could you fit the pieces back together? What clues might you use?

Re-Form an Image

1. Working with a partner, obtain photographs that are of interest to you from an old magazine. Do not look at each other's photographs.
2. You and your partner are each to cut one picture into small pieces.
3. Exchange picture pieces with your partner.
4. Using clues on surrounding pieces, re-form the image of the photograph your partner has cut into small pieces.

Science Journal

In your Science Journal, describe the characteristics of the cut-up photograph you used to re-form the image. Can you think of other examples in which characteristics of objects are used to match them up with other objects?

9·1 Continental Drift

What You'll Learn

- The hypothesis of continental drift
- Four pieces of evidence supporting continental drift

Vocabulary
continental drift
Pangaea

Why It's Important

- The hypothesis of continental drift led to plate tectonics, a theory that explains many dynamic processes in Earth.

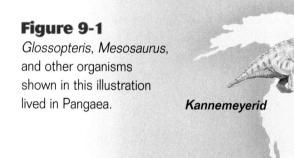

Evidence for Continental Drift

When you look at a map of Earth's surface, one thing is obvious. In **Figures 9-1** and **9-2,** you can see that the edges of some continents look as if they would fit together like a puzzle. In the early 1800s, as accurate maps of Earth's surface were first being developed, other people also noticed this fact.

Pangaea

Alfred Wegener (VEG nur) thought that the fit of the continents wasn't just a coincidence. He suggested that all the continents were joined together at some point in the past. In a 1912 lecture, he proposed the idea of continental drift. According to the hypothesis of **continental drift,** continents have moved slowly to their current locations. Wegener suggested that all continents were once connected as one large landmass that broke apart about 200 million years ago. He called this large landmass **Pangaea** (pan JEE uh), which means "all land."

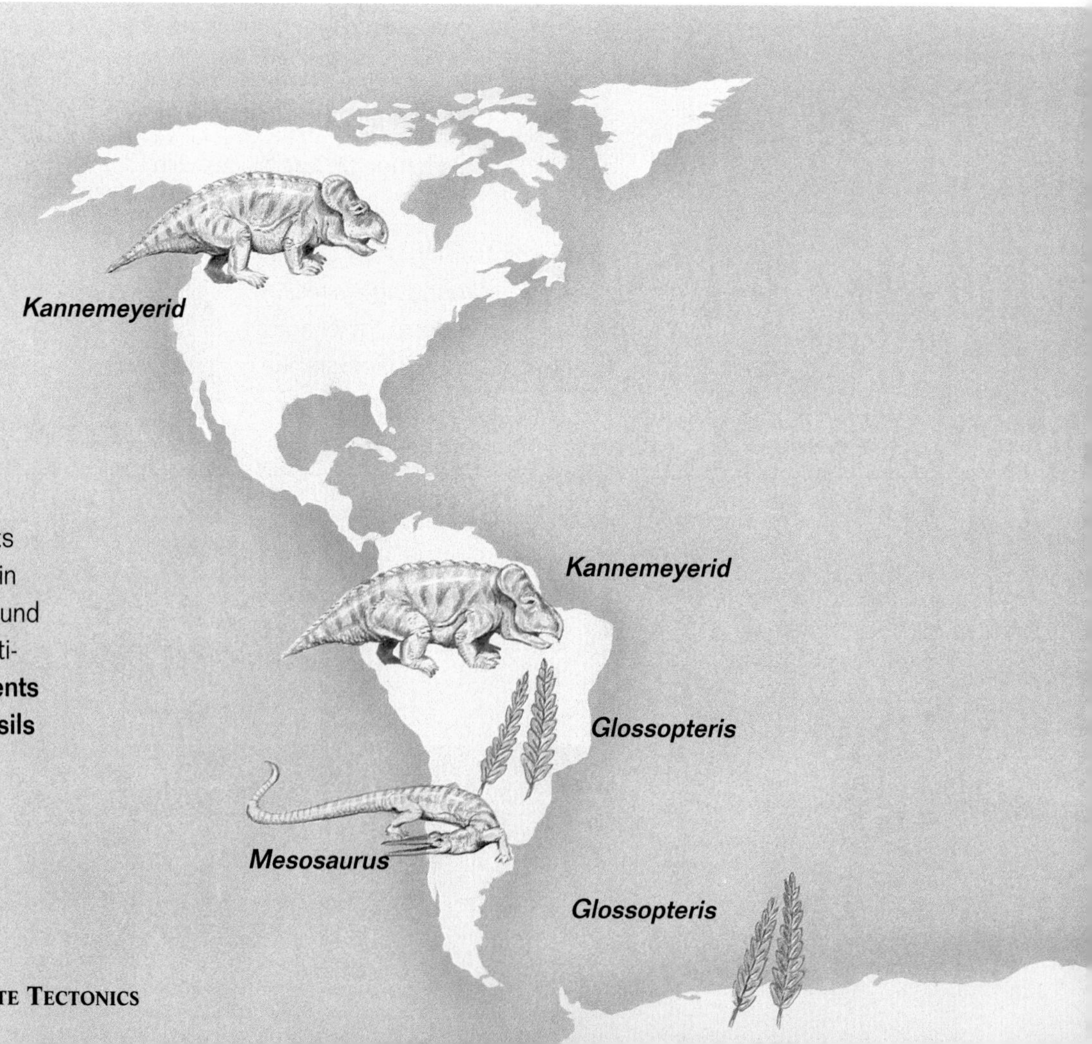

Figure 9-1
Glossopteris, *Mesosaurus*, and other organisms shown in this illustration lived in Pangaea.

A Fossil remains of plants and animals that lived in Pangaea have been found on more than one continent. **In which continents have *Mesosaurus* fossils been discovered?**

Long after Wegener's death in 1930, his basic hypothesis, that the continents have moved, was accepted. The evidence Wegener had to support his idea hadn't been enough to convince many people during his lifetime. However, Wegener's early evidence has since been joined by other important observations. Let's explore both Wegener's clues and some newer ones.

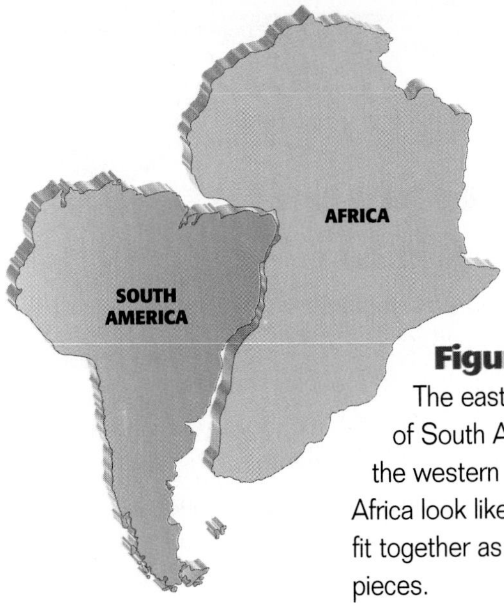

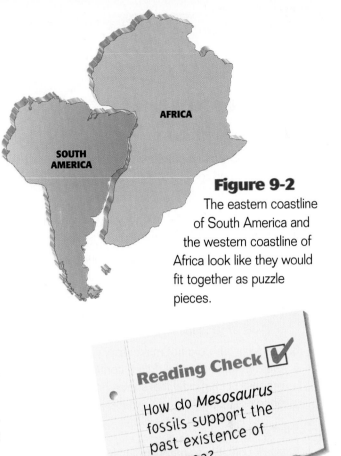

Figure 9-2
The eastern coastline of South America and the western coastline of Africa look like they would fit together as puzzle pieces.

Fossil Clues

Besides the puzzlelike fit of the continents, other clues were found from fossils. Fossils of the reptile *Mesosaurus* have been found in South America and Africa, as shown in **Figure 9-1.** This swimming reptile lived in freshwater and on land. How could fossils of *Mesosaurus* be found so far apart? It's unlikely that it could have swum between the continents. Wegener thought this reptile lived on both continents when they were joined as one giant landmass.

Reading Check
How do *Mesosaurus* fossils support the past existence of Pangaea?

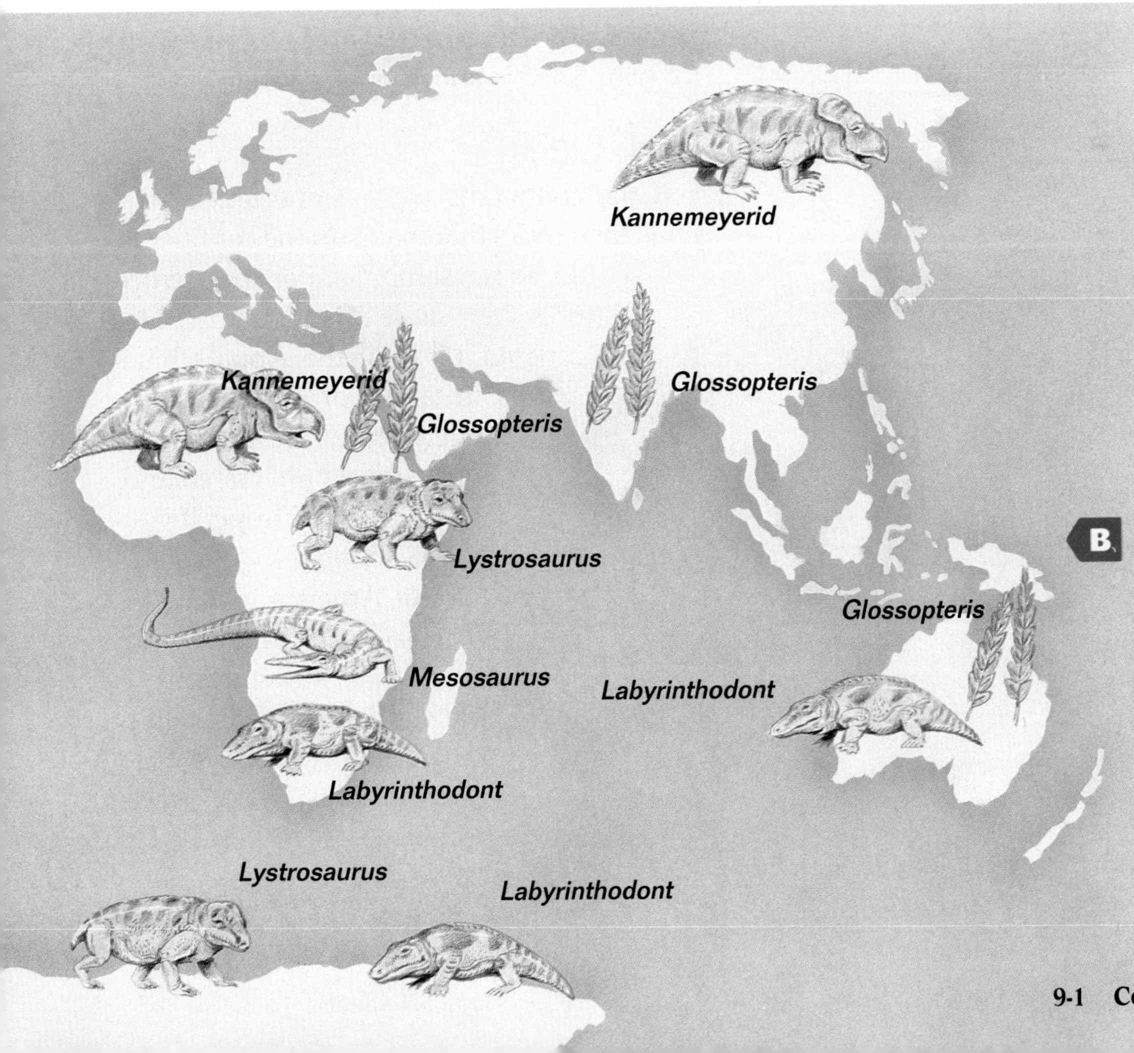

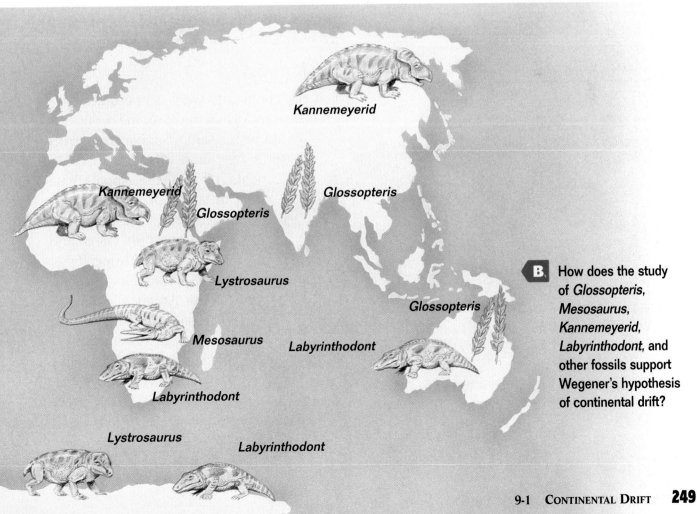

B How does the study of *Glossopteris, Mesosaurus, Kannemeyerid, Labyrinthodont*, and other fossils support Wegener's hypothesis of continental drift?

Try at Home MiniLab

Interpreting Fossil Data

Procedure

1. Build a three-layer landmass using clay or modeling dough.
2. Mold the clay into mountain ranges.
3. Place similar "fossils" into the clay at various locations around the landmass.
4. Form five continents from the one landmass. Also, form two smaller landmasses out of different clay with different mountain ranges and fossils.
5. Place the five continents and two smaller landmasses around the room.
6. Students who did not make or place the landmasses will locate the drifted continents and reconstruct a model that shows how they were once positioned.

Analysis

1. Were you able to reconstruct all or part of the original clay landmass?
2. What clues, if any, were useful in reconstructing the original landmass?
3. How did you deal with continents that initially didn't seem to fit?

Figure 9-3 This fossil fern, *Glossopteris*, grew in a warm tropical climate.

Another fossil that helps support the hypothesis of continental drift is *Glossopteris.* **Figure 9-3** shows this fossil fern, which has been found in Africa, Australia, India, South America, and most recently in Antarctica. The presence of this fern in so many areas led Wegener to suggest that all of these regions were once connected and had a similar climate.

Climate Clues

Fossils of warm-weather plants were found on the island of Spitzbergen in the Arctic Ocean. Wegener hypothesized that Spitzbergen drifted from the tropic regions. He also used glacial clues to support his theory.

Glacial deposits and grooved bedrock found in South America, Africa, India, and Australia show that these continents were once covered with glaciers. How could you explain why glacial deposits were found in areas where no glaciers exist today? Wegener thought that these continents were all connected and covered with ice near Earth's south pole at one time.

Rock Clues

If the continents were connected at one time, then rocks that make up the continents should be the same. Similar rock structures *are* found on different continents. Parts of the Appalachian Mountains of the eastern United States are similar to those found in Greenland and western Europe. If you were to travel to eastern South America and western Africa, you would find rock structures that are similar. Rock clues like these support the idea that the continents were once connected.

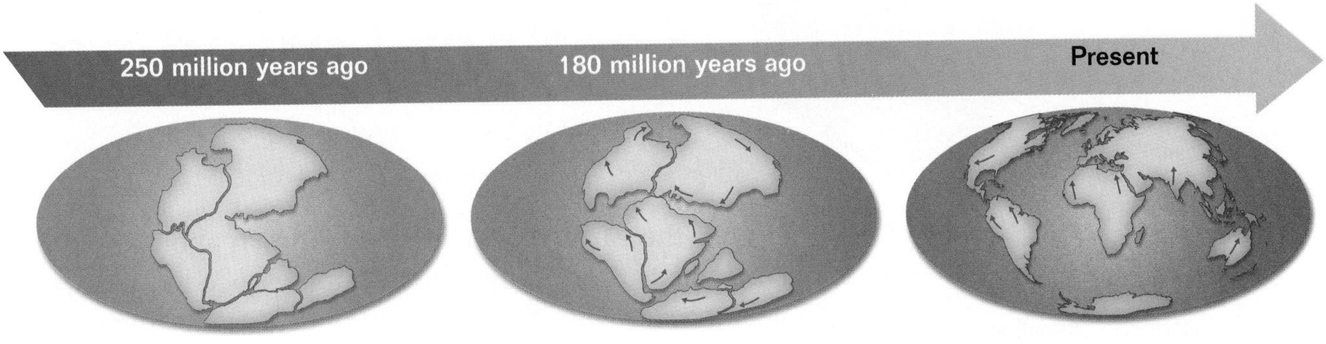

Figure 9-4 These computer models show the probable course that the continents have taken. On the far left is their position 250 million years ago. In the middle is their position 180 million years ago. At right is their current position. **Based on the diagrams, and assuming that the rate of movement will stay the same, what will happen to the Atlantic Ocean during the next 100 million years?**

How could continents drift?

Although Wegener provided evidence to support his hypothesis of continental drift, he couldn't explain how, when, or why these changes, shown in **Figure 9-4,** had taken place. Because other scientists at that time could not provide explanations either, Wegener's idea of continental drift was rejected. The idea was so different that most people closed their minds to it.

Rock, fossil, and climate clues were the main lines of evidence for continental drift. After Wegener's death, more clues were found and new ideas that supported continental drift were discovered. One of these new ideas, seafloor spreading, helped provide an explanation of how the continents could move.

Section Assessment

1. State one reason why Wegener's ideas about continental drift were not accepted.
2. How did Wegener use climate clues to support his hypothesis about continental drift?
3. **Think Critically:** Why would you expect to see similar rocks and rock structures on two landmasses that were connected at one time?
4. **Skill Builder**

   Comparing and Contrasting Compare and contrast the location of fossils of the tropical plant *Glossopteris,* as shown in **Figure 9-1,** with the climate that exists at each location today. If you need help, refer to Comparing and Contrasting in the **Skill Handbook** on page 672.

Science Journal

Imagine you are Alfred Wegener in the year 1912. In your Science Journal, write a letter to another scientist explaining your idea about continental drift. Try to convince this scientist that your hypothesis is correct.

9•2 Seafloor Spreading

What You'll Learn

- A description of seafloor spreading
- How age and magnetic clues support seafloor spreading

Vocabulary
seafloor spreading

Why It's Important

- Seafloor spreading helps explain how continents drift apart.

Clues on the Ocean Floor

Up until the early 1950s, little was known about the ocean floor. Scientists didn't have the technology needed to explore the deep oceans. But, the invention of echo-sounding devices allowed the development of accurate maps of the ocean floor. Soon, scientists discovered an ocean floor that had mountains and valleys just like on the continents. They also found a system of ridges and valleys in the Atlantic, the Pacific, and in other oceans around the world. The mid-ocean ridges form an underwater mountain range that stretches along the center of much of Earth's ocean floor. This discovery raised the curiosity of many scientists. What formed these mid-ocean ridges?

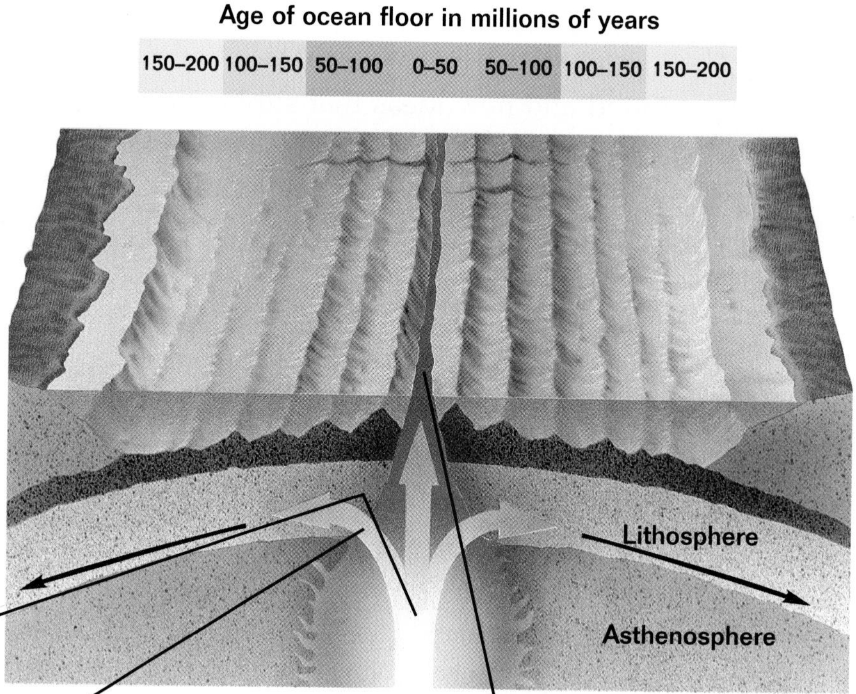

Figure 9-5 As the seafloor spreads apart at a mid-ocean ridge, new seafloor is created. The older seafloor moves away from the ridge in opposite directions. **If seafloor spreading is happening, what evidence should you expect to find by studying rocks taken from the seafloor?**

A Hot, less-dense, partially molten rock material from deep inside Earth is forced upward.

B As this hot material approaches the more rigid upper mantle, it is deflected, and the lithosphere moves along with it.

C Plates of Earth's lithosphere, which are composed of the crust and rigid upper mantle, are forced apart and moved in the direction of the moving hot rock material in the asthenosphere. A rift forms into which molten rock from the upper mantle is forced until it finally flows out onto Earth's surface as lava.

The Seafloor Moves

In the early 1960s, Princeton University scientist Harry Hess suggested an explanation. His now-famous and accepted theory is known as **seafloor spreading.** Hess proposed that hot, less-dense material below Earth's crust is forced upward toward the surface at a mid-ocean ridge. Then, it turns and flows sideways, carrying the seafloor away from the ridge in both directions, as seen in **Figure 9-5.**

As the seafloor spreads apart, magma moves upward and flows from the cracks. It becomes solid as it cools and forms new seafloor. The seafloor that is carried away from the ridge cools, contracts, and becomes more dense than the material below it. Colder seafloor begins to sink downward. The theory of seafloor spreading was later shown to be correct by the following lines of evidence.

Using Math

Measure the distance between North America and Africa at three locations on a world map. Determine an average distance between the two continents. Assuming the oldest seafloor (180 million years old) formed when Pangaea first broke up, how fast have the two continents been moving apart since then? Use the equation *rate = distance/time.*

Age Evidence

In 1968, scientists aboard the research ship *Glomar Challenger* began gathering information about the rocks on the seafloor. The *Glomar Challenger,* as shown in **Figure 9-6,** was equipped with a drilling rig that allowed scientists to drill into the seafloor to obtain rock samples. The scientists began drilling to study the ages of rocks in the seafloor and made a remarkable discovery. They found no rocks older than 180 million years. In contrast, some continental rocks are almost 4 billion years old. Why are these seafloor rocks so young?

Figure 9-6 The research ship *Glomar Challenger* helped in the exploration of the world's oceans and the seafloor.

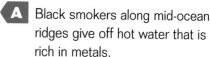

A Black smokers along mid-ocean ridges give off hot water that is rich in metals.

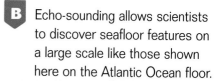

B Echo-sounding allows scientists to discover seafloor features on a large scale like those shown here on the Atlantic Ocean floor.

Figure 9-7 Many new discoveries have been made on the seafloor.

Scientists also found that the youngest rocks are located at the mid-ocean ridges. The ages of the rocks become increasingly older farther from the ridges on both sides. The evidence for seafloor spreading was getting stronger. New seafloor features and life-forms were also discovered along mid-ocean ridges, as shown in **Figure 9-7.**

PHYSICS INTEGRATION

Magnetic Clues

Earth's magnetic field has a north and a south pole. Magnetic lines, or directions, of force leave Earth near the south pole and enter Earth near the north pole. During a *magnetic reversal,* the magnetic forces run the opposite way. Scientists have determined that Earth's magnetic field has reversed itself many times in the past. These reversals occur over thousands or even millions of years.

Iron-bearing minerals, such as magnetite, that are found in basalt record Earth's magnetic field direction when they form. If Earth's magnetic field reverses, new iron minerals being formed will reflect that magnetic reversal. ☑

Reading Check ☑

What materials on the seafloor record magnetic field reversals?

Scientists found that rocks on the ocean floor show many magnetic reversals. A magnetometer (mag nuh TAHM ut ur), a sensitive instrument that records magnetic data, is used. The magnetic alignment in the rocks reverses back and forth over time in strips parallel to the mid-ocean ridges, as shown in **Figure 9-8.**

This discovery provided strong support that seafloor spreading was indeed happening. The magnetic reversals showed that new rock was being formed at the mid-ocean ridges.

The ideas of Alfred Wegener and Harry Hess changed the way people think about Earth's crust. Fossil, rock, and climate evidence supporting the hypothesis of continental drift is too strong to be discounted. Seafloor spreading shows that ocean floors change, too. You'll soon see how these two ideas are closely related.

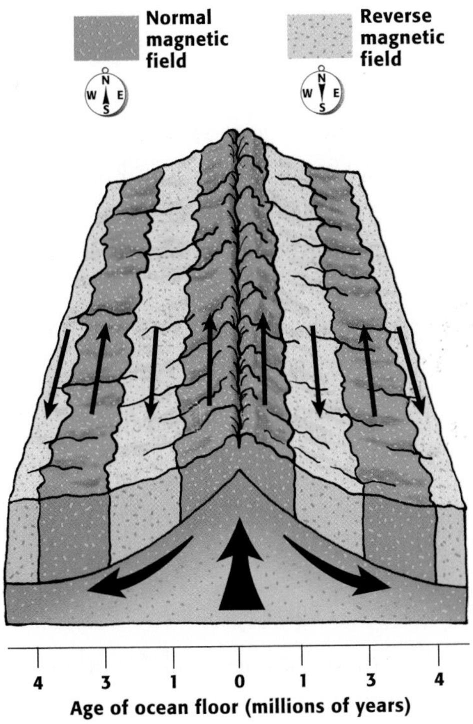

Figure 9-8 Changes in Earth's magnetic field are preserved in rock that forms on both sides of mid-ocean ridges. The time line on this diagram shows how this happens over millions of years. **Why is this considered evidence for seafloor spreading?**

CHEMISTRY INTEGRATION

Curie Point

Find out what the Curie point is and describe in your Science Journal what happens to iron-bearing minerals when they are heated to the Curie point. Explain how this is important to studies of seafloor spreading.

Section Assessment

1. How does the recording of Earth's magnetic field in iron-bearing minerals help support the theory of seafloor spreading?
2. What eventually happens to seafloor that is carried away from a mid-ocean ridge?
3. **Think Critically:** How is seafloor spreading different from continental drift?
4. **Skill Builder**
   Concept Mapping Make a concept map that discusses the evidence for seafloor spreading using the following terms and phrases: *ages increase away from ridge, pattern of magnetic field reversals, mid-ocean ridge, pattern of ages around ridge,* and *reverses back and forth.* If you need help, refer to Concept Mapping in the **Skill Handbook** on page 666.

Using Math

On average, North America is moving 1.25 cm per year away from the Mid-Atlantic Ridge. Using this rate, determine how much farther apart the continents of North America and Africa will be after 200 million years.

Activity 9•1

Seafloor Spreading Rates

Materials
- Metric ruler
- Pencil

So far, you've learned a lot about seafloor spreading and magnetic field reversals. How can you use your knowledge to reconstruct Pangaea? Try this activity to see how you can determine where a continent may have been located in the past.

What You'll Investigate

Can magnetic clues, such as magnetic field reversals on Earth, be used to help reconstruct Pangaea?

Goals
- **Interpret** data about magnetic field reversals.
- **Use** these magnetic clues to reconstruct Pangaea.

Procedure
1. **Study** the magnetic field graph below. You will be working only with normal polarity readings, which are the peaks above the baseline in the top half of the graph.
2. **Place** the long edge of a ruler vertically on the graph. Slide the ruler so that it lines up with the center of **peak #1 west** of the Mid-Atlantic ridge.
3. **Determine** and **record** the distance and age that line up with the center of **peak #1 west.** Repeat this process for **peak #1 east** of the ridge.
4. **Calculate** the average age and distance for this pair of peaks: **peaks #1 west** and **east.**
5. **Repeat** steps 1 through 4 for each remaining pair of normal polarity peaks.
6. For the six pairs of peaks, **calculate** the rate of movement in cm/year. Use the formula *rate = distance/time* to **calculate** the rate. You must **convert** kilometers to centimeters.

For example, to calculate a rate using Normal polarity peak #5, West from the ridge:

$$\text{rate} = \frac{125 \text{ km}}{10 \text{ million years}} = \frac{12.5 \text{ km}}{\text{million years}}$$

$$= \frac{1\,250\,000 \text{ cm}}{1\,000\,000 \text{ years}} = 1.25 \text{ cm/year}$$

Conclude and Apply
1. Compare the age of igneous rock found near the mid-ocean ridge with that of igneous rock found farther away from the ridge.
2. If the distance from a point on the coast of Africa to the Mid-Atlantic Ridge is approximately 2400 km, **calculate** how long ago that point in Africa was at or near the Mid-Atlantic Ridge.
3. How could you use this method to reconstruct Pangaea?

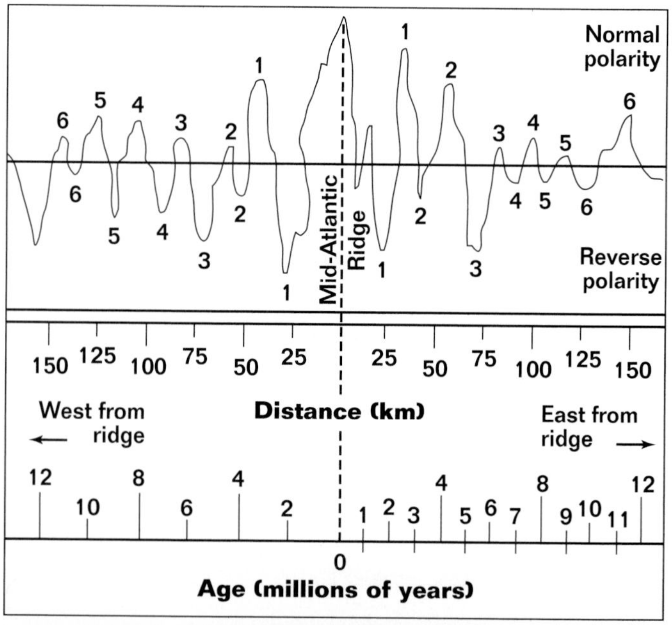

Plate Tectonics

9-3

Plate Tectonics

The discovery of seafloor spreading helped scientists understand what was happening to Earth's crust and upper mantle. The idea of seafloor spreading showed that more than just continents were moving, as Wegener had thought. It was now certain to scientists that sections of the seafloor and continents move around in relation to one another.

Plate Movements

In the 1960s scientists developed a new theory that combined the main ideas of continental drift and seafloor spreading. According to the theory of **plate tectonics,** Earth's crust and upper mantle are broken into sections. These sections, called **plates,** move around on a special layer of the mantle. The plates can be thought of as rafts that float and move around on this layer.

Composition of Earth's Plates

Plates are made of the crust and a part of the upper mantle, as seen in **Figure 9-9.** These two parts together are called the **lithosphere** (LIHTH uh sfihr). This rigid layer is about 100 km thick and is less dense than material underneath. The plastic-like layer below the lithosphere is called the **asthenosphere** (as THEN uh sfihr).

What You'll Learn

- How to compare and contrast different types of plate boundaries
- How convection currents might be the cause of plate tectonics
- The effects of plate tectonics found at each type of boundary

Vocabulary

plate tectonics
plate
lithosphere
asthenosphere
convection current

Why It's Important

- Plate tectonics explains how many of Earth's features form.

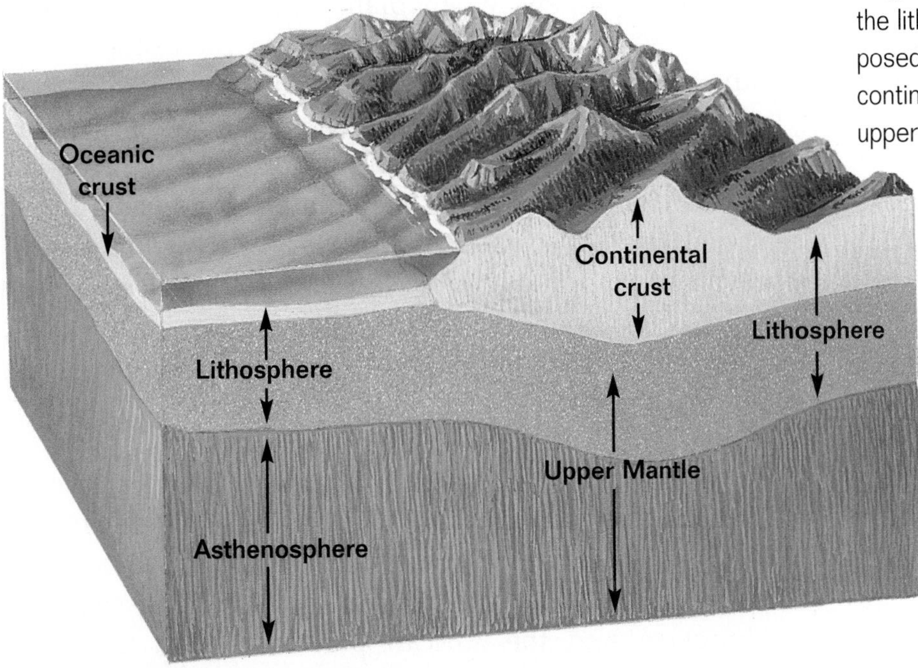

Figure 9-9 Plates of the lithosphere are composed of oceanic crust, continental crust, and rigid upper mantle.

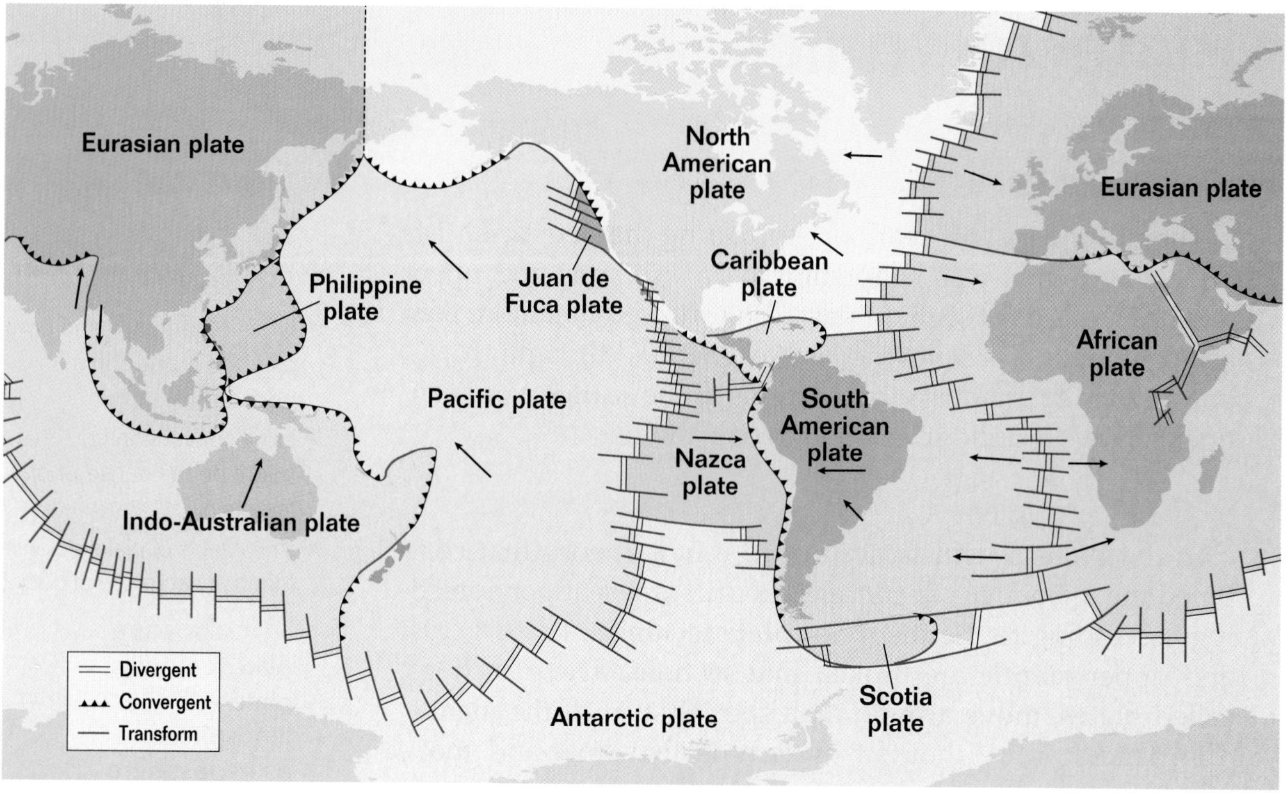

Figure 9-10 This diagram shows the major plates of the lithosphere, their direction of movement, and the type of boundary between them. **Based on what is shown in this figure, what is happening where the Nazca plate meets the Pacific plate?**

The rigid plates of the lithosphere "float" and move around on the asthenosphere. You can think of the plates on the asthenosphere as large, flat stones placed on top of putty. By applying force, you can easily slide the stones around on the putty.

Plate Boundaries

What happens when plates move? They can interact in three ways. They can move toward each other and collide, they can pull apart, or they can simply move past one another. When the plates interact, the result of their movement is seen at the plate boundaries, as in **Figure 9-10.**

Movement along any plate boundary means that changes must happen at other boundaries. What is happening to the Atlantic Ocean between the North American and African plates? Compare this with what is happening along the western margin of South America. ☑

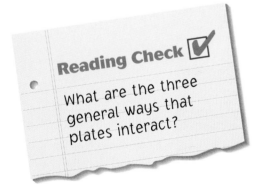

Reading Check ☑

What are the three general ways that plates interact?

Plates Moving Apart

The boundary between two plates that are moving apart is called a *divergent boundary.* You learned about divergent boundaries when you read about seafloor spreading. In the Atlantic Ocean, the North American plate is moving away from the Eurasian and the African plates, as seen in **Figure 9-10.**

That divergent boundary is called the Mid-Atlantic Ridge. The Great Rift Valley in eastern Africa is another example of a divergent plate boundary. Here, a valley has formed where two continental plates are separating. **Figure 9-11B** shows a side view of what a rift valley might look like and the hot material that rises up where plates separate.

Plates Moving Together

If new crust is being added at one location, why doesn't Earth's surface keep expanding? As new crust is added in one place, it disappears at another. The disappearance of crust can occur when seafloor cools, becomes more dense, and sinks. This happens where two plates collide at what is called a *convergent boundary.*

There are three types of convergent boundaries. When an oceanic plate collides with a less-dense continental plate, the oceanic plate is forced under the continental plate. The area where an oceanic plate is pushed down into the upper mantle is called a *subduction zone.* Volcanoes occur above subduction zones.

Figure 9-11C shows how this type of convergent boundary creates a deep-sea trench where one plate is forced beneath the other. High temperatures and pressures cause the

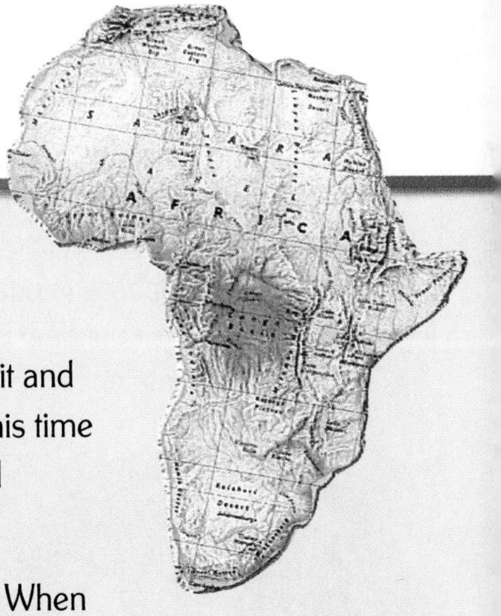

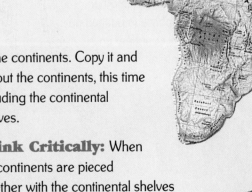

Problem Solving

The Fit Isn't Perfect

Recall the Explore Activity you performed at the beginning of this chapter. While you were trying to fit pieces of a cut-up photograph together, what clues did you use?

Take a copy of a map of the world and cut out each continent. Lay them out on a tabletop and try to fit them together, using techniques you used in the Explore Activity. You will find that the pieces of your Earth puzzle, the continents, do not fit together very well. Yet, several of the areas on some continents fit together extremely well.

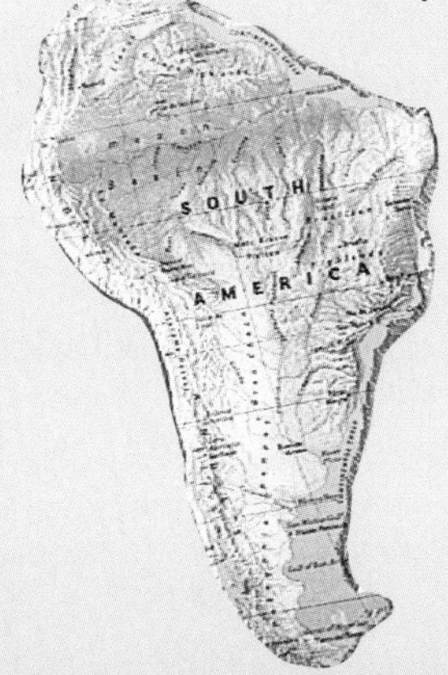

Take out another world map—one that shows the continental shelves as well as the continents. Copy it and cut out the continents, this time including the continental shelves.

Think Critically: When the continents are pieced together with the continental shelves attached, almost all of them fit together well. Why did this slight change of including the continental shelves solve the problem of fitting the continents together? What is true about the continental shelves that indicates they should be included with maps of the continents?

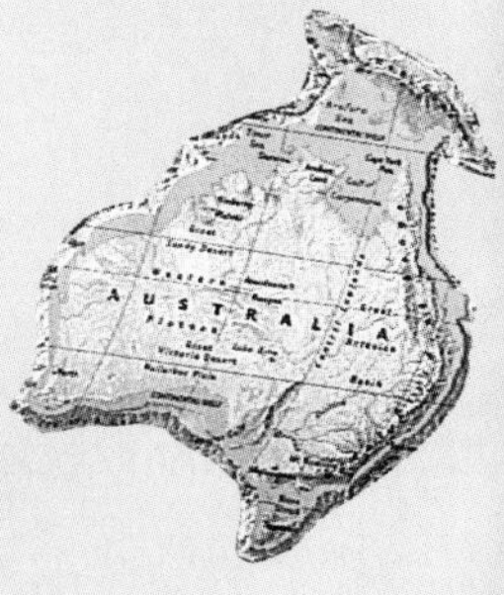

subducted plate to melt as it descends under the other plate. The newly formed magma is forced upward along these plate boundaries, forming volcanic mountains. The Andes mountain system of South America contains many volcanoes. They were formed at the convergent boundary of the Nazca and the South American plates.

The second type of convergent boundary occurs when two oceanic plates collide, and when seafloor that has become more dense due to cooling begins to sink. In this type of plate collision, one plate bends and slides under the other, forming a subduction zone as shown in **Figure 9-11E.** A deep-sea trench is formed, and new magma that is produced rises to form an island arc of volcanoes. The islands of Japan are an island arc formed where two oceanic plates collide.

VISUALIZING Plate Movement

Figure 9-11 Earth's plates pull apart at some boundaries and collide at others, forming mountains and volcanoes.

C As an oceanic plate collides with a less-dense continental plate, the continental plate is forced upward and the oceanic plate is forced under the continental plate. As the oceanic plate descends, it starts to melt. The melted rock is less dense than surrounding rock and is forced upward, forming volcanoes.

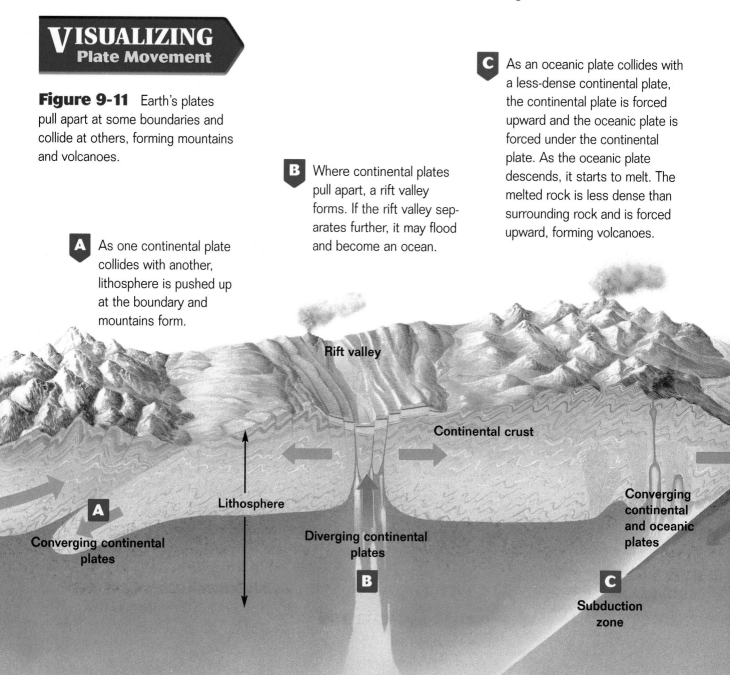

B Where continental plates pull apart, a rift valley forms. If the rift valley separates further, it may flood and become an ocean.

A As one continental plate collides with another, lithosphere is pushed up at the boundary and mountains form.

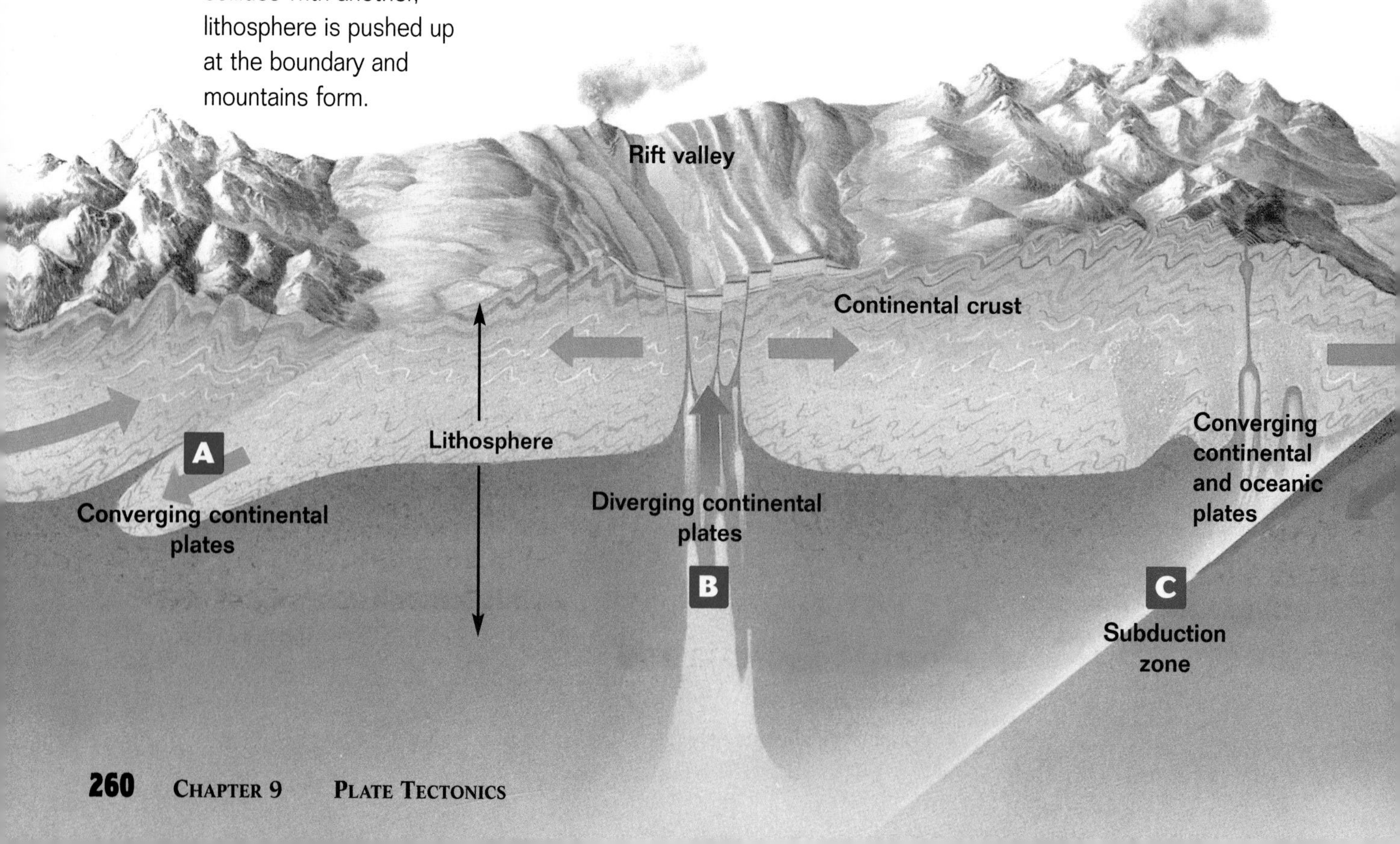

The third type of convergent boundary occurs when two continental plates collide as shown in **Figure 9-11A.** Because both of these plates are less dense than the material in the asthenosphere, usually no subduction occurs. The two plates just collide and crumple up, forming mountain ranges. Earthquakes are common at these convergent boundaries. But, volcanoes do not form because there is no subduction. The Himalaya in Asia are forming where the Indo-Australian plate crashes into the Eurasian plate.

Plates Sliding Past Each Other

The third type of plate boundary is called a *transform boundary.* Transform boundaries occur when two plates slide past one another. They move either in opposite directions or in the same direction at different rates. When one plate slips past another suddenly, earthquakes occur. The Pacific plate is sliding past the North American plate, forming the famous San Andreas Fault in California, as seen in **Figure 9-12.** The San Andreas Fault is part of a transform plate boundary. It has been the site of many earthquakes.

interNET CONNECTION

Visit the Glencoe Science Web Site at **www.glencoe.com/sec/science/ca** for more information about types of plate boundaries.

E When two oceanic plates collide, one oceanic plate becomes denser due to cooling and begins to sink under the other. Volcanoes form on the surface.

D A mid-ocean ridge forms whenever diverging plates continue to separate, creating a new ocean basin. As the rising magma cools, it forms new ocean crust.

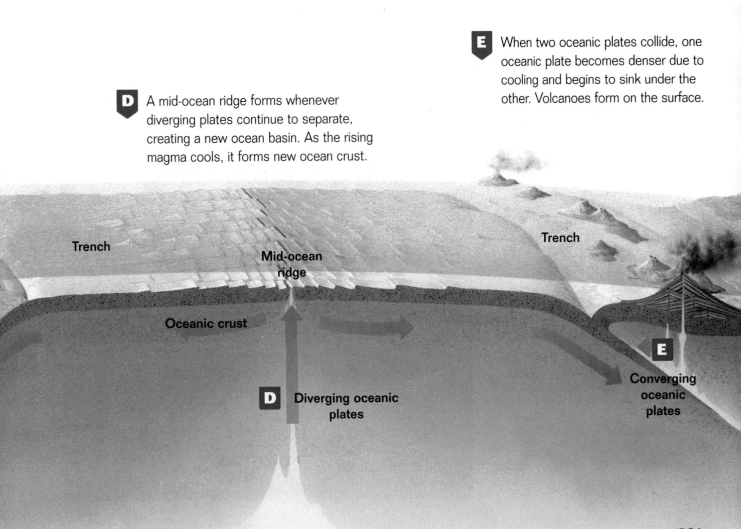

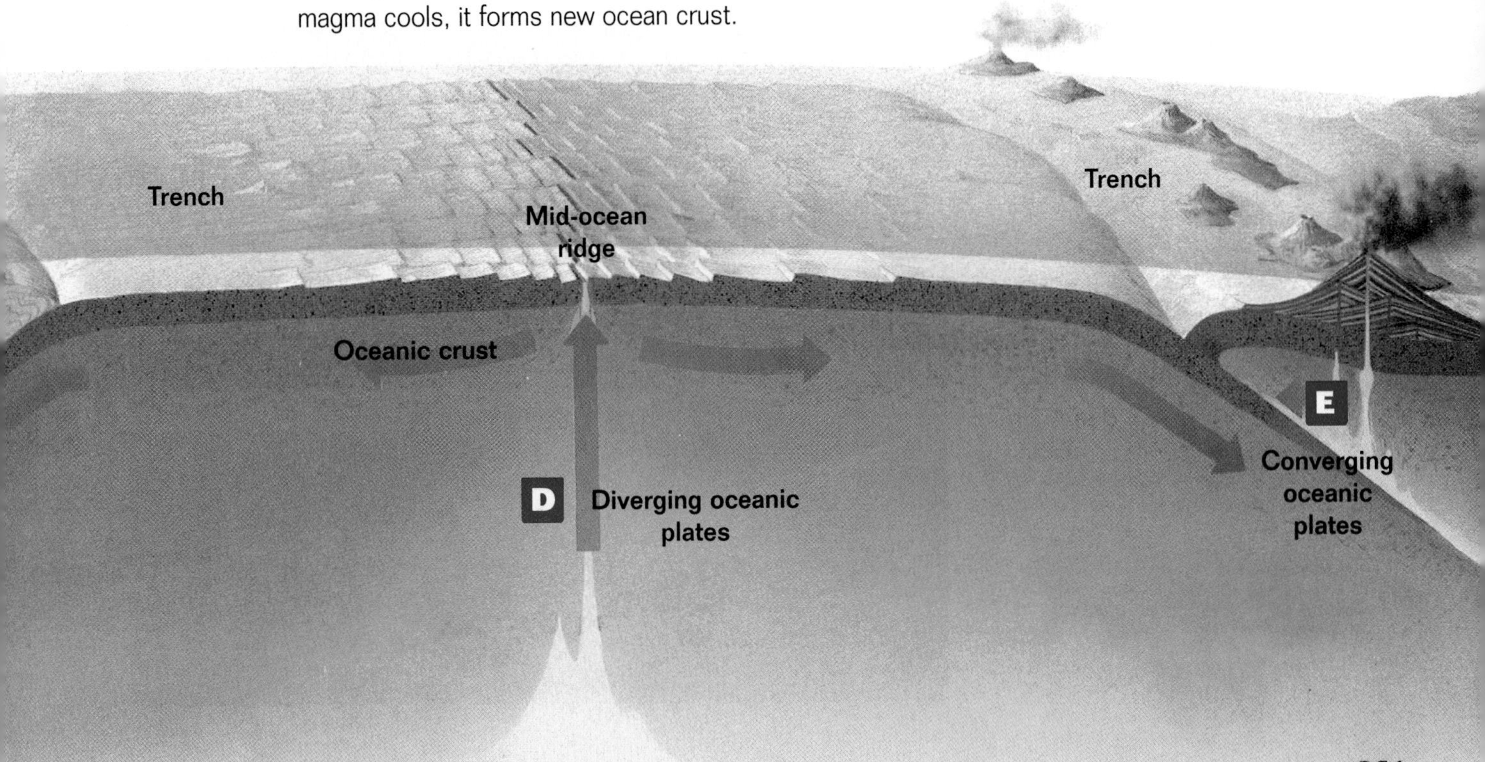

MiniLab

Modeling Convection Currents

Procedure

1. Fill a clear, colorless casserole dish with water to 5 cm from the top.
2. Center the dish on a hot plate and heat. **CAUTION:** *Wear thermal mitts to protect your hands.*
3. Add a few drops of food coloring to the water directly above the hot plate.
4. Looking from the side of the dish, observe what happens in the water.
5. In your Science Journal, describe what you observe. If possible, make an illustration.

Analysis

1. Determine whether any currents form in the water.
2. If so, infer what causes the currents to form.
3. If not, determine how to change the experiment in order to cause currents to form. Get permission from your teacher before you proceed.

Causes of Plate Tectonics

Many new discoveries have been made about Earth's crust since Wegener's day. But, one question still remains. What causes the plates to move and the seafloor to spread? Scientists now think they have a pretty good idea. They think that plates are moved by the same basic process that is used to heat some buildings.

Convection Currents

Many scientists have suggested that Earth's plates move because of slow circulation of rock in the mantle. Scientists have suggested that hot plasticlike rock deep in the mantle is forced upward toward Earth's surface. The rock is forced upward because it is less dense than surrounding rock. When this material reaches Earth's lithosphere, it moves horizontally and carries plates of lithosphere with it. As it cools, the plasticlike rock becomes more dense. It then sinks into the mantle, taking overlying lithosphere with it. The entire cycle of heating, rising, cooling, and sinking of mantle rock is called a **convection current.**

Figure 9-12 The San Andreas Fault in California occurs along the transform plate boundary where the Pacific plate is sliding past the North American plate.

A This photograph shows an aerial view of the San Andreas Fault.

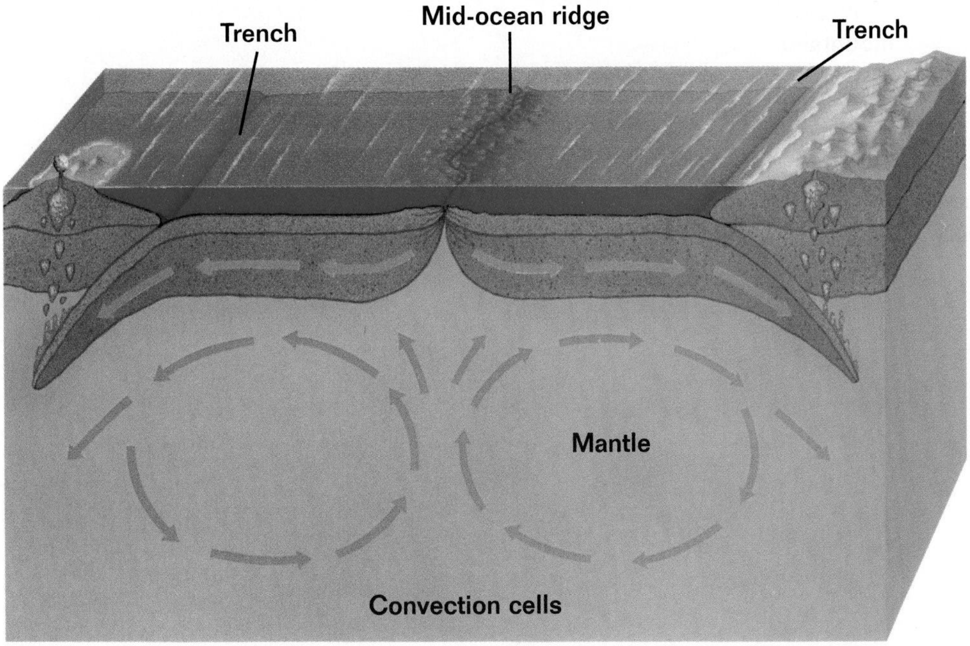

Figure 9-13 Pictured is one hypothesis of how convection currents (see arrows) are the driving force of plate tectonics. In this hypothesis, convection is limited to the upper mantle only. In another hypothesis, convection currents occur throughout the mantle.

These huge convection currents provide the energy to move plates as shown in **Figure 9-13.** They are, therefore, the cause of many of Earth's surface features. The convection currents also distribute heat. The hot plasticlike rock rising in Earth's mantle brings heat from Earth's interior to Earth's surface. Cooler rock then sinks into the mantle, where it is heated again.

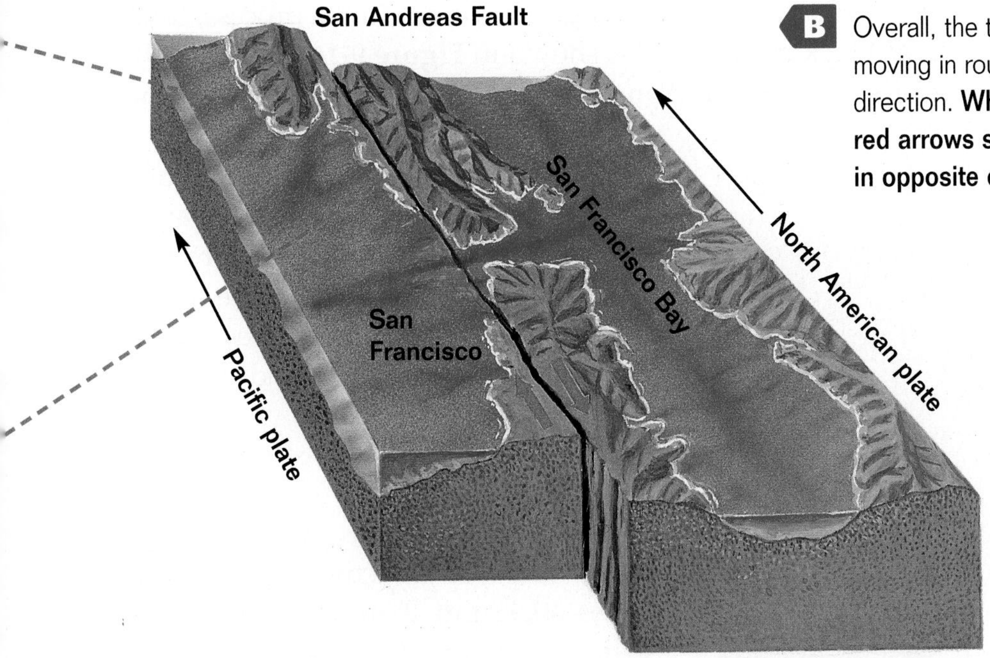

B Overall, the two plates are moving in roughly the same direction. **Why, then, do the red arrows show movement in opposite directions?**

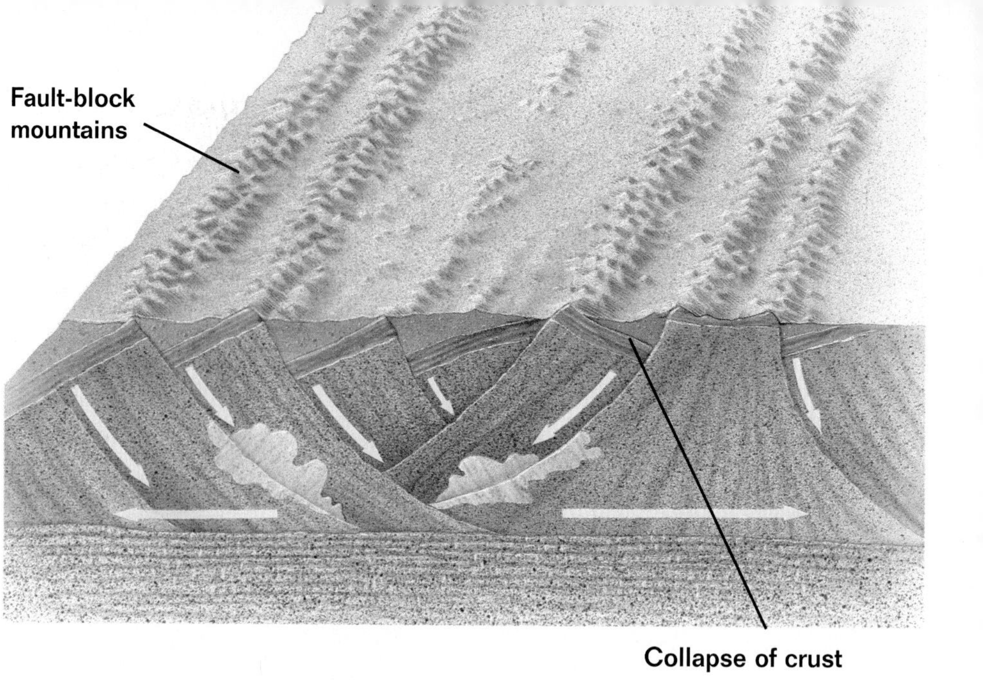

Figure 9-14 Fault-block mountains can form when Earth's crust is stretched by tectonic forces. The arrows indicate the directions that blocks have moved. **What type of force occurs when Earth's crust is pulled in opposite directions?**

*inter***NET**
CONNECTION

Visit the Glencoe Science Web site at **www.glencoe.com/sec/science/ca** for more information about the Great Rift Valley in Africa.

Effects of Plate Tectonics

Earth is a dynamic planet with convection currents inside that power the movement of plates. As the plates move, they interact. The interaction of plates produces forces that build mountains, create ocean basins, and cause volcanoes. Whenever rocks in Earth's crust break and move, a fault forms and energy is released in the form of seismic waves. Humans feel this release as earthquakes. You can see some of the effects of plate tectonics in the **Field Guide to Roadside Geology** at the end of this chapter.

Normal Faults and Rift Valleys

Diverging plates cause tension forces that stretch Earth's crust. This causes large blocks of crust to break and tilt or slide down. Entire mountain ranges may form in the process, called fault-block mountains, as shown in **Figure 9-14.** Generally, the faults that form from tension are normal faults. Once the divergence causes a separation in Earth's crust, rift valleys can form. Examples of rift valleys are the Great Rift Valley in Africa, shown in **Figure 9-15,** and the valleys that occur in the middle of mid-ocean ridges. Examples include the Mid-Atlantic Ridge and the East Pacific Rise.

Figure 9-15 The Great Rift Valley of Africa will probably become an ocean basin as rifting continues.

Strike-Slip Faults

If one plate is sliding past another, the forces are not directly opposite. The plates stick and then slide along large strike-slip faults. One such example is the San Andreas Fault. When plates move suddenly, vibrations are generated inside Earth that are felt as an earthquake. Plate tectonics explains how activity inside Earth can affect Earth's crust differently in different locations. We have seen how plates have moved since Pangaea separated. What was Earth like before that?

Mountains, Arcs, and Volcanoes

Most of Earth's mountain belts, volcanoes, and earthquakes occur at convergent plate boundaries. Compression forces produce several effects where plates move together. When continental plates converge, the forces generated cause massive folding of rock layers into mountain ranges such as the Himalaya, shown in **Figure 9-16,** or the Appalachian Mountains. Reverse faults also may occur if the forces are great enough. If the two converging plates are oceanic plates, one plate slides under the other, melting occurs, and island arcs and volcanoes form.

If an oceanic plate converges with a continental plate, the oceanic plate slides under the continental plate, melting occurs, and volcanoes form. Entire mountain ranges can form at this type of convergent boundary.

PHYSICS INTEGRATION

Tectonic Forces

In what directions are forces applied at convergent, divergent, and transform boundaries? Demonstrate these forces using wooden blocks or your hands.

Reading Check

What features occur where plates converge?

Testing for Plate Tectonics

Until recently, the only tests scientists could use to check for plate movement were indirect. They could study the magnetic characteristics of rocks on the seafloor. They could study volcanoes and earthquakes. However, these methods only provided indirect evidence that the plates have moved and are still moving. They did not provide proof—only support of the idea.

Figure 9-16 The Himalaya are still forming today as the Indo-Australian plate collides with the Eurasian plate.

Figure 9-17 When using the Satellite Laser Ranging System, scientists on the ground shoot laser pulses at a satellite, shown here. The pulses reflect off the satellite and are used to determine an exact location on the ground.

Now, scientists can measure exact movements of Earth's plates of as little as 1 cm/year. New methods had to be discovered to be able to measure the small amounts of movement of Earth's plates. One method uses lasers and a satellite, as shown in **Figure 9-17.**

Current data from these methods show that Hawaii is moving toward Japan at a rate of about 8.3 cm/year. Also, Maryland is moving away from England at a rate of about 1.7 cm/year. The total range of data from the methods taken all over the world shows that lithospheric plates move between 1 to 12 cm/year relative to the positions of other plates.

Section Assessment

1. What happens to plates at a transform plate boundary?
2. What occurs at plate boundaries associated with seafloor spreading?
3. Describe three types of plate boundaries where volcanic eruptions can occur.
4. **Think Critically:** Using **Figure 9-10** and a world map, determine what natural disasters might be likely to occur in Iceland.
5. **Skill Builder**
   Interpreting Scientific Illustrations Plate tectonic activity causes many events that can be dangerous to humans. One of these events is an earthquake that occurs on the seafloor. This can form a seismic sea wave, or tsunami. Learn how scientists predict the arrival time of a tsunami in a coastal area. Do the **Chapter 9 Skill Activity** on page 702.

Using Computers

Graphics Research ten recent earthquakes of magnitude 3.0 or greater. Make a bar graph that plots the number of earthquakes on the *y*-axis and their Richter magnitudes on the *x*-axis. Make the first bar on the *x*-axis have a Richter range of 3–4, the second a range of 4–5, etc. If you need help, refer to page 686.

Finding and Using Rates

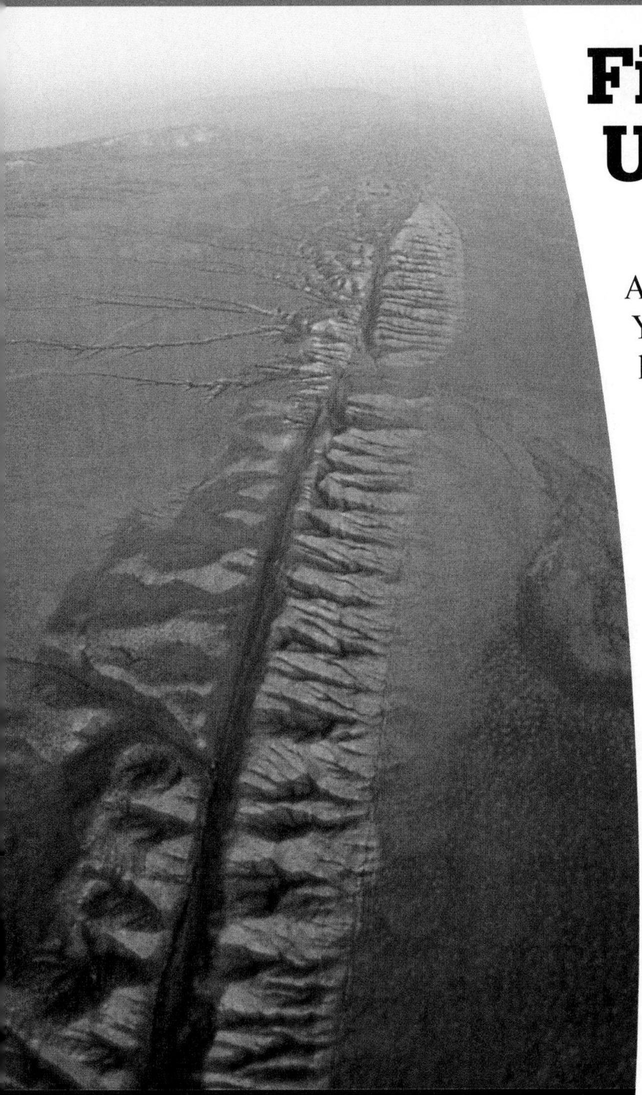

A rate is a ratio of two measurements with different units. You are familiar with some rates, such as kilometers per hour. Kilometers per hour is also a unit rate because the denominator of the rate is one unit. Finding unit rates can help you solve problems about the movement of geologic features in Earth's crust, such as strike-slip faults.

Problem

A well-known strike-slip fault is the San Andreas Fault in California (see aerial view at left). The fault has moved about 600 km in 150 million years. Follow the steps below to answer two questions. What is the rate of movement per year of the San Andreas Fault? At this rate, how far will the fault move in 1000 years?

Solution

1. Think: 150 million is a large number, and 600 is a much smaller number. You will be dividing to find the rate, so convert 600 km to millimeters. Since 1 km = 1000 m and 1 m = 1000 mm, multiply 600 by 1000 to get meters and again by 1000 to get millimeters. $600 \times 1000 \times 1000 = 600\ 000\ 000$; 600 km is 600 000 000 mm.

2. Find the unit rate: Write the rate as a fraction. Then, simplify the fraction to have a denominator of 1.

$$\frac{\text{mm}}{\text{years}} = \frac{600\ 000\ 000 \div 150\ 000\ 000}{150\ 000\ 000 \div 150\ 000\ 000} = \frac{4\ \text{mm}}{1\ \text{year}} = 4\ \text{mm/year}$$

The unit rate is 4 mm per year.

3. To find the movement of the fault over 1000 years: Multiply the unit rate by 1000. $4 \times 1000 = 4000$. The movement in 1000 years is 4000 mm, or 4 m.

Practice PROBLEMS

1. The Great Glen Fault in Scotland moved 8 km in 220 million years. What is the rate of movement per year of this fault?
2. How many times faster than the Great Glen Fault is the San Andreas Fault moving?
3. During the last 90 years, the San Andreas Fault has been moving much faster than in previous years. During this time period, the rate has been about 4 cm per year. About how much has the fault moved in the last 90 years?

On The Internet

Activity 9•2

Predicting Tectonic Activity

Earthquakes occur every day on Earth. Many of them are too small to be felt by humans, but all of them can tell us something about our planet. Active volcanoes can do the same. Active volcanoes often form at plate boundaries. The movement of plates on Earth causes forces that build energy in rocks. The release of this energy can produce vibrations in Earth (earthquakes).

Recognize the Problem

Can tectonically active areas be predicted by plotting locations of earthquake epicenters and volcanic eruptions?

Form a Hypothesis

Think about where earthquakes and volcanoes have occurred in the past. **Make a Hypothesis** about whether the locations of earthquake epicenters and active volcanoes can be used to predict tectonically active areas.

Goals

- **Plot** earthquake epicenters and the locations of volcanic eruptions obtained from the Glencoe Science Web Site.
- **Predict** tectonically active locations based on a plot of the locations of earthquake epicenters and active volcanoes.

Locations of Epicenters and Eruptions

Earthquake Epicenter/ Volcanic Eruption	Longitude	Latitude

Data Sources

Visit the Glencoe Science Web Site at **www.glencoe.com/sec/science/ca** for more information about earthquake and volcano sites. If you do not have access to the Internet, you can obtain the locations of earthquake epicenters and active volcanoes from the U.S. Geologic Survey or local newspapers.

Test Your Hypothesis

Plan

1. **Make a data table** like the one shown on the opposite page.
2. **Collect data** for earthquake epicenters and volcanic eruptions for at least the past two weeks. Your data should include the longitude and latitude for each location. For help, refer to the **data sources** given on the opposite page.
3. **Plot the locations** of earthquake epicenters and volcanic eruptions on a map of the world. Use an overlay of tissue paper or plastic.

Do

1. Make sure your teacher approves your plan and your data table before you proceed.
2. After you have collected and plotted the locations of earthquake epicenters and volcanic eruptions from at least the past two weeks, it's time to predict tectonically active areas on Earth.
3. Using your data, **predict** what areas of the world are tectonically active.
4. **Compare** and **contrast** the areas that you predicted to be tectonically active with the plate boundary map shown in **Figure 9-10.**

Analyze Your Data

1. What areas on Earth do you **predict** to be the locations of tectonic activity?
2. How close did your prediction come to the actual location of tectonically active areas?

Draw Conclusions

1. How could you make your predictions closer to the locations of actual tectonic activity?
2. Would data from a longer period of time help? **Explain.**
3. What types of plate boundaries were close to your locations of earthquake epicenters? Volcanic eruptions?
4. **Explain** which types of plate boundaries produce volcanic eruptions. Be specific.

FIELD GUIDE *to* Roadside Geology

FIELD *ACTIVITY*

Geologic forces slowly push and pull on Earth's crust, creating the surface features we can see around us. As you travel, look around you. The next time you drive along the road, whether on a personal journey or a field trip with your school, use this field guide to help you identify Earth structures you observe along the way. What forces are at work to form the structures you see? Record your observations and inferences about forces in your Science Journal.

Earthquakes! Landslides! Volcanic eruptions! These are some of the ways that Earth's surface can change quickly. However, most of the changes in Earth's crust are less spectacular and occur much more slowly. Because of the life span of humans, Earth's surface appears to change little. Features like mountains and rivers will not appear or disappear during a person's lifetime, but these features do change over much longer periods of time. In this field guide, you'll see some examples of how Earth's crust changes over time

Faults

- A fault is created when rocks move along a break or fracture.
- Faults can be small, with only centimeters of movement, or they can be large, stretching for hundreds of kilometers.
- There are three basic types of faults: normal faults, reverse faults, and strike-slip faults.

- Normal faults can form when tectonic forces pull on Earth's crust in opposite directions.

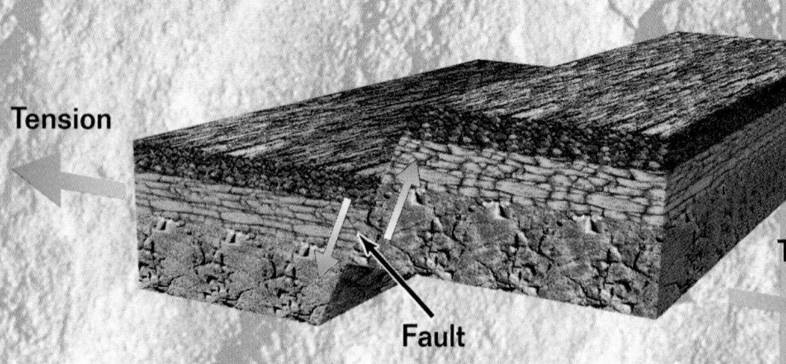

A Layers of rock have dropped downward along a normal fault.

B This normal fault located in Death Valley, California, shows a large amount of movement.

- When a section of Earth's crust is squeezed from both sides, a reverse fault can form.

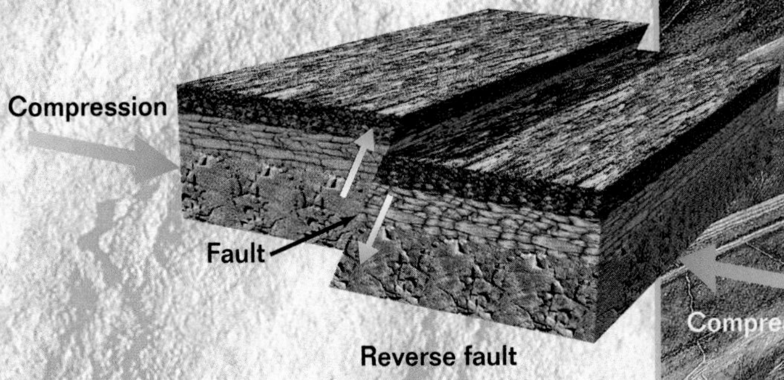

A Layers of rock have been displaced upward along a reverse fault.

B This reverse fault has shifted layers of sedimentary rock.

- Sometimes roads, sidewalks, and buildings are constructed across strike-slip faults. When the two sides along a fault move, human-made structures are often broken and shifted.

A The ground has been broken and shifted by movements along a strike-slip fault.

- Strike-slip faults form when tectonic forces cause slabs of Earth's crust to slide past one another.

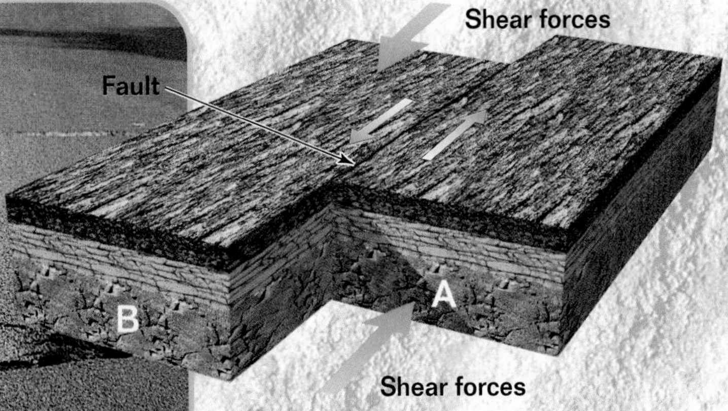

B In this strike-slip fault, side A of the block is being pushed away from you and side B is being pushed toward you.

Folds

- When rocks are subjected to stress, they do not always break and form faults. Under some conditions, rocks will bend and fold instead of breaking.
- Upward-arching folds are known as anticlines.
- Downward-sagging folds are called synclines.
- Folds can be large enough to form mountains or small enough to hold in your hand.

A

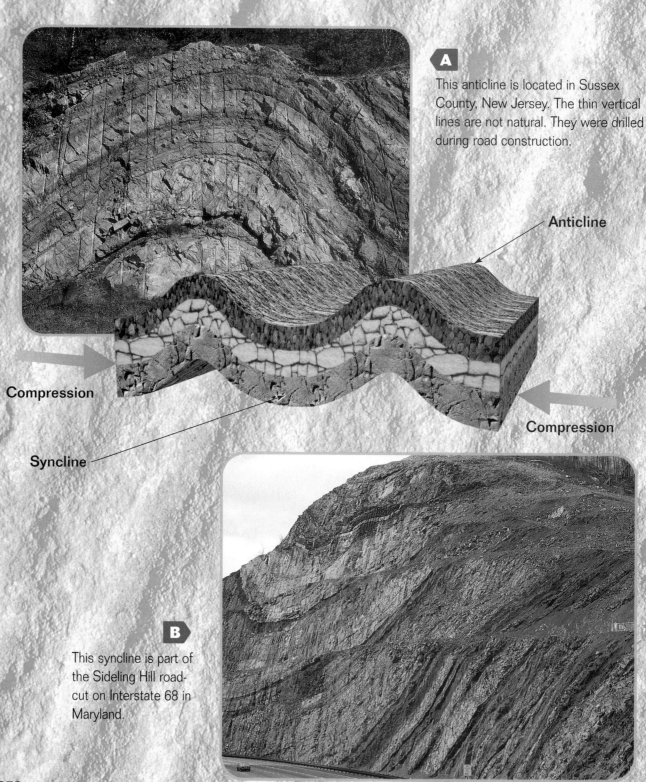

This anticline is located in Sussex County, New Jersey. The thin vertical lines are not natural. They were drilled during road construction.

B

This syncline is part of the Sideling Hill roadcut on Interstate 68 in Maryland.

Limestone Features

- Layers of limestone are common rock formations in Earth's crust.
- Water in nature is usually slightly acidic. When acidic water comes in contact with limestone, it reacts with the rock. Over time, the acidic water changes the rock into material that can then be washed away.
- Caves and sinkholes form when acidic water below Earth's surface slowly destroys the limestone.

A This cave in Luray Caverns, Virginia, is a hole left over after some limestone was removed by groundwater.

B This sinkhole in Winter Park, Florida, formed when limestone at Earth's surface collapsed into caves below.

Landslides

- A landslide happens when a mass of earth and rock moves downhill in response to gravity.
- Landslides often are triggered by heavy rains or sometimes by earthquakes.
- A landslide generally can be recognized by two surface features. A large curved depression, or scar, is left behind where the landslide started. A bumpy region of mixed-up rock and soil is formed where the landslide stops.

A

This landslide in the Madison Range, in Montana, was triggered by an earthquake on August 17, 1959.

B

This slump is a type of landslide that is common in oversteepened areas that are eroded by streams, lakes, and oceans. This slump is located in central California. The scar shows the area where the slump broke away from the slope.

Sedimentary Features

- Sediments are deposited in many different environments such as beaches, rivers, swamps, and mudflats. Leaf imprints, animal tracks, mud cracks, fossils, and even raindrop patterns have been preserved in sedimentary rocks.
- One type of sedimentary feature that is often observed in sandstone is ripple marks. When water flows over a sandy area, the sand forms a series of small ridges, or ripples.

A

This region of ripples was formed by flowing water at a beach in St. Johns County, Florida.

- If a rippled layer is gently buried by more sediments, the ripples can be preserved in the rock. Careful observation of sandstone layers often reveals ripple marks.

B

These ripple marks are preserved in a sandstone formation in Utah.

Chapter 9 Reviewing Main Ideas

For a **preview** of this chapter, study this Reviewing Main Ideas before you read the chapter. After you have studied this chapter, you can use the Reviewing Main Ideas to **review** the chapter.

GLENCOE TECHNOLOGY

The Glencoe MindJogger, Audiocassettes, and CD-ROM provide additional opportunities for review.

Section

9-1 CONTINENTAL DRIFT

The hypothesis of **continental drift** states that continents have moved to their present positions on Earth. Wegener believed that all continents were once connected into one large landmass he called **Pangaea.** The puzzlelike fit of the continents, fossils, climatic evidence, and similar rock structures supports Wegener's idea of continental drift. One problem with Wegener's idea was that he could not explain what process could be responsible for moving continents through the oceans. ***What is true of the fossils of*** **Mesosaurus** ***that Wegener felt supported the hypothesis of continental drift?***

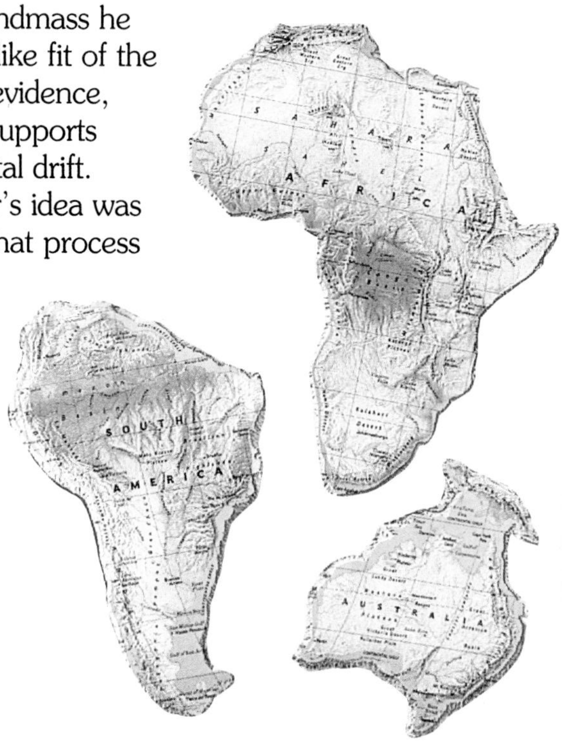

Section

9-2 SEAFLOOR SPREADING

Echo-sounding devices used to construct maps of the ocean floor showed underwater mountains and rift valleys. **Seafloor spreading** is the spreading apart of the seafloor at the mid-ocean ridges. The theory of seafloor spreading is supported by magnetic evidence in rocks and in the age of rocks on the ocean floor. The oldest rocks found on the ocean floor are 180 million years old. The youngest rocks are near the mid-ocean ridges, and the rocks become progressively older farther from the ridges. ***What type of magnetic evidence in rocks supports the theory of seafloor spreading?***

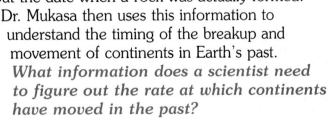

Reading Check

Suggest one or two additional illustrations for this chapter and explain why they would be valuable.

Section 9-3 PLATE TECTONICS

Plates move away from each other at divergent boundaries. Plates collide at convergent boundaries. At a transform boundary, two plates move horizontally past each other. Hot, plasticlike material from the mantle is forced upward to the **lithosphere,** moves horizontally, cools, and then sinks back into the mantle, causing **convection currents,** which are the driving force of **plate tectonics.** Most mountain belts, volcanoes, and earthquakes occur at convergent boundaries. Mid-ocean ridges and rift valleys occur at divergent boundaries. Major earthquakes occur at transform boundaries. ***At which type of plate boundary does subduction occur?***

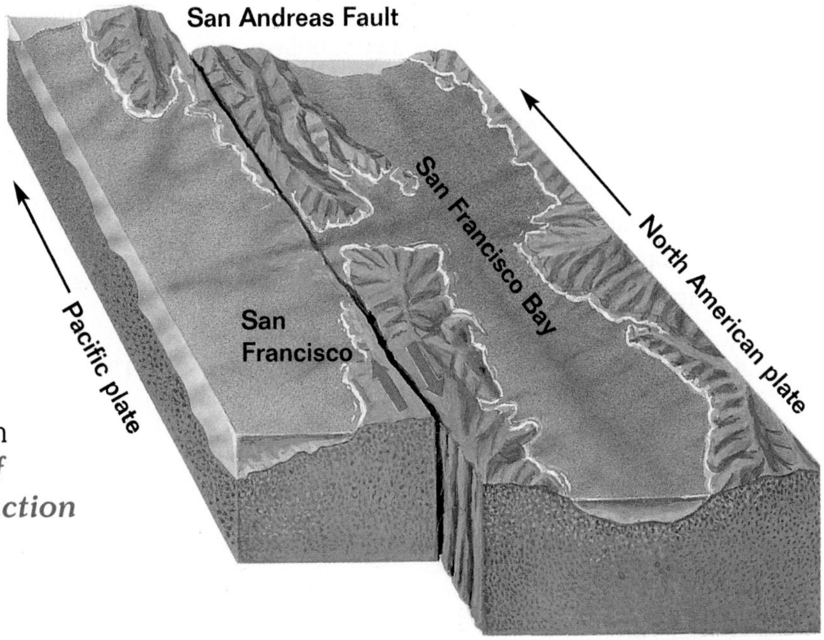

Career CONNECTION

Dr. Samuel B. Mukasa, Isotope Geochemist

As an isotope geochemist, Dr. Samuel Mukasa studies the elements that make up rocks. By comparing the concentrations of certain elements, he can figure out the date when a rock was actually formed. Dr. Mukasa then uses this information to understand the timing of the breakup and movement of continents in Earth's past. ***What information does a scientist need to figure out the rate at which continents have moved in the past?***

Chapter 9 Assessment

Using Vocabulary

a. asthenosphere
b. continental drift
c. convection current
d. lithosphere
e. Pangaea
f. plate
g. plate tectonics
h. seafloor spreading

Each phrase below describes a vocabulary term from the list. Write the term that matches the phrase describing it.

1. plastic-like layer below the lithosphere
2. idea that continents move on Earth's surface
3. large landmass made of all continents
4. process that forms new seafloor
5. driving force for plate movement

Checking Concepts

Choose the word or phrase that best answers the question.

6. Where is Earth's asthenosphere located?
   A) crust
   B) mantle
   C) outer core
   D) inner core
7. What type of plate boundary is the San Andreas Fault a part of?
   A) divergent boundary
   B) subduction boundary
   C) convergent boundary
   D) transform boundary
8. What hypothesis states that continents moved to their present positions?
   A) subduction
   B) seafloor spreading
   C) continental drift
   D) erosion
9. Which plate is subducting beneath the South American plate to form the Andes mountain system?
   A) North American
   B) African
   C) Indo-Australian
   D) Nazca
10. Evidence of which of the following features indicates that many continents were once near Earth's south pole?
    A) glaciers
    B) mid-ocean ridges
    C) volcanoes
    D) convection currents
11. What evidence in rocks supports the theory of seafloor spreading?
    A) plate movement
    B) subduction
    C) reversals of Earth's magnetic field
    D) convergence
12. Which type of plate boundary is the Great Rift Valley a part of?
    A) convergent
    B) divergent
    C) transform
    D) lithosphere
13. What theory states that plates move around on the asthenosphere?
    A) continental drift
    B) seafloor spreading
    C) subduction
    D) plate tectonics
14. What forms when one plate is forced under another plate?
    A) transform boundary
    B) divergent boundary
    C) subduction zone
    D) mid-ocean ridge
15. When oceanic plates collide, what volcanic landforms are made?
    A) folded mountains
    B) island arcs
    C) strike-slip faults
    D) mid-ocean ridges

Thinking Critically

16. Why are there few volcanoes in the Himalaya range but many earthquakes?
17. Glacial deposits often form at high latitudes near the poles. Explain why glacial deposits have been found in Africa.

18. How is magnetism used to support the theory of seafloor spreading?
19. Explain why volcanoes do not form along the San Andreas Fault.
20. Why wouldn't the fossil of an ocean fish found on two different continents be good evidence of continental drift?

Developing Skills

If you need help, refer to the Skill Handbook.

21. **Hypothesizing:** Mount St. Helens in the Cascade Mountain Range is a volcano. Use **Figure 9-10** and a U.S. map to hypothesize how it may have formed.
22. **Measuring in SI:** Movement along the African Rift Valley is about 2.1 cm per year. If plates continue to move apart at this rate, how much larger will the rift be (in meters) in 1000 years? In 15 500 years?
23. **Concept Mapping:** Make an events chain concept map that describes seafloor spreading along a divergent plate boundary. Choose from the following phrases: *magma cools to form new seafloor, magma rises, convection currents circulate hot material along boundary,* and *older seafloor is forced apart.*

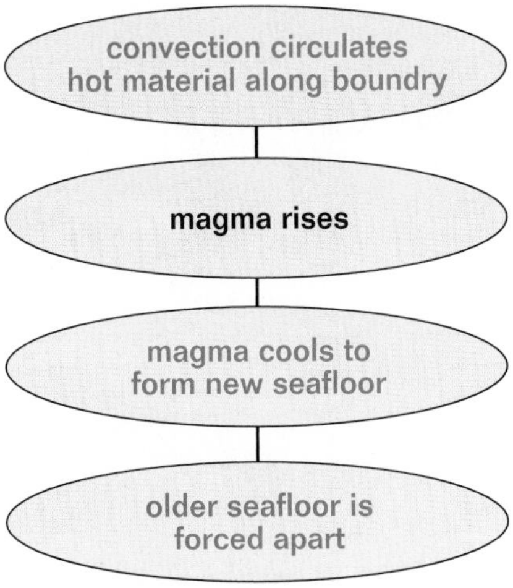
convection circulates hot material along boundry
magma rises
magma cools to form new seafloor
older seafloor is forced apart

THE PRINCETON REVIEW

Test-Taking Tip

The "Best" Answer Is Often the "Least Incorrect" If none of your answer choices look right, use the process of elimination to eliminate the *worst* ones. The one you've got left is the best choice.

Test Practice

Use these questions to test your Science Proficiency.

1. Alfred Wegener's original hypothesis of continental drift was not accepted by other scientists of his time. Which of the following statements **BEST** explains why this was true?
   A) Wegener had very little evidence to support his hypothesis.
   B) Wegener could not explain how continents move.
   C) Wegener was not a geologist.
   D) Wegener based his hypothesis only on the fossil record.
2. Island arcs form at convergent plate boundaries. Which of the following statements **BEST** explains this process?
   A) When two continental plates converge, subduction stops and mountains are built.
   B) When an oceanic plate converges on a continental plate, subduction leads to the formation of volcanoes.
   C) When two ocean plates diverge, magma is forced to Earth's surface, forming volcanoes.
   D) When two oceanic plates converge, subduction leads to the formation of volcanoes.

CHAPTER

10 Earthquakes

Chapter Preview

Skills Preview

Skill Builders
- Compare and Contrast
- Make and Use a Table

Activities
- Interpret Data
- Make and Use a Graph

MiniLabs
- Interpret a Graph
- Make a Model

Reading Check

As you read Section 10-1 of this chapter, complete a chart with these three columns: type of fault, its cause, its effects.

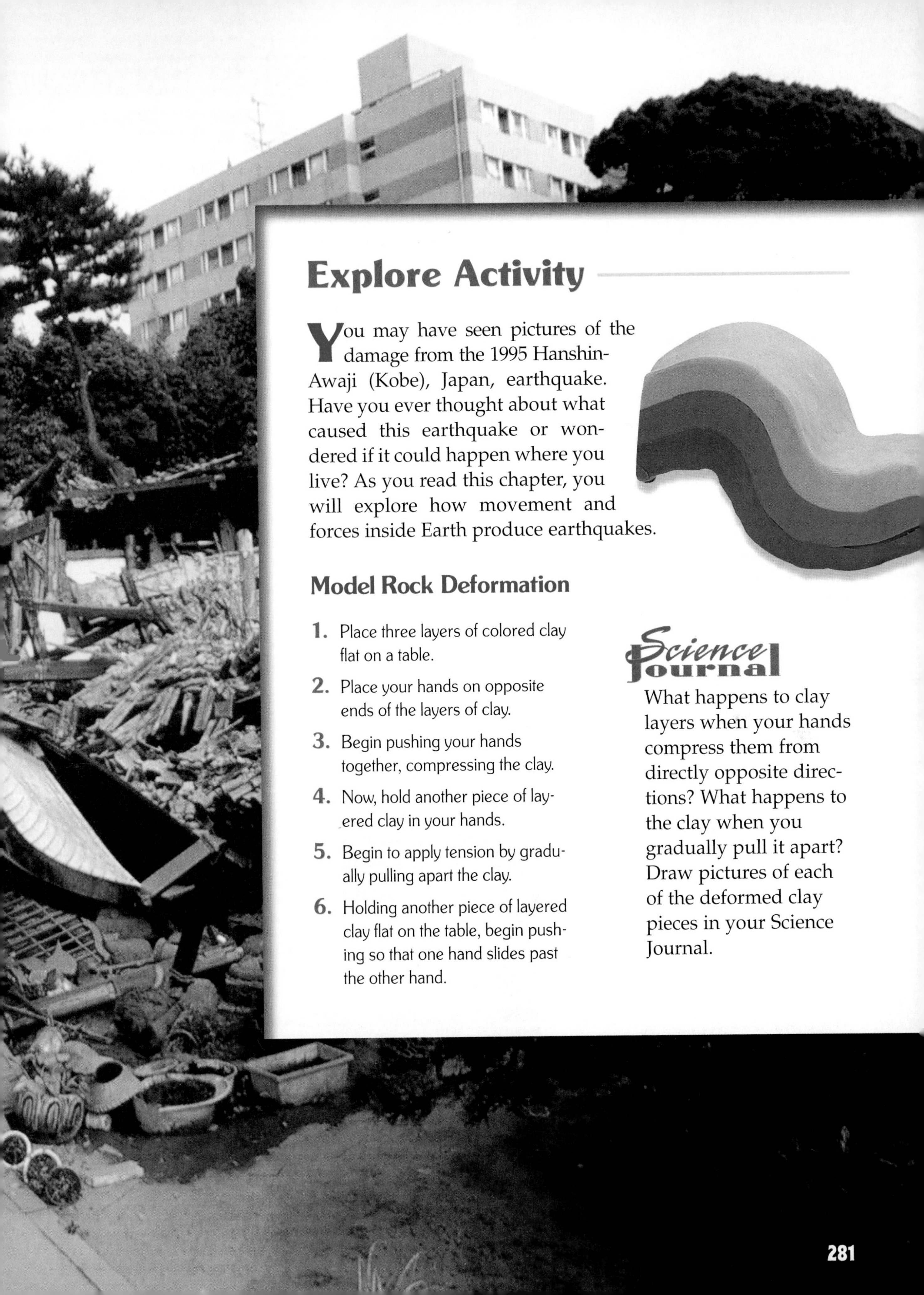

Explore Activity

You may have seen pictures of the damage from the 1995 Hanshin-Awaji (Kobe), Japan, earthquake. Have you ever thought about what caused this earthquake or wondered if it could happen where you live? As you read this chapter, you will explore how movement and forces inside Earth produce earthquakes.

Model Rock Deformation

1. Place three layers of colored clay flat on a table.
2. Place your hands on opposite ends of the layers of clay.
3. Begin pushing your hands together, compressing the clay.
4. Now, hold another piece of layered clay in your hands.
5. Begin to apply tension by gradually pulling apart the clay.
6. Holding another piece of layered clay flat on the table, begin pushing so that one hand slides past the other hand.

Science Journal

What happens to clay layers when your hands compress them from directly opposite directions? What happens to the clay when you gradually pull it apart? Draw pictures of each of the deformed clay pieces in your Science Journal.

10•1 Forces Inside Earth

Causes of Earthquakes

***What* You'll Learn**

- To explain how earthquakes result from the buildup of stress in Earth's crust
- The differences between normal, reverse, and strike-slip faults

Vocabulary

fault
earthquake
normal fault
reverse fault
strike-slip fault

***Why* It's Important**

- Studying the causes of earthquakes will help you tell where they can occur.

Think about the last time you used a rubber band to hold a roll of papers together. Rubber bands stretch when you use force on them. Because they are elastic, they return to their original shape once the force is released. A wooden ice-cream-bar stick behaves in much the same way. When force is first applied to the stick, it will bend and change shape, as shown by the student on the left in **Figure 10-1.** The energy needed to bend the stick is forced inside the stick as potential energy. If the force keeping the stick bent is removed, the stick will return to its original shape, and the stored energy will be released as energy of motion.

Passing the Elastic Limit Causes Faulting

There is a limit to how far a rubber band will stretch or to how far a wooden ice-cream-bar stick will bend. Once this elastic limit is reached, the rubber band or wooden stick breaks. Rocks near Earth's surface behave in much the same way. Up to a point, applied forces cause rocks to bend and stretch, undergoing elastic deformation. Once their elastic limit is passed, the rocks may break. This is demonstrated with an ice-cream-bar stick by the student on the right in **Figure 10-1.** When rocks break, they move along surfaces called **faults.**

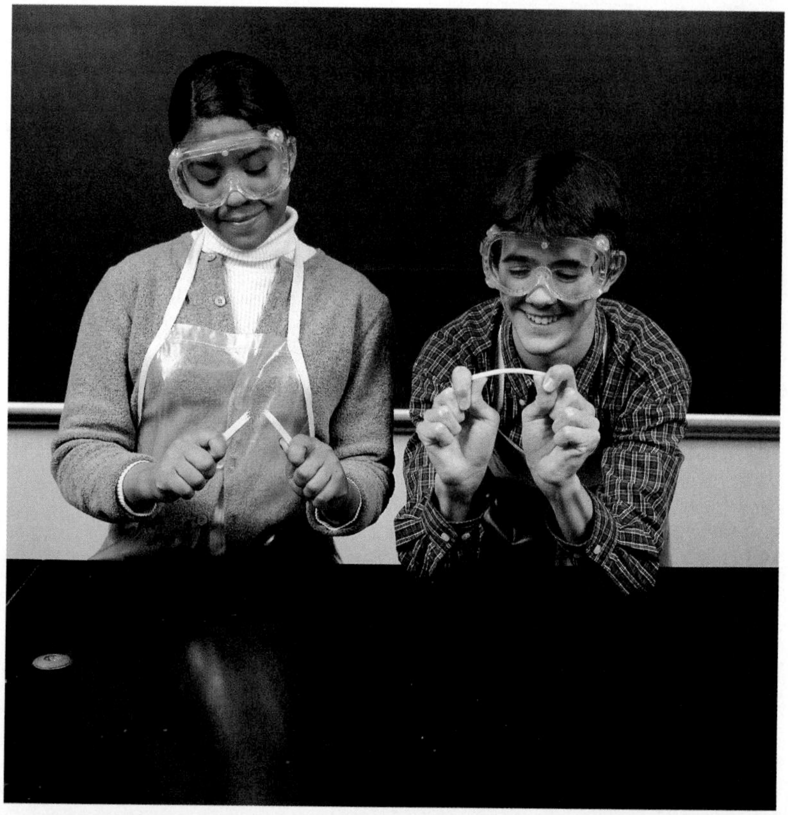

Figure 10-1
An ice-cream–bar-stick can be used to demonstrate elastic deformation.

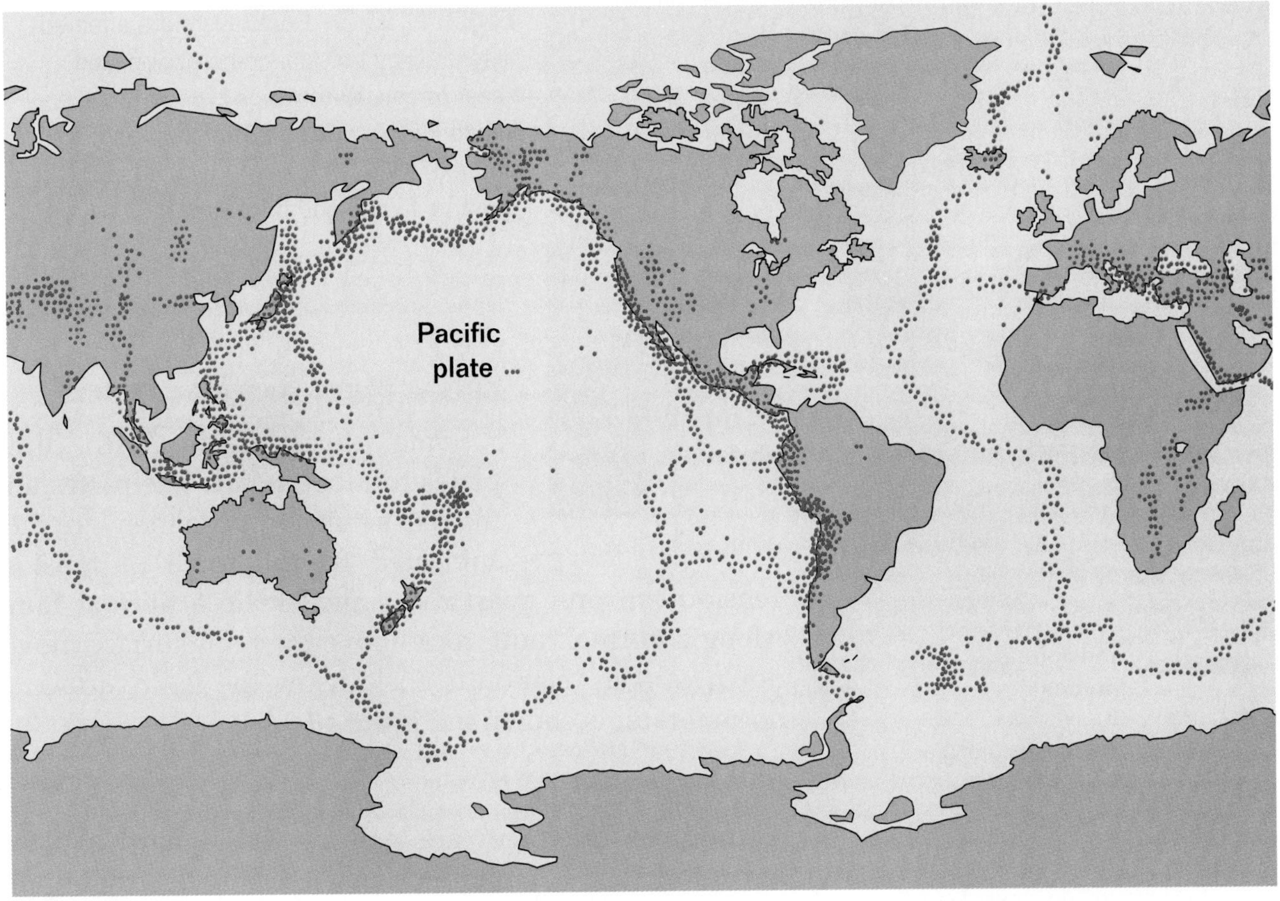

Figure 10-2 The dots represent the locations of major quakes over a ten-year period. Eighty percent of earthquakes occur along the edges of a section of Earth known as the Pacific plate.

What causes faults to form? Something must be forcing rocks to move. Otherwise, the rocks would just rest quietly. Earth's crust is in constant motion because of forces inside Earth. These forces cause sections of Earth's crust, called plates, to move, putting stress on rocks. Because of this stress, rocks tend to bend and stretch. However, if the force is great enough, rocks break. This breaking releases stored energy to produce the vibrations that we call **earthquakes. Figure 10-2** shows how the locations of earthquakes outline the sections of Earth's crust.

Types of Faults

PHYSICS INTEGRATION

Rocks go through several types of forces where sections or plates of Earth's crust and upper mantle meet. When you played with the layers of clay in the Explore Activity, you experimented with three forces—compression, tension, and shear. Compression is a force or stress that squeezes and compresses, while tension is the force that causes rocks to stretch and become longer. Shear is the force that causes rocks on either side of a fault to move past each other. Let's take a look at these three forces and the types of faults they create.

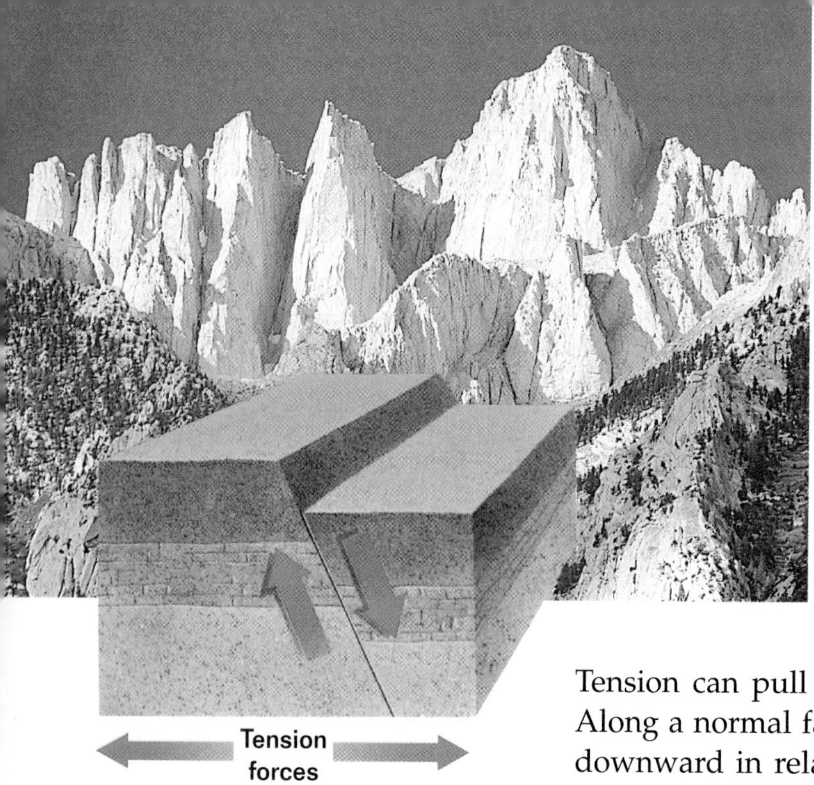

Figure 10-3 Rock layers are affected differently by tension, compression, and shear forces. **With which type of force would Earth's crust be stretched and thinned? With which type would Earth's crust be folded and thickened?**

A When rock moves along a fracture caused by tension forces, the break is called a normal fault. Rock above the fault moves downward in relation to the rock below the fault surface. Normal faults can form mountains such as the Sierra Nevada, which border California on the east.

Normal Faults

Some forces inside Earth cause plates to move apart. The plates and the rocks that compose them are then subjected to the force of tension. Tension can pull apart rocks and create a **normal fault.** Along a normal fault, rock above the fault surface moves downward in relation to rock below the fault surface. A normal fault is shown in **Figure 10-3A.**

Reverse Faults

Compression forces are present where Earth's plates move together. Compression pushes on rocks from opposite directions and causes them to bend and sometimes break. Once they break, the rocks continue to move along the fault surface. At a **reverse fault,** the rocks above the fault surface are forced up and over the rocks below the fault surface, as shown in **Figure 10-3B.**

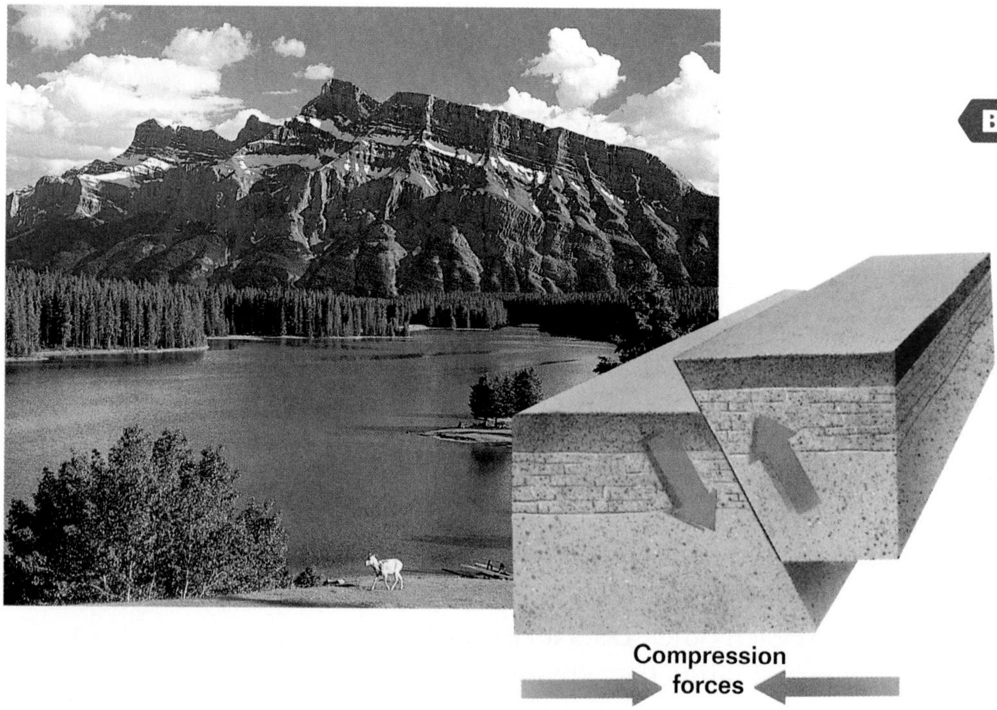

B When compression forces break rock, the rock above the fault surface moves upward in relation to the rock below the fault surface. The mountains shown, in Banff National Park in the Canadian Rocky Mountains, contain many reverse faults.

C Shear forces push on rock in opposite, but not directly opposite, horizontal directions. When they are strong enough, these forces split rock and create strike-slip faults. There is relatively little vertical movement along a strike-slip fault. When movement is sudden along faults like the San Andreas Fault shown here, earthquakes occur.

Strike-Slip Faults

You have probably heard about the San Andreas Fault in California. At this fault, shown in **Figure 10-3C,** two of Earth's plates are moving sideways past each other because of shear forces. This type of fault is called a strike-slip fault. At a **strike-slip fault,** rocks on either side of the fault surface are moving past each other without much upward or downward movement. Compare the faults in **Figure 10-3.** How do they differ? ☑

As the rocks move past each other at a strike-slip fault, their ragged surfaces catch each other, and the rocks are twisted and strained. Not only do they change shape, but the catching of their surfaces prevents movement along the faults. As forces keep driving the plates to move, energy builds up and the rocks reach their elastic limit. When the rocks are stressed past their elastic limit, they may break and an earthquake may result.

Some earthquakes can be dramatic—even devastating—events, while others go almost unnoticed. Regardless of their sizes, most earthquakes result from plates moving over, under, and past each other. If these plates simply slid smoothly by each other, tension, compression, and shear forces would not build up energy. But, rocks do experience these stresses and energy builds up in them, causing small

Reading Check ☑

What is a strike-slip fault?

PHYSICS INTEGRATION

Fault Forces

Explain what types of faults are produced by compression and by tension. How does the type of stress determine the nature of the fault in each case?

Figure 10-4
Geologists use surface evidence like these cracks in Costa Rica when searching for dangerous hidden fractures or faults.

changes in shape. When rocks break, as shown in **Figure 10-4**, energy is released along fault surfaces, and we observe the effects in the form of earthquakes.

Section Assessment

1. What type of force usually generates strike-slip faults?
2. The Appalachian Mountains formed when two of Earth's plates collided. What type of faults would you expect to find in these mountains? Why?
3. What happens to rocks when an earthquake occurs?
4. **Think Critically:** Why might it be easier to predict *where* an earthquake will occur than it is to predict *when* it will occur?
5. **Skill Builder**
Concept Mapping Make a cycle concept map that shows why many earthquakes occur along the San Andreas Fault. Use the following terms and phrases: *rocks, stress, bend and stretch, elastic limit reached,* and *earthquakes.* If you need help, refer to Concept Mapping in the **Skill Handbook** on page 666.

Using Computers

Graphics Use the graphics capabilities of a computer to make simple working models of the three types of faults: normal, reverse, and strike-slip. Have your computer model show how the forces that cause each fault differ. If you need help, refer to page 686.

Earthquake Information

10-2

Types of Seismic Waves

Have you ever seen a coiled-spring toy? When children play with a coiled-spring toy, they send energy waves through it. **Seismic** (SIZE mihk) **waves** made by an earthquake are like the waves of the toy. Where are seismic waves formed? How do they move through Earth, and how can we use the information that they carry? Let's investigate how scientists have answered these questions.

Earthquake Focus

As you have learned, when rocks move along a fault surface, energy is released and damage occurs, as seen in **Figure 10-5.** The point in Earth's interior where this energy release occurs is the **focus** of the earthquake. Seismic waves are produced at and travel outward from the earthquake focus.

What You'll Learn

- To compare and contrast primary, secondary, and surface waves
- How an earthquake epicenter is located
- The structure of Earth's interior

Vocabulary

seismic wave
focus
primary wave
secondary wave
epicenter
surface wave
inner core
outer core
mantle
crust

Why It's Important

- Seismic waves help scientists locate earthquakes and give information about Earth's interior.

Figure 10-5 This photograph shows buildings damaged during the 1989 Loma Prieta, California, earthquake. This earthquake was caused by the Pacific plate slipping past the North American plate by only 2 m.

interNET CONNECTION

Visit the Glencoe Science Web Site at **www.glencoe.com/sec/science/ca** for more information about seismic waves.

Seismic Waves

Waves that cause particles in rocks to move back and forth in the same direction the wave is moving are called **primary waves.** If you squeeze together several coils on one end of a coiled-spring toy and then release them, they compress and then stretch as the wave travels through the toy. Particles in rocks also squeeze together and stretch apart as primary waves move through them.

Now, if you and a friend stretch the coiled-spring toy between you and then move one end up and down, a different type of wave will pass through the toy. The spring will move up and down as the wave moves along it. **Secondary waves** move through Earth by causing particles in rocks to vibrate at right angles to the direction of the wave.

VISUALIZING Seismic Waves

Figure 10-6 Primary and secondary waves travel outward from the focus. Surface waves move outward from the epicenter.

A Sudden movement along a fault releases energy that causes an earthquake. The point beneath Earth's surface where the movement occurs is the focus of the earthquake.

B Primary waves and secondary waves originate at the focus and travel outward in all directions. Primary waves travel faster than secondary waves.

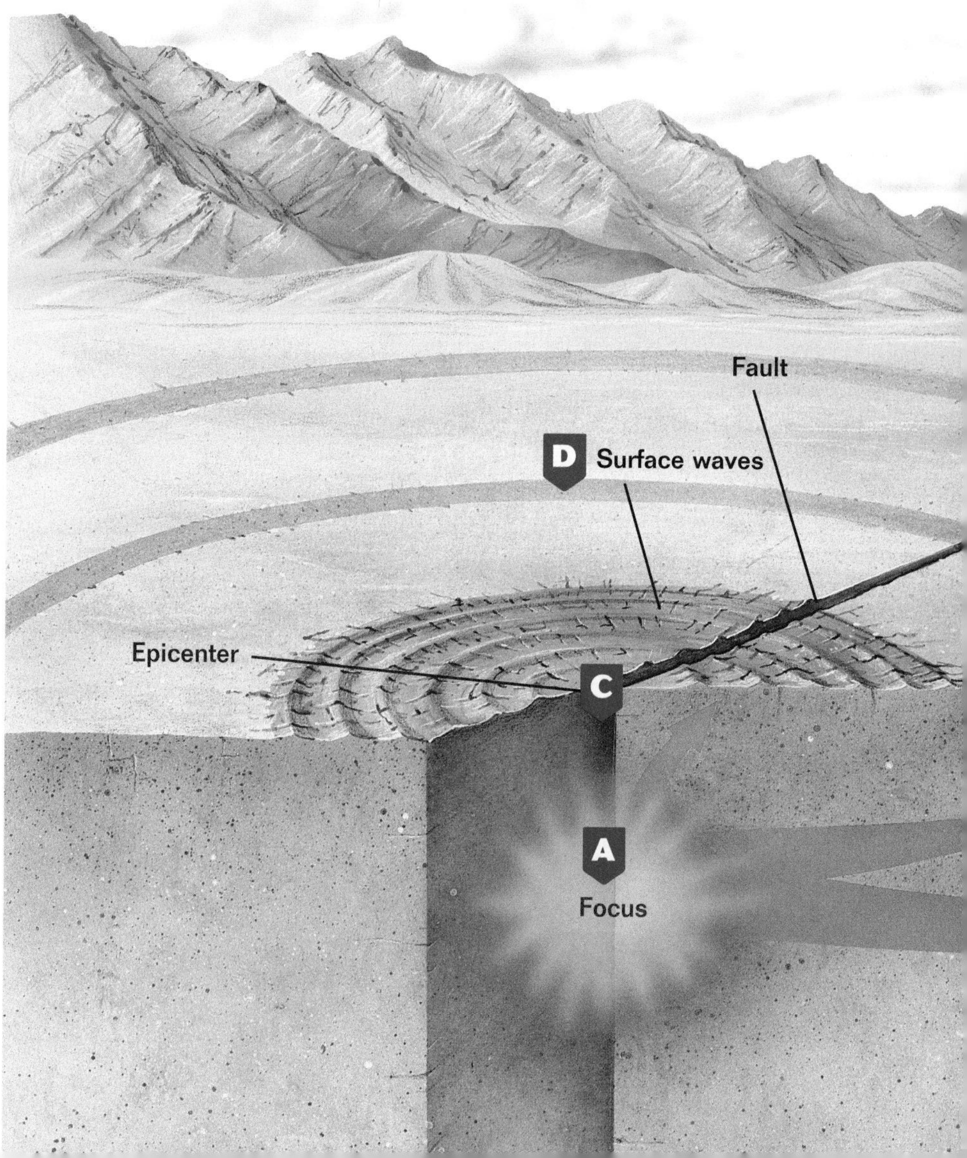

The point on Earth's surface directly above an earthquake's focus is the **epicenter** (EP ih sent ur), as shown in **Figure 10-6.** Energy that reaches the surface of Earth makes waves that travel outward from the epicenter. These waves, called **surface waves,** move particles up and down and side to side in a swaying motion.

Surface waves cause most of the destruction during an earthquake. Because most buildings are stiff and hard, they begin to fall apart when surface waves pass. The waves cause different parts of a building to move in different directions. This is because part of the surface wave motion is up and down, and part of the motion is side to side. ☑

Reading Check ☑

Which seismic waves cause most of the damage during an earthquake?

Locating an Epicenter

Primary, secondary, and surface waves don't travel through Earth at the same speed. Primary waves are the fastest. Surface waves are the slowest. Can you think of a way this information could be used to determine how far away an earthquake epicenter is? Think of the last time you and two friends rode your bikes to the store. You were fastest, so you arrived first. In fact, the longer you rode, the farther ahead of your friends you became. Scientists use the different speeds of seismic waves to find the distance to an earthquake epicenter.

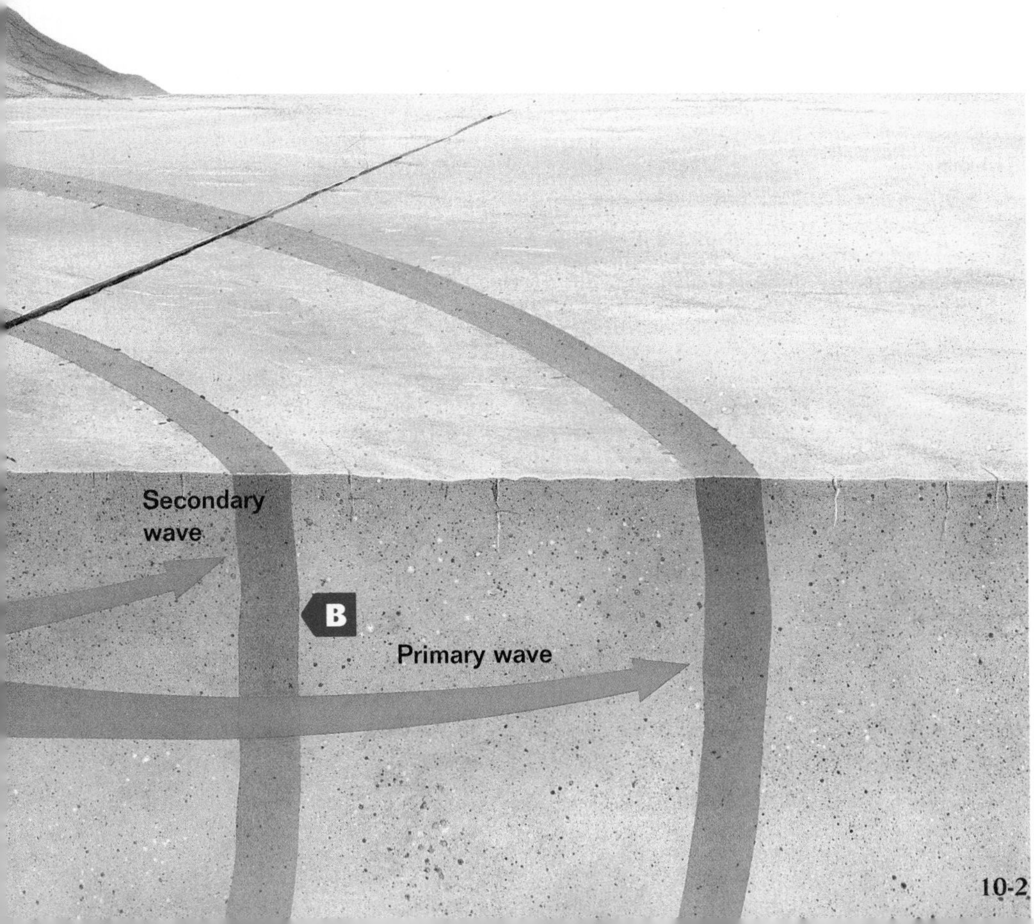

C The place on Earth's surface directly above the earthquake focus is called the epicenter. Surface waves radiate, or spread, outward from the epicenter in much the same way that ripples travel outward from a stone thrown into a pond.

D The amplitude, or height, of surface waves is greater than the amplitudes of primary and secondary waves. Surface waves cause the most damage during an earthquake.

Try at Home

MiniLab

Making and Using Tables and Graphs

Procedure

1. Use the graph in **Figure 10-7** to determine the difference in arrival times for primary and secondary waves at the distances listed in the data table below. Two examples are provided for you.
2. Use the graph to determine the differences in arrival times for at least two other distances of your choice.

Analysis

1. Interpret what happens to the difference in arrival times as the distance from the earthquake increases.
2. Explain how the distances you chose fit with what you interpreted in question 1.

Arrival Times

Distance (km)	Difference in Arrival Time
1500	2 minutes; 50 s
2250	
2750	
3000	
4000	5 minutes; 45 s
7000	
9000	

Seismograph Stations

Based on their different speeds, primary waves arrive first at recording stations, secondary waves second, as shown in **Figure 10-7,** and surface waves last. This allows scientists to determine the distance to an earthquake epicenter. The farther apart the wave arrivals, the farther away the epicenter is. When epicenters are far from the seismograph station, the primary wave has more time to put distance between it and the secondary and surface waves.

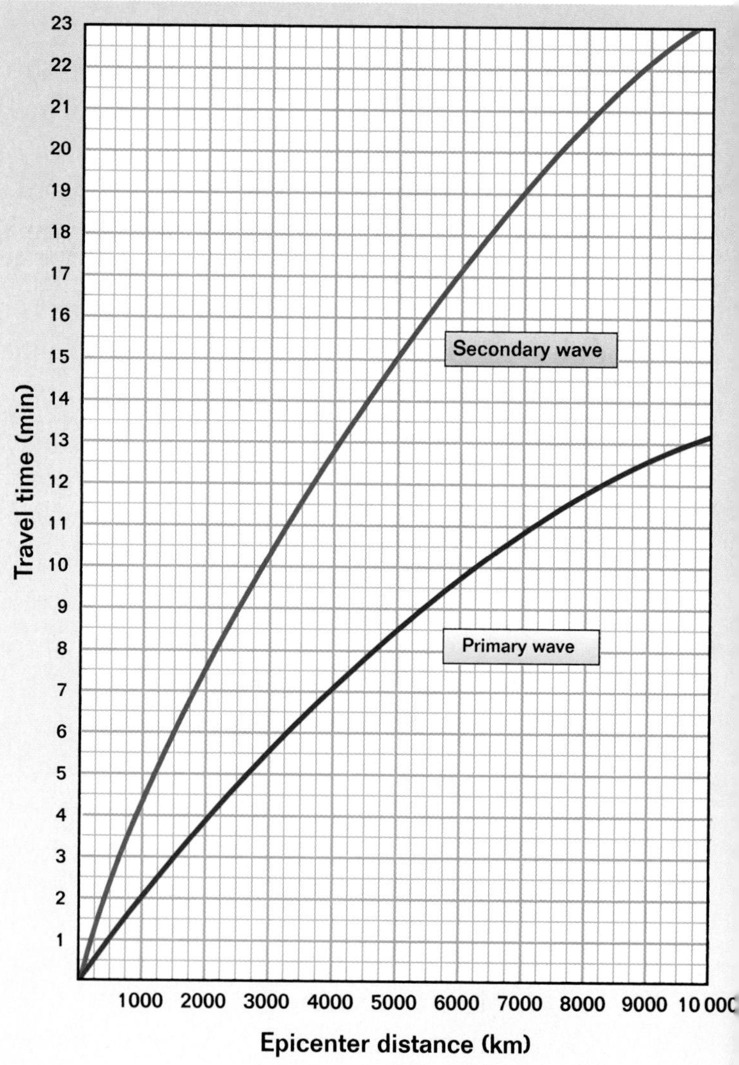

Figure 10-7 This graph shows the distance that primary and secondary waves travel over time. By measuring the difference in arrival times, a seismologist can determine the distance to the epicenter.

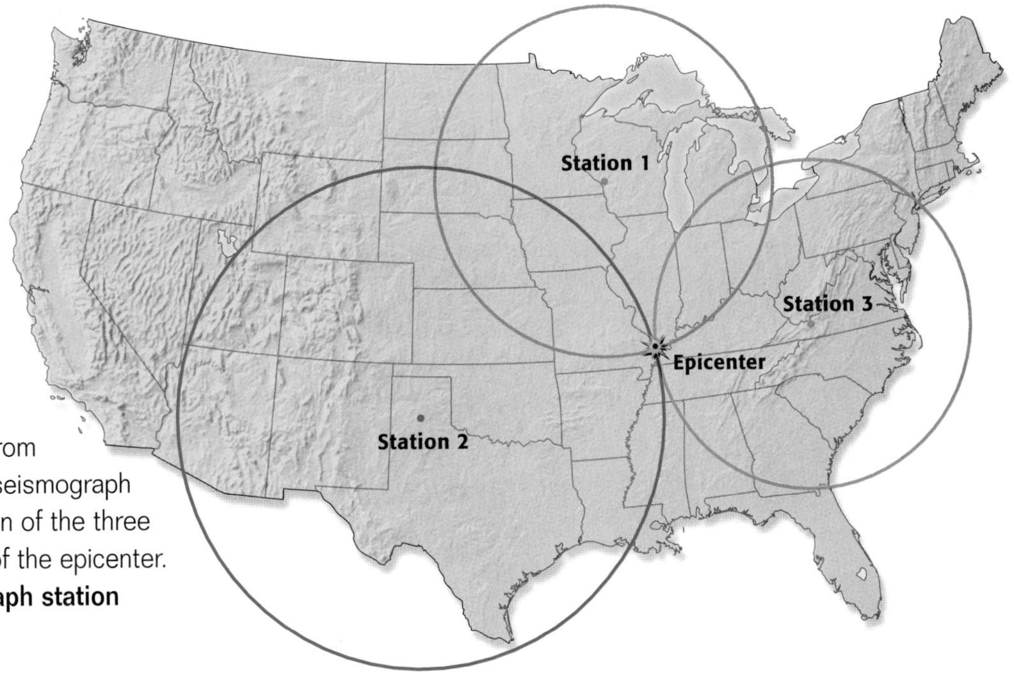

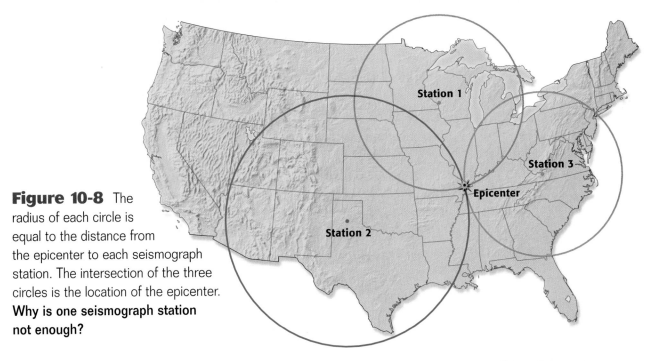

Figure 10-8 The radius of each circle is equal to the distance from the epicenter to each seismograph station. The intersection of the three circles is the location of the epicenter. **Why is one seismograph station not enough?**

Epicenter Location

If seismic wave information is recorded from at least three seismograph stations, the location of the epicenter can be determined, as shown in **Figure 10-8.** To locate an epicenter, scientists draw circles around each station on a map. The radius of each circle equals that station's distance from the earthquake epicenter. The point where all three circles meet is the location of the earthquake epicenter.

Mapping Earth's Interior

Scientists have found that at certain depths within Earth, the speed and path of seismic waves change. These changes mark the boundaries of the layers in Earth with different densities. Recall that the density of a material is mass per unit volume. In general, material in Earth's layers becomes denser toward the core as pressures increase. Using information from seismic waves, scientists have learned about Earth's interior without ever having been there, as shown in **Figure 10-9.**

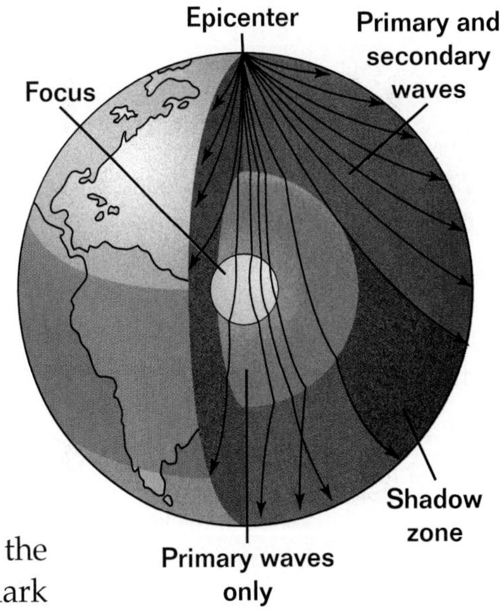

Figure 10-9 Primary waves bend when they contact the outer core (orange-red), and secondary waves are stopped completely. Primary waves also bend and speed up when they enter the inner core (yellow). In fact, as shown, seismic waves gradually bend and change speed as the density of rock changes.

Structure of Earth

Seismic wave studies allow scientists to make a model of Earth's interior, as shown in **Figure 10-10.** At the very center of Earth is a solid, dense **inner core** made mostly of iron with some nickel and smaller amounts of oxygen, silicon, and sulfur. Above the solid inner core lies the liquid **outer core,** also made mainly of iron. Earth's **mantle** is the largest layer, lying directly above the outer core. It is made mostly of silicon, oxygen, magnesium, and iron. Earth's thinnest, outermost layer is the **crust.**

Compared to the mantle, the crust contains more silicon and aluminum and less magnesium and iron. The crust is separated from the mantle by the Moho discontinuity.

Moho Discontinuity

Seismic waves speed up when they reach the bottom of the crust. This boundary between the crust and the mantle is called the *Moho discontinuity* (dis kahnt un EW ut ee). The boundary was discovered by the Yugoslavian scientist Andrija Mohorovičić, who inferred that seismic waves speed up because they're passing into a denser layer of Earth.

This denser layer is called the upper mantle, as shown in **Figure 10-10.** It is made up of minerals that are denser, on average, than minerals found in the crust.

VISUALIZING Layers of Earth

Figure 10-10 This wedge shows the layers inside Earth from the inner core. The inner core, outer core, and mantle are shown at the correct scale, but the crust is shown much thicker than it actually is.

A The crust of Earth varies in thickness. It is greater than 60 km in some mountainous regions, and less than 5 km thick under some oceans.

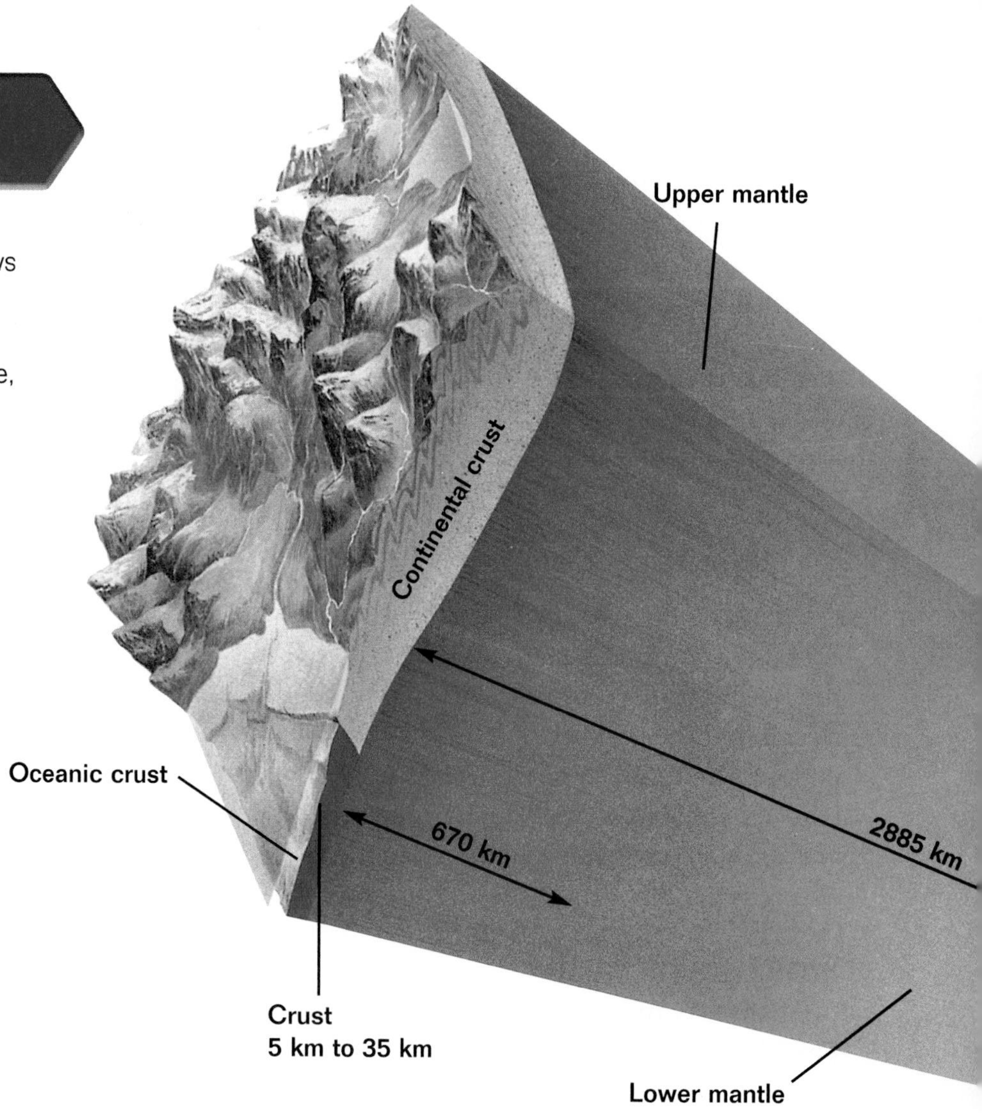

B There is a layer in the upper mantle where rock material is described as plasticlike. It is like a solid, but also flows like a liquid when under pressure. Some parts of this layer are thought to be molten.

Plasticlike Layer

Primary and secondary waves slow down when they hit a plasticlike layer that is part of the upper mantle. Then, seismic waves speed up again as they pass through the solid lower mantle. The denser the layer, the faster the seismic waves can travel through that layer.

Shadow Zone

An area exists on Earth where no seismic waves are detected after they are released by an earthquake. This area is called the *shadow zone.* Secondary waves don't pass through liquid, so they're stopped completely when they hit the liquid outer core. Primary waves are slowed and bent but not stopped by the liquid outer core. The bending of the primary waves and the stopping of the secondary waves create the shadow zone, as shown in **Figure 10-9.** These primary waves speed up again as they travel through the solid inner core. ✓

Reading Check ✓

Which seismic waves don't pass through liquid?

Mantle Samples

You can see that scientists learn a lot about Earth's interior by studying the behavior of seismic waves. But, did you ever wonder if anyone has ever held a piece of Earth's mantle or core in his or her hands? Some volcanic materials are a window to Earth's interior, containing minerals that scientists suggest are pieces of the upper mantle. Magma can break off and bring up pieces of the mantle as it forces its way to the surface as lava.

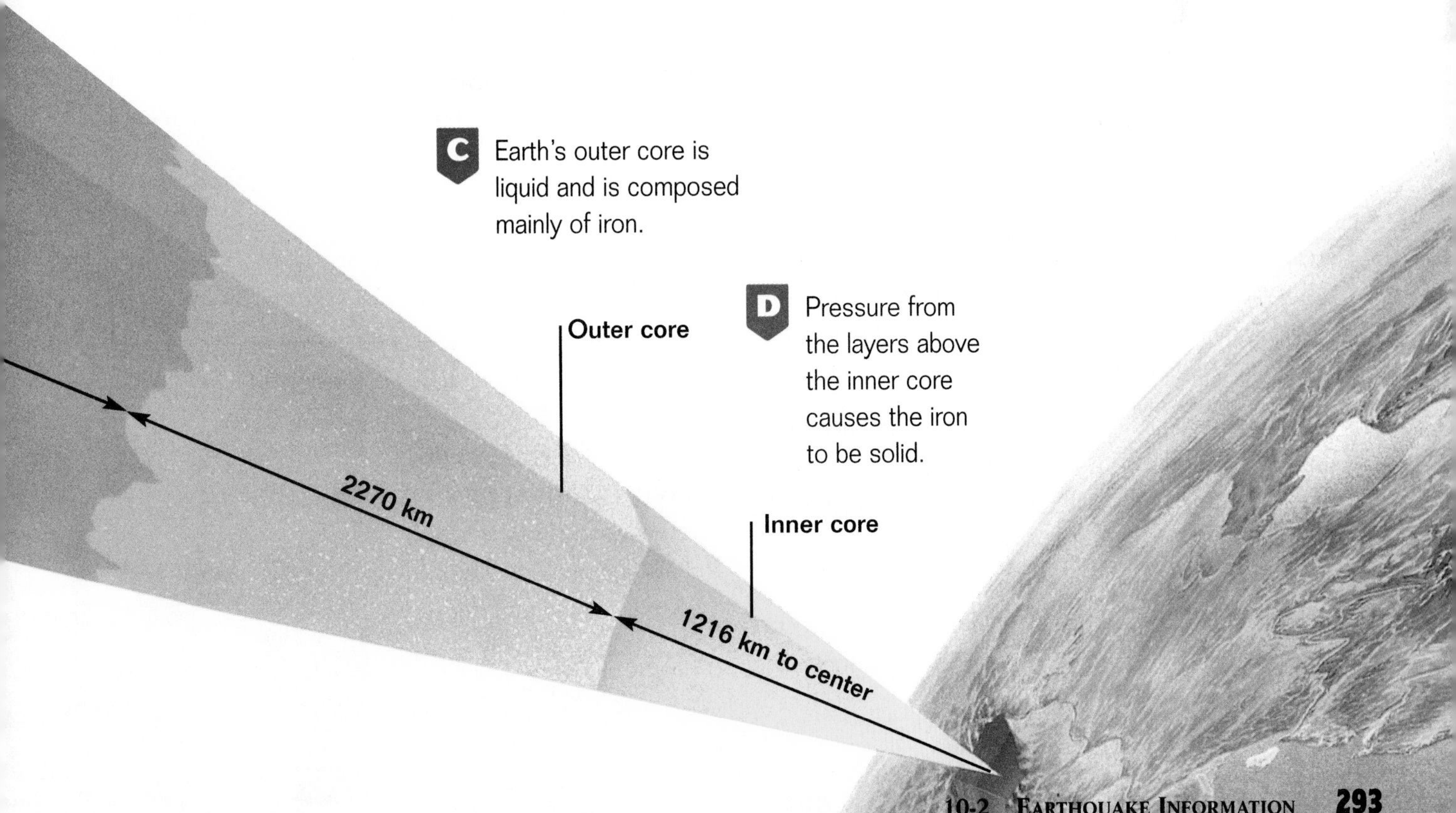

C
Earth's outer core is liquid and is composed mainly of iron.
D
Pressure from the layers above the inner core causes the iron to be solid.
Outer core
Inner core
2270 km
1216 km to center

Figure 10-11 Meteorites are made of minerals that are like those in different layers of Earth.

Meteorites

Samples of the deep mantle and core have never been collected. However, the rocky materials that make up our solar system, which includes Earth and meteorites, are thought to have formed at about the same time. Therefore, we can compare the composition of meteorites with that of Earth. Some meteorites have certain minerals that we know from rock formations and volcanic materials to be mantle minerals. Some meteorites are heavy and rich in iron, which studies show are the same materials in Earth's core. Scientists hypothesize that meteorites, such as the examples shown in **Figure 10-11,** contain samples that are like different parts of Earth's interior.

Problem Solving

Interpreting Data

Your teacher has placed five closed and sealed boxes in front of the class. The sizes of the five boxes are the same and equal to a sixth box that is empty. Your teacher has challenged you to complete problem-solving exercises in order to earn points. To earn all the points available, you must list at least three facts about the contents of each box. You are permitted to do anything you wish except open the boxes and look directly at the enclosed objects. The other rule is that you cannot damage any of the boxes in any way.

Determine what tests you will perform on each box that will reveal facts about its contents. You may wish to work with another student in case any of your tests require more than one person. In your Science Journal, make a table similar to the one above. Record all observations about the unknown box contents. List any inferences you have made concerning the contents of each box.

Box Interpretations

Box Number	Observations			Inferences
	Fact 1	Fact 2	Fact 3	
1				
2				
3				
4				
5				

Think Critically:
Compare the facts you discovered with those listed by your teacher. How is the challenge presented by your teacher related to a study of seismic waves and mapping of Earth's interior?

Using Math

Calculating Time

Example Problem: Primary waves travel at about 6 km/s through continental crust. The distance from Phoenix, Arizona, to Los Angeles, California, is about 600 km. How long would it take primary waves to travel between the two cities?

Problem-Solving Steps

1. What is known?
   distance, $d = 600$ km; average speed, $v = 6$ km/s
2. What is unknown? time, t
3. Use the equation, $t = d/v$
4. **Solution:** $t = d/v$
   $t = 600 \text{ km}/6 \text{ km/s} = 100 \text{ s}$ (1 minute, 40 s)

Practice Problem

Secondary waves travel at about 3.6 km/s through continental crust. How long would it take secondary waves to travel from Phoenix to Los Angeles?

Section Assessment

1. Which type of seismic wave does the most damage to property? Explain why.
2. Why is a seismic record from three locations needed to determine the position of an epicenter?
3. **Think Critically:** Suppose an earthquake occurs at the San Andreas Fault. What area on Earth would experience no secondary waves? Would China experience primary and secondary waves? Explain your answers.
4. **Skill Builder**
   Making and Using Graphs Use the data table below to make a graph of some travel times of earthquake waves. Which line represents primary waves? Which line represents secondary waves? If you need help, refer to Making and Using Graphs in the **Skill Handbook** on page 669.

Earthquake Wave Travel Times

Distance from Earthquake (km)	1500	2000	5000	5500	8600	10 000
Time (minutes)	5.0	2.5	14.0	7.0	11.0	23.5

Science Journal

When sound is produced, waves move through the air by pressing molecules together and then spreading them apart. Research sound waves and compare them to the types of seismic waves you have learned about. Relate what you learn to the fact that people report loud noise when earthquakes occur.

Activity 10-1

Using Scientific Methods

Epicenter Location

Materials

- **Figure 10-7**
- String
- Metric ruler
- Globe
- Chalk
- Paper

Try this activity to see how to plot the distance of several seismograph stations from the epicenters of two earthquakes and how to use these data to interpret where the earthquake epicenters were located.

What You'll Investigate

Can plotting the distance of several seismograph stations from two earthquake epicenters be used to interpret the locations of the two epicenters?

Goals

- **Plot** the distances of several seismograph stations based on primary and secondary wave arrival times.
- **Interpret** the location of earthquake epicenters from these plots.

Procedure

1. **Determine** the difference in arrival time between the primary and secondary waves at each station for each quake from the data table below.
2. Once you determine the arrival times of seismic waves for each seismograph station, use the graph in **Figure 10-7** to determine the distance in kilometers of each seismograph from the epicenter of each earthquake. **Record** these data in a data table provided by your teacher. The difference in arrival times in Paris for earthquake B is 9 minutes and 30 seconds. On the graph, the primary and secondary waves are separated along the vertical axis by 9 minutes and 30 seconds at 8975 km.
3. Using the string, **measure** the circumference of the globe. Determine a scale of centimeters of string to kilometers on Earth's surface. (Earth's circumference = 40 000 km.)
4. For each earthquake, A and B, place one end of the string at each seismic station location on the globe. Use the chalk to draw a circle with a radius equal to the distance from the earthquake's epicenter.
5. **Identify** the epicenter for each quake.

Conclude and Apply

1. How is the distance of a seismograph from the earthquake related to the arrival time of the waves?
2. What is the location of each earthquake epicenter?
3. How many stations were needed to accurately locate each epicenter?
4. **Predict** why some seismographs didn't receive secondary waves from some quakes.

Earthquake Wave Arrival Times

Location of Seismograph	Wave	Wave Arrival Times	
		Earthquake A	Earthquake B
(1) New York	P S	2:24:05 P.M. 2:29:15 P.M.	1:19:42 P.M. 1:25:27 P.M.
(2) Seattle	P S	2:24:40 P.M. 2:30:10 P.M.	1:14:37 P.M. 1:16:57 P.M.
(3) Rio de Janeiro	P S	2:29:10 P.M. 2:37:50 P.M.	— —
(4) Paris	P S	2:30:30 P.M. 2:40:10 P.M.	1:24:57 P.M. 1:34:27 P.M.
(5) Tokyo	P S	— —	1:24:27 P.M. 1:33:27 P.M.

Destruction by Earthquakes

10-3

Measuring Earthquakes

On January 25, 1999, a major earthquake struck Colombia, South America, leaving more than 1900 dead or missing. On February 4, 1998, and then again on May 30, 1998, major earthquakes of magnitudes 6.1 and 6.9 occurred at the Afghanistan-Tajikistan border. More than 6300 people were killed. On May 10, 1997, a magnitude-7.3 earthquake killed at least 1567 people in northern Iran. On January 17, 1995, a major earthquake occurred in Kobe, Japan, causing about $100 billion of property damage and 5502 deaths. On January 17, 1994, a major earthquake occurred in Northridge, California, causing billions of dollars of property damage, as seen in **Figure 10-12,** and 57 deaths. What determines the amount of damage done by an earthquake, and what can you do to protect yourself from the effects? With so many lives lost and such destruction, as shown in **Table 10-1,** it is important for scientists to learn as much as possible about earthquakes to try to reduce their damage.

What You'll Learn

- Definitions of *magnitude* and the *Richter scale*
- Ways to make your classroom and home more earthquake-safe

Vocabulary

seismologist
seismograph
magnitude
tsunami

Why It's Important

- People can prepare for earthquakes by building seismic-safe structures.

Figure 10-12
Several major highways were damaged in the January 17, 1994, earthquake in Northridge, California. **What happens during an earthquake that causes so much damage to highway overpasses?**

Seismology

Scientists who study earthquakes and seismic waves are **seismologists.** They use an instrument called a **seismograph** to record primary, secondary, and surface waves from earthquakes all over the world.

One type of seismograph has a drum holding a sheet of paper on a fixed frame. A pendulum with an attached pen is suspended from the frame. When seismic waves occur at the station, the drum vibrates but the pendulum remains at rest. The pen on the pendulum traces a record of the vibrations on a sheet of paper. The height of the lines traced on the paper is a measure of the energy released, or **magnitude,** of the earthquake.

Table 10-1

Large-Magnitude Earthquakes

Year	Location	Richter Value	Deaths
1556	Shensi, China	?	830 000
1737	Calcutta, India	?	300 000
1755	Lisbon, Portugal	8.8	70 000
1811–12	New Madrid, MO	8.3	few
1886	Charleston, SC	?	60
1906	San Francisco, CA	8.3	700–800
1920	Kansu Province, China	8.5	180 000
1923	Tokyo, Japan	8.3	143 000
1939	Concepcíón, Chile	8.3	30 000
1960	Southern Chile	8.6	5700
1964	Prince William Sound, AK	8.5	131
1970	Peru	7.8	66 800
1975	Laoning Province, China	7.5	few
1976	Tangshan, China	7.6	240 000
1985	Mexico City, Mexico	8.1	9500
1988	Armenia	6.9	28 000
1989	Loma Prieta, CA	6.9	63
1990	Iran	7.7	50 000
1990	Luzon, Philippines	7.8	1621
1993	Guam	8.1	none
1993	Marharashtra, India	6.4	30 000
1994	Northridge, CA	6.8	57
1995	Kobe, Japan	6.9	5502
1997	Northern Iran	7.3	>1500
1998	Afghanistan	6.1 & 6.9	>6300

Earthquake Magnitude

Not all seismographs measure vibrations in the same way. The Richter scale measures only local intensity on one kind of seismograph. However, seismologists also study magnitude in other ways.

The Richter magnitude is based on seismic waves that travel through Earth. It deals mainly with the strength of the break, not with the length or width of the fault. The Richter scale describes how much energy is released by the earthquake. For each increase of 1.0, the amplitude, or height, of the largest surface waves is ten times greater. However, about 32 times as much energy is released for every increase of 1.0 on the scale. For example, a magnitude-8.5 earthquake releases about 32 times as much energy as a magnitude-7.5

earthquake. **Table 10-2** shows how often various magnitude earthquakes are expected to occur.

Another magnitude used by seismologists is based on Earth movement or surface waves. Seismologists also use a magnitude called the moment magnitude. It comes from multiplying the length of the fault break by the amount of rock movement and then again by the rock stiffness. The moment magnitude depends on the strength and size of fault movement.

Table 10-2

Earthquake Occurrences	
Richter Magnitude	Number Expected per Year
1.0 to 3.9	> 949 000
4.0 to 4.9	6200
5.0 to 5.9	800
6.0 to 6.9	120
7.0 to 7.9	18
8.0 to 8.9	< 2

Tsunamis

Most earthquake damage happens when surface waves cause buildings, bridges, and roads to collapse. People living near the seashore, however, have another problem. An earthquake under the sea causes a sudden movement of the ocean floor. The movement pushes against the water, causing a powerful wave that can travel thousands of kilometers in all directions, as shown in **Figure 10-13.** Far from shore, a wave caused by an earthquake is so long that a large ship may ride over it without anyone noticing. But, when one of these waves breaks on a shore, it forms a towering crest that can reach 30 m in height. Ocean waves caused by earthquakes are called seismic sea waves, or **tsunamis** (soo NAHM eez).

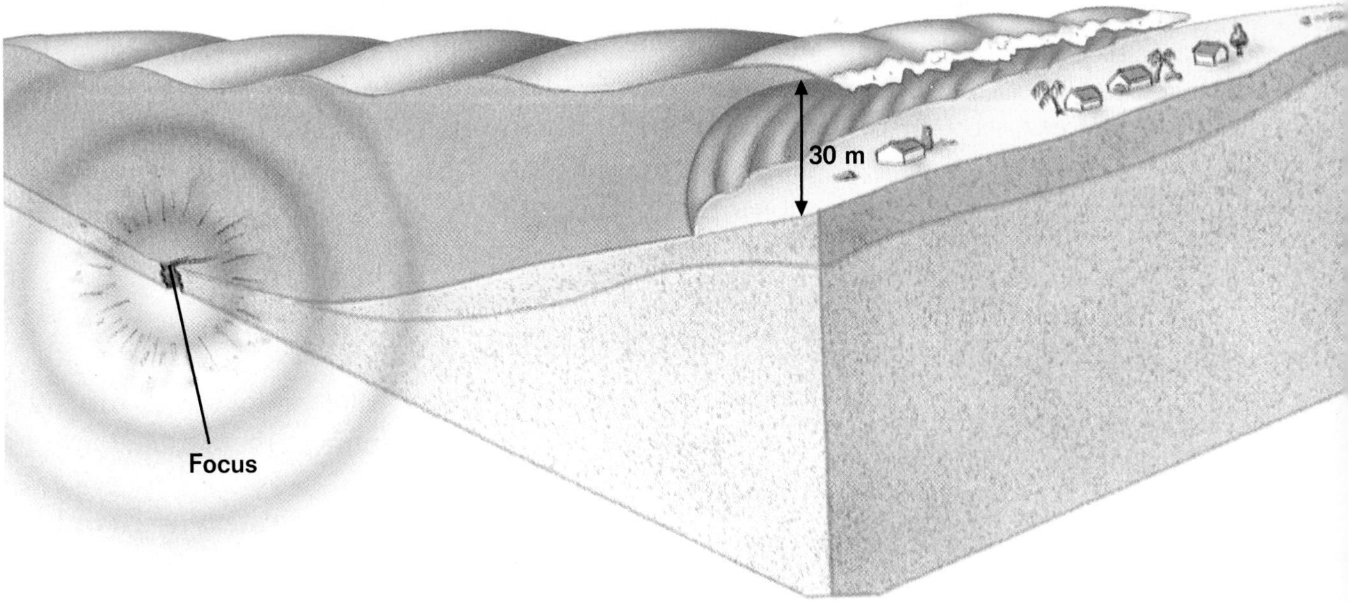

Figure 10-13 A tsunami begins over the earthquake focus. **What might happen to towns located near the shore?**

Figure 10-14 On July 17, 1998, a powerful tsunami swept away trees and houses along the northern coast of Papua, New Guinea. At least 2000 people died.

Just before a tsunami crashes on shore, the water along a shoreline may move rapidly toward the sea, exposing a large portion that is normally underwater. This should be taken as an immediate warning sign that a tsunami could strike. **Figure 10-14** shows some damage that was caused by the tsunami that struck Papua, New Guinea, on July 17, 1998.

*inter***NET**
CONNECTION

Visit the Glencoe Science Web Site at **www.glencoe.com/sec/science/ca** for more information about tsunamis.

Earthquake Safety

You've seen the destruction that earthquakes can cause. However, there are ways to minimize the damage and loss of life.

One of the first steps in earthquake safety is to study the earthquake history of a region, such as the one illustrated in **Figure 10-16.** If you live in an area that's had earthquakes in the past, you can expect them to occur there in the future. As you know, most earthquakes happen along plate boundaries. **Table 10-1** shows where severe earthquakes have happened. Being prepared is an important step in earthquake safety.

Quake-Proofing Your Home

Make your home as earthquake-safe as possible. Take heavy objects down from high shelves and place them on lower shelves. Reduce the chance of fire from broken gas lines by checking that hot-water heaters and gas appliances are held securely in place. During an earthquake, keep away from windows and avoid anything that could fall on you. Watch for fallen power lines and possible fire hazards. Stay clear of rubble that could contain sharp edges.

Seismic-Safe Structures

Seismic-safe structures stand up to vibrations that occur during an earthquake. **Figure 10-15** shows how buildings can be built to resist earthquake damage.

Today in California, some new buildings are held together by flexible, circular moorings placed under the buildings. The moorings are arranged in layers of steel plates and rubber parts. The rubber acts like a cushion to absorb earthquake waves.

MiniLab

Modeling Seismic-Safe Structures

Procedure

1. Obtain a set of building blocks from your teacher.
2. On a tabletop, build one structure out of the blocks by simply placing one block on top of another.
3. Build a second structure by wrapping sections of three blocks together with rubber bands. Then, wrap larger rubber bands around the entire completed structure.
4. Set the second structure on the tabletop and pound on the side of the table with a steady rhythm.

Analysis

1. Which of your two structures was better able to withstand the "earthquake" caused by pounding on the table?
2. How might the idea of wrapping the blocks with rubber bands be used in construction of supports for elevated highways?

Figure 10-15 The rubber portions of this building's moorings absorb most of the wave motion of an earthquake. The building itself only sways gently. **What purpose does the rubber serve?**

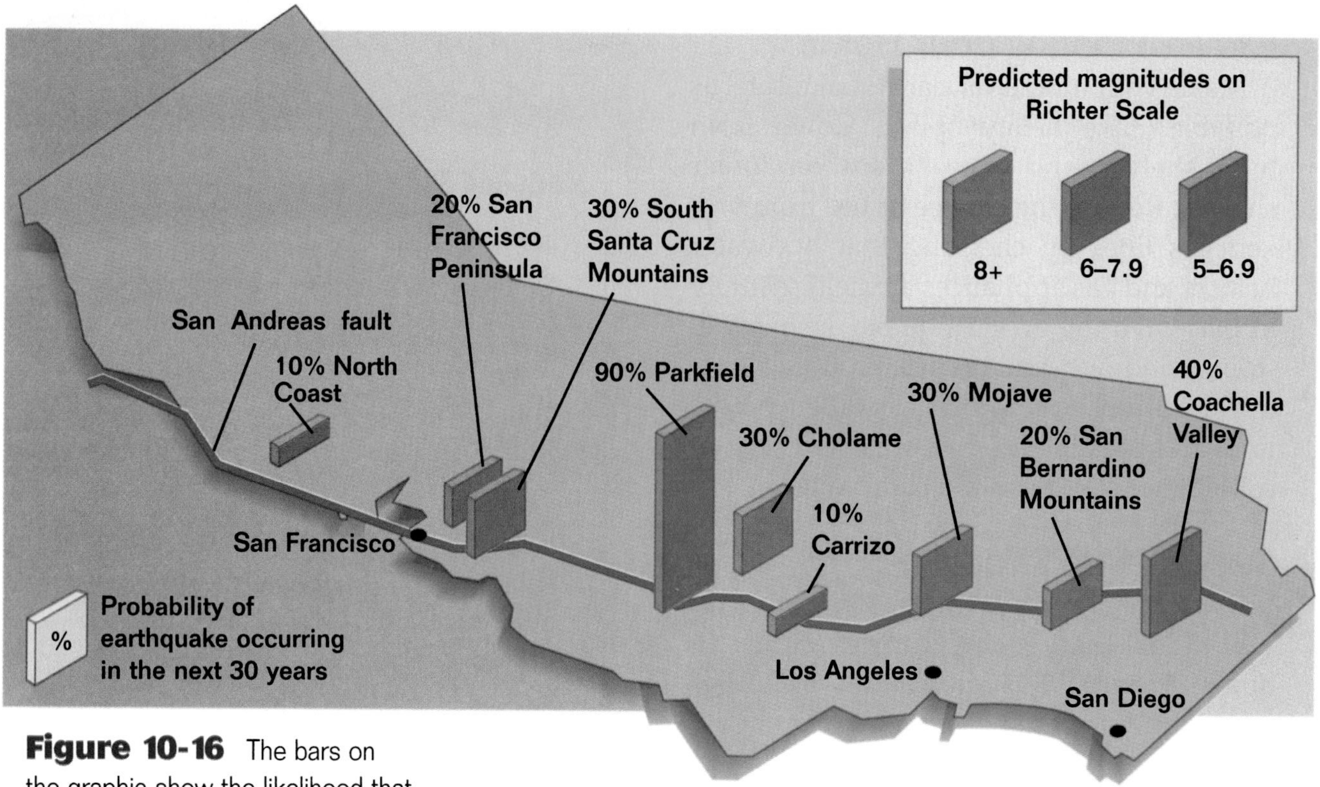

Figure 10-16 The bars on the graphic show the likelihood that an earthquake of a certain magnitude will strike these areas within the next 30 years. California residents are preparing for the major earthquakes predicted there.

Figure 10-15 shows how they work. Tests have shown that buildings supported in this way should be able to withstand an earthquake measuring up to 8.3 on the Richter scale without major damage.

Section Assessment

1. How do rubber moorings in a building help minimize damage during an earthquake?
2. Research how animal behavior has been studied to predict earthquakes. What changes may be occurring in the environment to cause animals to act differently?
3. **Think Critically:** Explain why a seismograph wouldn't work if the pen vibrated along with the rest of the machine.
4. **Skill Builder**
   Using Numbers Have you ever wondered what you would need to have stored up at home in the event of an earthquake? To find out what's important, and how much it costs, do the **Chapter 10 Skill Activity** on page 703.

Using Math

Calculate the difference in energy released between an earthquake of Richter magnitude 7.5 and one of magnitude 5.5.

Why We Have Earthquakes— A Korean Folktale

An earthquake is a shaking of Earth caused by the release of energy as rock suddenly breaks or shifts under stress. Most quakes happen along faults—breaks in Earth's crust along which rocks on either side can move. The Korean Peninsula is relatively stable compared to Japan, which is situated on a plate boundary. Of the nearly 2000 earthquakes that have been historically or scientifically recorded in Korea since 2 A.D., only 48 have been destructive.

Traditional Korean folktales, which have been passed on orally from generation to generation, explain natural events such as earthquakes. The tales also are told to teach moral lessons. Like the folktales and myths of other cultures throughout the world, Korean folktales reflect the peculiarities of the environment where they are told.

A Shoulder to Lean On

One Korean folktale tells of a time when one corner of Heaven began to sag. The King of Heaven took a gigantic pillar of red copper and placed one end on Earth and the other end under the sagging corner of Heaven.

The ground on Earth was soft, and, since Heaven was heavy, the pillar began to sink into Earth. The king sent the strongest man in Heaven to hold the pillar on his shoulder. This was the only way to keep the great weight of Heaven from sagging.

The man is still holding the pillar. He can't let it slip from his shoulder or all of Heaven will come crashing down. But, the great weight becomes painful for the man to hold on just one shoulder. So, from time to time, he shifts the pillar from one shoulder to the other. Every time the man shifts the weight of the pillar, the ground on Earth shakes with his efforts. According to the folktale, this is why we have earthquakes.

Science JOURNAL

Using what you have learned about earthquakes in this chapter, write your own story to explain why earthquakes occur. Use your stories to explain things about earthquakes that are still not well understood. Read your classmates' stories to find out what questions they still have about earthquakes. Make a list of these questions in your Science Journal.

Activity 10•2

Earthquake Depths

Materials

- Graph paper
- Pencil

You learned earlier in this chapter that Earth's crust is broken into sections called plates. Stresses caused by movement of these plates generate energy within rocks that must be released. When this release is sudden and rocks break, an earthquake occurs.

What You'll Investigate

Can a study of the foci of earthquakes tell us anything about how strain builds up in rocks and how it may be released?

Goals

- **Observe** any connection between earthquake-focus depth and epicenter location using the data provided on the next page.
- **Describe** any observed relationship between earthquake-focus depth and the movement of plates at Earth's surface.

Procedure

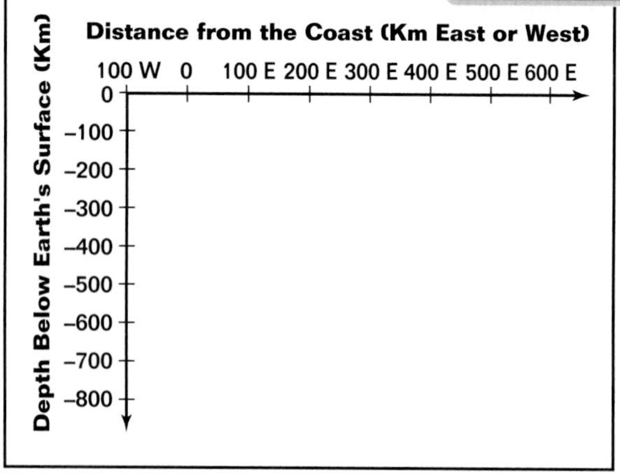

1. Use graph paper and the data table on the next page to make a line graph plotting the depths of earthquake foci and the distances from the coast of a continent for each earthquake epicenter.
2. **Place** "Distance from the coast" on the horizontal axis. Begin labeling at the far left with 100 km west. To the right of it should be 0 km, then 100 km east, 200 km east, 300 km east, and so on through 700 km east. What point on your graph would represent the coast?
3. Label the vertical axis "Depth below Earth's surface." **Label** the top of the graph 0 km to represent Earth's surface. **Label** the bottom of the vertical axis −800 km.
4. **Plot** the focus depths against the distance and direction from the coast for each earthquake in the table on the next page.

Conclude and Apply

1. **Describe** any observed relation between the location of earthquake epicenters and the depth of earthquake foci.
2. Based on the graph you have completed, **hypothesize** what is happening to the plates at Earth's surface in the vicinity of the plotted earthquake foci.
3. **Infer** what process is causing the earthquakes you plotted on your graph paper.
4. **Hypothesize** why none of the plotted earthquakes occurred below 700 km.

Focus and Epicenter Data

Quake	Focus Depth	Distance of Epicenter from Coast (km)
A	−55 km	0
B	−295 km	100 E
C	−390 km	455 E
D	−60 km	75 E
E	−130 km	255 E
F	−195 km	65 E
G	−695 km	400 E
H	−20 km	40 W
I	−505 km	695 E
J	−520 km	390 E
K	−385 km	335 E
L	−45 km	95 E
M	−305 km	495 E
N	−480 km	285 E
O	−665 km	545 E
P	−85 km	90 W
Q	−525 km	205 E
R	−85 km	25 W
S	−445 km	595 E
T	−635 km	665 E
U	−55 km	95 W
V	−70 km	100 W

Chapter 10 Reviewing Main Ideas

For a **preview** of this chapter, study this Reviewing Main Ideas before you read the chapter. After you have studied this chapter, you can use the Reviewing Main Ideas to **review** the chapter.

GLENCOE TECHNOLOGY

The Glencoe MindJogger, Audiocassettes, and CD-ROM provide additional opportunities for review.

Section 10-1 FORCES INSIDE EARTH

Plate movements put stress on rocks. To a point, the rocks bend and stretch. But, if the force is great enough and the rock's elastic limit is passed, the rocks will remain bent and may break. When the rocks break, they can move along surfaces called **faults.** Breaking rocks produce vibrations called **earthquakes.** ***How do rocks move relative to each other in a reverse fault?***

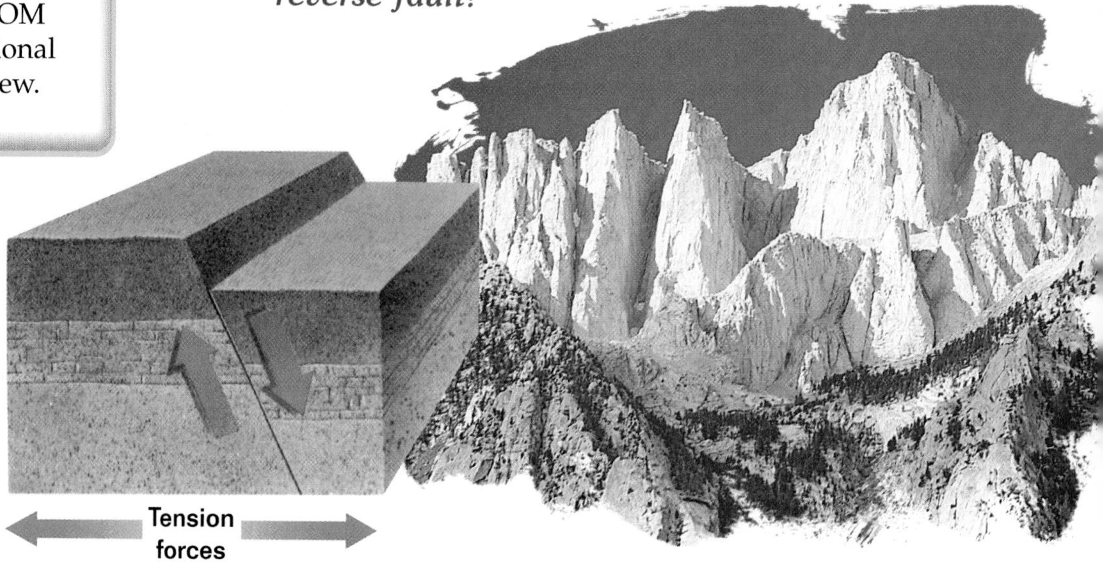

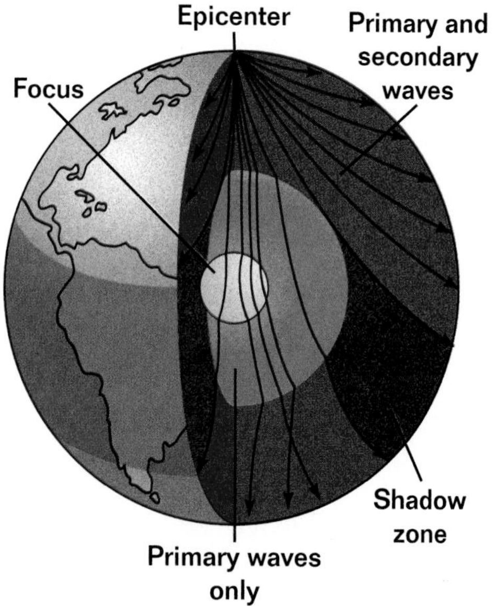

Section 10-2 EARTHQUAKE INFORMATION

Primary waves compress and stretch rock particles as the waves move. **Secondary waves** move by causing particles in the rocks to move at right angles to the direction of the waves. **Surface waves** move rock particles up and down and from side to side. Scientists can locate earthquake **epicenters** by measuring **seismic wave** speeds. By observing the speeds and paths of seismic waves, scientists are able to determine the boundaries among Earth's layers. ***What happens to the path and speed of seismic waves as they move from one layer to another inside Earth?***

Reading Check ☑

Write your own summary of Section 10-3 before reading the text on this page. Try to keep your summary within three to five sentences.

Section

10-3 DESTRUCTION BY EARTHQUAKES

Seismologists study **earthquakes** and the waves produced by earthquakes. The **magnitude** of an earthquake is a measure of the energy released by the earthquake. The Richter scale describes how much energy is released by an earthquake. For each difference of one on the Richter scale, an earthquake releases about 32 times more energy. ***How much more energy is released by an earthquake of magnitude 8.5 than an earthquake of magnitude 6.5?***

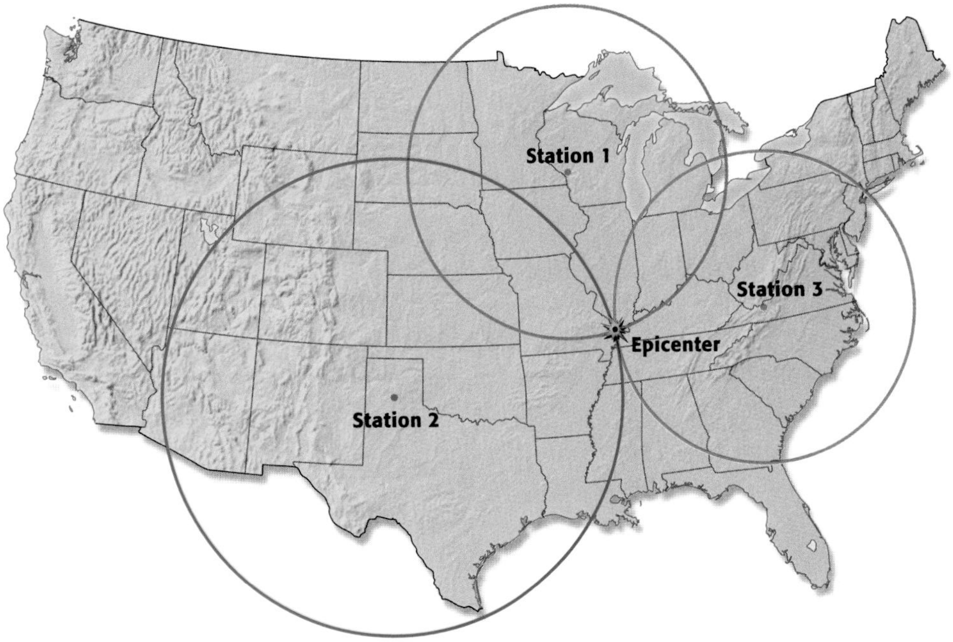

SEISMIC-SAFE STRUCTURES

Most lives lost during an earthquake are due to destruction of human-made structures. Seismic-safe structures are resistant to vibrations that occur during an earthquake. Buildings in areas with such structures are damaged during an earthquake but are less likely to collapse. ***Give suggestions for how to quake-proof your home.***

Chapter 10 Assessment

Using Vocabulary

a. crust
b. earthquake
c. epicenter
d. fault
e. focus
f. inner core
g. magnitude
h. mantle
i. normal fault
j. outer core
k. primary wave
l. reverse fault
m. secondary wave
n. seismic wave
o. seismograph
p. seismologist
q. strike-slip fault
r. surface wave
s. tsunami

Distinguish between the terms in each of the following pairs.

1. surface wave, tsunami
2. fault, focus
3. normal fault, reverse fault
4. seismologist, seismograph
5. inner core, outer core

Checking Concepts

Choose the word or phrase that best answers the question.

6. Earthquakes can occur when which of the following is passed?
   A) tension limit
   B) seismic limit
   C) elastic limit
   D) shear limit
7. When the rock above the fault surface moves down relative to the rock below the fault surface, what kind of fault forms?
   A) normal
   B) strike-slip
   C) reverse
   D) shearing
8. Primary and secondary waves move outward from which of the following?
   A) epicenter
   B) focus
   C) Moho discontinuity
   D) tsunami
9. What kind of waves stretch and compress rocks?
   A) surface
   B) primary
   C) secondary
   D) shear
10. What are the slowest seismic waves?
    A) surface
    B) primary
    C) secondary
    D) pressure
11. What is the fewest number of seismograph stations that are needed to locate the epicenter of an earthquake?
    A) two
    B) three
    C) four
    D) five
12. What happens to primary waves when they go from liquids into solids?
    A) slow down
    B) speed up
    C) stay the same
    D) stop
13. What part of a seismograph remains still?
    A) sheet of paper
    B) fixed frame
    C) drum
    D) pendulum
14. An earthquake of magnitude 7.5 has how much more energy than a quake of magnitude 6.5?
    A) 32 times more
    B) 32 times less
    C) twice as much
    D) about half as much
15. How are most lives lost during an earthquake?
    A) tsunamis
    B) primary waves
    C) collapse of buildings
    D) broken gas lines

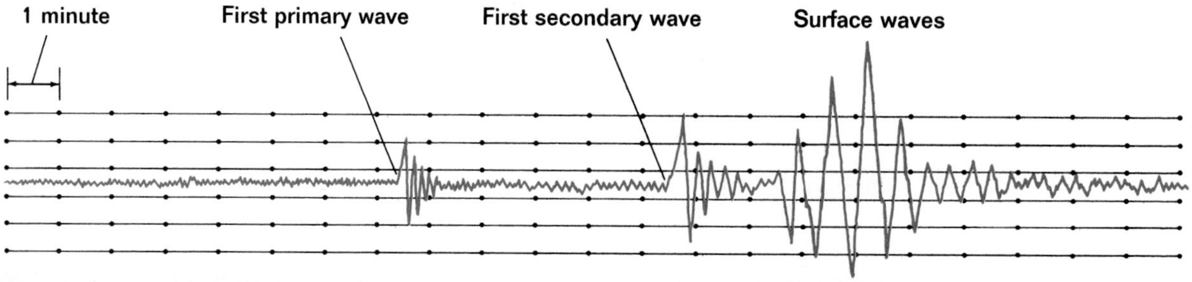

Thinking Critically

16. What kind of faults would you expect to be most common along the Mid-Atlantic Ridge? Explain.

17. Tsunamis often are called tidal waves. Explain why this is incorrect.

18. Which would probably be more stable during an earthquake—a single-story wood-frame house or a brick building? Explain.

Developing Skills

If you need help, refer to the **Skill Handbook.**

19. Interpreting Scientific Illustrations: The illustration on the opposite page is a typical record of earthquake waves made on a seismograph. How many minutes passed between the arrival of the first primary wave and the first secondary wave?

20. Concept Mapping: Complete the concept map below showing what faults result from the three forces. Use the following terms: *tension, compression, shear, normal faults, reverse faults,* and *strike-slip faults.*

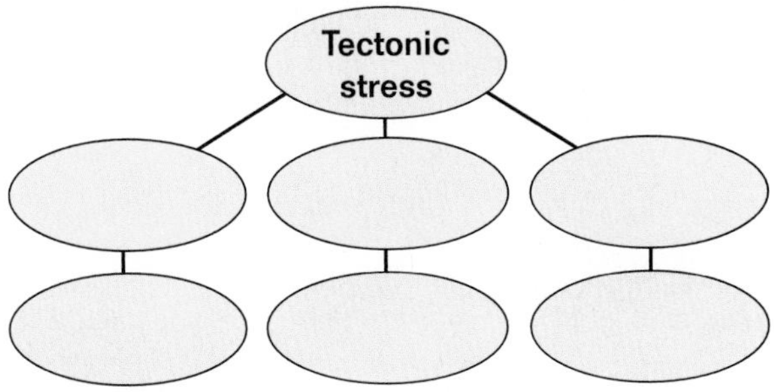

THE PRINCETON REVIEW

Test-Taking Tip

Work Weak Areas, Maintain Strong Ones It's sometimes difficult to focus on all the concepts needed for a test. So, ask yourself "What's my strongest area?" and "What's my weakest area?" Focus most of your energy on your weak areas. But, also put in some upkeep time in your best areas.

Test Practice

Use these questions to test your Science Proficiency.

1. Normal faults occur when tension is applied to rocks. Which of the following statements **BEST** supports this fact?
   A) As tension is applied, Earth's crust thins and can crack.
   B) When Earth's crust thins and cracks due to tension, the rock above the fault moves down relative to the rock below the fault.
   C) Tension causes Earth's crust to fold and eventually develop faults.
   D) When Earth's crust thins and cracks due to tension, the rock above the fault moves up relative to the rock below the fault.

2. Seismic records show that primary waves slow down and secondary waves stop when they reach Earth's outer core. What does this tell you about Earth's outer core?
   A) The density of Earth material increases in the outer core.
   B) Earth's outer core is solid.
   C) Earth's outer core is liquid and has a lower density than rock material at the bottom of the mantle.
   D) Earth's inner core is solid and more dense than the mantle.

CHAPTER 11

Volcanoes

Chapter Preview

Skills Preview

Skill Builders
- Map Concepts

Activities
- Measure
- Interpret Data

MiniLabs
- Make a Model

Reading Check

Before you begin this chapter, look up the word origins of unfamiliar terms like *tephra*, *batholith*, and *caldera*. Knowing the origins will help you understand these words.

Explore Activity

The explosive eruptions of Soufrière Hills volcano on the Caribbean island of Montserrat began in July 1995 and have blanketed much of the island with volcanic ash. Clouds of ash rose to heights of 12 000 m and covered much of the capital city of Plymouth. Volcanoes can be spectacular and dangerous. Massive eruptions of volcanic ash into Earth's atmosphere can cause drastic changes in the environment. On a smaller scale, and definitely in the case of Montserrat island's population, volcanic eruptions affect humans in many ways. List harmful and also helpful effects that volcanoes have.

Model a Volcano

1. Use clay to make a small model volcano with a crater at the top.
2. Place a small amount of baking soda (less than 1/4 teaspoon) and a drop of red food coloring in the crater.
3. Add approximately 20 mL of vinegar to the baking soda in the crater.

Science Journal

In your Science Journal, write a paragraph that explains what happens to the baking soda and food coloring when the vinegar is added. Hypothesize how your model eruption is similar to an actual eruption and how it is different.

11•1 What causes volcanoes?

What You'll Learn

- ► How volcanoes can affect people
- ► Conditions that cause volcanoes
- ► The relationship between volcanoes and Earth's moving plates

Vocabulary
volcano
vent
crater
hot spot

Why It's Important

- ► You'll understand why volcanoes are common in certain regions on Earth.

Volcanoes and You

A **volcano** is an opening in Earth's surface. It often forms a mountain when layers of lava and volcanic ash erupt and build up. Most of Earth's volcanoes are dormant, which means that they are not currently active, but more than 600 are active now. Active volcanoes sometimes erupt smoke, steam, ash, cinders, and flows of lava.

In 1980, Mount St. Helens in Washington State erupted. Geologists had warned people to leave the area surrounding the mountain. Most people left, but a few stayed. A total of 63 people were killed as a result of the eruption. The eruption also destroyed 400 km^2 of forested wildlife habitation on the north side of the volcano. Trees were blown over, or their branches were torn off.

Active Volcanoes

For centuries, the Kilauea volcano in Hawaii has been erupting, but not explosively. Most of the town of Kalapana Gardens was destroyed in May 1990. No one was hurt because the lava moved slowly. The most recent series of eruptions from Kilauea, as seen in **Figure 11-1,** began in January 1983.

Figure 11-1 Kilauea in Hawaii has been continually erupting since January 3, 1983, becoming the most active volcano on Earth. Living with volcanoes as active as Kilauea can create serious problems for home owners. Losses have reached 61 million dollars as at least 181 homes have been destroyed.

Figure 11-2 Volcanic ash covered several buildings in Iceland during an eruption in 1973. **Why might people continue to live close to a volcano despite the danger?**

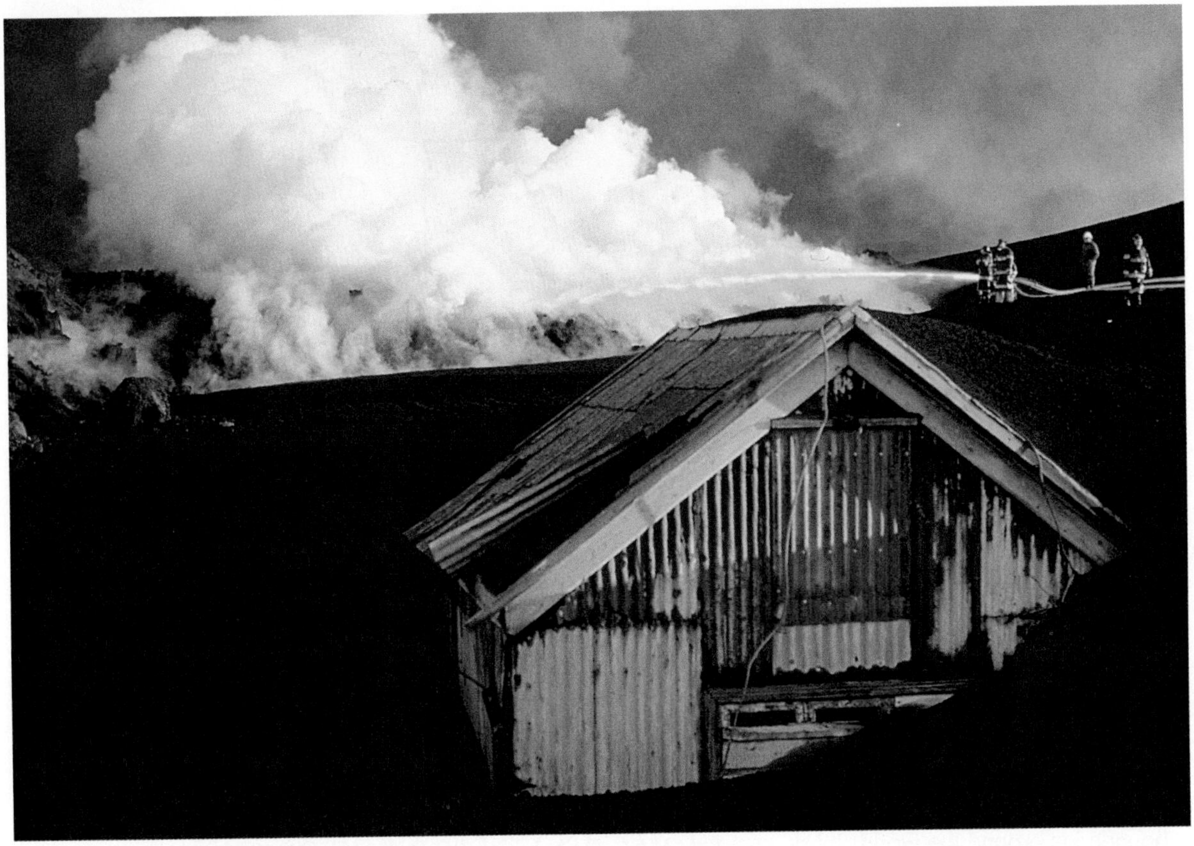

Kilauea is the world's most active volcano. Iceland is also famous for its active volcanoes and is known as the land of fire and ice. An Icelandic eruption is shown in **Figure 11-2.**

Eruptions of the Century

The largest volcanic eruption of the twentieth century occurred on the Alaska Peninsula. Beginning on June 6, 1912, Mount Katmai erupted an estimated 30 times greater volume of material than was expelled during the 1980 eruption of Mount St. Helens. In June 1991, Mount Pinatubo erupted in the Philippines, killing nearly 900 people. The eruption is considered the largest of any volcano in more than half a century. Millions of tons of sulfur dioxide and ash were thrown into Earth's upper atmosphere. It's possible that this material was the cause of the lowered global temperatures and record ozone losses that were observed as recently as 1993.

Just prior to the eruption of Mount Pinatubo, Mount Unzen in Japan erupted. Forty-four people lost their lives, including several volcanologists who were studying the erupting volcano and producing an educational program.

Using Math

Approximately 7000 quickly moving flows of hot gas and volcanic debris have occurred on Mount Unzen in Japan from 1991 through 1994. As long as Mount Unzen remains active, how many such flows, on average, can be expected to occur on Mount Unzen each month?

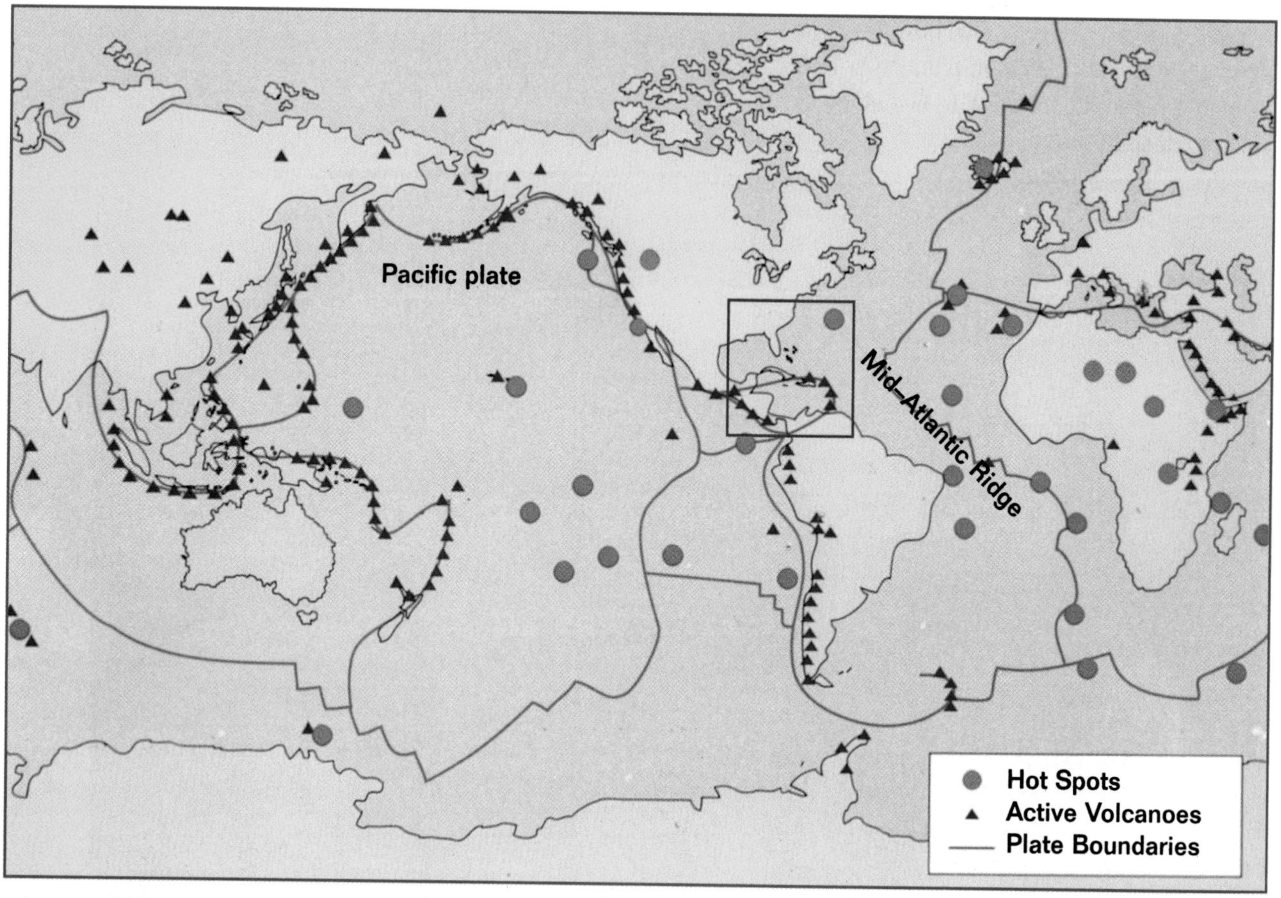

Figure 11-3 The diagram above shows the locations of active volcanoes, hot spots, and plate boundaries around the world. The squared-off area is shown in depth in **Figure 11-4B. How are the locations of active volcanoes related to the locations of hot spots and plate boundaries?**

Reading Check

Why is magma forced upward toward Earth's surface?

How do volcanoes form?

What happens inside Earth to create volcanoes? Why are some areas of Earth more likely to have volcanoes than others? Deep inside Earth, heat and pressure cause rock to melt and form magma. Some deep rocks already are melted. Others are hot enough that a small rise in temperature or drop in pressure can cause them to melt to form magma.

Magma Forced Upward

Magma is less dense than the rock around it, so it is slowly forced upward toward Earth's surface. You can see this process if you turn a bottle of cold syrup upside down. Watch the dense syrup force the less-dense air bubbles slowly toward the top of the bottle.

After many thousands or even millions of years, magma reaches Earth's surface and flows out through an opening called a **vent.** As lava flows out, it cools quickly and becomes solid, forming layers of igneous rock around the vent. The steep-walled depression around a volcano's vent is the **crater.**

Where do volcanoes occur?

Volcanoes form in places that are directly related to the movement of Earth's plates. Volcanoes occur where plates are moving apart, where plates are moving together, and at locations called hot spots. You can find locations of active volcanoes along with plate boundaries and hot spots on the map in **Figure 11-3.** There are many examples of volcanoes around the world at these three different areas. Let's explore volcanoes in Iceland, the Caribbean island of Montserrat, and Hawaii.

Plates Moving Apart

Iceland is a large island in the North Atlantic Ocean. It is near the Arctic Circle and has some glaciers. But, as seen in **Figure 11-2,** it also has volcanoes. Iceland has volcanic activity because it sits on top of the Mid-Atlantic Ridge.

The Mid-Atlantic Ridge is an area where Earth's plates are moving apart. Where plates separate, they form long, deep cracks called rifts. Magma flows from rifts as lava and is quickly cooled by seawater. **Figure 11-4A** shows how magma rises at rifts to form new volcanic rock. As more lava flows, it builds up from the seafloor. Sometimes, the volcanoes and rift eruptions rise above sea level, forming islands such as Iceland.

Plates Moving Together

Soufrière Hills volcano is located on the island of Montserrat, which is part of the Lesser Antilles islands of the Caribbean. Soufrière Hills volcano formed because it is located where Earth's plates move together as shown in **Figure 11-4B.** Here, the North and South American plates are forced under the less-dense Caribbean plate.

Figure 11-4 The locations of volcanoes depend on the motion of Earth's plates.

A Volcanic activity occurs where Earth's plates move apart. **Why does Iceland have volcanoes?**

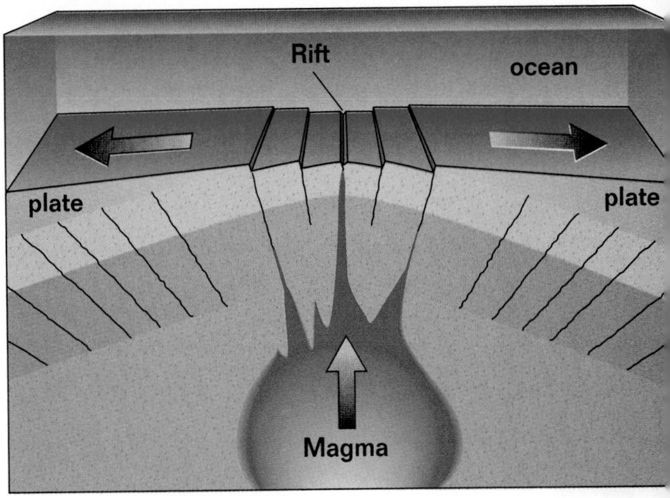

B Volcanoes form where the North and South American plates are forced below the Caribbean plate. **Why does magma form along this type of plate boundary?**

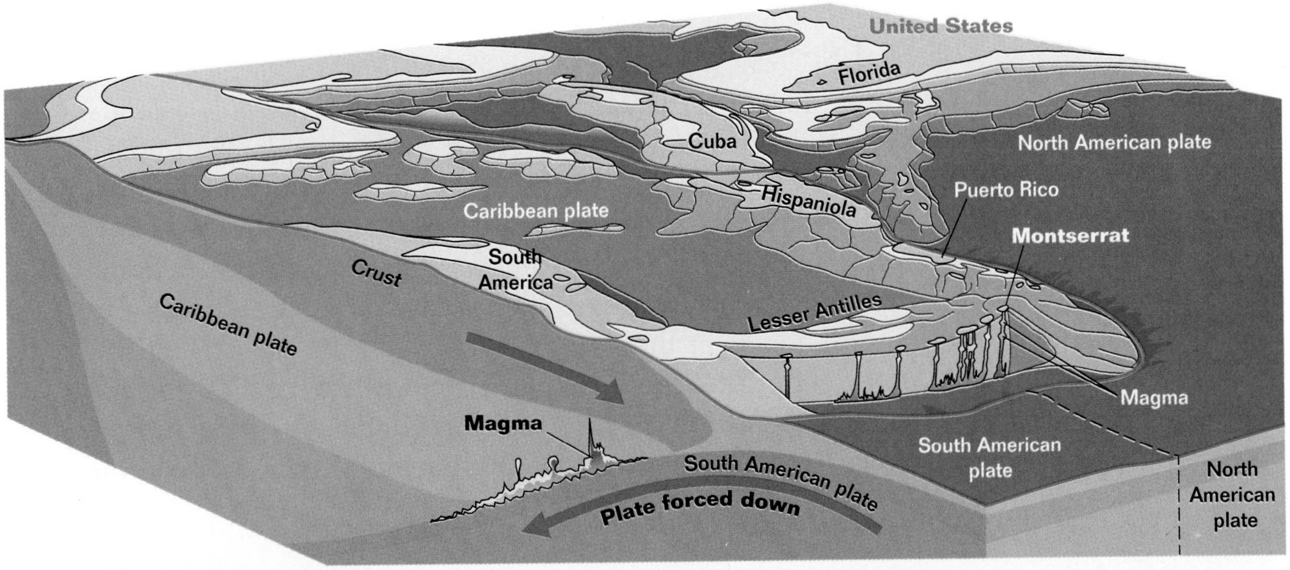

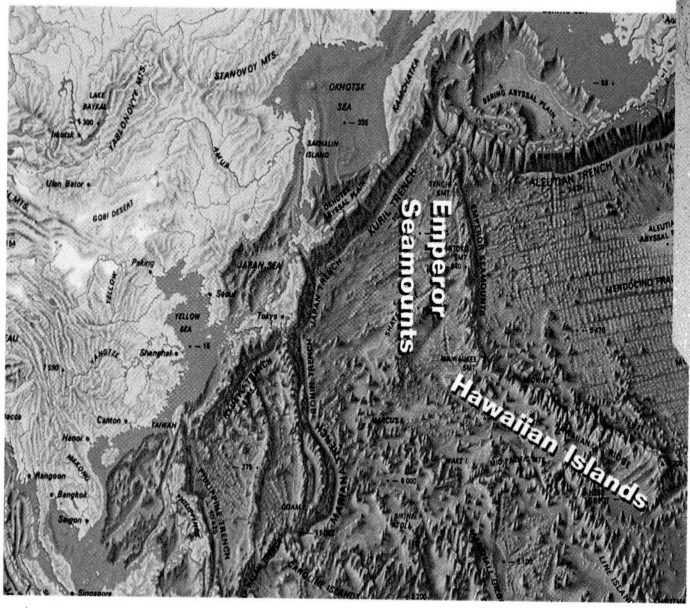

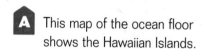

A This map of the ocean floor shows the Hawaiian Islands.

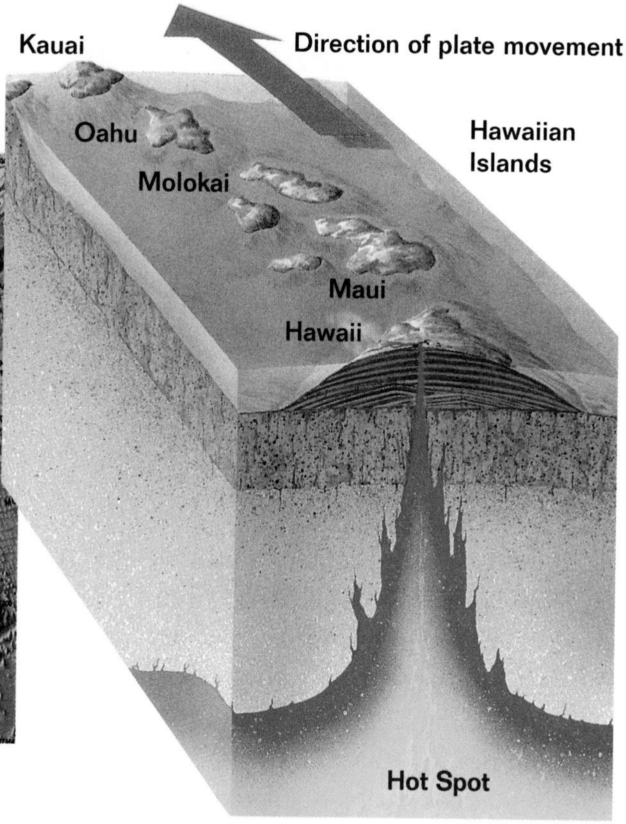

B The Hawaiian Islands have formed as the Pacific plate moves over a hot spot, with the earlier-formed islands northwest of the present hot-spot position. **Based on the position of the Emperor Seamounts shown in Figure 11-5A, infer whether or not the Pacific plate has always moved in the same direction. Explain your answer.**

Figure 11-5 Continued movement of the Pacific plate over a hot spot formed the islands of Kauai, Oahu, Molokai, Maui, and Hawaii over a period of about 5 million years. Scientists suggest that the Emperor Seamounts, which are extinct, underwater volcanoes, also formed in this way.

Magma forms when the plate being forced under the Caribbean plate gets deep enough and hot enough to partially melt. The magma is then forced upward to the surface, forming the volcanoes of the Lesser Antilles. **Figure 11-4B** shows how the North and South American plates are moving below the Caribbean plate.

Hot Spots

Like Iceland, the Hawaiian Islands are volcanic islands. But, unlike Iceland, they haven't formed at a plate boundary. The Hawaiian Islands are in the middle of the Pacific plate, far from its edges. What process could be forming them?

Geologists suggest that some areas in the mantle are hotter than other areas. Some geologists hypothesize that hot-spot magma forms at the boundary between the mantle and the outer core. This magma then rises toward Earth's surface, carrying heat from Earth's interior. The Hawaiian Islands sit on top of a hot spot under the Pacific plate. Magma from

C Computer image showing the island of Hawaii and Loihi, an underwater volcano. If Loihi reaches the surface, it will form a new island.

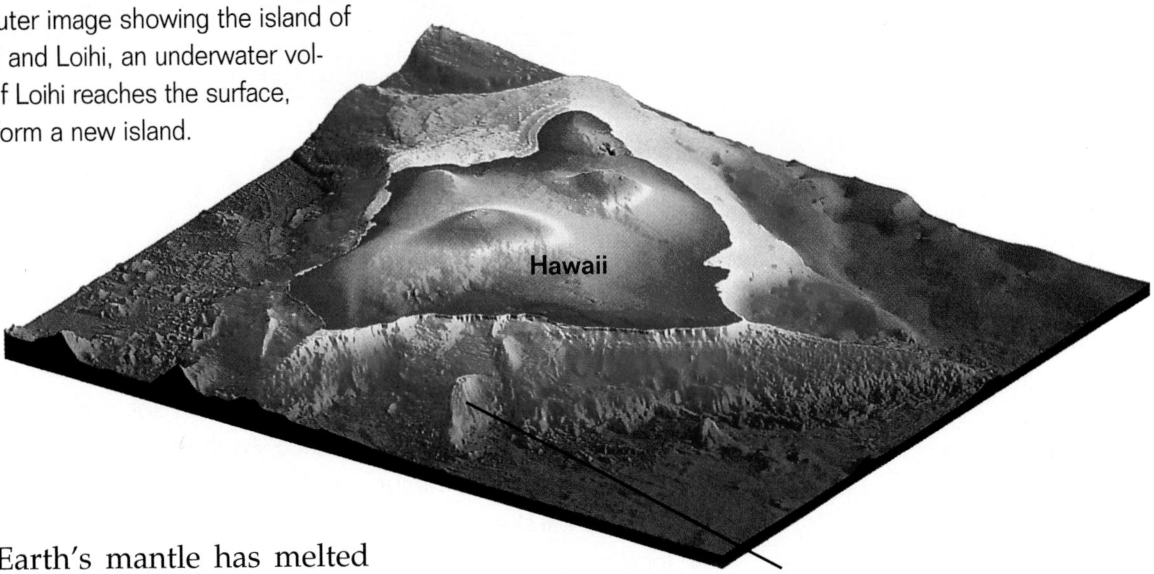

deep in Earth's mantle has melted through the crust to form several volcanoes. Those that rise above the water form the Hawaiian Islands, as shown in **Figure 11-5C.**

As you can see in **Figures 11-5A** and **11-5B,** the Hawaiian Islands are all in a line. This is because the Pacific plate is moving over the stationary hot spot. The island of Kauai is the oldest Hawaiian island and was once located where the big island of Hawaii is today. As the plate moved, Kauai moved away from the hot spot and became dormant. Continued movement of the Pacific plate formed Oahu, Molokai, Maui, and Hawaii over a period of about 5 million years.

Section Assessment

1. How are volcanoes related to Earth's moving plates?
2. As rock material melts, it becomes less dense. Explain what's happening to the atoms and molecules to cause this.
3. Why does lava cool rapidly along a mid-ocean ridge?
4. **Think Critically:** If the Pacific plate stopped moving, what would happen to the island of Hawaii?
5. **Skill Builder**
   Concept Mapping Make a concept map that shows how the Hawaiian Islands formed over a hot spot. Use the following terms and phrases: *volcano forms, plate moves, volcano becomes dormant,* and *new volcano forms.* If you need help, refer to Concept Mapping in the **Skill Handbook** on page 666.

Science Journal

Scientists were able to predict approximately when Mount Pinatubo in the Philippines would erupt. Research the changes in Earth's crust that were observed that led to this prediction. In your Science Journal, write a report on equipment used to predict volcanic eruptions.

Activity 11-1

Locating Active Volcanoes

Materials

- World map
- Tracing paper (2 to 4 pieces)
- Data table on the following page
- **Figure 9-10**
- **Figure 10-2**
- **Figure 11-3**

Have you ever wondered why volcanic eruptions occur in certain regions on Earth? Volcanoes form when hot, melted rock material is forced upward to Earth's surface. As the melted rock moves inside Earth, vibrations occur, which are felt as earthquakes. In this activity, you will see whether the locations of active volcanoes relate to the locations of recent earthquakes.

What You'll Investigate

Is there a correlation between the locations of active volcanoes and the locations of earthquake epicenters?

Goals

- **Plot** the locations of several active volcanoes.
- **Describe** any correlation you see between locations of volcanoes and locations of earthquake epicenters.

Procedure

1. Use tracing paper to outline the continents on a world map. Include the lines of latitude and longitude on your tracing.
2. Use the list of latitudes and longitudes of 21 active volcanoes to plot their locations on your tracing.
3. Compare your tracing with **Figure 10-2** and **Figure 11-3.**
4. In your Science Journal, and on a data table that you make, list the location of each volcano and indicate in a column whether an earthquake epicenter has been plotted close to the volcano. Also include three additional columns in your table to be used in step 5.
5. Using **Figure 9-10,** determine whether each volcano is located near a plate boundary or near a hot spot. Record this information in the extra three columns of your data table.

Volcano Locations

Volcano	Latitude	Longitude
#1	64° N	19° W
#2	28° N	34° E
#3	43° S	172° E
#4	35° N	136° E
#5	18° S	68° W
#6	25° S	114° W
#7	20° N	155° W
#8	54° N	167° W
#9	16° N	122° E
#10	28° N	17° W
#11	15° N	43° E
#12	6° N	75° W
#13	64° S	158° E
#14	38° S	78° E
#15	21° S	56° E
#16	38° N	26° E
#17	7° S	13° W
#18	2° S	102° E
#19	38° N	30° W
#20	54° N	159° E
#21	17° N	62° W

Conclude and Apply

1. **Describe** any patterns of distribution that active volcanoes form on Earth.
2. **Describe** any patterns of distribution of earthquake epicenters shown in **Figure 10-2.**
3. **Compare and contrast** any patterns that you observe with the locations of Earth's plate boundaries and hot spots shown in **Figures 11-3** and **9-10.**
4. **Write a hypothesis** to explain any patterns you observed for locations of active volcanoes, earthquake epicenters, tectonic plate boundaries, and hot spots. Suggest ways in which geologists might test your hypothesis.

11•2 Types of Volcanoes

***What* You'll Learn**

- How the explosiveness of a volcanic eruption is related to the silica and water vapor content of its magma
- Three forms of volcanoes

Vocabulary
shield volcano
tephra
cinder cone
composite volcano

***Why* It's Important**

- You'll understand what makes a volcano dangerous.

Styles of Eruptions

Some volcanic eruptions are explosive and violent, like those from Soufrière Hills volcano, Mount Pinatubo, and Mount St. Helens. In others, the lava quietly flows from a vent, as in the Kilauea (kihl ah WAY ah) eruptions. What causes these differences?

Two important factors control whether an eruption will be explosive or quiet. One is the amount of water vapor and other gases that are trapped in the magma. The other factor is how much silica is present in the magma. Silica is a compound composed of the elements silicon and oxygen.

Trapped Gases

Have you ever shaken a soft-drink container and then quickly opened it? The pressure from the gas in the drink builds up and is released suddenly when you open the can, spraying the drink. In the same way, gases such as water vapor and carbon dioxide are trapped in magma by the pressure of the surrounding magma and rock. As magma nears

Figure 11-6 A calm day in Washington was suddenly interrupted when Mount St. Helens erupted at 8:32 A.M. on May 18, 1980, as shown in this sequence of photographs. **Why was the eruption so violent compared with eruptions of volcanoes like Kilauea?**

A 8:32 A.M.

B 38 seconds later

the surface, there is less pressure. This allows the gas to escape from the magma. Gas escapes easily from some magma during quiet eruptions. Gas that builds up to high pressures eventually causes explosive eruptions such as the one shown in **Figure 11-6.**

PHYSICS INTEGRATION

Magma Composition

The second major factor that affects the type of eruption is the composition of the magma. Magma that is relatively low in silica is fluid and produces quiet, nonexplosive eruptions such as those at Kilauea. This type of lava pours from volcanic vents and runs down the sides of a volcano. These quiet eruptions form volcanoes over hot spots such as Hawaii. They also flow from rift zones, which are long, deep cracks such as those in Iceland. Because the magma is fluid when it is forced upward in a vent, trapped gases can escape easily in a nonexplosive manner.

Silica-rich magma, on the other hand, produces explosive eruptions such as those at Mount St. Helens. This magma sometimes forms where Earth's plates are moving together and one plate is forced under another. When the lower plate gets deep and hot enough, a portion of it is melted. This melting portion is richer in silica than the solid plate. As the melted portion is forced upward, it comes in contact with the crust and becomes more enriched in silica. Silica-rich magma is thick and gas gets trapped, causing pressure to build up. When an explosive eruption occurs, the gases expand rapidly, often carrying pieces of lava in the explosion.

LIFE SCIENCE INTEGRATION

Devastating Eruptions

Whenever a volcano erupts, people who live in its vicinity are affected in many ways. If the eruption is unexpected, lives can be lost. If people know the volcano is about to erupt, they can evacuate. Either way, their lives may never be the same. Research how the continuing eruption of the Soufrière Hills volcano on the Lesser Antilles Island of Montserrat has affected life on the island.

C 42 seconds later

D 53 seconds later

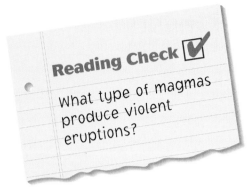

Reading Check ☑

What type of magmas produce violent eruptions?

Magma Water Content

Another factor that causes magma to erupt explosively is its high water content. The magma at some converging zones contains a lot of water vapor. This is because of water in the oceanic crust that is carried by one plate forced below another. The trapped water vapor in the magma causes explosive eruptions. Sometimes, gas causes lava fountains to form from basaltic magmas, as illustrated in **Figure 11-8.** ☑

VISUALIZING Forms of Volcanoes

Figure 11-7 The form of a volcano is determined by the nature of its eruption.

A When hot, fluid lava flows from one or more vents without erupting violently, it builds a gentle slope when it cools. This creates a shield volcano such as Mauna Loa, in background, in Hawaii.

B Explosive eruptions throw rock and lava high into the air. The lava cools and hardens into tephra. When tephra falls to the ground, it forms a steep-sided, loosely packed cinder cone volcano. Pictured here is a cinder cone in Arizona.

Forms of Volcanoes

A volcano's form depends on whether it is the result of a quiet or an explosive eruption and the type of lava it is made of—silica-poor, silica-rich, or a composition somewhere in between. Volcanoes are of three basic forms—shield volcanoes, cinder cone volcanoes, or composite volcanoes, as shown in **Figure 11-7.**

Shield Volcano

Quiet eruptions spread out silica-poor lava in flat layers. The buildup of these layers forms a broad volcano with gently sloping sides called a **shield volcano.** Examples of shield volcanoes are the Hawaiian Islands.

Cinder Cone Volcano

Explosive eruptions throw lava and rock high into the air. Bits of rock or solidified lava dropped from the air are called **tephra** (TEFF ruh). Tephra varies in size from volcanic ash—the smallest—to cinders, to larger rocks called

Figure 11-8 Usually, the hot, thin lava flows of Kilauea in Hawaii are nonviolent eruptions. **What could be causing the lava fountain shown above?**

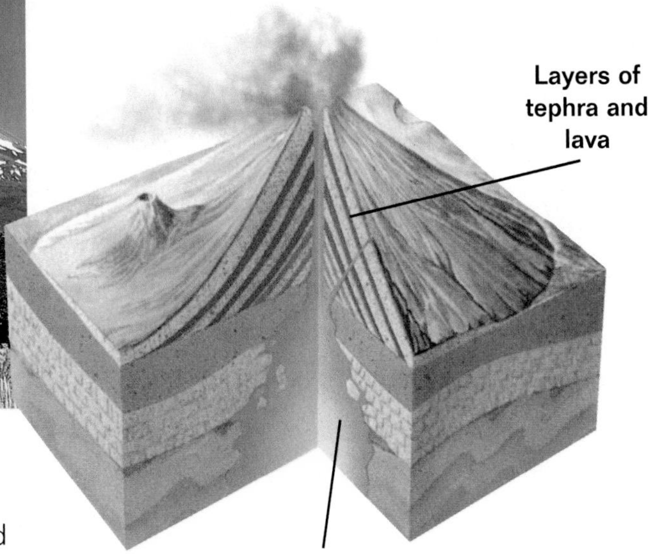

C Whenever volcanic eruptions vary between violent and quieter times, tephra layers alternate with lava layers. A volcano built by this layering of tephra and lava has a composite form, such as Mount Shasta in California, shown here, or Mount St. Helens.

bombs and blocks. When tephra falls to the ground, it forms a steep-sided, loosely packed **cinder cone** volcano, as seen in **Figure 11-7B.**

A Mexican farmer learned about cinder cones one morning when he went to his cornfield. He noticed that a hole in his cornfield that had been there for as long as he could remember was giving off smoke that smelled like sulfur. Throughout the night, hot glowing cinders were thrown high into the air. In just a few days, a cinder cone several hundred meters high covered his cornfield. This is the volcano named Paricutín.

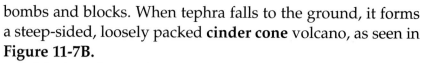

*inter***NET**
CONNECTION

Visit the Glencoe Science Web Site at **www.glencoe.com/sec/science/ca** for more information on forms of volcanoes.

Composite Volcano

Some volcanic eruptions can vary between quiet and violent. An explosive period can release gas and ash, forming a tephra layer. Then, the eruption can switch over to a quiet period, erupting lava over the top of the tephra layer. When this cycle of lava and tephra is repeated over and over in alternating layers, a **composite volcano** is formed. Composite volcanoes are found mostly where Earth's plates come together

Problem Solving

Comparing Volcanic Rocks

During your study of volcanoes and the material that is ejected from volcanoes, you are given four different igneous rocks. Your task is to determine how the rocks formed and what elements they likely contain.

The rocks are fine-grained and some are full of holes. The holes were caused by escaping gases during the cooling of these rocks. The color of volcanic rocks can indicate what minerals each rock contains. Dark-colored rocks tend to contain minerals high in iron and magnesium, whereas light-colored rocks tend to have a higher concentration of silica-rich minerals.

Study the photograph. Based on the overall color of the rocks, what elements do you think each is likely to contain?

Think Critically: Because some of these rocks are full of holes formed by gases as the rock cooled, it is possible that gases are also trapped inside these rocks. Is there a method to test the possible presence of trapped gas inside the rocks? Explain.

Figure 11-9 Mount Pinatubo in the Philippines erupted violently in 1991.

and one plate is forced below the other. Mount St. Helens is an example. As you can see in **Table 11-1,** many things affect volcanic eruptions and the form of a volcano.

Mount St. Helens formed as the Juan de Fuca plate was forced beneath the North American plate. The ocean floor of the Juan de Fuca plate partially melted as it was forced downward. Successive eruptions of lava and tephra were produced. They formed the majestic composite volcano that towers above the surrounding landscape. Before the 1980 eruption, silica-rich magma rose and was trapped beneath the surface. An earthquake-triggered landslide took place that released pressure on the underlying magma. This started a series of explosive eruptions, as seen in **Figure 11-6.**

The action of Earth's plates coming together also caused the 1991 eruption of the composite volcano Mount Pinatubo, in the Philippines, as seen in **Figure 11-9.** Mount Pinatubo erupted violently after lying quiet for more than 600 years. The islands of the Philippines are a volcanic island arc, formed where the Philippine plate meets the Eurasian plate.

Mini Lab

Modeling Volcanic Cones

Procedure

1. Pour dry sand or sugar onto one spot on a paper plate, forming a model of a cinder cone volcano. **CAUTION:** *Do not taste, eat, or drink any materials used in the lab.*
2. Mix a batch of plaster of paris and pour it onto one spot on another paper plate, forming a model of a shield volcano.
3. Allow the model of the shield volcano to dry. Use a protractor to measure the slope angles of the sides of the volcanoes.

Analysis

1. Which of your volcano models has steeper sides?
2. What form of volcano is represented by the model with steeper sides?
3. Infer why this is so.

Table 11-1

Thirteen Selected Eruptions in History							
Volcano and Location	Year	Type	Eruptive Force	Magma Content		Ability of Magma to Flow	Products of Eruption
				Silica	H_2O		
Etna, Sicily	1669	composite	moderate	high	low	medium	lava, ash
Tambora, Indonesia	1815	cinder	high	high	high	low	cinders, gas
Krakatau, Indonesia	1883	cinder	high	high	high	low	cinders, gas
Pelée, Martinique	1902	cinder	high	high	high	low	gas, ash
Vesuvius, Italy	1906	composite	moderate	high	low	medium	lava, ash
Katmai, Alaska	1912	composite	high	high	high	low	lava, ash, gas
Paricutín, Mexico	1943	cinder	moderate	high	low	medium	ash, cinders
Surtsey, Iceland	1963	shield	moderate	low	low	high	lava, ash
St. Helens, WA	1980	composite	high	high	high	low	gas, ash
Kilauea Iki, Hawaii	1989	shield	low	low	low	high	lava
Pinatubo, Philippines	1991	composite	high	high	high	low	gas, ash
Galeras, Colombia	1993	composite	high	high	high	low	gas, ash
Soufrière Hills, Montserrat	1995	composite	high	high	high	low	gas, ash, blocks

Section Assessment

1. Some volcanic eruptions are quiet and others are violent. What causes this difference?
2. Why are silica-rich magmas thicker than silica-poor magmas?
3. **Think Critically:** In 1883, Krakatau in Indonesia erupted. Infer which kind of lava Krakatau erupted: silica-rich or silica-poor? Support your inference using data in **Table 11-1.**
4. **Skill Builder**
   Making and Using Bar Graphs Have you ever wondered about how volcanic eruptions compare to one another? To find out more about the sizes of eruptions, do the **Chapter 11 Skill Activity** on page 704.

Using Math

When Mount St. Helens erupted in 1980, about 0.5 km^3 of material were ejected from the volcano. Tambora in Indonesia gave off 30 km^3 of material in 1815. How many times larger was the volume of material given off by Tambora?

Igneous Rock Features

11•3

Intrusive Features

We can observe volcanic eruptions because they are examples of igneous activity on the surface of Earth. But, far more igneous activity occurs underground because most magma never reaches the surface to form volcanoes. Intrusive rock forms when magma cools underground. What forms do intrusive igneous rocks take? You can look at some of these features in **Figure 11-10** and **Figure 11-11.**

Batholiths

The largest intrusive igneous rock bodies are **batholiths.** They can be many hundreds of kilometers wide and long and several kilometers thick. Batholiths form when magma cools underground before reaching the surface. However, not all of

What You'll Learn

- How intrusive igneous rock features form
- How a volcanic neck and a caldera form

Vocabulary

batholith
dike
sill
volcanic neck
caldera

Why It's Important

- Igneous activity formed many features you can observe on Earth's surface.

Figure 11-10 This diagram shows intrusive and other features associated with volcanic activity. **Which features shown are formed above ground? Which are formed by intrusive activities?**

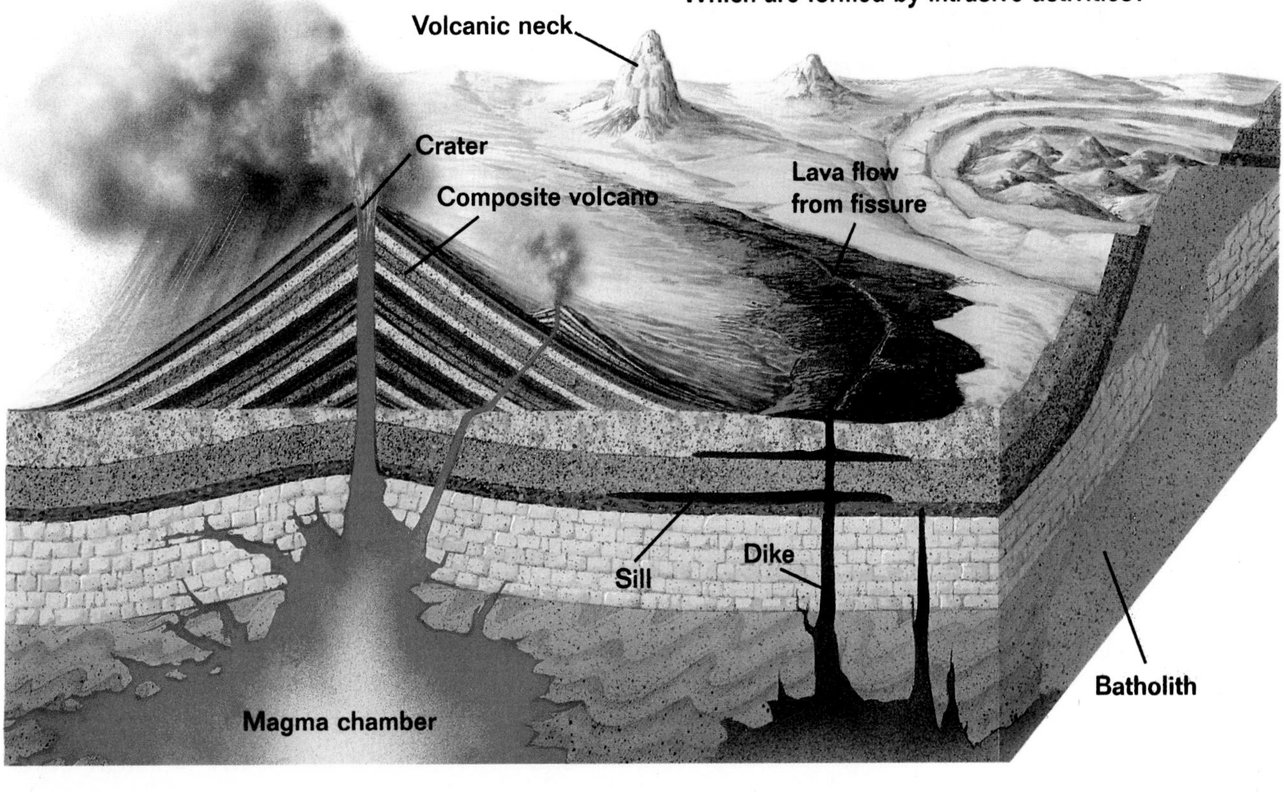

VISUALIZING
Igneous Features

Figure 11-11 Igneous features can form in many different sizes and shapes. Some of the most common are batholiths, dikes, sills, and volcanic necks. **Why are these features often exposed and jutting out at the surface?**

A Most of the bare rock visible in Yosemite National Park in California is a batholith that has been exposed by erosion.

B Ship Rock in New Mexico, seen in the background, is a volcanic neck.

Mini Lab

Modeling Magma Movement

Procedure

1. Pour water into a transparent, plastic cup.
2. Pour a small amount of cooking oil in to a separate plastic cup. Use oil that is slightly colored, such as olive oil.
3. Extract a small amount of oil with a dropper.
4. Submerge the dropper tip into the water cup and slowly squeeze oil drops into the water.

Analysis

1. Describe what happened to the oil.
2. How do your observations compare with the movement of magma within Earth's crust?

them are hidden in Earth. Some batholiths have been exposed at Earth's surface by erosion. The granite domes of Yosemite National Park, as seen in **Figure 11-11A,** are the remains of a huge batholith that stretches across much of the length of California.

Dikes and Sills

Magma sometimes squeezes into cracks in rock below the surface. This is like squeezing toothpaste into the spaces between your teeth. Magma that is squeezed into a generally vertical crack

C The horizontal sill shown here is located in Yellowstone National Park. It formed when magma squeezed between rock layers.

D The vertical dikes shown here are located in Nevada. They formed when magma was squeezed into vertical cracks in the surrounding rock layers.

that cuts across rock layers and hardens is called a **dike.** Magma that is squeezed into a horizontal crack between rock layers and hardens is called a **sill.** These features are shown in **Figures 11-11C** and **11-11D.** Most dikes and sills run from a few meters to hundreds of meters long. Some magma that forms a sill may continue to push the rock layers upward.

Other Features

When a volcano stops erupting, the magma hardens inside the vent. Erosion begins to wear away the volcano. The cone is much softer than the solid igneous rock in the vent. Thus, the cone erodes away first, leaving behind the solid igneous core as a **volcanic neck.** Ship Rock, New Mexico, is a volcanic neck. It is just one of many volcanic necks in the southwestern United States.

Sometimes after an eruption, the top of a volcano can collapse. This produces a large opening called a **caldera,** as shown in **Figure 11-12.** Crater Lake in Oregon is a caldera that is now a lake. Crater Lake formed after the violent eruption and destruction of Mount Mazama about 7000 years ago.

PHYSICS INTEGRATION

Rising Magma

You have learned that large bodies of magma underground are gradually forced upward toward Earth's surface. What forces push the magma upward through solid rock?

VISUALIZING
Caldera Formation

Figure 11-12 Crater Lake in Oregon formed when the top of a volcano collapsed, forming a caldera as shown in the sequence below.

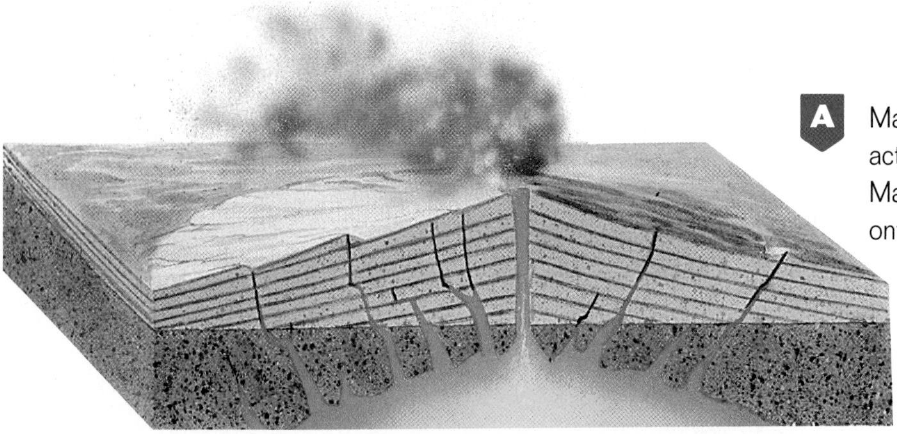

A Magma rises, causing volcanic activity of the former Mount Mazama. Magma is erupted onto the surface as lava.

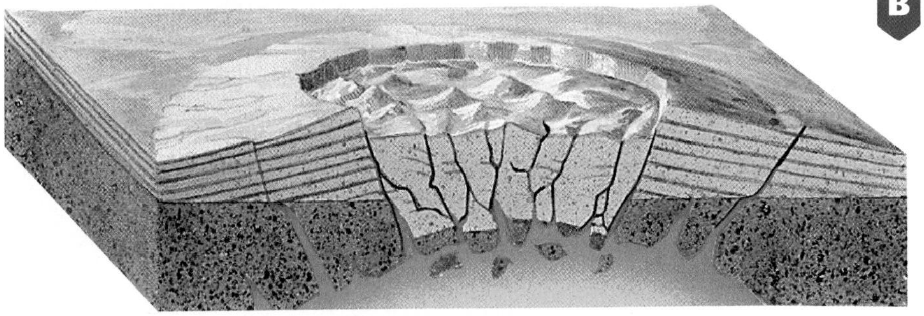

B Magma chamber partially empties, causing rock material to collapse down into the emptied chamber below the surface. This forms a circular-shaped caldera.

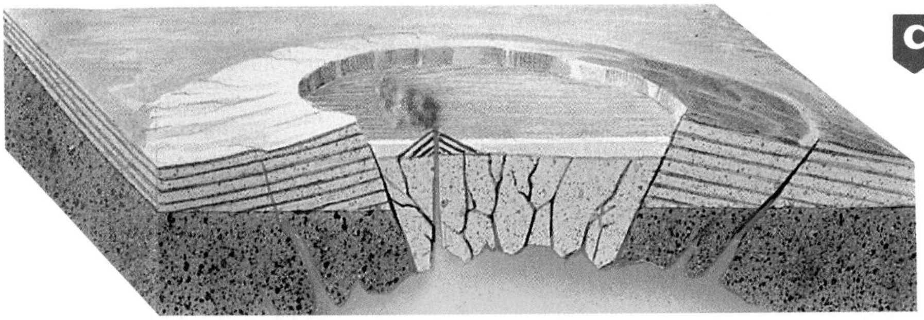

C Crater Lake formed when water collected into the circular space left when surface material collapsed.

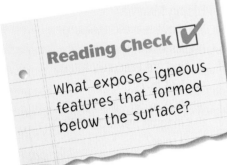

Reading Check

What exposes igneous features that formed below the surface?

Igneous Features Exposed

You have learned in this chapter about one way that Earth's surface is continually built up and how it is worn down. The surface of Earth is built up by volcanoes. Also, igneous rock is formed when magma hardens below ground. Eventually, the processes of erosion wear down rock at the surface, exposing features like batholiths, dikes, and sills.

D Wizard Island in Crater Lake, in Oregon, is a cinder cone volcano that erupted after the formation of the caldera.

Using Math

Crater Lake in Oregon measures between 8 km and 10 km across. If you use the average width of 9 km and assume the lake is circular, you can approximate the area of the lake inside this caldera. Use the equation:

$$A = \pi r^2$$

where A = the area of a circle and r = the radius of a circle.

Section Assessment

1. What's the difference between a caldera and a crater?
2. What is a volcanic neck and how does it form?
3. Explain how calderas form.
4. **Think Critically:** Why are the dome features of Yosemite National Park actually intrusive volcanic features when they are exposed at the surface in the park?
5. **Skill Builder**
   Comparing and Contrasting
   Compare and contrast dikes, sills, batholiths, and volcanic necks. If you need help, refer to Comparing and Contrasting in the **Skill Handbook** on page 672.

Using Computers

Graphics Use the graphics software available on your computer to produce an illustration of igneous rock features based on **Figure 11-10.** Be sure to include both intrusive features and features that form above ground. If you need help, refer to page 686.

Identifying Types of Volcanoes

Materials

- **Table 11-1**
- Paper
- Pencil

You have learned that certain properties of magma are related to the type of eruption and the form of the volcano that will develop. Try this activity to see how to make and use a table that relates the properties of magma to the form of volcano that develops.

What You'll Investigate

Are the silica and water content of a volcano related to the form of volcano that develops?

Goals

- **Determine** any relation between the ability of magma to flow and eruptive force.
- **Determine** any relation between magma composition and eruptive force.

Procedure

1. **Copy** the graph shown at right.
2. Using the information from **Table 11-1, plot** the magma content data for each of the volcanoes listed by writing the name of the basic type of volcano in the appropriate spot on the graph.
3. When the plotting of all 13 volcanoes has been completed, **analyze** the patterns of volcanic types on the diagram to answer the questions.

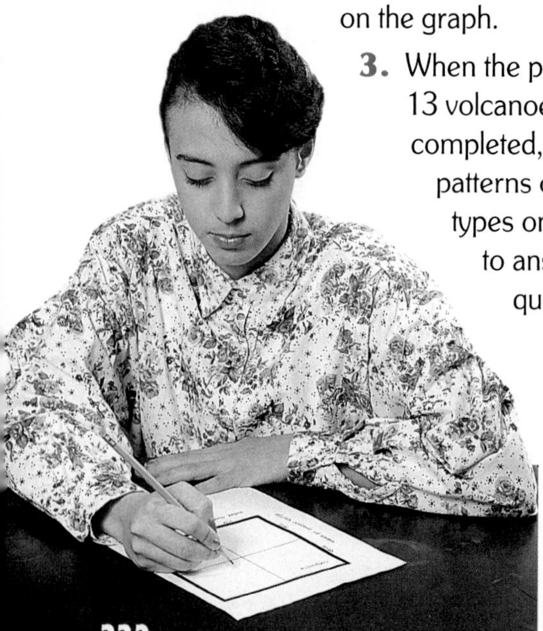

Conclude and Apply

1. What relation appears to exist between the ability of the magma to flow and the eruptive force of the volcano?
2. Which would be more liquidlike: a magma that flows easily or one that flows with difficulty?
3. What relation appears to exist between the silica or water content of the magma and the nature of the material ejected from the volcano?
4. How is the ability of a magma to flow related to its silica and water content?
5. **Infer** which of the two variables (silica or water content) appears to have the greater effect on the eruptive force of the volcano.
6. **Describe** the relation that appears to exist between the silica and water content of the magma and the type of volcano that is produced.

Types of Volcanoes

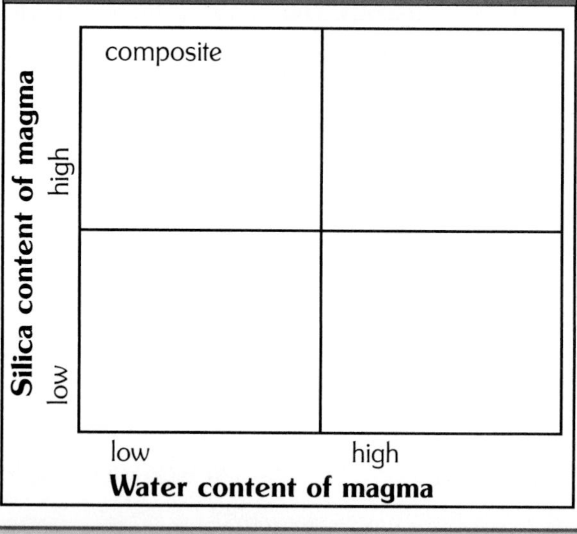

Predicting Volcanic Eruptions

Soufriére Hills volcano on the Caribbean island of Montserrat began erupting in July 1995 and continues to be very active. Although the volcano has killed 20 people in recent years, thousands of lives were saved because of advance warnings. Predicting eruptions doesn't protect buildings or roads, but it can save people and livestock. Scientists are now working on a worldwide volcano warning system.

Predicting Activity on Kilauea

The key to the volcano warning system is another system, the Global Positioning System (GPS), a collection of U.S. satellites orbiting Earth. The GPS makes it possible to take exact measurements of the Earth's surface and to pinpoint any location on the planet with great accuracy. It does this by measuring the distance between a receiver's position on Earth and at least three satellites orbiting Earth. GPS data can show whether the position being measured is moving. If the movement is associated with a volcanic eruption—such as moving magma—the information can be used to warn people about a coming eruption.

Giving Advanced Warning

This is exactly what a team of scientists from Stanford University hypothesized. They placed 13 receivers around a crater on Kilauea (left), a volcano on the island of Hawaii. On January 30, 1997, a new fissure eruption in and around the crater occurred. Eight hours before the eruption, the receivers showed that Kilauea's surface was moving. The volcano's summit was pulling apart, a movement that could have been caused by rising magma inside the volcano. Unfortunately, the volcano erupted before scientists received the information because data were only reported once every 24 hours. Research on this prediction method continues, however, and the Stanford team plans to put in place a better system that will report data continuously. This system will allow scientists to warn people before dangerous eruptions occur.

interNET CONNECTION

To learn more about Kilauea volcanism, use the link on the Glencoe Science Web Site at **www.glencoe.com/sec/science/ca** to visit the Hawaii Center for Volcanology.

Chapter 11 Reviewing Main Ideas

For a **preview** of this chapter, study this Reviewing Main Ideas before you read the chapter. After you have studied this chapter, you can use the Reviewing Main Ideas to **review** the chapter.

GLENCOE TECHNOLOGY

The Glencoe MindJogger, Audiocassettes, and CD-ROM provide additional opportunities for review.

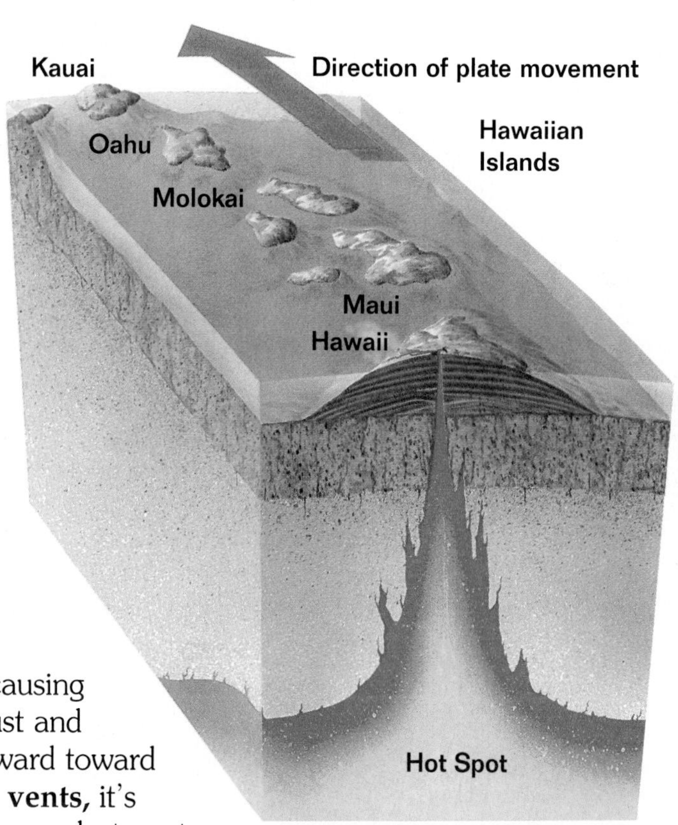

Section 11-1 CAUSES OF VOLCANOES

Volcanoes can be dangerous to people, causing deaths and destroying property. Rocks in the crust and mantle melt to form magma, which is forced upward toward Earth's surface. When the magma flows through **vents,** it's called lava and forms volcanoes. Volcanoes form over hot spots when magma flows onto the seafloor. Sometimes, the lava builds up from the seafloor to form an island. Volcanoes over **hot spots** and rifts sometimes form on land. Volcanoes also form when Earth's plates pull apart or come together. ***What happens to the lower plate where two plates come together in order for a volcano to form?***

Section 11-2 TYPES OF VOLCANOES

Some lavas are thin and flow easily, producing quiet eruptions. Other lavas are thick and stiff, and thus produce violent eruptions. Water vapor in magma adds to its explosiveness. **Shield volcanoes** are mountains made of silica-poor lava that have gently sloping sides. **Cinder cones** are steep sided and are made of **tephra. Composite volcanoes,** made of lava and tephra, are steep sided. ***Why are eruptions of composite volcanoes so explosive?***

Reading Check

Choose a topic in this chapter that interests you. Look it up in a reference book. Think of a way to share what you learn with others.

Section 11-3 IGNEOUS ROCK FEATURES

Intrusive igneous rock bodies such as batholiths, dikes, and sills form when magma solidifies underground. **Batholiths** are the most massive igneous rock bodies. **Dikes** form when magma squeezes into vertical cracks, cutting across rock layers. **Sills** form when magma squeezes in between rock layers. When a volcano stops erupting, the outer part of it erodes, leaving behind a **volcanic neck.** A **caldera** forms when the top of a volcano collapses, forming a large opening. ***What causes a volcano to collapse and form a caldera?***

Career CONNECTION

Robert Ballard, Oceanographer

Not all volcanic activity takes place on land. Robert Ballard, an oceanographer, explores volcanic activity deep in the ocean. He conducted the first manned exploration of the mid-ocean ridge, which is a chain of underwater volcanic rifts that spans the globe. Robert also discovered the hydrothermal vents of the Galápagos Rift.These underwater vents spew out hot, briny water that is heated by magma deep beneath the ocean floor. ***Do you think that volcanoes might affect the chemistry of the ocean?***

Chapter 11 Assessment

Using Vocabulary

a. batholith	g. hot spot
b. caldera	h. shield volcano
c. cinder cone	i. sill
d. composite volcano	j. tephra
e. crater	k. vent
f. dike	l. volcanic neck
	m. volcano

Each phrase below describes a science term from the list. Write the term that matches the phrase describing it.

1. mountain made of lava and tephra
2. large opening formed by the collapse of a volcano
3. volcano with gently sloping sides
4. steep-sided volcano made of tephra
5. an igneous intrusion formed between rock layers

Checking Concepts

Choose the word or phrase that best answers the question.

6. What type of plate boundary forms composite volcanoes?
   A) plates moving apart
   B) plates sticking and slipping
   C) plates moving together
   D) plates sliding past each other
7. Why is Hawaii made of volcanoes?
   A) Plates are moving apart.
   B) A hot spot exists.
   C) Plates are moving together.
   D) Rift zones exist.
8. What kind of magmas produce violent volcanic eruptions?
   A) those rich in silica
   B) those that are fluid
   C) those forming shield volcanoes
   D) those rich in iron
9. Magma that is low in silica produces what kind of eruptions?
   A) thick C) quiet
   B) caldera D) explosive
10. What is made entirely of tephra?
    A) shield volcano C) cinder cone
    B) caldera D) composite volcano
11. What kind of volcano is Kilauea?
    A) shield volcano C) cinder cone
    B) composite volcano D) caldera cone
12. What is magma that squeezes into a vertical crack and then hardens?
    A) sill C) volcanic neck
    B) dike D) batholith
13. What is the largest igneous intrusive body?
    A) dike C) sill
    B) volcanic neck D) batholith
14. Which describes solid material erupted from a volcano?
    A) lava C) tephra
    B) sand D) sill
15. What is the process that formed Mount St. Helens?
    A) plates sticking and slipping
    B) caldera formation
    C) plates sliding sideways
    D) plates moving together

Thinking Critically

16. Explain how glaciers and volcanoes can exist on Iceland.
17. What kind of eruption is produced when lava that is low in silica flows from a volcano? Explain.
18. How are volcanoes related to earthquakes?
19. A mountain called Misti is a volcano in Peru. Peru is on the western edge of South America. How might this volcano have formed?

20. Describe in detail what a composite volcano is made of. Which parts represent violent eruptions?

Developing Skills

If you need help, refer to the Skill Handbook.

21. **Concept Mapping:** Make a network tree concept map that compares quiet eruptions with explosive eruptions. Use the following words and phrases: *Hawaii, high-silica, flows easily, quiet, explosive, composite, Mount St. Helens, shield, low-silica,* and *resists flow.*

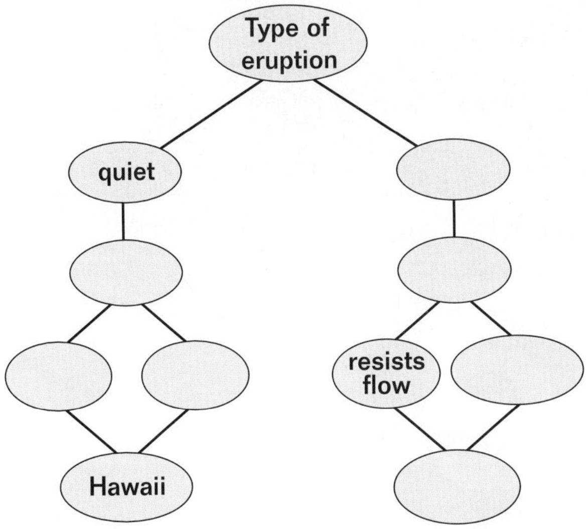

22. **Observing and Inferring:** A volcano erupted violently in Indonesia in 1883. What can you infer about the magma's composition? If people saw the eruption, what would they observe coming out of the volcano?

23. **Classifying:** Mount Fuji's steep sides are made of layers of silica-rich lava and ash. Classify Mount Fuji.

24. **Measuring in SI:** The base of the volcano Mauna Loa is about 5000 m below sea level. The total height of the volcano is 9170 m. What percentage of the volcano is above sea level? Below sea level?

THE PRINCETON REVIEW

Test-Taking Tip

All or None When filling in answer ovals, remember to fill in the entire oval. A computer will be scoring your answers. Don't give the right answer to a problem only to lose points on it because the computer couldn't read your oval.

Test Practice

Use these questions to test your Science Proficiency.

1. Not all volcanoes look or erupt the same. Which of the following statements **BEST** explains why this is true?
   - A) Volcanoes form at different locations.
   - B) Magmas of different compositions produce different forms of volcanoes because of the way they erupt.
   - C) Magma compositions do not vary. Volcanoes form differently because of the latitude at which they form.
   - D) The form of a volcano is related to the age of the volcano.

2. All Hawaiian Islands have formed in the same way. Which of the following statements **BEST** explains this?
   - A) The Hawaiian Islands have formed over an area where one plate is forced under another.
   - B) The Hawaiian Islands have formed over an area where plates are moving apart.
   - C) Each Hawaiian Island is supplied by its own hot spot of magma.
   - D) A hot spot provided magma for all islands as the Pacific plate slowly moved over the hot spot's location.

UNIT 4

Change Through Time

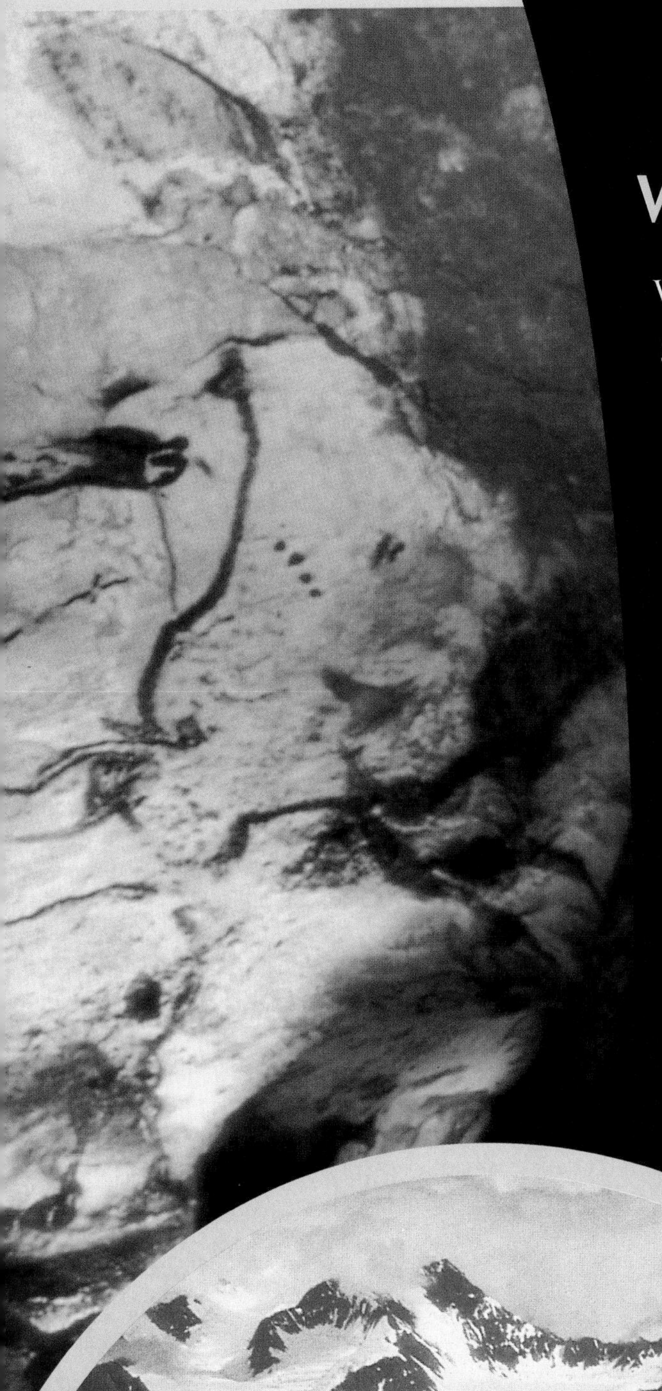

NATIONAL GEOGRAPHIC

What's Happening Here?

What traces of your existence will you leave for future generations to interpret? Long ago, someone painted these magnificent beasts on the walls of Lascaux (left), a cave in southern France. Archaeologists believe these drawings were created by Stone Age artists about 17 000 years ago. From the walls of this cave and others like it, scientists are piecing together the story of the ancestors of modern humans. While such drawings can help us interpret the human past, how can we figure out what happened before humans appeared on Earth? Even if you had been around and lived a long life, you could not have witnessed much of what happened. Why? Because like this glacier flowing into Prince William Sound, Alaska (below), many important changes happened too gradually to be seen. In this unit, you will learn about some of these slow changes and how to read the record these changes have left in the layers of Earth's crust.

interNET CONNECTION

Explore the Glencoe Science Web Site at **www.glencoe.com/sec/science/ca** to find out more about topics found in this unit.

CHAPTER 12

Clues to Earth's Past

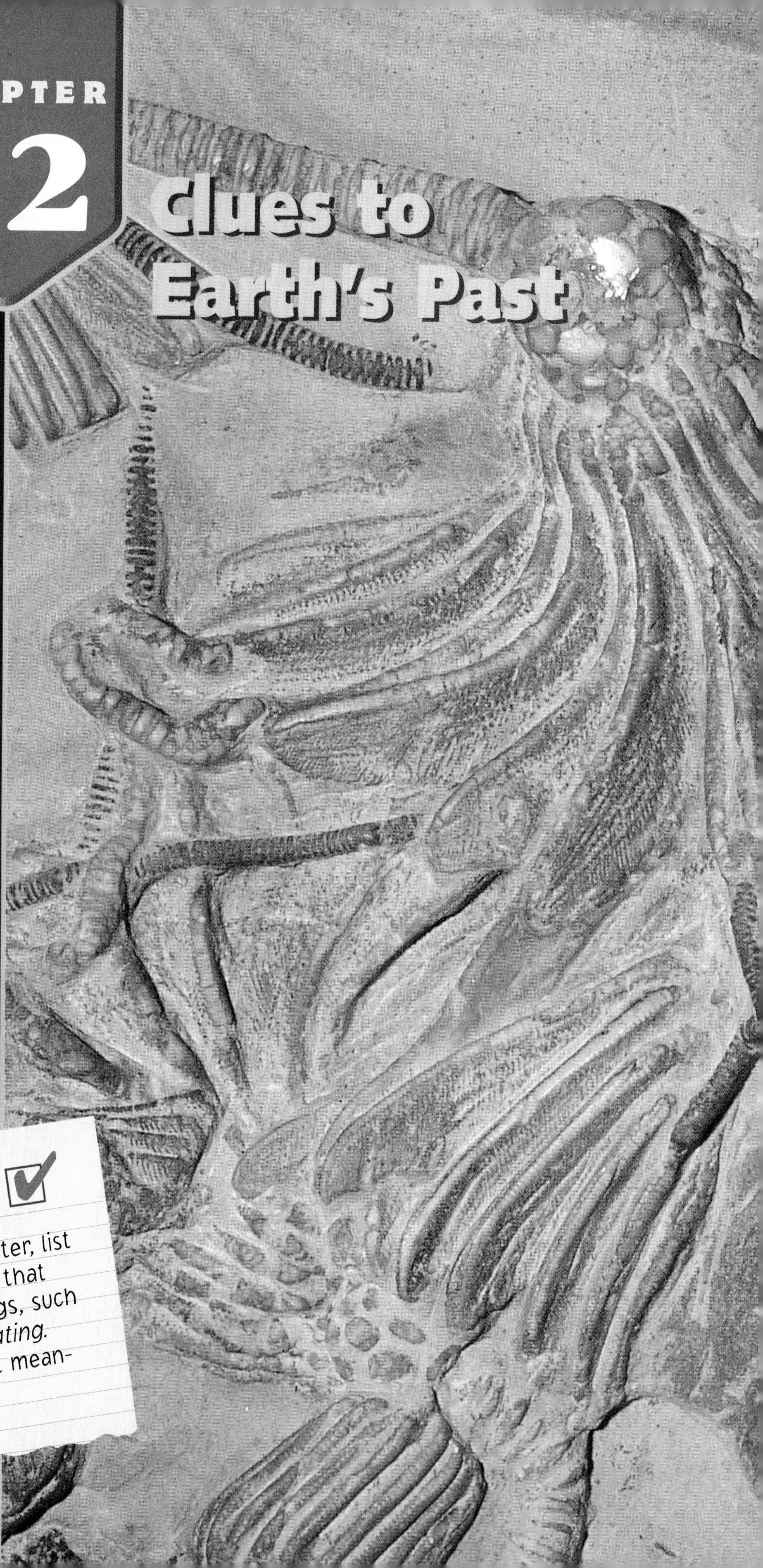

Chapter Preview

Section 12-1
Fossils

Section 12-2
Relative Ages of Rocks

Section 12-3
Absolute Ages of Rocks

Skills Preview

Skill Builders

- Interpret Data
- Make and Use a Table

Activities

- Interpret Data
- Analyze and Conclude

MiniLabs

- Observe
- Infer

Reading Check

As you read this chapter, list words you encounter that have several meanings, such as *mold, cast,* and *dating.* Explain the different meanings of these terms.

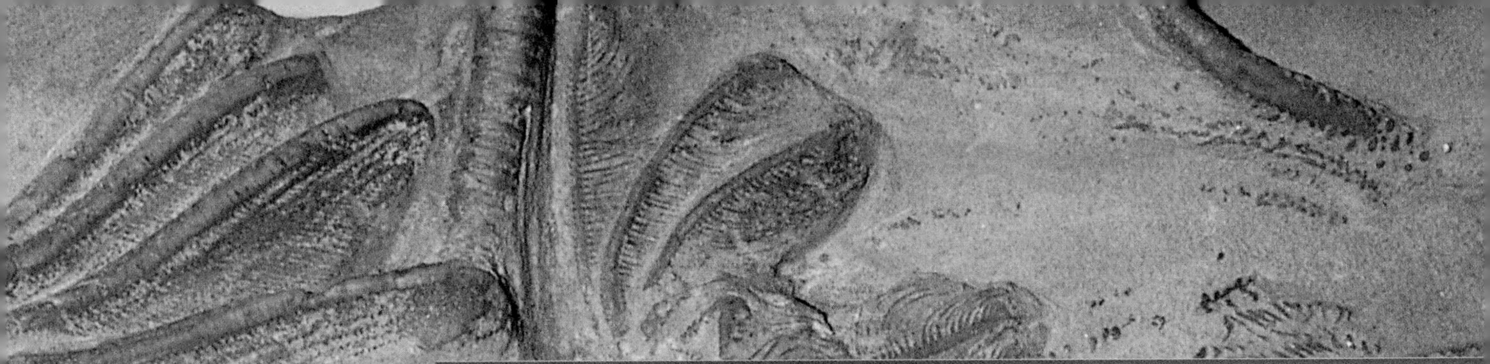

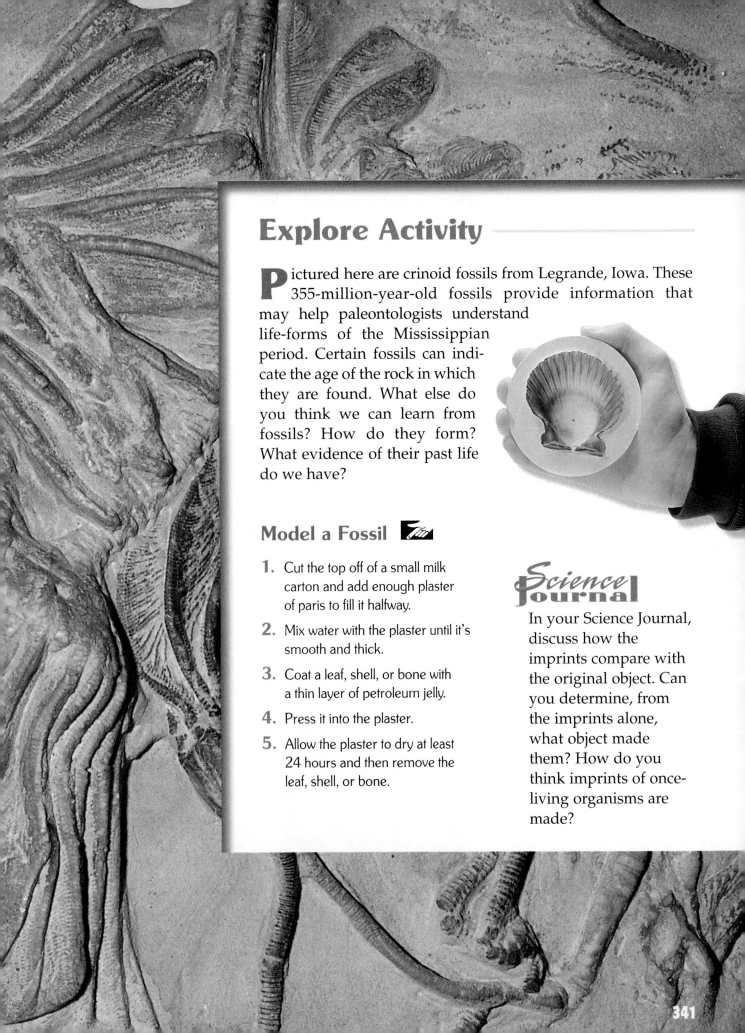

Explore Activity

Pictured here are crinoid fossils from Legrande, Iowa. These 355-million-year-old fossils provide information that may help paleontologists understand life-forms of the Mississippian period. Certain fossils can indicate the age of the rock in which they are found. What else do you think we can learn from fossils? How do they form? What evidence of their past life do we have?

Model a Fossil

1. Cut the top off of a small milk carton and add enough plaster of paris to fill it halfway.
2. Mix water with the plaster until it's smooth and thick.
3. Coat a leaf, shell, or bone with a thin layer of petroleum jelly.
4. Press it into the plaster.
5. Allow the plaster to dry at least 24 hours and then remove the leaf, shell, or bone.

Science Journal

In your Science Journal, discuss how the imprints compare with the original object. Can you determine, from the imprints alone, what object made them? How do you think imprints of once-living organisms are made?

12•1 Fossils

What You'll Learn

- Conditions necessary for fossils to form
- Processes of fossil formation
- How fossil correlation is used to determine rock ages

Vocabulary
fossil
petrified remains
carbonaceous film
mold
cast
index fossil

Why It's Important

- Fossils can help you interpret how life on Earth has changed through time.

Traces from Our Past

The thick forest shakes as an *Allosaurus* charges forward in search of an evening meal. On the other side of the swamp, a herd of apatosaurs moves slowly and cautiously. The adults surround the young to protect them from predators. Soon, night will fall on this prehistoric day, 160 million years ago.

Does this story sound familiar to you? It's likely that you've read about dinosaurs and other past inhabitants of Earth. But, how do you know they really lived? What evidence do we have of past life on Earth? Scientists reconstruct what an animal looked like from its fossil remains, as in **Figure 12-1.**

Fossil Formation

In the Explore Activity, you made imprints of parts of organisms. Imprints are records, or evidence, of life. Evidence such as the remains, imprints, or traces of once-living organisms preserved in rocks are **fossils.** By studying fossils, geologists help solve mysteries of Earth's past.

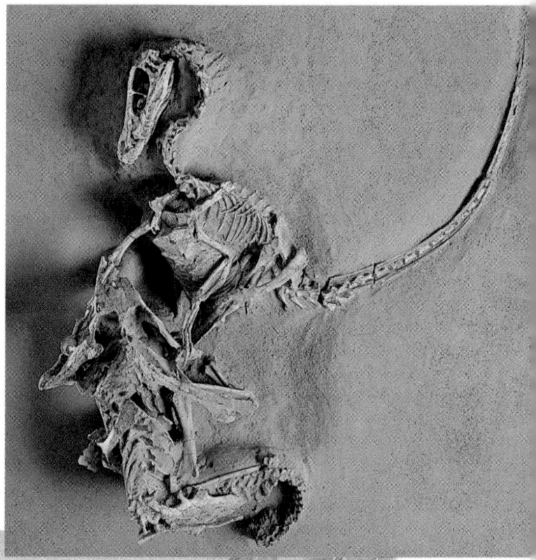
A

B

Figure 12-1 Scientists and artists can reconstruct what dinosaurs looked like using fossil remains. Two dinosaur fossils (A) were found in this position. Artists used the fossils to reconstruct a *Velociraptor* attacking a *Protoceratops* (B).

Fossils have helped geologists and biologists find out exactly when life began, when plants and animals first lived on land, and when certain types of organisms, such as the dinosaurs, disappeared. Fossils tell us not only *when* and *where* organisms once lived, but also *how* they lived.

Figure 12-2 The hard parts in plants, such as the cellulose in cell walls, made preservation of this fossil leaf possible.

Usually, the remains of dead plants and animals are quickly destroyed. Scavengers eat the dead organisms, or fungi and microorganisms cause them to decay. If you've ever left a banana on the shelf too long, you've seen this process begin. Compounds in the banana cause it to become soft and brown, and microorganisms move in and cause it to decay quickly. What keeps some plants and animals from decaying so that they become fossils?

Necessary Conditions

First of all, to become a fossil, the body of a dead organism must be protected from scavengers and microorganisms. One way this can occur is to have the body buried quickly by sediments. If a fish dies and sinks to the bottom of a pond, sediments carried into the pond by a stream will rapidly cover the fish. As a result, no animals or microorganisms can get to it. However, quick burial alone isn't enough to make a fossil.

Organisms have a better chance of being preserved if they have hard parts such as bones, shells, or teeth. As you may know, these hard parts are less likely to be eaten by other organisms, they decay more slowly, and they are less likely to weather away. Most fossils, such as the fossil leaf in **Figure 12-2,** are made of the hard parts of organisms. Fossils are most often found in sedimentary rocks. The heat and pressure involved in forming igneous and metamorphic rocks most often destroy fossil material.

Try at Home

MiniLab

Predicting Fossil Preservation

Procedure

1. Take a brief walk outside and observe the area near your school or home.
2. Look around and notice what type of litter has been discarded on the school grounds. Note whether there is a paved road near your school. Note anything else that was made by humans.

Analysis

1. Predict what human-made or natural objects from our time might be preserved far into the future.
2. Explain what conditions would need to exist for these objects to be preserved as fossils.

Figure 12-3 This pile of petrified wood is in the Petrified Forest National Monument in Arizona. Much of the original matter in these petrified plant remains has been replaced by quartz and other minerals. **Why have the fossils retained the shape of the original plant?**

Petrified Remains

You have some idea of what *Tyrannosaurus rex* looked like because you've seen drawings of this dinosaur. Perhaps you've also seen the skeletons of other dinosaurs in museums. Artists who draw *Tyrannosaurus rex* and other dinosaurs base their drawings on fossil bones. These bones are usually petrified.

Petrified (PEH truh fide) **remains** are hard and rocklike. Some or all of the original materials in the remains have been replaced by minerals. For example, a solution of water and dissolved quartz may flow through the bones of a dead organism. The water dissolves the calcium in the bone and deposits quartz in its place. Quartz is harder than calcium, so the petrified bone is rocklike.

We learn about past life-forms from bones, wood, and other remains that become petrified, like those in **Figure 12-3.** But, there are many other types of fossils to look at, too.

Figure 12-4 This fossil graptolite has been preserved as a carbonaceous film. Graptolites are extinct colonial animals that lived in the oceans from about 530 million to 320 million years ago.

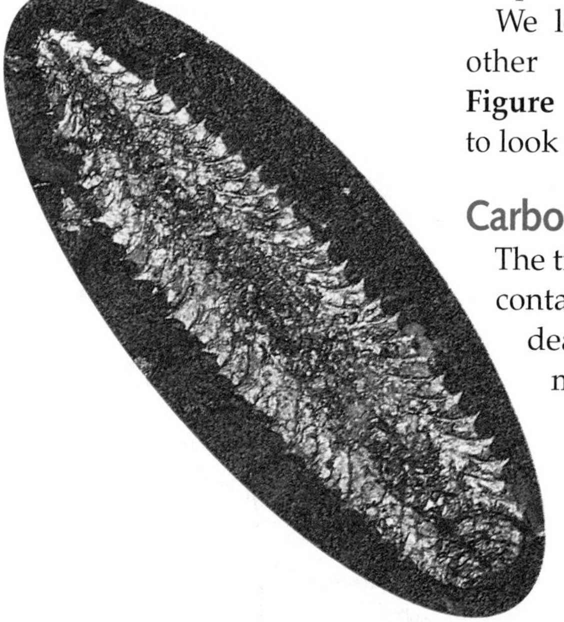

Carbonaceous Films

The tissues of most organisms are made of compounds that contain carbon. Sometimes, the only fossil remains of a dead plant or animal is this carbon. As you know, fossils most often form when a dead organism is buried in sediments. As more and more sediments pile up, the organism is exposed to pressure and heat. These conditions force gases and liquids from the organism. A thin film of carbon is left, forming an outline of the original organism. This type of fossil is called a **carbonaceous** (kar boh NAY shus) **film.** The process of chemically changing organic material is called carbonization. An example is shown in **Figure 12-4.**

In swamps and deltas, large amounts of plant matter accumulate. Over millions of years, these deposits become completely carbonized, forming the sedimentary rock coal. Coal is more important as a fuel than as a fossil because the makeup of the plant is most often lost when the coal forms.

Molds and Casts

Think again about the imprints in the plaster of paris you made earlier. In nature, such imprints are made when seashells or other hard parts of organisms fall into soft sediments such as mud. The object and sediments are then buried by more sediments. The sediments are squeezed and cemented together into rock. Holes in the rock let water and air reach the shell or hard part, causing it to dissolve, and leaving behind a hollow place in the rock called a **mold.** Later, other sediments may fill in the hollow place, harden into rock, and make a **cast** of the original organism, as shown in **Figure 12-5.**

Using Math

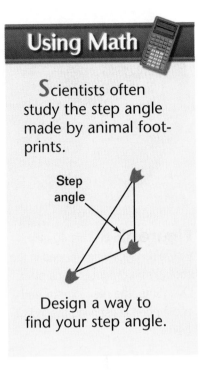

Scientists often study the step angle made by animal footprints.

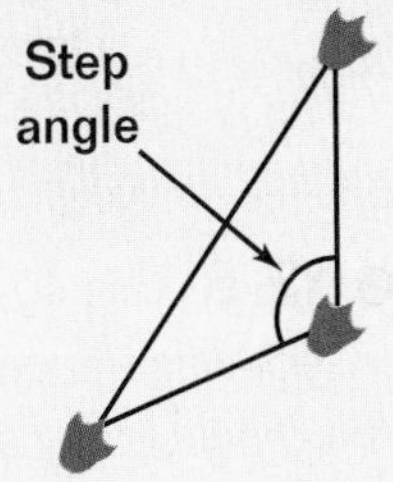

Design a way to find your step angle.

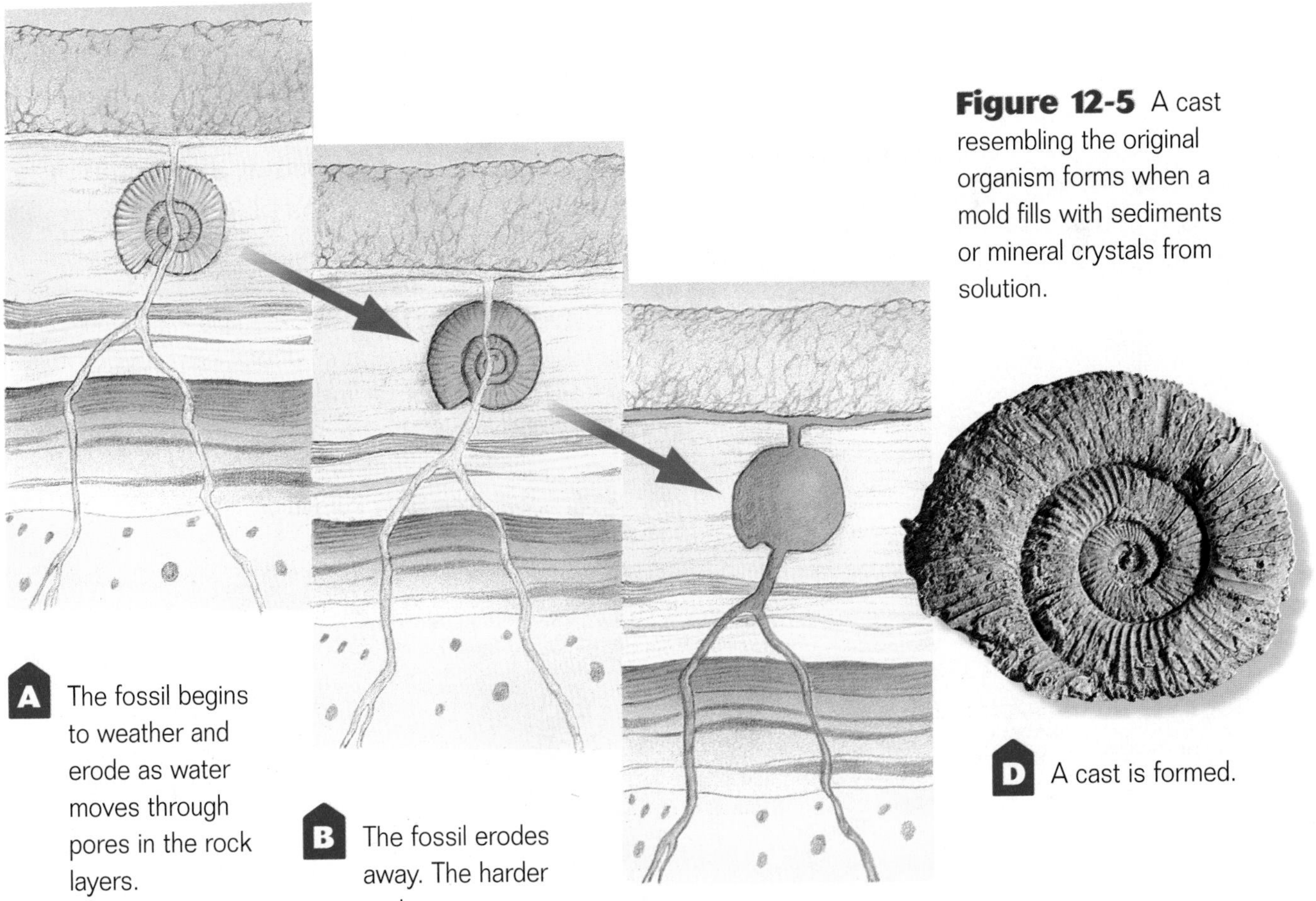

Figure 12-5 A cast resembling the original organism forms when a mold fills with sediments or mineral crystals from solution.

A The fossil begins to weather and erode as water moves through pores in the rock layers.

B The fossil erodes away. The harder rock once surrounding it forms a mold.

C Sediments are carried into the mold and deposited.

D A cast is formed.

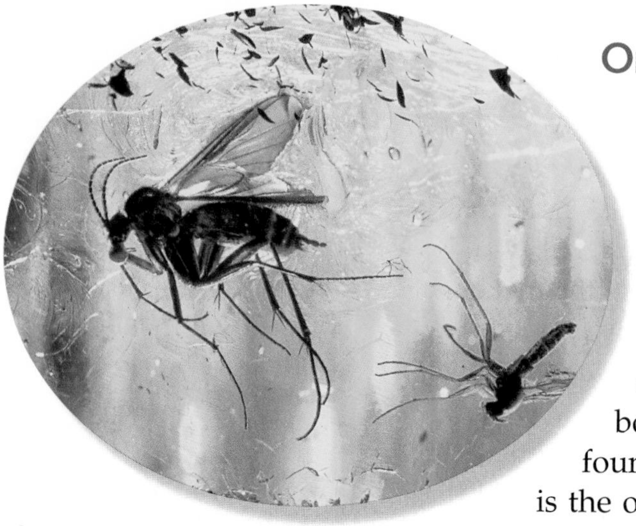

Figure 12-6 This 40-million-year-old insect was trapped in the sticky resin produced by a plant. Over time, the resin crystallized into amber, preserving the insect inside.

Original Remains

Sometimes the actual organism or parts of the organism are found. **Figure 12-6** shows an insect trapped in amber, a hard form of the sticky resin produced by some trees. The amber protects the insect's body from decay and petrification. Other organisms, such as woolly mammoths, have been found preserved in frozen ground. In 1991, the entire body of a man who lived 5300 years ago was found frozen in glacial ice in the southern Alps. It is the oldest complete human body ever discovered. Original remains have also been found in tar seeps such as the La Brea (BRAY ah) tar pits in California.

Trace Fossils

Fossilized tracks and other evidence of animal activity are called *trace fossils.* Perhaps your parents made your handprint or footprint in plaster of paris when you were born. If so, it's a record that tells something about you. From it, you can guess your size and maybe your weight at that age. Animals walking on Earth long ago have left similar tracks, such as those in **Figure 12-7.** In some cases, tracks can tell us more about how an organism lived than any other type of fossil. For example, the story described at the beginning of this chapter really took place.

A

Figure 12-7 Tracks made in soft mud, and now preserved in solid rock, can provide information about animal size, speed, and other behavior patterns. These tracks are located on the Navajo Reservation in Arizona (A) and in the Glenrose Rock Formation in Texas (B).

B

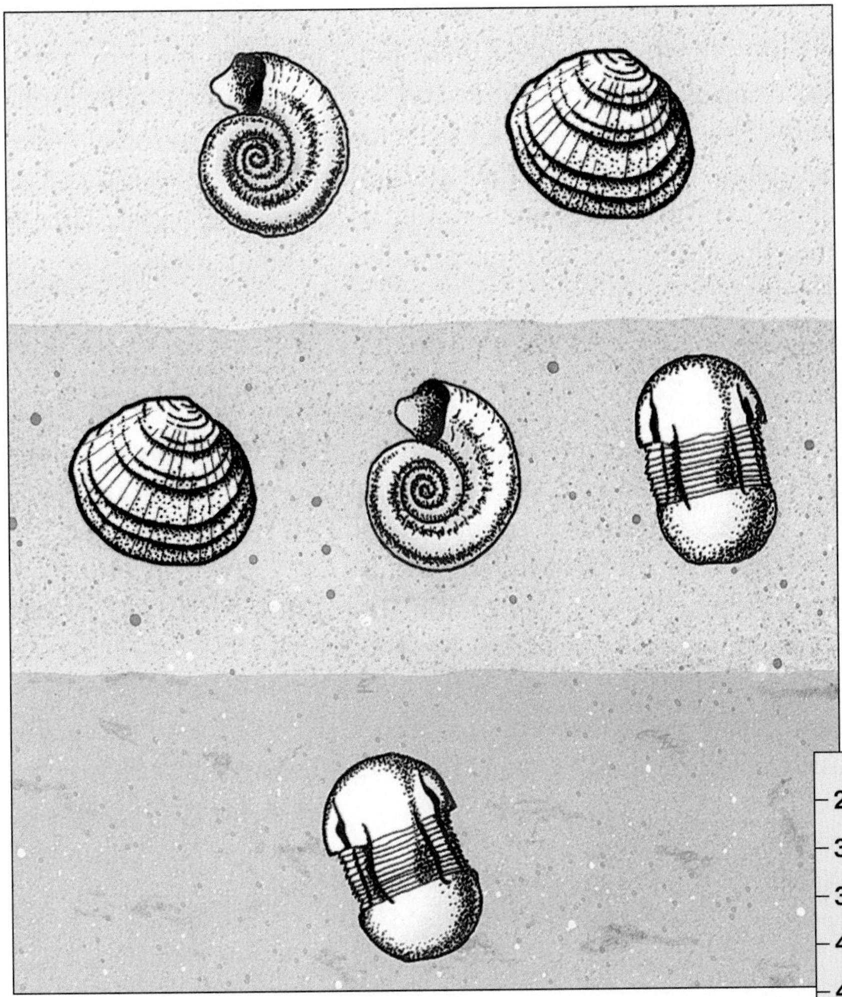

Figure 12-8 The sequence of sedimentary rock and the fossils each contains (A) can be used to date the rocks. The chart (B) shows when each organism inhabited Earth. **Why is it possible to say that the middle layer of rock had to be deposited between 438 and 408 million years ago?**

A Illustration of a sequence of rocks and the fossils they contain.

B Fossil Range Chart

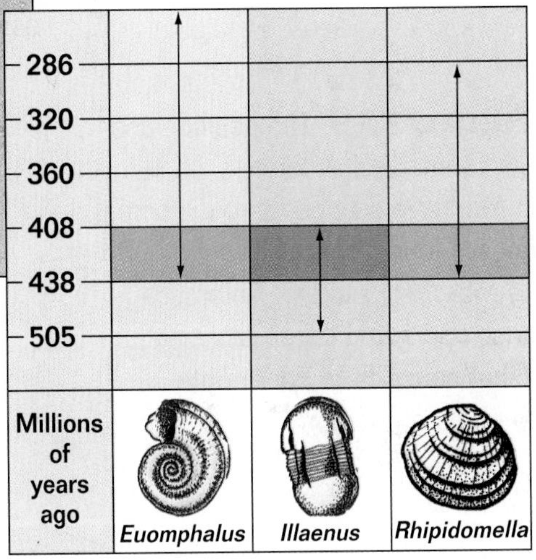

From a set of tracks at Davenport Ranch, Texas, we have learned something about the social life of *Apatosaurus*, one of the largest known dinosaurs. The largest tracks of the herd are on the outer edges and the smallest are on the inside. This suggests that the adult apatosaurs surrounded the young as they traveled—probably to protect them from enemies. In fact, a nearby set of allosaur tracks shows that one was stalking the herd.

Other trace fossils include worm holes and burrows made by marine animals. As you can see, a group of fossils can tell us a great deal about the individuals that lived on Earth before us. ☑

Reading Check ☑

How do fossil footprints provide information about social behavior?

Index Fossils

The study of fossils tells that species are constantly changing, or evolving. Evidence shows that species live on Earth for a certain period of time before they evolve into new species or they die out completely. Some species of organisms inhabit Earth for long periods of time without changing much. Other species remain unchanged for only a short time. It is these organisms that make index fossils.

Index fossils are species that lived on Earth for short periods of time, were abundant, and were widespread geographically. Scientists use index fossils to tell the age of rock layers. Because few fossils meet all the conditions to be an index fossil, groups of fossils are usually used to date rocks. This is how the rock layer in **Figure 12-8** was dated. Which fossil is the index fossil?

LIFE SCIENCE INTEGRATION

Trapped in Tar
You have learned that original remains of animals can be found in tar seeps. Hypothesize why so many animals became trapped in tar seeps. What would cause animals to walk into a tar pit?

Fossils and Ancient Environments

Fossils also can be used to tell what the environment of an area was like long ago. For example, rocks in Antarctica contain fossils of tropical plants. As shown in **Figure 12-9**, the environment of Antarctica today isn't tropical, but we hypothesize that it was at the time these fossilized plants were living.

How would you explain the presence of fossilized brachiopods, animals that lived in shallow seas, in the rocks of the midwestern United States? **Figure 12-10** shows an example of

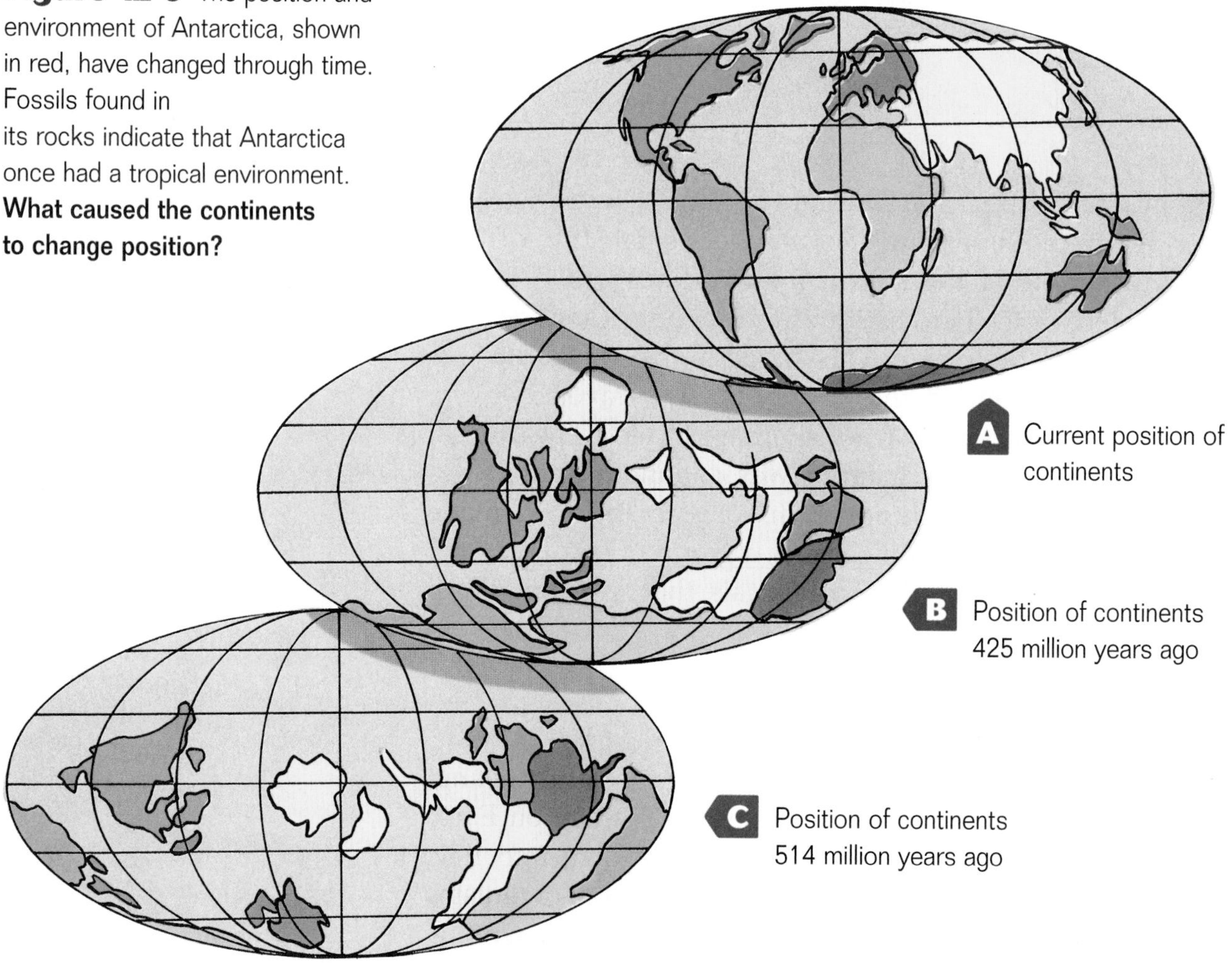

Figure 12-9 The position and environment of Antarctica, shown in red, have changed through time. Fossils found in its rocks indicate that Antarctica once had a tropical environment. **What caused the continents to change position?**

a modern brachiopod (BRAK ee uh pahd) and a fossil brachiopod. As shown in **Figure 12-9B** and **C,** North America was once found at the equator. The shallow seas that covered the central part of North America during some of this time were warm and hospitable to organisms such as brachiopods.

Fossils tell us not only about past life on Earth, but also about the history of the rock layers that contain them. Fossils can give information about environment, climate, and animal behavior, as well as dating the rocks.

Figure 12-10
(A) This Paleozoic-aged brachiopod lived in the warm shallow seas that once covered portions of North America.
(B) *Terebratulina septentrionalis* is a modern brachiopod. It lives off the coast of York, Maine. **How do the habitats of these brachiopod compare?**

Section Assessment

1. What conditions are needed for most fossils to form?
2. Describe how a mold-and-cast fossil might form.
3. Explain how index fossils are used.
4. **Think Critically:** What can be said about the ages of two geographically separated layers of rock that contain the same type of fossil?
5. **Skill Builder**
Concept Mapping Make a concept map that compares and contrasts petrified remains and original remains. Use the following terms and phrases: *types of fossils, original remains, evidence of former life, petrified remains, materials replaced by minerals,* and *actual parts of organisms.* If you need help, refer to Concept Mapping in the **Skill Handbook.**

Science Journal

Collect samples of fossils or visit a museum that has fossils on display. In your Science Journal, make an illustration of each fossil. Write a brief description, noting key facts about each. Also, write about how each fossil might have been formed.

12•2 Relative Ages of Rocks

What You'll Learn

- Several methods used to date rock layers relative to other rock layers
- How to interpret gaps in the rock record
- An example of how rock layers may be correlated with other rock layers

Vocabulary
principle of superposition
relative dating
unconformity

Why It's Important

- Being able to determine the age of rock layers is important in constructing a history of how Earth has changed through time.

The Principle of Superposition

It's a hot summer day in July, and you're getting ready to meet your friends at the park. You put on your helmet and pads and grab your skateboard. But, the bearings in one of the wheels are worn, and the wheel isn't spinning freely. You remember reading an article in a skateboarding magazine about how to replace wheels, and you decide to look it up. In your room is a stack of magazines from the past year, as seen in **Figure 12-11.** You know that the article came out in the January edition, so it must be near the bottom of the pile. As you dig downward, you find the magazine from March, then February. You know that January must be next.

How did you know that the January issue of the magazine would be on the bottom? To find the older issue under newer ones, you used the principle of superposition.

Youngest Rocks on Top

The **principle of superposition** states that for undisturbed layers of rock, the oldest rocks are on the bottom and the rocks become younger and younger toward the top. Why is this the case? Is it always true?

As you know, sediments are often deposited in horizontal beds, forming layers of sedimentary rock. The first layer to form is usually on the bottom. Each additional layer forms on top of the previous one. Unless forces such as those made

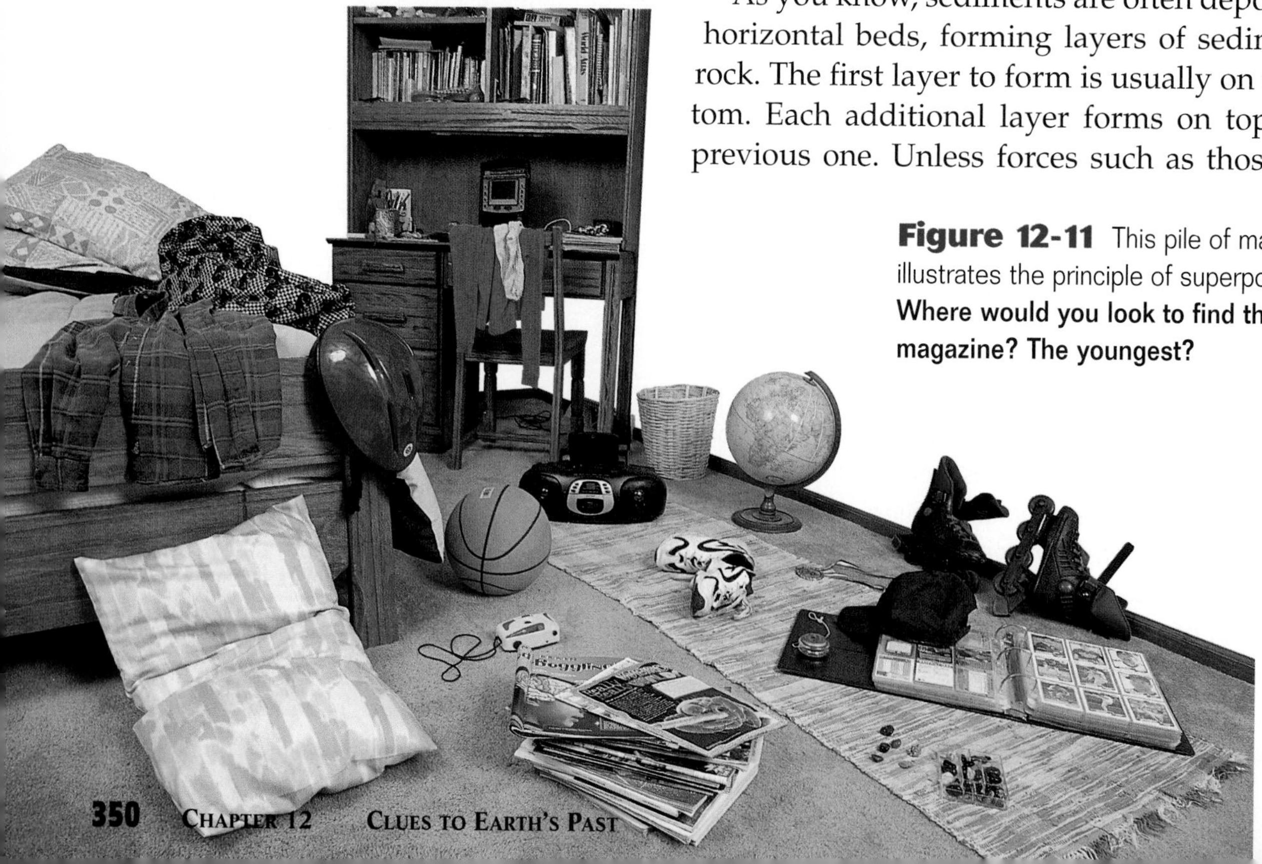

Figure 12-11 This pile of magazines illustrates the principle of superposition. **Where would you look to find the oldest magazine? The youngest?**

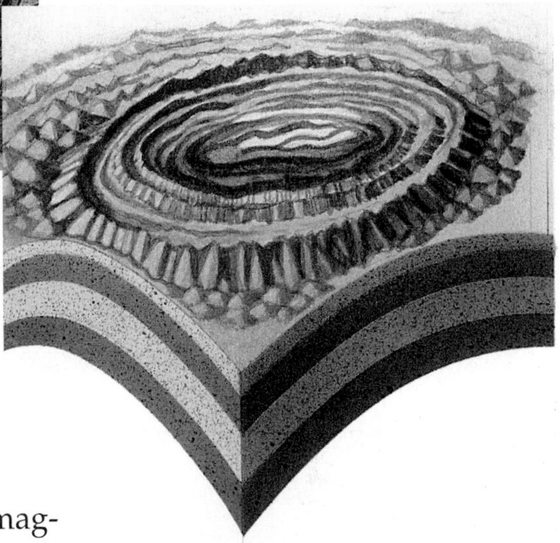

Figure 12-12 This illustration and photograph show a large-scale dome in sedimentary rocks with exposed rock layers in Wyoming. The oldest layers are folded up and exposed in the center. **Does the principle of superposition still apply here?**

by tectonic activity turn the layers upside down, the oldest rocks are found at the bottom. When layers have been turned upside down, geologists use other clues in the rock layers to tell their original positions.

Relative Dating

Suppose you now want to look for another issue of a magazine. You're not sure exactly how old it is—all you know is that it arrived after the January issue. You can find it in the stack by using relative dating.

Relative dating is used in geology to determine the order of events and the relative age of rocks by examining the position of rocks in a sequence. For example, if layers of sedimentary rock are offset by a fault, you know that the layers had to be there first before a fault could cut through them. The relative age of the rocks is older than the relative age of the fault. So, using the magazine example, how do you find the issue by relative dating?

Relative dating doesn't tell you anything about the exact age of rock layers. You don't know if a layer is 100 million or 10 000 years old—only that it's younger than the layers below it and older than the fault cutting through it.

Other Clues Help

Relative dating works well if rocks haven't been folded or overturned by tectonic processes. For example, look at **Figure 12-12.** Which layer is the oldest? In cases where rock layers have been disturbed, you may have to look for fossils and other clues to date the rocks. If you find a fossil in the top layer that's older than a fossil in a lower layer, you can hypothesize that layers have been turned upside down or faulted.

interNET CONNECTION

Visit the Glencoe Science Web Site at **www.glencoe.com/sec/science/ca** to learn more about how the relative dating of rocks is done.

Another clue you can use is the way the fossils are arranged in the layers. Most attached marine organisms grow upward, toward the sunlight. If you find a limestone formation with corals that are upright, you can infer that the rocks have not been tilted or overturned. Even something as simple as a hole in the rock can help. Sediments are always deposited horizontally at the bottom of a hole. If a sample looks like it is half filled from the top, it is upside down.

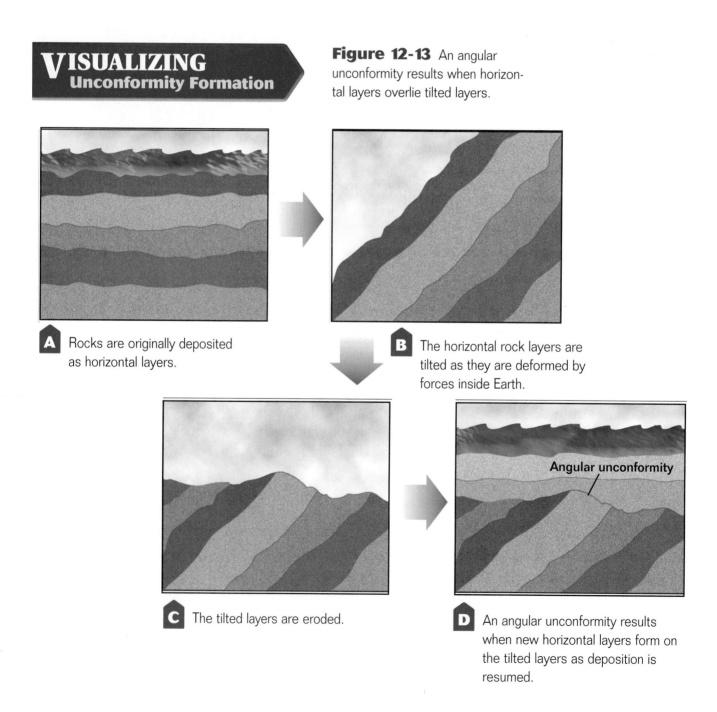

VISUALIZING Unconformity Formation

Figure 12-13 An angular unconformity results when horizontal layers overlie tilted layers.

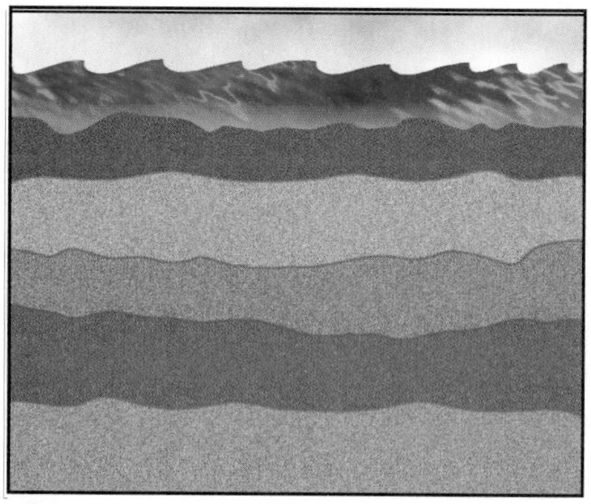

A Rocks are originally deposited as horizontal layers.

B The horizontal rock layers are tilted as they are deformed by forces inside Earth.

C The tilted layers are eroded.

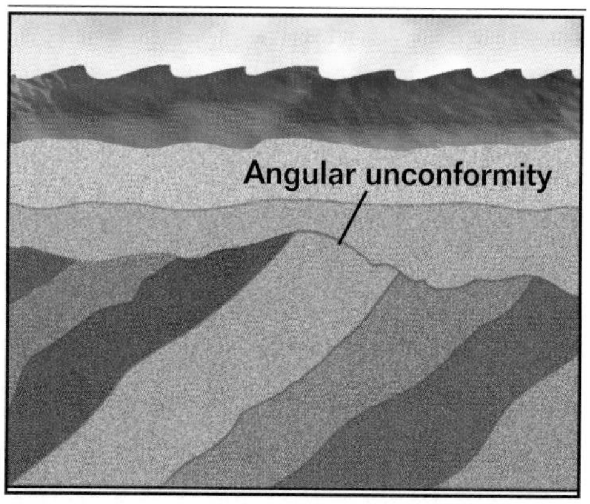

D An angular unconformity results when new horizontal layers form on the tilted layers as deposition is resumed.

Unconformities

As you have seen, a layer of rock is a record of past events. But, most rock records are not complete—layers are missing. These gaps in rock layers are called **unconformities** (un kun FOR miht eez).

Unconformities develop when agents of erosion remove existing rock layers. They also form when a period of time passes without any new deposition occurring to form new layers of rock.

Reading Check

What is an unconformity?

Angular Unconformities

Figure 12-13 illustrates one way an unconformity can form. Horizontal layers of sedimentary rock are tilted and uplifted, so that erosion and weathering wear them down. Eventually, younger sediment layers are deposited horizontally on top of the eroded and tilted layers. Such an unconformity is called an angular unconformity.

Disconformity

Suppose you're looking at a sequence of sedimentary rocks. They look complete, but layers are missing. If you look closely, you may find an old erosional surface. This records a time when the rocks were exposed and eroded. Later, younger rocks formed above the erosional surface when sediment deposition began again. Even though all the layers are horizontal, a gap still exists in the record. This type of unconformity, called a disconformity, is shown in **Figure 12-14.**

Figure 12-14 The buried erosional surface in the far right illustration is a disconformity. **How could you determine how much time and rock is missing?**

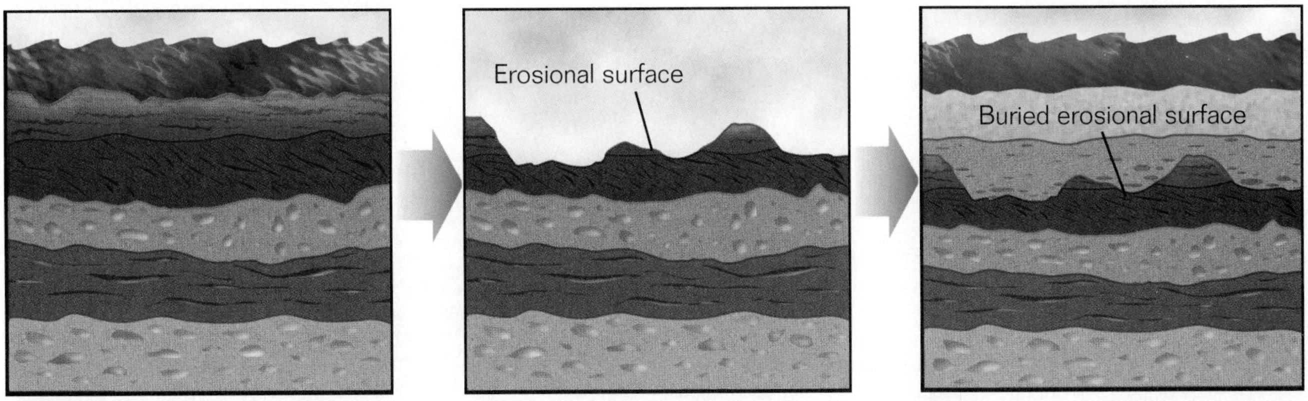

A Sedimentary rock layers are deposited horizontally.

B The layers are uplifted, exposed, and eroded.

C When deposition resumes, younger horizontal sediments are deposited on the buried erosional surface.

Nonconformity

Another type of unconformity, called a nonconformity, occurs when metamorphic or igneous rocks are uplifted and eroded. Sedimentary rocks are then deposited on top of this erosional surface. The surface between the two rock types is a nonconformity.

Correlating Rock Layers

Suppose you're studying a layer of sandstone in Bryce Canyon in Utah. Later, when you visit Canyonlands National Park, you notice that a layer of sandstone there looks just like the sandstone in Bryce Canyon, 250 km away. Above the sandstone in Canyonlands is a layer of limestone and then another sandstone layer. You return to Bryce Canyon and find the same sequence—sandstone, limestone, and sandstone. What do you infer? It's likely that you're actually looking at the same layer of rocks in two different locations. These rocks are parts of huge deposits that covered this whole area of the western United States, as seen in **Figure 12-15.** The sandstone and limestone you found at the two parks are the exposed surfaces of the same rock layers.

Figure 12-15 These rock layers, exposed at Hopi Point in Grand Canyon National Park, can be correlated, or matched up, with rocks from across large areas of the western United States.

Evidence Used for Correlation

Geologists match up, or correlate, layers of rocks over great distances, as seen in **Figure 12-16.** It's not always easy to say that a rock layer exposed in one area is the same as a rock layer exposed in another area. Sometimes it's possible to walk along the layer for kilometers and prove that it's a continuous layer. In other cases, such as at Canyonlands and Bryce Canyon, the rock layers are exposed only where rivers have cut through overlying layers of rock and sediment. How can you prove that the limestone sandwiched between the two layers of sandstone in Canyonlands is the same limestone as at Bryce Canyon? One way is to use fossil evidence. If the same types of fossils are found in both outcrops of limestone, it's likely that the limestone at each place is the same age, and therefore, one continuous deposit.

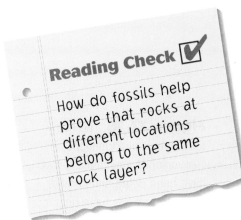

Reading Check

How do fossils help prove that rocks at different locations belong to the same rock layer?

Problem Solving

Interpreting Scientific Illustrations

When geologists study the rock outcrops in an area, they obtain rock samples from, measure the thickness of, and record a description of each rock layer. For example, one report might describe a 1-m-thick, massive sandstone of medium-brown color.

Once the descriptions are recorded for each layer of rock that is observed in one location, geologists draw a column that shows each of the rock layers. They then try to correlate or match up a rock column from one location to rock columns from other locations. A geologist can tell much about the geologic history of an area from a study of rock column correlations.

The rock column shown on the left is from Green River, Utah. The rock column on the right is from Westwater, Colorado. Using the rock columns, reconstruct the geologic history of the area. Correlate similar rock layers between the two locations. An example of how to correlate the rock columns is shown for rock layer 1. How many unconformities, and what types, can you recognize in each column?

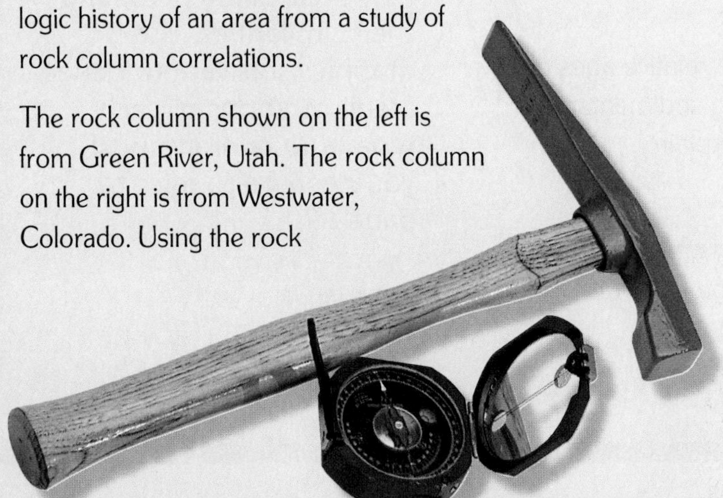

Think Critically: Explain the geologic history of the Green River area in terms of erosion and deposition. Why are some layers missing from the Westwater column?

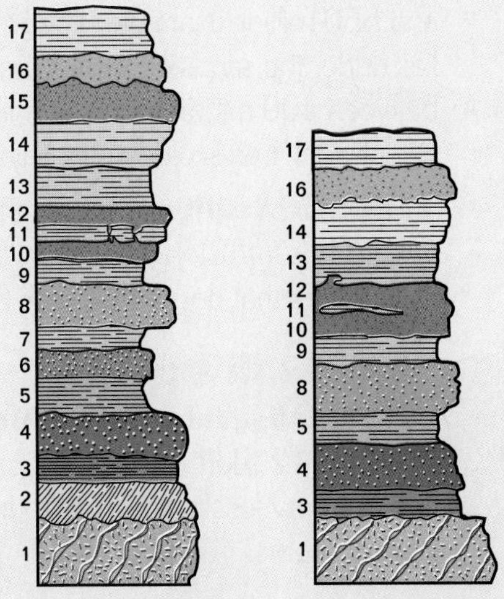

Green River, Utah   Westwater, Colorado

Are there other ways to correlate layers of rock? Sometimes relative dating isn't enough, and other dating methods must be used. In the next section, you'll see how the actual age of rocks can be determined and how geologists have used this information to determine the age of Earth.

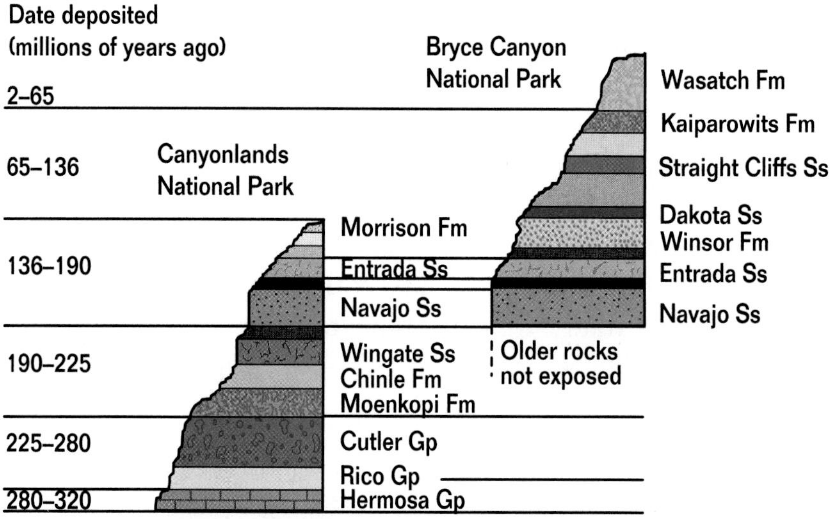

Figure 12-16 The many rock layers, or formations, in Canyonlands and Bryce Canyon have been dated and named. Some formations have been correlated between the two canyons. (NOTE: Fm = formation, Ss = sandstone, Gp = group.) **Which layers are present at both canyons?**

Section Assessment

1. Suppose you haven't cleaned out your locker all year. Where would you expect to find papers from the beginning of the year? What principle in geology would you use to find these old papers?
2. Why is it more difficult to recognize a disconformity than an angular unconformity?
3. A geologist finds a series of rocks. The sandstone contains a fossil that is 400 million years old. The shale contains fossils that are between 500 million and 550 million years old. The limestone, which lies under the sandstone, contains fossils that are between 400 million and 500 million years old. Which rock bed is oldest? Explain.
4. **Think Critically:** What are the relative ages of an igneous intrusion and overlying sedimentary rock layers that dome upward? Explain.
5. **Skill Builder**
Observing and Inferring Do the **Chapter 12 Skill Activity** on page 705 to find out how fossils are used to interpret environments.

Using Computers

Spreadsheet Use the information about unconformities on pages 352 and 353 to prepare an electronic spreadsheet listing the types of unconformities, their differences, and their similarities. Use graphics software to generate illustrations of each type of unconformity. If you need help, refer to page 690.

Relative Dating

Materials

- Paper
- Pencil

Can you tell which of two rock layers is older? You don't need to know the exact ages of the layers to tell. Geologists can learn a lot about rock layers simply by studying their arrangement.

What You'll Investigate

Can the relative ages of rocks be determined by studying the rock layers and structures?

Goals

- **Determine** the relative order of events by interpreting illustrations of rock layers.

Procedure

1. Study **Figures A** and **B**. The legend will help you interpret the figures.
2. Determine the relative ages of the rock layers, unconformities, igneous dikes, and fault in each figure.

Conclude and Apply

Figure A

1. Were any layers of rock deposited after the igneous dike formed? Explain.
2. What type of unconformity is shown? Is it possible that there were originally more layers of rock than are shown here? Explain.
3. What type of fault is shown?
4. Explain how to determine whether the igneous dike formed before or after the fault occurred?

Figure B

5. What type of fault is shown?
6. Is the igneous dike on the left older or younger than the unconformity near the top? Explain.
7. Are the two igneous dikes shown the same age? How do you know?
8. Which two layers of rock may have been much thicker at one time than they are now?

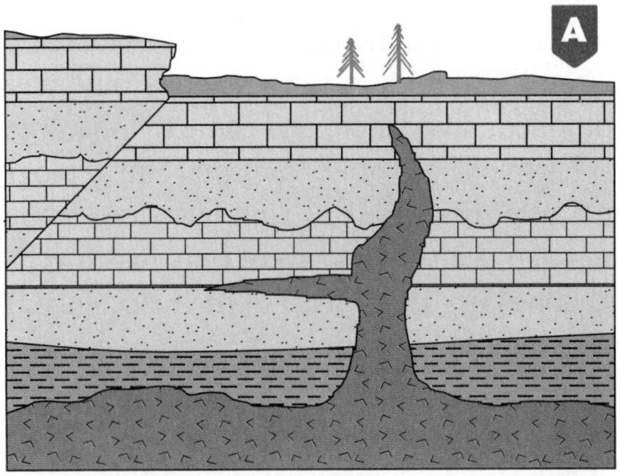

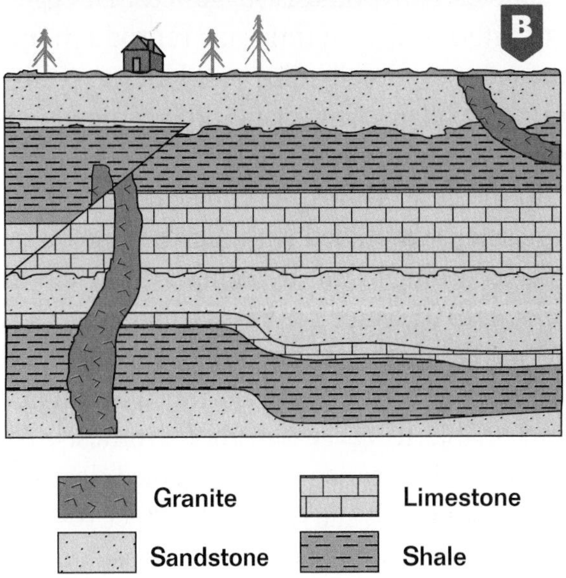

Interpreting Scientific Illustrations

1. Make a sketch of Figure A. On it, **identify** the relative age of each rock layer, igneous dike, fault, and unconformity. For example, the shale layer is the oldest, so mark it with a *1.* Mark the next-oldest feature with a *2,* and so on.
2. Repeat the procedure in question 1 for Figure B.

Extinction of Dinosaurs

What killed the dinosaurs?

The fossil record indicates that dinosaurs appeared between 230 and 220 million years ago. As time passed, dinosaurs multiplied, diversified, and came to inhabit every continent on Earth. Then quite abruptly, in geologic terms, the dinosaurs disappeared. This happened about 66 million years ago. Left behind were only fossilized tracks, teeth, and bones (right) as proof of their existence. What caused this dramatic extinction? No one really knows yet, but scientists have proposed several hypotheses to explain the disappearance of the dinosaurs.

One early hypothesis suggested that egg-eating mammals interfered with dinosaur reproduction, so that the dinosaurs eventually died out. However, this hypothesis did not explain why many other animals also became extinct when dinosaurs did.

In the early 1980s, several scientists proposed that a large asteroid collided with Earth some 66 million years ago. According to this hypothesis, the asteroid vaporized rocks and seawater on impact and sent clouds of dust and acidic gases into the atmosphere. The dust clouds would have blocked out so much sunlight that plants were unable to carry out photosynthesis. As vegetation withered, plant-eating dinosaurs died, leaving their meat-eating relatives to starve as well. Other researchers suggest that the asteroid impact led to widespread wildfires, acid rain, or global warming that caused the dinosaur extinction.

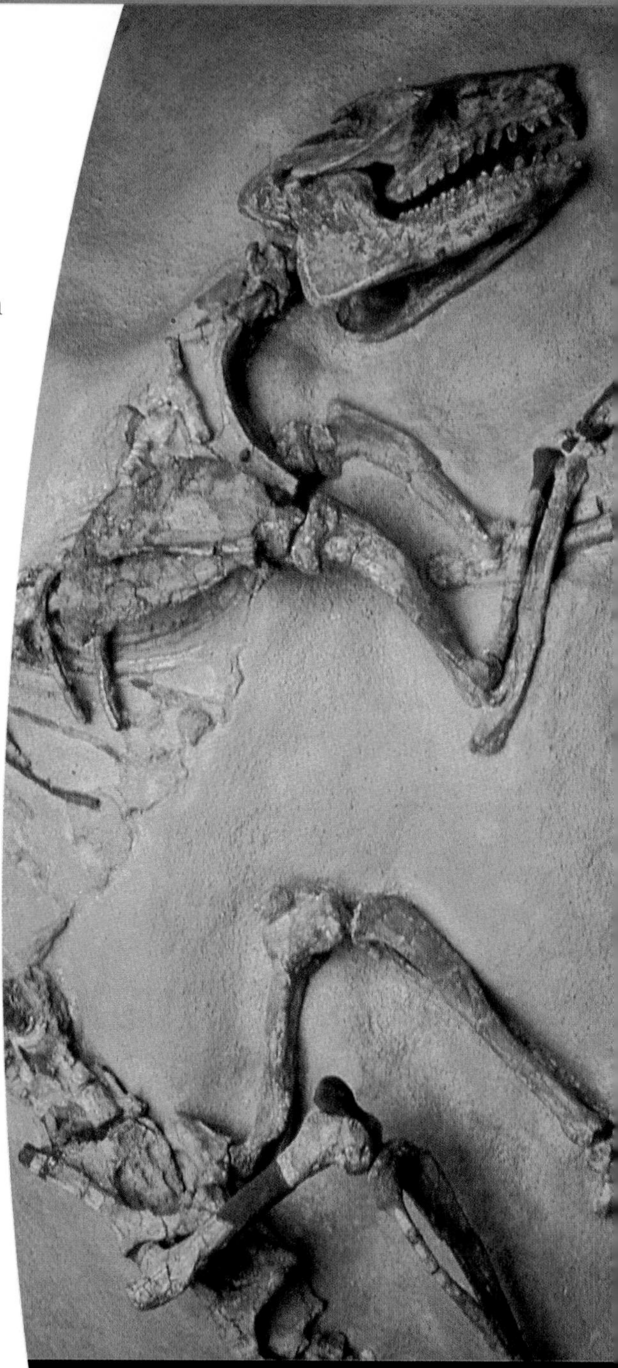

Other Hypotheses

Another hypothesis proposes that intense volcanic activity spewed enormous quantities of dust and gases into the ancient atmosphere and led to global cooling. Animals unable to adapt died out, including the dinosaurs. Any hypothesis regarding dinosaur extinction must take into account that many other species perished when the dinosaurs did, and yet many mammals survived. Scientists continue to search for evidence that will determine what event, or combination of events, ended the age of dinosaurs.

Science JOURNAL

How the dinosaurs became extinct remains an intensely debated topic. In your Science Journal, write an essay that discusses how one of the hypotheses could be supported and why.

Absolute Ages of Rocks

12•3

Absolute Dating

Remember the stack of magazines? As you continue to shuffle through them, looking for articles about wheels and bearings, you decide you need to restack them into a neat pile. By now, they're a mess and no longer in the order of their relative ages, as shown in **Figure 12-17.** How can you stack them so the oldest are on the bottom and the newest on top? Fortunately, magazines have their dates printed on their covers. Thus, stacking magazines in order is a simple process. Unfortunately for geologists, rocks don't have their ages stamped on them. Or do they?

Absolute dating is a method used to determine the age, in years, of a rock or other object. Absolute dating is a process that uses the properties of atoms in rocks and other objects to find their ages.

Radioactive Decay

An element can have atoms with different numbers of neutrons in their nuclei. These are called isotopes. Some of these isotopes undergo a process called **radioactive decay.** When an atom of some isotopes decays, one of its neutrons breaks down into a proton and an electron. The electron leaves the atom as a beta particle. The nucleus loses a neutron but gains a proton. Other isotopes give off two protons and two neutrons in the form of an alpha particle, as seen in **Figure 12-18.** As you know, when the number of protons in an atom is changed, as it is in radioactive decay, a new element is formed. For example, when an atom of the radioactive isotope uranium-238 decays, it eventually forms an atom of lead-206. Lead-206 isn't radioactive, so it does not decay any further.

Figure 12-17 The magazines that have been shuffled through no longer illustrate the principle of superposition.

What You'll Learn

- How absolute dating differs from relative dating
- How the half-lives of isotopes are used to determine a rock's age

Vocabulary

absolute dating
radioactive decay
half-life
radiometric dating
uniformitarianism

Why It's Important

- Determining the absolute age of rocks and minerals allows scientists to calculate the age of Earth.

PHYSICS INTEGRATION

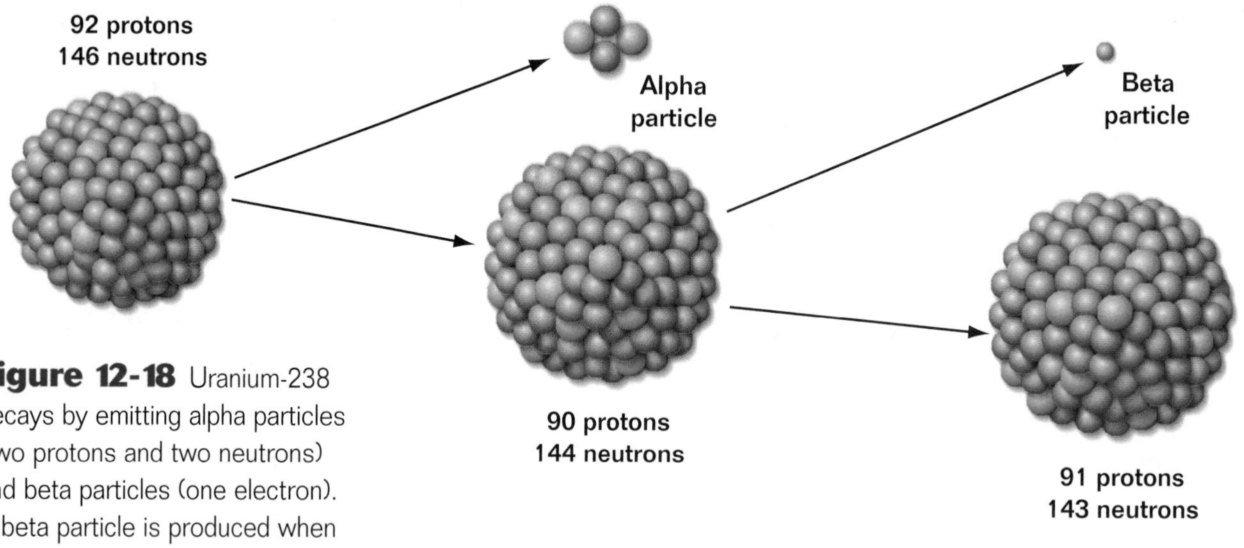

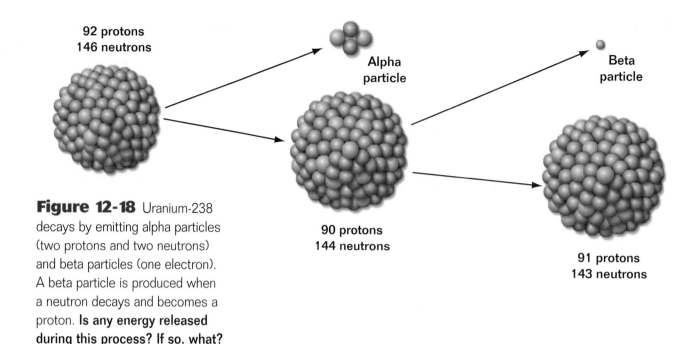

Figure 12-18 Uranium-238 decays by emitting alpha particles (two protons and two neutrons) and beta particles (one electron). A beta particle is produced when a neutron decays and becomes a proton. **Is any energy released during this process? If so, what?**

MiniLab

Sequencing Earth's History

Procedure

1. Sequence these events in Earth's history in relative order: Earth forms, first many-celled organisms, first land plants, first mammals, dinosaurs become extinct, first amphibians, first human ancestors, oldest known fossils, first many-celled animals.
2. Make a time line using these dates: 4.6 billion years, 3.5 billion years, 1.25 billion years, 600 million years, 439 million years, 408 million years, 225 million years, 66 million years, and 4.4 million years ago.
3. Match each event with the absolute date on your time line.

Analysis

1. Check your time line with your teacher.
2. Did you correctly list the events in relative order?
3. How does the age of Earth compare with the presence of humans on the time line?

In the case of uranium decaying to lead, uranium-238 is known as the parent material and lead-206 as the daughter product. Another example of a parent material is carbon-14, which decays to its daughter, nitrogen-14. Each radioactive parent material has a certain rate at which it decays to its daughter product. This rate is known as its half-life.

Half-Life

The **half-life** of an isotope is the time it takes for half of the atoms in an isotope to decay. For example, the half-life of carbon-14 is 5730 years. So it will take 5730 years for half of the carbon-14 atoms in an object to decay to nitrogen-14.

You might guess that in another 5730 years, all of the remaining carbon-14 atoms will have decayed to nitrogen-14. However, this is not the case. Only half of the atoms of carbon-14 remaining after the first 5730 years will decay during the second 5730 years. So, after two half-lives, one-fourth of the original carbon-14 atoms still remain. Half of the remaining carbon-14 will decay during another 5730 years. After many half-lives, such a small amount of the parent material remains that it may not be measurable.

Radiometric Dating

To a geologist, the decay of radioactive isotopes is like a clock ticking away. The clock is keeping track of time that's passed since rocks have formed. As time passes, the amount of parent material in a mineral decreases as the amount of daughter product increases, as seen in **Figure 12-19.** By measuring the ratio of daughter product to parent isotope in a mineral and by knowing the half-life of the parent, a geologist can calculate the absolute age of the mineral. This process is called **radiometric dating.**

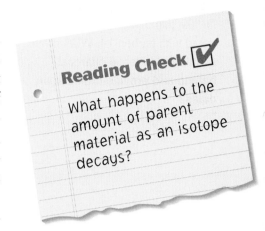

Reading Check

What happens to the amount of parent material as an isotope decays?

A scientist must decide which parent and daughter materials to measure when dating a mineral or a fossil. If the object to be dated is very old, then a parent isotope with a long half-life must be used. For example, carbon-14 dating would be useful to date a fossil shell that is 10 000 years old but could not be used to date a fossil that is 100 million years old. However, the half-life of uranium-238 is 4.5 billion years. This isotope has been used to date minerals that are billions of years old.

Radiocarbon Dating

Carbon-14 is useful for dating fossils, bones, and wood up to 75 000 years old. Organisms take in carbon from the environment to build tissues in their bodies. The amount remains constant throughout their lives. After the organism dies, the carbon-14 slowly decays and escapes as nitrogen-14 gas. The amount of carbon-14 remaining can be measured to determine the age of the fossil or when humans used a fire site, as in **Figure 12-20.**

Figure 12-19 After each half-life, one-half the amount of parent material remains. Eventually, such a small amount of the parent material is left that it may not be measurable. The radioactive decay curve shows how much parent isotope remains at any time. **How much parent material is left after a fifth half-life?**

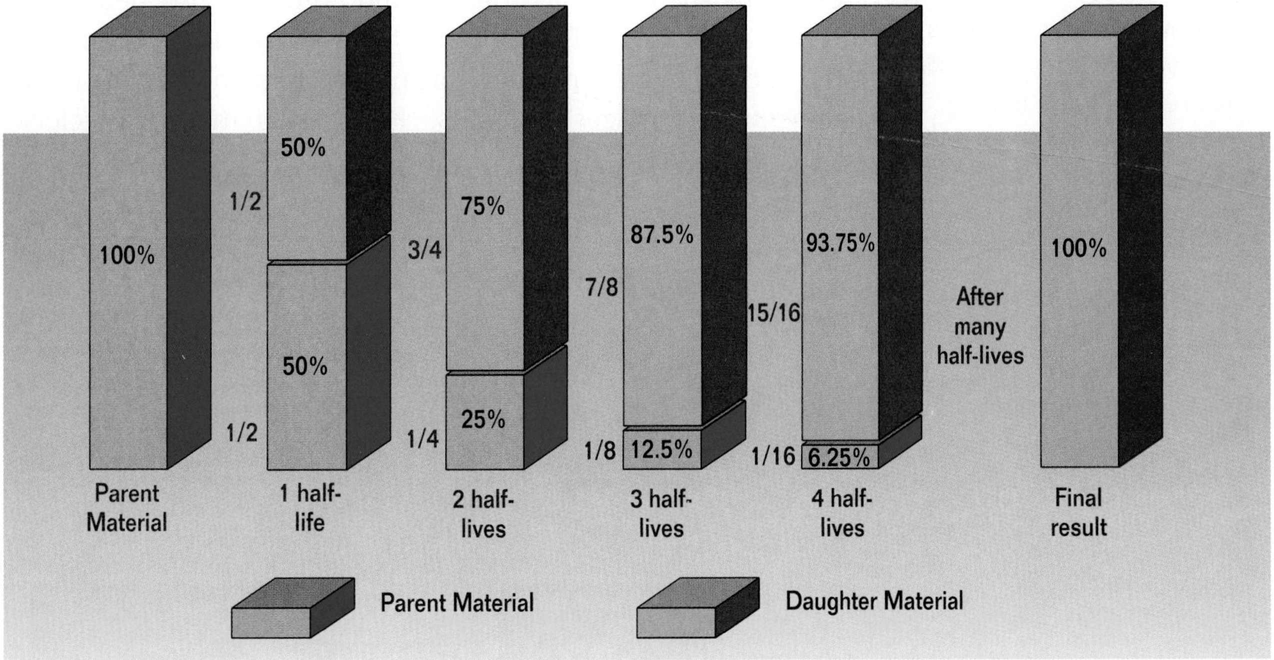

Figure 12-20 Human activity, like this campfire, also can be dated with carbon-14. **What other events could leave charcoal behind and provide radiocarbon dates?**

Rocks that can be radiometrically dated are mostly igneous although some metamorphic rocks can be used too. Sedimentary rocks cannot be dated by this method because only the absolute age of the sediment grains in the rock can be determined, not the rock itself. Radiometric dating has been used to date the oldest rocks found on Earth. These rocks are 3.96 billion years old. In western Australia sandstones, zircon mineral grains have been dated to about 4.1 to 4.3 billion years. Scientists have estimated the age of Earth at 4.6 billion years.

Source for Error

How sure can scientists be that the dates they calculate are accurate? First, they must make sure that no parent material is added to the mineral after decay has begun and no daughter product is removed after forming. This can be difficult when elements such as potassium (K) and argon (Ar) are being analyzed, as shown in **Figure 12-21.** Second, care must be taken if the rocks have been metamorphosed. Remember that metamorphism changes minerals. This resets the decay clock.

Figure 12-21 Over time, the potassium in the mineral decays to argon. The argon escapes, making the ratio of potassium to argon decrease. **Why does Argon (Ar) escape so easily?**

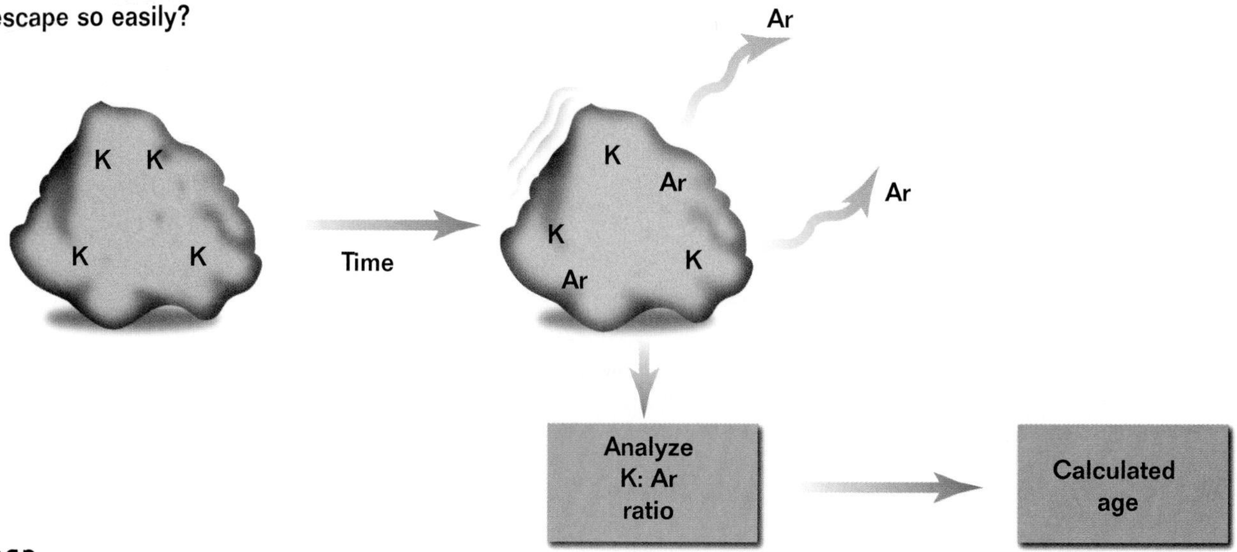

Scientists detect and compensate for wrong ages by using several different parent and daughter pairs in several different minerals. This cross-check also may help scientists to learn more about what has happened to a rock.

Uniformitarianism

Before radiometric dating was known, many people had estimated the age of Earth to be only a few thousand years old. But in the 1700s, Scottish scientist James Hutton estimated that Earth was much older. He used the principle of **uniformitarianism** (yew nih for mih TAHR ee ah nizm). This principle states that Earth processes taking place today are similar to those that took place in the past. Observing that the processes that changed the rocks and land around him were slow, he inferred that these processes had been just as slow throughout Earth's history. Hutton hypothesized that it took much longer than a few thousand years to form the rock layers around him and to erode mountain peaks to hills. John Playfair advanced Hutton's theories, but an English geologist, Sir Charles Lyell, is given the most credit for advancing uniformitarianism. What processes operating on Earth today also operated in the distant past?

interNET CONNECTION

Visit the Glencoe Science Web Site at **www.glencoe.com/sec/science/ca** for more information about the ages of rocks.

Section Assessment

1. You discover three undisturbed rock layers. The absolute age of the middle layer is 120 million years. What can you say about the ages of the layers above and below it?
2. How old would a fossil be if it had only one-eighth of its original carbon-14 content remaining?
3. **Think Critically:** Suppose you radiometrically date an igneous dike running through only the bottom two layers in question 1. The dike is cut off by the upper rock layer. The dike is 70 million years old. What can you say about the absolute age of the upper layer?
4. **Skill Builder**
   Making and Using Tables Make a table that shows the amounts of parent and daughter materials left of a radioactive element after four half-lives if the original parent material had a mass of 100 g. If you need help, refer to Making and Using Tables in the **Skill Handbook** on page 668.

Science Journal

Research Sir Charles Lyell in a geology book or encyclopedia. In your Science Journal, write a one-page report about his contribution to uniformitarianism.

Activity 12•2

Radioactive Decay

Materials

- Shoe box with lid
- Brass fasteners (100)
- Paper clips (100)
- Graph paper
- Pennies (100)
- Colored pencils (2)

Radioactive isotopes, elements that contain atoms with different numbers of neutrons, decay into their daughter elements in a specific amount of time. The rate of decay varies for each individual isotope. This rate can be used to determine the age of rocks that contain the isotopes under study. In this activity, you will develop a model that demonstrates how the half-life of certain radioactive isotopes can be used to determine absolute ages.

What You'll Investigate

What materials can be used to model age determination using radioactive half-lives?

Goals

- **Model** radioactive half-lives using listed materials.
- **Model** absolute age determination using the half-lives of radioactive isotopes.

Safety Precautions

Hold the lid of the box on tight to avoid having objects flying out of the box.

Procedure

1. Place 100 pennies into the shoe box with all heads up.
2. Place the lid on the box and shake it one time.
3. Remove the lid. Replace the pennies that are now tails up with paper clips. Record the number of pennies remaining in the box in a data table similar to the one shown on the next page.
4. Repeat steps 2 and 3 until all the pennies have been removed.

5. Remove the paper clips from the box. Put an "X" on one of the shorter sides of the box. Place 100 fasteners in the box, all pointed away from the "X".
6. Repeat step 2.
7. Remove the lid. Replace the fasteners that point toward the "X" with paper clips. Record the number of fasteners remaining in the box in a data table similar to the one shown at right.
8. Repeat steps 2 and 7 until all the fasteners have been removed.
9. Plot both sets of data on the same graph. Graph the "shake number" on the horizontal axis and the "number of pennies or fasteners remaining" on the vertical axis. Be sure to use a different colored pencil for each set of data.

Half-life Data

Shake Number	Number Remaining	
	Pennies	Fasteners

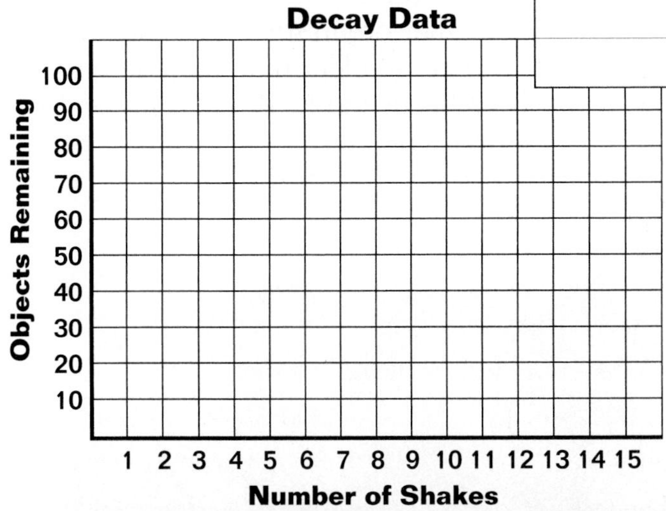

Conclude and Apply

1. In this model of radioactive decay, what do the coins and fasteners represent? The paper clips? The box? Each shake?
2. What was the half-life of the pennies? The fasteners?
3. How does the difference between the two objects affect the half-life? Compare the objects to the differences among radioactive elements.
4. Suppose you could make only one shake in 100 years. How many years would it take to have 25 coins and 75 paper clips remaining? To have 25 fasteners and 75 paper clips remaining?
5. How can absolute age of rocks be determined?

Chapter 12 Reviewing Main Ideas

For a **preview** of this chapter, study this Reviewing Main Ideas before you read the chapter. After you have studied this chapter, you can use the Reviewing Main Ideas to **review** the chapter.

GLENCOE TECHNOLOGY

The Glencoe MindJogger, Audiocassettes, and CD-ROM provide additional opportunities for review.

Section 12-1 FOSSILS

Fossils are more likely to form if hard parts of the dead organisms are buried quickly. Some fossils form when original materials that made up the organisms are replaced with minerals. Other fossils form when remains are subjected to heat and pressure, leaving only a **carbonaceous film** behind. When an organism is buried, decays, and leaves a cavity in the rock that is later filled with sediment, a **mold** and **cast** fossil forms. Some fossils are merely the tracks or traces left by former organisms. As a rule, a rock layer can be no older than the age of the fossils embedded in it. ***What type of fossil forms when original remains have been replaced with minerals?***

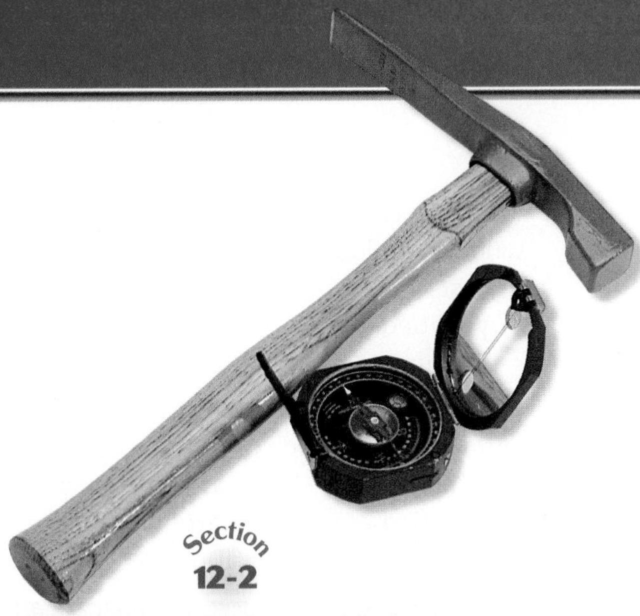

Reading Check

List any questions you still have about the chapter content. Review the chapter and try to answer them.

Section 12-2

RELATIVE AGES OF ROCKS

The **principle of superposition** states that older rocks lie underneath younger rocks in areas where the rocks haven't been disturbed. Faults are always younger than the rocks they cut across. Relative ages indicate if one layer of rock is younger or older than another. They do not indicate the layer's exact age in years. **Unconformities,** or gaps in the rock record, are due to erosion, nondeposition, or both. Three different types of unconformities can occur: angular unconformities, disconformities, and nonconformities. Fossils and rock types are often helpful when correlating similar rock bodies. ***What process or processes occur to form a disconformity?***

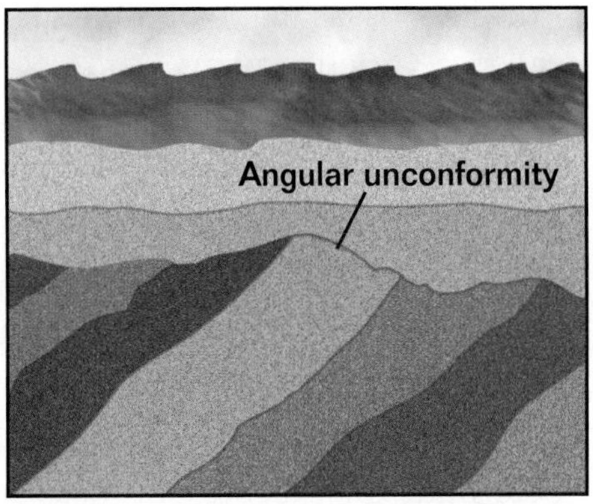

Section 12-3

ABSOLUTE AGES OF ROCKS

Unlike relative dating of rocks, **absolute dating** gives geologists a method by which they can determine the age in years of a rock or other object. The **half-life** of a radioactive isotope is the time it takes for half of the atoms in the isotope to decay. One half of the carbon-14 present in an object will decay to nitrogen-14 over a period of 5730 years. Because half-lives are constant, absolute ages of rocks containing radioactive elements can be determined. ***How are geologists able to determine a rock layer's age due to radiometric dating?***

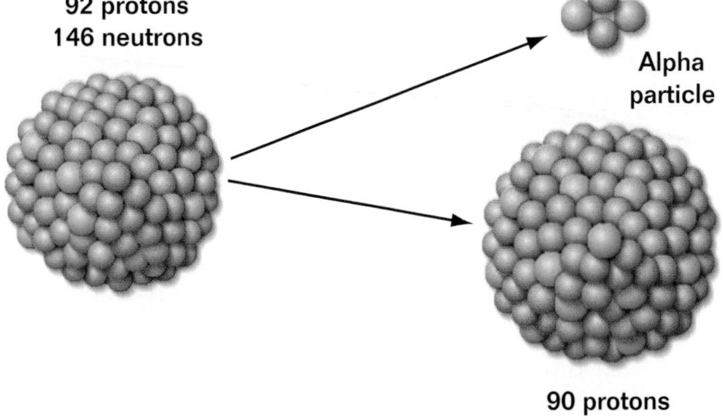

Chapter 12 Assessment

Using Vocabulary

a. absolute dating
b. carbonaceous film
c. cast
d. fossil
e. half-life
f. index fossil
g. mold
h. petrified remains
i. principle of superposition
j. radioactive decay
k. radiometric dating
l. relative dating
m. unconformity
n. uniformitarianism

The sentences below include terms that have been used incorrectly. Change the incorrect terms so that the sentence reads correctly.

1. Rocklike fossils made of minerals are called petrified remains.
2. Correlation fossils are fossils of species that existed for a short time and were abundant and widespread.
3. The principle of uniformitarianism explains the fact that younger rock layers overlie older rock layers.
4. Relative dating allows geologists to determine the exact age of rocks and fossils.
5. Radiometric dating is the time it takes for half of the atoms of a radioactive isotope to decay.

Checking Concepts

Choose the word or phrase that completes the sentence.

6. What are remains of organisms in rocks called?
   A) half-lives
   B) fossils
   C) unconformities
   D) extinctions
7. What conditions allow dead organisms to change into fossils?
   A) slow burial
   B) exposure to microorganisms
   C) soft parts present
   D) hard parts present
8. What are cavities left in rocks called when a shell or bone decays?
   A) casts
   B) petrified remains
   C) molds
   D) carbon films
9. Which of the following is evidence of animal activity, such as fossilized tracks?
   A) a trace fossil
   B) petrified remains
   C) original remains
   D) carbonaceous film
10. "The present is the key to the past" is an explanation of which principle?
    A) superposition
    B) succession
    C) radioactivity
    D) uniformitarianism
11. A fault can be used to find what kind of age of a group of rocks?
    A) relative
    B) radiometric
    C) index
    D) absolute
12. What is an unconformity between horizontal rock layers called?
    A) fault
    B) angular unconformity
    C) disconformity
    D) nonconformity
13. During which process are new elements formed?
    A) superposition
    B) radioactive decay
    C) evolution
    D) uniformitarianism
14. In one type of radioactive decay, what breaks down, releasing an electron?
    A) alpha particle
    B) proton
    C) beta particle
    D) neutron
15. According to radiometric dating, how many years old is Earth?
    A) 2000
    B) 5000
    C) 3.5 billion
    D) 4.6 billion

Thinking Critically

16. We don't have a complete fossil record of life on Earth. Give some reasons why.

17. Suppose a lava flow were found between two sedimentary rock layers. How could the lava flow be used to date the rocks? (Hint: Most lava contains radioactive isotopes.)

18. A set of dinosaur tracks, as in **Figure 12-7,** is found. How might the tracks be used to determine how tall the dinosaur was or how fast it was moving?

19. Suppose you're correlating rock layers in the western United States. You find a layer of shale that contains volcanic dust deposits. How can this layer help you in your correlation over a large area?

20. Why is carbon-14 not suitable for dating fossils formed about 2 million years ago?

Developing Skills

If you need help, refer to the Skill Handbook.

21. **Concept Mapping:** Make a concept map listing the following possible steps in the process of making a cast of a fossil: *replacement by minerals, organism dies, mineral crystals form from solution, burial, fossil erodes away, protection from scavengers,* and *bacteria.*

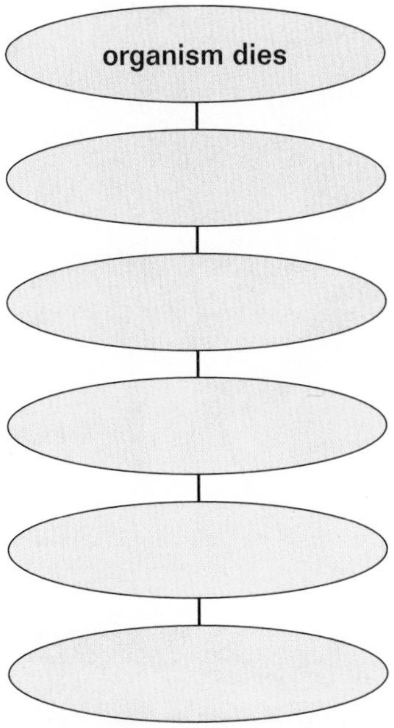

THE PRINCETON REVIEW

Test-Taking Tip

Make Yourself Comfortable When you take a test, try to make yourself as comfortable as possible. You will then be able to focus all your attention on the test.

Test Practice

Use these questions to test your Science Proficiency.

1. Many small fossil tracks of one type of animal are found surrounded by larger tracks of the same type of animal. What might this indicate about their social structure?
   A) Larger animals were attacking the smaller ones.
   B) Animals of different sizes were playing in a group.
   C) Large animals were surrounding the smaller ones for protection.
   D) Large animals run faster and therefore move to the outside of the herd.

2. An object was radiometrically dated and determined to be 90 000 years old. The half-life of the parent isotope is 30 000 years. Which statement **BEST** explains how this date was determined?
   A) In the object, 87.5 percent of the parent isotope and 12.5 percent of the daughter isotope are present.
   B) In the object, 50 percent of the parent isotope and 50 percent of the daughter isotope are present.
   C) In the object, 25 percent of the parent isotope and 75 percent of the daughter isotope are present.
   D) In the object, 12.5 percent of the parent isotope and 87.5 percent of the daughter isotope are present.

CHAPTER

13 Geologic Time

Chapter Preview

- Section 13-1
  - Life and Geologic Time
- Section 13-2
  - Early Earth History
- Section 13-3
  - Middle and Recent Earth History

Skills Preview

Skill Builders
- Make and Use a Table

Activities
- Make a Model

MiniLabs
- Measure in SI

Reading Check

After reading Section 1, compare the different types of trilobites shown. How could you put them in order, if they were not labeled by time period?

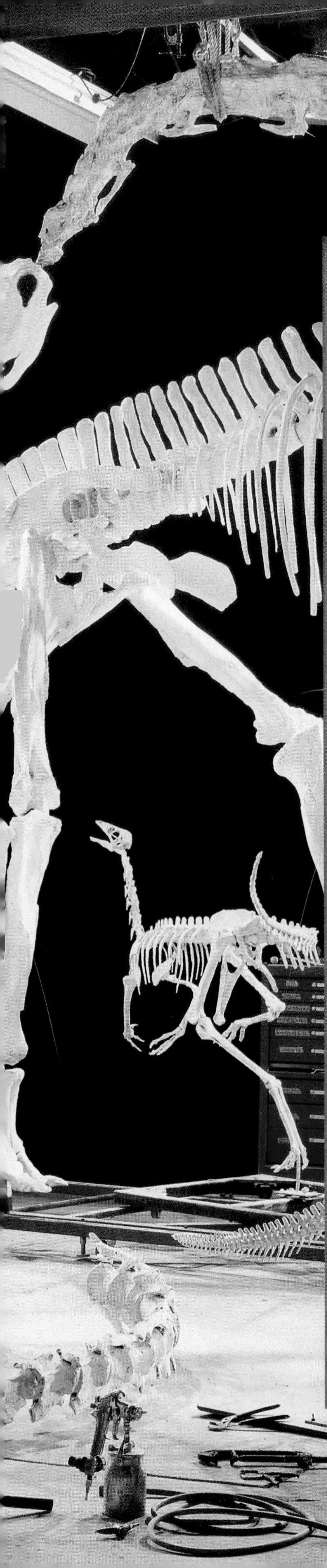

Explore Activity

Studying fossils has helped scientists understand the conditions that existed in Earth's past. Fossils and reproductions of fossils, such as the dinosaur skeletons the welder is working on here, provide evidence of Earth's environment at one time in the past. These fossils also represent a certain time in Earth's history. In this activity, you will record important events in your life and arrange them in the order in which they occurred. You will learn how recording certain events allows you to create a time scale, much like the time scale used by geologists worldwide. If you had to construct a time scale, how would you start? This activity will help you out.

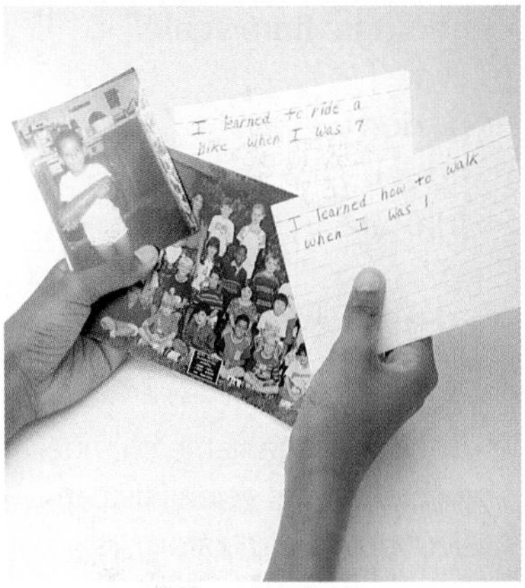

Make a Time Scale of Your Life

1. On 3 × 5 cards, write important events that have happened in your lifetime, one event per card.
2. Arrange the cards in the order in which the events happened. Then cut two blank cards in half to make the following labels: *Preschool Years, Early Elementary Years, Late Elementary Years,* and *Middle School Years.*
3. Place each label before the group of events that occurred during its time description.

Science Journal

In your Science Journal, draw a time line that puts all of these events in order. Did you know exact dates for some of the events? Was knowing exact dates helpful? What did they add to the time line?

13•1 Life and Geologic Time

What You'll Learn

- How geologic time is divided into units
- How trilobites from different periods of the Paleozoic era may have evolved through geologic time
- How plate tectonics affects changes in species

Vocabulary
geologic time scale
era
period
epoch
trilobite

Why It's Important

- Because organisms change through time, scientists can describe Earth history using the Geologic Time Scale.

Geologic Time

A group of students went digging for fossils with their teacher. They knew that paleontologists study geologic history by collecting and studying fossils of organisms that lived long ago. The students were hoping to find some fossils from the Paleozoic era and, in particular, trilobites (TRI luh bites). They were told that they would be looking in rocks that are about 510 million years old.

Some examples of what they found are shown in **Figure 13-1.** The fossils are small and appear to have segments over much of their bodies. Some of them seem to be curled into a ball. What are they? Are these the trilobites their teacher told them about? Finding out about Earth's history will help you determine if these fossils are trilobites.

The Geologic Time Scale

The appearance and disappearance of types of organisms throughout Earth's history give scientists data to mark important changes or geologic occurrences in time. We can divide Earth's history into smaller units based on the types of lifeforms living during certain periods. The division of Earth's history into smaller units makes up the **geologic time scale.** All the divisions in the geologic time scale are based on changes in fossil organisms. Changes in the fossils can be caused by geologic events such as changes in sea level or mountain building.

Figure 13-1 The physical appearance of many types of organisms, such as the trilobites shown here, has changed throughout geologic time.

A *Modocia typicales* is from Cambrian rocks in Utah.

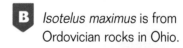

B *Isotelus maximus* is from Ordovician rocks in Ohio.

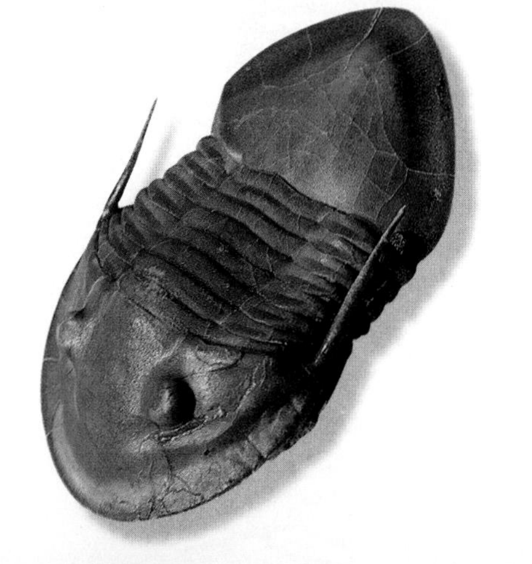

The geologic time scale is a record of Earth's history, starting with Earth's formation about 4.6 billion years ago. Each period of time is named. When the ages of fossils and rock layers are determined, scientists can assign them to a specific place on the geologic time scale.

Subdivisions of Geologic Time

Geologic time is divided into three subdivisions: eras, periods, and epochs. **Eras** are major subdivisions of the geologic time scale based on differences in life-forms. There are three named eras—the Paleozoic, which means ancient life, the Mesozoic, or middle life, and the Cenozoic, or recent life. As you can see in **Figure 13-2** on the next page, the Mesozoic era began about 245 million years ago. Its end is marked by the extinction of the dinosaurs and many other organisms about 66 million years ago. When did trilobites first appear? Were the students looking in rocks of the correct age to find trilobites?

Eras are subdivided into **periods.** Periods are based on the types of life that existed at the time. Periods are divided into smaller units of time called **epochs.** Generally, only the Cenozoic era is shown subdivided further into epochs as seen in **Figure 13-2.** The epochs of the other periods are usually called early, middle, and late. Why is this so? The fossil record is more complete in these recent rock layers. As a result, geologists have more data with which to divide the time scale.

interNET CONNECTION

Visit the Glencoe Science Web Site at **www.glencoe.com/sec/science/ca** to find out more about fossils.

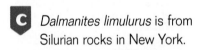

C *Dalmanites limulurus* is from Silurian rocks in New York.

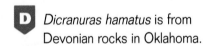

D *Dicranuras hamatus* is from Devonian rocks in Oklahoma.

VISUALIZING Geologic Time

Figure 13-2 The geologic time scale is divided into subunits based on the appearance and disappearance of types of organisms. The numbers listed show the beginning of each subunit. **Beginning at the bottom, which events do you think were most important in Earth history?**

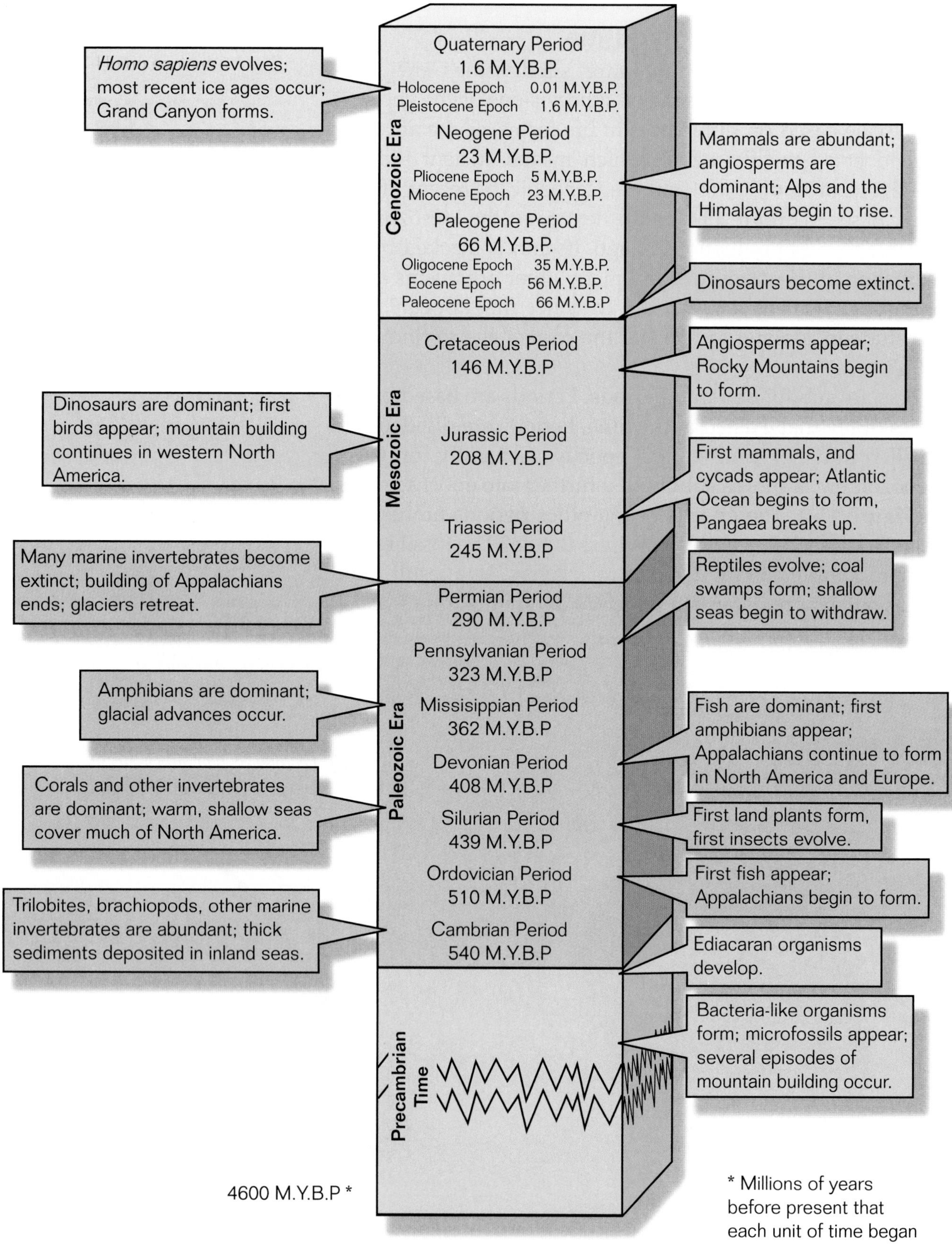

Cenozoic Era
Quaternary Period
1.6 M.Y.B.P.
Holocene Epoch 0.01 M.Y.B.P.
Pleistocene Epoch 1.6 M.Y.B.P.
Homo sapiens evolves; most recent ice ages occur; Grand Canyon forms.
Neogene Period
23 M.Y.B.P.
Pliocene Epoch 5 M.Y.B.P.
Miocene Epoch 23 M.Y.B.P.
Mammals are abundant; angiosperms are dominant; Alps and the Himalayas begin to rise.
Paleogene Period
66 M.Y.B.P.
Oligocene Epoch 35 M.Y.B.P.
Eocene Epoch 56 M.Y.B.P.
Paleocene Epoch 66 M.Y.B.P
Dinosaurs become extinct.
Mesozoic Era
Cretaceous Period
146 M.Y.B.P
Angiosperms appear; Rocky Mountains begin to form.
Jurassic Period
208 M.Y.B.P
Dinosaurs are dominant; first birds appear; mountain building continues in western North America.
Triassic Period
245 M.Y.B.P
First mammals, and cycads appear; Atlantic Ocean begins to form, Pangaea breaks up.
Many marine invertebrates become extinct; building of Appalachians ends; glaciers retreat.
Paleozoic Era
Permian Period
290 M.Y.B.P
Reptiles evolve; coal swamps form; shallow seas begin to withdraw.
Pennsylvanian Period
323 M.Y.B.P
Amphibians are dominant; glacial advances occur.
Missisippian Period
362 M.Y.B.P
Devonian Period
408 M.Y.B.P
Fish are dominant; first amphibians appear; Appalachians continue to form in North America and Europe.
Corals and other invertebrates are dominant; warm, shallow seas cover much of North America.
Silurian Period
439 M.Y.B.P
First land plants form, first insects evolve.
Ordovician Period
510 M.Y.B.P
First fish appear; Appalachians begin to form.
Trilobites, brachiopods, other marine invertebrates are abundant; thick sediments deposited in inland seas.
Cambrian Period
540 M.Y.B.P
Ediacaran organisms develop.
Precambrian Time
Bacteria-like organisms form; microfossils appear; several episodes of mountain building occur.
4600 M.Y.B.P *
* Millions of years before present that each unit of time began

Geologic Time and Fossils

Geologists study fossils to help describe Earth's past environments, to interpret how extinct organisms lived, and to document changes in organisms through time. A brief study of trilobites illustrates how this is done.

When people look for fossils, they like to find trilobites. **Trilobites** (TRI luh bites) were organisms that lived hundreds of millions of years ago. They crawled on the seafloor and occasionally swam through the water. They ranged in size from 6 mm to 75 cm in length, with most between 2 cm and 7 cm in length and between 1 cm and 3 cm in width.

Reading Check

From what characteristic did trilobites get their name?

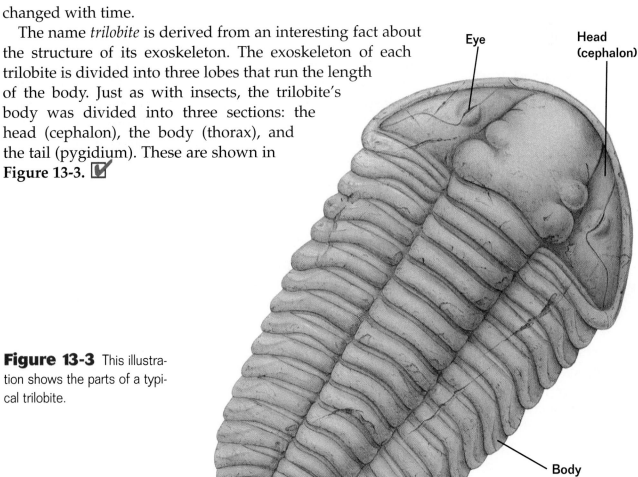

Trilobites first appeared during the Cambrian period and existed on Earth throughout the Paleozoic era. They became extinct at the end of the Permian period. Numerous species of trilobites lived on Earth for more than 300 million years. Although trilobites existed throughout Paleozoic time, they did not all look the same. The characteristics of trilobites changed with time.

The name *trilobite* is derived from an interesting fact about the structure of its exoskeleton. The exoskeleton of each trilobite is divided into three lobes that run the length of the body. Just as with insects, the trilobite's body was divided into three sections: the head (cephalon), the body (thorax), and the tail (pygidium). These are shown in **Figure 13-3.**

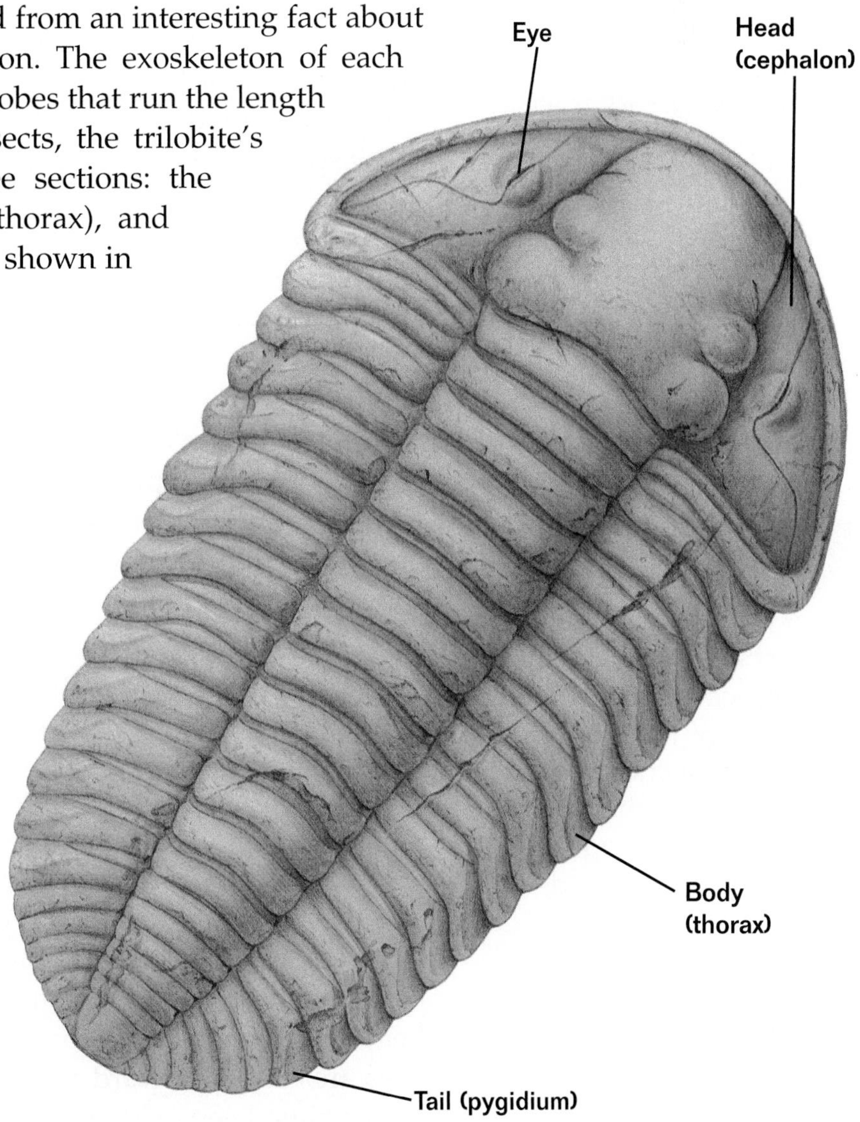

Figure 13-3 This illustration shows the parts of a typical trilobite.

A *Olenellus roddyi* is a Cambrian trilobite found in Pennsylvania.

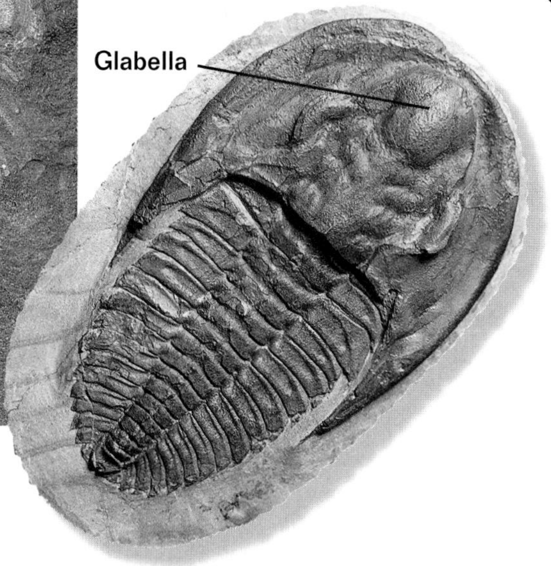

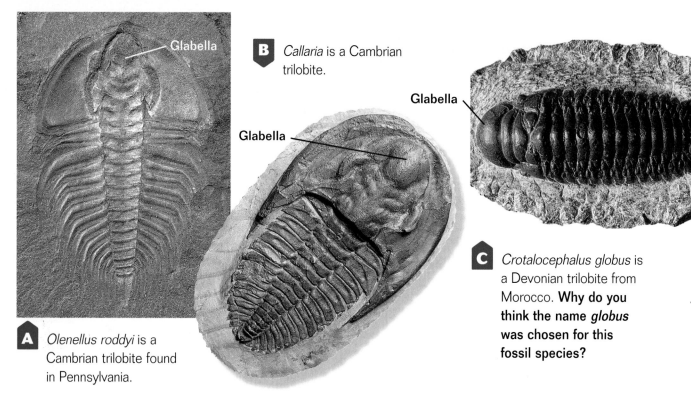

B *Callaria* is a Cambrian trilobite.

C *Crotalocephalus globus* is a Devonian trilobite from Morocco. **Why do you think the name *globus* was chosen for this fossil species?**

Figure 13-4 The *glabella* is a part of the trilobite's head. **Describe how the glabella changed through time.**

Changing Characteristics of Trilobites

Trilobites were common during the Cambrian period. Some species of trilobites became extinct at the close of the Cambrian period, others at the close of the Devonian period. Some species, however, survived until the end of the Permian period. Species of trilobites that lived during one period of the Paleozoic era show characteristics different from species of other periods. The different characteristics are used to show a gradual change of trilobites through geologic time as shown in **Figures 13-1** and **13-4.** Additionally, trilobites lived over large areas of the world during the Paleozoic era. They are considered an index fossil of the Paleozoic era. Index fossils are fossils that pinpoint a particular time in geologic history. In order to be an index fossil, the organism must have been geographically widespread, have lived for a relatively short period of time, and have distinct characteristics that help it stand out from other fossils. Because of physical changes through time, many species can be used as index fossils for specific geologic periods, such as the Cambrian period.

LIFE SCIENCE INTEGRATION

Using Math

Make a circle graph comparing the periods of the Paleozoic era. Sections of the circle graph should represent the lengths of the various periods of the Paleozoic era. Based on the circle graph, which period is the longest? Which period is the shortest?

Trilobite Eyes

Trilobites may have been the first organisms with true eyes and the capability to look out on their world. The position of the eyes on a trilobite fossil tells much about where the organism lived. If the eyes are located toward the front of the head, the organism was probably an active swimmer. If the eyes are located toward the back of the head, the organism might have been an ocean bottom dweller. In most species,

Figure 13-5 Changes in trilobite eyes allowed species to adapt to their environment. (A) *Modocia typicalis* had long, crescent-shaped eyes; (B) *Calymene granulosa's* eyes were reduced in size; (C) *Peronopsis interstrictus* had no eyes and was blind; (D) The eyes of *Phacops rana* were compound like many modern-day insects.

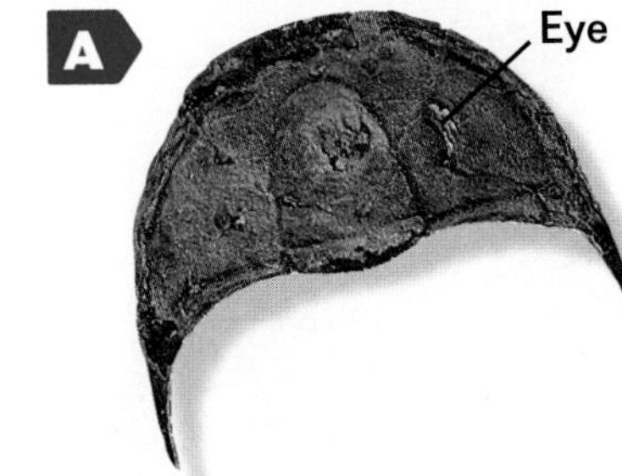

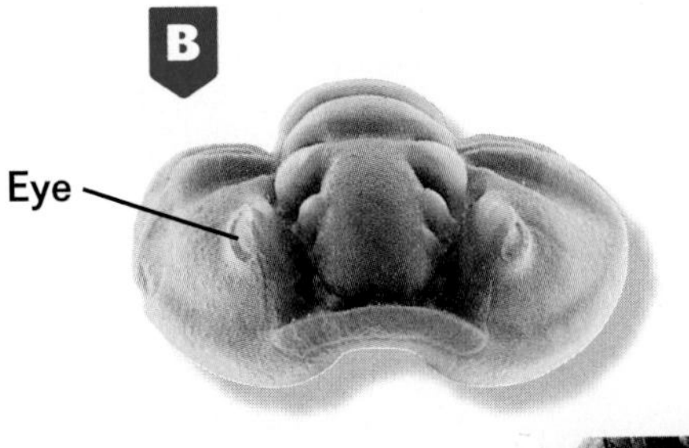

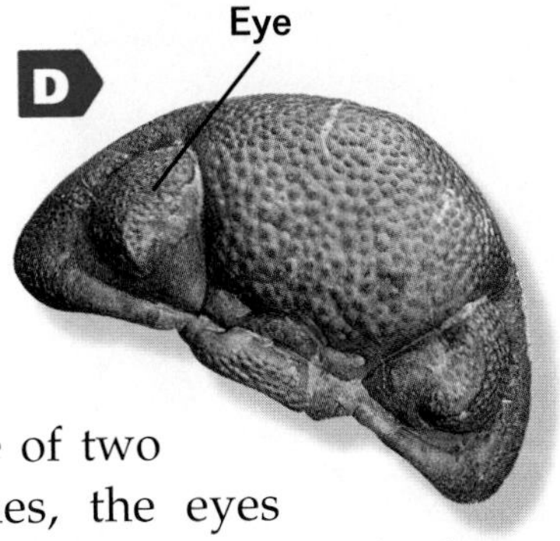

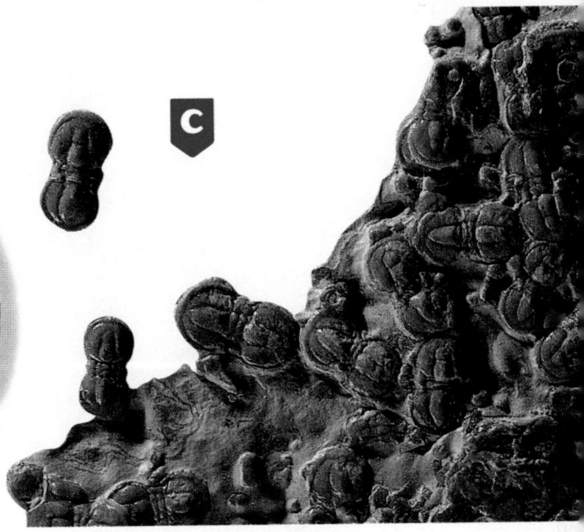

the eyes were located midway on the head—ideal for an organism that both crawled on the seafloor and swam in the water.

Trilobite eyes changed in one of two ways. In many trilobite species, the eyes became progressively smaller until they completely disappeared, as shown in **Figure 13-5.** The blind trilobites might have burrowed into the sediments on the seafloor or lived deeper than light could penetrate. In other species, the eyes became more complex. One genus, *Aeglina*, developed large compound eyes composed of numerous individual lenses. Some eyes developed stalks that held the eyes upward. Where do you think this would be useful?

The trilobite body and tail also underwent major changes in form through time as shown in **Figure 13-6.** Of special note is *Olenellus*, as shown in **Figure 13-7A.** This genus of trilobite from the Lower Cambrian period has pronounced spines. Although the exact use of the spines is not understood, the appearance of them is limited to earlier species. No spines are found in fossils between the Mississippian to the Permian periods. These differences also help identify different species and can be used to infer how and where they lived.

Figure 13-6 The physical features of trilobites changed throughout the Paleozoic era. **Which environments do you think each of these trilobites was adapted for?**

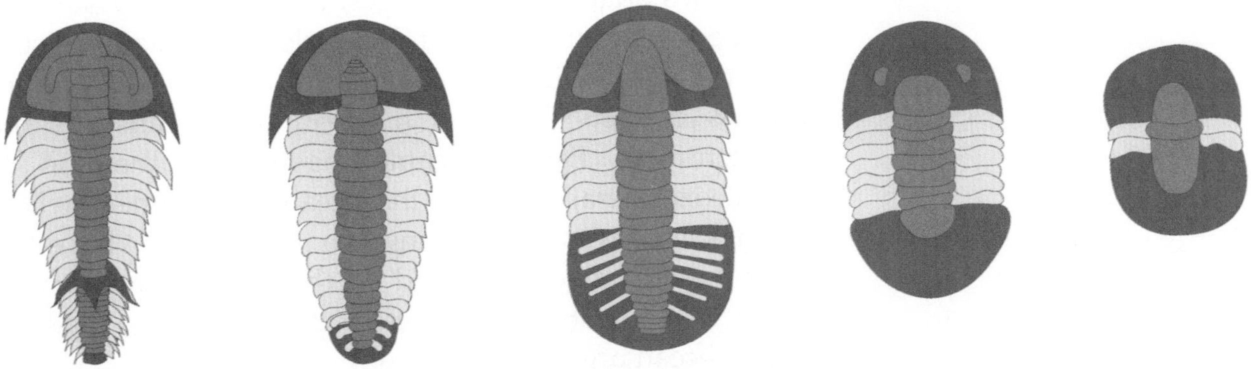

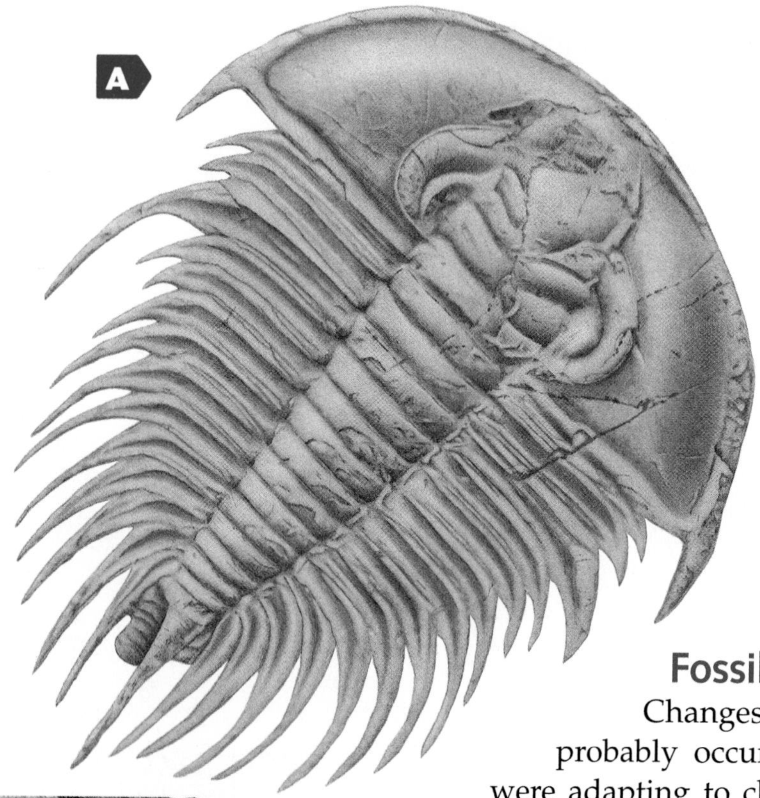

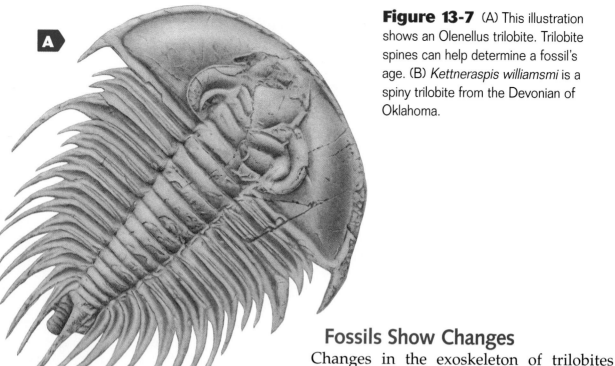

Figure 13-7 (A) This illustration shows an Olenellus trilobite. Trilobite spines can help determine a fossil's age. (B) *Kettneraspis williamsmi* is a spiny trilobite from the Devonian of Oklahoma.

Fossils Show Changes

Changes in the exoskeleton of trilobites probably occurred at least in part because they were adapting to changing environments, geographic isolation, how they lived, and the competition for survival. You have learned how paleontologists use the physical features of individual fossil species to interpret their life modes and environments. As you read through the rest of this chapter, you will see how studies such as the trilobite example helped enable geologists to interpret Earth history and create the geologic time scale.

The Effect of Plate Tectonics

Plate tectonics is one process that causes changing environments on Earth. As plates on Earth's surface moved over time, continents collided with and separated from each other many times. Continental collisions caused mountain building and the draining of seas. Continental separations caused deeper seas to develop between continents. This rearranging of land and sea still causes changes in climates today.

If species adapt to the changes, or evolve, they survive. If a species doesn't have individuals with characteristics needed to survive in the changing environment, the species becomes extinct. Trilobites lived in the oceans. As the supercontinent Pangaea came together at the end of the Paleozoic era, much of the ocean environment where trilobites lived was either changed or destroyed. What effect might these changes have had on the trilobite population? **Figure 13-8** illustrates the effect plate tectonics had on another ocean organism, coral.

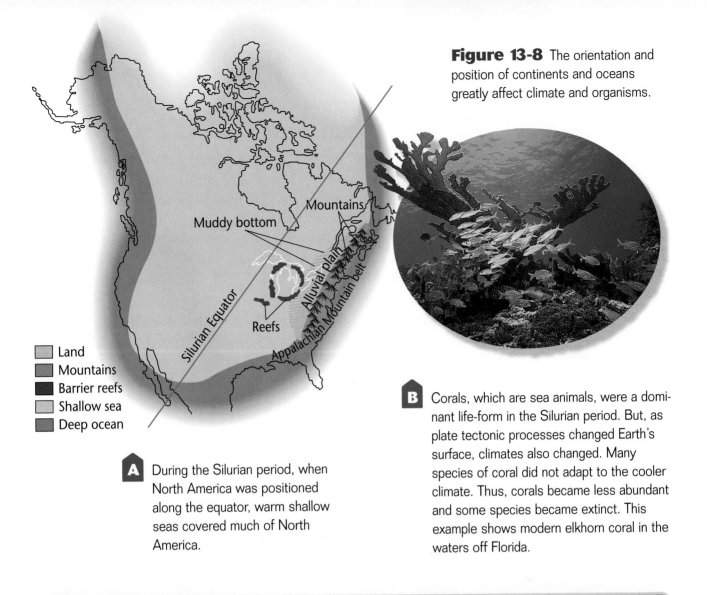

Figure 13-8 The orientation and position of continents and oceans greatly affect climate and organisms.

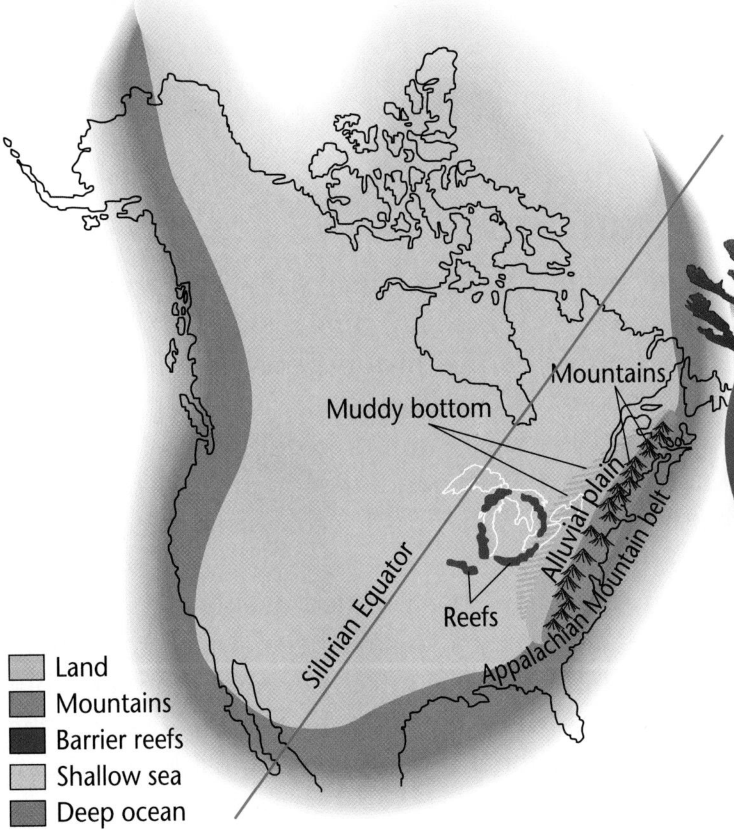

A During the Silurian period, when North America was positioned along the equator, warm shallow seas covered much of North America.

B Corals, which are sea animals, were a dominant life-form in the Silurian period. But, as plate tectonic processes changed Earth's surface, climates also changed. Many species of coral did not adapt to the cooler climate. Thus, corals became less abundant and some species became extinct. This example shows modern elkhorn coral in the waters off Florida.

Section Assessment

1. What are the major subdivisions of the geologic time scale based on?
2. Compare and contrast trilobite eyes and the type of environment they might have been adapted to.
3. How might plate tectonics affect all life on Earth?
4. **Think Critically:** How might movement of the continents have affected trilobite survival?
5. **Skill Activity**
   Interpreting Data Do the **Chapter 13 Skill Activity** on page 706 to interpret data about the age relationship between different dinosaurs.

Science Journal

Write a paragraph in your Science Journal that explains how various characteristics of trilobites from different periods of geologic time provide evidence that organisms belonging to the same genus or family change physically through time.

13•2 Early Earth History

What You'll Learn

- Dominant life-forms in Precambrian time and the Paleozoic era
- How organisms adapted to changing environments in Precambrian time and the Paleozoic era
- Changes in Earth and its life-forms at the end of the Paleozoic era

Vocabulary
Precambrian time
cyanobacteria
Paleozoic era
amphibian
reptile

Why It's Important

- The world you know today was created by physical and biological changes that occurred in the Mesozoic and early Cenozoic eras.

Precambrian Time

Look again at the geologic time scale in **Figure 13-2.** **Precambrian** (pree KAM bree un) **time** represents the longest geologic time unit of Earth's history. This time lasted from 4.6 billion to about 540 million years ago. Although the Precambrian was the longest unit of geologic time, relatively little is known about Earth and the organisms that lived during this time. Why is the fossil record from Precambrian time so sparse?

Precambrian rocks have been buried deeply and changed by heat and pressure. They also have been eroded more than younger rocks. These changes affect not only the rocks, but the fossil record, as well. Most fossils can't withstand the metamorphic and erosional processes that most Precambrian rocks have undergone.

Figure 13-9 In some conditions, cyanobacteria produce mound-shaped layers of calcium carbonate called stromatolites. Stromatolites were common about 2.8 billion years ago and are still being formed today. **What does this imply about the life-form cyanobacteria?**

A Stromatolites have changed little throughout geologic time. These modern ones in Australia look much like ancient stromatolites.

Early Life

It wasn't until fossilized cyanobacteria forming layered mats, called stromatolites, were found that scientists could begin to unravel Earth's complex history. Stromatolites are shown in **Figure 13-9.** Cyanobacteria first appeared on Earth about 3.5 billion years ago. **Cyanobacteria** are thought to be one of the earliest forms of life on Earth. They contain chlorophyll and as they photosynthesize, they give off oxygen. As these organisms evolved, they contributed to changes in Earth's atmosphere. During the few billion years following the appearance of cyanobacteria, oxygen became a major gas in Earth's atmosphere. The ozone layer in the stratosphere also began to develop, shielding Earth from ultraviolet rays. These major changes in the air allowed species of single-celled organisms to evolve into more complex organisms.

Animals without backbones, called invertebrates, developed near the end of Precambrian time. Imprints of jellyfish and marine worms have been found in late Precambrian rocks. However, because these early invertebrates were soft-bodied, they weren't easily preserved as fossils. This is another reason the Precambrian fossil record is so sparse.

CHEMISTRY INTEGRATION

Bacteria and Air
Cyanobacteria are thought to have been one of the mechanisms by which Earth's early atmosphere became richer in oxygen. Research the composition of Earth's early atmosphere. Describe where these gases originated.

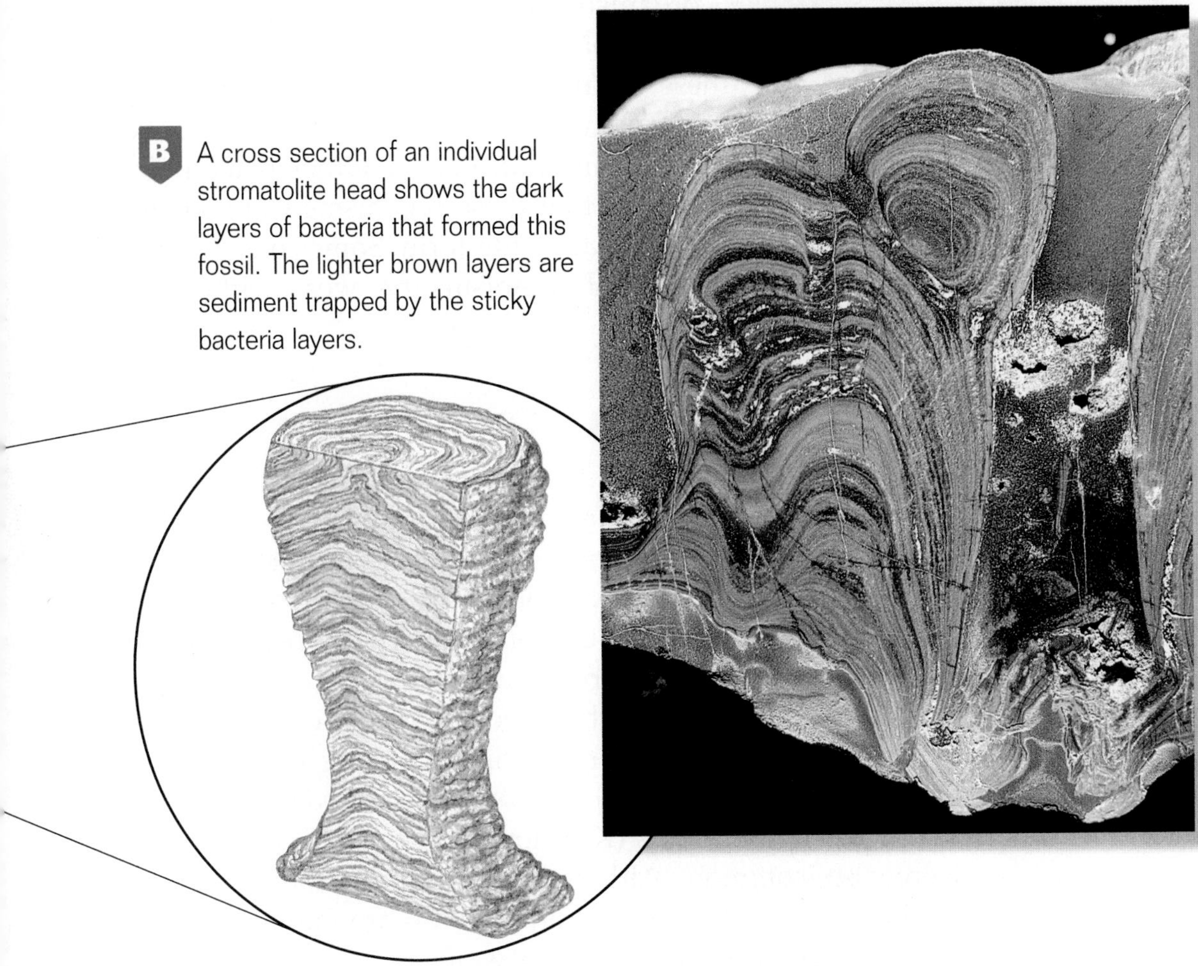

B A cross section of an individual stromatolite head shows the dark layers of bacteria that formed this fossil. The lighter brown layers are sediment trapped by the sticky bacteria layers.

Figure 13-10 These fossils are some of the first soft-bodied organisms preserved. They were first found in the Ediacara Hills in Australia.

A Some Ediacaran life-forms were attached to the ocean bottom, while others were able to freely move.

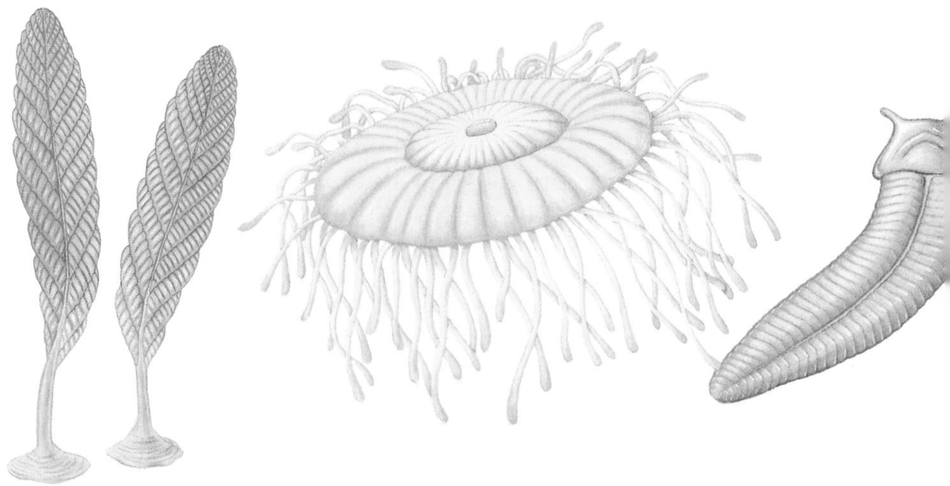

B *Dickinsonia* was a worm-like organism.

Unusual Life-Forms

Also developing at this time was a group of soft-bodied animals, first found in the Ediacara Hills of southern Australia. This group of organisms has become known as the *Ediacaran fauna*. Examples of these organisms are shown in **Figure 13-10.** Some paleontologists hypothesize that these organisms are the soft-bodied ancestors of many of the life-forms that developed during the Cambrian period. Other paleontologists hypothesize that these organisms were a completely different, now-extinct life-form. Some consider that the Ediacaran fossils are of organisms that were neither animal nor plant.

The Paleozoic Era

Fossils are more likely to form if organisms have hard parts. The beginning of the **Paleozoic** (pay lee uh ZOH ihk) **era** is marked by the presence of the first organisms with hard parts. Organisms were then more easily preserved.

The Paleozoic era, or era of ancient life, began about 544 million years ago. Warm, shallow seas covered much of Earth's surface during early Paleozoic time. Because of this, most of the life-forms were marine, meaning they lived in the ocean. Trilobites were common. Brachiopods (BRAH kee uh pahdz) and crinoids (KRI noyds), which still exist today, were also common. Although these animals may not be familiar to you, one type of animal you are familiar with—fish—evolved during this era, as well.

The Paleozoic era is broken into seven periods. The Cambrian period marks the appearance of marine animals with hard parts or skeletons. The most conspicuous and well known of these are trilobites. The start of the Ordovician period is marked by the beginning of the Appalachian Mountain–building process. This was probably caused by the collision of the Eurasian or African continental plate with the North American plate.

The first vertebrates, animals with backbones, developed during the Ordovician period. Plant life evolved on land during the Silurian period. Fish became dominant in the Devonian period, as seen in **Figure 13-11.** By this time, animals began to move onto land with the plants.

Try at Home

MiniLab

Interpreting Rock Layers

Procedure

1. Draw a sequence of three sedimentary rock layers.
2. Number the rock layers 1 through 3, bottom to top.
3. Identify the fossils in each layer as follows: Layer 1, contains fossils B and A; layer 2 contains fossils A, B, and C; layer 3 contains only fossil C.
4. Assign each of the fossils to one or more geologic periods. For example, fossil A lived from the Cambrian through the Devonian periods. Fossil C lived from the Devonian through the Permian periods, and so on.
5. Analyze the fossils' occurrence in each layer to help you determine the ages of each rock layer.

Analysis

1. Which layer or layers were you able to date to a specific period?
2. Why isn't it possible to determine during which specific period the other layers formed?
3. What is the age or possible age of each layer?

Figure 13-11 The giant fish, *Dunkleosteus*, which grew to more than 9 m long, lived during the Devonian period. This fossilized skull was found in Ohio. **What can you infer about the environment in Ohio during the Devonian?**

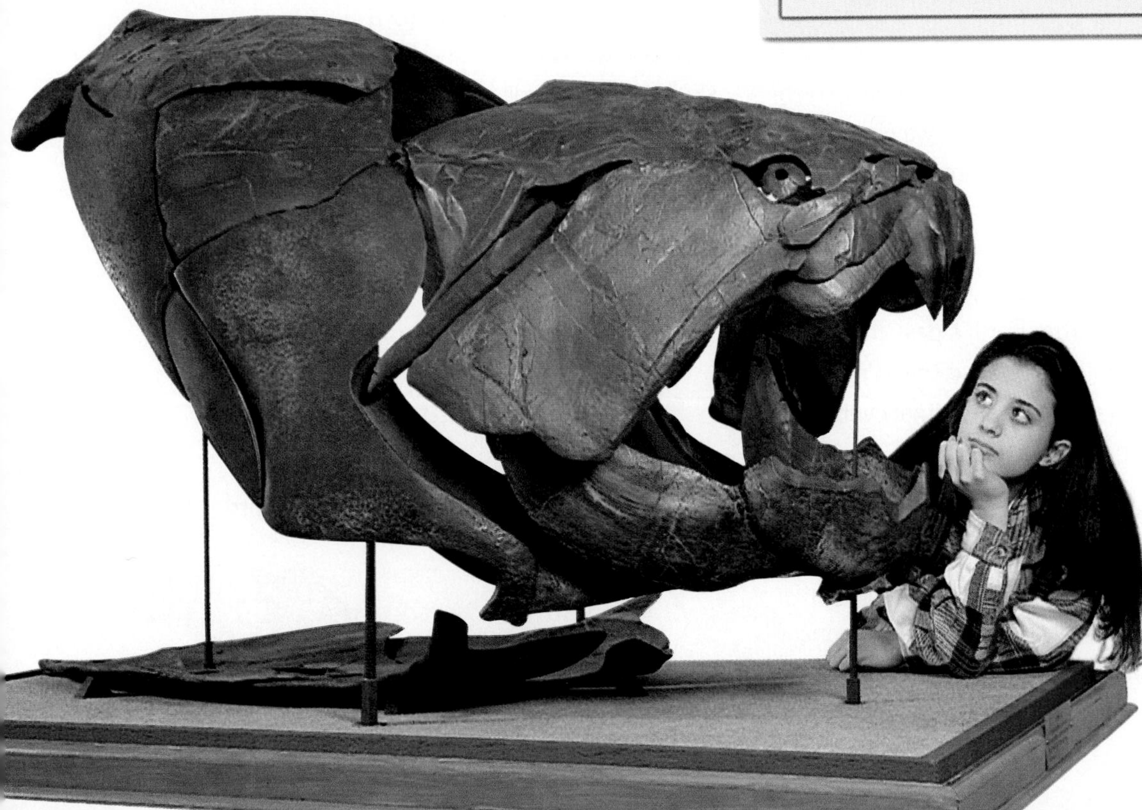

Life on Land

One type of aquatic animal evolved a lung that enabled it to survive on land. This animal used its fins to move across the ground. Other aquatic animals evolved into amphibians. **Amphibians** live on land and breathe air, but they must return to water to reproduce. Their eggs must be kept moist in water. They first appeared during the Devonian period and became the dominant form of vertebrate life on land by the Mississippian period.

Over time, amphibians evolved an egg with a strong outer shell that protected it from drying out. The egg also contained a nutritious yolk for the embryo. Because of this, they no longer needed to return to water to reproduce. By the Pennsylvanian period, reptiles had evolved, probably from the same ancestor as amphibians. **Reptiles** do not need to return to water to reproduce, as shown in **Figure 13-12.** Reptiles have skin with hard scales that prevent loss of body fluids. This adaptation enables them to survive farther from water. They can survive in relatively dry climates, whereas amphibians with their thin, moist skins, cannot. ☑

Reading Check ☑

What developed that allowed amphibians to reproduce away from water?

Problem Solving

Skull Structures

Scientists study the structure of bones and other preserved fossil parts in an attempt to determine which organisms are related. Bones, or the way bones are connected at joints, in related organisms show similar structures or connections. For example, if the skull from a modern organism shows similar eye openings and a similar structure of the nasal passages to the fossil skull of an animal from Earth's past, the two organisms may be related. Some scientists might even hypothesize that the modern animal evolved from the earlier animal.

The photographs show the shape and structure of four different organisms. One of the skulls is a fossil of an ancient, now-extinct life-form. The other three skulls are from modern-day organisms: an iguana, a bird, and a muskrat. Compare and contrast the shape and structure of the four skulls.

Think Critically: Which of the modern skulls looks most like the fossil skull? Hypothesize about which of the modern animals may have evolved from the ancient life-form.

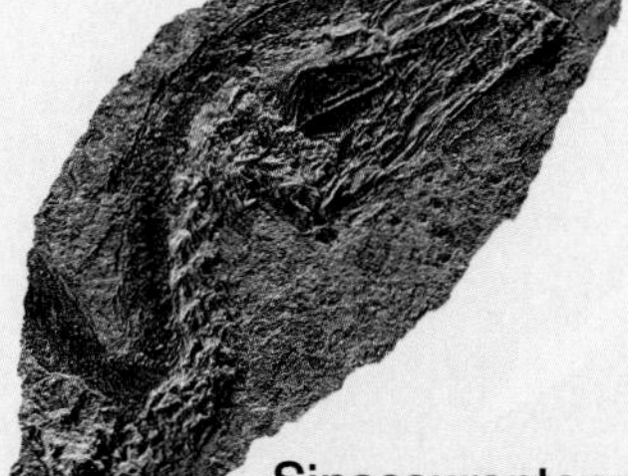

Sinosauropteryx

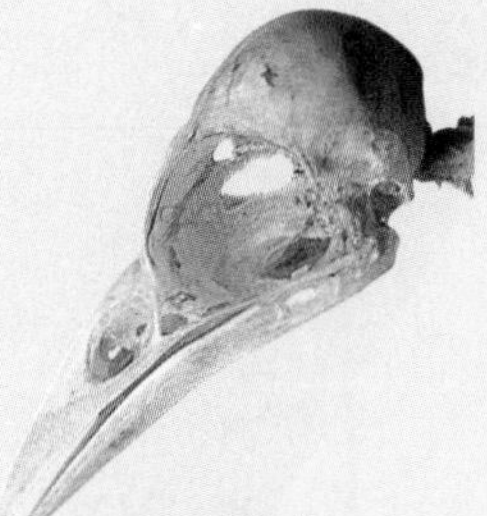

Bird

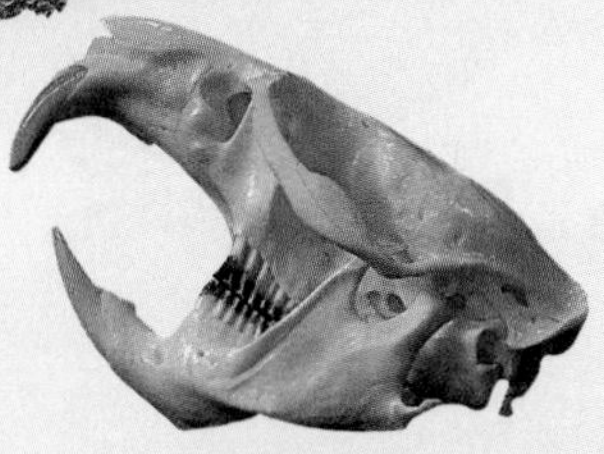

Muskrat

Iguana

Figure 13-12 Unlike frogs, salamanders, and other amphibians, reptiles such as these snakes can lay their eggs on land. This allows them to survive in relatively dry environments. **What characteristic of reptile eggs prevents the developing embryos from drying out?**

Many of the coal deposits mined today began forming during the Pennsylvanian period. Inland seas were cut off from the oceans. These freshwater seas covered much of the land. Swamps similar to those found in the Florida Everglades formed. When the swamp vegetation died, it was deposited in layers and quickly buried. This material later changed to today's coal beds. **Figure 13-13** shows what a forest might have looked like in the Pennsylvanian period.

Figure 13-13 The plants that make up the coal layers in the United States once lived in swampy areas.

A This illustration reconstructs what a Pennsylvanian-period forest might have looked like 300 million years ago.

B The plants end up as layers, or seams, of coal, as seen in this strip mine in southeastern Montana.

End of an Era

Mass extinctions of many land and sea animals have occurred. One mass extinction occurred at the end of the Paleozoic era. The cause of mass extinctions may have been changes in the environment following movement of continents through plate tectonics. Near the end of the Permian period, all continental plates came together to form the single landmass Pangaea, and major glaciers formed.

The slow, gradual collision of continental plates caused mountain building. Mountain-building processes caused seas to drain away, and interior deserts spread over parts of the United States and Europe. Climates changed from mild and warm to cold and dry. Many species, especially marine organisms, weren't able to adapt to these and other changes and became extinct.

interNET CONNECTION

Visit the Glencoe Science Web Site at **www.glencoe.com/sec/science/ca** for more information on mass extinctions.

Section Assessment

1. What geologic events occurred at the end of the Paleozoic era?
2. How might geologic events at the end of the Paleozoic era have caused the mass extinctions that occurred?
3. Why is the Precambrian fossil record so sparse?
4. What major change occurred in the atmosphere during the Precambrian?
5. **Think Critically:** What adaptations were needed for life to move onto the land?
6. **Skill Builder**
   Recognizing Cause and Effect
   Describe the cause-and-effect relationship between amphibians, reptiles, and the eggs they use in reproduction. If you need help, refer to Recognizing Cause and Effect in the **Skill Handbook** on page 673.

Using Computers

Using a Database
Research trilobites, brachiopods, and crinoids in a computer database of historical geology. Write a paragraph in your Science Journal describing each of these organisms and its habitat. Include hand-drawn illustrations, and compare them with the illustrations in the computer database of historical geology. If you need help, refer to page 685.

Changing Species

Materials

- Deck of playing cards

In this activity, you will observe how adaptation within a species might cause the evolution of a particular trait, leading to the development of a new species.

What You'll Investigate

How might adaptation within a species cause the evolution of a particular trait?

Goals

- **Model** adaptation within a species.

Procedure

1. **Remove** all of the kings, queens, jacks, and aces from a deck of playing cards.
2. Each remaining card represents an individual in a population of animals called "varimals." The number on each card represents the height of the individual. For example, the 5 of diamonds is a varimal that's 5 units tall.
3. **Calculate** the average height of the population of varimals represented by your cards.
4. Suppose varimals eat grass, shrubs, and leaves from trees. A drought causes many of these plants to die. All that's left are a few tall trees. Only varimals at least 6 units tall can reach the leaves on these trees.
5. All the varimals under 6 units leave the area to seek food elsewhere or die from starvation. **Discard** all of the cards with a number value less than 6. **Calculate** the new average height of the population of varimals.
6. Shuffle the deck of remaining cards.
7. **Draw** two cards at a time. Each pair represents a pair of varimals that will mate and produce offspring.
8. The offspring of each pair reaches a height equal to the average height of his or her parents. **Calculate** and **record** the height of each offspring.
9. Repeat by discarding all parents and offspring under 8 units tall. Now **calculate** the new average height of varimals. Include both the parents and offspring in your calculation.

Conclude and Apply

1. How did the average height of the population change over time?
2. If you hadn't discarded the shortest varimals, would the average height of the population have changed as much? **Explain.**
3. What trait was selected for?
4. Why didn't every member of the original population reproduce?
5. If there had been no varimals over 6 units tall in step 5, what would have happened to the population?
6. If there had been no variation in height in the population before the droughts occurred, would the species have been able to evolve into a taller species? **Explain.**
7. How does this activity **demonstrate** that traits evolve in species?

Fast Track to Extinction

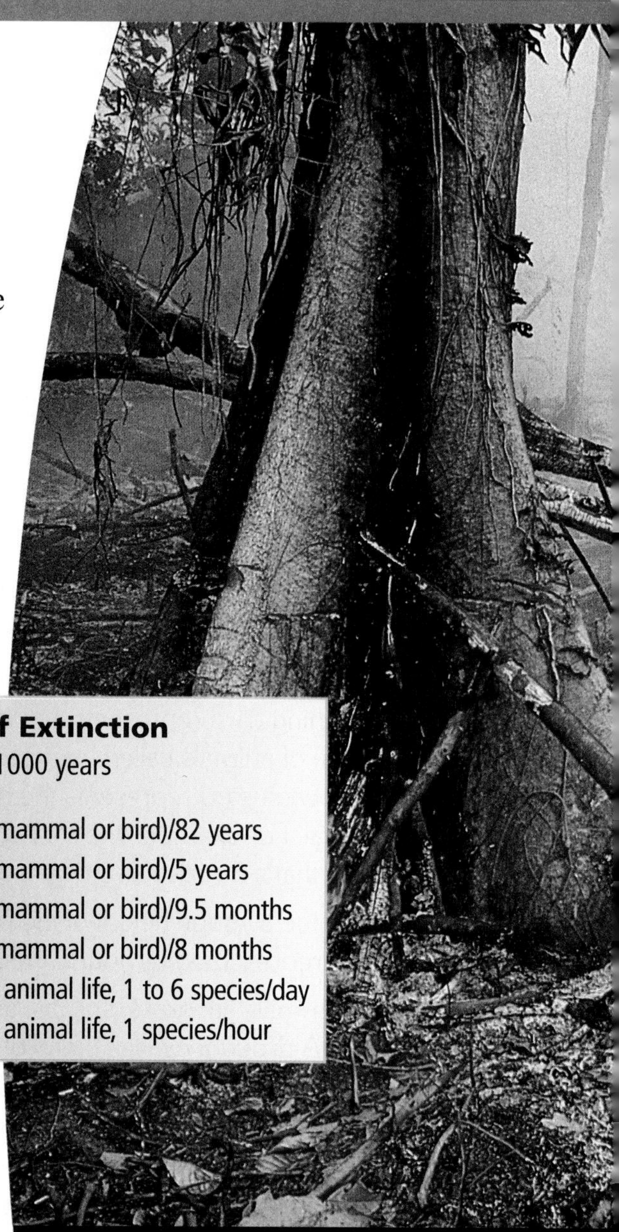

Human Impact

Extinctions—the loss of all members of a species—have occurred throughout Earth's history. In past millennia, extinctions were due to changes in the environment or competition for resources. Some extinctions may have been caused by early humans. Today, humans are causing extinctions at a much higher rate. See the chart below.

When members of a species die out faster than they reproduce, so that only few of its members are living, a species is considered endangered. If the population continues to decline, the species will become extinct.

Humans contribute to extinction directly by overhunting and overcollecting and indirectly by changing a species' habitat—where the species lives. If that habitat is altered or destroyed and the species cannot adapt, that species will die.

Time	Rates of Extinction
70 000 000 years ago (disappearance of the dinosaurs)	1 species/1000 years
1 A.D. to 1650	1 species (mammal or bird)/82 years
1650 to 1850	1 species (mammal or bird)/5 years
1850 to 1900	1 species (mammal or bird)/9.5 months
1900 to 1950	1 species (mammal or bird)/8 months
1992	All plant & animal life, 1 to 6 species/day
2000	All plant & animal life, 1 species/hour

Rain Forests

In the past decade, people cleared tropical rain forests for farming, logging, and other industries at an unprecedented rate. At right, a charred tree still burns as a farmer clears more land. Destroying rain forest eliminates habitats for many plants and animals. It is estimated that the destruction of all rain forests could result in a 90 percent loss of Earth's biodiversity, the variety of species on Earth.

Development with Habitat Protection

To slow or prevent loss of habitat, governments can restrict construction to allow both development and preservation. Development can include plans for preserving habitats or disturbing them as little as possible. Ecotourism (tourism that minimizes ecological impact), replanting efforts, and cultivating renewable crops are all ways to protect the world's rain forests.

interNET CONNECTION

Many organizations are working to slow the rate of extinction of animals and plants. Visit the Glencoe Science Web Site at **www.glencoe.com/sec/science/ca** to learn more about the preservation of wildlife. What is being done to help endangered species? Do you think this type of effort is effective? Why or why not?

Middle and Recent Earth History

13•3

The Mesozoic Era

Some of the most fascinating life-forms ever to live on Earth evolved during the Mesozoic era. One group of organisms you're probably familiar with—the dinosaurs—appeared during this geologic era.

The Breakup of Pangaea

The **Mesozoic** (mez uh ZOH ihk) **era,** or era of middle life, began about 245 million years ago. At the beginning of the Mesozoic era, all continents were joined as a single land-mass. This landmass was called Pangaea, as shown in **Figure 13-14.** Pangaea separated into two large landmasses during the Triassic period. The northern mass was *Laurasia,* and *Gondwana* was in the south. As the Mesozoic era continued, *Laurasia* and *Gondwana* broke up and formed the present-day continents.

Species that survived the mass extinctions of the Paleozoic era adapted to new environments. Recall that the hard scales of a reptile's skin help to retain body fluids. This trait, along with the hard shell of their eggs, enabled them to adapt to the drier climate of the Mesozoic era. They became the dominant animal life-form in the Jurassic period. Some of the reptiles evolved into archosaurs, suggested as being the common ancestor of crocodiles, dinosaurs, and birds.

What You'll Learn

- How dominant life-forms in the Mesozoic and Cenozoic eras compare and contrast
- How changes caused by plate tectonics affected the evolution of life during the Mesozoic era
- When humans probably first appeared on Earth

Vocabulary
Mesozoic era
gastrolith
Cenozoic era

Why It's Important

- As Earth's environments, plants, and animals changed through time, Earth became suitable for human life.

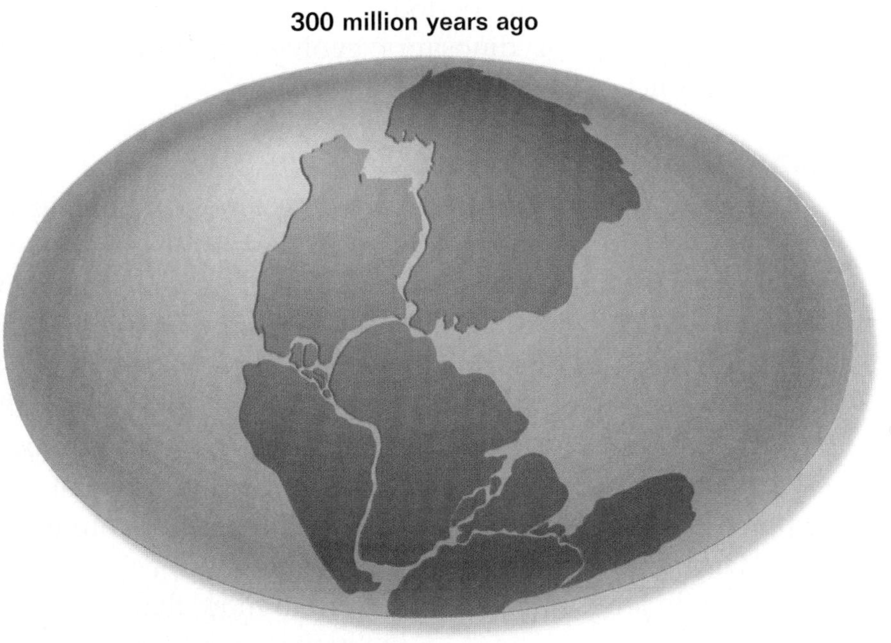

Figure 13-14 The supercontinent Pangaea formed at the end of the Paleozoic era. It began to break up at the end of the Triassic period. **Based on the position of the equator, describe the climate as tropical, temperate, or cold on each major landmass.**

Figure 13-15 Fossil evidence suggests that some dinosaurs, such as *Maiasaura*, may have nurtured their young. Fossil nests contain newly hatched and juvenile young. **What type of evidence might support this idea?**

Dinosaurs

What were dinosaurs like? Dinosaurs ranged in height from less than 1 m to enormous creatures such as *Apatosaurus,* which grew to 30 m in length, and *Tyrannosaurus,* which grew to 6 m in height. Some dinosaurs ate meat, whereas others ate only plants.

The first dinosaurs were small, and they appeared during the Triassic period. Larger species appeared during the Jurassic and Cretaceous periods. Throughout the Mesozoic era, new species of dinosaurs evolved as other species became extinct.

Good Mother Dinosaurs

The fossil record indicates that some dinosaurs nurtured their young and traveled in herds in which the adults surrounded their young. One such dinosaur is *Maiasaura,* shown in **Figure 13-15.** This dinosaur built nests in which it laid its eggs and raised its offspring. Nests have been found in clusters, indicating that more than one family of dinosaurs built in the same area. Some fossils of hatchlings have been found close to the adult animal. This has led some scientists to hypothesize that some dinosaurs nurtured their young. In fact, *Maiasaura* hatchlings may have stayed in the nest while they grew in length from about 35 cm to more than 1 m.

Reptile or Mammal?

Dinosaurs were reptiles. Recent studies indicate that dinosaurs may not have been cold-blooded, as are present-day reptiles. Tracks left in the mud by individual reptiles are usually close together. Tracks close together indicate that an animal moves slowly. Some dinosaur tracks that have been found indicate that they were much faster than most reptiles. This faster speed would be expected of warm-blooded animals, which need speed to be successful in hunting. *Gallimimus* was 4 m long and from its tracks, it is known that it could reach speeds of 80 km/h—as fast as a modern racehorse.

Other evidence that leads scientists to hypothesize that dinosaurs may have been warm-blooded has to do with their bone structure. Cross sections of the bones of cold-blooded animals exhibit rings similar to growth rings in trees. The bones of some dinosaurs don't show this ring structure. Instead, they are similar to bones found in birds and mammals. These observations indicate that dinosaurs may have been warm-blooded, fast-moving, nurturing animals somewhat like present-day mammals and birds. They may have been quite different from present-day reptiles.

Birds

Many scientists hypothesize that birds evolved from dinosaurs. Some scientists have even suggested that birds may have evolved from the advanced theropod called *Troodon,* shown in **Figure 13-16.** Theropods form a group of meat-eating dinosaurs that walked mainly on their hind legs.

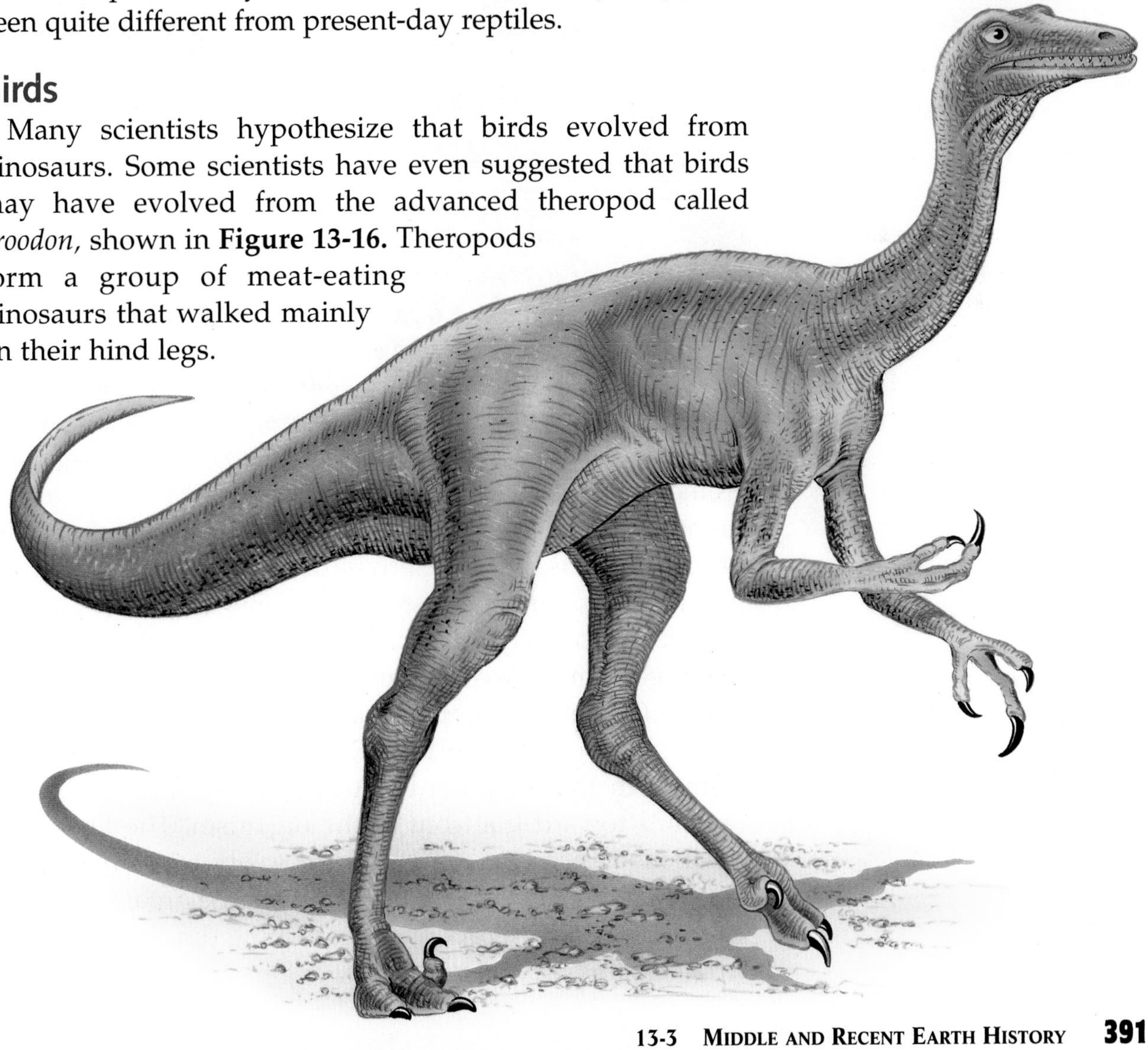

Figure 13-16 A highly evolved dinosaur called *Troodon* had a birdlike stance, much like a modern ostrich.

Figure 13-17 Fossils of *Archaeopteryx* that are about 150 million years old show both birdlike features and dinosaurlike features. **What birdlike and dinosaurlike features can you recognize?**

A A reconstruction of what *Caudipteryx* may have looked like.

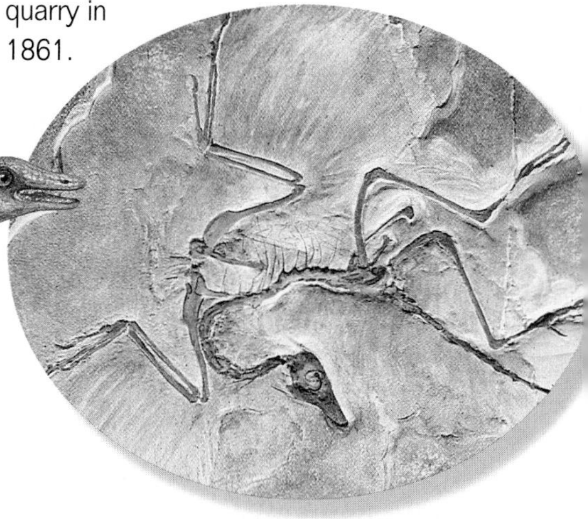

B Considered the world's most priceless fossil, *Archaeopteryx* was found in a limestone quarry in Germany in 1861.

C This *Caudipteryx* fossil shows tail feathers and gastroliths.

D This reconstruction shows what *Archaeopteryx* may have looked like.

Evidence for this is found in fossils of the first birds. They appeared during the Jurassic period of the Mesozoic era, as seen in **Figure 13-17.** The animal *Archaeopteryx* had wings and feathers like a bird but teeth and claws like a meat-eating dinosaur. *Archaeopteryx* may not have been a direct ancestor of today's birds. But, modern birds and *Archaeopteryx* probably share a common ancestor. ☑

A new discovery in China is a fossil of an earlier birdlike organism with dinosaurlike characteristics. It has been named *Caudipteryx*. Imprints of feathers were found on the fossil, shown in **Figure 13-17C.** *Caudipteryx* shows different teeth from those shown by *Archaeopteryx.* The teeth point outward toward the front of the organism. The teeth were positioned such that they could fit easily into a beak, similar to that of a bird's. Also, the shape of the organism's body was more like a theropod, a meat-eating dinosaur, than like *Archaeopteryx*.

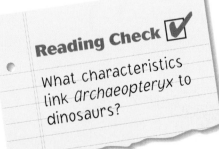

Reading Check ☑

What characteristics link *Archaeopteryx* to dinosaurs?

Also found associated with the fossil were **gastroliths,** stones swallowed to help with digestion. These can be found in the gizzards of modern birds. Fossils of *Caudipteryx* demonstrate strong evidence that this animal is related to the earliest birds, yet it looks more like a small, meat-eating dinosaur from that age.

Gymnosperms

During the Cretaceous period, seas expanded inland and species of plants, animals, and other organisms continued to adapt to new environments. Gymnosperms (JIHM nuh spurmz), which first appeared in the Paleozoic era, continued to adapt to their changing environment. The seeds of gymnosperms are not produced inside a fruit, as are the seeds of flowering plants. Pines, sequoias, and firs are gymnosperms.

Angiosperms

A new type of plant, called angiosperms (AN jee uh spurmz), evolved in the early Cretaceous period. Angiosperms, or flowering plants, produce seeds inside a fruit. Common angiosperms are magnolias and willows.

Many angiosperms survived while nonseed plants did not because their seeds were enclosed and protected in a fruit, allowing them to develop in varied environments. Angiosperms are so adaptive that they remain the dominant land plant today. A flower from an angiosperm is shown in **Figure 13-18.** Present-day angiosperms that evolved during the Mesozoic era include maple and oak trees.

MiniLab

Measuring Seafloor Spreading

Procedure

1. On a globe or world map, measure the distance in kilometers between a point near the east coast of South America and a corresponding point on the west coast of Africa.
2. Assuming that the rate of spreading has been about 3.5–4.0 cm per year, calculate how many years it took to create the present Atlantic Ocean if the continents were once joined.
3. Measure the distance across the Atlantic Ocean in several other locations and calculate the average of your results.
4. Check your calculations with the information provided in **Figure 13-2.**

Analysis

1. Did the values used to obtain your average value vary much?
2. How close did your average value come to the accepted estimate for the beginning of the breakup of Pangaea?

Figure 13-18 Angiosperms and pollinating insects evolved together to become dependent upon each other. The sweet nectar produced by many flowers attracts insects in search of food. The pollen of the flower sticks to the insect, which carries it to another flower. Some angiosperms wouldn't be able to reproduce without a particular species of insect.

VISUALIZING Cenozoic Life

Figure 13-19 Many prehistoric North American animals became extinct during the ice ages in the Pleistocene epoch.

Pangaea broke up during the Mesozoic era, and continents continued to move toward their present positions. Landmasses were breaking up and seas were draining from the land. There also was increased volcanic activity. Many life-forms, including the dinosaurs, became extinct. These extinctions probably were caused by changing environments. Scientists still are investigating what caused the environments to change.

Woolly mammoth

The Cenozoic Era

The **Cenozoic** (sen uh ZOH ihk) **era,** or era of recent life, began about 66 million years ago when dinosaurs and many other life-forms became extinct. Many of the mountain ranges throughout North and South America began to form at this time.

During the Cenozoic era, the climate became cooler and ice ages occurred. The Cenozoic era is subdivided into three periods. The present-day period is the Quaternary. We live in the Holocene epoch, which began after the last ice age. Many changes on Earth, its climate, and its life-forms, shown in **Figure 13-19,** occurred in the Cenozoic era. The two other periods (Neogene and Paleogene) were previously listed together as the Tertiary period.

Times of Mountain Building

The Alps formed when the African plate collided with the Eurasian plate. The Himalayas started to form when the Indo-Australian plate collided with the Eurasian plate.

As the number of flowering plants increased, their pollen and fruit provided food for the many insects and small, plant-eating mammals. The plant-eating mammals provided food for meat-eating mammals.

Horses

Camels

Dire wolves

Irish elk

Saber-toothed tiger

Further Evolution of Mammals

Many kinds of mammals evolved into larger life-forms. The first mammals were most likely small insect eaters that developed about the same time as the dinosaurs. Not all mammals remained on land. Fossil evidence shows that ancestors of the present-day whales and dolphins once lived on land.

As Australia and South America separated from Antarctica in the continuing breakup of Pangaea, many life-forms became isolated. They evolved separately from life-forms in other parts of the world. Evidence of this can be seen today with the dominance of marsupials in Australia. Marsupials are mammals that carry their young in a pouch, as seen in **Figure 13-20.**

Our species, *Homo sapiens,* probably appeared about 500 000 years ago but became a dominant animal only about 10 000 years ago. As the climate remained cool and dry, many of the larger mammals became extinct. Some scientists hypothesize that the appearance of early humans may have led to the extinction of these mammals. Fossil records indicate that early humans were hunters. As their numbers grew, humans competed for food that other animals relied upon. They may have contributed to extinctions by overkill.

Figure 13-20 Kangaroos are marsupials that live in Australia and carry their young (a joey) in a pouch.

Section Assessment

1. In which era, period, and epoch did *Homo sapiens* first appear?
2. How did the development of hard seeds enable angiosperms to survive in a wide variety of climates?
3. What evidence indicates that dinosaurs were warm-blooded?
4. **Think Critically:** What is the connection between plate tectonics and the occurrence of marsupials?
5. **Skill Builder**
   Sequencing Arrange these organisms in sequence according to when they first appeared on Earth: *mammals, reptiles, dinosaurs, fish, ediacaran fauna, angiosperms, birds, insects, amphibians, first land plants,* and *bacteria.* If you need help, refer to Sequencing in the **Skill Handbook** on page 666.

Using Math

Make a graph comparing the periods of time that make up the Mesozoic and Cenozoic eras. Express how long dinosaurs were dominant compared with the time humans have been dominant.

On The Internet

Activity 13•2

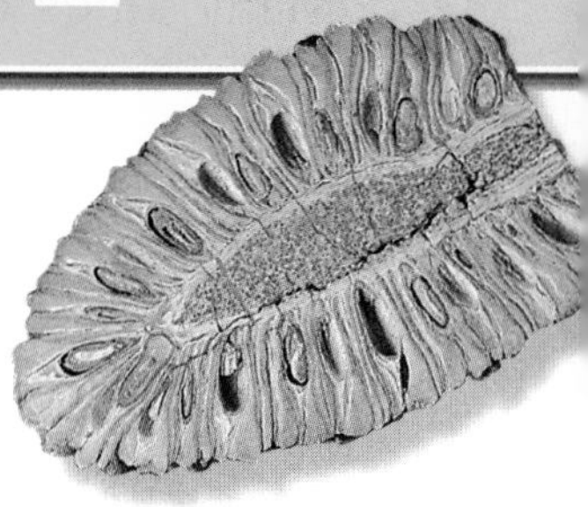

Discovering the Past

Imagine how the world looked millions of years ago. What animals might have been roaming around the spot where you are now sitting? You might be having trouble picturing the prehistoric world. Fortunately, the animals and plants of the past left a record of their existence—fossils. Scientists use fossils to find out what Earth looked like in the past. Fossils can help determine whether an area used to be dry land or an ocean. They also can help scientists determine what the climate in the past was like. Using the resources of the Internet and sharing data with your peers, you can start to discover how North America has changed through time.

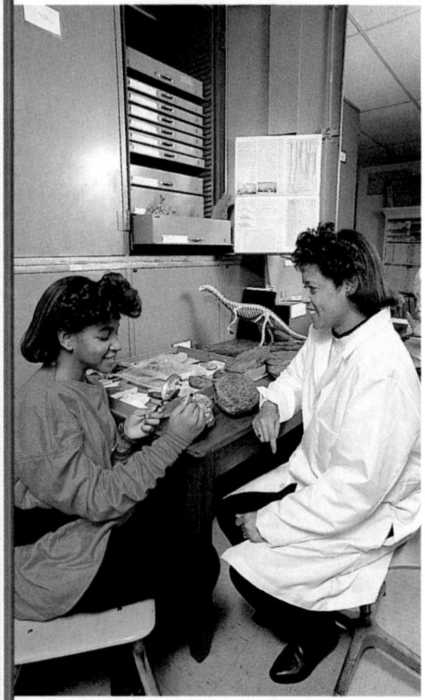

Recognize the Problem

How has your area changed over geologic time?

Form a Hypothesis

How might the area where you are now living have looked thousands or millions of years ago? Do you think the types of animals and plants have changed much over time? **Form a hypothesis** concerning the change in organisms and geography from long ago to the present day in your area.

Goals

- **Gather and communicate** details about fossils found in your areas.
- **Synthesize** information from various sources to make conclusions about the fossil record and the changes in your area over time.
- **Form conclusions** about the fossil record and changes in your area over time based on information from various sources.

Data Sources

Go to the Glencoe Science Web Site at **www.glencoe.com/sec/science/ca** to find links to data on the Internet and hints on how to locate information. You also can visit a local natural history museum or library to gather information on fossils.

Test Your Hypothesis

Plan

1. **Choose** one of the following geologic time periods to research: the Pleistocene epoch, the Cretaceous period, the Pennsylvanian period, or the Ordovician period.
2. **Gather information** from the links on the Glencoe Science Web Site or the library about the fossil plants and animals found in your area during one of these geologic time periods. Find information on where and how the fossil organisms lived.

Do

1. Obtain descriptions of other fossils in your area from the sites listed on the Glencoe Science Web Site.
2. Complete a data table in your Science Journal like the one below. Add any additional information that you think is important. One example has been given.
3. Post the information on the data table for this activity on the Glencoe Science Web Site.

Analyze Your Data

1. Is there a present-day relative of your prehistoric animals or plants?
2. How have the organisms in your area changed over time? Is your hypothesis supported?

Draw Conclusions

1. **Infer** from the fossil organisms found in your area what the geography and climate were like during the geologic time period you chose.
2. Using information posted on the Glencoe Science Web Site, write a report about what North America looked like during one of the geologic time periods listed.

Fossil Data

Fossil Name	Location	Period or Epoch	How or Where Fossil Lived	Additional Information
snail or gastropod	Kansas City, Kansas	Cretaceous period	lived in a shallow ocean, climate was tropical	had thick shell and spines to protect it from predators

Reviewing Main Ideas

For a **preview** of this chapter, study this Reviewing Main Ideas before you read the chapter. After you have studied this chapter, you can use the Reviewing Main Ideas to **review** the chapter.

The Glencoe MindJogger, Audiocassettes, and CD-ROM provide additional opportunities for review.

Section

13-1 LIFE AND GEOLOGIC TIME

Geologic time is divided into **eras, periods,** and **epochs.** Divisions within the geologic time scale are based on major evolutionary changes in organisms. The fossil record indicates that life-forms have changed over time. These changes include the physical appearance of organisms. Plate movements cause changes in Earth's climate that affect changes in organisms. ***Why is the Cenozoic era the only one in which periods are separated into named epochs on the geologic time scale?***

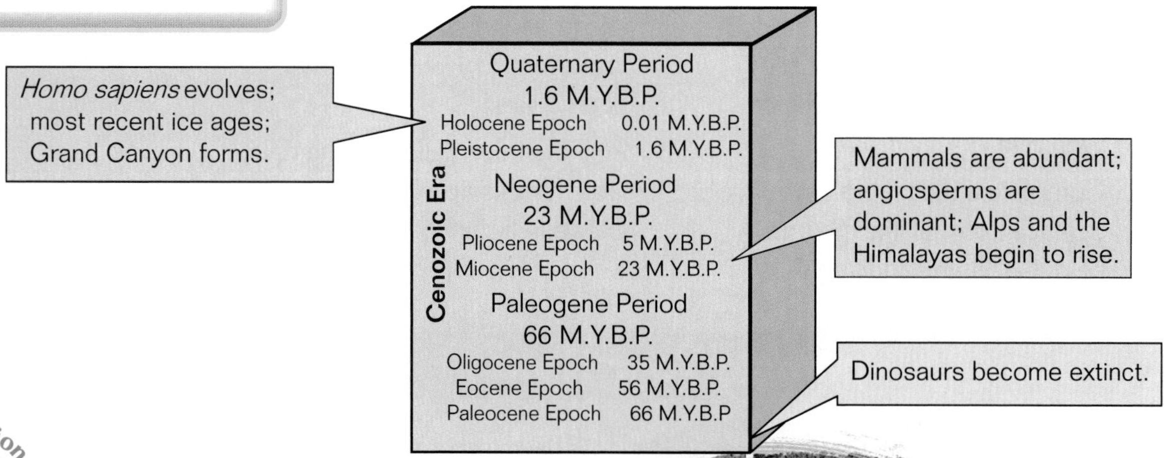

Section

13-2 EARLY EARTH HISTORY

Cyanobacteria were an early form of life that evolved during **Precambrian time. Trilobites,** brachiopods, fish, and corals were abundant during the **Paleozoic era.** Through time, bacteria evolved into higher life-forms, which evolved into many marine invertebrates during the early Paleozoic era. Plants and animals began to move onto land once a protective ozone layer had been established. During the Paleozoic era, glaciers advanced and seas withdrew from the continents. Many marine invertebrates became extinct. ***What was different between life-forms of Precambrian time and life-forms of the Cambrian period that allowed a better fossil record to be preserved?***

Reading Check

After you read this Reviewing Main Ideas, choose a sentence in each section that you feel best represents the main idea of that section.

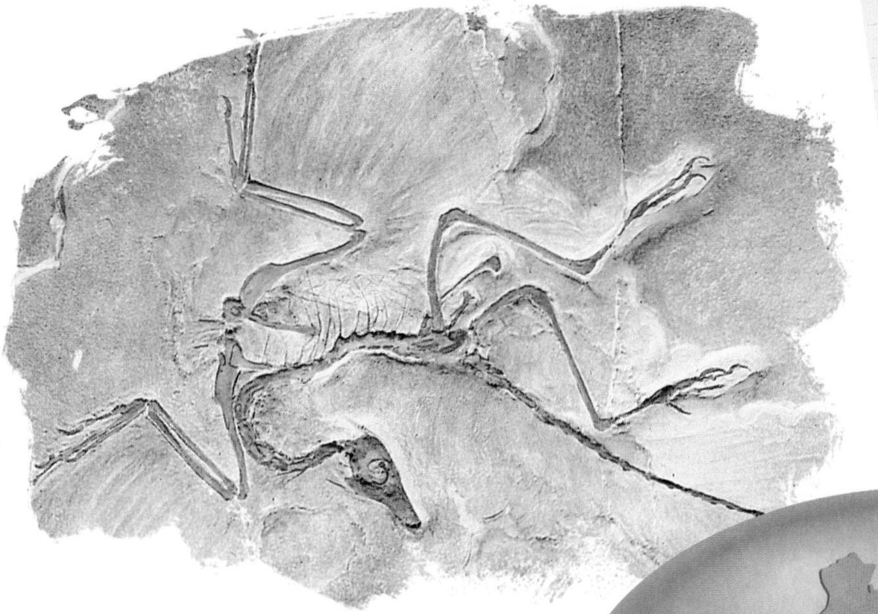

Section

13-3 MIDDLE AND RECENT EARTH HISTORY

Reptiles and gymnosperms were dominant land life-forms in the **Mesozoic era.** All continents were together as one landmass called Pangaea at the beginning of the Mesozoic era. Pangaea separated into two landmasses during the Triassic period. While animals and birds evolved during the Jurassic period, dinosaurs continued to dominate throughout the Jurassic and Cretaceous. Angiosperms evolved in the early Cretaceous. They were dominant throughout the Cretaceous and continue to be dominant today. Mammals also began to dominate the land in the Cenozoic era. Plate tectonic changes in the Mesozoic era caused climates to become drier and seas to expand. *Homo sapiens* evolved during the Pleistocene epoch. ***What caused a change in Earth's climate during the Mesozoic era?***

Chapter 13 Assessment

Using Vocabulary

a. amphibian
b. Cenozoic era
c. cyanobacteria
d. epoch
e. era
f. gastrolith
g. geologic time scale
h. Mesozoic era
i. Paleozoic era
j. period
k. Precambrian time
l. reptile
m. trilobite

Each phrase below describes a science term from the list. Write the term that matches the phrase describing it.

1. record of events in Earth history
2. geologic time with poorest fossil record
3. probably evolved from the same ancestor as amphibians
4. the geologic era in which we live
5. used by dinosaurs and birds to help digest food

Checking Concepts

Choose the word or phrase that best answers the question.

6. How many millions of years ago did the era in which you live begin?
   A) 650 C) 1.6
   B) 245 D) 66
7. What is one of the most important fossils for determining age from the Paleozoic era?
   A) dinosaur C) fish
   B) angiosperm D) trilobite
8. Which is the longest division of geologic time?
   A) the Paleozoic era
   B) the Cenozoic era
   C) Precambrian time
   D) the Mesozoic era
9. What is the next-smaller division of geologic time after the era?
   A) period C) epoch
   B) stage D) eon
10. During which period was the most recent ice age?
    A) Pennsylvanian C) Paleogene
    B) Triassic D) Quaternary
11. What was one of the earliest forms of life on Earth?
    A) gymnosperm C) angiosperm
    B) cyanobacterium D) dinosaur
12. Which had the same ancestors as amphibians?
    A) trilobites C) angiosperms
    B) lungfish D) gymnosperms
13. In which era did the dinosaurs live?
    A) Mesozoic C) Miocene
    B) Paleozoic D) Cenozoic
14. What has seeds without protective coverings?
    A) angiosperms C) gymnosperms
    B) flowering plants D) magnolias
15. What evolved to become the dominant land plant during the Cenozoic era?
    A) gymnosperms C) ginkgoes
    B) angiosperms D) algae

Thinking Critically

16. Why couldn't plants move onto land prior to the establishment of an ozone layer?
17. Why are some trilobites classified as index fossils?
18. What is the most significant difference between Precambrian and Paleozoic life-forms?
19. How might the extinction of plant species from a tropical rain forest affect animals that live in the forest?

20. Explain why the discovery of gastroliths supports the theory that dinosaurs are ancestors of birds.

Developing Skills

If you need help, refer to the Skill Handbook.

21. **Observing and Inferring:** Use the outlines of the present-day continents to make a sketch of the Mesozoic supercontinent Pangaea.
22. **Hypothesizing:** Why did trilobites become extinct at the end of the Paleozoic era?
23. **Interpreting Data:** Fernando found what he thought was a piece of coral in a chunk of coal. Was he right? Explain.
24. **Interpreting Scientific Illustrations:** The circle graph below represents geologic time. Determine which era of geologic time is represented by each portion of the graph.

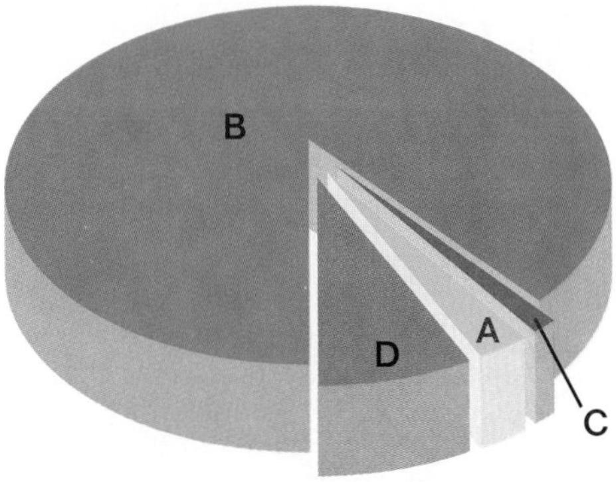

25. **Interpreting Scientific Illustrations:** The Cenozoic era has lasted 66 million years. What percentage of Earth's 4.6-billion-year history is that? How many degrees on the pie graph represent the Cenozoic era?

THE PRINCETON REVIEW

Test-Taking Tip

Use the Buddy System Study in a group. A small gathering of people works well because it allows you to draw from a broader base of skills and expertise. Keep it small and keep on target.

Test Practice

Use these questions to test your Science Proficiency.

1. The fossil record increased greatly around 544 million years ago. What one fact about organisms alive at that time **BEST** explains the change in the fossil record?
   A) Organisms became more mobile.
   B) Organisms had developed hard parts.
   C) Organisms were composed mostly of soft parts.
   D) Organisms moved onto land.
2. The fossil record is limited for Precambrian time. What does this tell you about the life-forms from that age?
   A) Organisms from Precambrian time did not have hard parts and were not preserved well.
   B) Few life-forms existed then.
   C) Precambrian life-forms were too small for fossilization.
   D) Precambrian time is too long for fossils to remain.

UNIT 5

Earth's Air and Water

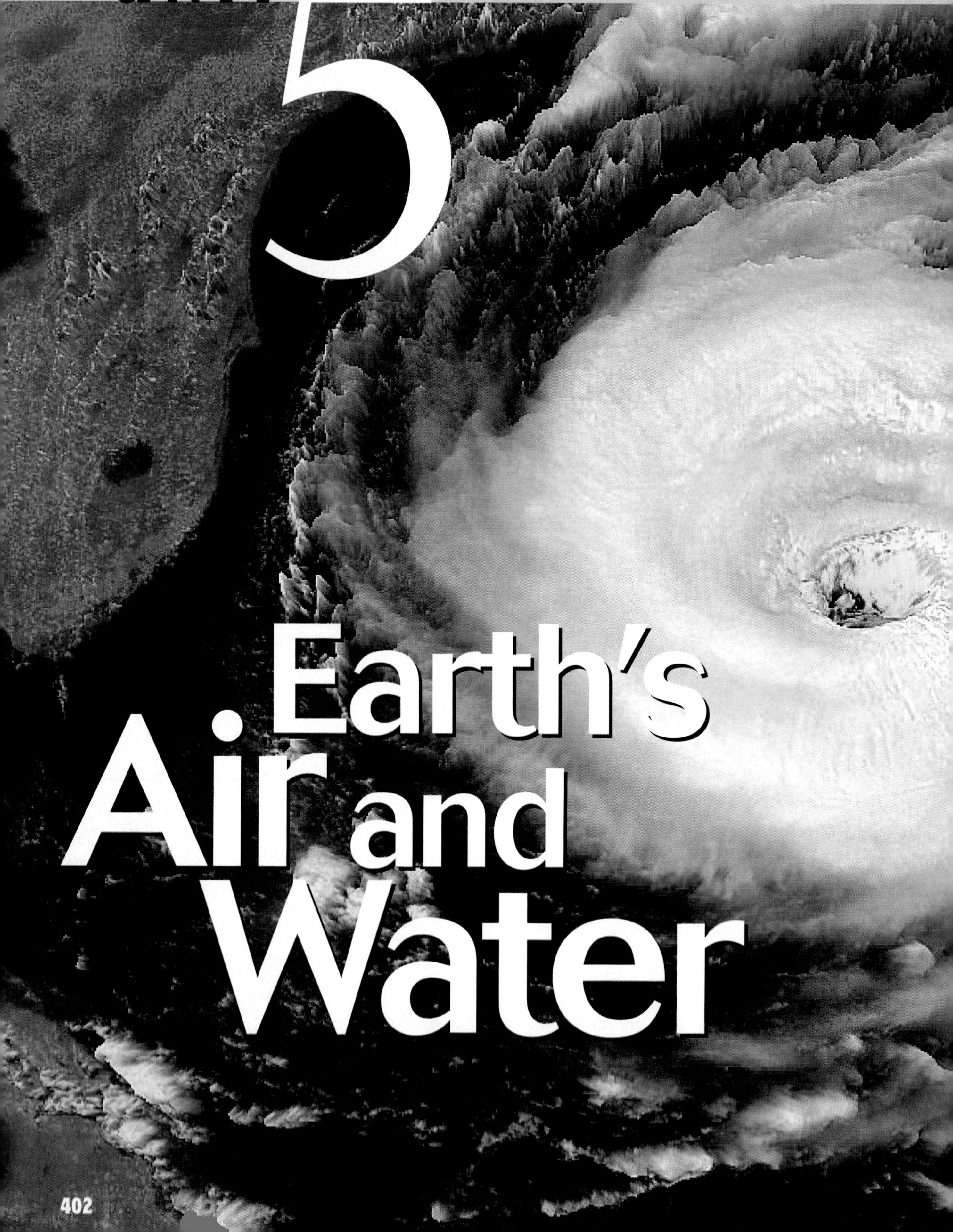

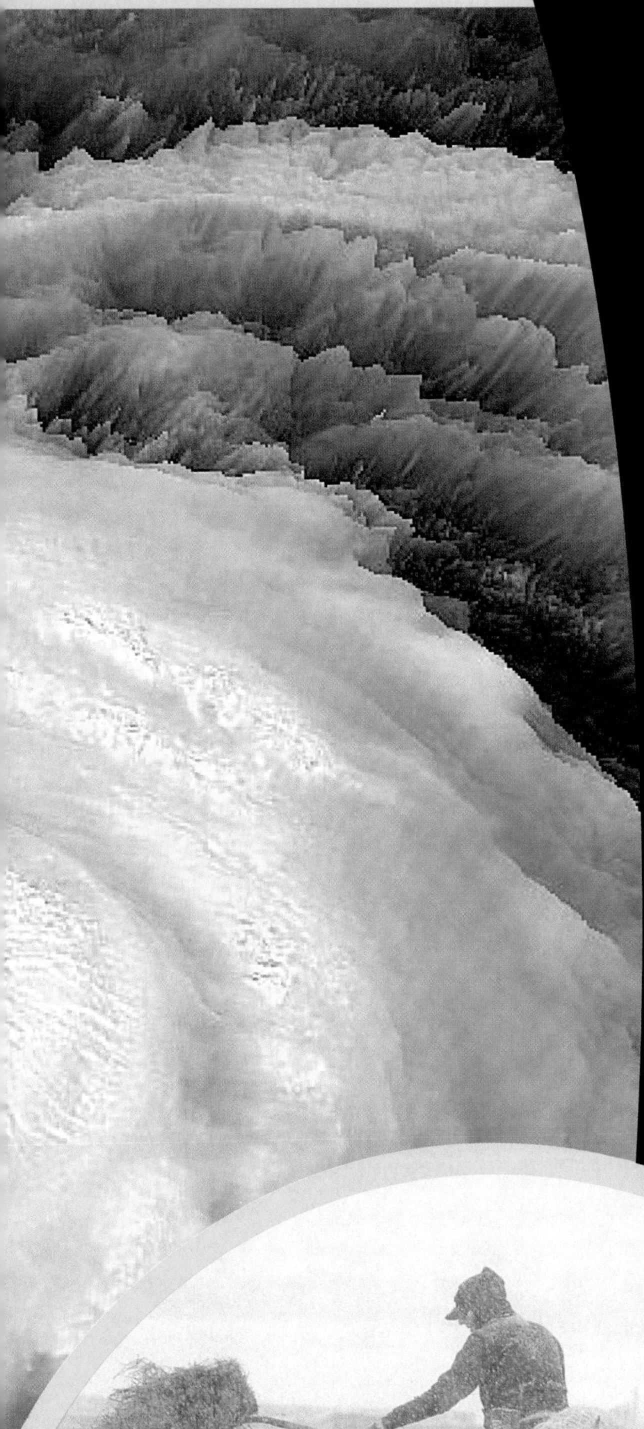

NATIONAL GEOGRAPHIC

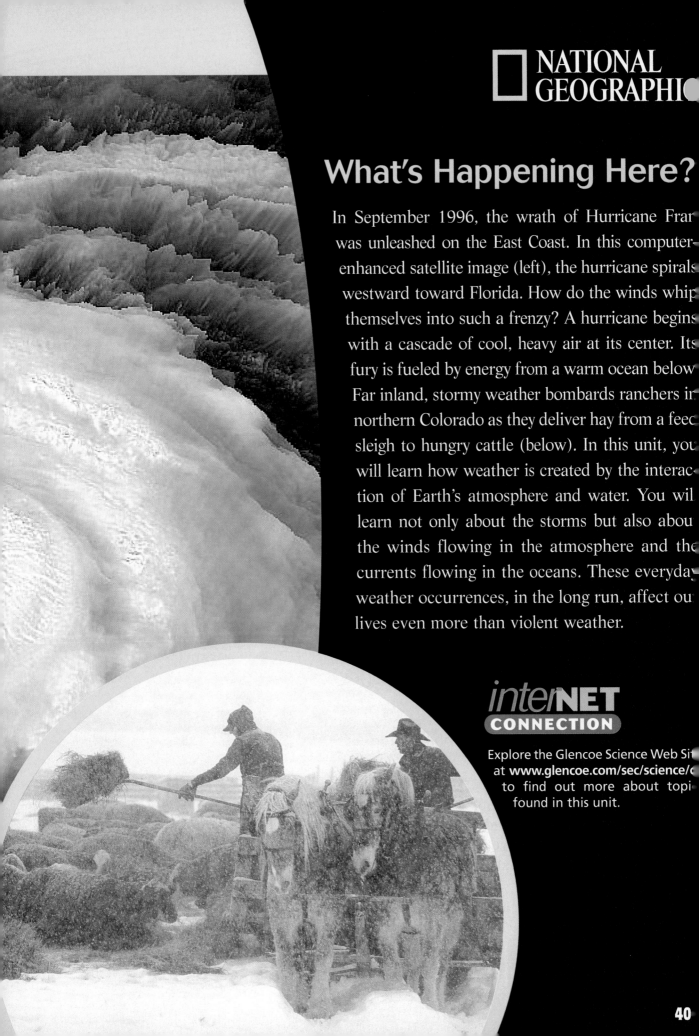

What's Happening Here?

In September 1996, the wrath of Hurricane Fran was unleashed on the East Coast. In this computer-enhanced satellite image (left), the hurricane spirals westward toward Florida. How do the winds whip themselves into such a frenzy? A hurricane begins with a cascade of cool, heavy air at its center. Its fury is fueled by energy from a warm ocean below. Far inland, stormy weather bombards ranchers in northern Colorado as they deliver hay from a feed sleigh to hungry cattle (below). In this unit, you will learn how weather is created by the interaction of Earth's atmosphere and water. You will learn not only about the storms but also about the winds flowing in the atmosphere and the currents flowing in the oceans. These everyday weather occurrences, in the long run, affect our lives even more than violent weather.

interNET CONNECTION

Explore the Glencoe Science Web Site at www.glencoe.com/sec/science/c to find out more about topi found in this unit.

CHAPTER

14 Atmosphere

Chapter Preview

Skills Preview

Skill Builders
- Predict
- Map Concepts

Activities
- Analyze Data
- Compare and Contrast

MiniLabs
- Observe and Infer
- Measure in SI

Reading Check ✓

Before reading this chapter, list the vocabulary terms for each section. As you read, write a definition next to each term.

Explore Activity

Do you know how windsurfing works? A surfer uses the power of the wind to skim a surfboard across water. You've probably used the power of wind to fly a kite or to sail a boat. Do you know where wind comes from? Temperature differences in the air play a large role in creating wind. The Explore Activity that follows will help you observe the effects of temperature.

Observe Temperature Effects

1. Your teacher will pour a small quantity of water into a soda can.
2. The can will be heated until the water boils.
3. Then the heat will be turned off, and the can will be submerged upside down in cold water.

Science Journal

What happens as the can cools? In your Science Journal, hypothesize why this happens. How is this related to windsurfing?

14•1 Earth's Atmosphere

Makeup of the Atmosphere

It's early morning in the future. You're getting dressed for work. As you eat breakfast, the weather report comes over the computer screen: "Smog levels higher than normal. Temperatures near 38°C. The ozone layer in the stratosphere thinner than yesterday." You'll need your filter mask to protect your lungs from the smog. Pollution in the atmosphere has raised the temperature. You'll have to wear cool clothing. The thinner ozone layer requires you to use a strong sunblock lotion to protect yourself from skin cancer.

This scenario may not sound pleasant, but it's a future you may face. Because your life depends on the air you breathe, you need to know about the atmosphere, its composition, its structure, how it affects you, and how you affect it.

What You'll Learn

- The gases in Earth's atmosphere
- The structure of Earth's atmosphere
- What causes air pressure

Vocabulary

troposphere
ionosphere
ozone layer
ultraviolet radiation
chlorofluorocarbon

Why It's Important

- The makeup and structure of the atmosphere affect the weather and, in turn, you.

Atmospheric Gases

The atmosphere surrounding Earth extends from Earth's surface to outer space. The atmosphere is a mixture of gases with some suspended solids and liquids. **Figure 14-1** is a graph of the gases in Earth's atmosphere. Nitrogen is the most common gas. Oxygen makes up 21 percent of our atmosphere. We need oxygen to breathe. Water vapor makes up from zero to four percent of the atmosphere. When the percentage of water vapor is higher, the percentages of other gases are slightly
lower.

Figure 14-1 This graph shows the percentages of the gases that make up our atmosphere.

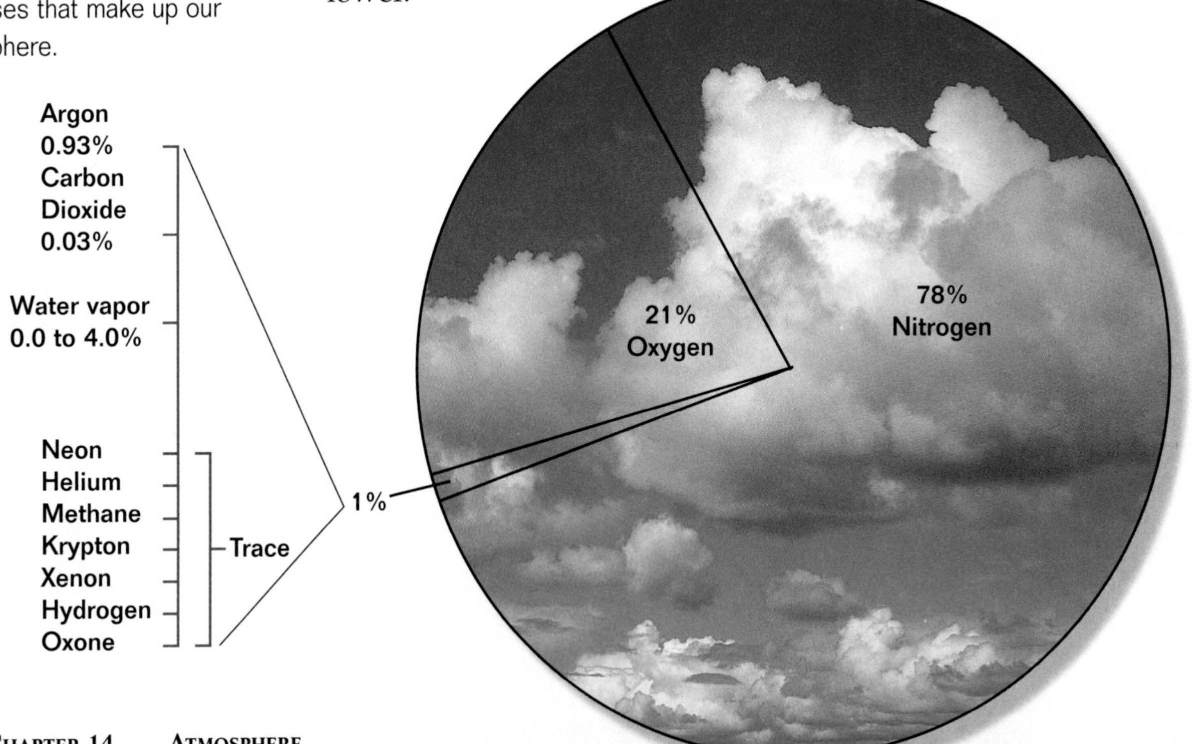

Figure 14-2 Smog lies over Mexico City. **How does brown smog form?**

The atmosphere also contains smog, a type of pollution. The kind of smog affecting an area depends on the pollutants. Car exhaust expels dust and gases into the air. These pollutants mix with oxygen and other chemicals in the presence of sunlight, causing a brown smog, as shown in **Figure 14-2.** Other gases caused by burning coal or oil cause a gray smog.

Another component of smog is ozone. Ozone is a gas made up of three oxygen molecules bonded together. Ozone occurs naturally in the upper atmosphere, but it is not normally found in the lower part of the atmosphere. When it is formed in the air above cities, ozone is considered a pollutant. In the lower atmosphere, ozone can harm plants and damage our lungs.

Atmospheric Solids and Liquids

Gases aren't the only thing making up Earth's atmosphere. Dust, salt, and ice are three common solids found in the atmospheric mixture. Dust gets into the atmosphere when wind picks it up off the ground and carries it along. Ice is common in the form of hailstones and snowflakes. Salt is picked up from ocean spray.

The atmosphere also contains liquids. The most common liquid in the atmosphere is water droplets found in of clouds. Water is the only substance that exists as a solid, liquid, and gas in Earth's atmosphere.

Figure 14-3 Earth's atmosphere extends hundreds of kilometers upward. The first 15 km on this diagram are not to scale.

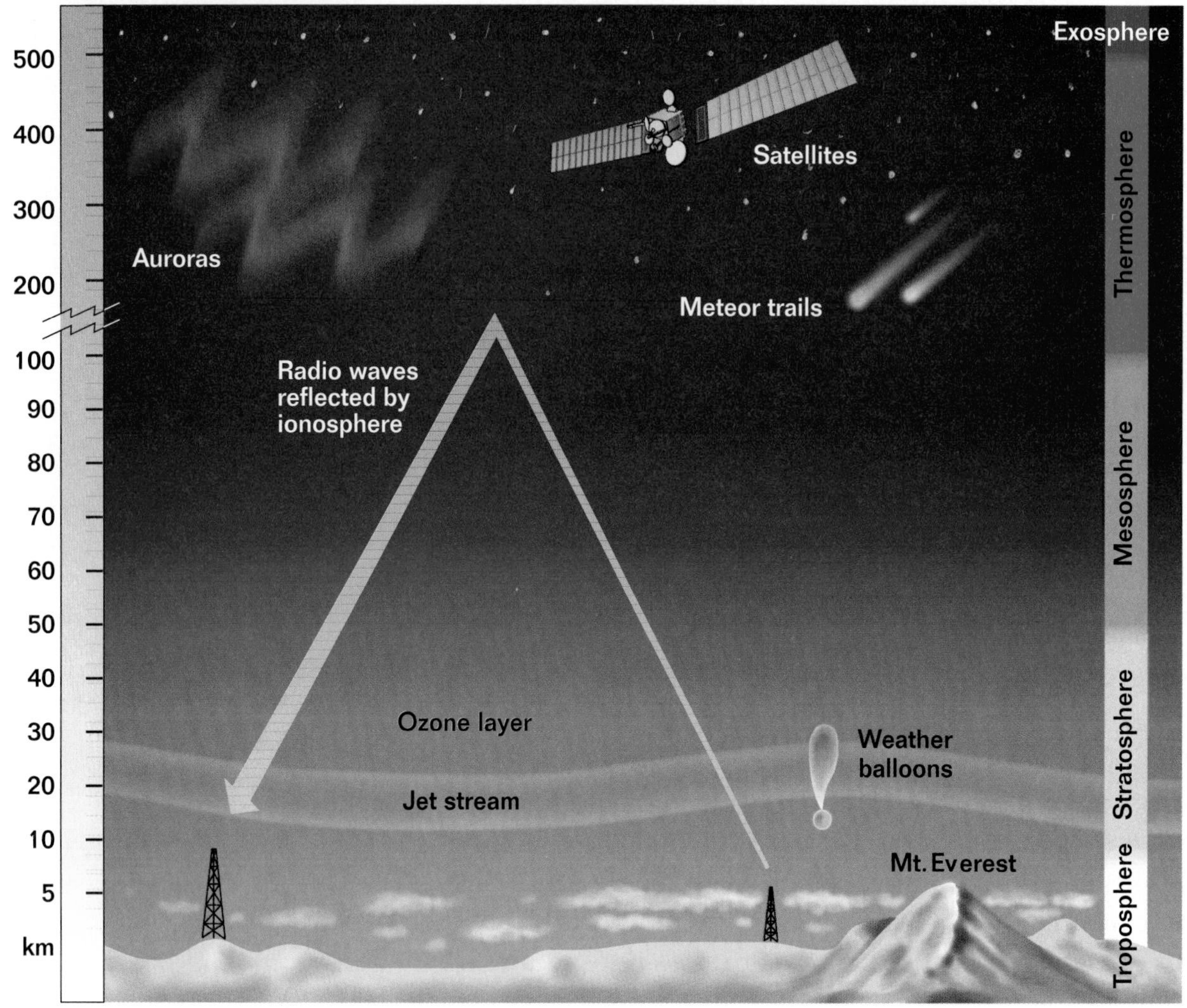

Structure of the Atmosphere

In the beginning of this chapter, you read about an imaginary weather forecast from the future. The forecast predicted a high smog level and a thin ozone layer in the stratosphere. Both conditions affect your health but in different ways. Where in the atmosphere does smog occur? Where can you find not just ozone but the ozone layer?

Figure 14-3 illustrates Earth's five main atmospheric layers: the troposphere, stratosphere, mesosphere, thermosphere, and exosphere. Each layer has unique characteristics.

Lower Layers of the Atmosphere

We live in the **troposphere,** the layer closest to the ground. The troposphere contains 75 percent of the atmospheric gases, as well as dust, ice, and liquid water. Weather, clouds, and smog occur in the troposphere.

Above the troposphere lies the stratosphere. As **Figure 14-3** shows, a layer of ozone exists within the stratosphere. This ozone layer was mentioned in the future forecast because the ozone layer directly affects your health. You'll learn more about this layer in Section 14-2.

Upper Layers of the Atmosphere

Beyond the stratosphere are the mesosphere, thermosphere, and exosphere. One important layer of the thermosphere is the **ionosphere,** a layer of electrically charged particles. When solar energy hits these particles, the particles can interfere with certain kinds of radio waves sent from Earth. During the daytime, energy from the sun interacts with the particles in the ionosphere, which causes the particles to absorb AM radio waves. At night, without solar energy, AM radio transmissions bounce off the ionosphere. This bouncing allows radio transmissions from one side of the globe to be received on the other side of the globe. **Figure 14-4** illustrates this.

The exosphere is the uppermost part of Earth's atmosphere. Beyond it lies space. If you were an astronaut traveling upward through the exosphere, you would encounter fewer and fewer molecules. Eventually, you would find so few molecules that, for all practical purposes, you would be out of Earth's atmosphere and in space. But, there's no clear boundary between the atmosphere and space.

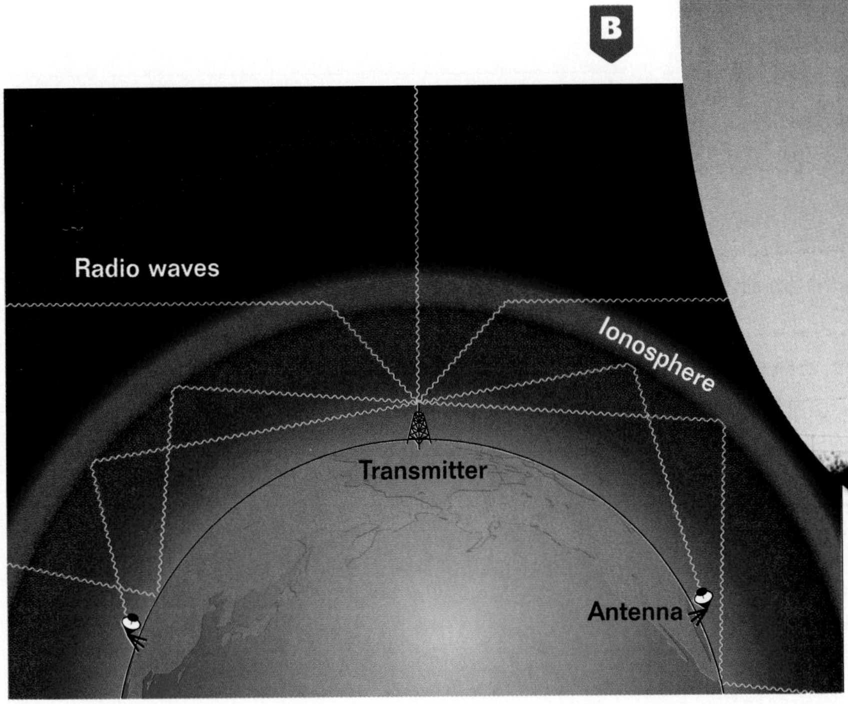

Figure 14-4 Radio waves can be received by antennas around the globe (A). At night, AM radio waves that strike the ionosphere at sharp angles pass through to space, but other waves strike at lower angles and are reflected back toward Earth (B).

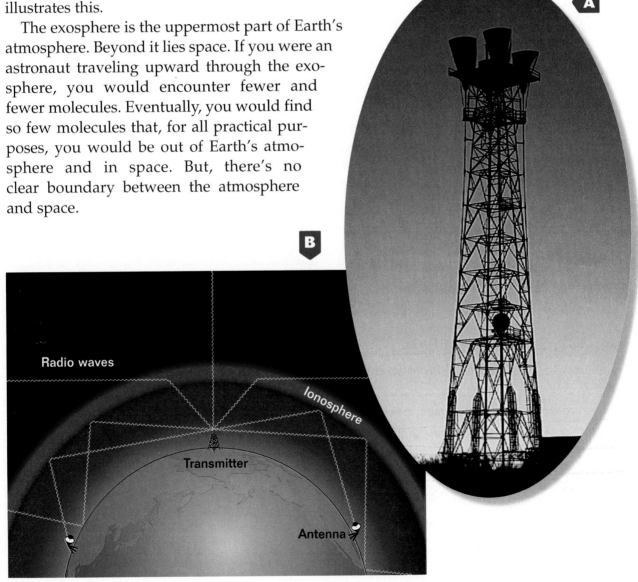

The space shuttle orbits Earth in the exosphere, 280 km above Earth's surface. So few molecules exist here that the wings of the shuttle, used in the lower atmosphere, are useless. The spacecraft must rely on bursts from small rocket thrusters to maneuver. ☑

Reading Check ☑

How does the space shuttle maneuver?

Atmospheric Pressure

Gases in the atmosphere have mass and a gravitational attraction to other matter. The gravitational attraction between Earth and molecules of gas causes atmospheric gases to be pulled toward Earth. Yet, atmospheric gases extend upward hundreds of kilometers. The weight of the gases at the top of the atmosphere presses down on the air below, compressing the molecules and increasing the density of the air. The air at the bottom of the atmosphere, close to Earth, is more dense. This dense air exerts more force than the less-dense air at the top of the atmosphere. Force exerted on an area is known as pressure.

Where do you think air pressure is greater—in the exosphere at the top of the atmosphere or in the troposphere near Earth's surface? Air pressure is greater nearer Earth. At sea level on Earth's surface, more molecules are pushing down from above.

Problem Solving

Interpreting Atmospheric Pressure

Atmospheric gases extend hundreds of kilometers above Earth's surface, but the molecules that make up these gases are fewer and fewer in number the higher you go. This means that air pressure decreases with altitude. The graph on this page shows these changes in air pressure. Note that altitude on the graph only goes up to 36 km. The troposphere and the stratosphere are represented on the graph, but other layers of the atmosphere are not. Study the graph, then answer the questions below.

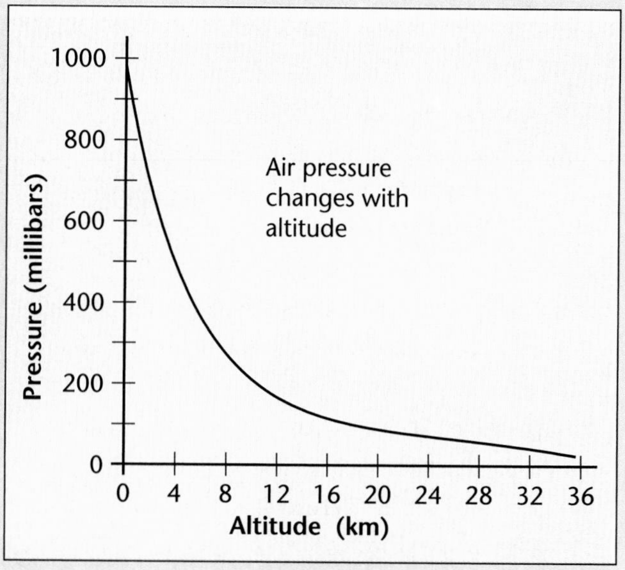

Think Critically: Does air pressure increase more rapidly at high or low altitudes? Why doesn't air pressure drop to zero on the graph? At what altitude would it drop to zero?

Figure 14-5 Air pressure decreases with elevation. **How might this affect a mountain climber?**

Going Up

In general, atmospheric pressure is greatest near Earth's surface and decreases as you move upward away from sea level. That means air pressure decreases as you go up in the mountains. **Figure 14-5** shows a mountain climber. Some people find it harder to breathe in high mountains. Fewer molecules exist at high elevations, so air pressure is less.

Atmospheric Temperatures

You don't have to climb a mountain to find lower air pressure. Anywhere on Earth where the atmosphere is heated, air molecules move with greater energy. In heated air, fewer molecules occupy a cubic centimeter of space. As a result, there is less air pressure. Colder air has more molecules occupying a cubic centimeter of space. This causes high air pressure. These areas of high and low pressure are often marked on weather maps because they affect our weather. Tracking the movement of these high- and low-pressure areas helps meteorologists forecast the weather.

Temperatures affect Earth's atmosphere in another way. The atmosphere is divided into layers based on temperature differences. Earth's atmospheric gases are heated by absorbing energy from the sun. In the troposphere near Earth's surface, temperatures decrease with an increase in altitude. Just above it in the stratosphere, molecules of ozone absorb the sun's ultraviolet radiation, heating that layer. While some layers contain gases that easily absorb the sun's energy, other layers do not. Because of this, the various layers have different temperatures.

MiniLab

Measuring the Mass of Air

Procedure

1. On a pan balance, find the mass of an inflatable ball that is completely deflated.
2. Hypothesize about the change in the mass of the ball when it goes from being deflated to inflated.
3. Inflate the ball to its maximum recommended inflation pressure.
4. Determine the mass of the fully inflated ball.

Analysis

1. What change occurs in the mass of the ball from deflation to inflation?
2. Infer from your data whether air has mass.

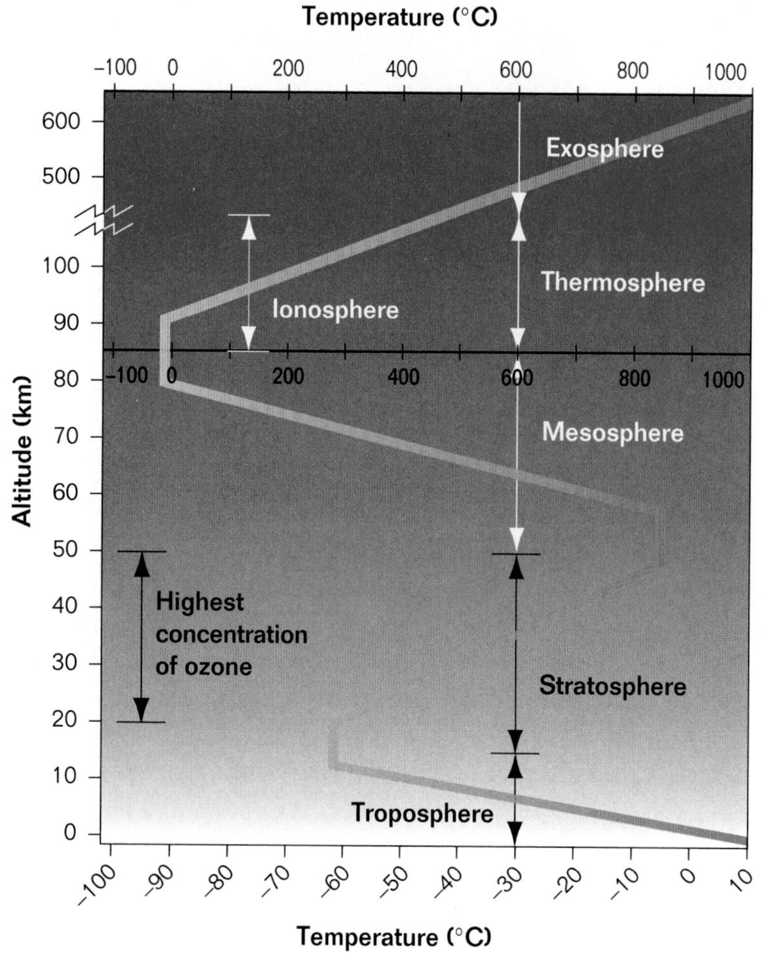

Figure 14-6 The division of the atmosphere into layers is based mainly on differences in temperature. **What is the temperature of the troposphere at a height of 10 km?**

Notice in **Figure 14-6** how the temperature of the atmosphere changes in different layers. Which layer is the coldest? Which layer is the warmest?

The Ozone Layer

Is the ozone layer in danger?

About 20 km above your head lies the ozone layer. The **ozone layer** is an atmospheric layer with a high concentration of ozone. This layer, located in the stratosphere, cannot be seen, yet your life depends on it. The ozone layer shields you from harmful energy from the sun.

Ozone is a form of oxygen. The oxygen we breathe has two atoms per molecule. An ozone molecule, however, binds three oxygen atoms together. The layer of ozone molecules absorbs most of the ultraviolet radiation that enters the atmosphere. **Ultraviolet radiation** is one of the many types of energy that comes to Earth from the sun. Too much exposure to ultraviolet radiation can damage the skin. Ultraviolet radiation can cause cancer and other health problems in many types of plants and animals.

Ozone Holes

LIFE SCIENCE INTEGRATION

Each year, more than 800 000 Americans develop skin cancer, and more than 9000 die from it. If the ozone layer disappeared, cancer rates might increase. **Figure 14-7** shows that the ozone layer is thinning and developing holes. In 1986, scientists found areas in the stratosphere with extremely low amounts of ozone. One very large hole opened over Antarctica. A smaller hole was discovered over the north pole. Since that time, these holes appear during certain seasons and disappear during others. The ozone layer changes due to natural processes such as seasons, sunspots, and volcanic eruptions, but pollutants may also be at fault.

CFCs

Some scientists hypothesize that pollutants in the environment are destroying the ozone layer. These pollutants destroy ozone much faster than it can be naturally replaced. Blame has fallen on **chlorofluorocarbons** (CFCs), a group of chemical compounds used in refrigerators, aerosol sprays, and foam packaging. When these products are manufactured and used, CFCs enter the atmosphere. Recently, many governments have restricted the production and use of CFCs.

Chlorofluorocarbon molecules destroy ozone. Recall that an ozone molecule is composed of three oxygen atoms bonded together (O_3). When a chlorine atom from a chlorofluorocarbon molecule comes near a molecule of ozone, the ozone molecule breaks apart. It forms a regular two-atom molecule (O_2). This oxygen can't absorb ultraviolet radiation. The result is that more ultraviolet radiation reaches Earth's surface.

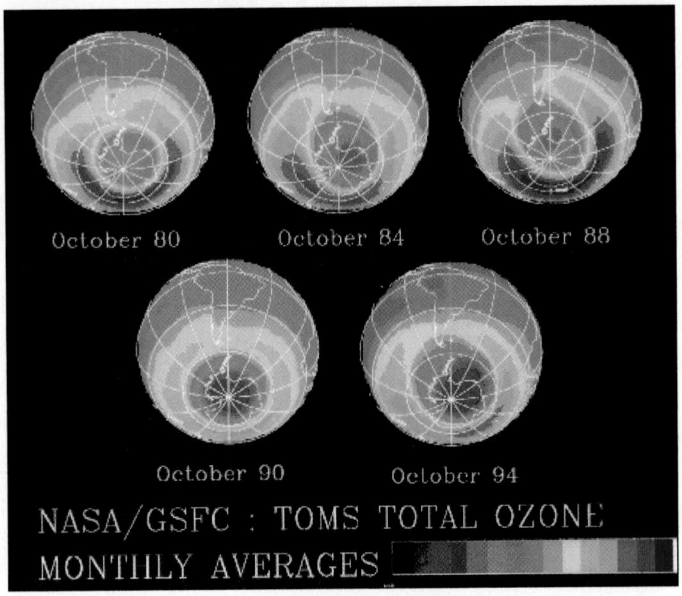

Figure 14-7 These images were produced using data from a NASA satellite. The purple color shows how the ozone hole has grown bigger over time.

Section Assessment

1. Explain why the temperature of the atmosphere does not increase or decrease steadily as you move from Earth's surface toward space.
2. What causes air pressure?
3. **Think Critically:** Imagine you're a football player running with the ball. Six players tackle you and pile on top—one on top of the other. Relate the pressure that you and each player above you feels to the pressure in the layers of the atmosphere.
4. **Skill Builder**
   Predicting Solar activity such as sunspots interact with Earth's atmosphere. Do the **Chapter 14 Skill Activity** on page 707 to predict when sunspots occur.

Science Journal

The names of the atmospheric layers end with the suffix *-sphere*. In these names, *sphere* means "layer." Use a dictionary to find out what *meso-*, *thermo-*, and *exo-* mean. In your Science Journal, write the meaning of these prefixes and explain why the layers are appropriately or inappropriately named.

Activity 14•1

Using Scientific Methods

Making a Barometer

Materials

- Small coffee can
- Drinking straw
- Large, rubber balloon
- Construction paper
- Transparent tape
- Scissors
- Rubber band

If you have flown in an airplane or zoomed to the top of a building in an elevator, you have experienced an air pressure change inside your ears. When you rapidly increased your altitude, air pressure outside your eardrums became lower than the pressure inside your eardrums. The air inside your ears pushed against your eardrums. In this activity, you'll see that a barometer reacts as your eardrums did when exposed to differences in pressure.

What You'll Investigate

How does a barometer react to a change in air pressure?

Goals

- **Make** a barometer.
- **Observe** the effects of weather changes on a barometer.

Procedure

1. **Cut** the balloon and **stretch** it tightly over the can. **Secure** it in place with the rubber band.
2. Using tape, **attach** a piece of construction paper vertically to the side of the coffee can as shown in the photo.
3. **Trim** one end of the straw to a point. **Tape** the other end of the straw to the balloon and **point** the trimmed end toward the paper.
4. Make a horizontal mark on the paper where the pointed end of the straw touches. **Write** *high* above this mark and *low* below it.
5. **Design** a data table to record your observations. **Record** the movement of the straw for a period of a week. Also **record** the weather conditions each day. **Plot** the movement of the straw on a graph.

Conclude and Apply

1. How did your barometer react to changes in air pressure?
2. **Analyze** your data to see what type of weather was associated with the pressures you recorded.
3. **Conclude** from your activity how a weather forecaster can use barometric pressure to help predict weather.

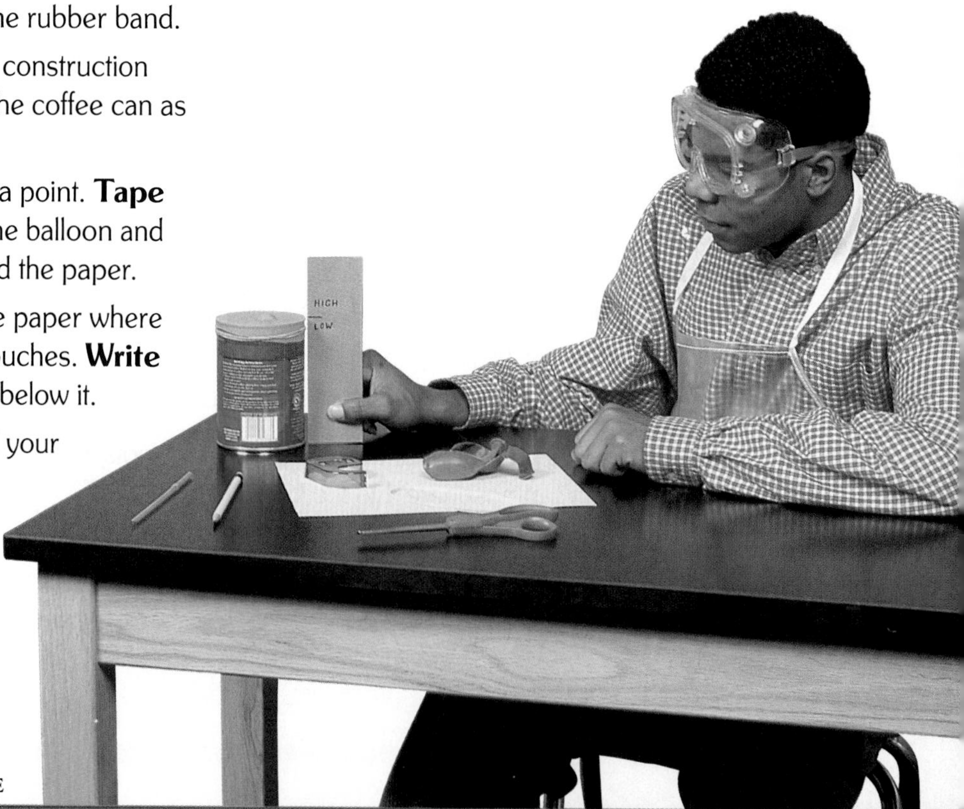

History of Science

NATIONAL GEOGRAPHIC

Where does river water come from?

Centuries ago, people noted that rivers flowed from mountains into the oceans. Because the oceans had not overflowed, they thought there must be a way for the water to pass through Earth and back up to the tops of mountains. In the Middle Ages, the years between 500 and 1500 A.D., some philosophers tried to explain this mechanism.

Many Explanations

One suggestion was that the water was somehow attracted upward, like iron filings to a magnet. Another theory was that spaces and cracks in Earth pulled in water vapor to avoid a vacuum. The vapors then condensed into water that later emerged as springs. Others thought that nature acted like a pump, with tides and strong winds putting pressure on the water at the sea bottom to force it up tunnels to the mountaintops.

Scientists during the Renaissance, the years between 1300 and 1600 A.D., concluded that the water in the rivers and streams came from rain and snow falling on the mountains. One scientist in the sixteenth century said that to understand rivers, it was more important to study nature than to study ancient philosophers' ideas about nature. He wrote that the sun's heat evaporates great amounts of water from the ocean into clouds. The water then falls as rain or snow. This water flows downhill as streams or sinks into Earth's crust until it meets impermeable rock and is forced back to the surface as springs. Fluids cannot pass through impermeable rock.

Observing the Alps

In 1715, an Italian scholar made a trip to the Alps to trace streams to their origins. He observed that water ran down slopes from the snowpack at the top. The rivers all came from melting snow and ice.

In another part of the Alps, he found great snowpacks but few streams. The local shepherds showed him where the water ran into cracks in the ground. He realized that this explained the origin of springs. Underground streams flowed from high in the Alps, seeped into the earth, and came to the surface as springs.

Science JOURNAL

Research the pros and cons associated with dam building. Predict the consequences that could result from damming a river. If you need help, refer to Predicting Consequences in the **Skill Handbook**.

14•2 Energy from the Sun

What You'll Learn

- Three things that happen to the energy Earth receives from the sun
- The differences among radiation, conduction, and convection
- The water cycle

Vocabulary
radiation
conduction
convection
hydrosphere
water cycle

Why It's Important

- The sun is the source of most energy in our atmosphere.

Energy Transfer in the Atmosphere

In the future scenario, you return from work. You eat dinner and read the evening news transmitted on the computer network. You see that the Space Agency is still trying to create a hospitable atmosphere on Mars. It's studying the atmospheres of Earth and Venus to understand how they work and how an Earthlike atmosphere might be produced on Mars or Venus. The atmospheres of Earth and its neighboring planets of Venus and Mars are shown in **Figure 14-8.** The atmosphere on

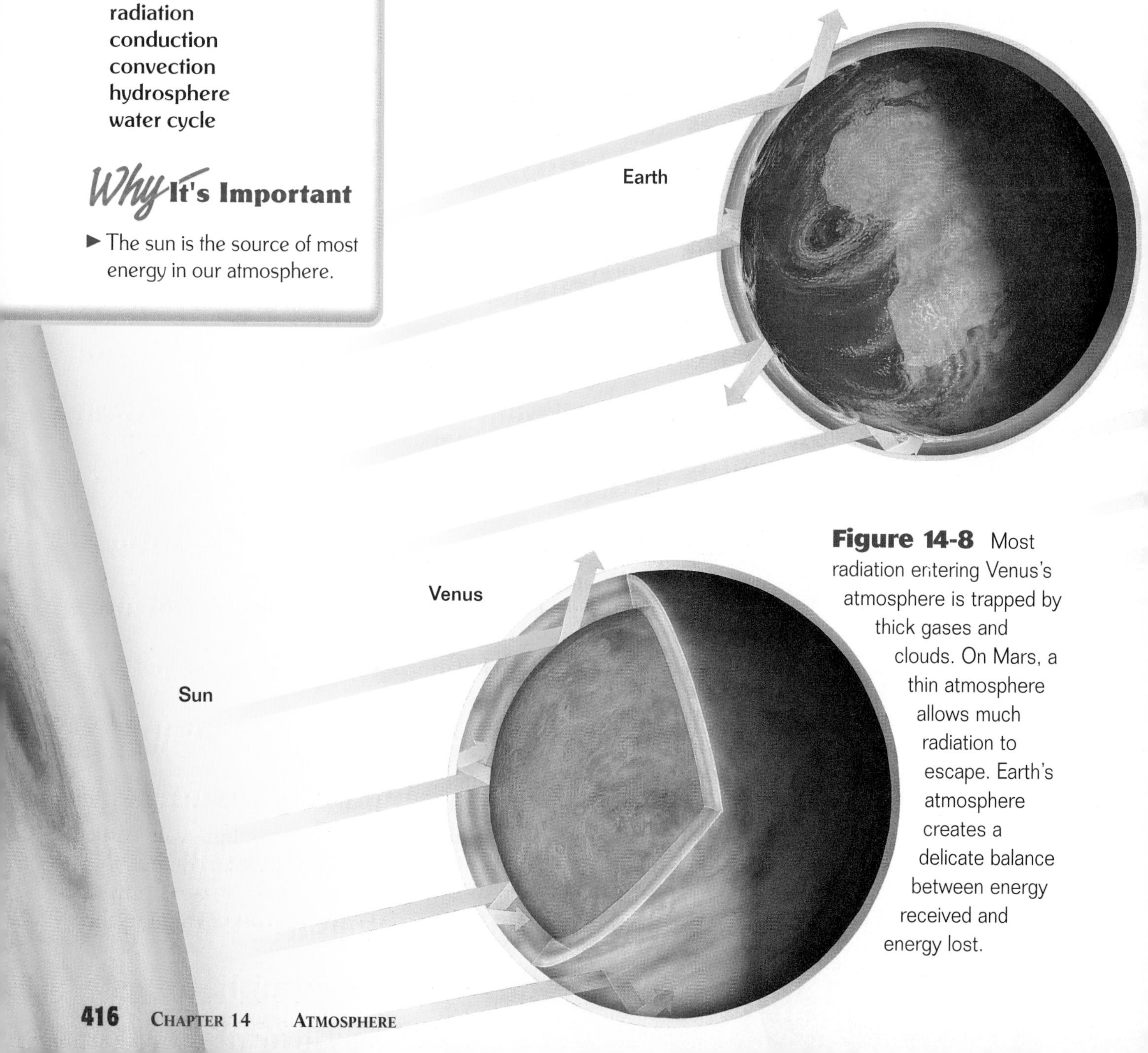

Figure 14-8 Most radiation entering Venus's atmosphere is trapped by thick gases and clouds. On Mars, a thin atmosphere allows much radiation to escape. Earth's atmosphere creates a delicate balance between energy received and energy lost.

Mars is currently too thin to support life or to hold much thermal energy from the sun. As a result, Mars is a cold, lifeless world. On the other hand, Venus's atmosphere is so dense that almost no thermal energy coming from the sun can escape. Venus is so hot that a living thing would instantly burn if it were put on Venus's surface.

In our solar system, nine planets circle the star we call the sun. Earth supports life, but the nearby planets, Mars and Venus, do not support life. How does the interaction between Earth's atmosphere and the sun provide an environment suitable for life?

Using Math

Most weather activity occurs in the airspace between the ground and an altitude of 11 km. Suppose the temperature in this airspace drops about 7°C for each kilometer of increase in altitude. If the ground temperature is 15°C, what is the temperature at an altitude of 3 km?

The Sun

The sun is the source of all energy in our atmosphere. When Earth receives energy from the sun, three different things happen to that energy. Some energy is reflected back into space. Some is absorbed by the atmosphere, and some is absorbed by land and water surfaces. The balance among these three events controls the characteristics of our atmosphere and the life that it supports. Let's take a look at what happens to the energy that reaches Earth.

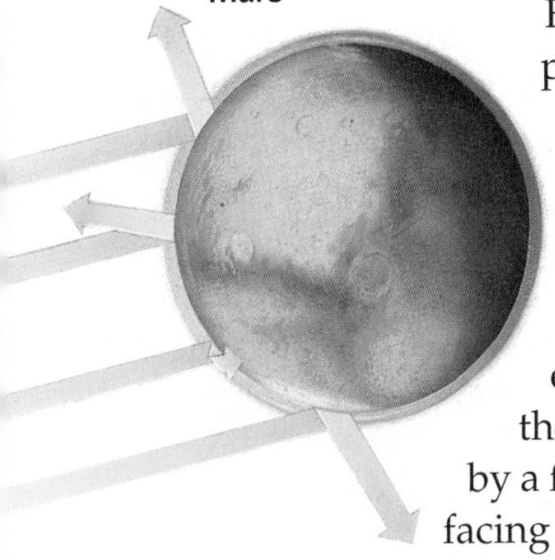

Radiation

Energy from the sun reaches our planet in the form of radiant energy, or radiation. **Radiation** is the transfer of energy by electromagnetic waves. Radiation from the sun travels through empty space, as well as through our atmosphere. You experience radiation as light and heat. When the sun warms your face or when you sit by a fire and it warms the side of your body facing it, you experience radiant energy. You aren't in direct contact with the sun or the fire, but the energy still reaches you. ☑

Reading Check ☑

What is radiation?

Heat

When radiation from the fire reaches you, the molecules of your skin absorb the energy and you feel heat. Heat is energy that flows from an object with a higher temperature to an object with a lower temperature. Once objects at Earth's surface, such as asphalt roads, rocks, houses, or ocean water, absorb radiation, they heat up. These heated surfaces then radiate energy. Much of the radiation coming from the sun passes through the atmosphere. Most radiation coming from Earth's surface is absorbed and heats up our atmosphere.

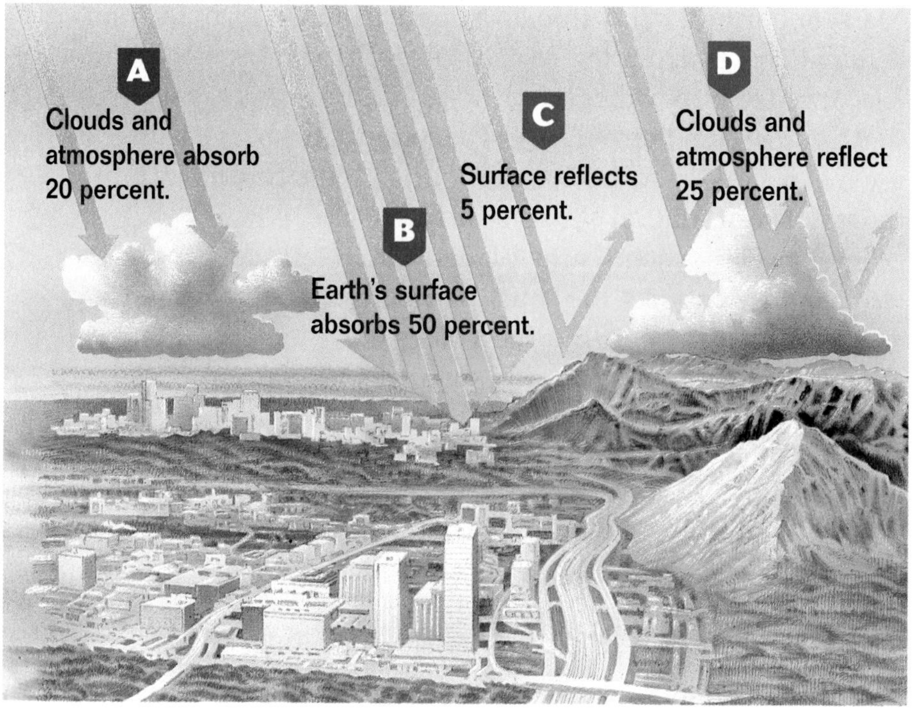
A
Clouds and
atmosphere absorb
20 percent.
B
Earth's surface
absorbs 50 percent.
C
Surface reflects
5 percent.
D
Clouds and
atmosphere reflect
25 percent.

Figure 14-9 The sun is the source of energy in our atmosphere. Thirty percent of incoming solar radiation is reflected back into space. **How much is absorbed by Earth's surface?**

The ozone layer absorbs ultraviolet radiation. When ozone and other gases absorb radiation, the temperature of the atmosphere rises, as you saw in **Figure 14-6.**

On Venus, even less radiation is able to escape back to space, making Venus hotter than Earth. On Earth, a delicate balance exists between energy received from the sun and energy escaping back to space. In the future weather forecast at the beginning of this chapter, high temperatures were forecast. This may be because smog and other pollutants in the atmosphere are preventing radiation from returning to space. Air pollution can upset the balance of incoming and outgoing radiation on Earth.

Some radiation from the sun isn't absorbed by Earth's atmosphere or surface objects. Instead, it simply reflects off the atmosphere and surface, like a ball bouncing off a wall. **Figure 14-9** illustrates the percentages of radiation absorbed and reflected by Earth's surface and atmosphere.

Conduction

If you walk barefoot on hot asphalt, your feet heat up because of conduction. Radiation from the sun heated the asphalt, but direct contact with the asphalt heated your feet. In a similar way, Earth's surface transfers energy directly to the atmosphere. As air moves over warm land or water, air molecules are heated by direct contact. A warm layer of molecules on Earth's surface comes in direct contact with a layer of air molecules and transfers energy.

Conduction is the transfer of energy that occurs when molecules bump into one another. Molecules are always in motion, but molecules in hotter objects move more rapidly than those in cooler objects. When substances are in contact, energy is transferred from energized, fast-moving molecules to lower-energy molecules until all molecules are moving at about the same rate. **Figure 14-10** illustrates how the processes of heat transfer affect the atmosphere.

Convection

After the atmosphere is warmed by radiation or conduction, the heat is transferred throughout the atmosphere by a third process, convection. **Convection** is the transfer of heat by the flow of a heated material. Convection occurs in gases and liquids. Let's see how this works with air.

When air is warmed, the molecules move apart. This increases the volume of the air, which makes the air less dense. Air pressure decreases because fewer molecules are pressing in on each other. Cold temperatures affect the air in just the opposite way. In cold air, molecules move closer together. The air becomes more dense and air pressure increases. Because cold air is dense, it sinks. As the cold air falls toward Earth, it pushes up less-dense, warm air. A circular movement of air, called a convection current, results.

PHYSICS INTEGRATION

Conduction
Infer which of the following would transfer heat by conduction the best: solids, liquids, or gases.

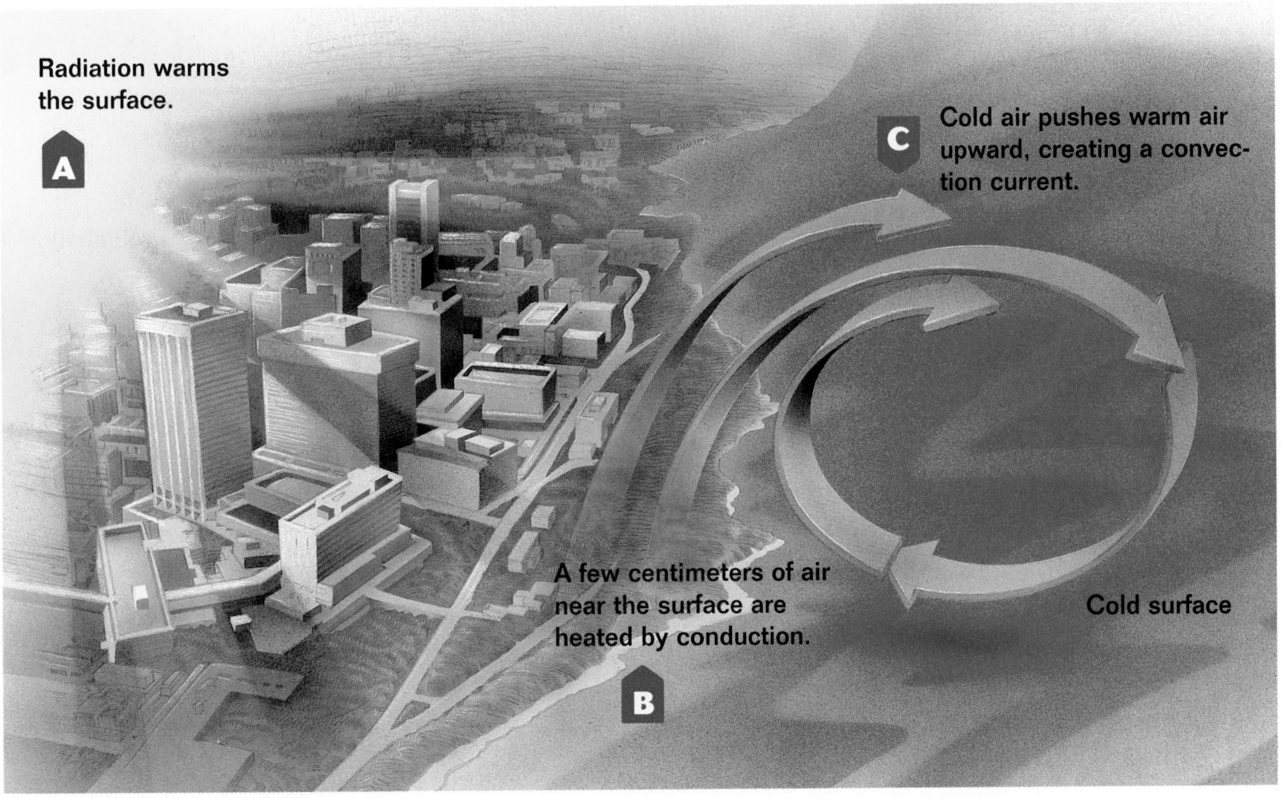

Radiation warms the surface.
A
C
Cold air pushes warm air upward, creating a convection current.
A few centimeters of air near the surface are heated by conduction.
B
Cold surface

Figure 14-10 Heat is transferred within Earth's atmosphere by radiation, conduction, and convection.

Our Unique Atmosphere

Convection currents and other processes that transfer energy control our environment. As you have seen, radiation from the sun can escape back into space, be absorbed by the atmosphere, or be absorbed by bodies on Earth's surface. Once it's been absorbed, heat can be transferred by radiation, conduction, or convection. Just how much radiation is absorbed determines the type of life that can exist on this planet. Other planets in the solar system that are similar to Earth, such as Venus and Mars, don't absorb and lose the same amounts of radiation as Earth. Their atmospheres don't support life as we know it.

*inter***NET**
CONNECTION

Visit the Glencoe Science Web Site at **www.glencoe.com/sec/science/ca** for more information about Earth's atmosphere.

The Water Cycle

Another thing that allows our atmosphere to support life is water. All life as we know it needs water. Although most of Earth's water is in the oceans, it is also found in lakes, streams, rivers, groundwater, glaciers, and the atmosphere. All the water that is found at Earth's surface is the **hydrosphere.** Although there's a lot of water on Earth, 97 percent is salt water and only three percent is freshwater. Two-thirds of the freshwater is frozen in ice caps at the north and south poles. That leaves only one percent available for us to use. This one percent of freshwater is important because it is constantly moving between the atmosphere and Earth in the **water cycle,** as shown in **Figure 14-11.**

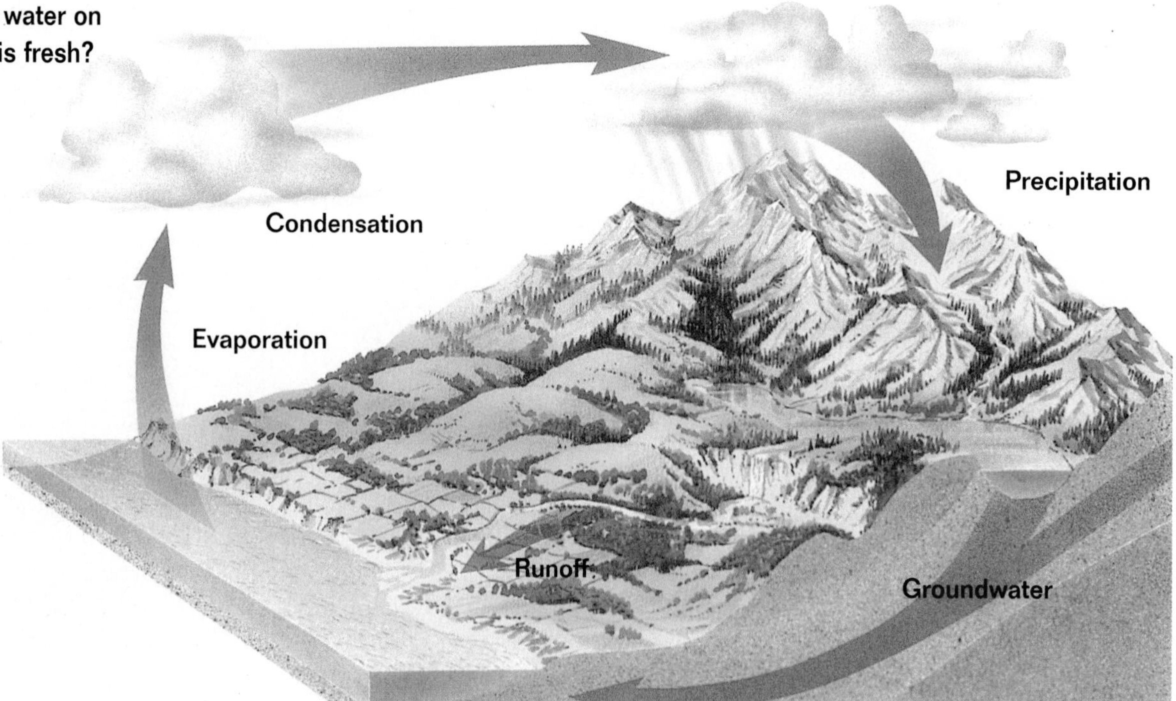

Figure 14-11 Water moves from Earth to the atmosphere and back to Earth again. **How much of the water on Earth is fresh?**

The sun provides the energy for the water cycle. Radiation from the sun causes water to change to a gas called water vapor. The process of water changing from a liquid state to a gas is called *evaporation*. Water evaporates from lakes, streams, and oceans and rises into Earth's atmosphere.

Figure 14-12 Rain is one form of precipitation. **Describe another form.**

Forming Clouds

In the next step of the water cycle, water vapor rises in the atmosphere and cools. When it cools enough, it changes back into a liquid. This process of water vapor changing to a liquid is called *condensation*. When water vapor condenses, it forms clouds.

The third step in the water cycle is *precipitation*. Clouds are made up of millions of tiny water droplets that collide and form larger drops. When the drops grow so large that they can no longer stay suspended in the clouds, drops of water fall to Earth, and the water cycle continues. The moisture that falls from clouds is called precipitation. The forest in **Figure 14-12** is experiencing precipitation in the form of rain.

As you can see, many factors determine whether a planet will have an atmosphere capable of supporting life. How much energy is transferred to the atmosphere and how much energy escapes Earth's atmosphere are important to life on Earth. Learning about our atmosphere will help us protect it so it can continue to support life.

Section Assessment

1. Pollution may be making our atmosphere more like that of Venus. How can that happen and how might it affect temperatures on Earth?
2. How does the sun transfer energy to Earth, and how does the atmosphere get heated?
3. **Think Critically:** Describe the role of the sun in the water cycle.
4. **Skill Builder**
   Concept Mapping Make a cycle concept map that explains what happens to energy that reaches Earth as radiant energy. If you need help, refer to Concept Mapping in the **Skill Handbook** on page 666.

Using Math

Earth is about 150 000 000 km from the sun. The radiation coming from the sun travels at 300 000 km/s. About how long does it take for the radiation from the sun to reach Earth?

Design Your Own Experiment

Activity 14•2

The Heat Is On

Have you ever noticed how cool and refreshing a plunge in a pool or lake is on a hot summer day? Did you ever wonder why the land gets so hot when the water remains cool? At night, the water feels warmer than the land. Let's explore how water and land absorb heat.

Possible Materials

- Ring stand
- Soil
- Metric ruler
- Clear plastic boxes (2)
- Overhead light with reflector
- Thermometers (4)
- Water
- Masking tape
- Colored pencils (4)

Recognize the Problem

How do soil and water compare in their abilities to absorb and release heat?

Form a Hypothesis

Form a hypothesis to explain how soil and water compare in their abilities to absorb and release heat. Write another hypothesis about how air temperatures above soil and above water differ during the day and night.

Goals

- **Design** an experiment to compare the rates of heat absorption and of heat release of both soil and water.
- **Observe** how these differing rates of heat absorption and release affect the air above soil and above water.

Safety Precautions

CAUTION: *Be careful when handling the hot overhead light. Do not let the light or its cord make contact with water.*

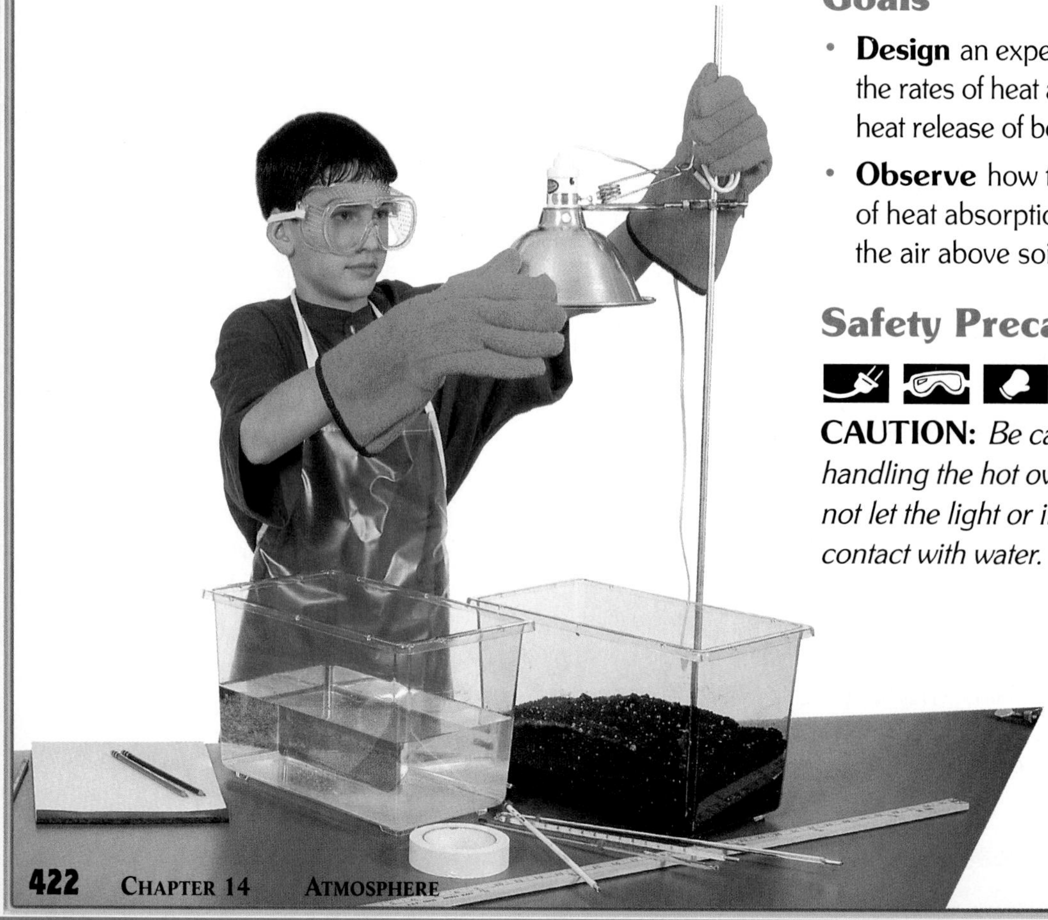

Test Your Hypothesis

Plan

1. As a group, agree upon and write out your hypotheses.
2. **List** the steps that you need to take to test your hypotheses. Include in your plan how you will use your equipment to compare the rates of heat absorption and heat release of water and soil.
3. **Design** a data table in your Science Journal for both parts of your experiment—when the light is on and energy can be absorbed and when the light is off and energy is released.

Do

1. Make sure your teacher approves your plan and your data table before you proceed.
2. Carry out the experiment as planned.
3. During the experiment, **record** your observations and complete the data tables in your Science Journal.
4. Include in your measurements the temperatures of the soil and the water. Also **compare** the rate of release of heat by water and soil. Include in your measurements the temperatures of the air above both of the substances. Do each test for 14 minutes.

Analyze Your Data

1. Use your colored pencils and the information in your data tables to **make line graphs.** Show the rate of energy absorption and energy release for both soil and water. If you need help, refer to Making and Using Graphs in the **Skill Handbook** on page 669.
2. **Analyze** your graphs. When the light was on, which heated up faster, the soil or the water?
3. **Compare** how fast the air heated up over the water with how fast the air heated up over the land.

Draw Conclusions

1. Were your hypotheses supported or not? **Explain.**
2. **Infer** from your graphs which lost heat faster—the water or the soil.
3. **Compare** the temperatures of the air above the water and above the soil after the light was turned off. How do water and soil compare in their abilities to absorb and release heat?

14•3 Movement of Air

What You'll Learn

- Why different latitudes receive different amounts of solar energy
- The Coriolis effect, sea breezes, and land breezes
- How to locate doldrums, trade winds, prevailing westerlies, polar easterlies, and jet streams

Vocabulary
Coriolis effect
jet stream
sea breeze
land breeze

Why It's Important

- Wind systems determine major weather patterns on Earth.

Wind Formation

Have you ever watched a tree swaying in the breeze and wondered where wind comes from? Wind is caused by the uneven heating of Earth and its atmosphere. This uneven heating causes temperature differences that create areas of pressure differences in the atmosphere. Air moving from areas of high pressure to areas of lower pressure creates a general circulation of air around Earth. Wind is the movement of air from an area of high pressure to an area of lower pressure.

Heated Air

Temperature differences at Earth's surface are caused in part by Earth's curved surface. Areas of Earth receive different amounts of solar radiation. **Figure 14-13** illustrates why more radiation is received at the equator than at other latitudes. Air above the equator is heated more than at any other place on Earth. As you know, heated air has a low density, so it is pushed upward by denser, cold air. **Figure 14-14** shows this general pattern of air circulation.

Where does this cold, denser air come from? It comes from the poles, which receive less radiation from the sun, making air at the poles much colder. This dense, high-pressure air

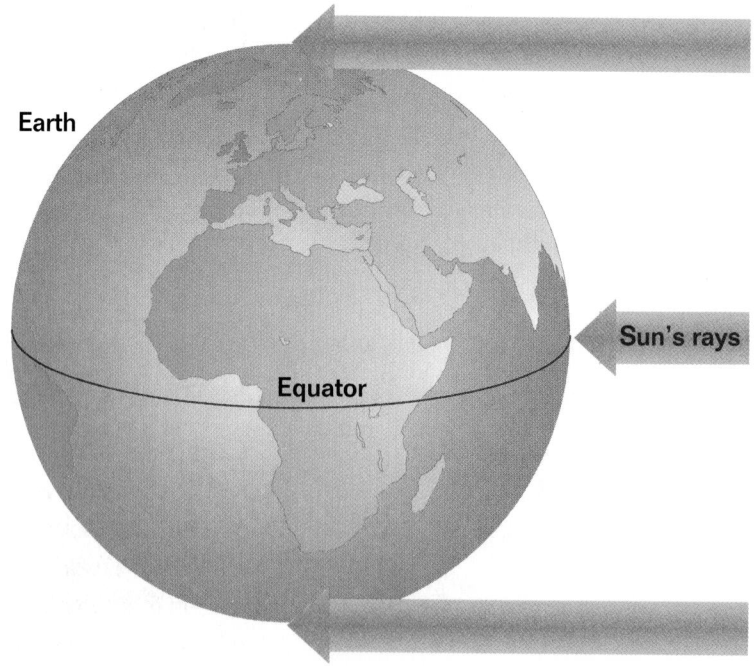

Figure 14-13 Because of Earth's curved surface, solar rays strike the equator more directly and areas away from the equator at angles. **Describe how rays strike the poles.**

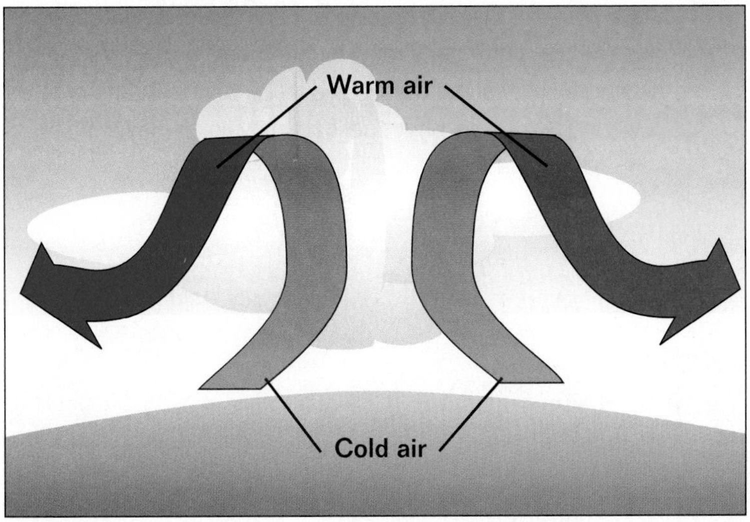

Figure 14-14 Wind develops from uneven heating on Earth. **As cold air sinks and moves under warm air, what happens to the warm air?**

sinks and moves along Earth's surface. As you read on, you'll see that large convection currents formed by rising warm air and sinking cold air distribute heat in Earth's atmosphere. This gives rise to Earth's wind systems.

The Coriolis Effect

The rotation of Earth creates the Coriolis effect. The **Coriolis effect** changes the direction of all free-moving objects such as air and water to the right north of the equator and left to the south. It causes air moving south in the northern hemisphere to turn westward. To someone at the equator, southbound air appears to move to the west as Earth turns east. The diagram of Earth in **Figure 14-15** shows this. The flow of air caused by differences in heating and by the Coriolis effect creates distinct wind patterns on Earth's surface. Not only do these wind systems influence the weather, but they also determine when and where ships and planes travel most efficiently.

Try at Home

MiniLab

Observing Convection Currents

Procedure

1. Fill a clear glass jar with hot water.
2. Place ice cubes on the water along with a few drops of food coloring and observe the motion of the food coloring.

Analysis

1. Describe the motion of the food coloring.
2. Compare and contrast the convection current that you made with convection currents in the atmosphere.

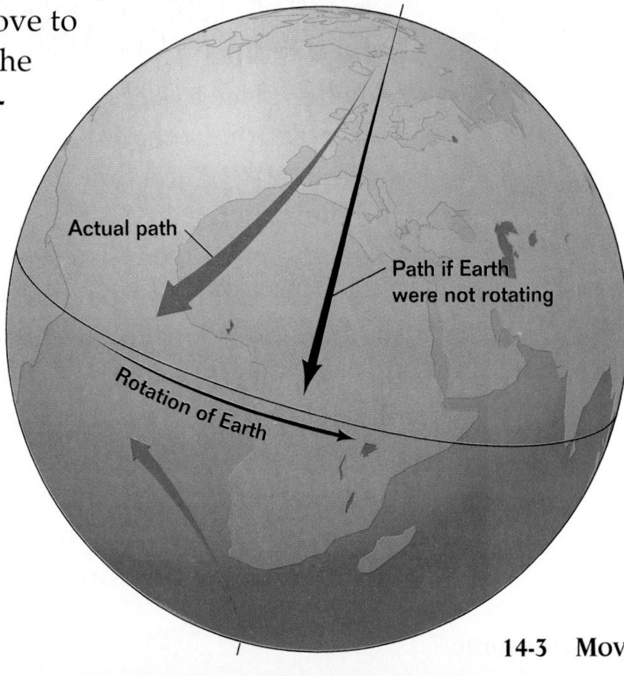

Figure 14-15 The Coriolis effect creates wind patterns across the world.

Figure 14-16 Uneven heating of Earth's surface produces major convection currents, shown by the purple arrows (A). The blue arrows (B) show the world's major wind systems created when the Coriolis effect deflects moving air westward.

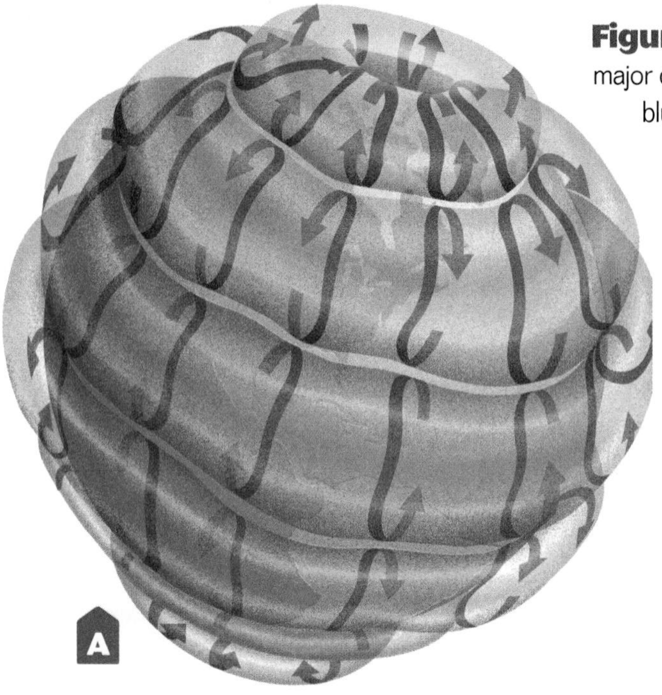

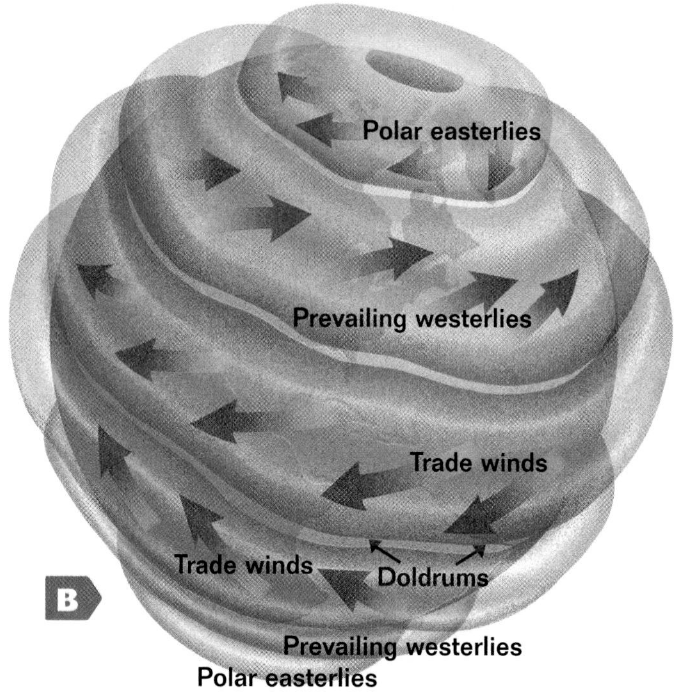

Wind Systems

Let's venture into the past to imagine sailing the oceans during the time of the great sailing ships. No motors propel the ship. You depend entirely on the winds for energy. That means you must avoid getting into the doldrums, which is the windless zone at the equator. In the doldrums, the air seems motionless. Actually, the air is moving almost straight up. Do you remember why this happens? ☑

Reading Check ☑

What are the doldrums?

Surface Winds

A better place to sail is between the equator and 30° latitude north or south. In that area, air descending to Earth's surface creates steady winds that blow to the southwest in the northern hemisphere. In the southern hemisphere, they blow toward the northwest. These are the trade winds. In the days of the great sailing ships, the northern trade winds provided a dependable route for trade. **Figure 14-16** shows the major wind systems on Earth, along with convection currents. Sailing ships like the one in **Figure 14-17** were designed to use such winds.

Between 30° and 60° latitude north and south of the equator, winds blow in the opposite direction from the trade winds. These winds are called the prevailing westerlies.

Sailors use the prevailing westerlies to sail from the Americas to Europe. The prevailing westerlies blow from the southwest to the northeast in the northern hemisphere. They are responsible for much of the movement of weather across the United States and Canada. In the southern hemisphere, the prevailing westerlies blow from the northwest to the southeast.

The last major wind systems at Earth's surface are the polar easterlies. These winds blow from the northeast to the southwest near the north pole and from the southeast to the northwest near the south pole.

interNET CONNECTION

Visit the Glencoe Science Web Site at **www.glencoe.com/sec/science/ca** for more information about global wind systems.

High-Altitude Winds

Winds also occur at higher altitudes. Narrow belts of strong winds, called **jet streams,** blow near the top of the troposphere. Two jet streams in each hemisphere blow from west to east at the northern and southern boundaries of the prevailing westerlies. These streams of air resemble fast-moving, winding rivers. Their speeds average between 97 and 185 km/h. Their positions in latitude and altitude change from day to day and season to season. They have a major effect on our weather.

Just as sailors seek the trade winds, prevailing westerlies, and polar easterlies to help propel their ships, jet pilots take advantage of jet streams. When flying eastward, planes save time and fuel. Going west, planes fly at different altitudes to avoid the jet streams.

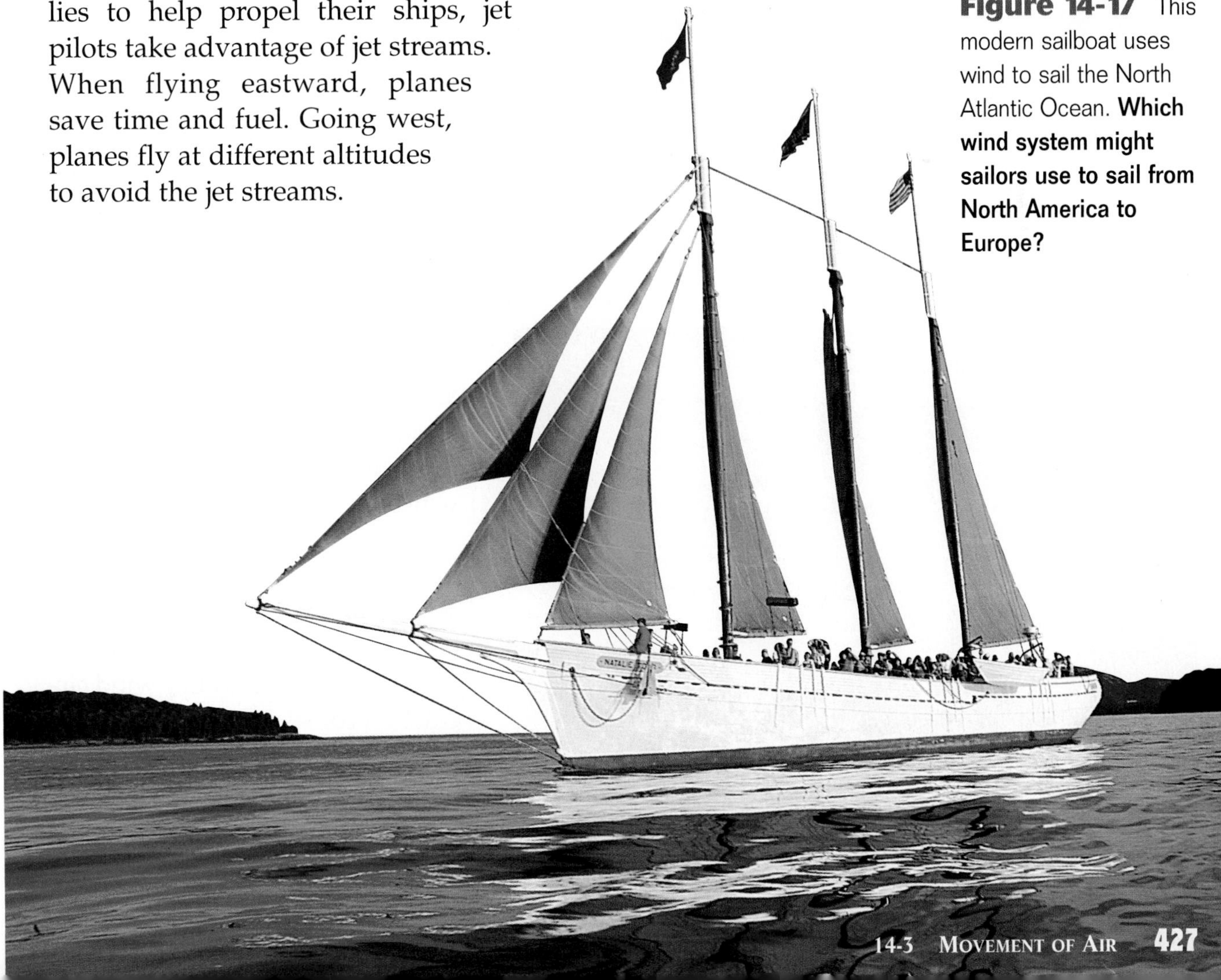

Figure 14-17 This modern sailboat uses wind to sail the North Atlantic Ocean. **Which wind system might sailors use to sail from North America to Europe?**

Daily and Seasonal Winds

The wind systems determine the major weather patterns for the entire globe. Smaller wind systems determine local weather. If you live near a large body of water, you're familiar with two such wind systems—land breezes and sea breezes.

Sea Breezes

Convection currents over areas where the land meets the sea cause sea breezes and land breezes. **Sea breezes** are created during the day because solar radiation warms the land more than the water. Air over the land is heated by conduction. This heated air becomes less dense and is forced upward by cooler, denser air moving inland from the ocean. A convection current results.

Figure 14-18 These daily winds occur because a convection current changes its direction.

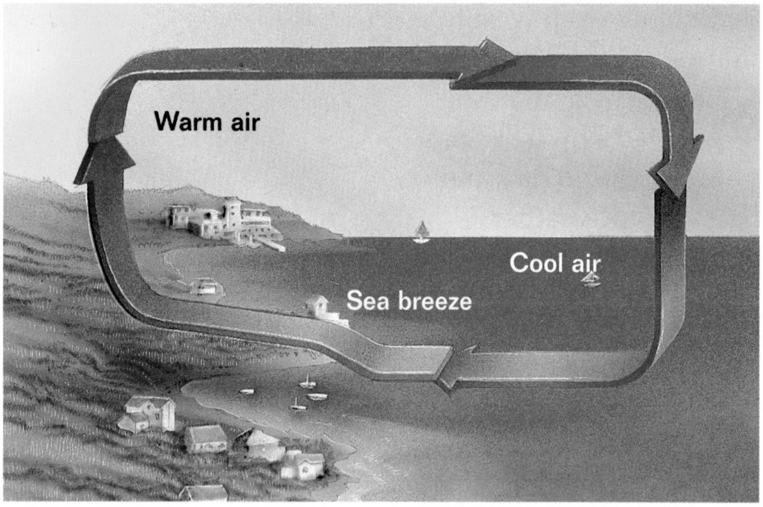

A During the day, cool air forces warm air over the land to rise, creating a sea breeze.

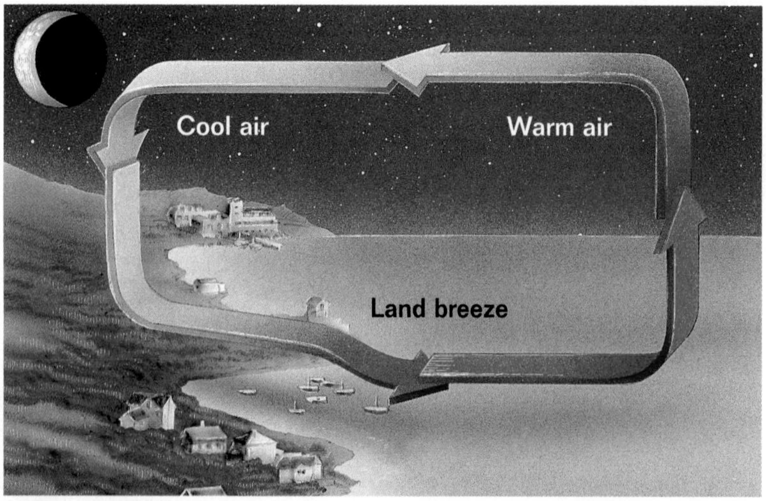

B At night, cold air over the land forces up the warmer air above the sea, creating a land breeze.

Land Breezes

At night, the land cools much more rapidly than the ocean water. Air over the land becomes cooler than the air over the ocean. The cool, dense air from the land moves out over the water, pushing the warm air over the water upward. Movements of air toward the water are called **land breezes. Figure 14-18** can help you understand how sea breezes and land breezes occur.

Mountain-valley wind is another wind that has a daily cycle. In the mountains, about three hours after sunrise, a valley wind starts flowing from the valley upward along the slope of the mountain. A few hours after sunset, a mountain wind begins to blow down the slope into the valley. This mountain-valley wind circulation comes from heating of the mountainsides during the day. At night, the mountain slopes cool quickly and the cooler, denser air drains into the valley.

Figure 14-19

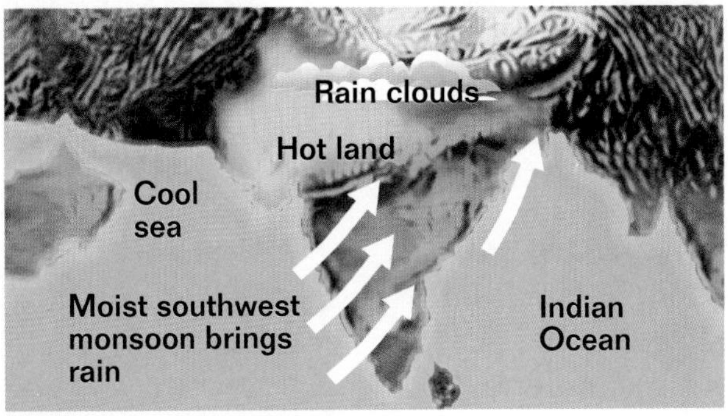

A When the land is intensely hot, the wet monsoon winds blow from the ocean onto the land, bringing rain.

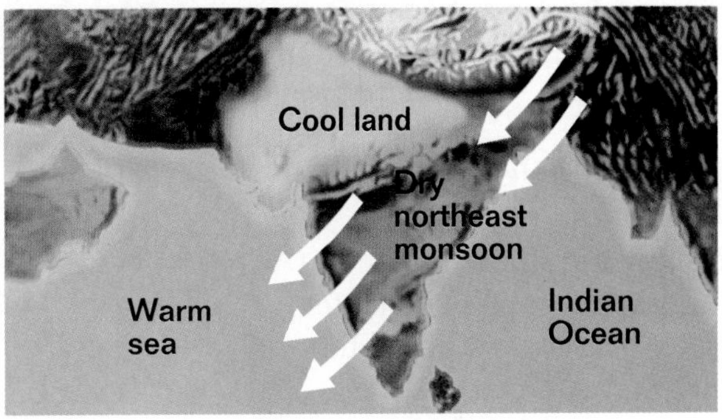

B When the sun is not shining directly over the land, the air above the ocean has a lower pressure. Dry winds flow from the land out over the ocean, bringing the dry season.

Monsoons

Other winds change with the seasons. **Figure 14-19** shows monsoon winds that occur in tropical areas. During the winter, when land is cooler than the ocean, air flows away from the land. During the summer, when land is warmer, the air blows inland. Where the monsoon winds are strong, the summer monsoon blows moist, ocean air over the land and brings extremely heavy rain. The wind during the winter brings dry weather.

Section Assessment

1. Why do latitudes differ in the amount of solar energy they receive?
2. How does the Coriolis effect influence the general wind circulation of Earth?
3. **Think Critically:** Explain why a jet that flies from North Carolina to California uses more fuel and takes longer to complete its journey than a similar jet that flies from California to North Carolina.
4. **Skill Builder**
   Comparing and Contrasting
   Compare and contrast land and sea breezes and seasonal winds versus daily winds. If you need help, refer to Comparing and Contrasting in the **Skill Handbook** on page 672.

Using Computers

Graphics Use a computer graphics package and **Figure 14-16** to draw the wind systems on Earth. Make separate graphics of major wind circulation cells shown by purple arrows. On another graphic, show major surface winds. On another, draw the jet streams. Print your graphics and share them with your class. If you need help, refer to page 686.

Chapter 14 Reviewing Main Ideas

For a **preview** of this chapter, study this Reviewing Main Ideas before you read the chapter. After you have studied this chapter, you can use the Reviewing Main Ideas to **review** the chapter.

The Glencoe MindJogger, Audiocassettes, and CD-ROM provide additional opportunities for review.

Section

14-1 EARTH'S ATMOSPHERE

The atmosphere is a thin blanket of air molecules that surrounds Earth. Its structure and composition are unique to our planet. Earth gets its thermal energy from the sun, but it's the atmosphere that transfers heat to all parts of the planet. Nitrogen and oxygen are the two most common gases in Earth's atmosphere. All gases in the atmosphere have mass, and thus, they push against one another, creating air pressure. Earth's atmosphere is classified into layers based on temperature differences. ***Why do different layers of the atmosphere have different temperatures?***

THE OZONE LAYER

The **ozone layer** protects Earth from too much **ultraviolet radiation.** When exposed to excessive amounts of ultraviolet radiation, humans can develop cancers and other health problems. ***How does a molecule of chloro fluorocarbon destroy a molecule of ozone?***

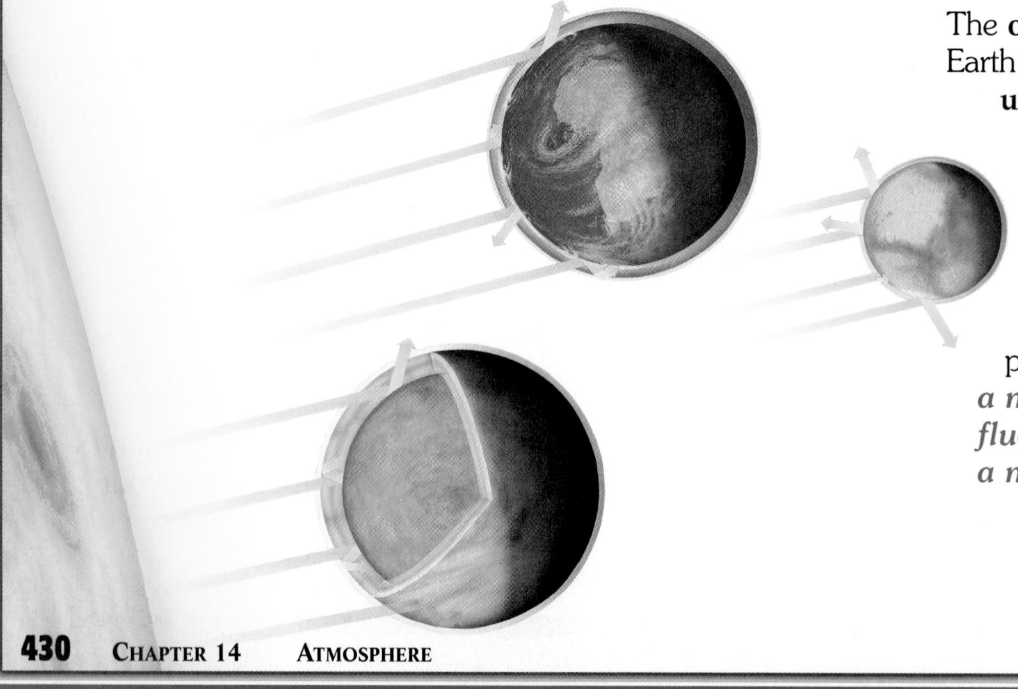

Reading Check

Choose a major illustration from this chapter, such as **Figure 14-3.** List things you learned from this illustration.

Section 14-2 ENERGY FROM THE SUN

Some of the sun's energy that reaches Earth escapes back into space. Other energy is absorbed by Earth's air, land, and water. Solar energy fuels the water cycle between the atmosphere and Earth's surface. ***How are the transfer of energy by convection and the water cycle similar?***

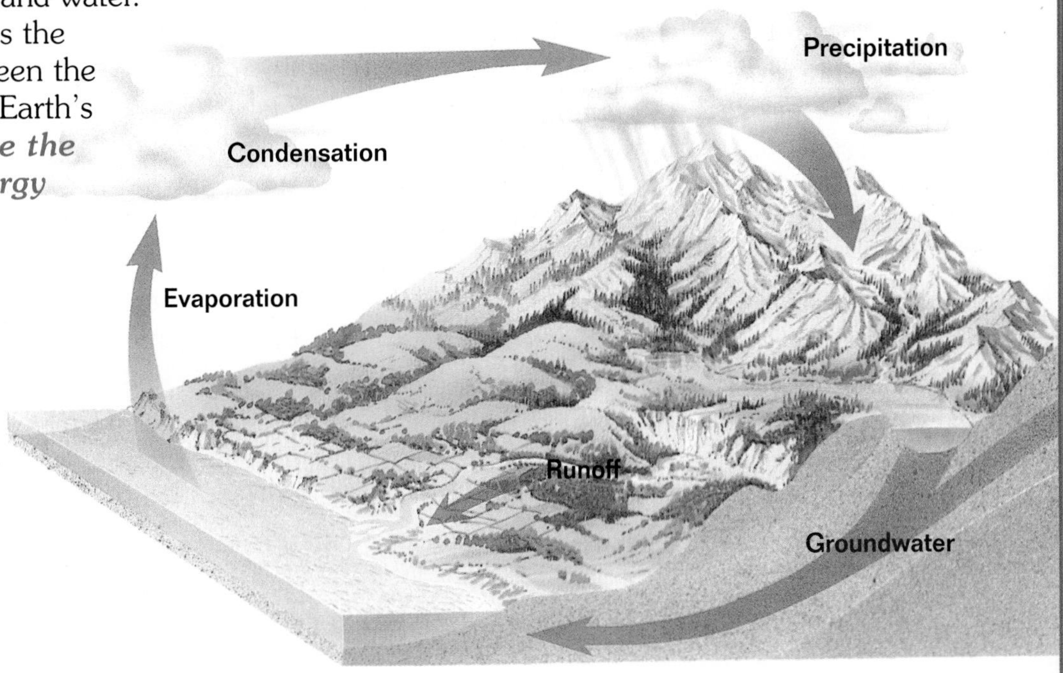

Section 14-3 MOVEMENT OF AIR

Because Earth's surface is curved, not all areas receive the same amount of solar radiation. This uneven heating causes temperature differences at Earth's surface, which, in turn, creates pressure differences. Pressure pushes air, creating winds. ***How do the doldrums and the trade winds differ?***

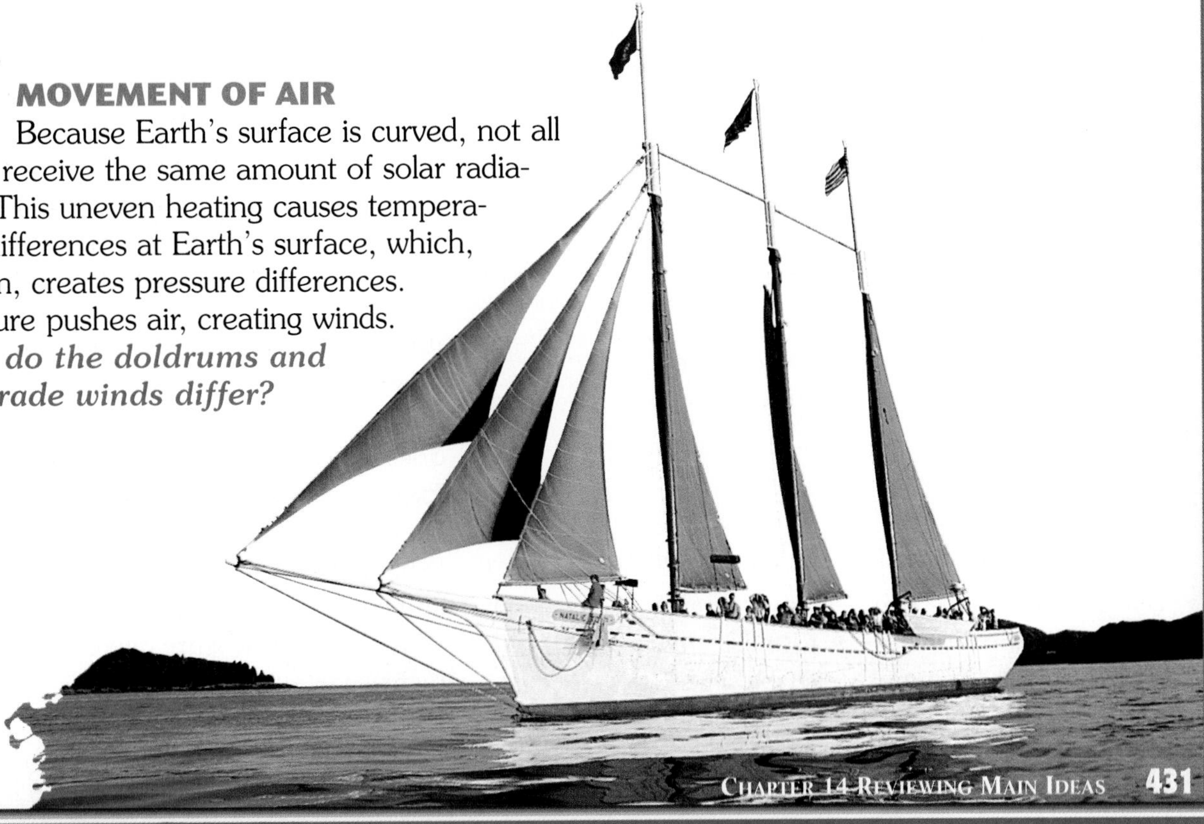

Chapter 14 Assessment

Using Vocabulary

a. chlorofluorocarbon
b. conduction
c. convection
d. Coriolis effect
e. hydrosphere
f. ionosphere
g. jet stream
h. land breeze
i. ozone layer
j. radiation
k. sea breeze
l. troposphere
m. ultraviolet radiation
n. water cycle

Use what you know about the above terms to answer the following questions.

1. How does a land breeze differ from a sea breeze?
2. What is the Coriolis effect?
3. Compare and contrast conduction and convection.
4. What are the layers of Earth's atmosphere?
5. Describe the water cycle.

Checking Concepts

Choose the word or phrase that best answers the question.

6. What is the most abundant gas in the air?
   A) oxygen C) argon
   B) water vapor D) nitrogen
7. What is smog?
   A) conduction C) pollution
   B) mud D) wind
8. What is the uppermost layer of the atmosphere?
   A) troposphere C) exosphere
   B) stratosphere D) thermosphere
9. What is the warmest layer of air?
   A) troposphere C) mesosphere
   B) stratosphere D) exosphere
10. What protects living things from too much ultraviolet radiation?
    A) the ozone layer
    B) oxygen
    C) nitrogen
    D) argon
11. Where is air pressure greatest?
    A) troposphere
    B) stratosphere
    C) exosphere
    D) thermosphere
12. When objects are in contact, how is energy transferred?
    A) trade winds
    B) convection
    C) radiation
    D) conduction
13. What does a barometer measure?
    A) temperature C) humidity
    B) air pressure D) wind speed
14. What type of wind is created by the movement of air toward water?
    A) sea breeze C) land breeze
    B) doldrum D) barometer
15. What are narrow belts of strong winds near the top of the troposphere called?
    A) doldrums C) polar easterlies
    B) jet streams D) trade winds

Thinking Critically

16. Why are there few or no clouds in the stratosphere?
17. It is thought that life could not have existed on land until the ozone layer formed about 2 billion years ago. Why does life on land require an ozone layer?
18. Explain how soup in a pan on a stove is heated by conduction and convection.
19. What happens when water vapor rises and cools?
20. Why does air pressure decrease with an increase in altitude?

Developing Skills

If you need help, refer to the Skill Handbook.

21. Concept Mapping: Complete the cycle concept map below using the following phrases to explain how air moves to form a convection current: *cool air pushes up warm air, cool air is warmed by conduction,* and *cool air sinks.*

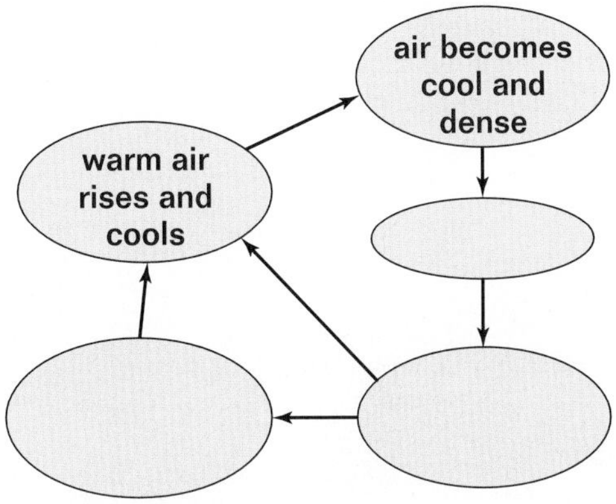

22. Observing and Inferring: In an experiment, a student measured the air temperature 1 m above the ground on a sunny afternoon and again one hour after sunset. The second reading was lower than the first. What can you infer from this?

23. Hypothesizing: Trees use carbon dioxide to photosynthesize. Carbon dioxide in the atmosphere prevents radiation from Earth's surface from escaping to space. Hypothesize how the temperature on Earth would change if many trees were cut down.

24. Using Variables, Constants, and Controls: Design an experiment to find out how plants are affected by differing amounts of ultraviolet radiation. In the design, use filtering film made for car windows. What is the variable you are testing? What are your constants? Your controls?

THE PRINCETON REVIEW

Test-Taking Tip

Cross It Out List the answer choice letters on scratch paper and cross out choices you've eliminated. You'll stop yourself from choosing an answer you've mentally eliminated.

Test Practice

Use these questions to test your Science Proficiency.

1. Early sailors avoided sailing into the doldrums. Why?

A) Doldrums only blew from east to west.

B) Doldrums only blew from west to east.

C) Doldrums kept changing wind direction.

D) Doldrums are a windless zone.

2. The upper part of the stratosphere is warmer than the upper part of the mesosphere. Which of the following **BEST** explains why?

A) The stratosphere is closer to the sun than the mesosphere.

B) The stratosphere is closer to Earth's surface than the mesosphere.

C) The stratosphere has greater air pressure than the mesosphere.

D) The stratosphere has gases that more easily absorb solar energy than the gases in the mesosphere.

CHAPTER

15 Weather

Chapter Preview

Skills Preview

Skill Builders
- Recognize Cause and Effect
- Compare and Contrast

Activities
- Predict
- Use Numbers

MiniLabs
- Infer
- Make a Model

Reading Check

Before beginning this chapter, read the What You'll Learn feature at the beginning of each section. Explain why each section could include this feature.

Explore Activity

Dark clouds, thunder, lightning, heavy rain—when you see any of these, take cover soon. You're about to experience some severe weather. Tornadoes are a type of severe weather event that comes with little or no warning. A tornado can roar through farms and cities, smashing everything in its path, leaving a trail of destruction. Winds in a tornado sometimes reach 500 km/hour—strong enough to flatten buildings and uproot trees. Updrafts in the center can act like a giant vacuum cleaner, sucking homes, cars, and even animals high into the air.

Model a Tornado

1. Obtain two 2-L plastic bottles.
2. Fill one about three-quarters full of water and add one drop of dish-washing soap to the water.
3. Put the empty bottle on top and tape the bottles securely, opening to opening.
4. Flip the bottles to put the one with water in it on top. Move the top bottle in a circular motion.

Science Journal

Describe what happens in the bottles. Use this description to compare this model of a tornado with a real tornado as you learn about the features of this weather phenomenon.

15•1 What is weather?

What You'll Learn

- The role of water vapor in the atmosphere and how it affects weather
- How clouds form and how they are classified
- How rain, hail, sleet, and snow develop

Vocabulary
weather
humidity
relative humidity
dew point
fog
precipitation

Why It's Important

- Your daily activities are affected by weather changes.

Factors of Weather

"What's the weather going to be today?" That's probably one of the first things you ask when you get up each day. Weather information can affect what you wear to school, how you get to and from school, and what you do after school.

Everyone discusses the weather. Can you explain what it is? **Weather** refers to the present state of the atmosphere. Weather describes current conditions such as air pressure, wind, temperature, and the amount of moisture in the air. One kind of weather is seen in **Figure 15-1.**

In the water cycle, the sun provides the energy to evaporate water into the atmosphere, where it forms clouds and eventually falls back to Earth.

The water cycle forms the basis of our weather. But, the sun does more than just evaporate water. It also heats air, causing the formation of the global winds. The interaction of air, water, and the sun causes weather.

Figure 15-1 The weather influences what you can do, especially outdoor activities such as a trip to the playground.

Humidity

The sun evaporates water into the atmosphere. How does this happen? How can the atmosphere hold water? The air of the atmosphere is somewhat like a sponge. The holes in a sponge enable it to hold water. The atmosphere holds water in a similar way. Water vapor molecules fit into spaces between the molecules that make up air. The amount of water vapor held in air is called **humidity.**

Humidity varies from day to day because the temperature of the air changes. The amount of water vapor that air can hold depends on the temperature. At cooler temperatures, molecules in air move more slowly. This slow movement in cool air allows water vapor molecules to join together (condense). At warmer temperatures, air and water vapor molecules move too quickly to join together.

If you look at **Figure 15-2,** you'll see that at 25°C, a cubic meter of air can hold a maximum of 22 g of water vapor. The same air cooled to 15°C can hold only about 13 g of water vapor. ☑

Try at Home MiniLab

Making Rain

Procedure

1. Pour a few centimeters of hot water into a tall, clear, widemouthed jar.
2. Put ice cubes in a small plastic bag. Suspend the bag from the top of the jar and let it hang down inside *above* the water level.

Analysis

1. In your Science Journal, describe what you see.
2. Describe what is happening to the water vapor in the jar.

Reading Check ☑

How does temperature affect humidity?

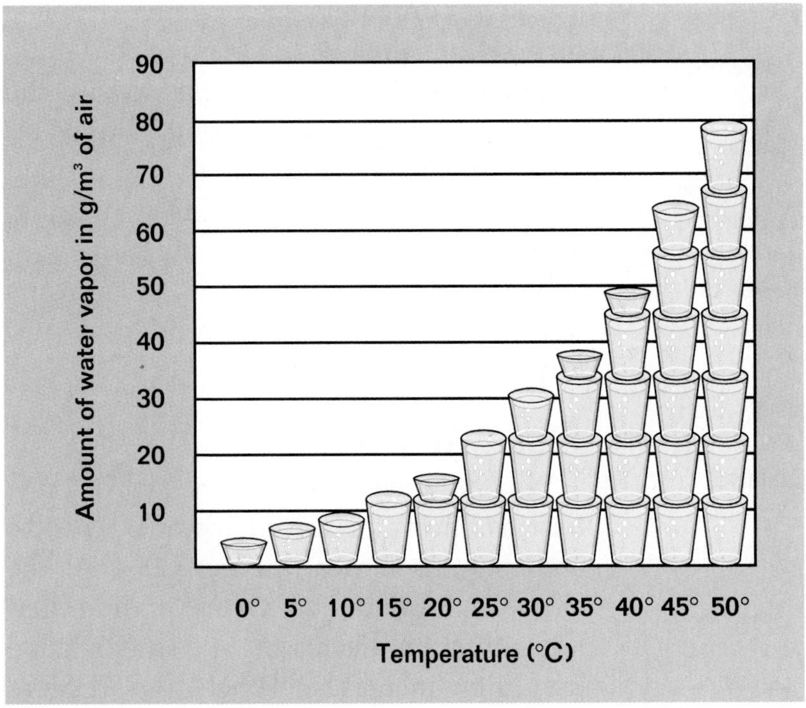

Figure 15-2 This graph shows the maximum amount of water vapor in air at various temperatures. **What happens to the amount of water vapor as the temperature decreases?**

Figure 15-3 When the air next to the glass cools to its dew point, condensation forms on the glass.

On hot summer days when the air seems damp and sticky, people often comment on the high humidity. When they mention humidity, they are actually talking about the relative humidity.

Relative Humidity

Have you ever heard a weather forecaster speak of relative humidity? **Relative humidity** is a measure of the amount of water vapor that air is holding compared to the amount it can hold at a specific temperature. When air contains as much moisture as possible at a specific temperature, it is saturated. If you hear a weather forecaster say the relative humidity is 50 percent, that means the air on that day contains 50 percent of the water needed for the air to be saturated.

As shown in **Figure 15-2,** air at 40°C is saturated when it contains about 50 g of water vapor per cubic meter of air. Air at 25°C is saturated when it contains 22 g of water vapor per cubic meter of air. If air at 25°C contains only 11 g of water vapor in each cubic meter of air, the relative humidity is 50 percent. Saturated air has a relative humidity of 100 percent.

When there is more water vapor than the air can hold, it will condense back to a liquid or freeze, depending on the temperature. The temperature at which air is saturated and condensation forms is the **dew point.** The dew point changes with the amount of moisture in the air.

You've probably seen water droplets form on the outside of a glass of cold milk, as in **Figure 15-3.** The cold glass cooled the air next to it to its dew point. The water vapor in the air condensed and formed water droplets on the glass. Dew on grass in the early morning forms the same way. When air near the ground is cooled to its dew point, water vapor condenses and forms droplets on the grass.

Cloud Formation

Why are there clouds in the sky? Clouds form as warm air is forced upward, expands, and cools, as shown in **Figure 15-4.** As the air cools, the amount of water vapor needed for saturation decreases and the relative humidity increases. When the relative

MiniLab

Determining Dew Point

Procedure

1. Partially fill a metal can with room-temperature water. Dry the outer surface of the can.
2. Slowly stir the water and add small amounts of ice.
3. In a data table in your Science Journal, note the exact water temperature at which a thin film of moisture first begins to form on the outside of the metal can.
4. Repeat steps 1–3 two more times.
5. The average of the three temperatures at which the moisture begins to appear is the dew point temperature of the air around the container.

Analysis

1. What factors determine the dew point?
2. Why does change in air temperature cause the dew point to change?

humidity reaches 100 percent, the air is saturated. Water vapor begins to condense in tiny drops around small particles such as dust, salt, and smoke in the atmosphere. These drops of water are so small they become suspended in the air. When millions of these drops collect, a cloud forms.

Cloud Classification

As you will see in the **Field Guide to Clouds** at the end of this chapter, many different types of clouds can be seen in the sky. Clouds are classified mainly by shape and by height. Some clouds stack up, reaching high into the sky, while others are low and flat. Some dense clouds bring rain or snow, while thin clouds appear on mostly sunny days. Refer to the Field Guide for more details.

Shape

The three main cloud types are stratus, cumulus, and cirrus. Cumulus clouds are masses of puffy, white clouds, often with flat bases. Some people refer to them as cauliflower clouds. They form when air currents rise. They may rise to great heights and can be associated with both fair weather and thunderstorms.

Stratus clouds form layers or smooth, even sheets in the sky. When layers of air cool below their dew point temperatures, stratus clouds appear. Stratus clouds usually form at low altitudes. Stratus clouds are associated with fair weather and precipitation. Sometimes, they form a dull, gray blanket that hangs low in the sky and brings drizzle.

Figure 15-4 Clouds form when moist air is pushed high enough to reach its dew point. The water vapor condenses, forming water droplets that group together.

A Clouds form when warm air is forced up in a convection current caused by solar radiation heating Earth's surface.

C Clouds form when two air masses meet. Warmer air is forced up over the cold air. As the warm air cools, the water vapor in it condenses. **Is the warm air on the left or the right?**

B Clouds form when warm, moist air is forced to rise over a mountain. The air cools and the water vapor condenses.

Figure 15-5 When water vapor in air collects on particles to form water droplets, the type of precipitation that is received on the ground depends on the temperature of the air.

A When the air near the ground is warm, water vapor forms raindrops that fall as rain.

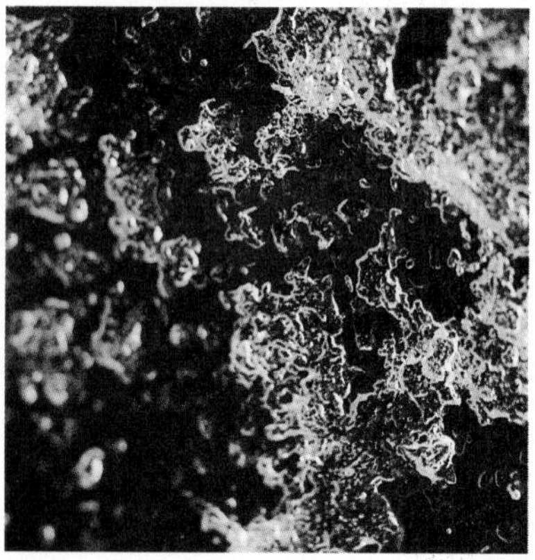

B When the air near the ground is cold, sleet, made up of many small ice pellets, falls.

C When the air is very cold, water vapor forms snowflakes.

D Hailstones are pellets of ice that form as the ice nuclei go up and down in the cloud.

When air is cooled to its dew point and condenses near the ground, it forms a stratus cloud called **fog. Figure 15-6** shows a stratus cloud fog in San Francisco.

Cirrus clouds appear fibrous or curly. They are high, thin, white, feathery clouds containing ice crystals. Cirrus clouds are associated with fair weather, but they may indicate approaching storms.

Height

Some prefixes of cloud names describe the height of the cloud base. The prefix *cirro-* describes high clouds, *alto-* describes middle-elevation clouds, and *strato-* refers to clouds at low elevations. Some clouds' names combine the altitude prefix with the term *stratus* or *cumulus*.

Cirrostratus clouds are high clouds that look like fine veils. They are made of ice crystals that appear to form halos around the moon or sun.

Altostratus clouds form at middle levels. They look like thick veils or sheets of gray or blue. If the clouds are not too thick, sunlight can filter through them. They produce light, continuous precipitation.

Rain Capacity

Nimbus clouds are dark clouds associated with precipitation. They are so full of water that no sunlight penetrates them. When a nimbus cloud is also a towering cumulus cloud, it is called a cumulonimbus cloud. Some cumulonimbus clouds grow huge, starting near Earth's surface and towering to nearly 18 000 m. Sudden, gigantic thunderstorms can be unleashed from them. Nimbostratus clouds are low, dark gray clouds that bring long, steady rain. They often have streaks that extend to the ground.

As long as the water drops in a cloud remain small, they stay suspended in the air. But when the water droplets combine and reach the size of 0.2 mm, they become too heavy and fall out of suspension in the form of precipitation.

Precipitation

Water falling from clouds is called **precipitation.** Air temperature determines whether the water droplets form rain, snow, sleet, or hail—the four main types of precipitation. **Figure 15-5** shows how the four types of precipitation form. Drops of water falling in temperatures above freezing come down as rain. Snow forms when the air temperature is below freezing and water vapor changes directly to a solid. Sleet forms when snow passes through a layer of warm air, melts, and then refreezes near the ground.

Figure 15-6 Fog surrounds the Golden Gate Bridge, San Francisco. Fog is a stratus cloud near the ground.

Problem Solving

Interpret When Dew Will Form

Sometimes in the early morning, you have probably noticed that some outdoor surfaces are wet and glisten in the sunlight. You are observing droplets of dew. In order for dew to form, the temperature must drop low enough to cause condensation in the air immediately above the ground. Dew will form on any solid surface such as grass, cobwebs, and even insect wings. Use **Figure 15-2** and the graph to the right to answer the following questions.

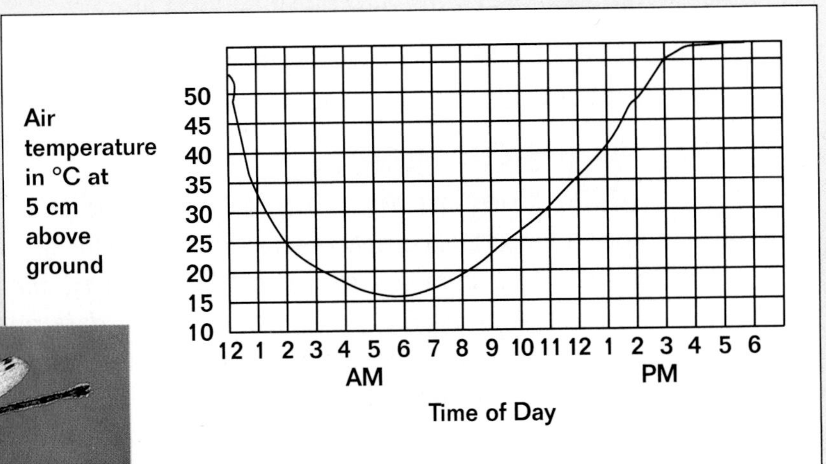

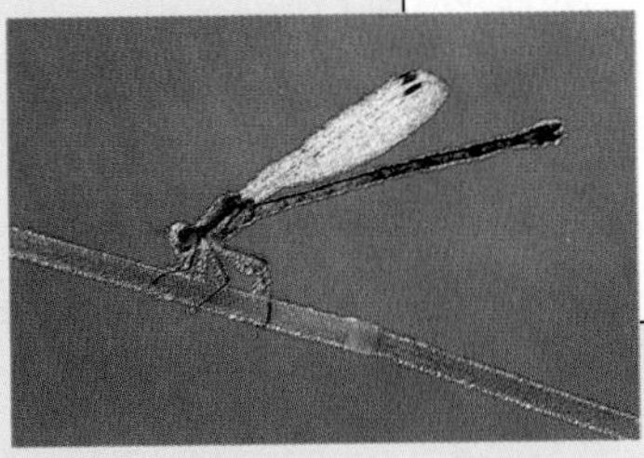

Think Critically: If the humidity on the day shown in the graph is 50 g of water vapor per cubic meter of air, at what time would you expect dew to form? At what hour will it disappear?

Figure 15-7 A large hailstone appears to have a layered structure much like an onion.

Hail

Hail is precipitation in the form of lumps of ice as shown in **Figure 15-7.** Hail forms in cumulonimbus clouds of a thunderstorm when drops of water freeze in layers around a small nucleus of ice. Hailstones grow larger as they're tossed up and down by rising and falling convection currents. Most hailstones are smaller than 2.5 cm but can grow much larger. Hail can be the most damaging form of precipitation, especially if winds blow during a hailstorm. Falling hailstones can break windows and destroy crops.

PHYSICS INTEGRATION

By understanding the role of water vapor in the atmosphere, you can begin to understand weather. The relative humidity helps determine whether a location will have a dry day or some form of precipitation. The temperature of the atmosphere determines the form of precipitation. Studying clouds can add to your ability to forecast weather.

Section Assessment

1. When does water vapor in air condense?
2. How do clouds form?
3. What is the relationship between air temperature and the amount of water vapor that can be in the air?
4. **Think Critically:** How can the same cumulonimbus cloud produce both rain and hail?
5. **Skill Builder**
   Concept Mapping Make a network tree concept map that compares four clouds. Use these terms: *cirrus, cumulus, stratus, nimbus, feathery, fair weather, puffy, layered, precipitation, clouds, dark,* and *steady precipitation.* If you need help, refer to Concept Mapping in the **Skill Handbook** on page 666.

Using Math

Use the graph in **Figure 15-2** to determine the amount of water vapor air can hold when its temperature is 50°C.

The Heat Index

"It's not the heat, it's the humidity," people say, and they're right. High humidity affects your body's ability to cool itself, so you feel hotter. The "heat index" describes how your body feels at different levels of temperature and humidity. You can figure out the heat index using the chart below. For example, locate the air temperature of 90°F at the top of the chart. Then, locate the humidity of 70 percent. At this temperature and humidity, the heat index is 106°F.

Problem

What is the relationship between air temperature and relative humidity?

Heat Index Table

Relative Humidity	Air Temperature (Degrees Fahrenheit) 70°	75°	80°	85°	90°	95°	100°	105°	110°	115°	120°
	Apparent Temperature (Heat Index)										
0%	64	69	73	78	83	87	91	95	99	103	107
10%	65	70	75	80	85	90	95	100	105	111	116
20%	66	72	77	82	87	93	99	105	112	120	130
30%	67	73	78	84	90	96	104	113	123	135	148
40%	68	74	79	86	93	101	110	123	137	151	
50%	69	75	81	88	96	107	120	135	150		
60%	70	76	82	90	100	114	132	149			
70%	70	77	85	93	106	124	144				
80%	71	78	86	97	113	136					
90%	71	79	88	102	122						
100%	72	80	91	108							

Practice PROBLEMS

1. Make graphs by plotting actual air temperature versus apparent temperature (heat index) at 50 percent humidity and at 70 percent humidity.
2. Write a paragraph describing what happens to the heat index as the humidity rises. Give some specific examples to justify your ideas. You may want to make a new graph showing 20 percent, 50 percent, 70 percent, and 100 percent humidity all on the same graph. This will help you see any patterns.

Solution

1. Make a graph comparing the air temperature and the apparent temperature, or heat index, at a 20 percent humidity level.
2. On graph paper, draw a horizontal axis labeled "Actual Air Temperature" and a vertical axis labeled "Apparent Temperature (Heat Index)." Mark off a temperature scale on each axis, starting with 65°F, increasing in increments of five degrees.
3. In the table above, find 20 percent Relative Humidity in the light-blue area and move to the right. On your graph, locate 70° on the horizontal axis and 66° on the vertical axis. Make a dot at the intersection of the two grid lines. Continue to plot the data for the other temperatures in the table at 20 percent humidity.

15•2 Weather Patterns

What You'll Learn

- What weather is associated with fronts and high- and low-pressure areas
- How low-pressure systems form at fronts
- How tornadoes develop from thunderstorms

Vocabulary

air mass
front
tornado
Doppler radar
hurricane

Why It's Important

- Air masses, pressure systems, and fronts cause weather to change constantly.

Changes in Weather

Why do you ask about the weather in the morning when you get up? Isn't it safe to think that the weather is the same as it was the day before? Of course not! Weather is always changing because of the continuing movement of air and moisture in the atmosphere. These changes are generally related to the development and movement of air masses.

Air Masses

An **air mass** is a large body of air that has the same properties as Earth's surface over which it develops. For example, an air mass that develops over land is dry compared with one that develops over water. Also, an air mass that develops in the tropics is warmer than one that develops at a higher latitude. When you observe a change in the weather from one day to the next, it is due to the movement of air masses. **Figure 15-8** shows air masses that affect the United States.

Pressure Systems

You have heard weather forecasters mention high- and low-pressure systems. What are they? In the atmosphere, great masses of air molecules push down from above, creating atmospheric pressure at Earth's surface. Atmospheric pressure at sea level varies over the surface of Earth. The atmospheric

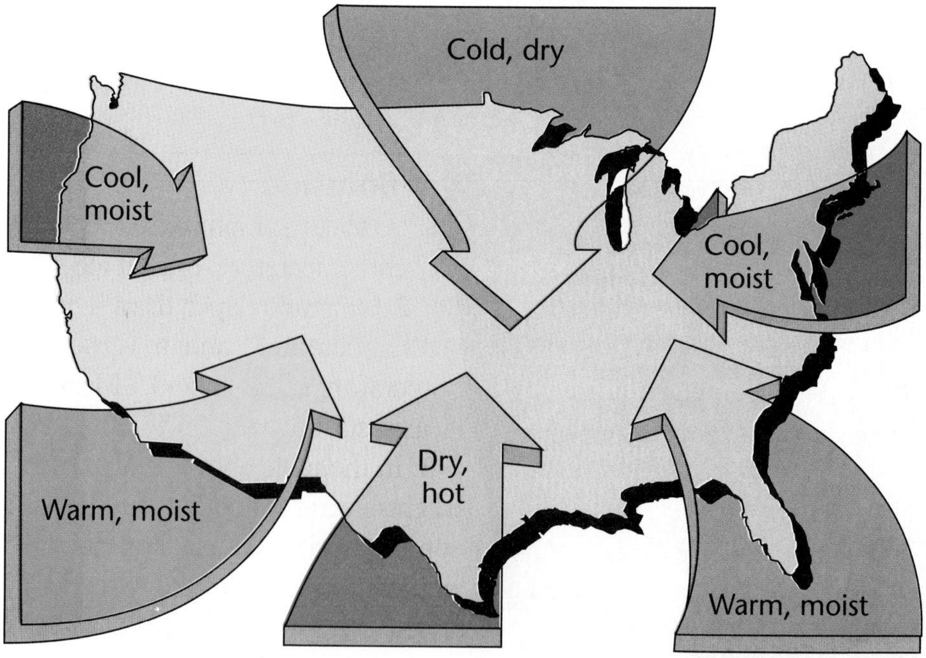

Figure 15-8 Six major air masses affect weather in the United States. Each air mass has the same characteristics of temperature and moisture content as the area over which it forms. **What air masses affect the weather in your region of the country?**

pressure is determined by three things: the temperature and density of the air and the amount of water vapor in the air.

Variation in atmospheric pressure affects the weather. Areas of high pressure at Earth's surface are regions of descending air. Section 15-1 explained that clouds form when air rises and cools. The sinking motion of high-pressure air masses makes it difficult for air to rise and clouds to form. That's why high pressure usually means good weather. Areas of low pressure usually have cloudy weather.

Fronts

Low-pressure systems form along the boundaries of air masses. The boundary between cold and warm air masses is called a **front.** All fronts involve both a warm and a cold air mass. Storms and precipitation occur at these fronts.

At a front, air at the surface moves from the high-pressure systems into the low-pressure systems. As the air flows into the low-pressure area, it flows under the less dense, warm air, forcing it upward. As the air in a low-pressure system rises, it cools. At a certain elevation, the air reaches its dew point and the water vapor in it condenses, forming clouds. **Figure 15-9** shows how a low-pressure system can develop at the boundary between cold and warm air.

At fronts where two different air masses meet, the air does not mix. Instead, the cold air mass moves under the warm air. The warm air rises. Winds begin. As surface winds blow from a high-pressure area into a low-pressure area, the Coriolis (kor ee OH lus) effect turns the winds. The Coriolis effect makes them circulate counterclockwise around a low-pressure area in the northern hemisphere and clockwise in the southern hemisphere.

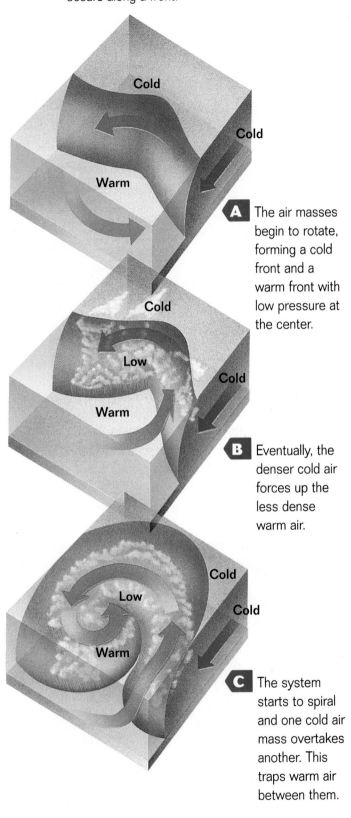

Figure 15-9 These diagrams show how a low-pressure system occurs along a front.

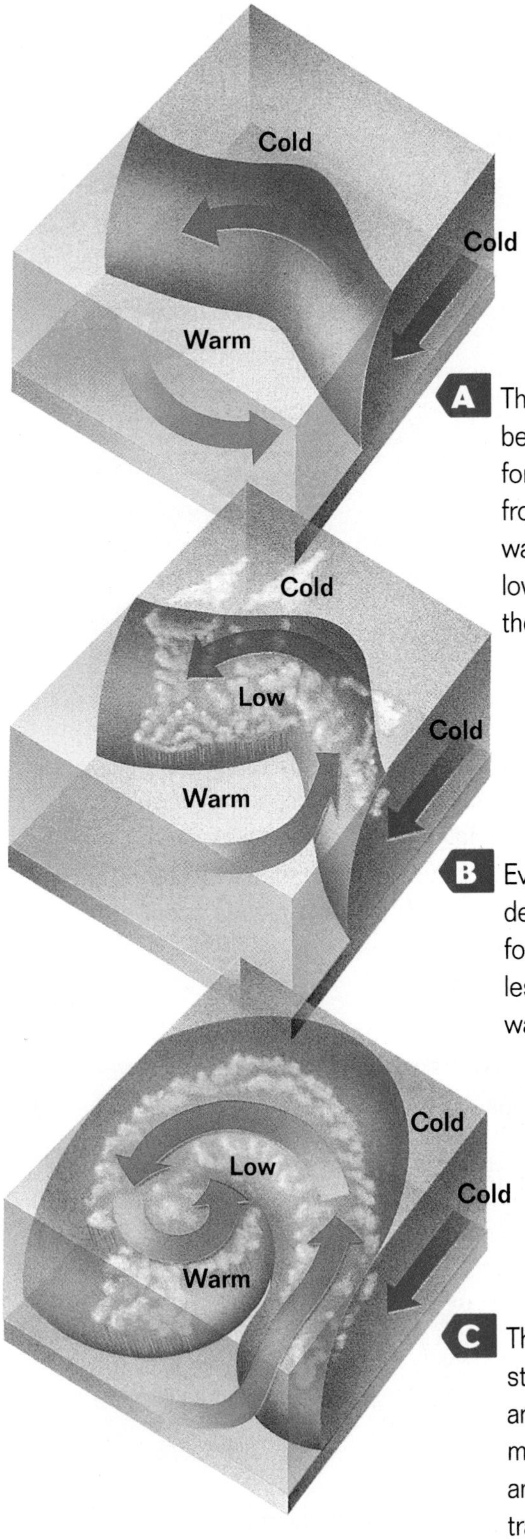

A The air masses begin to rotate, forming a cold front and a warm front with low pressure at the center.

B Eventually, the denser cold air forces up the less dense warm air.

C The system starts to spiral and one cold air mass overtakes another. This traps warm air between them.

Most changes in weather occur at one of four types of fronts—warm, cold, occluded, or stationary, as illustrated in **Figure 15-10.** Fronts usually bring a change in temperature and always bring a change in wind direction.

VISUALIZING Fronts

Figure 15-10 These diagrams show the structure of a warm, a cold, an occluded, and a stationary front.

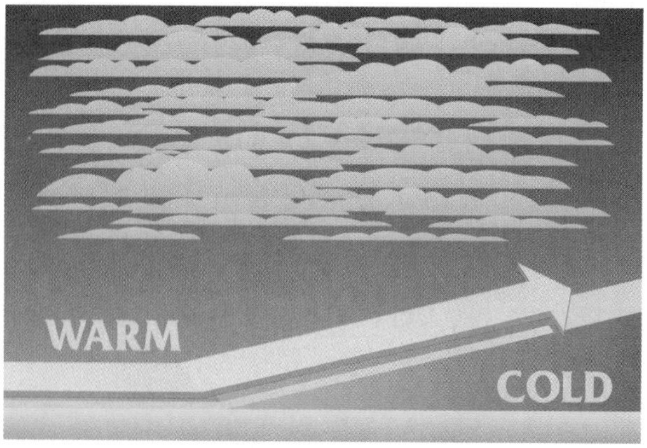

A A warm front develops when a less dense, warm air mass slides over a departing cold air mass. Precipitation occurs over a wide area. Look for high cirrus clouds to form as water vapor condenses. **What other clouds occur at a warm front?**

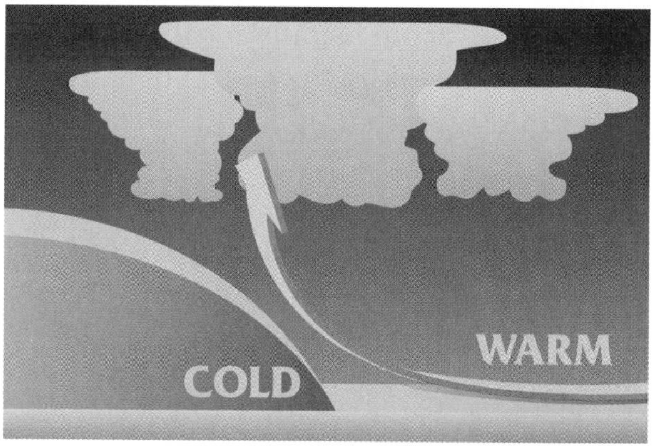

B In a cold front, a cold air mass pushes under a warm air mass and forces the warm air aloft along a steep front. This results in a narrow band of violent storms. Cold fronts often move at twice the speed of warm fronts. Cumulus and cumulonimbus clouds form along the front. **What kinds of weather do these clouds bring?**

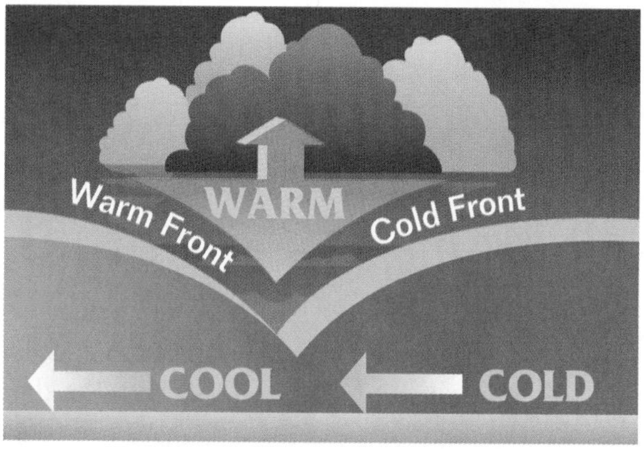

C The faster-moving cold front overtakes the slower-moving warm front and forms an occluded front. The warm air is forced to rise off the ground. Strong winds and heavy precipitation may occur. **Why is the warm air forced up between the cold air masses?**

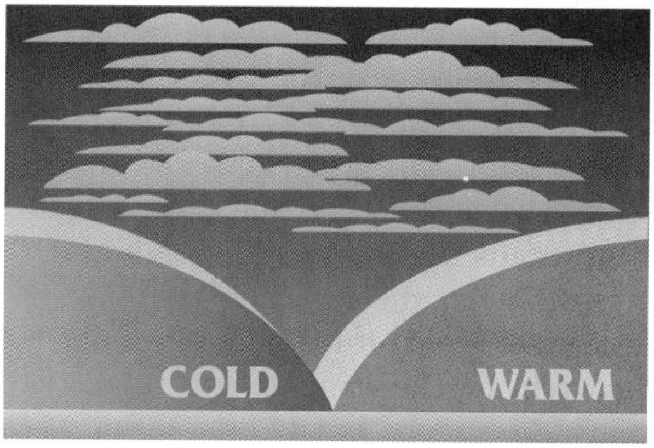

D A stationary front occurs when pressure differences cause a warm front or a cold front to stop moving. A stationary front may remain in the same place for several days. Light wind and precipitation occur across the entire frontal region. **What might happen if a stationary front remains for a long period of time?**

Severe Weather

Weather does affect you every day. Usually, you can still go about your business regardless of the weather. If it's raining, you can still go to school. Even if it snows a little, you can still get there. But, some weather conditions, such as those caused by blizzards, thunderstorms, and tornadoes, prevent you from going about your normal routine. Severe weather poses danger to people and animals.

Figure 15-11 This time-elapsed photo shows a thunderstorm over Arizona.

Thunderstorms

In a thunderstorm, heavy rain falls, lightning flashes, thunder roars, and maybe hail falls. What forces cause such extreme weather conditions? Thunderstorms occur inside warm, moist air masses and at fronts. When the warm, moist air moves upward rapidly, cools, and condenses, it forms cumulonimbus clouds that can reach heights of 18 km. As the rising air reaches its dew point, water droplets and ice form and begin falling the long distance through the clouds toward Earth's surface. The falling droplets collide with other droplets and grow larger. The heavier raindrops fall, dragging down the air with them. This creates downdrafts of air that spread out at Earth's surface. These downdrafts cause the strong winds associated with thunderstorms.

Lightning

Thunderstorms also produce thunder and lightning. Lightning, like that in **Figure 15-11,** occurs when a rapid uplift of air builds up electric charges in the clouds. Some places in the clouds have a positive electrical charge and some have a negative electrical charge. When current flows between regions of opposite electrical charge, lightning flashes. Bolts of lightning can leap from cloud to cloud and from Earth to clouds.

Thunder results from the rapid heating of the air around a bolt of lightning. Lightning can reach temperatures of about 30 000°C, which is more than five times the temperature of the surface of the sun. This extreme heat causes the air around the lightning to expand rapidly. Then, it cools quickly and contracts. The rapid movement of the molecules forms sound waves heard as thunder.

PHYSICS INTEGRATION

Moving Air

The air over a city is usually warmer than the air over rural communities because of the concrete and asphalt in a city. Because of this difference, convection currents develop at the boundaries of cities and rural areas. Make a drawing of a city skyline in your Science Journal. Illustrate the drawing with arrows showing the direction the convection currents move in air.

Thunderstorms can cause a lot of damage. Their heavy rain sometimes causes flooding, and lightning can strike objects and set them on fire. Strong winds generated by thunderstorms also can cause damage. If a thunderstorm has winds traveling faster than 89 km/hour, it is classified as a severe thunderstorm. Hail from a thunderstorm can make dents in cars and the aluminum siding on houses. Although rain from thunderstorms helps crops grow, hail has been known to flatten and destroy a crop in a matter of minutes.

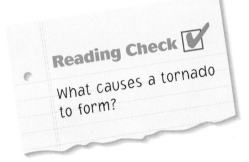

Reading Check ✓

What causes a tornado to form?

Tornadoes

Some of the most severe thunderstorms produce tornadoes. A **tornado** is a violent, whirling wind that moves in a narrow path over land. It usually moves from southwest to northeast. Most tornadoes form along a front. In severe thunderstorms, the wind at different heights blows in different directions and at different speeds. This difference in wind direction and speed is called *wind shear.* A strong updraft will tilt the wind shear and produce rotation inside the thunderstorm. A funnel cloud appears. **Figure 15-12** shows how a tornado funnel forms. Recall the tornado you made in the Explore Activity. ✓

Some tornado funnels do not reach Earth. When funnel clouds touch down, they pick up dirt and debris from the ground. This material gives the funnels their dark gray or black color. Sometimes, tornadoes strike Earth, go back up into the atmosphere, then dip down and strike another area.

When tornadoes touch the ground, their destructive winds rip apart

Figure 15-12 A funnel cloud, such as the one in this farm field (A), is formed by winds (B). The destructive winds of a tornado can reach up to 500 km/hour.

A

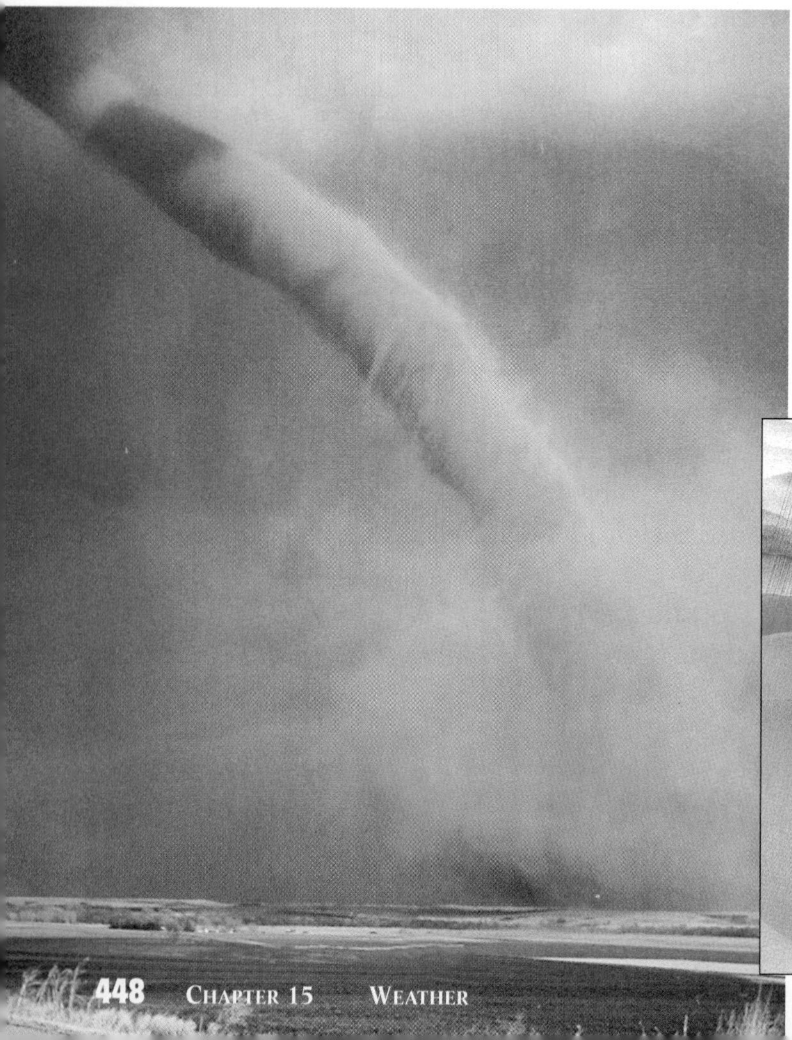

B

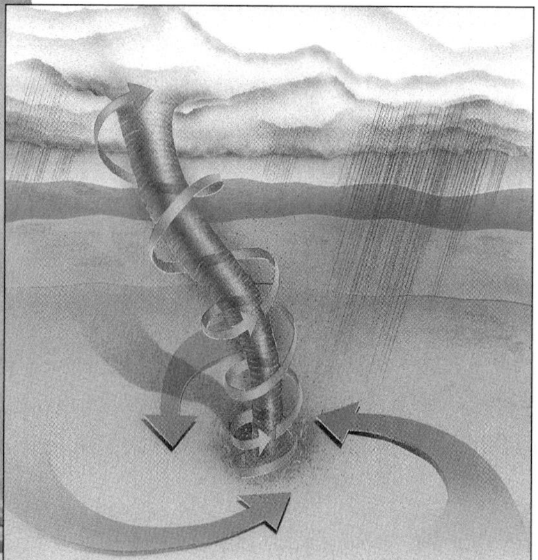

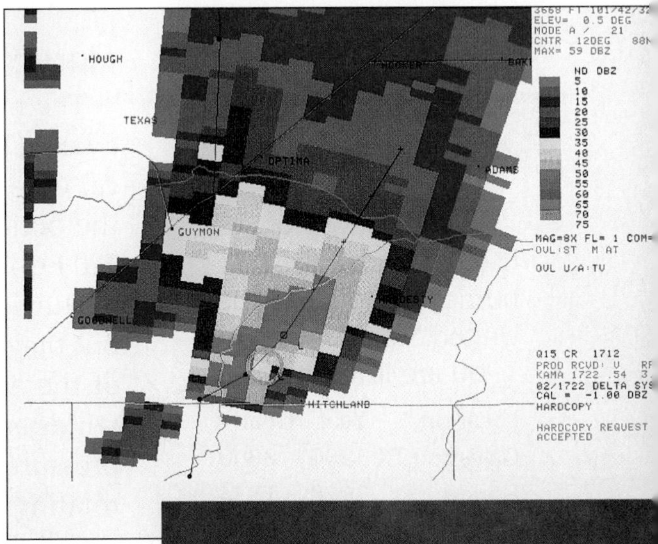

Figure 15-13 The hook-shaped image on the Doppler radar screen indicates a possible tornado in Texas. **Explain how you could determine the direction the storm is moving.**

buildings and trees. High winds can blow through broken windows. When winds blow inside a house, they can lift off the roof and blow out the walls, making it look as though the building exploded. The updraft in the center of a powerful tornado can lift animals, cars, and even houses into the air. Although tornadoes rarely exceed 200 m in diameter and usually last only a few minutes, they are often extremely destructive.

Tornadoes occur worldwide, but most tornadoes touch down in the United States—about 700 per year. Tornadoes most frequently strike the Midwest and South, usually in spring or early summer. Texas, Oklahoma, and Kansas report the most tornadoes.

NEXRAD and Doppler Radar

Tracking a tornado can help prevent loss of life. Thanks to Next Generation Weather Radar, or NEXRAD, severe storms that may evolve into tornadoes can be tracked. NEXRAD is a nationwide system of radar stations that use a specialized radar system called Doppler radar.

Doppler radar sends out repeated radio waves and monitors the reflected waves from distant storms. It can tell the direction a storm is moving.

If a storm is moving toward the radar, the reflected radio waves are squeezed and shift to a higher frequency. If a storm is moving away from the radar, the waves are lengthened and shift to a lower frequency. These frequency differences appear on the Doppler radar screen as different colors, as shown in **Figure 15-13.**

Bright green indicates winds coming toward the radar. Red indicates winds moving away from the radar. Where red and green are close together, rotation is occurring. This indicates a funnel cloud such as the one shown in **Figure 15-14.** If this cloud touches down, it becomes a tornado. Tornado advisories are issued by the National Weather Service. A tornado watch occurs when conditions are right for a tornado to form and a tornado warning is issued if a funnel cloud is observed by tornado spotters or Doppler radar. This usually provides time for people to get to safety.

Figure 15-14 This funnel cloud could become a tornado in a split second.

***inter*NET CONNECTION**

Visit the Glencoe Science Web Site at **www.glencoe.com/sec/science/ca** for more information about weather.

Using Math

The locations of five of the deadliest hurricanes to strike the United States since 1900 are listed below.

Location	Year	Deaths
Galveston, TX	1900	8000
Florida	1928	1836
Southern TX	1919	600
New England	1938	600
Florida Keys	1935	498

Make a bar graph of these data, plotting the hurricane location on the *x*-axis and the number of deaths on the *y*-axis.

Hurricanes

The most powerful storm is the hurricane. A **hurricane** is a large, swirling, low-pressure system that forms over tropical oceans. It is like a machine that turns heat energy from the ocean into wind. A storm must have winds of at least 120 km/hour to be called a hurricane.

Hurricanes are similar to low-pressure systems on land, but they are much stronger. **Figure 15-15** illustrates the parts of the hurricane. In the North Atlantic, the southeast trade winds and the northeast trade winds sometimes meet. A low-pressure area develops in the middle of the swirl and begins rotating counterclockwise in the northern hemisphere. This usually happens between 5° and 20° north latitude, where the water is quite warm. Around the middle of the low-pressure area, warm, moist air is forced upward. As it rises to higher elevations, it cools and moisture condenses.

Figure 15-16 shows a hurricane hitting land. When a hurricane strikes land, the high winds, tornadoes, heavy rains, and high waves of the storm surge cause a lot of damage. Floods from the heavy rains can damage buildings and cover large areas of wildlife habitat. The weather of the hurricane can destroy crops, demolish buildings, and kill people and

Figure 15-15

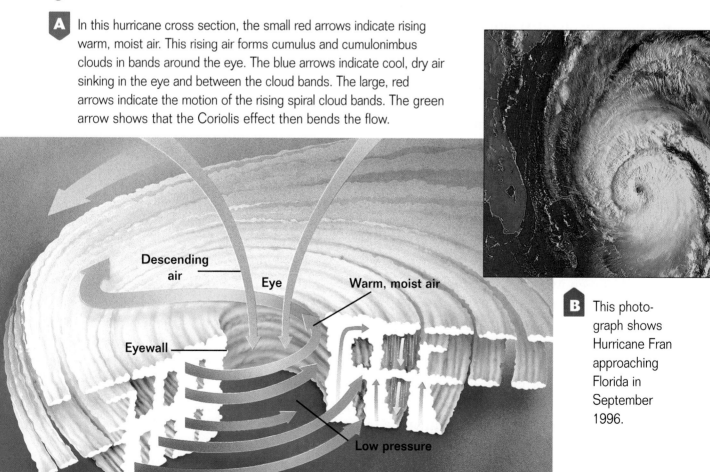

A In this hurricane cross section, the small red arrows indicate rising warm, moist air. This rising air forms cumulus and cumulonimbus clouds in bands around the eye. The blue arrows indicate cool, dry air sinking in the eye and between the cloud bands. The large, red arrows indicate the motion of the rising spiral cloud bands. The green arrow shows that the Coriolis effect then bends the flow.

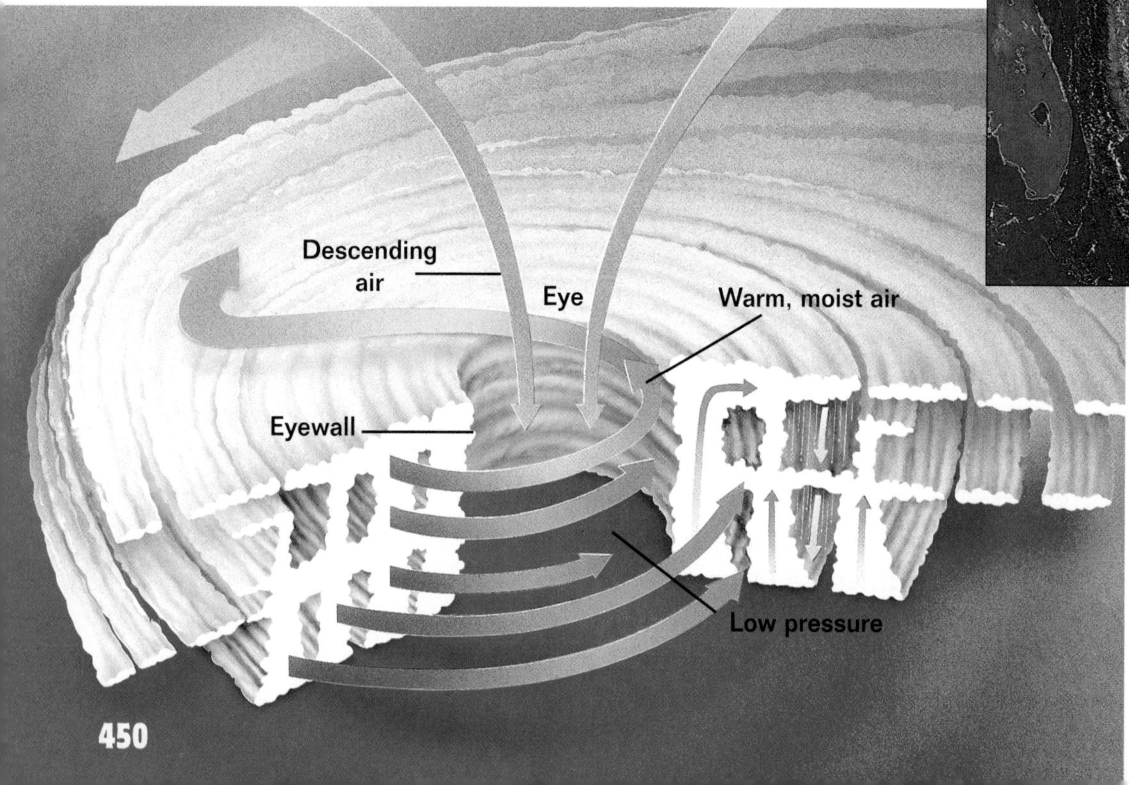

B This photograph shows Hurricane Fran approaching Florida in September 1996.

animals. In 1998, Hurricane Mitch hit Central America. In Honduras, more than 10 000 people were killed. Nearly 70 percent of the nation's crops were destroyed. Seventy percent of the nation's roads, water supplies, and bridges were severely damaged.

As long as a hurricane is over water, the warm, moist air rises and provides energy for the storm. When a hurricane reaches land, however, its supply of warm, moist air disappears and the storm loses power.

Figure 15-16 Hurricanes can be destructive, killing people and destroying property.

Most hurricanes in the United States strike along the Gulf of Mexico or along the Atlantic Coast. Mexico often sustains damage from hurricanes along its Pacific coast, as well as its Atlantic coast. Find out what happens to the islands of the Caribbean Sea during an average hurricane season.

Changes in weather affect your life. The interaction of air and water vapor causes constant change in the atmosphere. Air masses meet and fronts form, causing changes in weather. Severe weather can affect human lives and property.

Section Assessment

1. Why do high-pressure areas usually have clear skies?
2. Explain how a tornado develops from a thunderstorm.
3. How does Doppler radar determine the direction a storm is moving?
4. **Think Critically:** How do two converging fronts form a low-pressure area? Which front would bring the most severe weather?
5. **Skill Builder**
Interpreting Scientific Illustrations For more practice in interpreting illustrations, do the **Chapter 15 Skill Activity** on page 708.

Using Computers

Spreadsheet Make a spreadsheet comparing warm fronts, cold fronts, stationary fronts, and occluded fronts. Indicate what kind of clouds and weather systems form with each. If you need help, refer to page 690.

Reading a Weather Map

Materials

- Magnifying glass or hand lens
- **Figure 15-19**
- Appendix I

Meteorologists use a series of symbols to provide a picture of local and national weather conditions. These symbols give information on the temperature, air pressure, cloud cover, and more. Let's see how you can interpret weather information from weather map symbols.

What You'll Investigate

How do you read a weather map?

Goals

- **Interpret** weather map symbols.
- **Predict** weather using weather map information.

Procedure

Use the information provided in the questions below and Appendix I to learn how to read a weather map.

Conclude and Apply

1. Locate the station models on the map for Tucson, Arizona, and Albuquerque, New Mexico. Find the dew point, cloud coverage, pressure, and temperature at each location.
2. Review information about the spacing of isobars and wind speed in Section 15-3 and determine whether the wind would be stronger at Roswell, New Mexico, or at Fort Worth, Texas. Record your answer.
3. Determine the type of front near Key West, Florida. Record your answer.
4. The triangles or half-circles on the weather front symbol are on the side of the line toward the direction the front is moving. In what direction is the cold front located over Colorado and Kansas moving?
5. **Locate** the pressure system over Winslow, Arizona. Review Section 15-3 and **describe** what would happen to the weather of Wichita, Kansas, if this pressure system were to move there.
6. Prevailing westerlies are winds responsible for the movement of much of the weather across the United States and Canada. Based on this, would you expect Charleston, South Carolina, to continue to have clear skies? **Explain** your answer.
7. Use the **Field Guide to Clouds** at the end of this chapter to **predict** the types of clouds that might be present over Tucson, Arizona; Key West, Florida; and Charleston, South Carolina.

Forecasting Weather

15-3

Weather Observations

You can determine current weather conditions by observing the temperature and looking to see if clouds are in the sky. You know if it's raining. You also have a general idea of the weather because you are familiar with the typical weather where you live. If you live in Florida, you probably don't worry about snow in the forecast. But, if you live in Maine, you assume it will snow every winter. What weather concerns do you have in your region?

A **meteorologist** (meet ee uh RAHL uh just) studies weather. Meteorologists take measurements of temperature, air pressure, winds, humidity, and precipitation. Meteorologists use weather satellites, Doppler radar, computers, and instruments attached to balloons to gather data such as shown in **Figure 15-17.** Instruments for observing weather improve meteorologists' ability to predict weather. Meteorologists use the information provided by weather instruments to make weather maps. They use these maps to make weather forecasts.

What You'll Learn

- How data are collected for weather maps and forecasts
- The symbols used in a weather station model

Vocabulary

meteorologist
station model
isotherm
isobar

Why It's Important

- Reading a weather map allows you to interpret weather information and make predictions.

Weather Forecasts

Storms such as hurricanes, tornadoes, blizzards, and thunderstorms can be dangerous. When conditions show that severe weather may occur or when dangerous weather is observed, meteorologists at the National Weather Service issue advisories.

Figure 15-17 This tornado chaser uses a Doppler radar unit to obtain weather data about the severe storm.

When they issue a weather watch, you should prepare for severe weather. Watches are issued for severe thunderstorms, tornadoes, floods, blizzards, and hurricanes. During a watch, stay tuned to a radio or television station reporting the weather. When a warning is issued, severe weather conditions already exist. You should take immediate action. During a severe thunderstorm warning, take shelter. During a tornado warning, go to the basement or a room in the middle of the house away from windows.

Weather Information

The National Weather Service depends on two sources for its information: meteorologists from around the world and satellites. Meteorologists take measurements in a specific location and give the data to the National Weather Service. The National Weather Service uses this information to make weather maps. The Service records the information on maps with a combination of symbols, forming a **station model.** A station model shows the weather conditions at one specific location, as shown in **Figure 15-18.** Weather satellites provide cloud maps, surface temperatures, photos of Earth, and other data. All this information is used to forecast weather and to issue warnings about severe weather.

Temperature and Pressure

In addition to station models, weather maps have lines that indicate atmospheric pressure and temperature. These lines connect locations of equal temperature or pressure. A line that connects points of equal temperature is called an **isotherm** (I suh thurm). *Iso* means "same" and *therm* means "temperature." You've probably seen isotherms on weather maps on TV or in the newspaper.

An **isobar** is a line drawn to connect points of equal atmospheric pressure. You can tell how fast wind is blowing in an area by noting how closely isobars are spaced. Isobars close together indicate a large pressure difference over a small area. A large pressure difference causes strong winds. Isobars

Figure 15-18
A station model shows the weather conditions at one specific location.

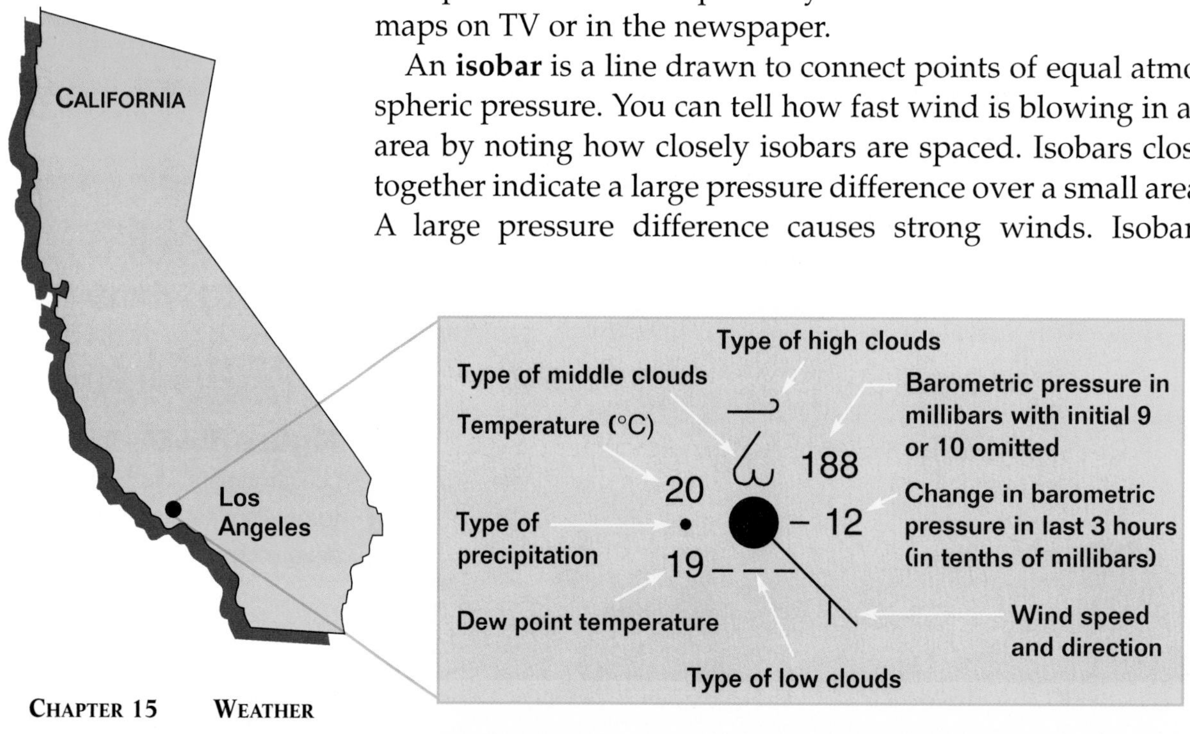

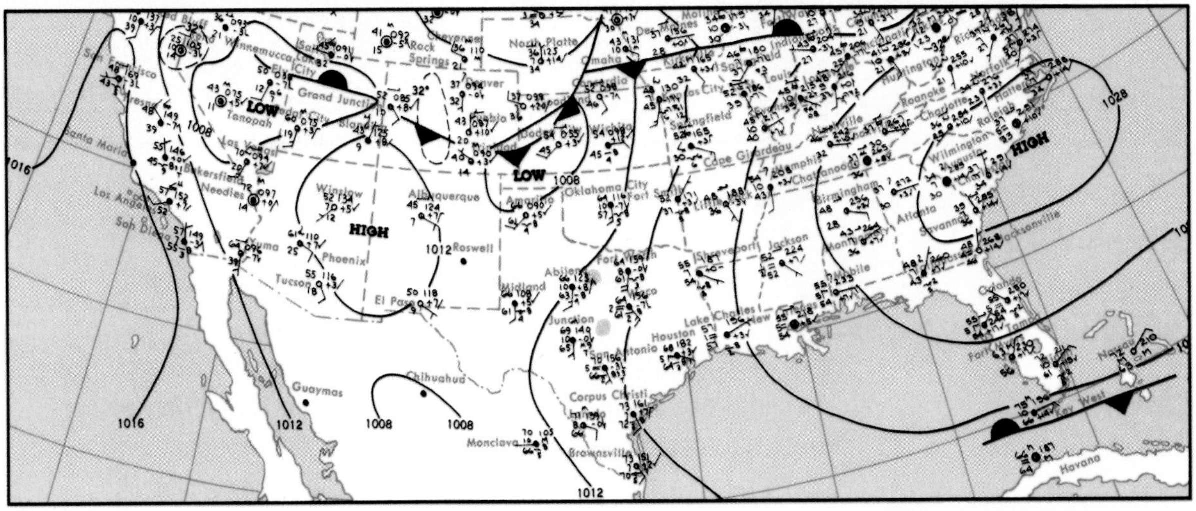

Figure 15-19 Highs, lows, isobars, and fronts on this weather map help meteorologists forecast the weather.

spread apart indicate a smaller difference in pressure. Winds in this area are more gentle. Isobars also indicate the locations of high- and low-pressure areas. On a weather map like the one in **Figure 15-19**, these areas are drawn as circles with a *High* or a *Low* in the middle. ☑

When you watch the weather forecasts on television, notice how weather fronts move across the United States from west to east. This is a pattern that meteorologists depend on in forecasting the weather. However, weather forecasters cannot always predict the exact weather because weather conditions change rapidly. Local conditions also influence the weather. However, improved technologies enable forecasters to be increasingly more accurate.

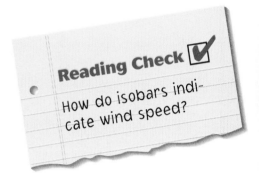

Reading Check ☑

How do isobars indicate wind speed?

Section Assessment

1. What symbols are used in a station model?
2. What do the different lines on a weather map indicate?
3. **Think Critically:** Use Appendix I to analyze the station model shown in **Figure 15-18.** What is the temperature, type of clouds, wind speed and direction, and type of precipitation at that location?
4. **Skill Builder**
   Comparing and Contrasting Contrast a weather watch and a weather warning. If you need help, refer to Comparing and Contrasting in the **Skill Handbook** on page 672.

Science Journal

Weather affects history. Research what happened to American troops at Valley Forge during the War of Independence in the winter of 1777–1778. Imagine that you were a soldier there during that winter. In your Science Journal, describe your experiences.

On The Internet

Activity 15•2

Weather or Not

It's raining cats and dogs! Red sky at night, sailor's delight. These sayings are about the weather. You may check out the weather forecast to decide if a concert will be rained out or if you need to wear a coat to the park. Knowing what the weather will be like is important. But, how do scientists predict or forecast the weather? They collect weather data every day all over the country and try to find a pattern in the data.

Recognize the Problem

How can you use weather data to forecast the weather?

Form a Hypothesis

Think about what the weather was like yesterday and what it is like today. **Make a hypothesis** about what the weather will be like in your area for the next several days.

Goals

- **Organize** weather data available on the Glencoe Science Web Site, in newspapers, and on television.
- **Predict** the weather in your area based on the data.

Data Sources

Go to the Glencoe Science Web Site at **www.glencoe.com/sec/science/ca** for information about weather data. You also can find weather data on television news shows, in newspapers, or on the radio. Or, you can make your own weather station. You'll need a thermometer, a barometer, a rain gauge, and a wind vane.

Test Your Hypothesis

Plan

1. Make a data table like the one below in your Science Journal.
2. Collect data in your area every day for at least two weeks. Your weather data should include each of the items listed in the table.
3. You can post your weather data on the Glencoe Science Web Site and collect data from other schools around the country.
4. Use the data to make your own weather maps. Print the map from the Glencoe site or post your data on a large map of the United States, using an overlay of tissue paper or plastic.

Do

1. Make sure your teacher approves your plan and your data table before you proceed.
2. Carry out the experiment as planned.
3. While doing the experiment, **record** your observations and **complete** the data tables in your Science Journal.

Analyze Your Data

1. How close did your predictions come to actual weather? Was your hypothesis supported?
2. Were your forecasts for the first few days more accurate than the later day's forecasts? **Explain.**

Draw Conclusions

1. How could you make your predictions more accurate?
2. Would data from other areas help? Explain your answer.

Weather Data Collection Table					
Date					
Location					
Temperature					
Barometric Pressure					
Wind Speed					
Wind Direction					
Type of Precipitation					
Amount of Precipitation					
Cloud Cover					

FIELD GUIDE to Clouds

Clouds are like people—they come in many different sizes and shapes. Some tower thousands of meters into the sky. Others are like fragile wisps of cotton candy floating in the air. All clouds are formed by atmospheric conditions that in turn form our weather. Using this field guide, you can learn to identify different types of clouds and try your hand at weather forecasting.

FIELD ACTIVITY

For a week, use this field guide to help you identify the clouds in your area. Observe the clouds two to three times each day. In your Science Journal, record the date, time, types of clouds observed, and the general weather conditions. What relationships can you infer between the weather and the types of clouds that are present?

How Clouds Are Classified

- Clouds are classified based on their shape and height.
- The height of a cloud is represented by the prefix used in its name. For example, a cirrocumulus (cirro + cumulus) cloud is a high cloud with a puffy shape.

Key to Cloud Classification

The following symbols are used in this field guide to represent the height and shape of common clouds.

Height

symbol | prefix

Cirro

Describes high clouds with bases starting above 6000 m.

Alto

Describes middle clouds with bases between 2000 m to 6000 m.

Strato

Refers to low clouds below 2000 m.

Shape

symbol | prefix

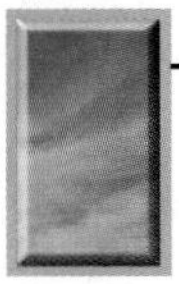

Cirrus

Latin meaning: hair
Describes wispy, stringy clouds

Cumulus

Latin meaning: pile or heap
Describes puffy, lumpy-looking clouds

Stratus

Latin meaning: layer
Describes featureless sheets of clouds

Nimbus

Latin meaning: cloud
Describes low, gray rain clouds

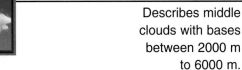

Cirrus

- Feathery cirrus clouds are the highest clouds of all.
- They are formed of ice crystals.
- They usually signal fair weather.
- They also can be a sign of changing weather.

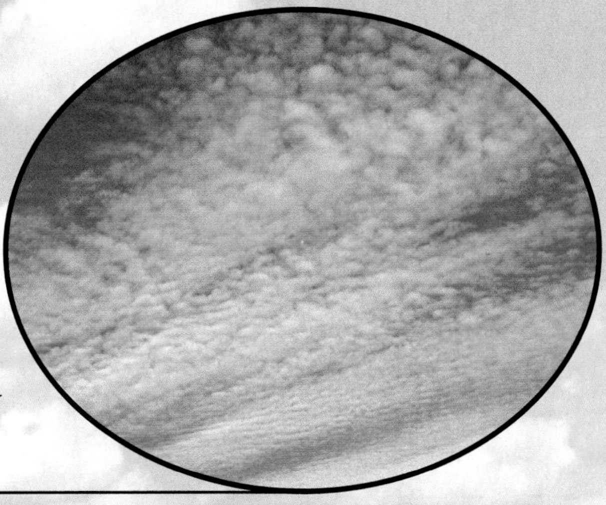

Cirrostratus

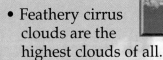

- These thin, sheet-like clouds often form ahead of advancing storms, particularly if they're followed by middle clouds.

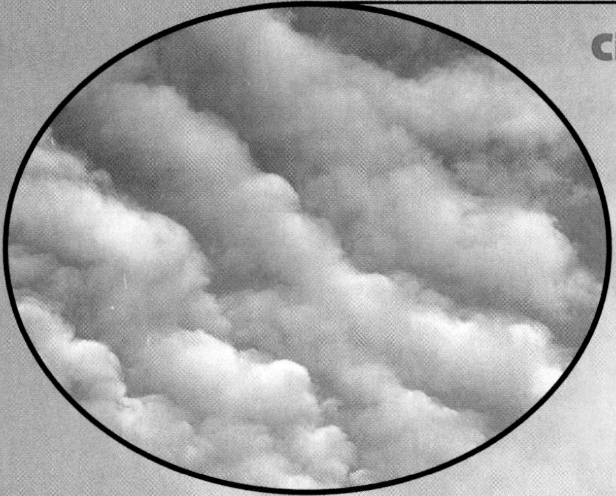

Cirrocumulus

- Cirrocumulus clouds are small, rounded, white puffs.
- They appear individually or in long rows.
- Their rippled pattern resembles the scales of fish. Hence, a sky full of cirrocumulus clouds is called a "mackerel sky."

Altostratus

- Gray or blue-gray altostratus clouds—they're never white—often cover the entire sky.
- They are a sign of widespread, steady rain ahead.

Altocumulus

- These puffy, white or gray clouds look like rows of soft cotton balls.
- Randomly scattered altocumulus clouds may mean several days of fair weather.
- When the clouds resemble little castles, expect a thunderstorm by day's end.

Nimbostratus

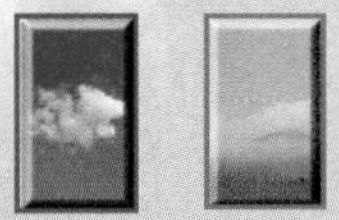

- Dark gray, wet-looking nimbostratus clouds are associated with steady rain or snow.
- The precipitation is light to moderate, never heavy.
- Nimbostratus clouds often have streaks that extend to the ground.

Stratus

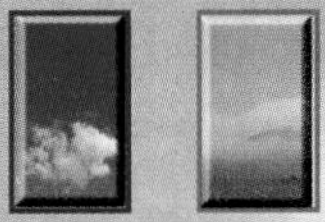

- Low-lying stratus clouds cover the sky in a blanket of gray.
- Light rain or drizzle usually accompanies these clouds.

Stratocumulus

- Low, lumpy stratocumulus clouds are often a sign of fair weather.
- To distinguish them from altocumulus clouds, extend your arm toward the cloud.
- An altocumulus cloud will be roughly the size of your thumbnail. A stratocumulus cloud will be about the size of your fist.

Cumulus

- Small, scattered cumulus clouds with slight vertical growth signal fair weather.
- They have dome-shaped or tower-shaped tops, like cauliflowers.

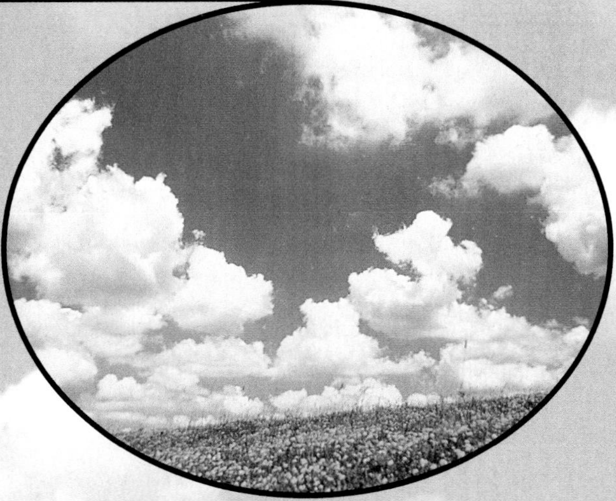

Cumulonimbus

- These are thunderstorm clouds.
- They form near Earth's surface and grow to nearly 18 000 m.
- Lightning, thunder, and strong winds are associated with cumulonimbus clouds.

Chapter 15 Reviewing Main Ideas

For a **preview** of this chapter, study this Reviewing Main Ideas before you read the chapter. After you have studied this chapter, you can use the Reviewing Main Ideas to **review** the chapter.

GLENCOE TECHNOLOGY

The Glencoe MindJogger, Audiocassettes, and CD-ROM provide additional opportunities for review.

Section

15-1 WHAT IS WEATHER?

Humidity is created by water vapor in the air. When air cools to its **dew point,** water vapor condenses and forms clouds. **Precipitation** forms when the **relative humidity** reaches 100 percent, water condenses in drops around dust and other particles in the air, and the water droplets reach at least 0.2 mm in size. Rain, hail, sleet, and snow are types of precipitation. ***What is the difference between humidity and relative humidity?***

Section

15-2 WEATHER PATTERNS

The temperature and the density of the air and the amount of water vapor in the air help determine the atmospheric pressure. High pressure brings clear skies and fair weather. Low-pressure areas are cloudy. Low-pressure systems form along the boundaries of **air masses.** ***Why do clouds usually develop in a region that is experiencing low pressure?***

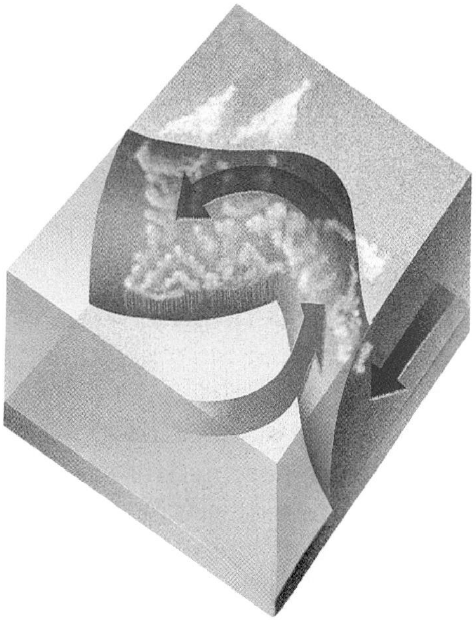

Reading Check ☑

Make up a new cloud type. Name it, using a prefix from the field guide. Describe when it would occur and what kind of weather it would bring.

SEVERE WEATHER

Fronts form at the boundary of two air masses. Warm fronts may produce precipitation over a wide area. Cold fronts produce a narrow band of violent storms. A stationary front produces weak winds and precipitation. Occluded fronts are sometimes associated with high winds and heavy precipitation. Thunderstorms, **tornadoes,** and **hurricanes** are examples of severe weather that can develop from low-pressure systems. All can result in loss of lives and destruction of property. Tornadoes are intense, whirling windstorms that can result from strong winds and low pressure in thunderstorms. *How do hurricanes form?*

Section 15-3 FORECASTING WEATHER

Meteorologists use information from radar, satellites, computers, and other instruments to make weather maps and forecasts. Symbols on a **station model** indicate the weather at a particular location. *Draw a station model to describe the weather conditions shown here.*

Chapter 15 Assessment

Using Vocabulary

a. air mass	**i.** isotherm
b. dew point	**j.** meteorologist
c. Doppler radar	**k.** precipitation
d. fog	**l.** relative humidity
e. front	**m.** station model
f. humidity	**n.** tornado
g. hurricane	**o.** weather
h. isobar	

Using the list above, replace the underlined words with the correct key science term.

1. Severe weather often occurs at the <u>boundary between air masses</u>.
2. Thunderstorms may produce a <u>violent swirling storm moving in a narrow path</u>.
3. Low-pressure systems over oceans often produce a <u>large, swirling tropical storm</u>.
4. Weather forecasts can be gotten by checking <u>symbols that describe local weather conditions</u> on weather maps.
5. To determine the air pressure in an area, you can look at the <u>lines on a weather map that indicate points of equal pressure</u>.

Checking Concepts

Choose the word or phrase that best answers the question.

6. What is the condition of the air when water vapor condenses from it?
   A) hot C) dry
   B) temperate D) saturated
7. What is a large body of air that has the same properties as the area over which it formed?
   A) air mass C) front
   B) station model D) isotherm
8. What has been reached when water vapor in air condenses?
   A) dew point C) front
   B) station model D) isobar
9. What forms when water vapor changes directly into a solid?
   A) rain C) sleet
   B) fog D) snow
10. What are high, feathery clouds made of ice crystals called?
    A) cirrus C) cumulus
    B) nimbus D) stratus
11. What type of front forms when two cool air masses merge?
    A) warm C) stationary
    B) cold D) occluded
12. What increases when the temperature of air increases?
    A) humidity C) cloud cover
    B) precipitation D) weather
13. What is issued when severe weather conditions exist and immediate action should be taken?
    A) front C) station model
    B) watch D) warning
14. What term describes the amount of water vapor in the air?
    A) dew point C) humidity
    B) precipitation D) relative humidity
15. What is a stratus cloud near the ground called?
    A) cumulus C) cirrus
    B) dew D) fog

Thinking Critically

16. If you learn that there is 79 percent relative humidity, what does that mean?
17. How do water and the sun interact to cause our weather?
18. Why don't hurricanes form in polar regions?

19. If a barometer shows that the air pressure is dropping, what general weather prediction could you make?
20. What weather conditions would the tall, thick, anvil-shaped clouds indicate?

Developing Skills

If you need help, refer to the Skill Handbook.

21. **Comparing and Contrasting:** Compare and contrast tornadoes and severe thunderstorms.
22. **Observing and Inferring:** You take a hot shower. The mirror in the bathroom clouds up. Infer from this information what has happened.
23. **Interpreting Scientific Illustrations:** Use the cloud descriptions in the **Field Guide to Clouds** to describe the weather at your location today. Then, try to predict tomorrow's weather.
24. **Concept Mapping:** Construct events chains, one for each type of precipitation. Show the sequence from evaporation to falling precipitation. The number of events may vary.
25. **Interpreting Scientific Illustrations:** Describe the weather conditions shown on the station model below.

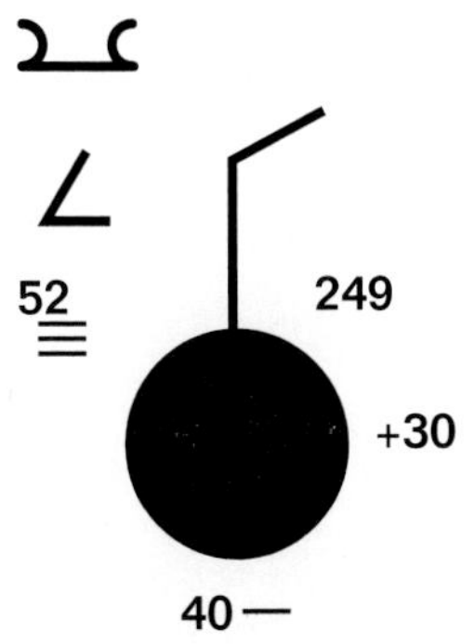

THE PRINCETON REVIEW

Test-Taking Tip

Your Answers Are Better Than the Test's When you know the answer, answer the question in your own words before looking at the answer choices. Often, more than one answer choice will look good, so arm yourself with yours before looking.

Test Practice

Use these questions to test your Science Proficiency.

1. If the actual amount of humidity in the air does not change, what is the cause-and-effect relationship of temperature and relative humidity?
   A) As temperature increases, relative humidity increases.
   B) As temperature decreases, relative humidity increases.
   C) As relative humidity increases, temperature increases.
   D) As relative humidity decreases, temperature increases.
2. Making long-range, accurate weather predictions is difficult. Why is this true?
   A) Weather instruments are not accurate.
   B) Weather instruments are not precise.
   C) Meteorologists do not communicate with one another.
   D) Atmospheric conditions are constantly changing.

CHAPTER

16 Climate

Chapter Preview

Skills Preview

Skill Builders

- Compare and Contrast
- Form a Hypothesis

Activities

- Measure in SI
- Make a Model

MiniLabs

- Analyze Data
- Observe and Infer

Reading Check

As you read this chapter, list five things you already knew about climate and ten things you are learning.

Explore Activity

Brrr. . . this penguin lives in Antarctica, where temperatures are cold year-round. Other places on Earth are almost always hot. Some areas are dry, while others are rainy. Why do temperature and precipitation vary so much from place to place? The amount of sun energy that a place receives plays an important part in weather patterns. Energy from the sun also creates wind. Wind systems distribute moisture and heat around the world, as you will see in the following activity.

Observe Deserts and Wind Systems

1. Obtain a world globe or atlas.
2. Locate several of the world's deserts.
3. Find the latitudes of these deserts.
4. Research major wind systems such as the trade winds and the prevailing westerlies to determine which winds affect these latitudes.

Science Journal

Many deserts are located next to mountain ranges. In your Science Journal, explain how mountains might affect precipitation patterns in different regions.

16•1 What is climate?

What You'll Learn

- What determines the climate of an area
- How latitude and natural features affect the climate of a region

Vocabulary
climate
tropics
polar zone
temperate zone

Why It's Important

- Many factors affect the climate you live in.

Climate

If you ever have a chance to travel around the world or around the United States, you'll experience a variety of climates. **Climate** is the pattern of weather that occurs in an area over many years. If you ever visit a rain forest, you'll find the climate there wetter than in a desert. The wettest rain forest averages 1168 cm of precipitation annually. A desert receives less than 25 cm of rain per year. Some places closer to the equator are much warmer than places near the poles. Temperatures on Earth range from –89.2°C to 57.8°C.

Climate is determined by averaging the weather of a region over a long period of time, such as 30 years. Scientists average temperature, precipitation, air pressure, humidity, and days of sunshine to determine an area's climate. Other factors that affect the climate of a region include latitude, landforms, location of lakes and oceans, availability of moisture, global wind patterns, ocean currents, and location of air masses.

Latitude Affects Climate

As you can see in **Figure 16-1,** latitudes close to the equator receive the most solar radiation. Latitude also affects climate. **Figure 16-2** shows a comparison of cities at different latitudes. The **Tropics,** the region between latitudes 23.5° N and 23.5° S, receive the most solar radiation because the sun shines almost directly overhead. Year-round temperatures in the tropics are always hot, except at high elevations. The **polar zones** extend from 66.5° north and south latitudes to the poles. Solar energy hits the polar zones at a low angle, spreading energy over a large area. Also, polar ice reflects some of this solar radiation back out to space. During winter, polar regions are tilted away from the sun and receive no solar radiation at all. Therefore, polar regions are never warm. Some are covered with ice year-round.

Between the tropics and the polar zones are the **temperate zones.** Temperatures in these zones are moderate. The United States, except for Alaska and Hawaii, is in a temperate zone.

Figure 16-1 The Tropics are warmer because they receive the most direct solar energy.

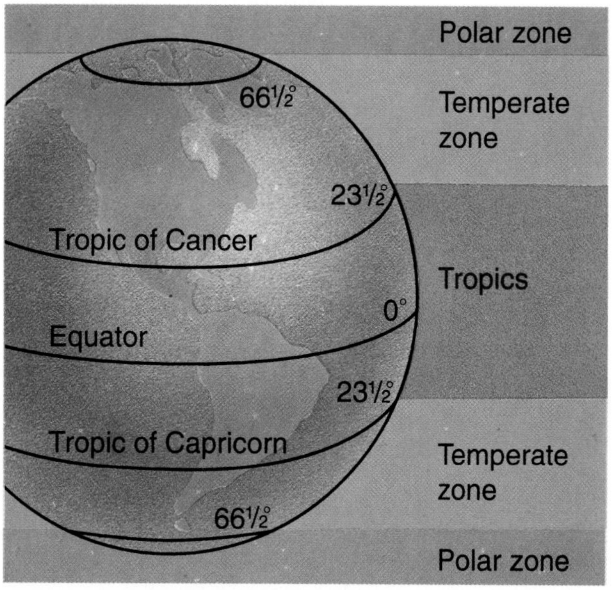

VISUALIZING Climate

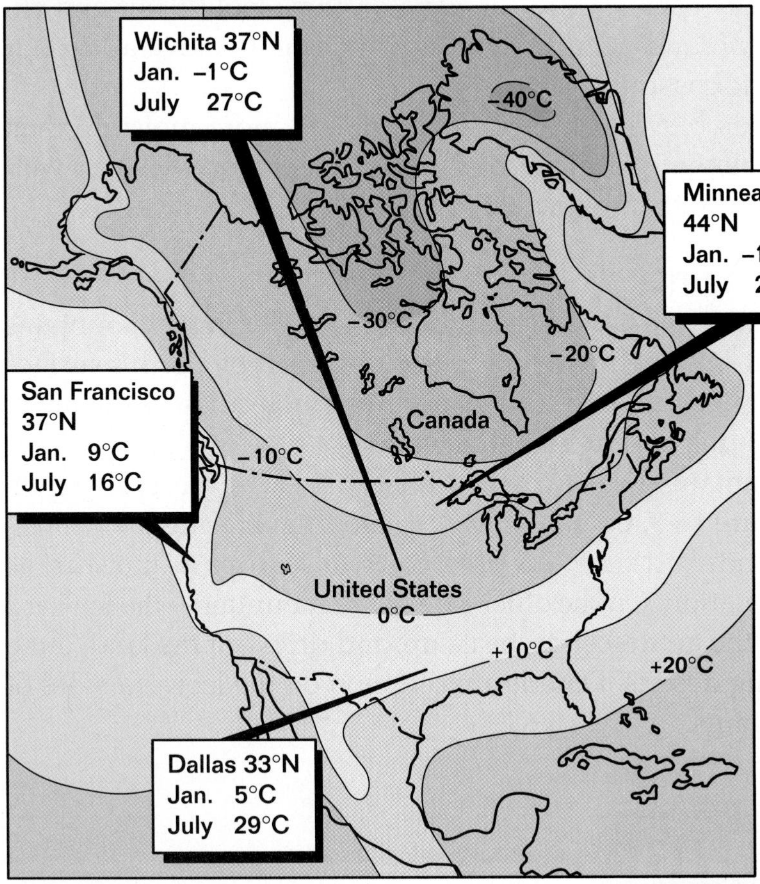

Figure 16-2 This map shows daily minimum temperatures (°C) in January and July throughout the United States.

A Minneapolis, Minnesota, at 44°N, receives less solar radiation than Dallas, Texas.

B San Francisco's climate is affected by the nearby ocean. **Compare these temperatures to those of Wichita, Kansas, on the same 37°N latitude line.**

C Dallas, Texas, at 33°N, receives more solar radiation than Minneapolis. **Compare the temperature range of Dallas to that of Minneapolis.**

Other Factors

There's more to climate than the general divisions of polar, temperate, and tropical. Within each zone, natural features, such as mountains and large bodies of water, affect climate. Large cities also change weather patterns, which can influence the local climate.

Large Bodies of Water

If you live near an ocean, you may have noticed that water heats up and cools down more slowly than land. Large bodies of water affect the climate of coastal areas. Many coastal regions are warmer in the winter and cooler in the summer than inland areas of similar latitude. Look at **Figure 16-2B** again. You can see the effect of an ocean by comparing the temperatures in a coastal city and a continental city, both at 37°N latitude.

Mini Lab

Observing Solar Radiation

Procedure

1. Darken the room.
2. Hold a flashlight about 30 cm from a globe. Shine the light directly on the equator. With your finger, trace around the light.
3. Without moving the location of the light, tilt it to shine on 30°N latitude. The size of the illuminated area should increase. Repeat at 60°N latitude.

Analysis

1. How did the size and shape of the light beam change as you directed the light toward higher latitudes?
2. How does the tilt of Earth affect the solar radiation received by different latitudes?

Ocean currents also affect coastal climate. Warm currents begin near the equator and flow toward the higher latitudes, warming the regions they pass by. When the currents cool off and flow back toward the equator, they cool the air and climates of land nearby. Some warm currents move along our Atlantic coast.

Reading Check

How do ocean currents affect climate?

Winds blowing from the sea contain more moisture than those blowing from the land. Thus, coasts tend to have a wetter climate than places inland.

Mountains

At the same latitude, the climate is colder in the mountains than at sea level. When radiation absorbed by Earth's surface is reflected upward, there are fewer molecules in the air to absorb this heat at higher elevations.

Mountains also affect the climate of nearby areas, as shown in **Figure 16-3.** On the side of the mountain facing the wind—the windward side—air rises, cools, and drops its moisture as precipitation. On the other side of the mountain—the leeward side—the air descends, heats up, and dries out the land, often forming deserts. Deserts are common on the leeward sides of mountains.

Problem Solving

The Lake Effect

Depending on their temperature, ocean currents either warm or cool nearby coastal regions. Ocean breezes, filled with moisture, give coastal regions wetter climates than areas farther inland. If oceans modify the climate of nearby coastal areas, do you think large lakes do this, as well? The following data were collected from four different Ohio cities near Lake Erie. Examine the data and answer the questions.

Climate Data

Location	A	B	C	D
Distance from the lake in kilometers	0	1.6	48.3	80.5
Average monthly range of temperature in °C	7.6	8.8	10.8	11.9
Frost-free days	205	194	162	154
Annual precipitation in centimeters	73.6	81.4	94.0	97.5

Think Critically

1. How is the distance from Lake Erie related to frost-free days?
2. What is the relationship between distance from the lake and annual precipitation?
3. Is the climate of a city near Lake Erie affected by the lake? Explain.
4. Some fruit, such as grapes, need long growing seasons. Which of the four locations would be best for growing grapes?

Large Cities

Large cities affect local climates. Solar radiation that strikes cities is absorbed by streets, parking lots, and buildings. These paved surfaces and structures heat up and radiate energy into the atmosphere. Automobile exhaust and other pollutants in the air trap this heat energy, creating what some people call a heat island effect. Summer temperatures in a city can be ten degrees higher than in surrounding rural areas.

In addition to raising temperatures, cities affect the climate in other ways. Skyscrapers act as small mountains and change local wind and precipitation patterns. A study of St. Louis, Missouri, found that 25 percent more rainfall, 45 percent more thunderstorms, and 31 percent more hailstorms occurred over the city than over the surrounding rural areas.

Figure 16-3 Climate differs on either side of a mountain range. This map shows the leeward and windward sides of the Andes, a mountain system between Chile and Argentina.

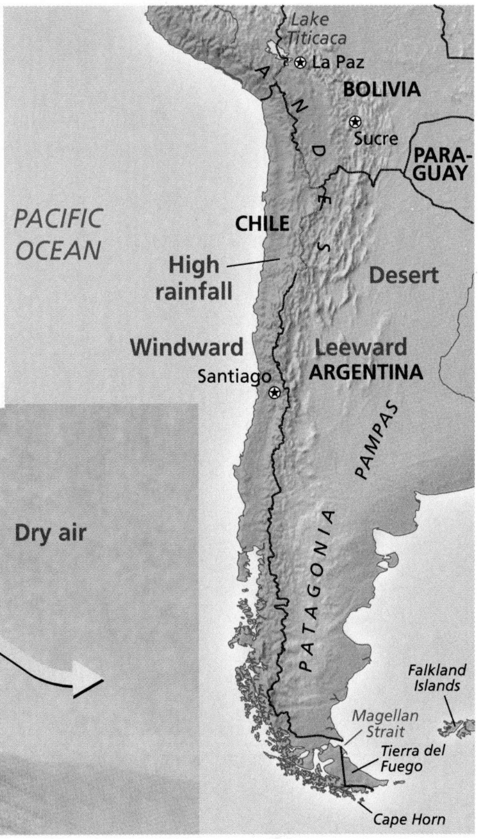

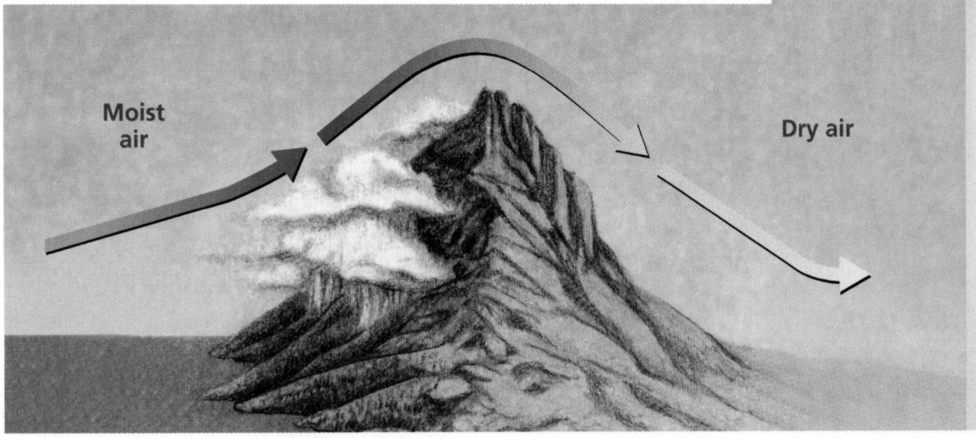

Section Assessment

1. What factors help determine the climate of a region?
2. How do mountains affect climate?
3. Explain how two cities located at the same latitude can have different climates.
4. **Think Critically:** Explain why types of plants and animals found on different sides of the same mountain range might differ.
5. **Skill Builder**
   Comparing and Contrasting Compare and contrast tropical, temperate, and polar climates. If you need help, refer to Comparing and Contrasting in the **Skill Handbook** on page 672.

Using Math

Using the data from the Problem Solving activity, predict the annual precipitation for a location 60 km from Lake Erie. Explain how you determined your answer.

Design Your Own Experiment

Activity 16•1

Microclimates

Possible Materials

- Thermometers
- Psychrometer
- Paper strip or wind sock
- Large cans (4–5)
  ** beakers or rain gauges (4–5)*
- Piece of unlined paper

A microclimate is a localized climate that differs from the main climate surrounding it. Buildings in a city, for instance, can affect the climate of the area surrounding the buildings.

Recognize the Problem

Does your school building create microclimates?

Form a Hypothesis

Hypothesize how a building affects the climate of the area around it.

Goals

- **Observe** temperature, wind speed, relative humidity, and precipitation in areas outside your school.
- **Infer** how the building might affect these climate factors.

Safety Precautions

If a thermometer breaks, do not touch it. Have your teacher dispose of the glass safely. Do NOT use a mercury thermometer.

Relative Humidity

Dry Bulb Temperature	Dry Bulb Temperature Minus Wet Bulb Temperature, °C									
	1	2	3	4	5	6	7	8	9	10
13°C	89	79	69	59	50	41	32	22	15	7
14°C	90	79	70	60	51	42	34	26	18	10
15°C	90	80	71	61	53	44	36	27	20	13
16°C	90	81	71	63	54	46	38	30	23	15
17°C	90	81	72	64	55	47	40	32	25	18
18°C	91	82	73	65	57	49	41	34	27	20
19°C	91	82	74	65	58	50	43	36	29	22
20°C	91	83	74	66	59	51	44	37	31	24
21°C	91	83	75	67	60	53	46	39	32	26
22°C	92	83	76	68	61	54	47	40	34	28
23°C	92	84	76	69	62	55	48	42	36	30
24°C	92	84	77	69	62	56	49	43	37	31
25°C	92	84	77	70	63	57	50	44	39	33

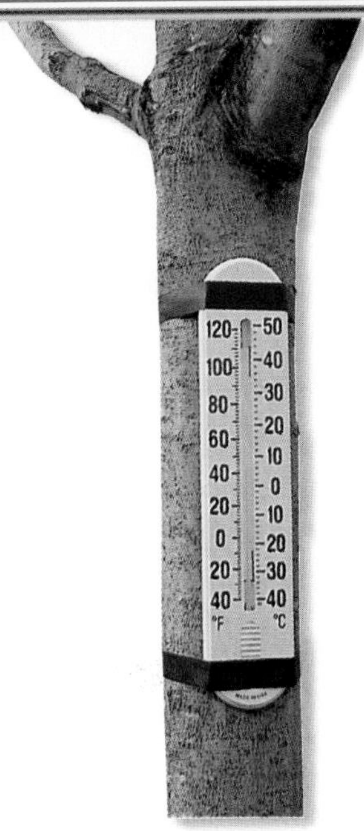

Test Your Hypothesis

Plan

1. As a group, agree upon and write out your hypothesis statement.
2. **List** the steps needed to test your hypothesis. Include in your plan how you will use your equipment to measure the temperature, wind speed, relative humidity, and precipitation at four or five sites around your school building.
3. To find relative humidity, you'll need to use a psychrometer. A psychrometer is an instrument with two thermometers, one wet and one dry. As moisture from the wet thermometer evaporates, it takes heat energy from its environment, and the environment immediately around the wet thermometer cools. The thermometer records a lower temperature. Relative humidity can be found by finding the difference between the wet thermometer and the dry thermometer and by using the chart on the previous page.
4. **Select** your test sites. Select a control site that is not affected by the building.
5. **Make a map** of the school building and the test sites.
6. **Design a data table** in your Science Journal to use as your group collects data.

Do

1. Make sure your teacher approves your plan and your data table before you proceed.
2. Carry out the experiment as planned.
3. While the experiment is going on, **record** your observations and **complete** the data table in your Science Journal.

Analyze Your Data

1. **Map** your data. Color code the areas to show which microclimates had the highest and lowest temperatures, the greatest and least wind speed, the greatest and least relative humidity, and the greatest and least precipitation.
2. **Analyze** your data to find patterns.

Draw Conclusions

1. How did your test sites differ from your control site?
2. **Analyze** your hypothesis and the results of your experiment. Was your hypothesis supported?

16•2 Climate Types

Climate Classification

If your job were to classify climates, where would you begin? Climates can be classified in several ways. Climatologists, people who study climates, usually use a system developed in 1918 by Russian-German meteorologist and climatologist Wladimir Köppen. Köppen observed that the type of vegetation found in a region depended on the climate of the area. **Figure 16-4** shows differences Köppen might have observed. His classification system is based on his studies of temperature and precipitation.

What You'll Learn

- A climate classification system
- How organisms adapt to particular climates

Vocabulary
adaptation
hibernation

Why It's Important

- Your climate differs from others on Earth.

Climate Types

The climate classification system shown in **Figure 16-5** divides climates into six groups: tropical, mild, dry, continental, polar, and high elevation. These groups are further divided into types. For example, the dry climate classification is divided into semiarid and arid.

Examine the map and count how many different climates are found in the United States. Why do so many different types of climates exist here? What climate exists where you live?

Figure 16-4 The type of vegetation in a region depends on the climate.

A Short grasses grow in fairly dry climates.

B Ferns and trees draped with Spanish moss grow in climates that have heavy rainfall.

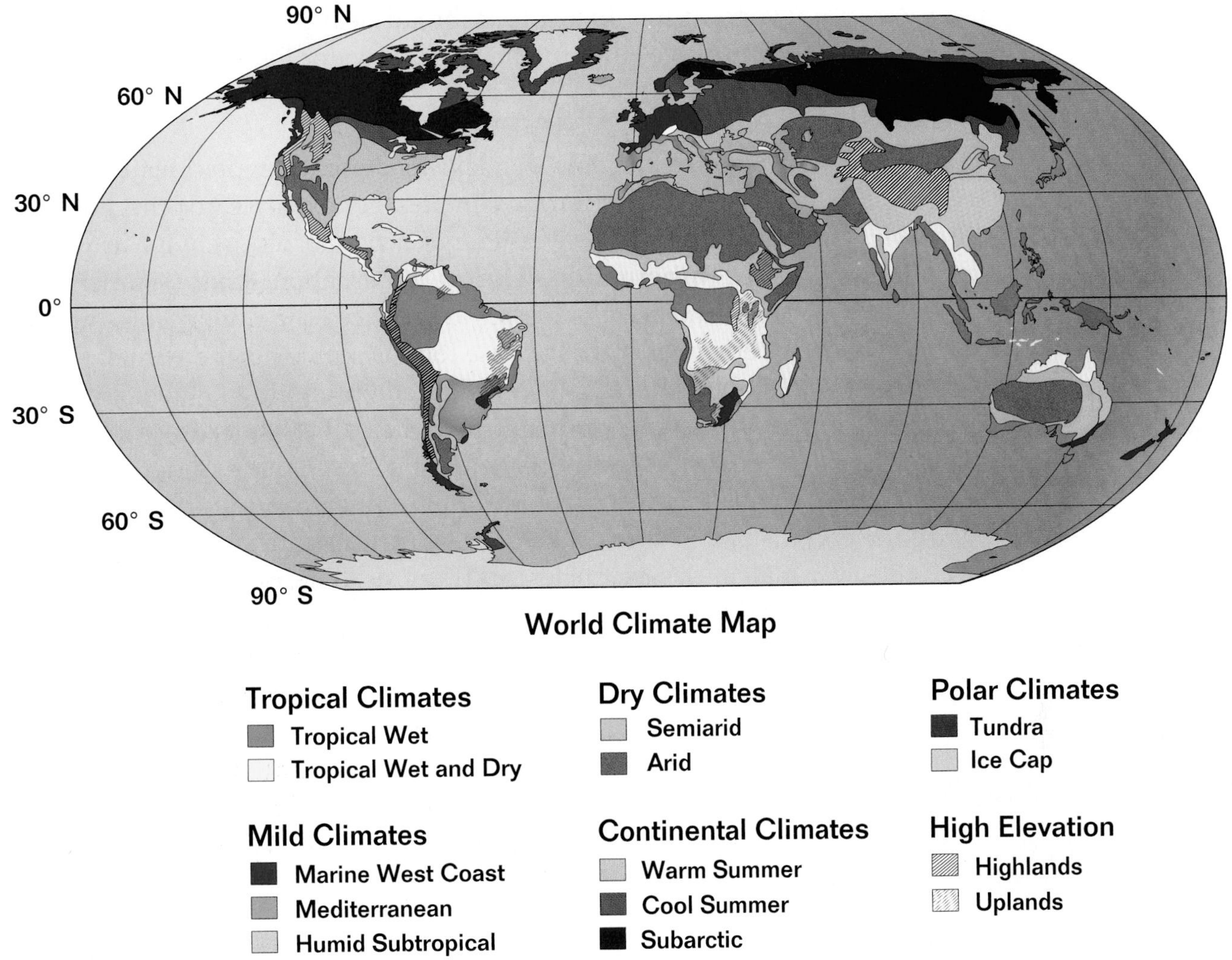

Figure 16-5 Study the climate classification system shown on this map. Notice that most wet climates are located between latitudes 30° N and 30° S. **What other patterns do you see on this map?**

Organism Adaptations

Climates vary around the world, and as Köppen observed, the type of climate that exists in an area determines the vegetation found there. Fir trees aren't found in deserts, nor are cacti found in rain forests. In fact, all organisms have certain adaptations that allow them to survive in some climates but not in others. An **adaptation** is any structure or behavior that helps an organism survive in its environment. Adaptations develop in a population over a long period of time. Some adaptations are shown in **Figure 16-6** on the following page. Climatic factors that may limit where an organism can live are temperature, moisture, and amount of daylight.

Structural Adaptations

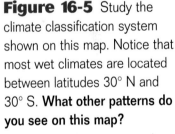

LIFE SCIENCE INTEGRATION

Some organisms have body structures that help them survive in certain climates. The fur of mammals insulates them from cold temperatures. A cactus has a thick, fleshy stem. This structural adaptation helps a cactus hold water. The waxy texture of the stem keeps water inside the plant from evaporating. Instead of broad leaves, cactus plants have spiny leaves that further reduce water loss.

Reading Check ☑

What is hibernation?

Behavioral Adaptations

Some organisms display behavioral adaptations that help them survive in certain climates. For example, rodents and certain other mammals undergo a period of inactivity in winter called **hibernation.** During hibernation, body temperature drops and body processes are reduced to a minimum. Animals hibernate, in part, because food is scarce during winter. ☑

Other animals have adapted differently. When it's cold, bees cluster together in a tight ball to keep from freezing. During hot, sunny days, desert snakes hide under rocks. At night, when it's cooler, they slither out in search of food. Instead of drinking water as turtles and lizards do in wet climates, desert turtles and lizards obtain the moisture they need from their food.

Figure 16-6 Organisms have structural and behavioral adaptations that help them survive in particular climates.

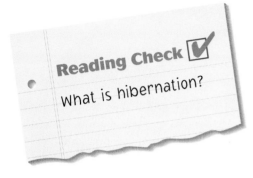

A Honeybees fan in fresh air to keep the hive cool. **How do bees keep warm?**

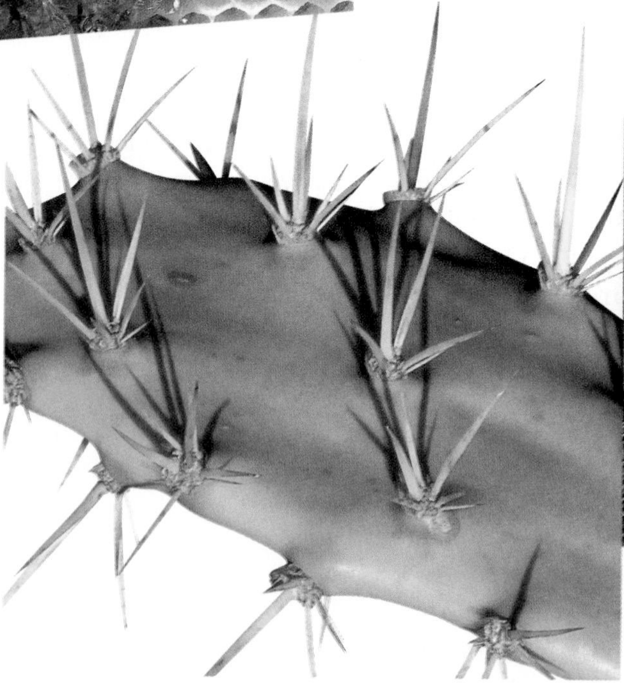

B The needles and the waxy skin of a cactus reduce water loss.

C A wolf's fur keeps it warm. Fur is hair. The spaces between the hairs trap air and heat and keep out the cold and rain.

Figure 16-7 People have adaptations that help them to survive in every climate.

Lungfish survive periods of intense heat by going through an inactive state called estivation. As weather gets hot and water begins evaporating, the fish burrows into mud and secretes a covering around itself. It lives this way until the warm, dry months pass.

Like other organisms, you have structural adaptations that help you adjust to climate. You can maintain a fairly constant body temperature, regardless of the outside temperature. In hot weather, your sweat glands release water onto your skin. The water evaporates. As a result, you become cooler. What other adaptations help the people in **Figure 16-7** adjust to climate?

Section Assessment

1. Use **Figure 16-5** and a world map to identify the climate type for each of the following locations: Cuba, North Korea, Egypt, and Uruguay.
2. What are some behavioral adaptations that allow animals to stay warm?
3. **Think Critically:** What special adaptations must plants and animals have to live in dry regions?
4. **Skill Builder**
   Forming a Hypothesis Some scientists think Earth is becoming hotter. Suppose this is true. Form a hypothesis about which adaptations will allow some present-day organisms to survive this change. If you need help, refer to Forming a Hypothesis in the **Skill Handbook** on page 674.

Science Journal

Research the ways people have adapted their behavior to survive in the six climate regions shown in **Figure 16-5.** Consider clothing, housing, and transportation. Write about these adaptations in your Science Journal.

16•3 Climatic Changes

Seasons

In temperate zones, weather generally changes with the season. **Seasons** are short-term periods of climate change caused by regular differences in daylight, temperature, and weather patterns. These differences are due to changes in the amount of solar radiation an area receives. **Figure 16-8** shows Earth revolving around the sun. Because Earth is tilted as it revolves, different areas of Earth receive changing amounts of solar radiation throughout the year. That affects wind patterns. In turn, wind patterns and natural features help create seasonal climatic changes.

What You'll Learn

- What causes seasons
- How El Niño affects the climate
- Theories about climatic change

Vocabulary
season
El Niño
greenhouse effect
global warming
deforestation

Why It's Important

- Global warming is a serious, yet hotly debated environmental concern.

Effects of Latitude

The middle latitudes or temperate zones often have warm summers and cool winters. Spring and fall are usually mild. Because of fairly constant solar radiation at the low latitudes near the equator, the Tropics do not have as much seasonal temperature change as the middle latitudes. But, tropical areas do experience dry and rainy seasons.

During the year, the high latitudes near the poles have great differences in temperature and number of daylight hours. As shown in **Figure 16-8,** during summer in the northern hemisphere, the north pole is tilted toward the sun. The north pole has 24 hours of daylight each day for six months. During that same time, the south pole experiences 24-hour days of darkness. At the equator, days are about the same length all year long.

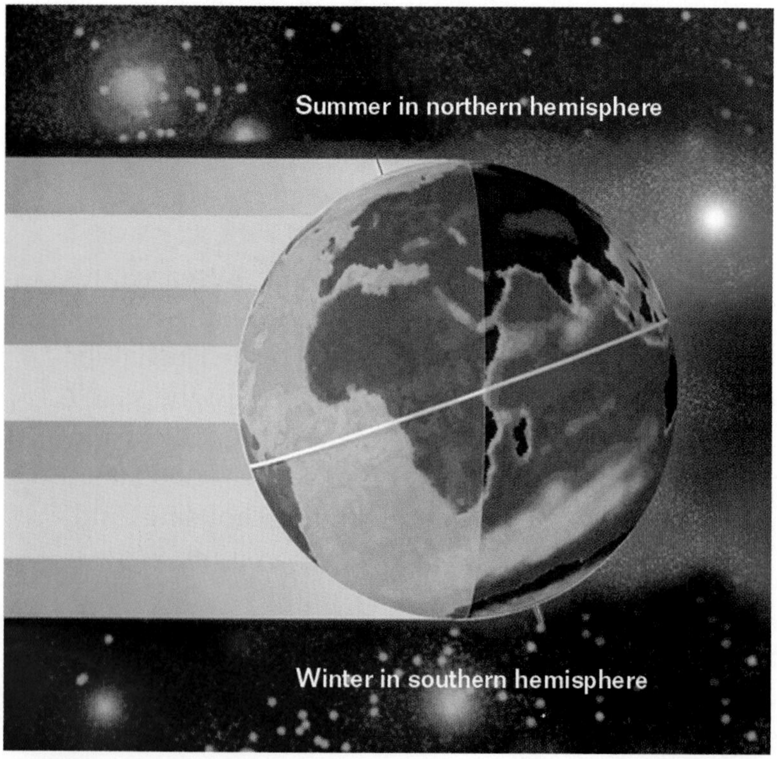

Figure 16-8 As Earth moves around the sun, different areas of Earth tilt toward the sun, bringing different seasons. In the southern hemisphere during winter, the south pole tilts away from the sun, making the sunlight less concentrated. At the same time in the northern hemisphere, the north pole tilts toward the sun. It's summer and days are long.

El Niño

Some climatic changes last longer than a season. **El Niño** (el·NEEN yoh) is a climatic event that starts in the tropical Pacific Ocean and sets off changes in the atmosphere. El Niño used to occur every three to seven years. Now, it happens more frequently, although scientists are not sure why. In El Niño, the Pacific Ocean warms along the equator. Near the equator, trade winds that blow east to west weaken and sometimes reverse. The change in the trade winds allows warm tropical water in the upper layers of the Pacific to flow eastward to South America. Ocean temperatures increase by 1°C to 7°C off the coast of Peru. The increase in temperatures causes the spaces around water molecules to expand, and sea level rises slightly.

El Niño does not directly cause unusual weather but instead affects the atmosphere and ocean, making stormy weather more likely. Warmer water brings more evaporation. Heavy rains fall over South America. During El Niño, one of the jet streams often splits. This changes the atmospheric pressure off California and wind and precipitation patterns around the world. Such changes can cause drought in Australia and Africa. They also affect dependable monsoon rains in Indonesia and cause storms in California, as shown in **Figure 16-9.**

LIFE SCIENCE INTEGRATION

Deadly El Niño?
During El Niño, some aquatic plants and animals living in waters off California die. Infer how El Niño may be the cause of their deaths.

Figure 16-9 The effects of El Niño are felt around the world. A strong El Niño occurred in 1998.

A A severe drought struck Indonesia.

B California was plagued by mudslides and floods.

Climatic Change

Figure 16-10 The length of growing seasons is recorded in tree rings. **Was Earth's climate always the same in the past? Explain.**

Although some years are warmer, colder, drier, or wetter than others, Earth's climate remains fairly constant. However, in Earth's past the climate was sometimes much colder or much warmer than it is today.

Geological records show that in the past, the climate of different areas changed. Fossils of tropical plants and animals found in polar as well as temperate regions indicate warmer worldwide climates in the past. **Figure 16-10** illustrates how living things can be used to study climate changes. Glacial erosion and deposition around the world show that in the past 2 million years, glaciers covered large parts of Earth's surface. These periods of extensive glaciers are called ice ages. During Earth's past, ice ages have alternated with warm periods called interglacial intervals. Some ice ages lasted 60 000 years. Most interglacial periods lasted about 12 000 years. We are now in an interglacial interval, which began about 11 500 years ago. Ice cores drilled in Greenland show that cold spells, lasting 1000 years or more, changed rapidly to warm spells that lasted as long. **Figure 16-11** shows a scientist working with ice cores.

Figure 16-11 By examining air bubbles trapped in ice cores, scientists learn about climates of past geologic eras.

Climatic Change Theories

Research into the causes of climatic change suggests a variety of possibilities. Catastrophic events such as meteorite collisions and volcanic eruptions may have occurred, or perhaps the sun's output of energy isn't constant. It could be that when Earth's plates move, they change climate patterns, or perhaps Earth's movements in space cause climatic change.

Catastrophic events such as large meteorite collisions and volcanic eruptions put enormous volumes of dust, ash, and smoke into the atmosphere. These dust and smoke particles could have blocked so much solar radiation that they cooled the planet and changed the climate. **Figure 16-12** illustrates how a major volcanic eruption affects Earth's atmosphere.

Clouds

Evidence suggests that an increase in cloud cover can affect global temperatures. Thick clouds can block solar radiation from reaching Earth's surface. It is possible that an increase in cloud cover could lead to a cooling effect similar to that produced by volcanic ash. Clouds, however, also can absorb solar energy that has already reached Earth's surface. Thus, clouds have two effects—they both reflect and absorb solar energy. The reflection of solar energy can make Earth's climate cooler. The absorption of solar energy can make Earth's climate warmer.

Solar radiation provides Earth's energy. If the output of the radiation from the sun varies—regardless of cloud cover—this also could change Earth's climate.

Mini Lab

Analyzing Tree Rings

Procedure

1. As a tree grows, it adds layers of growth rings. When conditions for growth are good, growth rings occur far apart. When conditions are poor, growth rings appear close together.
2. Examine the growth rings of a cross section of wood. Note that the oldest wood is in the center.
3. Measure the thickness of several rings in your sample.

Analysis

1. How did the length of the growing seasons change as the tree grew older? Describe what evidence you found for this.
2. If scientists examine growth rings in petrified wood samples from different geologic times, what can they learn about climates of earlier geologic periods?

Figure 16-12 When Mount Pinatubo in the Philippines erupted in 1991, its volcanic ash cooled temperatures around the world.

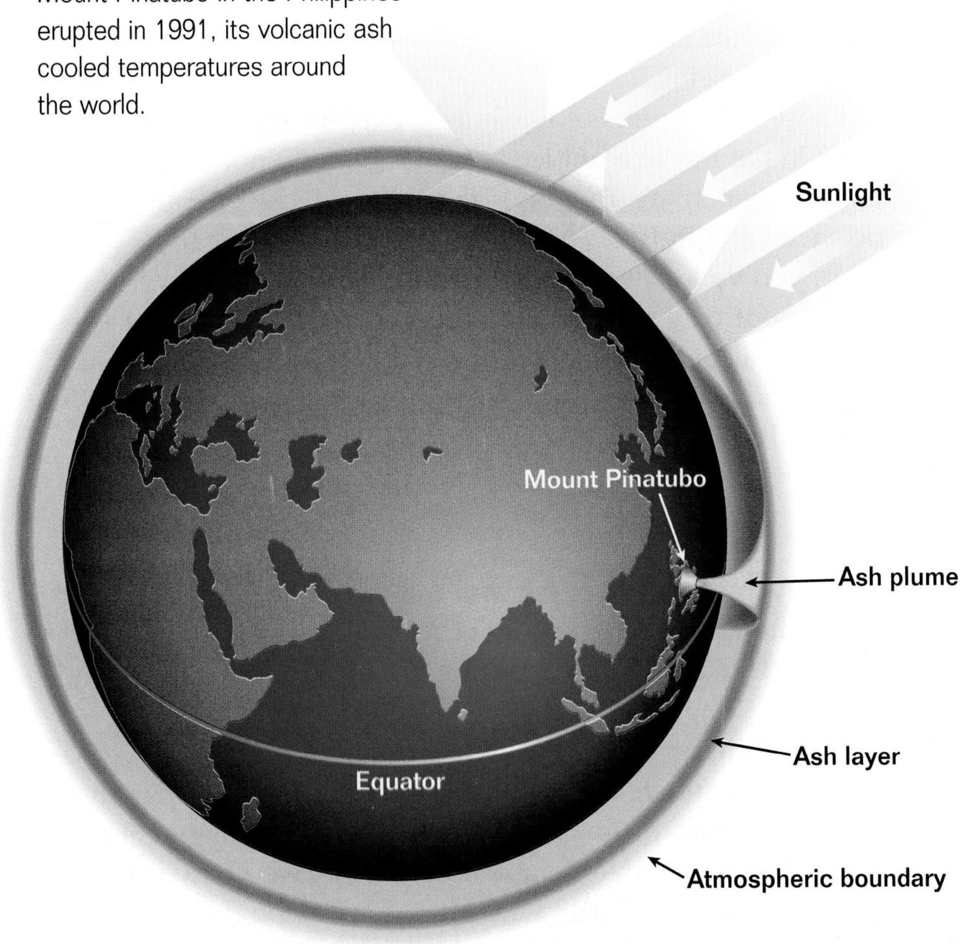

interNET CONNECTION

Visit the Glencoe Science Web Site **www.glencoe.com/sec/science/ca** for more information about climate changes.

Figure 16-13 This glacier in Argentina is similar to those that covered large parts of North America during the last ice age. **What is an ice age?**

Earth Moves

Another possible explanation for major climatic change concerns the movement of the plates on Earth's crust. The movement of continents and oceans affects the transfer of heat on Earth's surface, which in turn affects wind and precipitation patterns. Through time, these altered patterns may change the climate.

Another theory relates to Earth's movements in space. Earth is currently tilted on its axis at 23.5° to the plane of its orbit around the sun. In the past, this tilt has increased to 25° and has decreased to 22°. When this tilt is at its maximum, the poles receive more solar energy. When the tilt is at its minimum, the poles receive less solar energy. Earth's tilt changes about every 41 000 years. Some scientists hypothesize that the change in tilt may affect climates.

Another Earth movement that may affect climatic change is the change in the shape of Earth's orbit around the sun. The shape of Earth's orbit changes over a 100 000-year cycle. When the orbit is more circular than at present, Earth is farther from the sun and temperatures are colder than those we are experiencing.

These movements of Earth may explain some of the variations in the most recent ice age. But, they do not explain why glaciers, such as the one shown in **Figure 16-13,** have occurred so rarely over the long span of geologic time.

As you've learned, many theories attempt to answer questions about why Earth's climate has changed through the ages. Probably all of these things play some role in changing climates. More study needs to be done before we can understand all the factors that affect climate.

interNET CONNECTION

Visit the Glencoe Science Web Site at **www.glencoe.com/sec/science/ca** for more information about the greenhouse effect.

Climatic Changes Today

Today, many newspaper and magazine headlines warn us about the greenhouse effect and global warming. The greenhouse effect and global warming are related, but they are not the same thing.

The **greenhouse effect** is natural heating caused when gases in our atmosphere trap heat. The greenhouse effect is illustrated in **Figure 16-14.** Carbon dioxide is the main greenhouse gas. Without the greenhouse effect, life as we know it would not be possible on Earth. Like Mars, Earth would be too cold.

Global Warming

Global warming means global temperatures are rising. One reason for global warming is the increase of greenhouse gases in our atmosphere. An increase in greenhouse gases increases the greenhouse effect. In the last 100 years, surface temperature on Earth has increased 0.5°C. This may be from global warming. ☑

Reading Check ☑

What is global warming?

If the mean temperature continues to rise, ice caps will melt. Low-lying areas might experience increased flooding. Already some ice caps are beginning to break apart and sea level is rising in certain areas. Some scientific studies show that these events are related to Earth's increased temperature.

You learned in the previous section that organisms are adapted to their environments. When environments change, can organisms adjust? In some tropical waters around the world, corals are dying. Are these deaths caused by warmer water? Many people think so.

Figure 16-14
The sun's radiation travels through our atmosphere and heats Earth's surface. Greenhouse gases in our atmosphere trap the heat. **How is this similar to the way a greenhouse works?**

Using Math

When ice sheets melt, sea level rises. Between 1900 and 1970, sea level at New York City rose 23 cm. What was the average rise in sea level per year from 1900 to 1970? The present elevation of New York City is 396 cm above sea level. If sea level continues to rise at the same rate, when will New York City start to go under water?

Some climate models show that in the future, Earth's temperatures will increase faster than they have in the last 100 years. Next, you will learn how people's activities may add to global warming, and you will find out what you can do to help lessen this problem.

Human Activities and Carbon Dioxide

Human activities affect the air in our atmosphere. Burning fossil fuels and removing vegetation add carbon dioxide to the atmosphere and contribute to global warming. Each year, the amount of carbon dioxide in our atmosphere continues to increase.

Burning Fossil Fuels

When natural gas, petroleum, and coal are burned for energy, the carbon in these fossil fuels is combined with oxygen. This increases the amount of carbon dioxide (CO_2) in our atmosphere.

Deforestation

Destroying and cutting down forests, called **deforestation,** also affects the amount of carbon dioxide in our atmosphere. Forests, such as the one shown in **Figure 16-15,** are cleared for mining, roads, buildings, and grazing cattle. Forests also are dying from the effects of pollution.

Figure 16-15 When forests are cleared or burned, carbon dioxide levels increase in the atmosphere. **What can people do to help reduce CO_2 levels in the atmosphere?**

As they grow, trees take in carbon dioxide. When trees are removed, the carbon dioxide they could have removed from the atmosphere is left. Cut-down trees are often burned. Burning produces more carbon dioxide.

Ways to Reduce CO_2

What can we each do to help reduce the amount of CO_2 in the atmosphere? Conserving electricity is one answer. When we conserve electricity, we reduce the amount of fossil fuels that must be burned. One way to save fuel is to change daily activities that rely on energy from burning fossil fuels. Turn off the TV, for instance, when no one is watching it. Walk or ride a bike to the store, if possible, instead of driving a car. We also can use different energy sources to meet our energy needs, such as the wind farm shown in **Figure 16-16.**

Another way to reduce CO_2 is to plant vegetation. As you've learned, plants remove carbon dioxide from the atmosphere. Correctly planted vegetation also can shelter homes from cold winds or blazing sun and reduce the use of electricity.

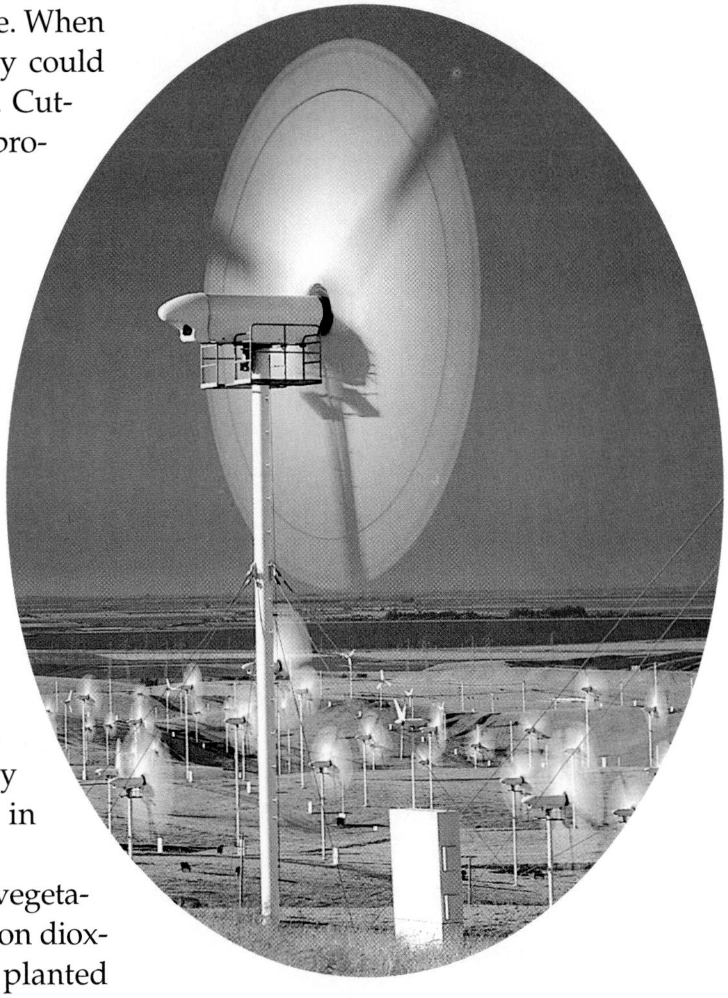

Figure 16-16 This wind farm in California generates electricity without adding CO_2 to the atmosphere.

Section Assessment

1. What causes seasons?
2. In what way does El Niño change the climate?
3. **Think Critically:** How do we know that climates of earlier geologic eras were different from today's climates?
4. **Skill Builder**
   Interpreting Data Ice cores help scientists study Earth's past climate. Do the **Chapter 16 Skill Activity** on page 709 to determine how average global temperatures have changed over the last 165 000 years.

Using Computers

Word Processing
Design a pamphlet to inform people why Earth's climate changes. What are your predictions for the future? On what evidence do you base these predictions? Include this evidence in your pamphlet. If you need help, refer to page 684.

Activity 16•2

Using Scientific Methods

The Greenhouse Effect

Materials

- Identical large, empty glass jars (2)
- Lid for one jar
- Thermometers (3)

Have you ever climbed into a car on a warm day and burned yourself on the seat? Why was it so hot inside the car when it wasn't that hot outside? It was hotter in the car because the car functioned like a greenhouse. You experienced the greenhouse effect.

What You'll Investigate

How can you demonstrate the greenhouse effect?

Goals

- **Make a model** to demonstrate the greenhouse effect.
- **Measure** and **graph** temperature changes.

Safety Precautions

Be careful when you handle glass thermometers. If a thermometer breaks, do not touch it. Have your teacher dispose of the glass safely.

Procedure

1. Lay a thermometer inside each jar.
2. Place the jars next to each other by a sunny window. Lay the third thermometer between the jars.
3. **Record** the temperatures of the three thermometers. They should be the same.
4. Place the lid on one jar.
5. **Record** the temperatures of all three thermometers at the end of five, ten, and 15 minutes.
6. **Make a line graph** that shows the temperatures of the three thermometers for the 15 minutes of the experiment.

Conclude and Apply

1. **Explain** why you placed a thermometer between the two jars.
2. What were the constants in this experiment? What was the variable?
3. Which thermometer experienced the greatest temperature change during your experiment? Why?
4. **Analyze** what occurred in this experiment. How was the lid in this experiment like the greenhouse gases in the atmosphere?
5. **Infer** from this experiment why you should never leave a pet inside a closed car in warm weather.

History of Science

NATIONAL GEOGRAPHIC

Climate

Climate usually changes slowly over long periods of time. But, over the past few hundred years, scientists have learned that climate can sometimes change rapidly. The earliest climate records were written accounts of notable events, such as how much grain was harvested in a year. It wasn't until the 1800s that scientists began to draw conclusions about past climatic conditions based on their observations of the natural world.

Tree Rings

In the early 1900s, a unique method for obtaining information on climate was developed. Called dendrochronology, it is based on measuring the width of annual growth rings (see inset) in trees. In general, wet years produce wide rings while dry years produce narrow rings. By analyzing the annual rings of a large, old tree, wet and dry periods can be identified in the tree trunk. Climate records going as far back as 8000 years ago have been obtained from some of the world's oldest trees.

Ice Cores

Perhaps the most widely used method for obtaining climatic information measures the ratio of uncommon heavier types of water molecules to ordinary water molecules in the environment. When raindrops and snow crystals form, this ratio changes as the temperature changes. By measuring this ratio in ice cores from Greenland and Antarctica, temperature records as old as 100 000 years can be obtained. At left, a scientist saws an ice core sample. Such cores show that major climate changes sometimes occurred in just a few decades.

Other new techniques make use of ancient coral deposits, fossils, and sediments in lake and ocean beds. Data gathered from these sources help researchers explain the climate of today and better predict the climate of the future.

Science JOURNAL

Imagine that you are living on a thick sheet of glacial ice during an ice age. In your Science Journal, describe what you would need to survive.

Chapter 16 Reviewing Main Ideas

For a **preview** of this chapter, study this Reviewing Main Ideas before you read the chapter. After you have studied this chapter, you can use the Reviewing Main Ideas to **review** the chapter.

The Glencoe MindJogger, Audiocassettes, and CD-ROM provide additional opportunities for review.

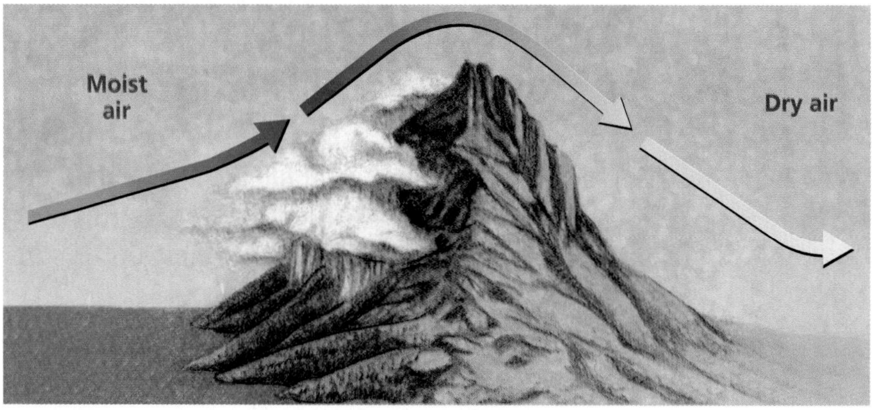

Section

16-1 WHAT IS CLIMATE?

The **climate** of an area is the average weather over a long period of time, such as 30 years. The three main types of climate are tropical, polar, and temperate. In general, higher latitudes experience cooler climates than lower latitudes do. Natural features such as oceans, mountains, and even large cities affect climate. ***In what ways do large cities affect the climate of nearby areas?***

Section

16-2 CLIMATE TYPES

Climates are classified by various characteristics, such as temperature, precipitation, and vegetation. Organisms have structural and behavioral **adaptations** that help them survive in particular climates. Adaptations develop in a population over a long period of time. ***What are some adaptations of organisms that live in tropical, wet climates?***

Reading Check

Is the greenhouse effect a fact or an opinion? How do you know? What are two facts related to climate? What are two opinions?

Section 16-3 CLIMATIC CHANGES

Seasons are caused by Earth's tilt on its axis as it revolves around the sun. **El Niño** disrupts the normal wind and precipitation patterns around the world. Geological records show that in the past, Earth's climate alternated between ice ages and warm periods called interglacial intervals. ***Why are seasons and El Niño considered to be short-term climatic changes?***

GLOBAL WARMING

The **greenhouse effect** occurs naturally when certain gases trap Earth's heat. **Global warming** occurs when global temperatures rise because of an increased greenhouse effect. Many people feel that humans are contributing to global warming. ***How does planting vegetation help decrease the amount of carbon dioxide in the atmosphere?***

Chapter 16 Assessment

Using Vocabulary

a. adaptation
b. climate
c. deforestation
d. El Niño
e. global warming
f. greenhouse effect
g. hibernation
h. polar zone
i. season
j. temperate zone
k. tropics

Explain the differences between the terms in each of the following sets.

1. global warming, greenhouse effect
2. polar zone, temperate zone
3. adaptation, hibernation
4. climate, season
5. deforestation, El Niño

Checking Concepts

Choose the word or phrase that best answers the question.

6. What is commonly found in places where warm air crosses a mountain and descends?
   A) lakes
   B) rain forests
   C) deserts
   D) glaciers
7. What do the fossils of tropical plants and animals found in polar regions tell scientists?
   A) the temperature of earlier geologic eras
   B) the relative length of growing seasons
   C) behavioral adaptations
   D) the amount of carbon dioxide in the air in prehistoric times
8. What is the main greenhouse gas in our atmosphere?
   A) helium
   B) carbon dioxide
   C) hydrogen
   D) oxygen
9. What latitude receives the most direct rays of the sun year-round?
   A) 60°N
   B) 90°
   C) 30°S
   D) 0°
10. What happens as you climb a mountain?
    A) temperature decreases
    B) temperature increases
    C) air pressure increases
    D) air pressure remains constant
11. Which of the following is true of El Niño?
    A) It occurs every ten to 20 years.
    B) It causes flooding in Australia.
    C) It cools the waters off Alaska.
    D) It sometimes reverses the direction of the trade winds.
12. What do changes in Earth's orbit affect?
    A) Earth's shape
    B) Earth's temperatures
    C) Earth's rotation
    D) Earth's tilt
13. The Köppen Climate Classification System is based on precipitation and what other factor?
    A) temperature
    B) air pressure
    C) winds
    D) latitude
14. Which of the following is an example of structural adaptation?
    A) hibernation
    B) migration
    C) fur
    D) estivation
15. How can people help reduce global warming?
    A) conserve energy
    B) burn coal
    C) produce methane
    D) remove trees

Thinking Critically

16. Why will global warming lead to the extinction of some organisms?
17. What can you infer if you find fossils of tropical plants in a desert?
18. On a summer day, why would a Florida beach be cooler than an orange grove 2 km away?
19. What would happen to global climates if the sun became larger?
20. Why would it be cooler if you climb to a higher elevation in a desert?

Developing Skills

If you need help, refer to the Skill Handbook.

21. **Interpreting Scientific Illustrations:** Study the graph below. How many years does it span?

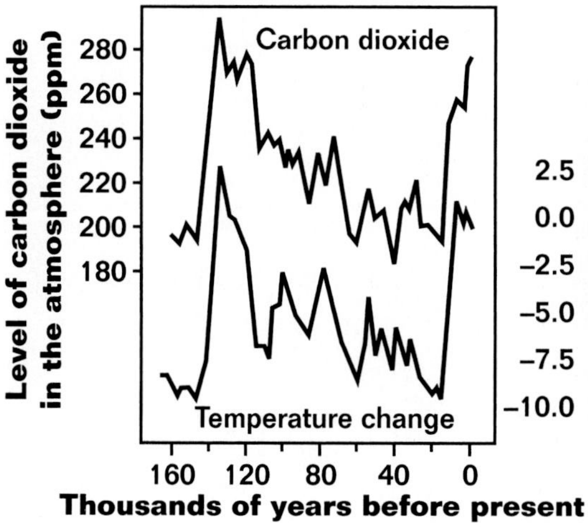

22. **Infer:** Explain how atmospheric pressure over the Pacific Ocean might affect the direction that the trade winds blow.
23. **Sequencing:** Make a chain-of-events chart to explain the effect of a major volcanic eruption on climate.

THE PRINCETON REVIEW

Test-Taking Tip

Investigate Ask what kinds of questions to expect on the test. Ask for practice tests so that you can become familiar with the test-taking materials.

Test Practice

The graph on this page shows long-term variations in atmospheric carbon dioxide levels and global temperature. Study this graph and answer the following questions. Use these questions to test your Science Proficiency.

1. Which of the following statements **BEST** describes the information on this graph?
   A) As carbon dioxide in the atmosphere has increased, so has global temperature.
   B) As carbon dioxide in the atmosphere has increased, global temperature has decreased.
   C) As global temperature has increased, carbon dioxide in the atmosphere has decreased.
   D) There is no relationship between carbon dioxide in the atmosphere and global temperatures.
2. Which of these statements is true according to the information in this graph?
   A) Earth's global-mean temperature has never been hotter than today.
   B) There has never been a higher level of carbon dioxide on Earth than today.
   C) The global-mean temperature 60 000 years ago was at its lowest point.
   D) The highest level of carbon dioxide in the atmosphere 80 000 years ago was 235 ppm.

CHAPTER

17 Ocean Motion

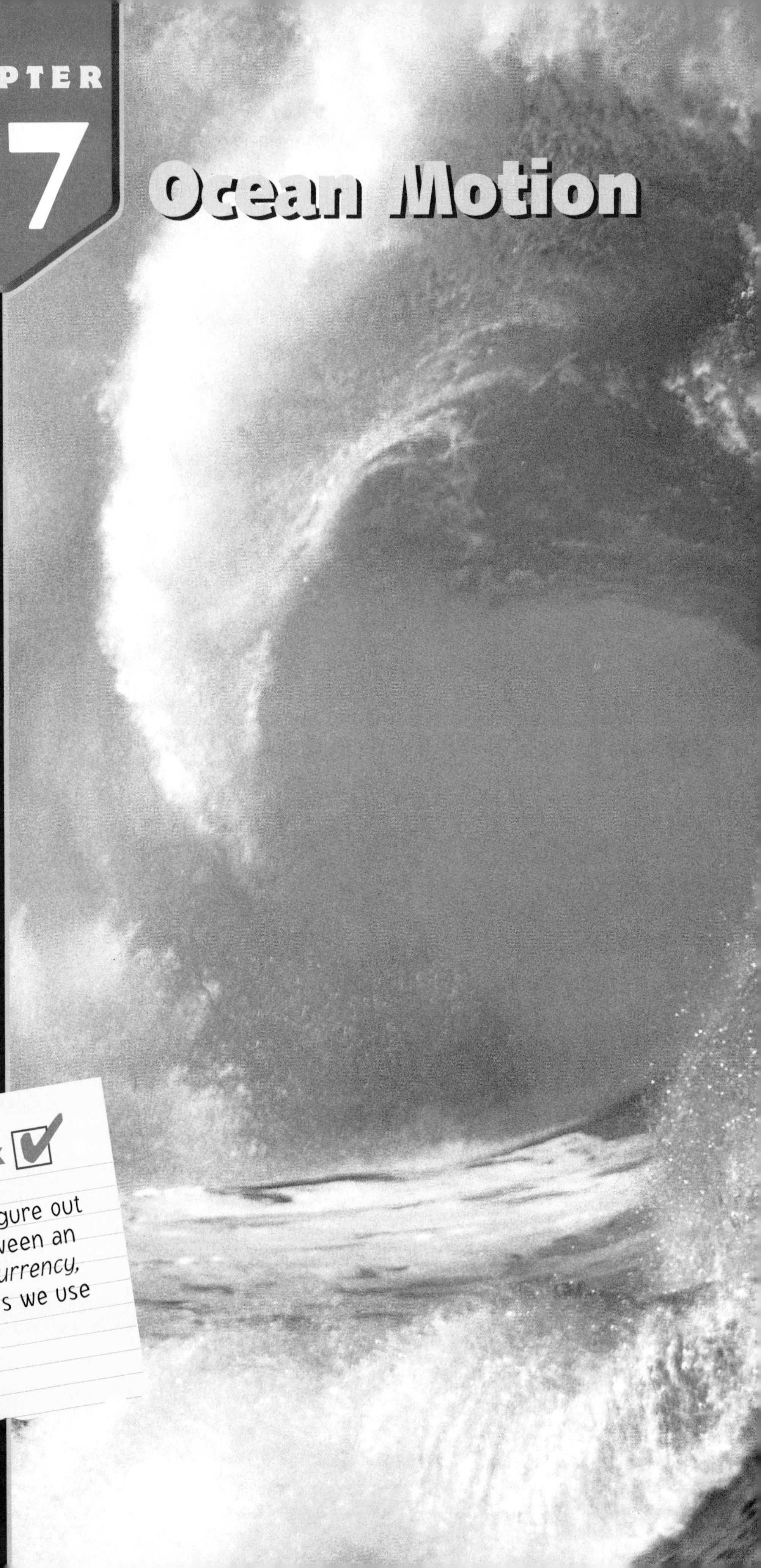

Chapter Preview

Skills Preview

Skill Builders

- Predict
- Compare and Contrast

Activities

- Recognize Cause and Effect
- Measure in SI

MiniLabs

- Make a Model
- Observe and Infer

Reading Check

Use a dictionary to figure out the relationship between an ocean *current* and *currency,* the coins and dollars we use to buy things.

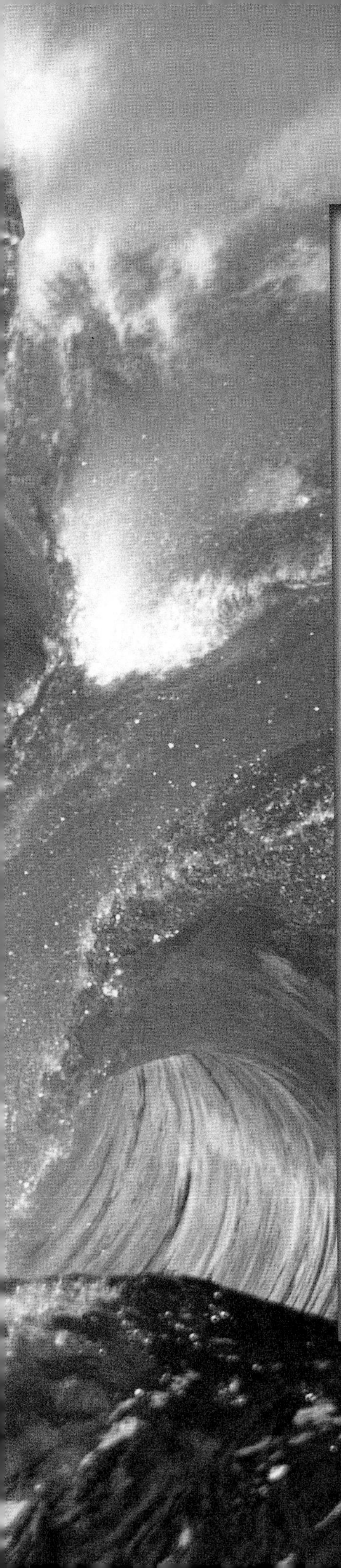

Explore Activity

The ocean is constantly in motion. Waves, such as the one on the left, break against the shore with great energy. Wind causes most waves in the ocean, ranging in size from small ripples to the giant waves of hurricanes. Some reach more than 30 m high. Winds also cause general movements of ocean water in currents around the world. In this chapter, you will learn more about the interaction between the atmosphere and the oceans, as well as how waves, currents, and tides work.

Observe Currents

1. In a bowl, melt some ice to make ice water.
2. Add three drops of food coloring to the ice water.
3. Fill a 250-mL beaker with warm water.
4. Use a dropper to place three to four drops of the ice water on the surface of the warm water.
5. Repeat the experiment, but this time, *slowly* insert the full dropper until the tip is 1 cm from the bottom of the beaker. Squeeze out the dropper and *slowly* pull it back out.

Science Journal

In your Science Journal, record which procedure produced a current. Describe what the current looked like. Look up the word *convection* in the dictionary. Infer why the current created is called a convection current.

17•1 Ocean Water

What You'll Learn

- The origin of the water in Earth's oceans
- Why the ocean is salty
- The composition of seawater

Vocabulary
basin
salinity

Why It's Important

- Oceans affect weather and provide food, oxygen, and natural resources.

Oceans and You

Oceans affect your life, and your life affects oceans. No matter where you live, the ocean influences you. When it rains, most of the water that falls comes from oceans. If the day is sunny, it is partly due to weather systems that develop over oceans. Oceans are a source of food and resources. **Figure 17-1A** shows a rig drilling oil from beneath the ocean floor. Fish taken from the sea are shown in **Figure 17-1B.**

Oceans also act as barriers between continents. The price of clothing, cars, and gasoline may include the cost of shipping these materials across oceans. To go from the United States to Europe, a traveler must fly or take a ship across the ocean. In the past, humans have migrated across oceans to new lands. Oceans also provide a means of transportation for plants and animals. Animals migrate with ocean currents. Plant seeds are washed from one coast to another by oceans.

Figure 17-1 We depend on the oceans. Some of our oil comes from wells drilled through rock layers under the oceans (A). Some food comes from the oceans (B).

B

A

Human activity also affects the oceans. If you live near a stream that is polluted, that pollution can travel to an ocean. Cities near oceans regularly dump sewage sludge into the ocean. Oil spills destroy beaches and marshes along the ocean.

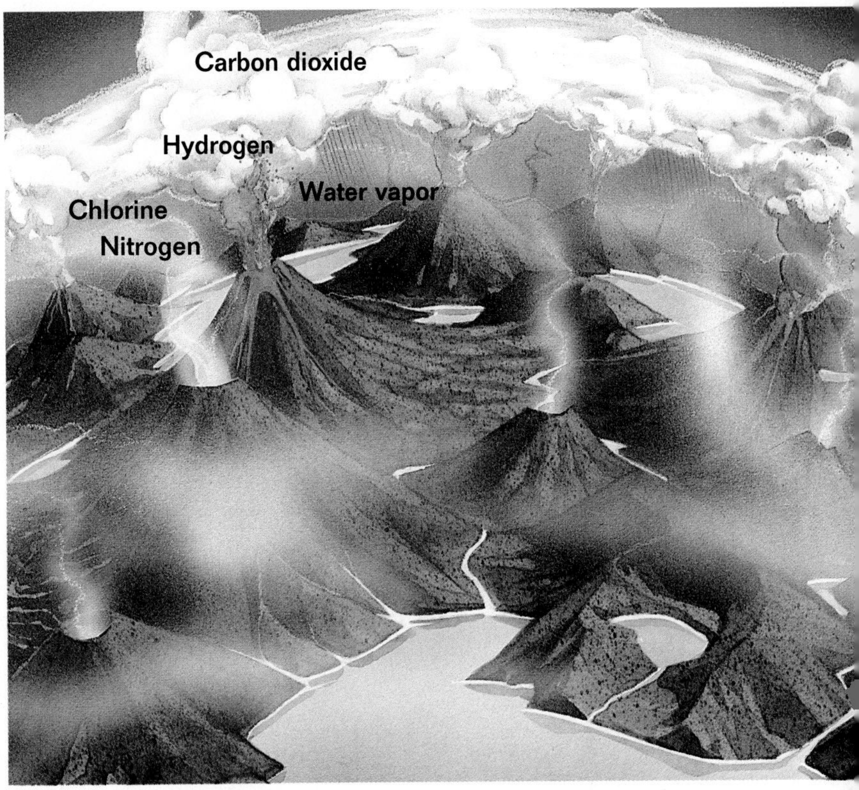

Figure 17-2 Earth's oceans may have formed from water vapor. This water vapor was released into the atmosphere by volcanoes that also gave off chlorine, carbon dioxide, nitrogen, and hydrogen.

Origin of Oceans

In the first billion years after Earth formed, its surface was much more volcanically active than it is today, as illustrated in **Figure 17-2.** When volcanoes erupt, they spew lava and ash, and they also give off water vapor, carbon dioxide, and other gases. Scientists hypothesize that about 4 billion years ago, this water vapor began to be stored in Earth's early atmosphere. Over millions of years, it cooled enough to condense into storm clouds. Torrential rains began to fall. Oceans were formed as this water filled low areas on Earth called **basins.**

Composition of Oceans

Humans use a lot of water each day. In some areas, freshwater is limited. When water demand in these areas increases, too much water may be pumped from aquifers. This can cause a decrease in the freshwater supply.

Seventy percent of Earth's surface is covered by ocean water. If we could use ocean water to meet our water needs, the demand on the freshwater supply would be decreased. But, water from an ocean is different from drinking water. It tastes salty because the ocean contains many dissolved salts. In the water, these salts are separated into chloride, sodium, sulfur, magnesium, calcium, and potassium.

These salts come from rivers and groundwater that slowly dissolve elements such as calcium, magnesium, and sodium from rocks and minerals. Rivers carry these elements to the oceans. Erupting volcanoes add elements, such as sulfur and chlorine, to the atmosphere and oceans.

Using Math

Make a circle graph to show the percentage of Earth's surface that is ocean. Explain the steps you took to complete your graph. Compare your procedures and graph with those of other students.

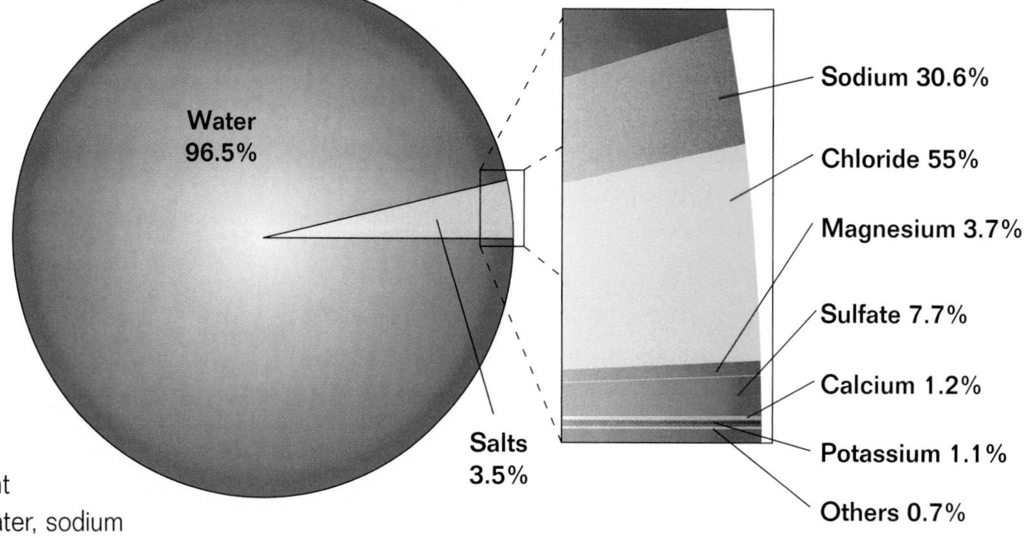

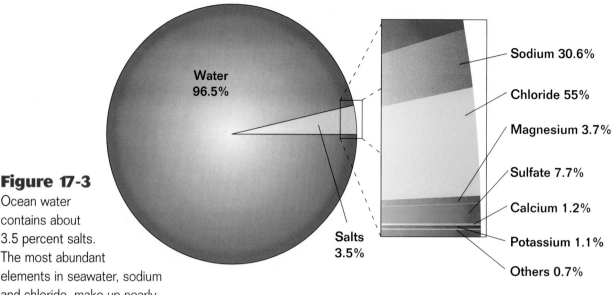

Figure 17-3 Ocean water contains about 3.5 percent salts. The most abundant elements in seawater, sodium and chloride, make up nearly 86 percent of the substances in seawater.

Salinity

The most abundant elements in seawater are sodium and chlorine. As rivers flow to the ocean, they dissolve sodium along the way. Volcanoes add chlorine gas. These elements also make up most of the salt in seawater. If seawater evaporates, the sodium and chlorine combine to form a salt called halite. Halite is the salt you use to season food. It is this salt and similar ones that give ocean water its salty taste. ☑

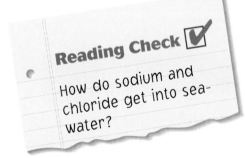

Reading Check ☑

How do sodium and chloride get into seawater?

Salinity (say LIH nuh tee) is a measure of the amount of salts dissolved in seawater. It is usually measured in grams of salt per kilogram of water. One kilogram of ocean water contains about 35 g of dissolved salts, or about 3.5 percent dissolved salts. The graph in **Figure 17-3** lists the most abundant salts in ocean water. The proportion and amount of dissolved salts in seawater remain nearly constant and have stayed about the same for hundreds of millions of years. This tells us that the composition of the oceans is in balance. Oceans are not growing saltier.

Element Removal

LIFE SCIENCE INTEGRATION ➤

Although rivers, volcanoes, and the atmosphere constantly add substances to the ocean, the oceans are considered to be in a steady state. As new substances are added to the oceans, elements are being removed. They are removed by becoming sediment and by biological processes. Sea animals and algae use dissolved substances. Some marine animals use calcium to form bones. Other animals, such as oysters and clams, use calcium to form shells. Some algae, called diatoms, have silica shells. Because many organisms use calcium and silica, these substances are removed more quickly from seawater than substances such as chloride or sodium.

Desalination

Salt also can be removed from ocean water. The process that removes salt from ocean water is called desalination. If you have ever gone swimming in the ocean, you know what happens when your skin dries. The white, sticky substance on your skin is salt. As seawater evaporates, the salt is left behind. As the demand for freshwater increases throughout the world, scientists are developing technology to remove salt from seawater and make it drinkable. A desalination plant is shown in **Figure 17-4.** Some methods include evaporating the seawater and collecting the freshwater as it condenses on a glass roof. An electric current can be passed through the water to collect the salt. Also, frozen seawater can be separated into salt crystals and freshwater ice crystals.

The oceans originally formed from water vapor that condensed and fell as rain, then collected in basins. Volcanoes, groundwater, and rivers added salts and other elements to seawater, giving the oceans their compositions.

Figure 17-4 This desalination plant is in Saudi Arabia. **Which body of water do you think Saudi Arabia uses to make freshwater from salt water?** (Hint: Locate Saudi Arabia on a map.)

Section Assessment

1. According to scientific theory, how were Earth's oceans formed?
2. Why does ocean water taste salty?
3. How have ocean currents affected the distribution of plants and animals on Earth?
4. **Think Critically:** Why does the salinity of Earth's oceans remain constant?
5. **Skill Builder**
   Concept Mapping Make a concept map that shows how halite becomes dissolved in the oceans. Use the terms *rivers, volcanoes, halite, source of, sodium, chlorine,* and *combine to form.* If you need help, refer to Concept Mapping in the **Skill Handbook** on page 666.

Science Journal

What is happening in this excerpt from "The Rime of the Ancient Mariner" by S. T. Coleridge?

As idle as a painted ship
Upon a painted ocean.
Water, water, everywhere,
And all the boards did shrink;
Water, water, everywhere,
Nor any drop to drink.

Water, Water, Everywhere

Materials

- Pan balance
- Table salt
- Water (500 mL)
- Flask (1000 mL)
- Beaker (600 mL)
- Plastic spoon
- Hot plate
- Scissors
- Ice
- 1-hole rubber stopper with curved or bent plastic tubing
- Rubber tubing (60 cm)
- Cardboard sheet (12 cm^2)
- Metal washers (4–5)
- Shallow pan
- Watch glasses (2)

Imagine being stranded on an island. You're thirsty, but you can't find any freshwater. There's plenty of salt water. How can you remove the salts from the water so that you can drink it?

What You'll Investigate

How can you make freshwater from salt water?

Goals

- **Make a model** to demonstrate desalination.
- **Observe** and **infer** how desalination works.

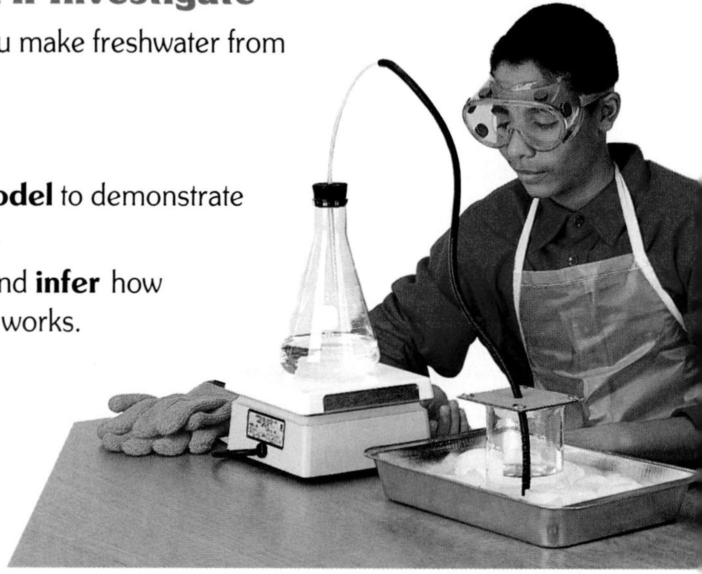

Procedure

1. **Dissolve** 18 g of table salt in a beaker containing 500 mL of water. Use the spoon to thoroughly mix the saltwater solution.
2. **Pour** the solution into the flask. **Insert** the stopper into the flask. Make sure the plastic tubing is above the surface of the solution. Place the flask on the hot plate. Do not turn on the hot plate.
3. Use the scissors to cut a small hole in the piece of cardboard. **Insert** the free end of the rubber tubing through the hole. Be sure to keep the tubing away from the hot plate.
4. **Place** the cardboard over a clean beaker. Add several washers to the cardboard to hold it in place.
5. Set the beaker in a shallow pan filled with ice.
6. Turn on the hot plate. Bring the solution to a boil. **Observe** what happens in the flask and in the beaker.
7. Continue boiling until the solution is almost, but not quite, boiled away. Turn off the hot plate and let the water in the beaker cool.
8. **Measure** the volume of water in the beaker and the volume of salt water remaining in the flask.
9. **Pour** a small sample of water from the beaker into one watch glass and water from the flask into the other watch glass. **Evaporate** the water samples on the hot plate. **Observe** each sample.

Conclude and Apply

1. **Compare** the combined volumes of water in the beaker and flask with the volume of the salt water at the beginning. Are they the same? Explain.
2. **Explain** your results by drawing a diagram of the experiment. **Label** the processes involved.

Ocean Currents

17-2

Surface Currents

The ocean is always moving. A mass movement or flow of ocean water is called a current. When you stir chocolate flavoring into milk or stir a pot of soup, you make currents with the spoon. The currents are what mix the liquid. An ocean current is like a river within the ocean. It moves masses of water from place to place.

Ocean currents carry water in various directions. **Surface currents** move water horizontally—parallel to Earth's surface. Surface currents are powered by wind. The wind and the currents force the ocean to move in huge circular patterns all around the world. **Figure 17-5** shows these major surface currents. Surface currents in the ocean also are related to the general circulation of wind on Earth.

What You'll Learn

- How winds, the Coriolis effect, and continents influence surface currents
- The temperatures of coastal waters
- Density currents

Vocabulary

surface current
upwelling
density current

Why It's Important

- Ocean currents and atmosphere transfer heat to create the climate you live in.

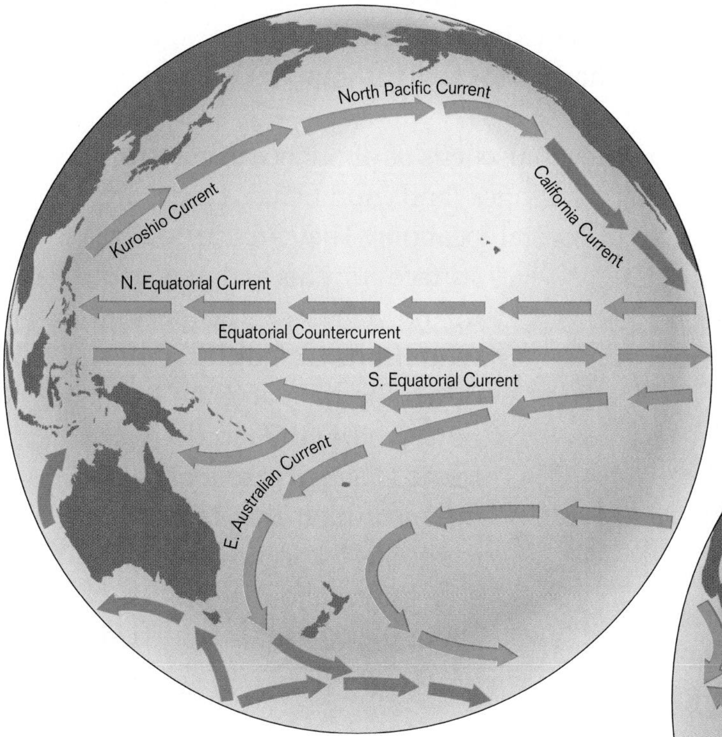

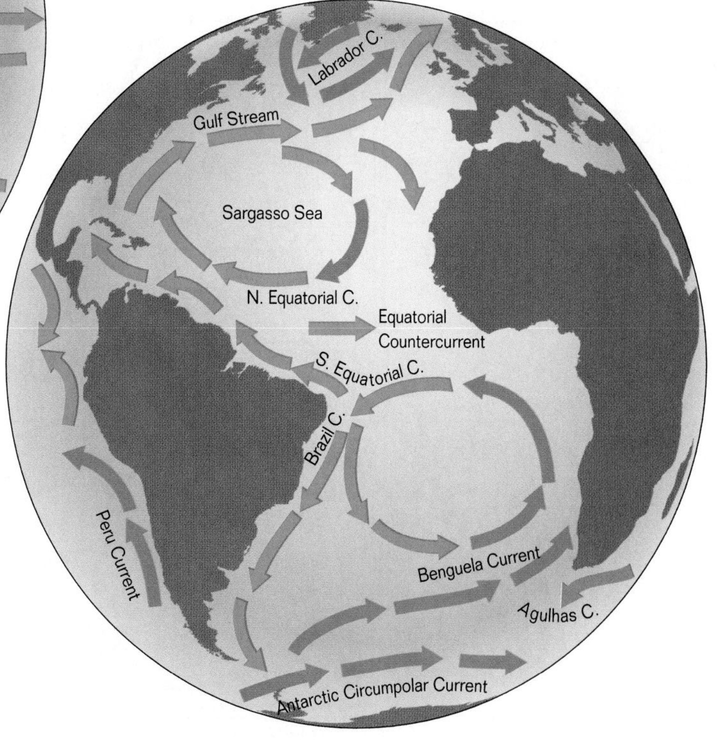

Figure 17-5 These are the major surface currents of Earth's oceans. Red arrows indicate a warm current. Blue arrows indicate a cold current.

Surface currents move only the upper few hundred meters of seawater. Seeds and plants are carried between continents by surface currents. Sailors use these currents along with winds to sail more efficiently from place to place. The Antarctic Circumpolar current is the strongest current in the ocean.

LIFE SCIENCE INTEGRATION

Marine Animals
When marine animals such as eels, turtles, and whales migrate, they often use surface ocean currents. Infer what would happen to animal migration without surface currents.

The Gulf Stream

Although satellites provide new information about ocean movements, much of what we know about surface currents comes from records that were kept by sailors in the nineteenth century. Sailors always have used surface currents to help them travel quickly. Sailing ships depend on one surface current to carry them west and another to carry them east. During the American colonial era, ships floated on the 100-km-wide Gulf Stream current to go quickly from North America to England. On the map in **Figure 17-5,** find the Gulf Stream current in the Atlantic Ocean.

In the late 1600s, the British explorer William Dampier first wrote about the Gulf Stream in his *Discoveries on the Trade Winds.* A century later, Benjamin Franklin published a map of the Gulf Stream that his cousin Captain Timothy Folger, a Massachusetts whaler, had drawn. This map is shown in **Figure 17-6.**

What washes up on beaches also tells us about ocean currents. Drift bottles containing messages and numbered cards are released from a variety of coastal locations. They are carried by surface currents and may end up on a beach. The person who finds a bottle writes down the date and the location where the bottle was found. Then, it is sent back to the institution that launched the bottle. By doing this, valuable information is provided about the current that carried the bottle.

Figure 17-6 Captain Timothy Folger drew this map of the Gulf Stream around 1770.

Other Factors That Influence Surface Currents

Surface ocean currents and surface winds are affected by the Coriolis effect. The Coriolis effect is caused by the rotation of Earth. Imagine that you throw a ball straight up into the air. If it could stay up long enough and come straight back down, the ball would not return to you. Why? Because Earth has rotated while the ball was in flight. And, because you are standing on Earth, you have moved also. The same thing happens to wind. Although the wind may be blowing in a straight line, Earth's rotation causes the wind to be turned. It is turned clockwise in the northern hemisphere and counterclockwise in the southern hemisphere. Surface currents are produced by surface winds. As the surface winds are turned, so are the surface currents. The Coriolis effect turns currents north of the equator, such as the Gulf Stream, clockwise. Currents south of the equator are turned counterclockwise. Look again at the map of surface currents in **Figure 17-5.**

The continents also influence ocean currents. Notice that currents moving toward the west in the Pacific Ocean are turned north and south by Asia and Australia. Then, currents affected by the Coriolis effect move eastward until North and South America turn them. According to the map in **Figure 17-5,** what other surface currents are turned by continents?

*inter***NET**
CONNECTION

Visit the Glencoe Science Web Site at **www.glencoe.com/sec/science/ca** for more information about ocean currents.

Why are surface currents important?

Currents on the west coast of continents are usually cold, but currents on eastern coasts are warm. West coast currents begin near the poles where the waters are colder. East coast currents originate near the equator where the water is warmer. **Figure 17-7** shows the warm waters of the Gulf Stream. How do warm and cold surface currents affect the east and west coasts of the United States?

Surface currents distribute heat from equatorial regions to other areas of Earth. As warm waters flow away from the equator, heat is released to the atmosphere. The atmosphere is warmed. This transfer of heat influences climate.

Figure 17-7 Data on ocean temperature collected by a satellite were used to make this surface-temperature image of the Atlantic Ocean. The warm Gulf Stream waters appear as orange and red, and cooler waters appear as blue and green.

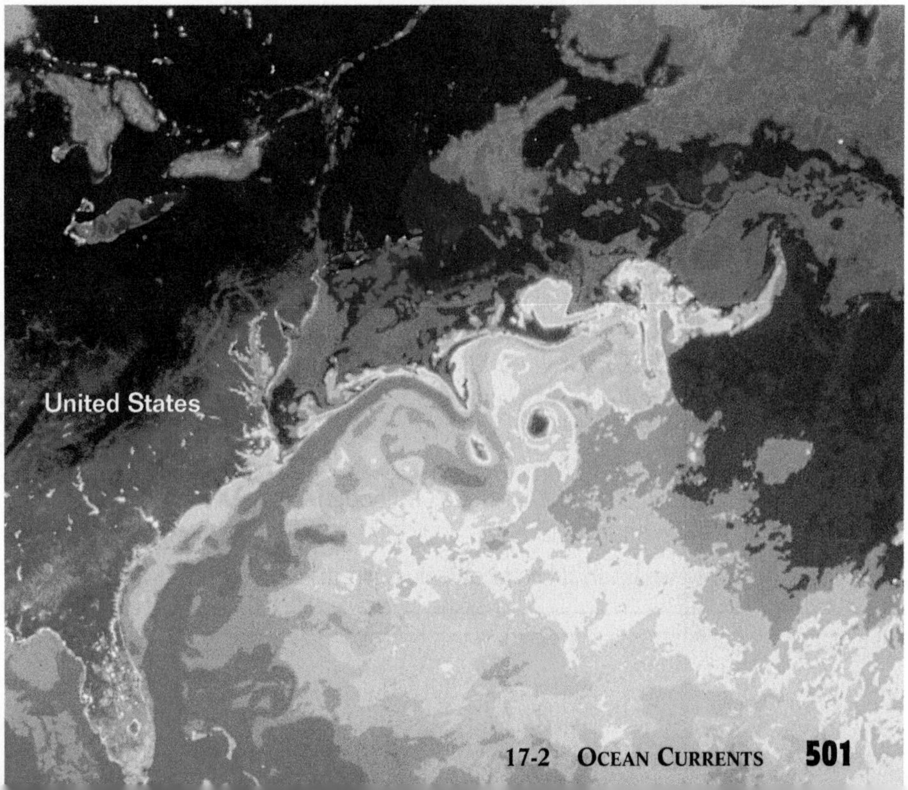

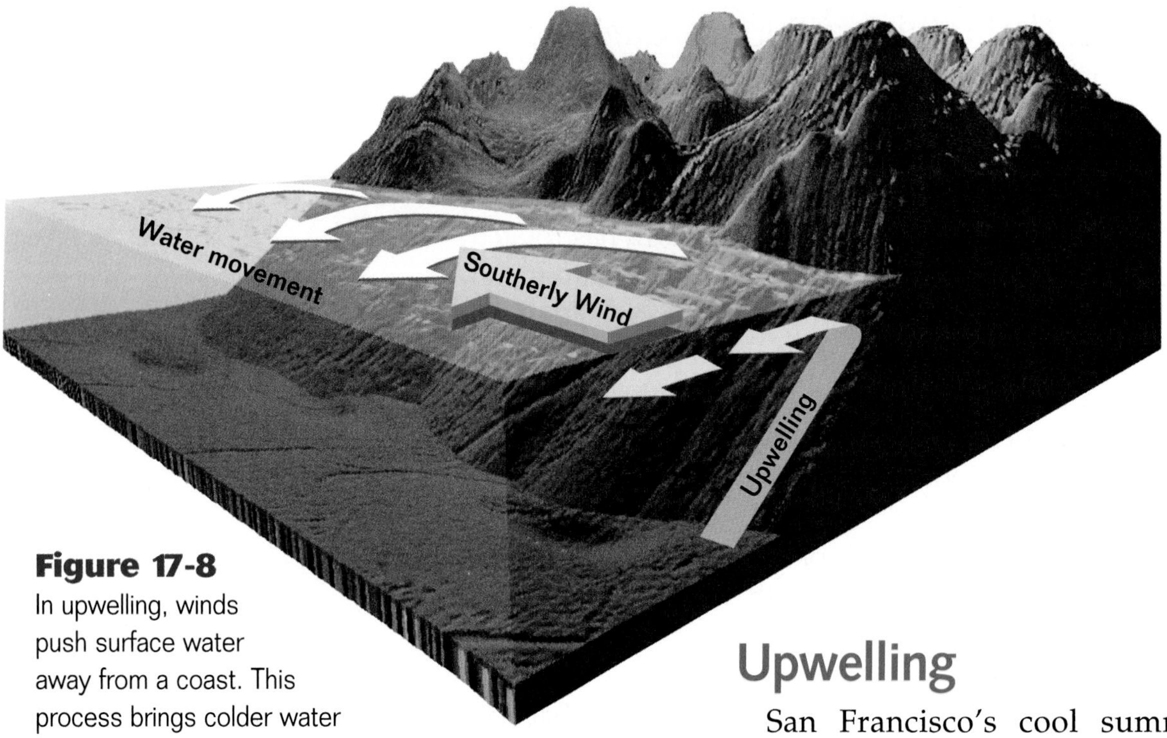

Figure 17-8
In upwelling, winds push surface water away from a coast. This process brings colder water to the surface.

Upwelling

San Francisco's cool summers and famous fogs are due, in part, to upwelling. **Upwelling** is a circulation in the ocean that brings deep, cold water to the ocean surface. Wind blowing offshore or parallel to the coast carries water away from the land as shown in **Figure 17-8.** Cold, deep ocean water rises to the surface and replaces the water that has been blown away. This water contains high concentrations of nutrients from organisms that died, sank to the bottom, and decayed. These nutrients bring fish to areas of upwelling along the coasts of Oregon, Washington, and Peru, which are known as good fishing areas. Upwelling also affects the climate of nearby coastal areas.

Density Currents

Wind-driven surface currents affect only the upper layers of Earth's oceans. Deep in the ocean, waters circulate not because of wind but because of density differences.

A **density current** is a type of convection current. It forms when more dense seawater sinks under less dense seawater. This movement pushes surface ocean water deeper into the ocean.

Try at Home

Mini Lab

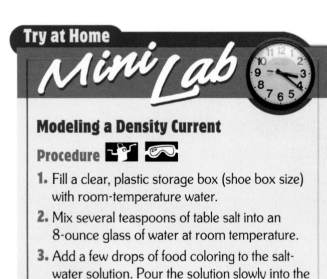

Modeling a Density Current

Procedure

1. Fill a clear, plastic storage box (shoe box size) with room-temperature water.
2. Mix several teaspoons of table salt into an 8-ounce glass of water at room temperature.
3. Add a few drops of food coloring to the salt-water solution. Pour the solution slowly into the freshwater in the large container.

Analyze

1. Describe what happened when you added salt water to freshwater. Explain.
2. How does this lab relate to density currents?

You made a density current in the Explore Activity at the beginning of this chapter. The cold water was more dense than the warm water in the beaker. The cold water sank to the bottom. This created a density current that moved the food coloring.

The density of seawater can be increased by an increase in salinity or by a decrease in temperature. Changes in temperature, salinity, and pressure work together to create density currents. Density currents circulate ocean water slowly. These currents distribute heat throughout Earth's oceans, and some scientists suggest they may have an important effect on Earth's climate. ☑

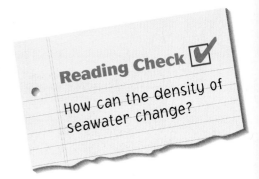

Reading Check ☑

How can the density of seawater change?

An important density current occurs in Antarctica where the most dense ocean water forms during the winter. As ice forms on the surface, seawater freezes, but the salt is left behind in the unfrozen water. This extra salt increases the density of the ocean water until it is very dense. This dense water sinks and slowly spreads along the ocean bottom toward the equator, forming a density current. In the Pacific Ocean, this water may take 1000 years to reach the surface at the equator. In the Atlantic Ocean, dense surface waters that sink circulate more quickly. In the Atlantic, a density current may take 275 years to bring water from the bottom to the surface.

Problem Solving

Interpreting Ocean Temperatures

Imagine that your job is to analyze the data shown in the chart below. The data were collected from three different water masses in the North Atlantic Ocean. You know that one sample came from near the surface, one came from a depth of 750 m, and a third came from the ocean floor. The samples are not labeled and became mixed up in shipment.

Ocean Water

Sample #	Temperature (°C)	Density (g/mL)
1	6	1.02 716
2	3	1.02 781
3	14	1.02 630

Solve the Problem

1. Which sample came from near the surface? How do you know?
2. Which sample of water came from the bottom? How do you know?
3. Hypothesize how less dense seawater can be colder than denser seawater.

Think Critically: During El Niño, the surface winds blow toward South America. How do you think the usual upwelling near Peru is affected?

Figure 17-9 Surface currents in the ocean carry objects from long distances. In May 1991, thousands of sneakers washed up on Oregon beaches. The North Pacific drift and California current had carried 80 000 new shoes from the site of a shipping accident a year earlier in the mid-Pacific and deposited them on the western edge of the United States.

A density current also occurs in the Mediterranean, a nearly enclosed sea. Warm temperatures evaporate water from the surface, increasing the salinity and the density of the water. This dense water from the Mediterranean flows into the less dense water of the Atlantic Ocean. When it reaches the Atlantic, it flows deeper in a density current.

Our knowledge has come a long way since early investigations of the Gulf Stream. Today, we can track ocean currents by objects that wash up on shore as shown in **Figure 17-9** and by satellite. This information helps ships navigate, fishing fleets locate upwellings, and us to understand climate and track hurricanes.

Section Assessment

1. How does the energy from wind affect surface currents?
2. How do density currents affect the circulation of water in deep parts of the oceans?
3. **Think Critically:** The latitudes of San Diego, California, and Charleston, South Carolina, are exactly the same. However, the average yearly water temperature in the ocean off Charleston is much higher than the water temperature off San Diego. Why?
4. **Skill Builder**
   Predicting A river flows into the ocean. Predict what will happen to this layer of freshwater. Explain your prediction. If you need help, refer to Predicting in the **Skill Handbook** on page 682.

Using Computers

Spreadsheet Make a spreadsheet that compares surface and density currents. Focus on characteristics such as wind, horizontal and vertical movement, temperature, and density. If you need help, refer to page 690.

Ocean Waves and Tides

17-3

What You'll Learn

- Wave formation
- How water particles move in a wave and how wave energy moves
- How ocean tides form

Vocabulary

wave, crest, trough, breaker, tide, tidal range

Why It's Important

- Waves and tides influence how we use oceans and affect life in coastal areas.

Waves

If you've been to the seashore or seen a beach on TV, you've watched waves roll in. Waves in water are caused by winds, earthquakes, and the gravitational force of the moon and sun. You have probably heard about ocean waves or tsunamis that are caused by earthquakes. But, what is an ocean wave? A **wave** is a rhythmic movement that carries energy through matter or space. In the ocean, waves move through seawater.

Several terms are used to describe waves. **Figure 17-10** shows that the **crest** is the highest point of a wave. The **trough** (TROF) is the lowest point. Wave height is the vertical distance between crest and trough. Wavelength is the horizontal distance between the crests or troughs of two waves.

Wave Movement

When you watch an ocean wave, it looks as though the water is moving forward. But, unless the wave is breaking onto shore, the water itself does not move forward. Each molecule of water stays in about the same place as the wave passes. **Figure 17-11** shows this. To see another example of a wave carrying energy, tie a rope to a tree. Shake the rope up and down until a wave starts across it. Notice that as the

Figure 17-10 The crest, trough, wavelength, and wave height are parts of a wave. **What other types of waves have you learned about?**

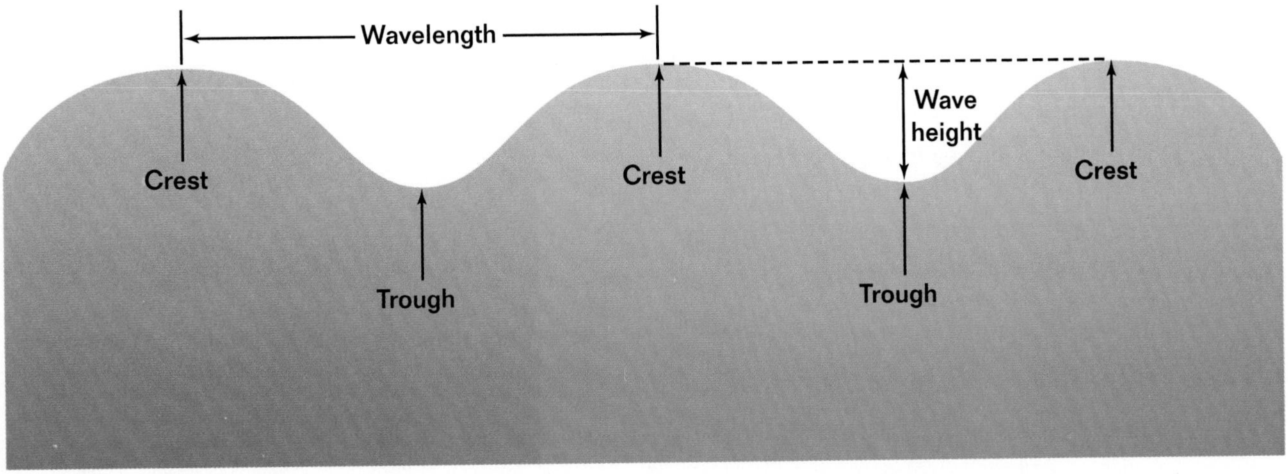

energy passes along the rope, the rope moves. But, each piece of rope is still the same distance from the tree.

In the same way, an object floating on water will rise and fall as a wave passes, but the object will not move forward. Only the energy moves forward, while the water particles remain in the same place.

A wave changes shape in the shallow area near shore. Friction with the ocean bottom slows water at the bottom of the wave. As the wave slows, its crest and trough come closer together. The wave height increases. The top of a wave, not slowed by friction, moves faster than the bottom. Eventually, the top of the wave outruns the bottom and collapses. The wave crest falls, and water tumbles over on itself. The wave breaks onto the shore. **Figure 17-12** illustrates this process. This collapsing wave is a **breaker.** It is the collapse of this wave that propels a surfer and surfboard onto shore. After a wave breaks onto shore, gravity pulls the water back into the sea.

Reading Check

What causes an ocean wave to slow down?

VISUALIZING Waves

Figure 17-11 In a wave, individual particles of water move in circles as the energy passes through.

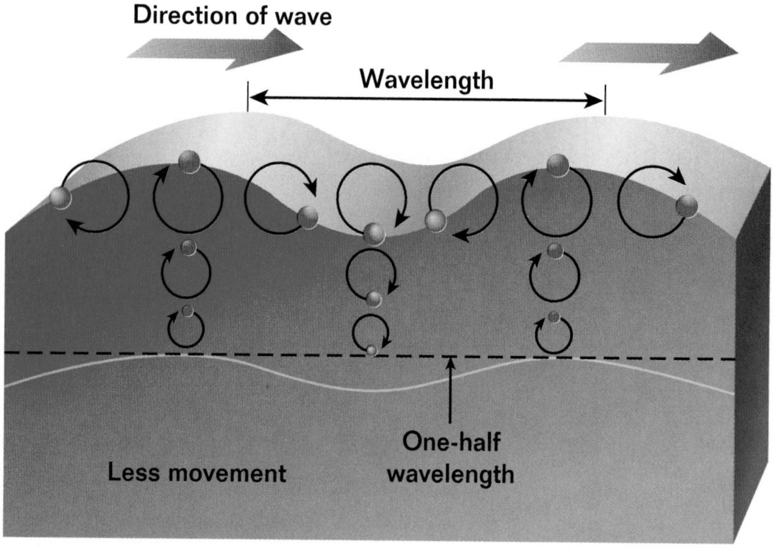

Little water movement occurs below a depth equal to one-half wavelength.

A Particles of water in a wave move around in circles. The farther below the surface, the smaller the circles are. Below a depth equal to about half the wavelength, particle movement stops.

B Wave energy moves forward somewhat like the motion of falling dominoes. Like water particles, individual dominoes remain near where they were standing as they fall, transferring energy to the next domino.

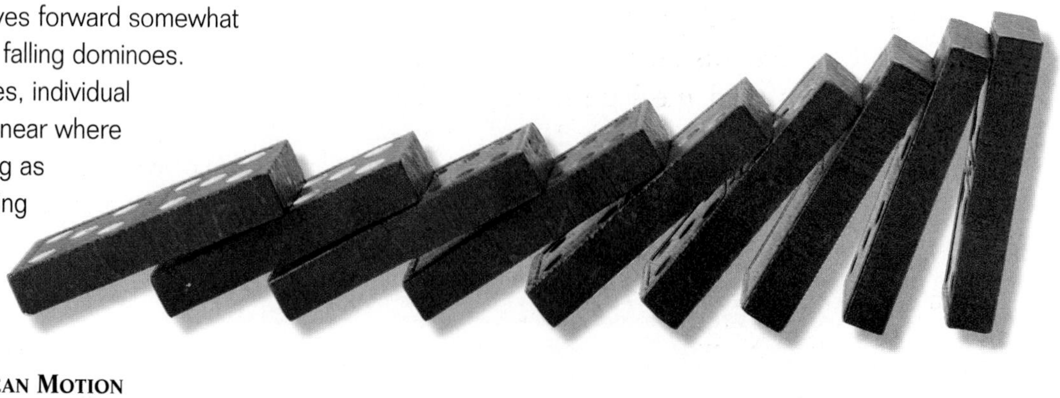

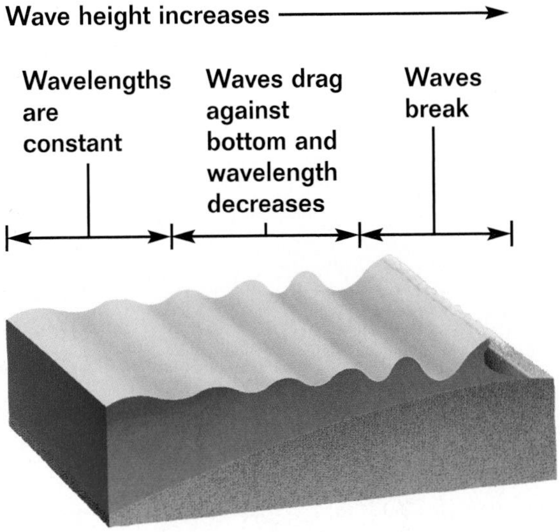

Figure 17-12 Wavelength decreases and wave height increases as waves approach the shore. This causes breakers to form.

There are two different types of ocean waves—the common sea waves caused by wind and the long waves of the tides.

Waves Caused by Wind

When wind blows across a body of water, friction causes the water to move along with the wind. If the wind speed is great enough, the water begins to pile up, forming a wave. As the wind continues to blow, the wave increases in height. The height of waves depends on the speed of the wind, the distance over which the wind blows, and the length of time the wind blows. When the wind stops blowing, waves stop forming. But, once set in motion, waves continue moving for long distances even if the wind stops. Waves at a seashore may have originated halfway around the world.

MiniLab

Modeling Water Movement in a Wave

Procedure

1. Put a piece of tape on the outside bottom of a clear, rectangular, plastic storage box. Fill the box with water.
2. Float a cork in the container above the piece of tape.
3. Use a spoon to make gentle waves in the container.
4. Observe the movement of the waves and the cork.

Analysis

1. Describe the movement of the waves and the motion of the cork.
2. Compare the movement of the cork with the movement of water particles in a wave.

Tides

Have you ever been to the beach and noticed the level of the sea rise and fall during the day? This rise and fall in sea level is called a **tide.** A tide is caused by a giant wave. This wave is only 1 m or 2 m high but thousands of kilometers long. As the crest of this wave approaches the shore, sea level appears to rise. This is called high tide. A few hours later, as the trough of the wave approaches, sea level appears to drop. This is referred to as low tide.

One low-tide–high-tide cycle takes 12 hours and 25 minutes. A daily cycle of two high and two low tides occurs in most places and takes 24 hours and 50 minutes—slightly more than a day. The **tidal range** is the difference between the level of the ocean at high tide and low tide. Notice the tidal range in the photos of **Figure 17-13.**

Figure 17-13 The large difference between high and low tide is seen at Mt. Saint Michel off the northwestern coast of France on a summer day.

A High tide at 6 A.M.

B Low tide at 6:25 P.M.

The Gravitational Effect of the Moon

For the most part, these tides are caused by the interaction of gravity in the Earth-moon system. The moon's gravity exerts a strong pull on Earth. The water in the oceans responds to this pull. The water is pulled outward as Earth and the moon revolve around a common center of mass between them. These events are explained in **Figure 17-14.**

Two bulges of water form, one at the point closest to the moon and one on the exact opposite side of Earth. As Earth spins, these bulges follow the moon. To the earthbound observer, these bulges appear as waves traveling across the oceans. The crests of the waves are the high tides.

As Earth rotates, different locations on Earth's surface pass through high and low tide. The change between high and low tide is different across the world. Near the equator, where the water is spread out over a large area, the difference in high and low tide is hardly noticeable. But, as seen in **Figure 17-13,** water in a smaller area experiences a much larger tidal range.

The Gravitational Effect of the Sun

The sun also affects tides. The sun can strengthen or weaken the moon's effects. When the moon, Earth, and sun are lined up together, they cause spring tides. During spring tides, high tides are higher and low tides are lower than normal. When the sun, Earth, and moon form a right angle, high tides are lower and low tides are higher than normal. These are called neap tides.

Figure 17-14 (A) The moon doesn't really revolve around Earth. They both revolve around a common center of mass. The action of the moon and Earth around the common center causes the bulge of water on the side of Earth opposite the moon. The bulge of water on the side of Earth nearest the moon is caused by the moon's gravity exerting a force on Earth. (B) When the sun, moon, and Earth are aligned, spring tides occur. (C) When the sun, moon, and Earth form a right angle, neap tides occur.

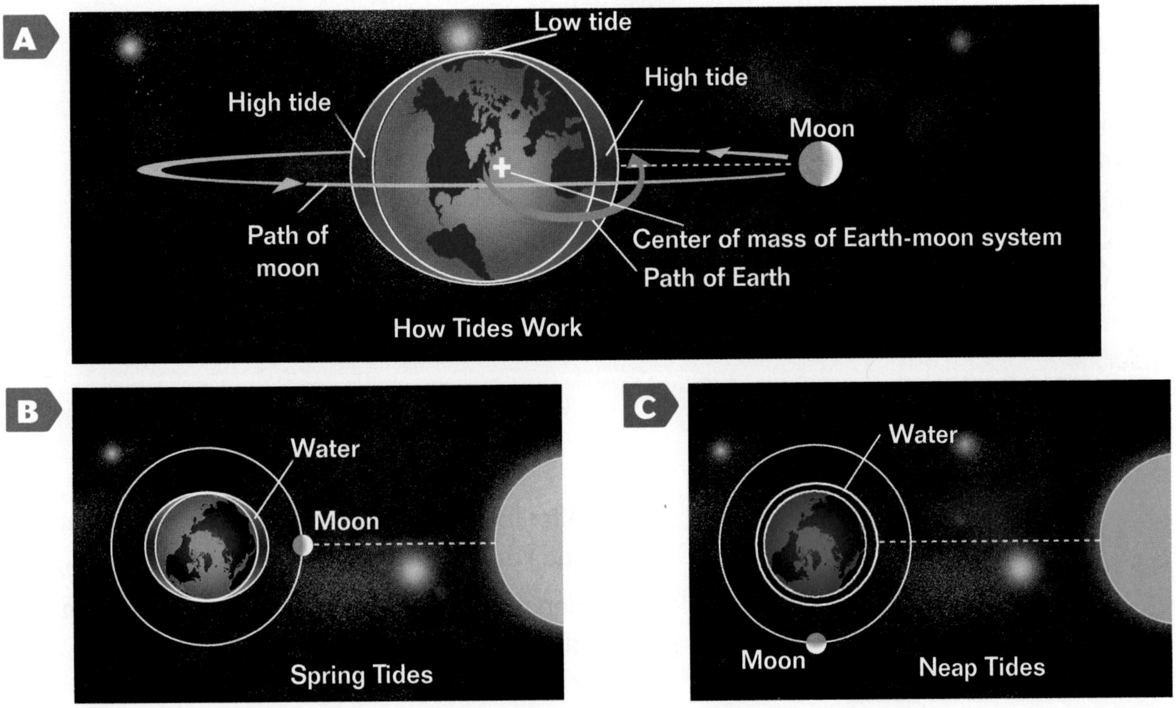

In this section, you've learned how the energy of the wind causes the formation of surface waves. You've also learned how gravity affects the motion of the ocean, with help from Earth, the moon, and sun on the longest waves—tides.

Section Assessment

1. Describe the parts of an ocean wave.
2. What causes high tides?
3. **Think Critically:** At the ocean, you spot a wave about 200 m from shore. A few seconds later, the wave breaks on the beach. Explain why the water in the breaker is not the same water that was in the wave 200 m away.
4. **Skill Builder**
   Comparing and Contrasting To learn more about tides, do the **Chapter 17 Skill Activity** on page 710.

Using Math

The crest of a wave is 35 m above the ocean floor. The trough of a wave is 28 m above the ocean floor. Calculate the wave height.

Making Waves

Materials

- White paper (11" × 14")
- Electric fan (three-speed)
- Light source
- Clock or watch
- Rectangular, clear-plastic storage box
- Ring stand with clamp
- Water
- Metric ruler

Wind helps generate some waves. The energy of motion is transferred from the wind to the surface water of the ocean. The force of the wind affects the waves that are created. What other factors influence the generation of waves?

What You'll Investigate

How does the speed of the wind and the length of time it blows affect the height of a wave?

Goals

- **Observe** how wind speed and duration affect wave height.

Procedure

1. **Position** the box on white paper beside the ring stand.
2. **Clamp** a light source on the ring stand or use a gooseneck lamp. Direct the light onto the box. Fill the plastic box with water to within 3 cm of the top. **CAUTION:** *Do not allow any part of the light or cord to come in contact with the water.*
3. **Place** the fan at one end of the box to create waves. Start on slow. Keep the fan on during measuring. **CAUTION:** *Do not allow any part of the fan or cord to come in contact with the water.*
4. After three minutes, **measure** the height of the waves caused by the fan. **Record** your observations in a table similar to the one shown. Through the plastic box, **observe** the shadows of the waves on the white paper.
5. After five minutes, **measure** the wave height and **record** your observations.
6. Repeat steps 3 to 5 with the fan on medium, then on high.
7. Turn off the fan. Observe what happens.

Conclude and Apply

1. **Analyze** your data to determine whether the wave height is affected by the length of time that the wind blows. Explain.
2. **Analyze** your data to determine whether the height of the waves is affected by the speed of the wind. Explain.
3. **Infer** how wave energy could be used to reduce Earth's dependence on its decreasing supply of fossil fuels.

Wave Data

Fan speed	Time	Wave height	Observations
Low			
Medium			
High			

NATIONAL GEOGRAPHIC

Tidal Power

Are you looking for an energy supply that just won't quit? Try harnessing tides. Tides are the movement of Earth's oceans primarily in response to the gravitational pull of the moon. At high tide, the water is pulled toward shore. At low tide, it is pulled away. Tidal range is a measure of the difference in water level at low tide and at high tide. The Bay of Fundy in eastern Canada boasts the greatest tidal range on Earth—16 m. This immense range makes the Bay of Fundy a perfect place to tap the energy of the tides. In the early 1980s, the Canadian government built a pilot power-generating plant there (left).

Tidal Dams

Tidal power is harnessed by tidal dams. At high tide, the gates of the dam open to let water enter. Then, the gates close, storing the water behind the dam. As the tide goes out, the dammed-up water is passed over turbines in the dam. The turbines contain blades similar to those of a fan. When the water pushes against the blades, the turbines spin and generate electricity.

Electric power-generating plants that use tidal power also have been built in Russia, China, and France. The largest tidal power plant constructed so far is located on the Rance River in France. It provides enough power for the region of Brittany and surrounding areas (about the size of the state of Kentucky).

Generating electric power using tides has many advantages. Tidal energy does not run out. There are no expenses for fuel, pollution control, or waste disposal. The cost of the power to customers is relatively low.

Possible Problems

Building a tidal dam is expensive, and tidal dams don't always produce electricity at times of peak demand because the electricity can't be stored. Tidal dams can cause environmental problems such as loss of habitat for shorebirds and fish. Also, boating can be affected if water becomes too shallow due to dam operation.

interNET CONNECTION

Visit the Glencoe Science Web Site at **www.glencoe.com/sec/science/ca** to research the latest development in the Bay of Fundy project. Has a larger plant been built? How much power is the current one generating? Have there been environmental consequences?

Chapter 17 Reviewing Main Ideas

For a **preview** of this chapter, study this Reviewing Main Ideas before you read the chapter. After you have studied this chapter, you can use the Reviewing Main Ideas to **review** the chapter.

The Glencoe MindJogger, Audiocassettes, and CD-ROM provide additional opportunities for review.

Section

17-1 OCEAN WATER

The oceans are an important feature of Earth; they provide habitat for many organisms, and food and transportation for humans. The oceans are a mix of water and dissolved salts in constant motion. Water that fills Earth's oceans may have started as water vapor released from volcanoes. Over millions of years, the water vapor condensed and rain fell, forming the oceans. ***How does early Earth's volcanic activity compare to today's activity?***

OCEAN SALTS

Ocean water is salty because groundwater and rivers dissolve elements from rocks on land and release them into the water. Once in the oceans, these elements combine chemically with the elements released from underwater volcanoes. ***What kind of salt makes up nearly 90 percent of the salt in the ocean?***

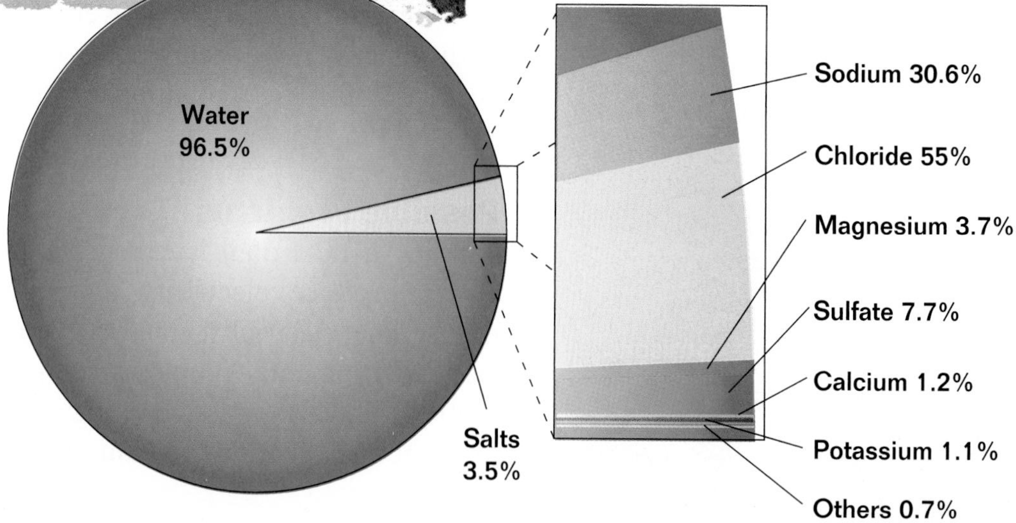

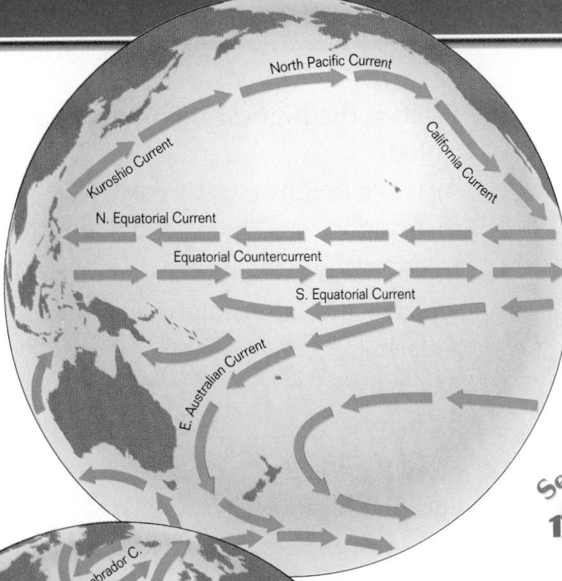

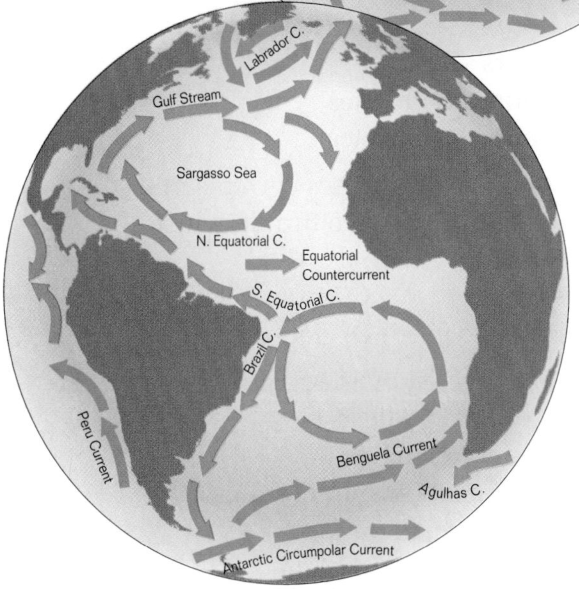

Reading Check

Write three generalizations about the ocean. Exchange them with a partner and discuss whether each other's generalizations are accurate.

Section 17-2 OCEAN CURRENTS

Friction between air and the ocean's surface causes **surface currents.** Surface currents are affected by the Coriolis effect. Currents are also deflected by landmasses. Surface currents can greatly affect climate and economic activity, such as fishing. Ocean transportation is also affected by surface currents. ***Why are some currents cold, while others are warm?***

DEEP-WATER CURRENTS

Differences in temperatures and densities between water masses in the oceans set up circulation patterns called **density currents.** ***How do density currents originate in the Mediterranean Sea?***

Section 17-3 OCEAN WAVES and TIDES

A **wave** is a rhythmic movement that carries energy. The **crest** is the highest point of the wave. The **trough** is the lowest point. Energy moves forward while water particles move in place. Wind causes most water waves, but **tides** are not caused by wind. ***What causes tides?***

Chapter 17 Assessment

Using Vocabulary

- a. basin
- b. breaker
- c. crest
- d. density current
- e. salinity
- f. surface current
- g. tidal range
- h. tide
- i. trough
- j. upwelling
- k. wave

Answer the following questions using complete sentences.

1. Explain the difference between a surface current and a density current.
2. How are breakers and crests related?
3. How is a tide like a wave?
4. Describe the relationship between rivers and a basin.
5. What does *salinity* mean?

Checking Concepts

Choose the word or phrase that best answers the question.

6. Where might ocean water have originated?
   A) salt marshes
   B) volcanoes
   C) basins
   D) surface currents
7. What causes chlorine gas to enter the oceans?
   A) volcanoes
   B) rivers
   C) density currents
   D) groundwater
8. What is the most common ocean element?
   A) chloride
   B) calcium
   C) boron
   D) sulfate
9. What causes most surface currents?
   A) density differences
   B) the Gulf Stream
   C) salinity
   D) wind
10. What is the highest point on a wave called?
    A) wave height
    B) trough
    C) crest
    D) wavelength
11. In the ocean, what are movements in which water alternately rises and falls called?
    A) currents
    B) waves
    C) crests
    D) upwellings
12. How long is the cycle of one low tide and one high tide?
    A) 12 hours
    B) 24 hours
    C) 12 hours, 25 minutes
    D) 24 hours, 50 minutes
13. The Coriolis effect causes currents in the northern hemisphere to turn in which direction?
    A) eastward
    B) southward
    C) counterclockwise
    D) clockwise
14. Tides are affected by the positions of which celestial bodies?
    A) Earth and the moon
    B) Earth, the moon, and the sun
    C) Venus, Earth, and Mars
    D) the sun, Earth, and Mars
15. What affects surface currents?
    A) crests
    B) upwellings
    C) the Coriolis effect
    D) calcium

Thinking Critically

16. Describe the position of the moon and sun when a low tide is higher than normal.
17. Halite makes up nearly 90 percent of the salt in ocean water. How much halite is found in 1000 kg of ocean water?
18. Why do silica and calcium remain in seawater for a shorter time than sodium?
19. Describe the Antarctic density current.
20. How might the use of fertilizers on farm crops affect the composition of the oceans?

Developing Skills

If you need help, refer to the Skill Handbook.

21. **Recognizing Cause and Effect:** What causes upwelling? What effect does it have? When upwelling disappears from an area, what effect can this have?
22. **Comparing and Contrasting:** Compare and contrast ocean waves and ocean currents.
23. **Interpreting Data:** Refer to the graph below. On what day(s) is the high tide highest? Lowest? On what day(s) is the low tide lowest? Highest? On which day would Earth, the moon, and the sun be lined up? On which day would the moon, Earth, and the sun form a right angle?

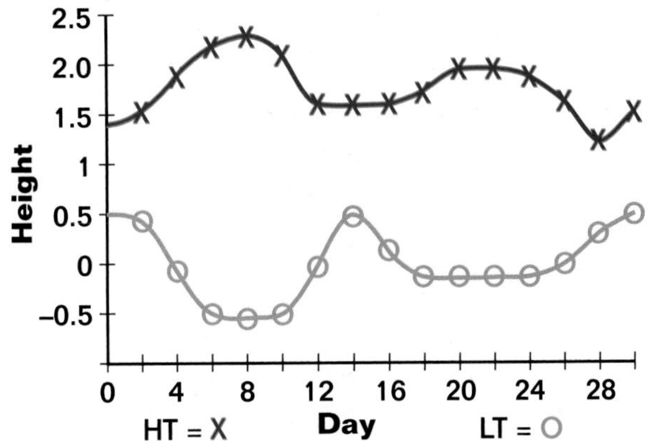

24. **Recognizing Cause and Effect:** In the Mediterranean Sea, a density current forms because of the high rate of evaporation of water from the surface. Explain how evaporation can lead to the formation of a density current.

THE PRINCETON REVIEW

Test-Taking Tip

Take Five and Stay Sharp Wanting to perform well on your exam is good. But, if you take it too seriously, you'll actually end up hurting your chances for a good score. Remember to take frequent, short breaks in your studies to keep your mind fresh.

Test Practice

Use these questions to test your Science Proficiency.

1. When a wave enters shallow water, what happens?
   A) Its crest and trough come closer together, and the wave height increases.
   B) Its crest and trough get farther apart, and the wave height increases.
   C) Its wavelength gets longer, and the wave height increases.
   D) Its wavelength gets shorter, and the wave height decreases.
2. The table below shows the high and low tides on four different beaches on the same day. Which beach experienced the greatest tidal range on this day?

Beach	High tide in meters	Low tide in meters
Glomar	2.3	1.4
Travelers	1.8	–0.4
Station	5.2	4.1
State	3.0	–0.6

A) Glomar
B) Travelers
C) Station
D) State

UNIT 6

Astronomy

NATIONAL GEOGRAPHIC

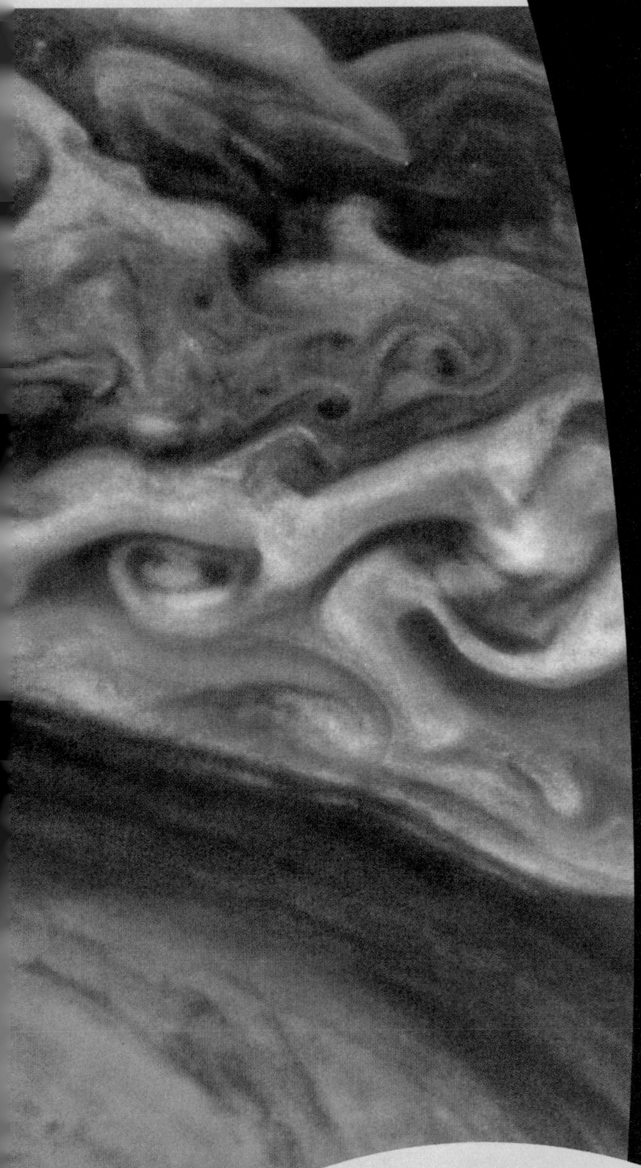

What's Happening Here?

Much of the light you see twinkling in the night sky bears witness to a distant past. How so? If you peered at one of those stars through a powerful telescope, you would discover not how the star appears today but how it appeared millions of years ago. Likewise, if people on a distant planet were to aim a telescope at you, they would see Earth as it existed in the age of the dinosaurs. Outer space is so vast that light traveling at 300 000 kilometers a second takes millions of years to span the distance from a distant star to Earth. To grasp the subject of astronomy, you must expand your notion of distance to the unfathomable. In this unit, you will learn how the lure of this vastness has triggered a new age of exploration. En route into deep space, the *Voyager* probes launched in 1977 photographed Jupiter's Great Red Spot (left), a massive storm in the planet's outer gases. In 1996, this astronaut (inset) tested a minirocket backpack by flying solo above the space shuttle *Discovery*.

interNET CONNECTION

Explore the Glencoe Science Web Site at **www.glencoe.com/sec/science/ca** to find out more about topics found in this unit.

CHAPTER

18 The Sun-Earth-Moon System

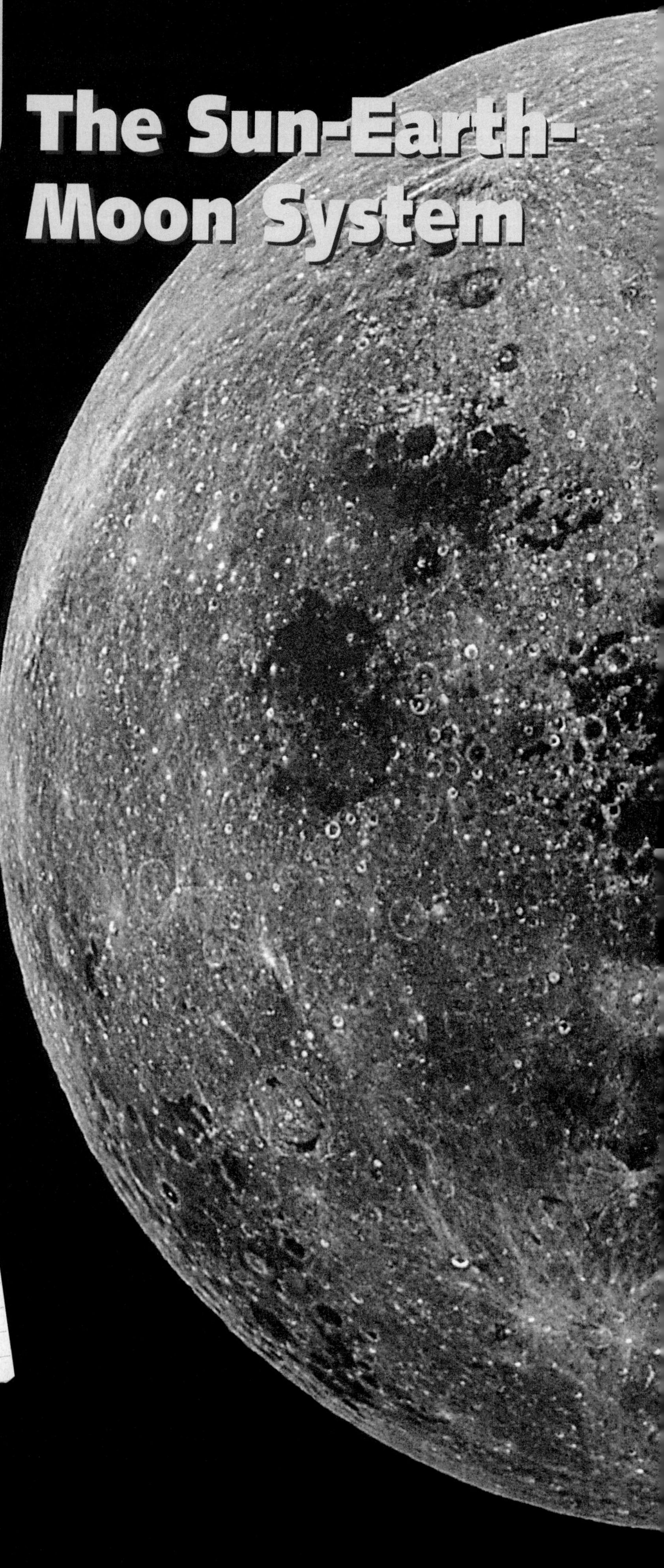

Chapter Preview

Section 18-1
Planet Earth
Section 18-2
Earth's Moon
Section 18-3
Exploration of the Moon

Skills Preview

Skill Builders
- Sequence

Activities
- Make a Model
- Interpret Data

MiniLabs
- Compare and Contrast
- Use Numbers

Reading Check

As you read about the phases of the moon and other topics in this chapter, write down the signal words that indicate a sequence, such as *shortly after* and *just before.*

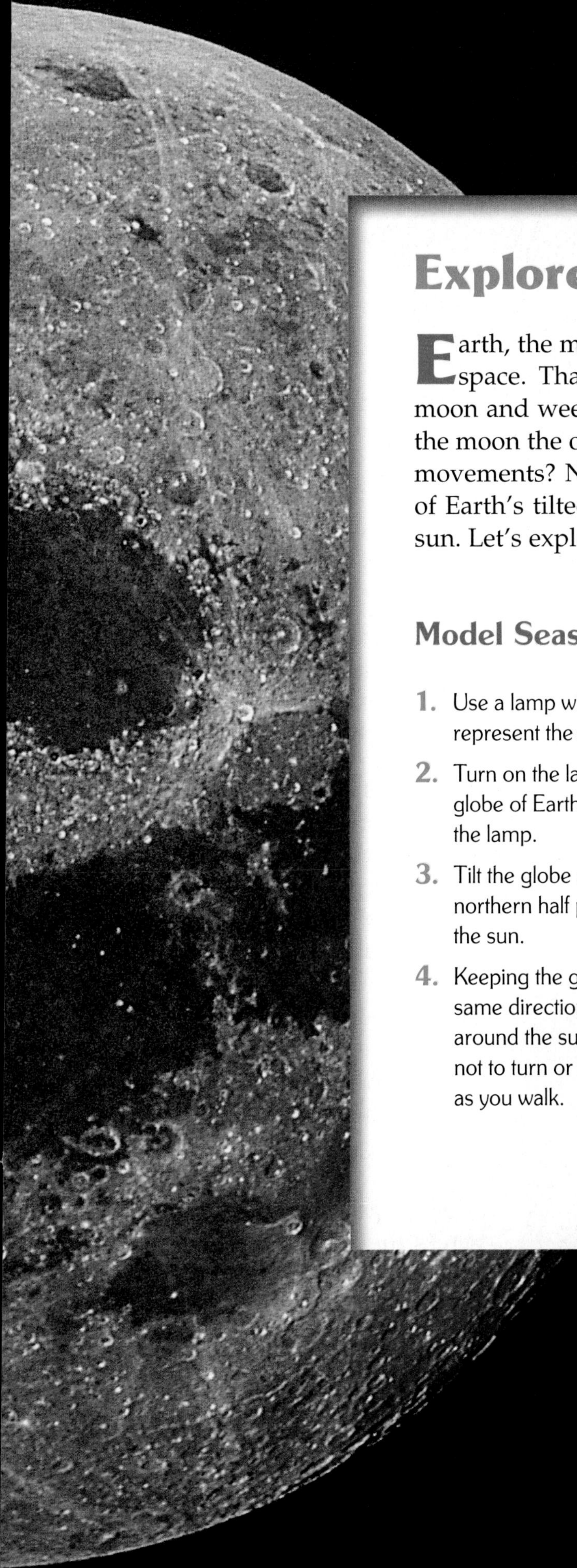

Explore Activity

Earth, the moon, and the sun are constantly moving through space. That's why one night you may see a shining full moon and weeks later see no moon at all. Is the appearance of the moon the only thing that changes because of these movements? No, seasons change, too, because of Earth's tilted axis as it moves around the sun. Let's explore how this happens.

Model Seasons

1. Use a lamp without a shade to represent the sun.
2. Turn on the lamp and hold a globe of Earth about 2 m from the lamp.
3. Tilt the globe slightly so the northern half points toward the sun.
4. Keeping the globe tilted in the same direction, walk halfway around the sun. Be careful not to turn or twist the globe as you walk.

Science Journal

In which direction is the northern hemisphere pointing relative to the sun in step 3? In step 4? In your Science Journal, describe which seasons these positions represent for the northern hemisphere.

18•1 Planet Earth

What You'll Learn

- Physical data about Earth
- The difference between the rotation and revolution of Earth
- How Earth's revolution and tilt cause seasons to change on Earth

Vocabulary

sphere
axis
rotation
revolution
ellipse
equinox
solstice

Why It's Important

- The movements of Earth cause night and day.

Planet Earth Data

You rise early in the morning, while it's still dark outside. You sit by the window and watch the sun come up. Finally, day breaks, and the sun begins its journey across the sky. But, is the sun moving, or are you?

Today, we know that the sun appears to move across the sky because Earth is spinning as it travels around the sun. But, it wasn't long ago that people believed Earth was the center of the universe. They believed Earth stood still and the sun traveled around it.

As recently as the days of Christopher Columbus, some people also believed Earth was flat. They thought that if you sailed far out to sea, you eventually would fall off the edge of the world. How do you know this isn't true? How have scientists determined Earth's shape?

Earth's Shape

Space probes and artificial satellites have sent back images that show Earth is sphere-shaped. A **sphere** (SFIHR) is a round, three-dimensional object. Its surface at all points is the same distance from its center. Tennis balls and basketballs are examples of spheres. But, people had evidence of Earth's true shape long before cameras were sent into space.

Around 350 B.C., the Greek astronomer and philosopher Aristotle reasoned that Earth was spherical because it always casts a round shadow on the moon during an eclipse, as shown in **Figure 18-1.** Only a spherical object always produces a round shadow. If Earth were flat, it would cast a straight shadow.

Other evidence of Earth's shape was observed by early sailors. They watched as ships approached from across the ocean and saw that the top of the ship would come into view first. As they continued to watch the ship, more and more of it

Figure 18-1 If Earth were flat, its shadow during an eclipse would be straight on the moon, not curved, as shown.

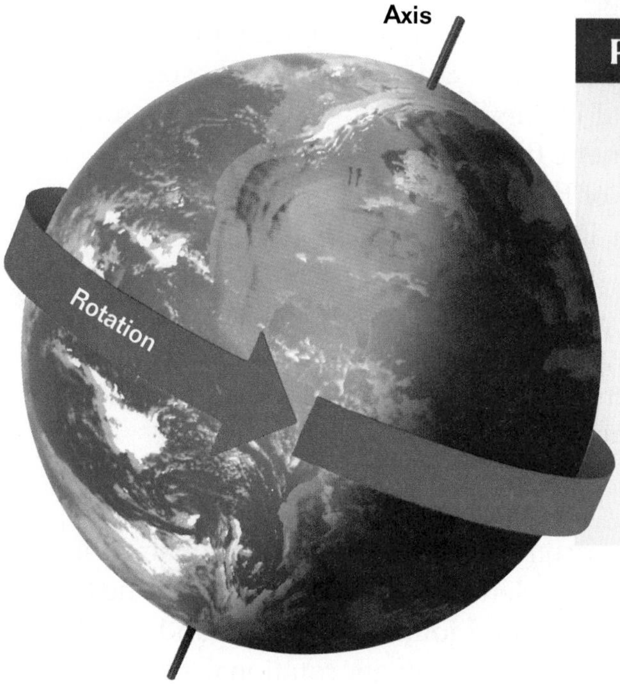

Table 18-1

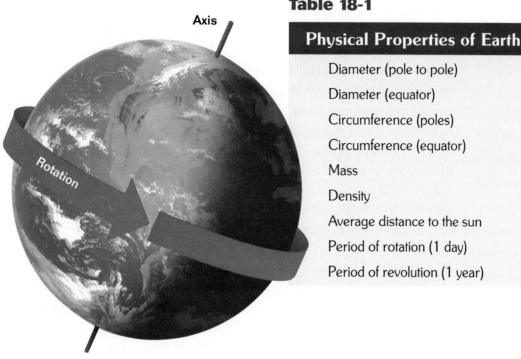

Physical Properties of Earth	
Diameter (pole to pole)	12 714 km
Diameter (equator)	12 756 km
Circumference (poles)	40 008 km
Circumference (equator)	40 075 km
Mass	5.98×10^{27} g
Density	5.52 g/cm^3
Average distance to the sun	149 600 000 km
Period of rotation (1 day)	23 hr, 56 min
Period of revolution (1 year)	365 days, 6 hr, 9 min

would appear until they could see all of it. This was possible only if Earth was a sphere.

Today, we know that Earth is sphere-shaped, but it is not a perfect sphere. It bulges slightly at the equator and is somewhat flattened at the poles. The poles are located at the north and south ends of Earth's axis. Earth's **axis** is the imaginary line around which Earth spins. The spinning of Earth on its axis, called **rotation,** causes day and night to occur.

Earth's Rotation

As Earth rotates, the sun comes into view at daybreak. Earth continues to spin, making it seem as if the sun moves across the sky until it sets at night. During night, your area of Earth has spun away from the sun. Because of this, the sun is no longer visible. Earth continues to rotate steadily, and the sun eventually comes into view the next morning. One complete rotation takes about 24 hours, or one day. How many rotations does Earth complete during one year? As you can see in **Table 18-1,** it completes about 365 rotations during its journey around the sun.

Try at Home

MiniLab

Comparing Spheres

Procedure

1. Use a long piece of string to measure the circumference of a basketball or volleyball.
2. Measure the circumference of the ball at a right angle to your first measurement.
3. Determine the roundness ratio by dividing the larger measurement by the smaller one.
4. Compare these data with the roundness ratio data about Earth's circumference provided in **Table 18-1.**

Analysis

1. How round is Earth compared with the ball?
2. Is Earth larger through the equator or through the poles?
3. Explain how your observations support your answer.

Earth's Magnetic Field

PHYSICS INTEGRATION

Convection currents inside Earth's mantle power the movement of tectonic plates. Scientists hypothesize that movement of material inside Earth along with Earth's rotation generates a magnetic field, as shown in **Figure 18-2.**

The magnetic field of Earth is much like that of a bar magnet. Earth has a north and a south magnetic pole, just as a bar magnet has opposite magnetic poles at its ends. **Figure 18-3** illustrates the effects of sprinkling iron shavings over a bar magnet. The shavings align with the magnetic field of the magnet. Earth's magnetic field is similar, almost as if Earth had a giant bar magnet in its core.

Magnetic North

When you observe a compass needle pointing toward the north, you are seeing evidence of Earth's magnetic field. Earth's magnetic axis, the line joining its north and south magnetic poles, does not align with its rotational axis. The magnetic axis is inclined at an angle of 11.5° to the rotational axis. If you followed a compass needle pointing north, you would end up at the magnetic north pole rather than the geographic (rotational) north pole.

Earth's magnetic field and other physical properties affect us every day. What occurrences can you explain in terms of Earth's physical properties and movement in space?

Figure 18-2 Heat and pressure within Earth cause the liquid outer core to move continuously. Driven by Earth's rotation and convection currents deep within Earth, the molten liquid forms spiraling columns. These spirals generate mechanical energy, which in turn generates electricity that creates the magnetic field.

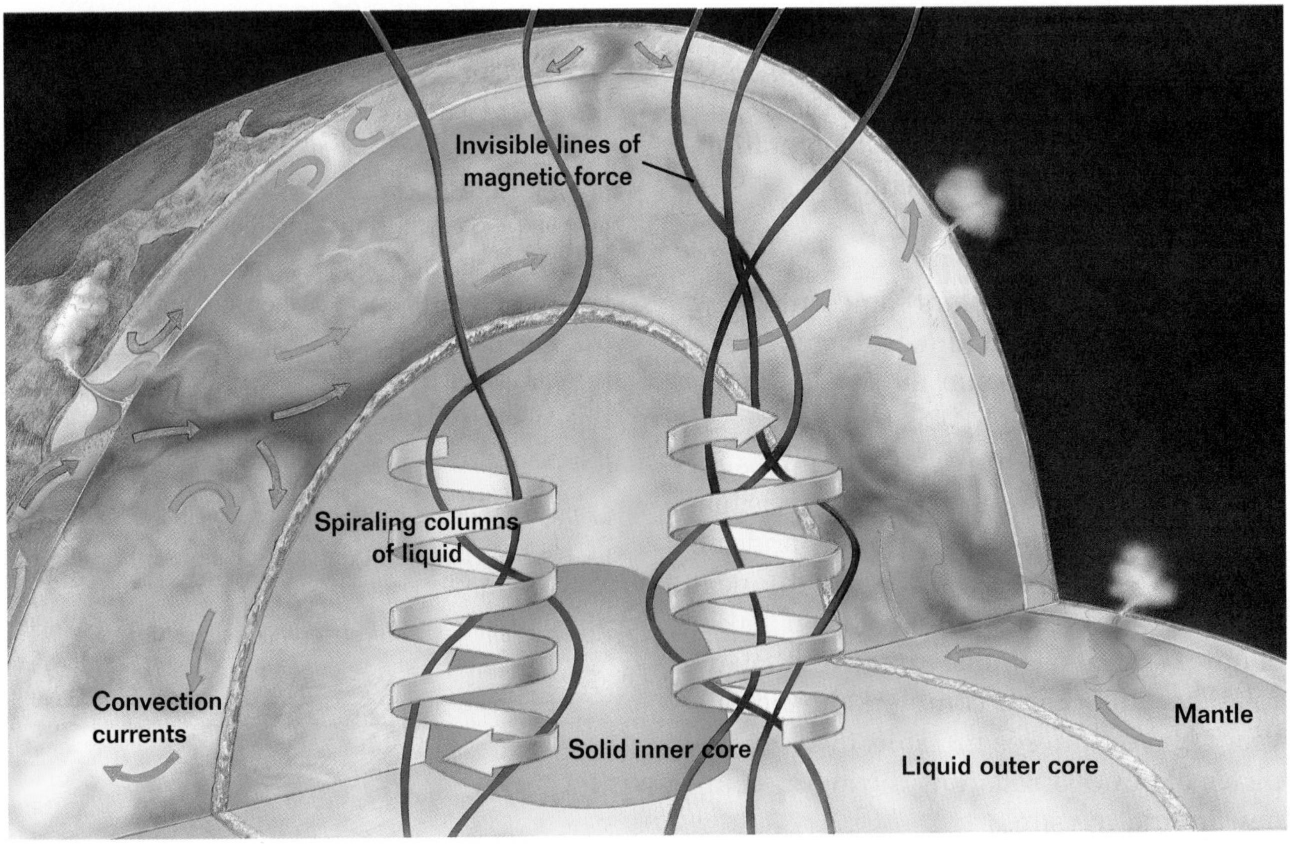

Figure 18-3 Particles in the solar wind streaming through space from the sun distort Earth's magnetic field. As a result, Earth's magnetic field isn't symmetrical. It doesn't have the same shape as a magnetic field surrounding a bar magnet, which is symmetrical.

Seasons

Autumn is coming, and each day it gets colder outside. Dawn comes later each morning, and the sun appears lower in the sky. A month ago, it was light enough to ride your bike at 8:00 P.M. Now, it's dark at 8:00 P.M. What is causing this change?

Earth's Revolution

You learned earlier that Earth's rotation causes day and night. Another important motion of Earth is its **revolution,** or yearly orbit around the sun. Just as the moon is a satellite of Earth, Earth is a satellite of the sun. If Earth's orbit were a circle and the sun were at the center of the circle, Earth would maintain a constant distance from the sun. However, this is not the case. Earth's orbit is an **ellipse** (ee LIHPS), which is an elongated, closed curve. As **Figure 18-4** shows, the sun is offset from the center of the ellipse. Because of this, the distance between Earth and the sun changes during Earth's yearlong orbit. Earth gets closest to the sun—about 147 million km away—around January 3. The farthest point in Earth's orbit is about 152 million km away from the sun and is reached around July 4. ☑

Reading Check ☑

What is an ellipse?

Does this elliptical orbit cause seasonal temperatures on Earth? If it did, you would expect the warmest days in January. You know this isn't the case in the northern hemisphere. Something else causes the change.

Even though Earth is closest to the sun in January, the overall amount of energy Earth receives from the sun changes little throughout the year. However, the amount of energy any one place on Earth receives can vary greatly.

Figure 18-4 The northern hemisphere experiences summer when Earth is farthest from the sun. It experiences winter when Earth is closest to the sun. **Is the change of seasons caused by Earth's elliptical orbit? Explain your answer.**

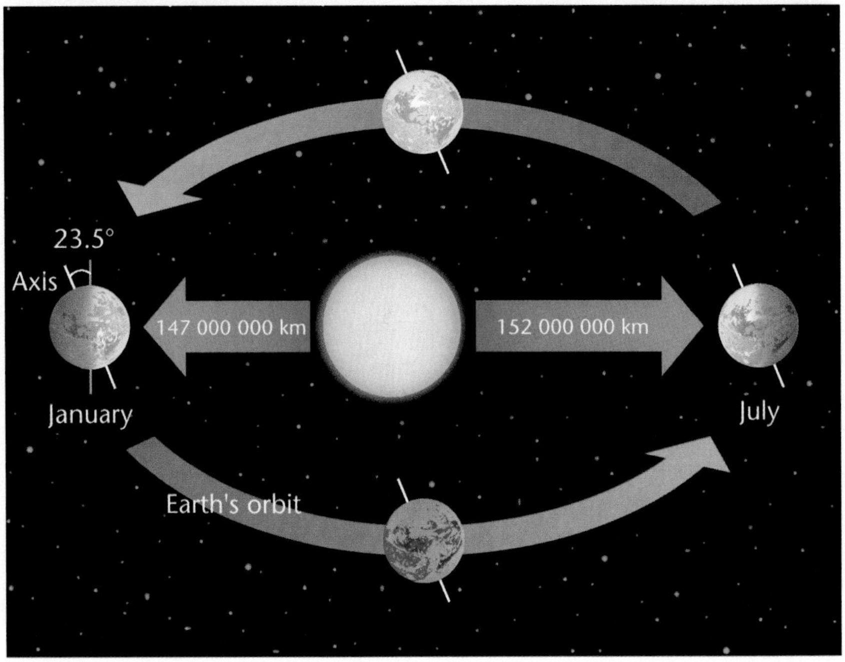

Earth's Tilted Axis

Earth's axis is tilted 23.5° from a line perpendicular to its orbit. This tilt causes the seasons. Daylight hours are longer for the hemisphere tilted toward the sun. Think of how early it gets dark in the winter compared to the summer. As shown in **Figure 18-4,** the hemisphere tilted toward the sun receives more hours of sunlight than the hemisphere tilted away from the sun.

Earth's tilt also causes the sun's radiation to strike the hemisphere tilted toward it at a higher angle than it does the other hemisphere. Because of this, the hemisphere tilted toward the sun receives more electromagnetic radiation per unit area than the hemisphere tilted away. In other words, if you measured the amount of radiation received in a 1-km^2 area in the northern hemisphere and, at the same time, measured it for 1 km^2 in the southern hemisphere, you would find a difference. The hemisphere tilted toward the sun would be receiving more energy.

A summer season results when the sun's electromagnetic radiation strikes Earth at a higher angle. Just the opposite occurs during winter. **Figure 18-5** shows scenes from winter and summer.

Figure 18-5 Temperatures during summer are warmer than those during winter. **Why?**

Equinoxes and Solstices

Because of the tilt of Earth's axis, the sun's position relative to Earth's equator constantly changes. Most of the time, the sun is north or south of the equator. Two times during the year, however, the sun is directly over the equator.

Equinox

Look at **Figure 18-6.** When the sun reaches an **equinox** (EE kwuh nahks), it is directly above Earth's equator, and the number of daylight hours equals the number of nighttime hours all over the world. At that time, neither the northern nor the southern hemisphere is tilted toward the sun. In the northern hemisphere, the sun reaches the spring equinox on March 20 or 21 and the fall equinox on September 22 or 23. In the southern hemisphere, the equinoxes are reversed. Spring occurs in September and fall occurs in March.

Solstice

The **solstice** is the point at which the sun reaches its greatest distance north or south of the equator. In the northern hemisphere, the sun reaches the summer solstice on June 21 or 22, and the winter solstice occurs on December 21 or 22. Just the opposite is true for the southern hemisphere. When the sun is at the summer solstice, there are more daylight

interNET CONNECTION

Visit the Glencoe Science Web Site at **www.glencoe.com/sec/science/ca** for more information about seasons.

Figure 18-6 At summer solstice in the northern hemisphere, the sun is directly over the Tropic of Cancer, 23.5° north latitude at noon. At winter solstice, the sun is directly over the Tropic of Capricorn, 23.5° south latitude at noon. At both fall and spring equinoxes, the sun is directly over the equator at noon.

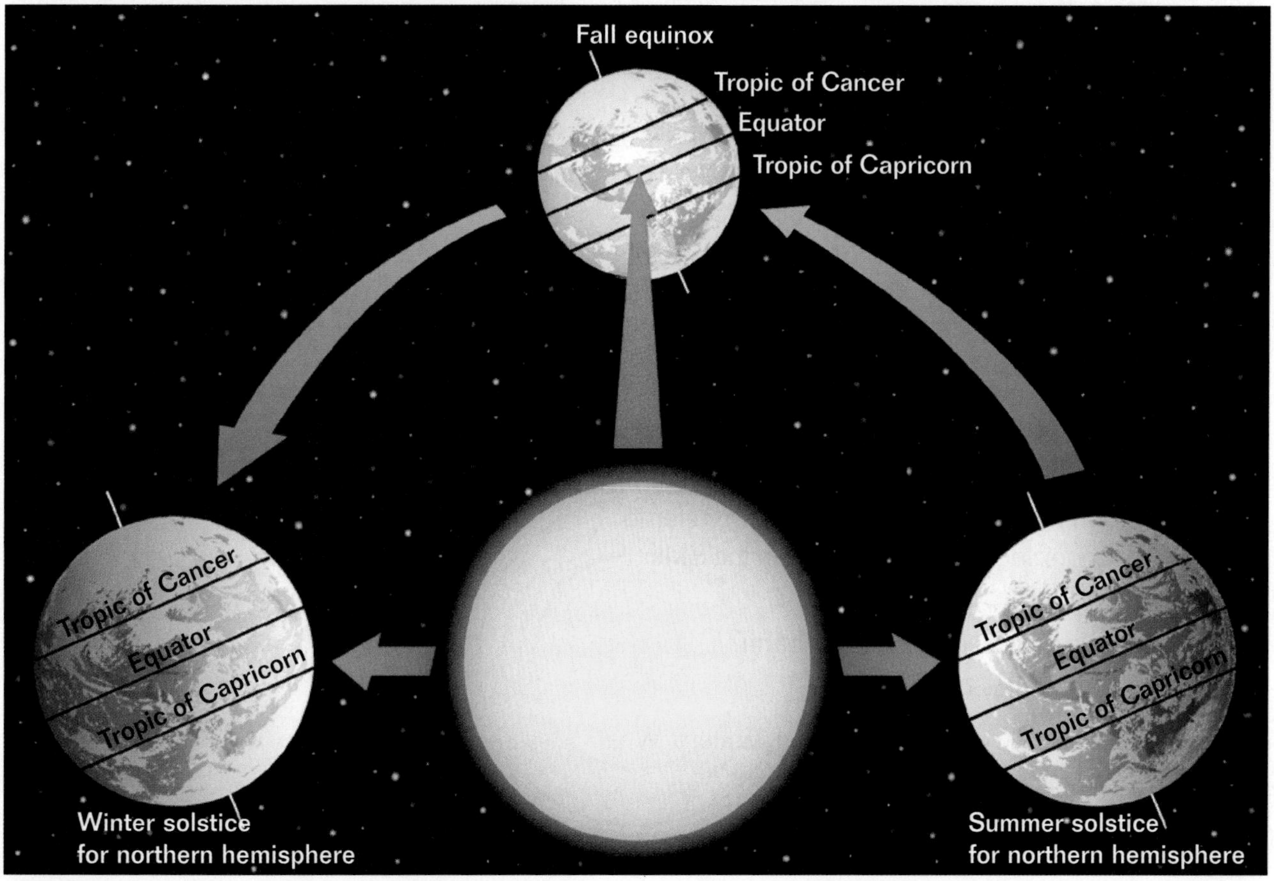

hours than during any other day of the year. When it's at the winter solstice, on the shortest day of the year, the most nighttime hours occur.

Earth Data Review

Earth, shown in **Figure 18-7,** is an imperfect sphere that bulges very slightly at the equator and is somewhat flattened at the poles. The rotation of Earth causes day and night. Earth's tilted axis is responsible for the seasons you experience, and our revolution around the sun marks the passing of a year. In the next section, you will read how Earth's nearest neighbor, the moon, is also in constant motion and how you observe this motion each day.

Figure 18-7 In this photo, Earth appears to be nearly a perfect sphere. In reality, its diameter is 42 km larger at the equator than at the poles.

Section Assessment

1. Which Earth motion causes night and day?
2. Why does summer occur in Earth's northern hemisphere when Earth's north pole is tilted toward the sun?
3. **Think Critically: Table 18-1** lists Earth's distance from the sun as an average. Why isn't there one exact measurement of this distance?
4. **Skill Builder**
   Recognizing Cause and Effect
   Answer these questions about the sun-Earth-moon relationship. If you need help, refer to Recognizing Cause and Effect in the **Skill Handbook** on page 673.
   a. What causes seasons on Earth?
   b. What causes winter?
   c. Earth is closest to the sun in January. What effect does this have on seasons?

Using Computers

Spreadsheet Using the table or spreadsheet capabilities of a computer program, generate a table of Earth's physical data showing its diameter, mass, period of rotation, and other data. Then, write a description of the planet based on the table you have created. If you need help, refer to page 690.

NATIONAL GEOGRAPHIC

A Brave and Startling Truth
by Maya Angelou

In this chapter, you have learned some of the physical characteristics of our planet. Now, find out how one poet, Maya Angelou, uses Earth-science imagery to describe the human race and the quest for world peace. Below are several excerpts, or parts, from her poem "A Brave and Startling Truth."

We, this people, on a small and lonely planet
Traveling through casual space
Past aloof stars, across the way of indifferent suns
To a destination where all signs tell us
It is possible and imperative that we learn
A brave and startling truth...

When we come to it
Then we will confess that not the Pyramids
With their stones set in mysterious perfection
Nor the Gardens of Babylon
Hanging as eternal beauty
In our collective memory
Not the Grand Canyon
Kindled into delicious color
By Western sunsets
These are not the only wonders of the world...

When we come to it
We, this people, on this wayward, floating body
Created on this earth, of this earth
Have the power to fashion for this earth
A climate where every man and every woman
Can live freely without sanctimonious piety
And without crippling fear

When we come to it
We must confess that we are the possible
We are the miraculous, the true wonder of this world
That is when, and only when
We come to it.

interNET CONNECTION

Visit the Glencoe Science Web Site at **www.glencoe.com/sec/science/ca** to learn more about Maya Angelou and her works. Do her other books and poems also contain Earth-science imagery? Using your knowledge of Earth science, write a short poem that uses Earth-science imagery to describe a social issue important to you.

Design Your Own Experiment

Activity 18•1

Tilt and Temperature

Possible Materials

- Tape
- Black construction paper (one sheet)
- Gooseneck lamp with 75-watt bulb
- Celsius thermometer
- Watch
- Protractor

Have you ever noticed how hot the surface of a blacktop driveway can get during the day? The sun's rays hit Earth more directly as the day progresses. Now, consider the fact that Earth is tilted on its axis. How does this affect the amount of heat an area on Earth receives from the sun?

Recognize the Problem

How is the angle at which light strikes an area on Earth related to the changing of the seasons?

Form a Hypothesis

State a hypothesis about how the angle at which light strikes an area affects the amount of heat energy received by that area.

Goals

- **Measure** the amount of heat generated by a light as it strikes a surface at different angles.
- **Describe** how light striking a surface at different angles is related to the changing of the seasons on Earth.

Safety Precautions

Do not touch the lamp without safety gloves. The lightbulb and shade can be hot even when the lamp has been turned off. Handle the thermometer carefully. If it breaks, do not touch anything. Inform your teacher immediately.

Test Your Hypothesis

Plan

1. As a group, agree upon and write out your hypothesis statement.
2. As a group, **list the steps** you need to take to test your hypothesis. Be specific, describing exactly what you will do at each step. List your materials.
3. **Make a list** of any special properties you expect to observe or test.
4. Read over your entire experiment to make sure that all steps are in a logical order.
5. **Identify** any constants, variables, and controls in the experiment.
6. Will you **summarize** data in a graph, table, or some other format?
7. How will you **determine** whether the length of time the light is turned on affects heat energy?
8. How will you **determine** whether the angle at which light strikes an area causes changes in heat and energy?

Do

1. Make sure your teacher approves your plan before you proceed.
2. **Carry out** the experiment as planned.
3. **Complete** the data table in your Science Journal.

Analyze Your Data

1. **Describe** your experiment, including how you used independent variables to test your hypothesis.
2. What happened to the temperature of the area being measured as you modified your variables?
3. **Identify** the dependent variable in your experiment.

Draw Conclusions

1. Did your experiment support your hypothesis? **Explain.**
2. If not, **determine** how you might change the experiment in order to retest your hypothesis. How might you change your hypothesis?

18•2 Earth's Moon

What You'll Learn

- How the moon's phases depend on the relative positions of the sun, the moon, and Earth
- Why eclipses occur and how solar and lunar eclipses compare
- What the surface features of the moon may tell us about its history

Vocabulary

moon phase **new moon** **waxing** **first quarter** **full moon** **waning** **third quarter** **solar eclipse** **lunar eclipse** **maria**

Why It's Important

- The moon is our closest neighbor in space.

Motions of the Moon

You have probably noticed how the moon's apparent shape changes from day to day. Sometimes, just after sunset, you can see a full, round moon low in the sky. Other times, only half of the moon is visible, and it's high in the sky at sunset. Sometimes, the moon is visible during the day. Why does the moon look the way it does? What causes it to change its appearance and position in the sky?

The Moon's Rotation and Revolution

Just as Earth rotates on its axis and revolves around the sun, the moon rotates on its axis and revolves around Earth. The moon's revolution causes changes in its appearance. If the moon rotates on its axis, why don't we see it spin around in space? The moon rotates on its axis once every 27.3 days. It takes the same amount of time to revolve once around Earth. As **Figure 18-8** shows, because these two motions take the same amount of time, the same side of the moon always faces Earth.

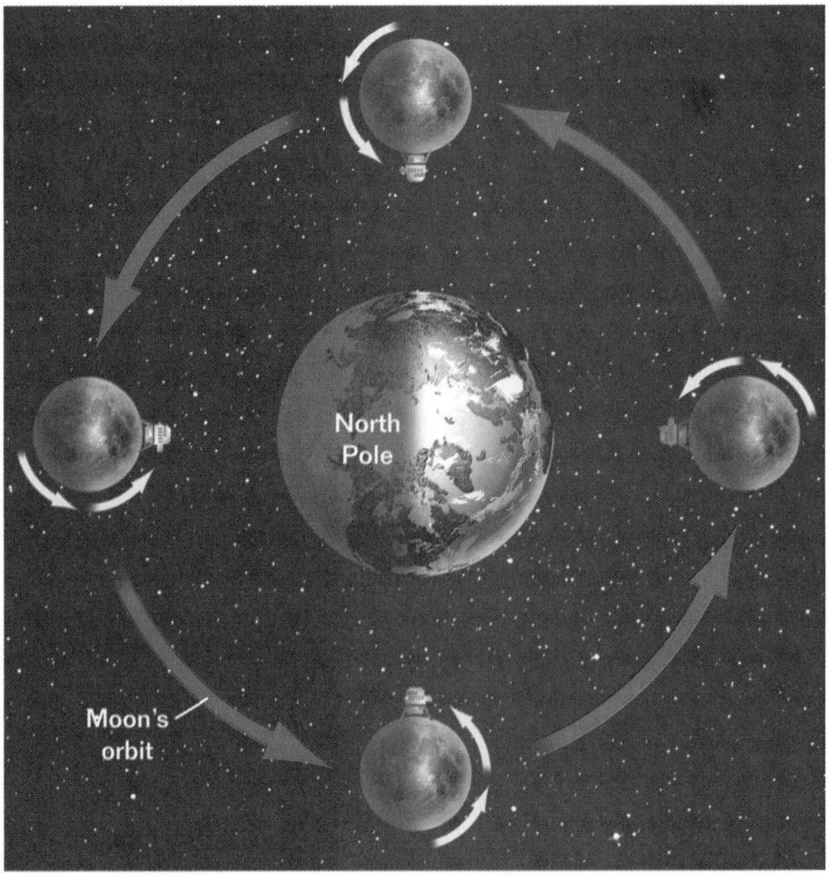

Figure 18-8 In about one month, the moon orbits Earth. It also completes one rotation on its axis during the same period. **Does this affect which side of the moon faces Earth? Explain.**

Figure 18-9 The phases of the moon are: (A) new moon, (B) waxing crescent, (C) first quarter, (D) waxing gibbous, (E) full moon, (F) waning gibbous, (G) third quarter, and (H) waning crescent.

You can show this by having a friend hold a ball in front of you. Instruct your friend to move the ball around you while keeping the same side of it facing you. Everyone else in the room will see all sides of the ball. You will see only one side.

Why the Moon Shines

The moon shines because it reflects sunlight from its surface. Just as half of Earth experiences day as the other half experiences night, half of the moon is lighted while the other half is dark. As the moon revolves around Earth, you see different portions of its lighted side, causing the moon's appearance to change. **Moon phases,** as shown in **Figure 18-9,** are the changing appearances of the moon as seen from Earth. The phase you see depends on the relative positions of the moon, Earth, and the sun.

Phases of the Moon

A new moon occurs when the moon is between Earth and the sun. During a **new moon,** the lighted half of the moon is facing the sun and the dark side faces Earth. The moon is in the sky, but it cannot be seen.

Waxing Phases

Shortly after a new moon, more and more of the moon's lighted side becomes visible—the phases are **waxing.** About 24 hours after a new moon, you can see a thin slice of the side of the moon that is lighted by the sun. This phase is called the waxing crescent. About a week after a new moon, you can see half of the lighted side, or one-quarter of the moon's surface. This phase is **first quarter.**

The phases continue to wax. When more than one-quarter is visible, it is called waxing gibbous. A **full moon** occurs when all of the moon's surface that faces Earth is lit up.

Using Math

Earth rotates through an angle of 360° in one day. How many degrees does Earth rotate in one hour?

MiniLab

Comparing the Sun and Moon

Procedure

1. Find an area where you can make a chalk mark on pavement or another surface.
2. Tie a piece of chalk to one end of a string that's 400 cm long.
3. Hold the other end of the string to the pavement.
4. Have a friend pull the string tight and walk around you, leaving a mark on the pavement as he or she circles you.
5. Draw a circle with a 1-cm diameter in the middle of the large circle.

Analysis

1. The small circle represents the moon, and the larger circle represents the sun. How big is the sun compared to the moon?
2. The diameter of the sun is 1.39 million km. The diameter of the Earth is 12 756 km. Draw two new circles modeling the sizes of the sun and Earth.
3. What are the diameters of your two new circles?

Figure 18-10 The orbit of the moon is not in the same plane as Earth's orbit around the sun. If it were, we would experience a solar eclipse each month during the new moon. The plane of the moon's orbit is tilted about 5° to the plane of Earth's orbit.

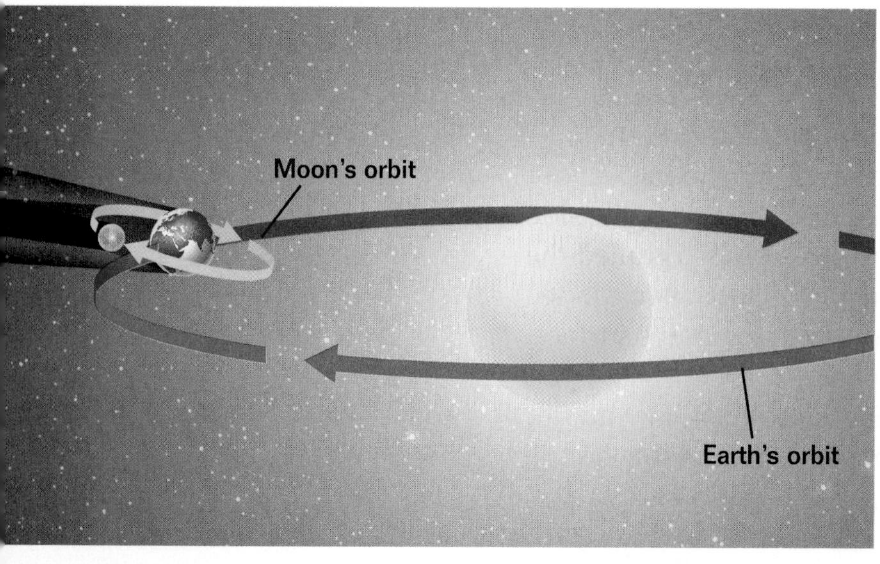

Waning Phases

After a full moon, the amount of the moon's lighted side that can be seen becomes smaller. The phases are said to be **waning.** Waning gibbous begins just after a full moon. When you can see only half of the lighted side, the **third-quarter** phase occurs. The amount of the moon that can be seen continues to become smaller. Waning crescent occurs just before another new moon. Once again, you can see a small slice of the lighted side of the moon.

The complete cycle of the moon's phases takes about 29.5 days. Recall that it takes about 27.3 days for the moon to revolve around Earth. The discrepancy between these two numbers is due to Earth's revolution. It takes the moon about two days to "catch up" with Earth's advancement around the sun.

Eclipses

Imagine yourself as one of your ancient ancestors, living 10 000 years ago. You are out foraging for nuts and other fruit in the bright afternoon sun. Gradually, the sun disappears from the sky, as if being swallowed by a giant creature. The darkness lasts only a short time, and the sun soon returns to full brightness. You realize something unusual has happened, but you don't know what caused it. It will be almost 8000 years before anyone can explain the event that you just experienced.

The event just described was a total solar eclipse (ih KLIPS). Today, we know what causes such eclipses, but for our early ancestors, they must have been terrifying events. Many animals act as if night has come. Cows return to their barns, and chickens go to sleep. What causes the day to suddenly change into night and then back into day?

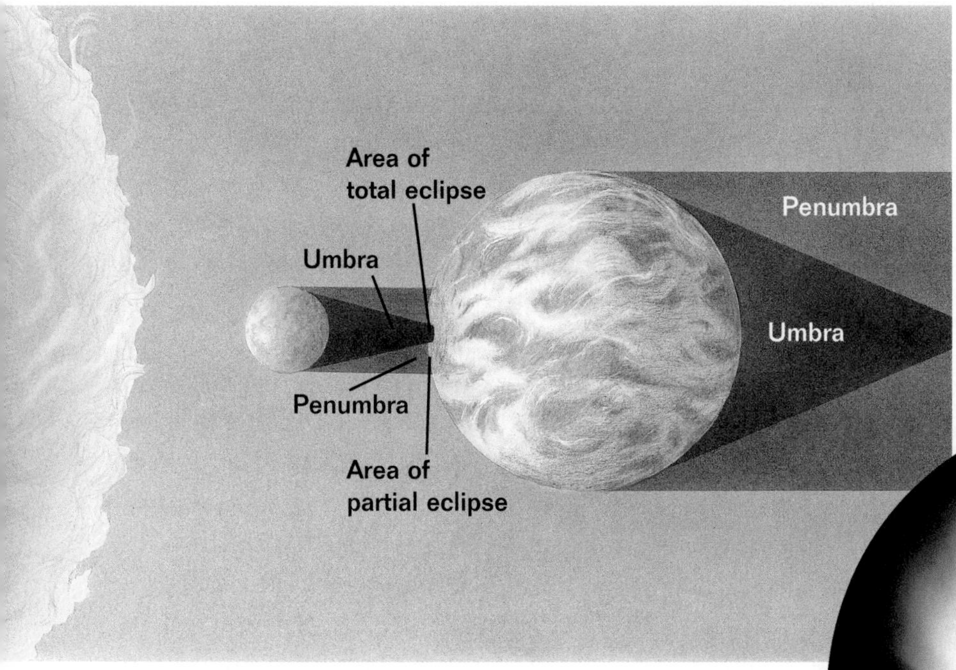

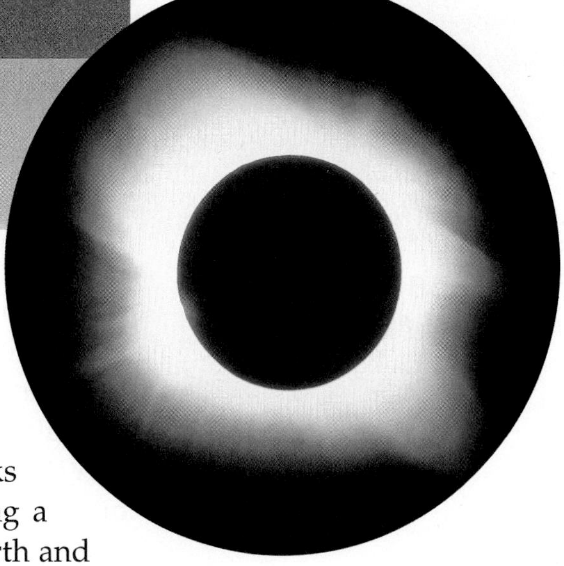

Figure 18-11 Only a small area of Earth experiences a total solar eclipse during the eclipse event. Only the outer portion of the sun's atmosphere is visible during a total solar eclipse. Distances are not drawn to scale.

The Cause of Eclipses

Revolution of the moon causes eclipses. Eclipses occur when Earth or the moon temporarily blocks the sunlight reaching the other. Sometimes, during a new moon, a shadow cast by the moon falls on Earth and causes a solar eclipse. During a full moon, a shadow of Earth can be cast on the moon, resulting in a lunar eclipse.

Eclipses can occur only when the sun, the moon, and Earth are lined up perfectly. Look at **Figure 18-10.** Because the moon's orbit is not in the same plane as Earth's orbit around the sun, eclipses happen only a few times each year.

Solar Eclipses

A **solar eclipse,** such as the one in **Figure 18-11,** occurs when the moon moves directly between the sun and Earth and casts a shadow on part of Earth. The darkest portion of the moon's shadow is called the umbra (UM bruh). A person standing within the umbra experiences a total solar eclipse. The only portion of the sun that is visible is part of its atmosphere, which appears as a pearly white glow around the edge of the eclipsing moon.

Surrounding the umbra is a lighter shadow on Earth's surface called the penumbra (puh NUM bruh). Persons standing in the penumbra experience a partial solar eclipse. **CAUTION:** *Regardless of where you are standing, never look directly at a solar eclipse. The light can permanently damage your eyes.*

LIFE SCIENCE INTEGRATION

Changing Seasons

Suppose that Earth's rotation took twice the time that it presently does. Write a report on how conditions such as global temperatures, work schedules, plant growth, and other factors might be different.

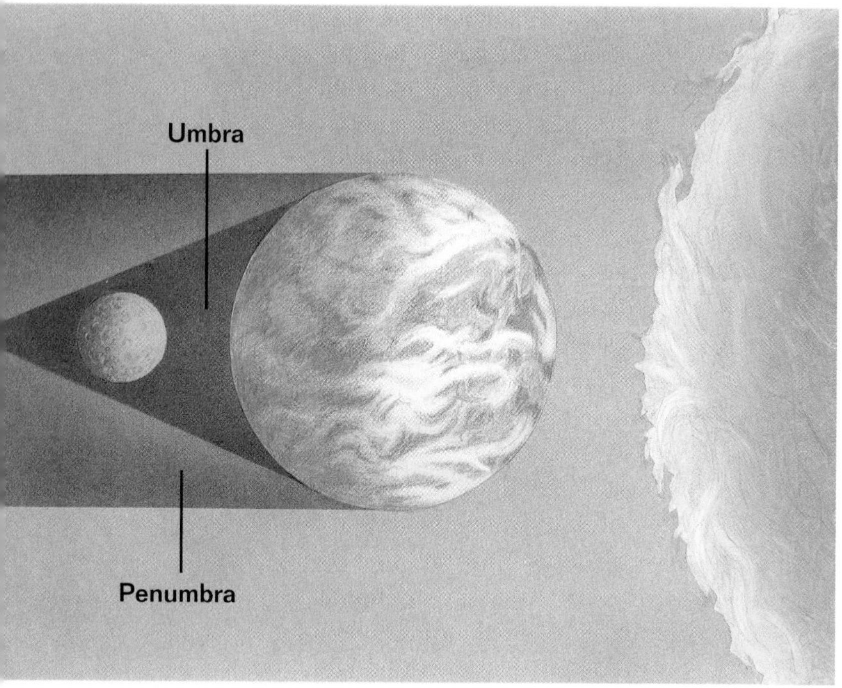

Figure 18-12 During a total lunar eclipse, Earth's shadow blocks light coming from the sun.

Lunar Eclipses

When Earth's shadow falls on the moon, a **lunar eclipse** like the one shown in **Figures 18-12** and **18-13** occurs. A lunar eclipse begins when the moon moves into Earth's penumbra. As the moon continues to move, it enters Earth's umbra and you see a curved shadow on the moon's surface. It was from this shadow that Aristotle concluded that Earth's shape was spherical. When the moon moves completely into Earth's umbra, the moon becomes dark red because light from the sun is refracted by Earth's atmosphere onto the moon. A total lunar eclipse has occurred.

A partial lunar eclipse occurs when only a portion of the moon moves into Earth's umbra. The remainder of the moon is in Earth's penumbra and, therefore, receives some direct sunlight.

A total solar eclipse occurs up to two times every year, yet most people live their entire lives without witnessing one. You may not be lucky enough to see a total solar eclipse, but it is almost certain you will have a chance to see a total lunar eclipse in your lifetime. The reason it is so difficult to view a total solar eclipse is that only those people in the small region where the moon's umbra strikes Earth can witness one. In contrast, anyone on the nighttime side of Earth can see a total lunar eclipse.

Figure 18-13 These photographs show the moon moving from right to left into Earth's umbra, then out again.

Structure of the Moon

When you look at the moon, you can see many of its larger surface features. The dark-colored, relatively flat regions are called **maria.** Maria formed when ancient lava flows from the moon's interior filled large basins on the moon's surface. The basins formed early in the moon's history.

Craters

Many depressions on the moon were formed by meteorites, asteroids, and comets, which strike the surfaces of planets and their satellites. These depressions are called craters. During impact, cracks may have formed in the moon's crust, allowing lava to reach the surface and fill in the large craters, forming maria. The igneous rocks of the maria are 3 to 4 billion years old. They are the youngest rocks found on the moon thus far.

The Moon's Interior

Seismographs left on the moon by *Apollo* astronauts have enabled scientists to study moonquakes. The study of earthquakes allows scientists to map Earth's interior. Likewise, the study of moonquakes has led to a model of the moon's interior. One model of the moon shows that its crust is about 60 km thick on the side facing Earth and about 150 km thick on the far side. Below the crust, a solid mantle may extend to a depth of 1000 km. A partly molten zone of the mantle extends farther down. Below this may be an iron-rich, solid core.

interNET CONNECTION

Visit the Glencoe Science Web Site at **www.glencoe.com/sec/science/ca** to learn more about the *Apollo* space missions.

Problem Solving

Survival on the Moon

You and your crew have crash-landed on the moon, far from your intended landing site at the moon colony. It will take one day to reach the colony on foot. The side of the moon that you are on will be facing away from the sun during your entire trip back. You manage to salvage the following items from your wrecked ship: food, rope, solar-powered heating unit, battery-operated heating unit, three 70-kg oxygen tanks, map of the constellations, magnetic compass, oxygen-burning signal flares, matches, 8 L of water, solar-powered radio receiver and transmitter, three flashlights and extra batteries, signal mirror, and binoculars. Keep in mind that the moon's gravity is about one-sixth that of Earth's, and it lacks a magnetic field. Determine which items will be of no use to you. Determine which items to take with you on your journey to the colony.

Think Critically: Based on what you have learned about the moon, describe why each of the salvaged items is useful or not useful.

1. How did the moon's physical properties affect your decisions?
2. How did the lack of sunlight affect your decisions?

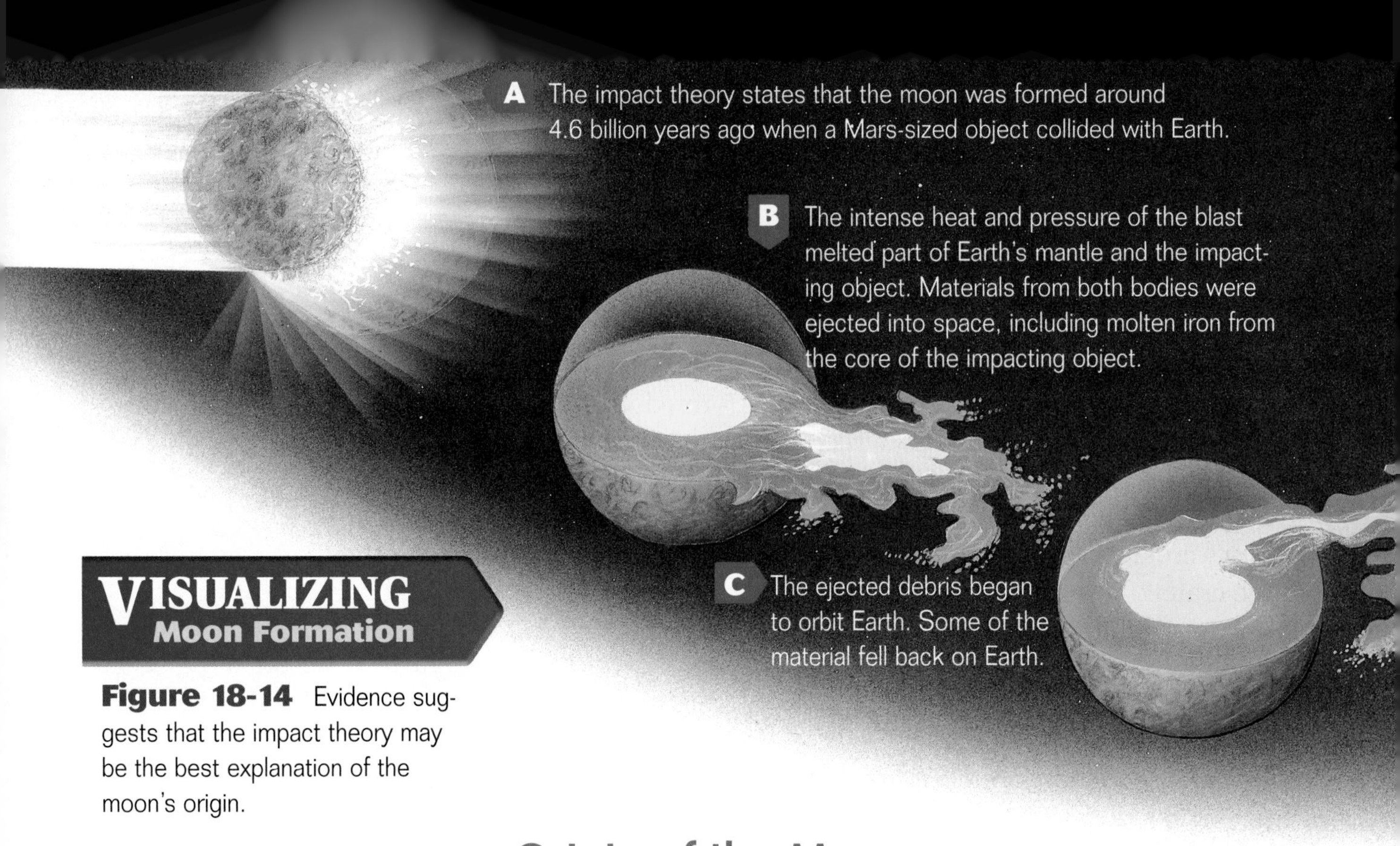

A The impact theory states that the moon was formed around 4.6 billion years ago when a Mars-sized object collided with Earth.
B The intense heat and pressure of the blast melted part of Earth's mantle and the impacting object. Materials from both bodies were ejected into space, including molten iron from the core of the impacting object.
C The ejected debris began to orbit Earth. Some of the material fell back on Earth.

VISUALIZING Moon Formation

Figure 18-14 Evidence suggests that the impact theory may be the best explanation of the moon's origin.

Origin of the Moon

Prior to the data obtained from the *Apollo* space missions, there were three theories about the moon's origin. The first was that the moon was captured by Earth's gravity. It had formed elsewhere and wandered into Earth's vicinity. The second theory was that the moon condensed from loose material surrounding Earth during the early formation of the solar system. The last theory was that a blob of molten material was ejected from Earth while Earth was still in its early molten stage.

Impact Theory

The data gathered by the *Apollo* missions have led many scientists to support a new impact theory. According to the impact theory, the moon was formed about 4.6 billion years ago when a Mars-sized object collided with Earth, throwing gas and debris into orbit. The gas and debris then condensed into one large mass, forming the moon. **Figure 18-14** illustrates the impact theory. ☑

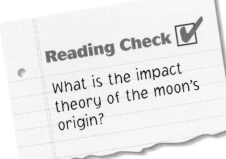

> **Reading Check ☑**
>
> What is the impact theory of the moon's origin?

Regardless of the moon's true origin, it has played an important role in our history. It was a source of curiosity for many early astronomers. Studying the phases of the moon and eclipses led people to conclude that Earth and the moon were in motion around the sun. Earth's shadow on the moon proved that Earth's shape was spherical. When Galileo first turned his telescope to the moon, he found a surface scarred by craters

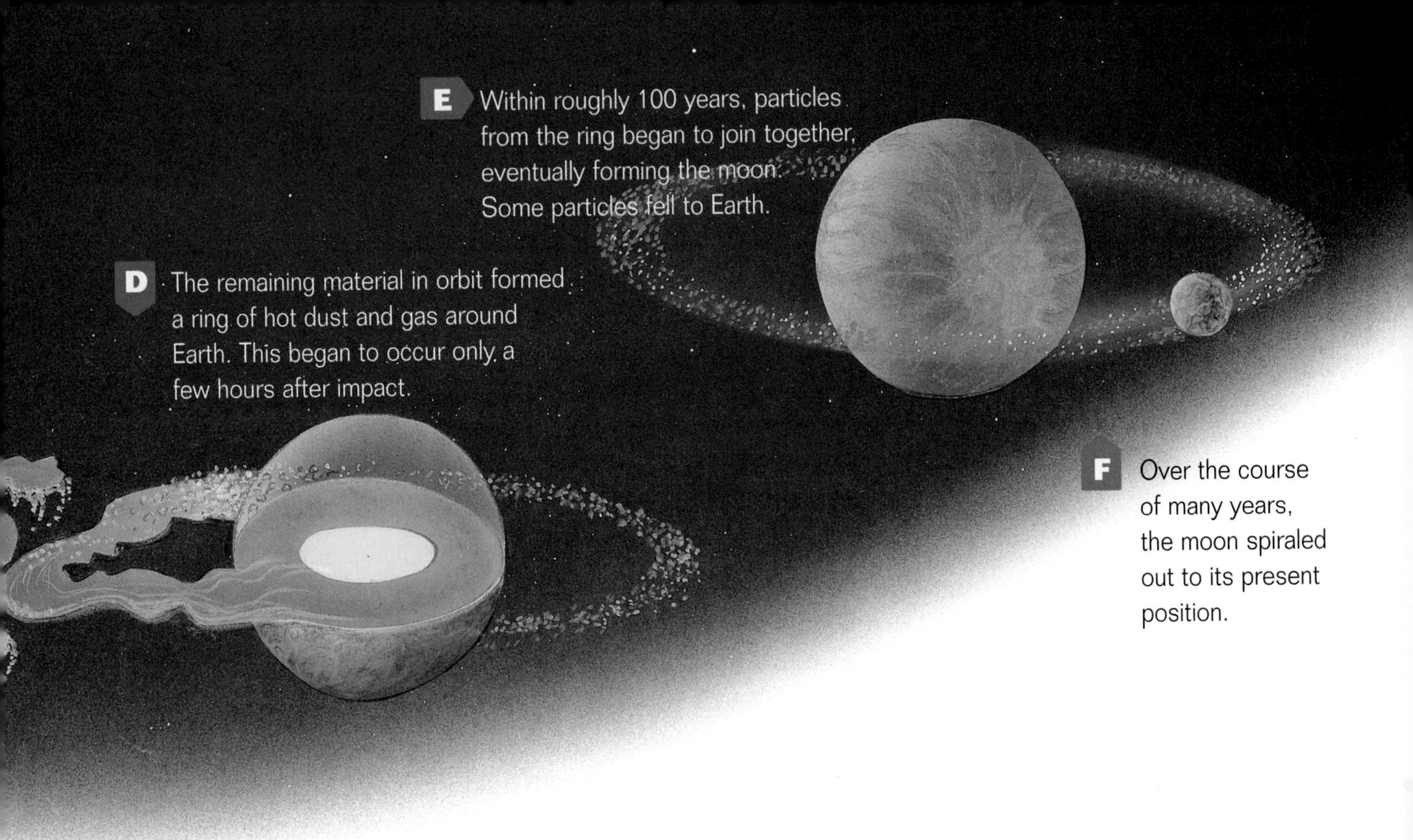
E Within roughly 100 years, particles from the ring began to join together, eventually forming the moon. Some particles fell to Earth.
D The remaining material in orbit formed a ring of hot dust and gas around Earth. This began to occur only a few hours after impact.
F Over the course of many years, the moon spiraled out to its present position.

and maria. Before that time, many people believed that all planetary bodies were perfect, without surface features.

By studying the moon, we can learn about ourselves and the planet we live on. As you will read in the next section, not only is the moon important as an object from our past, but it is important to our future, as well.

Section Assessment

1. What are the relative positions of the sun, the moon, and Earth during a full moon?
2. Why does a lunar eclipse occur only during a full moon?
3. Compare and contrast umbra and penumbra.
4. **Think Critically:** What provides the force necessary to form craters on the moon?
5. **Skill Builder**
Interpreting Scientific Illustrations By tracking the changing positions of the sun, Earth, and the moon, scientists can predict solar eclipses. Do the **Chapter 18 Skill Activity** on page 711 to see when and where future solar eclipses will occur.

Science Journal

Research the moon's origin in astronomy books and magazines. In your Science Journal, write a report about the various theories, including the theory about a Mars-sized object colliding with Earth. Make a drawing of each theory.

18·3 Exploration of the Moon

What You'll Learn

- Recent information about the moon discovered by spacecraft
- Facts about the moon's poles that may be important to future space travel

Vocabulary
mascon

Why It's Important

- Future missions to the moon may lead to important discoveries about Earth's origin.

Early Moon Missions

For centuries, astronomers have studied the moon for clues to its makeup and origin. In 1958, the former Soviet Union took studies of the moon into space with the launching of the *Luna* spacecraft. Three years later, the United States launched the first *Ranger* spacecraft, beginning its own lunar space exploration program.

Early U.S. moon missions, such as those involving the uncrewed *Ranger* and later the *Lunar Orbiter* spacecraft, focused on taking detailed photographs of the moon's surface. The *Lunar Orbiter* missions were followed by the *Surveyor* missions, wherein seven *Surveyor* spacecraft landed on the moon in preparation for the ultimate goal: to land astronauts on the moon. In 1969, this goal was realized with the launching of *Apollo 11*. By 1972 when the *Apollo* missions ended, 12 U.S. astronauts had walked on the moon.

Return to the Moon

More than 20 years passed before the United States resumed its studies of the moon from space. In 1994, the *Clementine* spacecraft was placed into lunar orbit to conduct a two-month survey of the moon's surface. *Clementine's* mission was to test new sensors for tracking cold objects, such as satellites, in space.

Figure 18-15 This false-color photograph, taken by cameras on the *Clementine* spacecraft, shows the moon, the sun, and the planet Venus.

In addition, *Clementine* was placed in lunar orbit to take high-resolution photographs in order to compile a detailed map of the moon's surface. **Figure 18-15** shows a photograph taken by *Clementine*. *Clementine's* four cameras were able to resolve features as small as 200 m across, enhancing our knowledge of the moon's surface. ☑

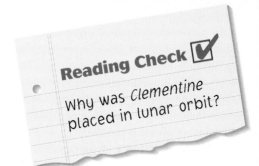

Reading Check ☑

Why was *Clementine* placed in lunar orbit?

The Moon's South Pole

The South Pole-Aitken Basin is the oldest identifiable impact feature on the moon's surface. It is also the largest and deepest impact basin or depression found thus far anywhere in the solar system, measuring 12 km in depth and 2500 km in diameter. Data returned by *Clementine* gave scientists the first set of high-resolution photographs of this area of the moon. Much of this depression stays in shadow throughout the moon's rotation, forming a cold area where ice deposits from impacting comets may have collected. Radio signals reflected from *Clementine* to Earth indicated the presence of ice at the moon's south pole. Also, a large plateau that is always in sunlight was discovered in this area. If there truly is ice near the plateau, this would be an ideal location for a moon colony powered by solar energy.

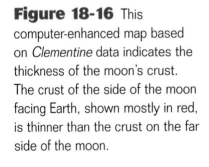

Figure 18-16 is a global map showing the moon's crustal thickness based on *Clementine* data. According to the data, the moon's crust thins under impact basins. Also, the moon's crust on the side facing Earth is much thinner than on the far side. Such maps show the location of **mascons,** which are concentrations of mass. Mascons are located under impact basins. Data collected by *Clementine* also provided information on the mineral content of moon rocks. In fact, this part of its mission was instrumental in naming the spacecraft. Clementine was the daughter of a miner in the ballad "My Darlin' Clementine."

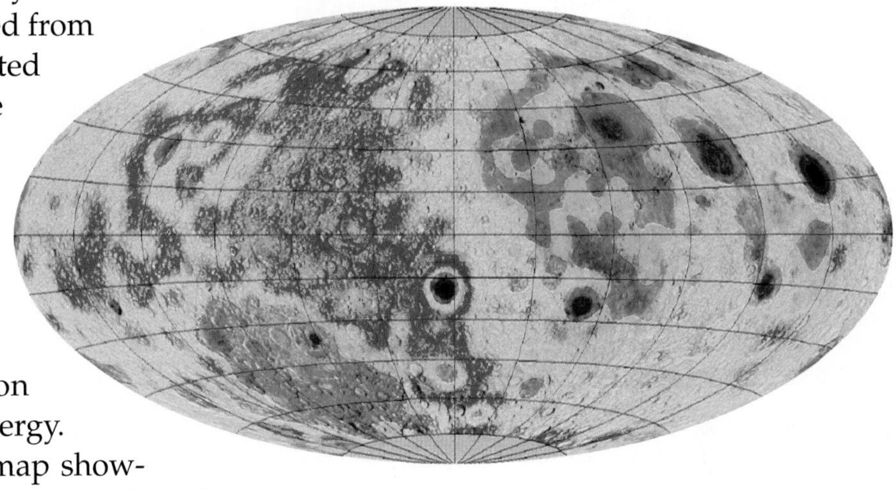

Figure 18-16 This computer-enhanced map based on *Clementine* data indicates the thickness of the moon's crust. The crust of the side of the moon facing Earth, shown mostly in red, is thinner than the crust on the far side of the moon.

The Lunar Prospector

The success of *Clementine* at a relatively low cost opened the door for further moon missions. In 1998, NASA launched the *Lunar Prospector* spacecraft. Its mission was to orbit the moon, taking photographs of the lunar surface for mapping purposes. These maps confirmed the *Clementine* data. The

Lunar Prospector also was scheduled to conduct a detailed study of the moon's surface, searching for clues as to the origin and makeup of the moon.

Icy Poles

Early data obtained from the *Lunar Prospector* indicate that hydrogen is present in the rocks found in the craters at the moon's poles, as shown in **Figure 18-17.** Hydrogen is one of the elements that make up water. These data, combined with data from *Clementine,* have led scientists to theorize that ice may exist in the floors of the craters at both of the moon's poles. These craters are deep and cold. Sunlight never reaches their floors, where temperatures are as low as –233°C—definitely cold enough to have preserved any ice that may have collected in the craters from colliding comets or meteorites.

Figure 18-17 Data from *Lunar Prospector* indicate the presence of twice as much ice at the moon's north pole as at its south pole.

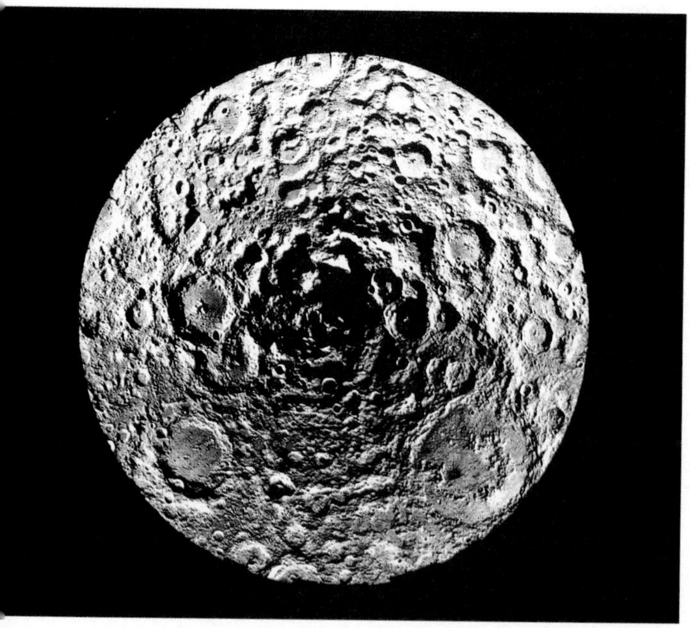

Based on the *Lunar Prospector* data, scientists estimate that 6 billion tons of ice lie under the surface of the moon's poles. The ice may be buried under about 40 cm of crushed rock. Data from *Lunar Prospector* also have enabled scientists to conclude that the moon has a small, iron-rich core about 600 km across.

Section Assessment

1. List two discoveries about the moon made by the *Clementine* spacecraft.
2. What was the main mission of the *Lunar Prospector?*
3. How did studies of the moon change after the 1950s?
4. **Think Critically:** Why would the discovery of ice at the moon's poles be important to future space flights?
5. **Skill Builder**
   Sequencing Sequence the following moon missions in the order in which they occurred: *Surveyor, Lunar Prospector, Apollo, Lunar Orbiter, Ranger,* and *Clementine.* If you need help, refer to Sequencing in the **Skill Handbook** on page 666.

Using Math

The moon's orbit is tilted at an angle of about 5° to Earth's orbit around the sun. Using a protractor, draw an angle of 5°. Draw a model of the moon's orbit around Earth.

Moon Phases and Eclipses

Materials

- Light source (unshaded)
- Polystyrene ball on pencil
- Globe

You know that moon phases and eclipses result from the relative positions of the sun, the moon, and Earth. In this activity, you will demonstrate the positions of these bodies during certain phases and eclipses. You also will see why only people on a small portion of Earth's surface see a total solar eclipse.

What You'll Investigate

Can a model be devised to show the positions of the sun, the moon, and Earth during various phases and eclipses?

Goals

- **Model** moon phases.
- **Model** solar and lunar eclipses.

Procedure

1. Review the illustrations of moon phases and eclipses shown in Section 18-2.
2. **Use** the light source as a model sun and a polystyrene ball on a pencil as a model moon. **Move** the model moon around the globe to duplicate the exact position that would have to occur for a lunar eclipse to take place.
3. **Move** the model moon to the position that would cause a solar eclipse.
4. **Place** the model moon at each of the following phases: first quarter, full moon, third quarter, and new moon. **Identify** which, if any, type of eclipse could occur during each phase. Record your data.
5. **Place** the model moon at the location where a lunar eclipse could occur. **Move** it slightly toward Earth, then away from Earth. Note the amount of change in the size of the shadow causing the eclipse. Record this information.
6. **Repeat** step 5 with the model moon in a position where a solar eclipse could occur.

Conclude and Apply

1. During which phase(s) of the moon is it possible for an eclipse to occur?
2. **Describe** the effect that a small change in the distance between Earth and the moon has on the size of the shadow causing the eclipse.
3. As seen from Earth, how does the apparent size of the moon **compare** with the apparent size of the sun? How can an eclipse be used to confirm this?
4. **Infer** why a lunar and solar eclipse do not occur every month.
5. Suppose you wanted to more accurately model the movement of the moon around Earth. **Explain** how your model moon moves around the globe. Would it always be in the same plane as the light source and the globe?
6. Why have only a few people seen a total solar eclipse?

Moon Phase Observations

Moon Phase	Observations
first quarter	
full	
third quarter	
new	

Chapter 18 Reviewing Main Ideas

For a **preview** of this chapter, study this Reviewing Main Ideas before you read the chapter. After you have studied this chapter, you can use the Reviewing Main Ideas to **review** the chapter.

GLENCOE TECHNOLOGY

The Glencoe MindJogger, Audiocassettes, and CD-ROM provide additional opportunities for review.

Section
18-1 PLANET EARTH

Earth is a **sphere** that is slightly flattened at its poles. Earth **rotates** once each day and **revolves** around the sun in a little more than 365 days. Seasons on Earth are due to the amount of solar radiation received by a hemisphere at a given time. The tilt of Earth on its **axis** causes the amount of solar energy to vary. ***How does Earth's interior act like an electromagnet?***

Section
18-2 EARTH'S MOON

Earth's moon goes through **phases** that depend on the relative positions of the sun, the moon, and Earth. Eclipses occur when Earth or the moon temporarily blocks sunlight from the other. A **solar eclipse** occurs when the moon moves directly between the sun and Earth. A **lunar eclipse** occurs when Earth's shadow falls on the moon. The moon's **maria** are the result of ancient volcanism. Craters on the moon's surface formed from impacts with meteorites, asteroids, and comets. ***If the moon is between Earth and the sun for each new moon, why are there only one or two solar eclipses each year?***

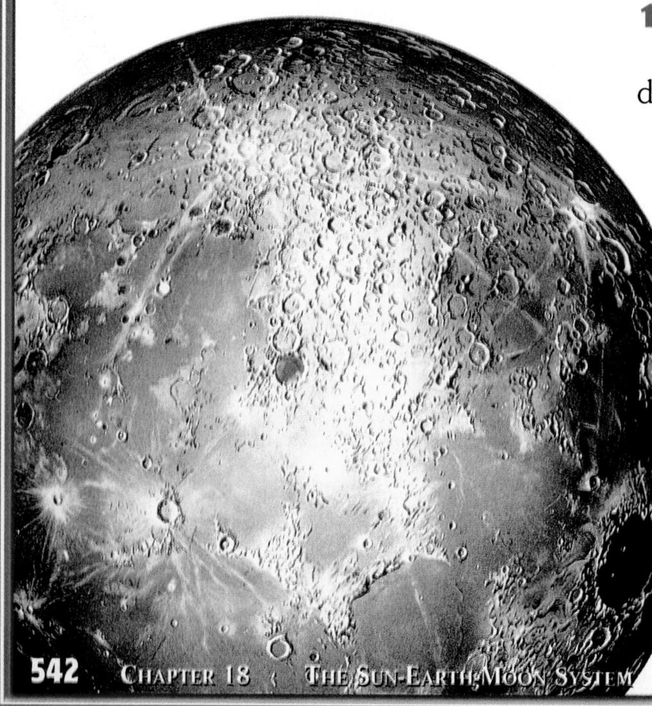

Reading Check

Use these words in sentences that do not relate to the sun, Earth, or moon: *sphere, axis, rotation, revolution, ellipse, waxing,* and *waning.*

Section

18-3 EXPLORATION OF THE MOON

The *Clementine* spacecraft took detailed, high-resolution photographs of the moon's surface. Data from *Clementine* indicate that the moon's South Pole-Aitken Basin may contain ice deposits that could supply water for a moon colony. The *Clementine* spacecraft also noted that **mascons** occur beneath impact basins on the moon. NASA has returned to exploring the moon with its latest spacecraft, the *Lunar Prospector*. Data from *Lunar Prospector* seem to support the ice theory and also indicate that the moon's north pole may contain twice as much ice as the south pole. ***How did the* Clementine *spacecraft get its name?***

Career CONNECTION

Gibor Barsi, Astronomer

Gibor Barsi is an astronomer who works with the Keck Telescopes on Mauna Kea, Hawaii. The summit of Mauna Kea is considered the world's premier site for astronomical observation. Gibor is interested in answering the questions, "How many planets are there around other stars, what are they like, and how do they form?" He feels that the next generation of astronomers and technology will answer these questions. ***Why do you suppose astronomers are interested in finding new planets?***

Chapter 18 Assessment

Using Vocabulary

a. axis
b. ellipse
c. equinox
d. first quarter
e. full moon
f. lunar eclipse
g. maria
h. mascon
i. moon phase
j. new moon
k. revolution
l. rotation
m. solar eclipse
n. solstice
o. sphere
p. third quarter
q. waning
r. waxing

Each phrase below describes a science term from the list. Write the term that matches the phrase describing it.

1. causes day and night to occur on Earth
2. occurs when the sun's position is directly above the equator
3. moon phase in which all of the lighted side of the moon is seen
4. eclipse that occurs when the moon is between Earth and the sun
5. concentration of mass on the moon located under an impact basin

Checking Concepts

Choose the word or phrase that completes the sentence.

6. How long does it take for the moon to rotate?
   A) 24 hours
   B) 365 days
   C) 27.3 hours
   D) 27.3 days
7. Where is Earth's circumference greatest?
   A) equator
   B) mantle
   C) poles
   D) axis
8. During an equinox, the sun is directly over what part of Earth?
   A) southern hemisphere
   B) northern hemisphere
   C) equator
   D) pole
9. Why does the sun appear to rise and set?
   A) Earth revolves.
   B) The sun moves around Earth.
   C) Earth rotates.
   D) Earth orbits the sun.
10. How long does it take for the moon to revolve?
   A) 24 hours
   B) 365 days
   C) 27.3 hours
   D) 27.3 days
11. As the lighted portion of the moon appears to get larger, what is it said to be?
   A) waning
   B) waxing
   C) rotating
   D) crescent shaped
12. During what kind of eclipse is the moon directly between the sun and Earth?
   A) solar
   B) new
   C) full
   D) lunar
13. What is the darkest part of the shadow during an eclipse?
   A) waxing gibbous
   B) umbra
   C) waning gibbous
   D) penumbra
14. What are depressions on the moon called?
   A) eclipses
   B) moonquakes
   C) phases
   D) craters
15. What fact do data gathered from the *Clementine* spacecraft support?
   A) The moon rotates once in 29.5 days.
   B) The moon has a thinner crust on the side facing Earth.
   C) The moon revolves once in 29.5 days.
   D) The moon has a thicker crust on the side facing Earth.

Thinking Critically

16. How would the moon appear to an observer in space during its revolution? Would phases be observable? Explain.
17. Would you weigh more at Earth's equator or at the north pole? Explain.

18. Tides occur due to the gravitational attraction among the sun, the moon, and Earth. During which phases of the moon are tides the highest? Explain.
19. If you were lost on the moon's surface, why would it be more beneficial to have a star chart rather than a compass?
20. Which of the moon's motions are real? Which are apparent? Explain.

Developing Skills

If you need help, refer to the Skill Handbook.

21. **Hypothesizing:** Why do locations near Earth's equator travel faster during one rotation than places near the poles?
22. **Using Variables, Constants, and Controls:** Describe a simple activity to show how the moon's rotation and revolution work to keep one side facing Earth at all times.
23. **Comparing and Contrasting:** Compare and contrast a waning moon with a waxing moon.
24. **Concept Mapping:** Copy and complete the cycle map shown on this page. Show the sequences of the moon's phases.

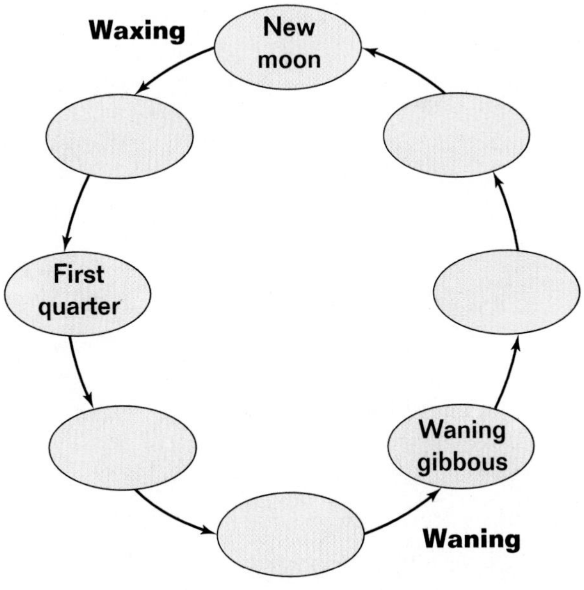

THE PRINCETON REVIEW

Test-Taking Tip

Practice, Practice, Practice Practice to improve *your* performance. Don't compare yourself with anyone else.

Test Practice

Use these questions to test your Science Proficiency.

1. As the moon revolves around Earth, it keeps the same side facing Earth. Which of the following statements **BEST** explains why this is so?
   A) The moon rotates once on its axis as it makes one complete revolution around Earth.
   B) The moon does not rotate as it revolves.
   C) The speed of rotation for the moon exactly equals its speed of revolution.
   D) The speed of revolution for the moon is constant and therefore keeps one side facing Earth at all times.
2. More craters are on the far side of the moon than on the side facing Earth. Which of the following statements would **BEST** explain this fact?
   A) A greater number of volcanoes occur on the far side of the moon.
   B) Earth's gravity attracts more of the objects that would produce craters on the side of the moon facing Earth.
   C) Earth blocks the paths of any objects that would collide with the side of the moon facing Earth.
   D) The far side of the moon is always facing away from the sun.

CHAPTER 19

The Solar System

Chapter Preview

Skills Preview

Skill Builders
- Map Concepts

Activities
- Make a Model

MiniLabs
- Observe and Infer

Reading Check

As you read this chapter, identify and describe the cause-effect relationships that control the structure of the solar system.

Explore Activity

The planets of our solar system are our neighbors in space. But to us on Earth, they look like tiny points of light among the thousands of others visible on a clear night. With the help of telescopes and space probes, the points of light become giant colorful spheres, some with rings, others pitted with countless craters. This false-color image of Mars shows the space rover *Sojourner* exploring the planet's surface. Mars has two heavily cratered moons. In this activity, you'll explore how craters are made on the surfaces of planets and moons.

Model Comet Collisions

1. Place fine white flour into a cake pan to a depth of 3 cm, completely covering the bottom of the pan.
2. Cover the flour with 1 cm of fine, gray, dry cement mix, or try different colors of gelatin powder.
3. From different heights ranging from 10 cm to 25 cm, drop various-sized objects into the pan. Use marbles, lead weights, bolts, and nuts.

Science Journal

In your Science Journal, draw what happened to the surface of the powder in the pan when each object was dropped from different heights.

19•1 The Solar System

What You'll Learn

- The sun-centered and Earth-centered models of the solar system
- Current models of the formation of the solar system

Vocabulary
solar system
inner planet
outer planet

Why It's Important

- You'll learn how views of the solar system have changed over time.

Early Ideas About the Solar System

Imagine yourself on a warm, clear summer night lying in the grass and gazing at the stars and the moon. The stars and the moon seem so still and beautiful. You may even see other planets in the solar system, thinking they are stars. Although the planets are different from the stars, they blend in with the stars and are usually hard to pick out.

Earth-Centered Model

It is generally known today that the sun and the stars appear to move through the sky because Earth is moving. This wasn't always an accepted fact. Many early Greek scientists thought the planets, the sun, and the moon were embedded in separate spheres that rotated around Earth. The stars were thought to be embedded in another sphere that also rotated around Earth. Early observers described moving objects in the night sky using the term *planasthai,* which means "to wander." The word *planet* comes from this term.

This model is called the Earth-centered model of the solar system. It included Earth, the moon, the sun, five planets—Mercury, Venus, Mars, Jupiter, and Saturn—and the sphere of stars.

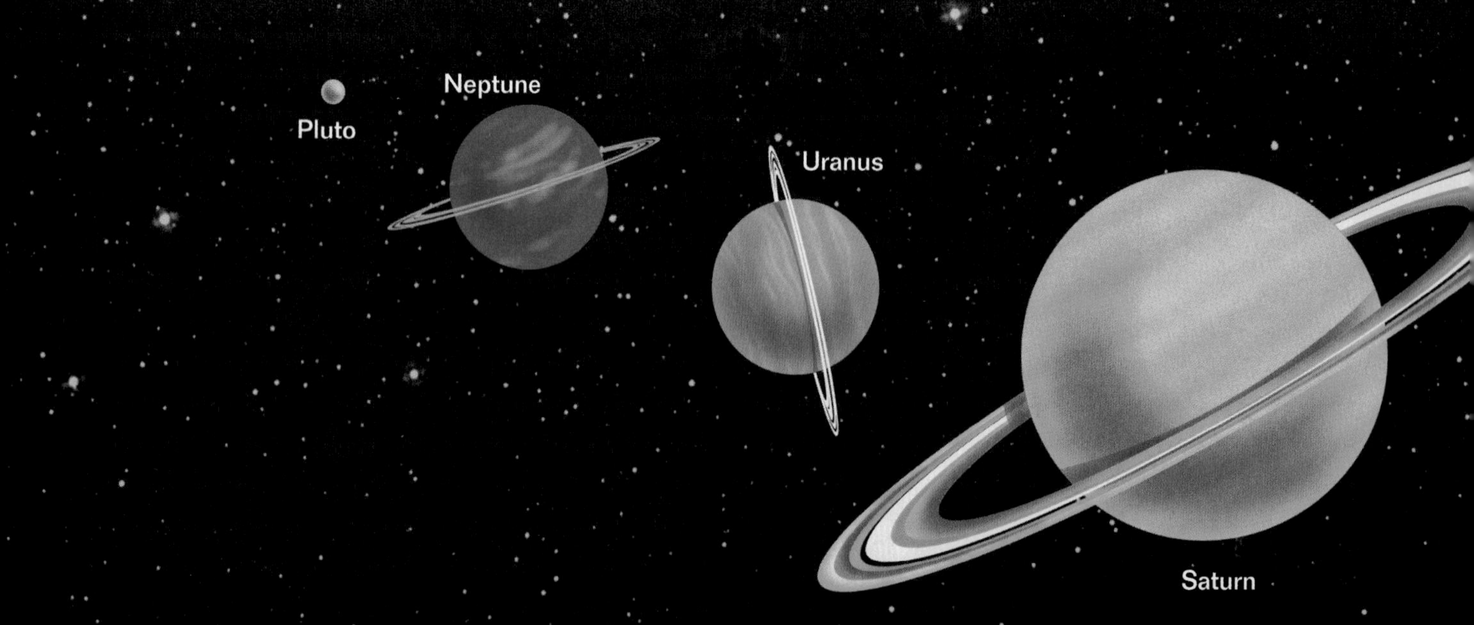

Figure 19-1 Each of the nine planets in the solar system is unique. The sizes of the planets and sun are drawn to scale but the distances between the planets and sun are not to scale.

Sun-Centered Model

The idea of an Earth-centered solar system was held for centuries until the Polish astronomer Nicholas Copernicus published a different view in 1543. Using an idea proposed by an early Greek scholar, Copernicus stated that the moon revolved around Earth, which was a planet. Earth, along with the other planets, revolved around the sun. He also stated that the daily movement of the planets and the stars was due to Earth's rotation. This is the sun-centered model of the solar system.

Using his telescope, the Italian astronomer Galileo Galilei found evidence that supported the ideas of Copernicus. He discovered that Venus went through phases like the moon's. These phases could be explained only if Venus were orbiting the sun. From this, he concluded that Venus revolves around the sun and that the sun is the center of the solar system.

Modern View of the Solar System

We now know that the **solar system** is made up of the nine planets, including Earth, and many smaller objects that orbit the sun. The sizes of the nine planets and the sun are shown to scale in **Figure 19-1.** However, the distances between the planets are not to scale. The dark areas on the sun are sunspots, which you will learn about later. Notice how small Earth is compared with some of the other planets and the sun, which is much larger than any of the planets.

The solar system includes a vast territory extending billions of kilometers in all directions from the sun. The sun contains 99.86 percent of the mass of the whole solar system. Because of its gravitational pull, the sun is the central object around which other objects of the solar system revolve.

VISUALIZING The Early Solar System

Figure 19-2 Through careful observations, astronomers have found clues that help explain how our solar system may have formed.

B As gravity pulled matter inward, the cloud began to contract and spin. The densely packed matter grew extremely hot.

A About 4.6 billion years ago, a large cloud of gas, ice, and dust occupied our place in space.

How the Solar System Formed

Scientists hypothesize that the sun and the solar system formed from a cloud of gas, ice, and dust about 4.6 billion years ago. **Figure 19-2** illustrates how this may have happened. This cloud was slowly rotating in space. A nearby star may have exploded, and the shock waves from this event may have caused the cloud to start contracting. At first, the cloud was rotating slowly. As it contracted, the matter in the cloud was squeezed into less space. The cloud's density became greater and the increased attraction of gravity pulled more gas and dust toward the cloud center. This caused the cloud to rotate faster, which in turn caused it to flatten into a disk with a dense center. ☑

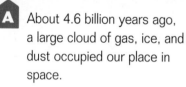

Reading Check ☑
When did the solar system begin to form?

As the cloud contracted, the temperature began to increase. Eventually, the temperature in the core of the cloud reached about 10 million °C and nuclear fusion began. A star was born—this was the beginning of our sun. Nuclear fusion occurs when atoms with low mass, such as hydrogen, combine to form heavier elements, such as helium. The new, heavy element contains slightly less mass than the sum of the light atoms that formed it. The lost mass is converted into energy.

Not all of the nearby gas, ice, and dust were drawn into the core of the cloud. Remaining gas, ice, and dust particles

C The center of the rotating disk continued to heat. Meanwhile, gas and dust particles in the outer rim clumped together, forming larger objects.

D The larger clumps continued to grow as more objects collided.

collided and stuck together, forming larger objects that in turn attracted more particles because of the stronger pull of gravity. Close to the sun, the temperature was hot, and the easily vaporized elements could not condense into solids. This is why light elements are more scarce in the planets closer to the sun than in planets farther out in the solar system. Instead, the inner solar system is dominated by small, rocky planets with iron cores.

The **inner planets**—Mercury, Venus, Earth, and Mars—are the solid, rocky planets closest to the sun. The **outer planets**—Jupiter, Saturn, Uranus, Neptune, and Pluto—are those farthest from the sun. Except for Pluto, which is made of rock and ice, the outer planets are made mostly of lighter elements such as hydrogen, helium, methane, and ammonia.

E Eventually, the larger clumps gathered enough matter to become planets. The core of the disk grew even denser and hotter.

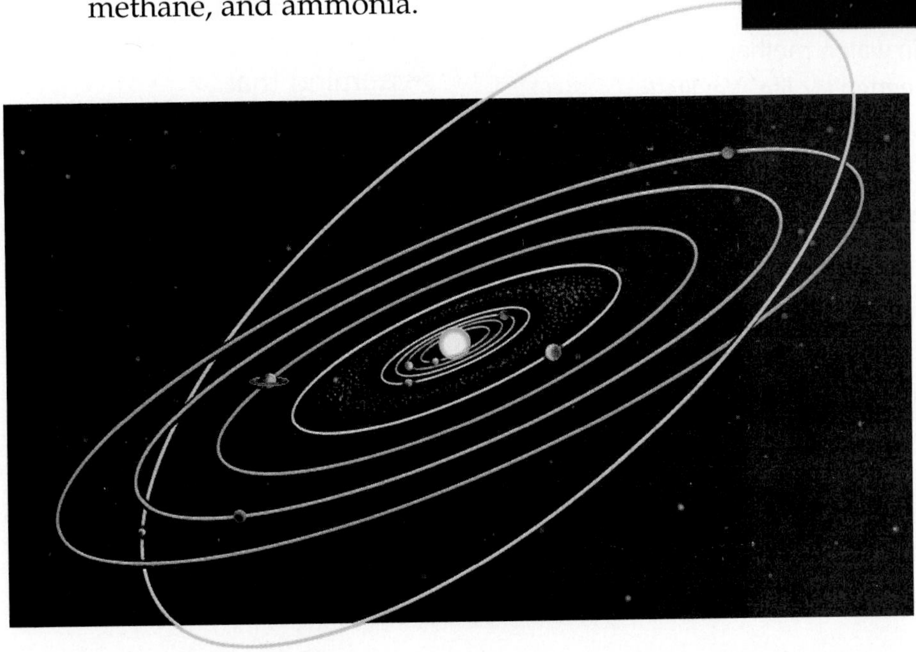

F Nuclear fusion began in the core, and the sun became a star. Some of the smaller objects became moons and rings around the planets.

PHYSICS INTEGRATION

Motions of the Planets

When Nicholas Copernicus developed his sun-centered model of the solar system, he thought that the planets orbited the sun in circles. In the early 1600s, the German mathematician Johannes Kepler began studying the orbits of the planets. He discovered that the shapes of the orbits are not circular, but elliptical. He also calculated that the sun is not at the center of the ellipse but is offset from the center.

Kepler also discovered that the planets travel at different speeds in their orbits around the sun. By studying these speeds, you can see that the planets closer to the sun travel faster than planets farther away from the sun. As a result, the outer planets take much longer to orbit the sun than the inner planets do.

Copernicus's ideas, considered radical at the time, led to the birth of modern astronomy. Early scientists didn't have technology such as space probes to learn about the planets. They used instruments such as the one shown in **Figure 19-3.** Nevertheless, they developed theories about the solar system that we still use today. In the next section, you'll learn about the inner planets—our nearest neighbors in space.

Figure 19-3 This instrument, called an astrolabe, was used for a variety of astronomical calculations.

Section Assessment

1. What is the difference between the sun-centered and the Earth-centered models of the solar system?
2. How do scientists hypothesize the solar system formed?
3. The outer planets are rich in water, methane, and ammonia—the materials needed for life. Yet life is unlikely on these planets. Explain.
4. **Think Critically:** Would a year on the planet Uranus be longer or shorter than an Earth year? Explain.
5. **Skill Builder**
   Concept Mapping Make a concept map that compares and contrasts the Earth-centered model with the sun-centered model of the solar system. If you need help, refer to Concept Mapping in the **Skill Handbook** on page 666.

Using Math

Assuming that the planets travel in nearly circular orbits, research their value of average orbital speeds to determine how much faster (in km/s) Mercury travels in its orbit than Earth travels in its orbit.

Planetary Orbits

Planets travel around the sun along fixed paths called orbits. Early theories about the solar system stated that planetary orbits were perfect circles. As you construct a model of a planetary orbit, you will observe that the shape of planetary orbits is an ellipse, not a circle.

Materials

- Thumbtacks or pins
- Metric ruler
- String (25 cm)
- Pencil
- Cardboard (23 cm × 30 cm)
- Paper (21.5 cm × 28 cm)

What You'll Investigate

How can a model be constructed that will show planetary orbits to be elliptical?

Goals

- **Model** planetary orbits.
- **Calculate** changes in ellipses.

Procedure

1. **Place** a blank sheet of paper on top of the cardboard and insert two thumbtacks or pins about 3 cm apart.
2. **Tie** the string into a circle with a circumference of 15 to 20 cm. **Loop** the string around the thumbtacks. With someone holding the tacks or pins, **place** your pencil inside the loop and **pull** it tight.

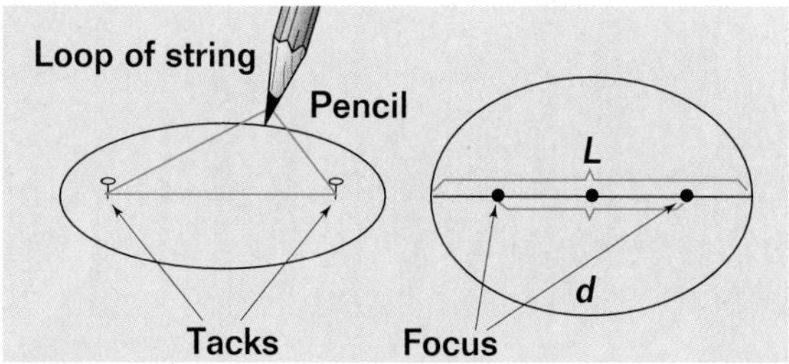

3. **Move** the pencil around the tacks, keeping the string tight, until you have completed a smooth, closed curve, called an ellipse.
4. **Repeat** steps 1 through 3 several times. First, **vary** the distance between the tacks, then **vary** the length of the string. However, change only one of these each time. Make a data table to record the changes in the sizes and shapes of the ellipses.
5. Orbits usually are described in terms of eccentricity (*e*). The eccentricity of any ellipse is determined by dividing the distance (*d*) between the foci (fixed points—here, the tacks) by the length of the major axis (*L*). See the diagram at left.
6. **Calculate** and **record** the eccentricity of the ellipses that you constructed.
7. **Research** the eccentricities of planetary orbits.
8. **Construct** an ellipse with the same eccentricity as Earth's orbit. **Repeat** this step with the orbit of either Pluto or Mercury.

Conclude and Apply

1. **Analyze** the effect a change in the length of the string or the distance between the tacks has on the shape of the ellipse.
2. **Hypothesize** what must be done to the string or placement of tacks to decrease the eccentricity of a constructed ellipse.
3. **Describe** the shape of Earth's orbit. Where is the sun located within the orbit?
4. **Identify** the planets that have the most eccentric orbits.
5. **Describe** the path of an orbit with an eccentricity of zero.

19·2 The Inner Planets

What **You'll Learn**

- The inner planets in their relative order from the sun
- Important characteristics of each inner planet
- How Venus and Earth compare and contrast

Vocabulary

Mercury, Venus, Earth, astronomical unit, Mars

Why **It's Important**

- Other planets have characteristics that are different from those of Earth.

Inner Planets

We have learned much about the solar system since the days of Copernicus and Galileo. Advancements in telescopes allow astronomers to observe the planets from Earth. The planets shine by sunlight reflected from their surfaces. In addition, space probes have explored much of our solar system, adding greatly to the knowledge we have about the planets. Let's take a tour of the solar system through the "eyes" of the space probes.

Mercury

The closest planet to the sun is **Mercury.** It is also the second-smallest planet. The first and only American spacecraft mission to Mercury was in 1974–1975 by *Mariner 10,* which flew by the planet and sent pictures back to Earth. *Mariner 10* photographed only 45 percent of Mercury's surface—we do not know what the other 55 percent looks like. What we do know is that the surface of Mercury has many craters and looks much like our moon. It also has cliffs as high as 3 km on its surface, as seen in **Figure 19-4.** These cliffs may have formed when Mercury apparently shrank about 2 km in diameter.

Why did Mercury apparently shrink? Scientists think the answer may lie inside the planet. *Mariner 10* detected a weak magnetic field around Mercury, indicating that the planet has a large iron core. Some scientists hypothesize that the crust of Mercury solidified while the iron core was still hot and

Figure 19-4 Giant cliffs on Mercury, like the one marked by the arrow, suggest that the planet might have shrunk.

Mercury

molten. Then, as the core cooled and solidified, it contracted, causing the planet to shrink. The large cliffs may have resulted from breaks in the crust caused by this contraction, similar to what happens when an apple dries out and shrivels up.

Because of Mercury's small size and low gravitational pull, most gases that could form an atmosphere escape into space. Mercury's thin atmosphere is composed of hydrogen, helium, sodium, and potassium. The sodium and potassium may diffuse upward through the crust. The thin atmosphere and the nearness of Mercury to the sun cause this planet to have large extremes in temperature. Mercury's surface temperature can reach 450°C during the day and drop to –170°C at night.

Using Math

The average distance from the sun to Earth is 150 million km. How many minutes does it take light traveling at 300 000 km/s to reach Earth? Use the equation

$$\text{Time} = \frac{\text{distance}}{\text{speed}}$$

Venus

The second planet outward from the sun is **Venus.** Venus is sometimes called Earth's twin because its size and mass are similar to Earth's. One major difference is that the entire surface of Venus is blanketed by a dense atmosphere. The atmosphere of Venus, which has 96 times the surface pressure of Earth's at sea level, is mostly carbon dioxide. The clouds in the atmosphere contain droplets of sulfuric acid, which gives them a slightly yellow color.

Clouds on Venus are so dense that only two percent of the sunlight that strikes the top of the clouds reaches the planet's surface. The solar energy that reaches the surface is trapped by the carbon dioxide gas and causes a greenhouse effect similar to but more intense than Earth's greenhouse effect. Due to this intense greenhouse effect, the temperature on the surface of Venus is 470°C.

The former Soviet Union led the exploration of Venus. Beginning in 1970 with the first *Venera* probe, the Russians have photographed and mapped the surface of Venus using radar and surface probes. Between 1990 and 1994, the *U.S. Magellan* probe used its radar to make the most detailed maps yet of Venus's surface. *Magellan* revealed huge craters, faultlike cracks, and volcanoes with visible lava flows, as seen in **Figure 19-5.**

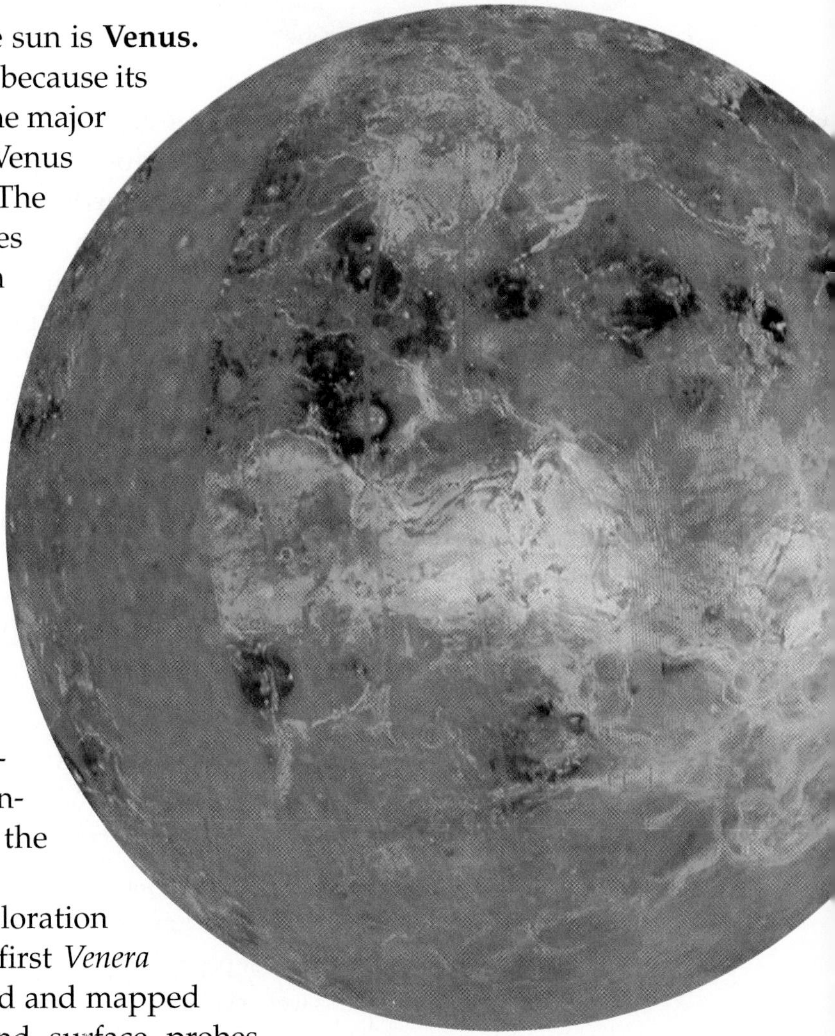

Figure 19-5 Although Venus is similar to Earth, there are important differences. **How could studying Venus help us learn more about Earth?**

Earth

Figure 19-6 More than 70 percent of Earth's surface is covered by liquid water. **What is unique about surface temperatures on Earth?**

Earth, shown in **Figure 19-6,** is the third planet from the sun. The average distance from Earth to the sun is 150 million km, or one astronomical unit (AU). **Astronomical units** are used to measure distances to objects in the solar system.

Unlike other planets, surface temperatures on Earth allow water to exist as a solid, liquid, and gas. Earth's atmosphere causes most meteors to burn up before they reach the surface. The atmosphere also protects life from the sun's intense radiation.

Mars

Mars, the fourth planet from the sun, is called the red planet because iron oxide in the weathered rocks on its surface gives it a reddish color, as seen in **Figure 19-7.** Other features of Mars visible from Earth are its polar ice caps, which get larger during the Martian winter and shrink during the summer. The ice caps are made mostly of frozen carbon dioxide and frozen water.

Most of the information we have about Mars came from the *Mariner 9, Viking* probes, *Mars Global Surveyor,* and *Mars Pathfinder. Mariner 9* orbited Mars in 1971–1972. It revealed long channels on the planet that may have been carved by

Problem Solving

Interpret Planetary Data

Your teacher asks you to determine which planet's surface is hotter, Mercury or Venus. You must also explain the temperature difference. You decide that this assignment is going to be easy. Of course, Mercury has to be hotter than Venus because it is much closer to the sun. Venus is almost twice as far away as Mercury. You write your answer and turn in your paper. Later, when you receive your paper back, you find out that your assumptions were evidently wrong. Your teacher suggests that you research the question further, using the table on this page as a guide. As a further hint, your teacher tells you to consider how a greenhouse works to keep it warmer inside than outside and to relate this to what might happen to a planet with a thick atmosphere.

Data for Mercury and Venus

	Mercury 0.39 AU from sun	Venus 0.72 AU from sun
Surface Temperature (High)		
Atmosphere Density		
Atmosphere Compostion		

Think Critically: What causes Venus to have a higher surface temperature than Mercury? Explain.

flowing water. *Mariner 9* also discovered the largest volcano in the solar system, Olympus Mons. Like all Mars's volcanoes, Olympus Mons is extinct. Large rift zones that formed in the Martian crust were also discovered. One such rift, Valles Marineris, is shown in **Figure 19-7.**

The Viking probes

In 1976, the *Viking 1* and *2* probes arrived at Mars. Each spacecraft consisted of an orbiter and a lander. The *Viking 1* and *2* orbiters photographed the entire surface of Mars from orbit, while the *Viking 1* and *2* landers touched down on the planet's surface to conduct meteorological, chemical, and biological experiments. The biological experiments found no evidence of life in the soil. The *Viking* landers also sent back pictures of a reddish-colored, barren, rocky, and windswept surface.

Try at Home

MiniLab

Inferring Effects of Gravity

Procedure

1. Suppose you are a crane operator who is sent to Mars to help build a Mars colony.
2. You know that your crane can lift 44 500 N on Earth, but the gravity on Mars is only 40 percent of Earth's gravity.
3. Using Appendix B, determine how much mass your crane could lift on Mars.

Analysis

1. How can what you have discovered be an advantage over construction on Earth?
2. In what ways might construction advantages change the overall design of the Mars colony?

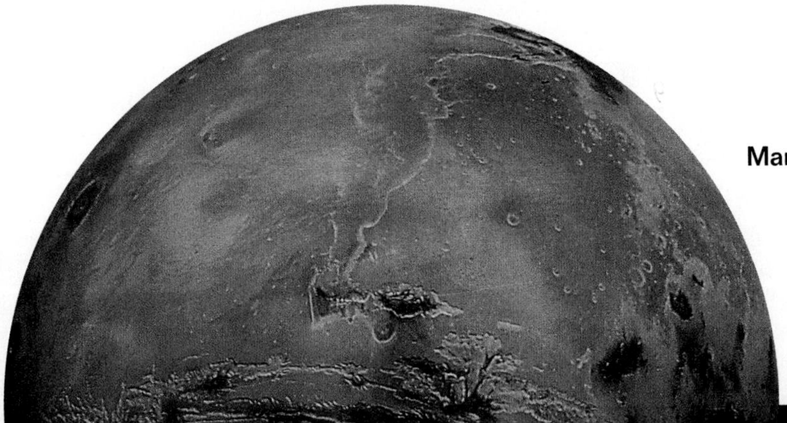

Mars

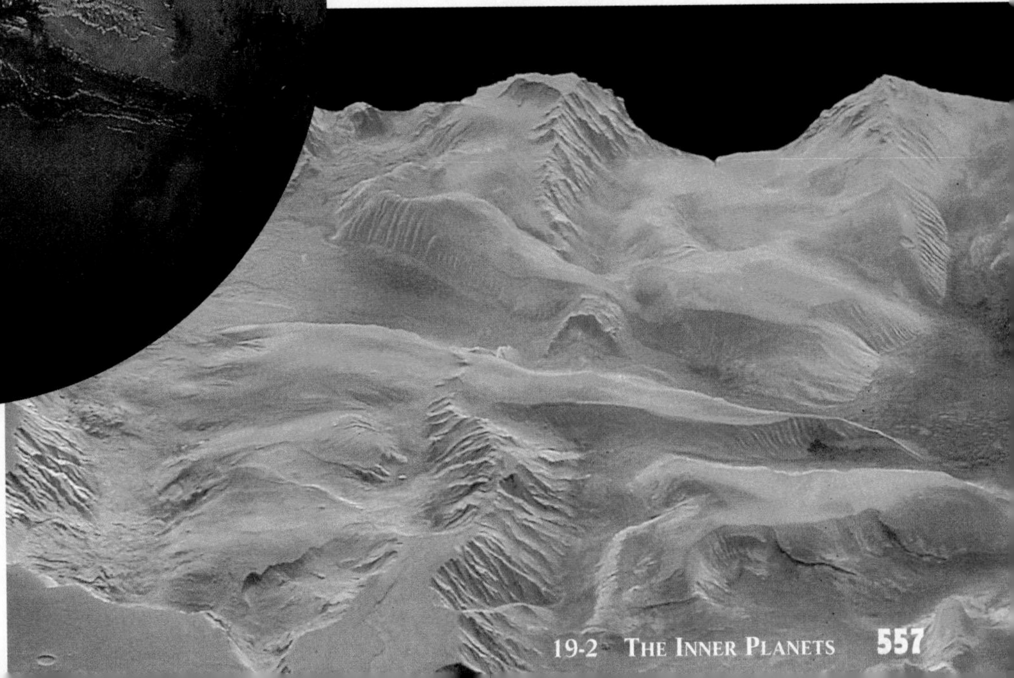

Figure 19-7 Valles Marineris is more than 4000 km long, up to 240 km wide, and more than 6 km deep.

Reading Check

In what way is Valles Marineris similar to the Grand Canyon?

CHEMISTRY INTEGRATION

Mars has always been known as the red planet. Research the composition of surface rocks on Mars. Describe the chemical reaction in the Martian soil responsible for the planet's red color.

Global Surveyor and Pathfinder

The *Mars Pathfinder,* shown in **Figure 19-8,** gathered data that indicated that iron in Mars's crust may have been leached out by groundwater. In addition, high-quality cameras on board *Global Surveyor* showed that the walls of Valles Marineris have distinct layers similar to the Grand Canyon on Earth. *Global Surveyor* also noticed that a vast flat region, similar to a dried-up seabed or mudflat, covers a large area of Mars's northern hemisphere. This evidence, combined with evidence gathered from *Mariner 9,* indicates that large amounts of water were once present on the planet. Where has all the water gone? Many believe it is frozen into Mars's crust at the poles, shown in **Figure 19-9,** or has soaked into the ground.

The Martian atmosphere is much thinner than Earth's and is composed mostly of carbon dioxide, with some nitrogen and argon. The thin atmosphere does not filter out harmful rays from the sun as Earth's atmosphere does. Surface temperatures range from 35°C to –170°C. The temperature difference between day and night sets up strong winds on the planet, which can cause global dust storms during certain seasons.

A

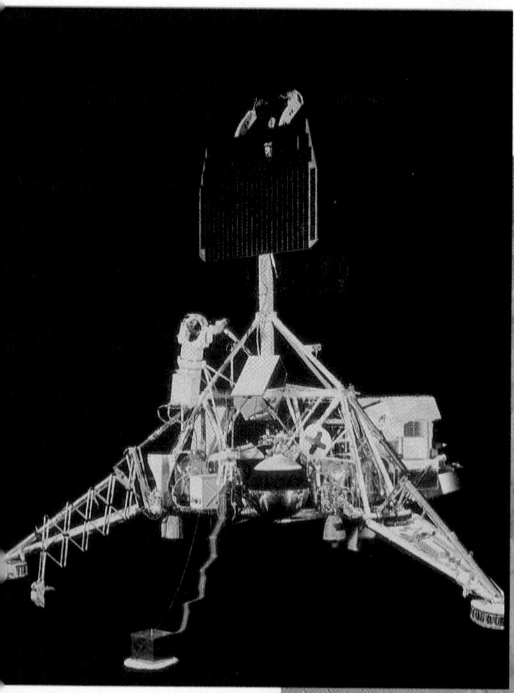

B

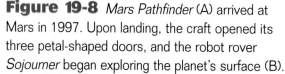

Figure 19-8 *Mars Pathfinder* (A) arrived at Mars in 1997. Upon landing, the craft opened its three petal-shaped doors, and the robot rover *Sojourner* began exploring the planet's surface (B).

Figure 19-9 These photos show two features of Mars.

A Olympus Mons is the largest volcano in the solar system.

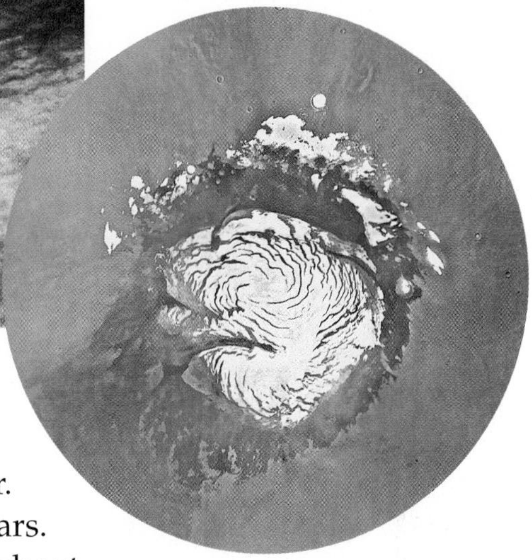

B Water that flowed on Mars long ago may now be frozen in polar ice caps.

Martian Moons

Mars has two small, heavily cratered moons. Phobos is 25 km in diameter, and Deimos is 13 km in diameter. Phobos's orbit is slowly spiraling inward toward Mars. Phobos is expected to impact the Martian surface in about 50 million years.

As you toured the inner planets using the "eyes" of the space probes, you saw how each planet is unique. Mercury, Venus, Earth, and Mars are different from the outer planets, which you'll explore in the next section.

Section Assessment

1. How are Mercury and Earth's moon similar?
2. List one important characteristic of each inner planet.
3. Although Venus is often called Earth's twin, why would life as we know it be unlikely on Venus?
4. Name the inner planets in order from the sun.
5. **Think Critically:** Do the closest planets to the sun always have the hottest surface temperatures? Explain your answer.
6. **Skill Builder**
   Interpreting Data Using the information in this section, explain how Mars is like Earth. How are they different? If you need help, refer to Interpreting Data in the **Skill Handbook** on page 676.

Science Journal

Use textbooks and NASA materials to investigate NASA's missions to Mars. In your Science Journal, report on the possibility of life on Mars and the tests that have been conducted to see whether life is there.

19•3 The Outer Planets

What You'll Learn

- The major characteristics of Jupiter, Saturn, Uranus, and Neptune
- How Pluto differs from the other outer planets

Vocabulary

Jupiter
Great Red Spot
Saturn
Uranus
Neptune
Pluto

Why It's Important

- You'll learn about the planets in our solar system that differ most from Earth.

Outer Planets

You have learned that the inner planets are small, solid, rocky bodies in space. By contrast, the outer planets, except for Pluto, are large, gaseous objects.

You may have heard or read about the *Voyager* and *Galileo* spacecraft. Although they were not the first probes to the outer planets, they have uncovered a wealth of new information about Jupiter, Saturn, Uranus, and Neptune. Let's follow the spacecraft on their journeys to the outer planets of the solar system.

Jupiter

In 1979, *Voyager 1* and *Voyager 2* flew past **Jupiter,** the largest planet and the fifth planet from the sun. *Galileo* reached Jupiter in 1995. The major discoveries of the probes include new information about the composition and motion of Jupiter's atmosphere and the discovery of three new moons. *Voyager* probes also discovered that Jupiter has faint dust rings around it and that one of its moons has volcanoes on it.

Jupiter is composed mostly of hydrogen and helium, with some ammonia, methane, and water vapor as well. Scientists theorize that the atmosphere of hydrogen and helium gradually changes to a planetwide ocean of liquid hydrogen and helium toward the middle of the planet. Below this liquid layer may be a solid rocky core. The extreme pressure and temperature, however, make the core different from any rock on Earth.

You've probably seen pictures from the probes of Jupiter's colorful clouds. Its atmosphere has bands of white, red, tan, and brown clouds, as shown in **Figure 19-10.** Continuous storms of swirling, high-pressure gas have been observed on Jupiter. The **Great Red Spot** is the most spectacular of these storms. Lightning also has been observed within Jupiter's clouds.

Jupiter

A

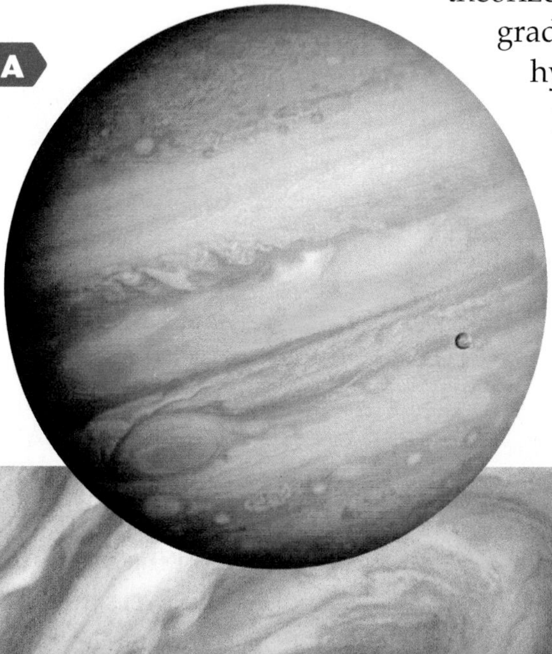

B

Figure 19-10 Jupiter (A) is the largest planet in our solar system, containing more mass than all of the other planets combined. The Great Red Spot (B) is a giant storm about 12 000 km from top to bottom.

Moons of Jupiter

Sixteen moons orbit Jupiter. The four largest, shown in **Table 19-1,** were discovered by Galileo in 1610. Io is the closest large moon to Jupiter. Jupiter's tremendous gravitational force and the gravity of Europa pull on Io. This force heats up Io, causing it to be the most volcanically active object in the solar system. The next large moon is Europa. It is composed mostly of rock with a thick, smooth crust of ice, which may indicate the presence of an ocean under the ice. Next is Ganymede, which is the largest moon in the solar system. It's larger than the planet Mercury. Callisto, the last of the large moons, is composed of ice and rock. Studying these moons and events such as the comet collision shown in **Figure 19-11** further our knowledge of the solar system.

Saturn

The next planet surveyed by the *Voyager* probes was Saturn, in 1980 and 1981. **Saturn** is the sixth planet from the sun and is also known as the ringed planet. Saturn is the second-largest planet in the solar system but has the lowest density. Its density is so low that the planet would float on water.

Table 19-1

Large Moons of Jupiter

Io The most volcanically active object in the solar system; sulfur lava gives it its distinctive red and orange color; has a thin oxygen, sulfur, and sulfur dioxide atmosphere.

Europa Rocky interior is covered by a 100-km-thick ice crust, which has a network of cracks, indicating tectonic activity; has a thin oxygen atmosphere.

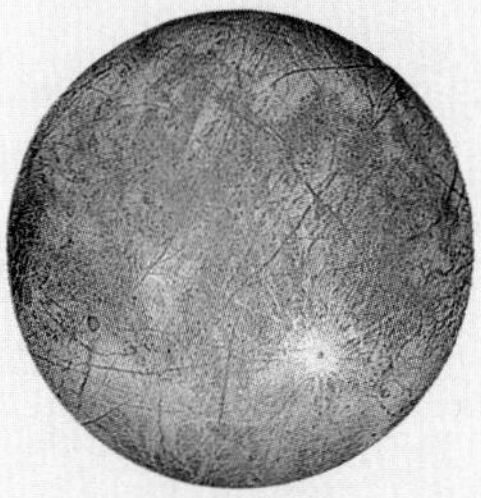

Ganymede Has an ice crust about 100 km thick, covered with grooves; crust may surround a mantle of water or slushy ice; has a rocky core and a thin hydrogen atmosphere.

Callisto Has a heavily cratered, ice-rock crust several hundred kilometers thick; crust may surround a salty ocean around a rock core; has a thin atmosphere of hydrogen, oxygen, and carbon dioxide.

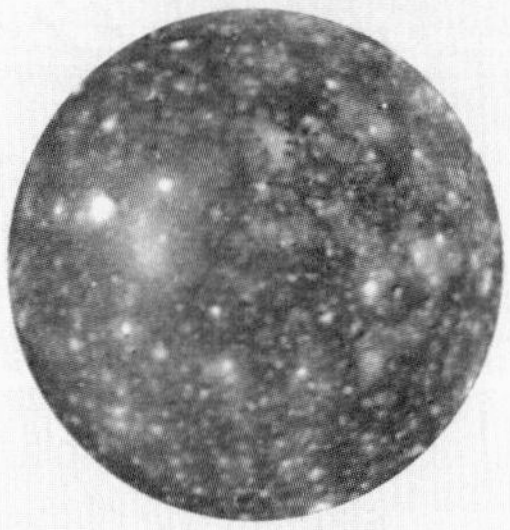

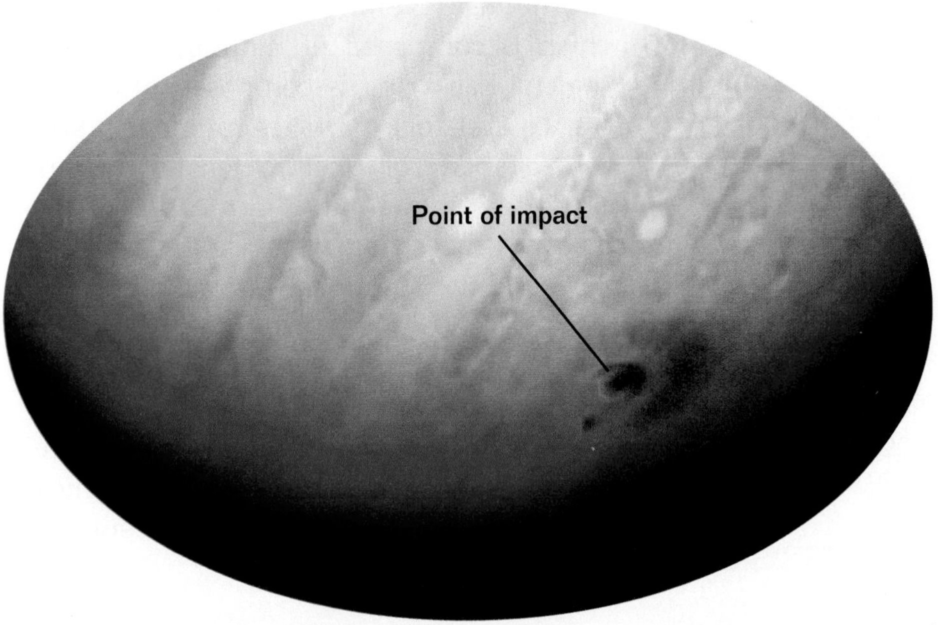

Figure 19-11 In 1994, comet Shoemaker-Levy 9 collided into Jupiter causing a series of spectacular explosions. Information from this impact gives us clues about what might happen if such an impact occurred on Earth.

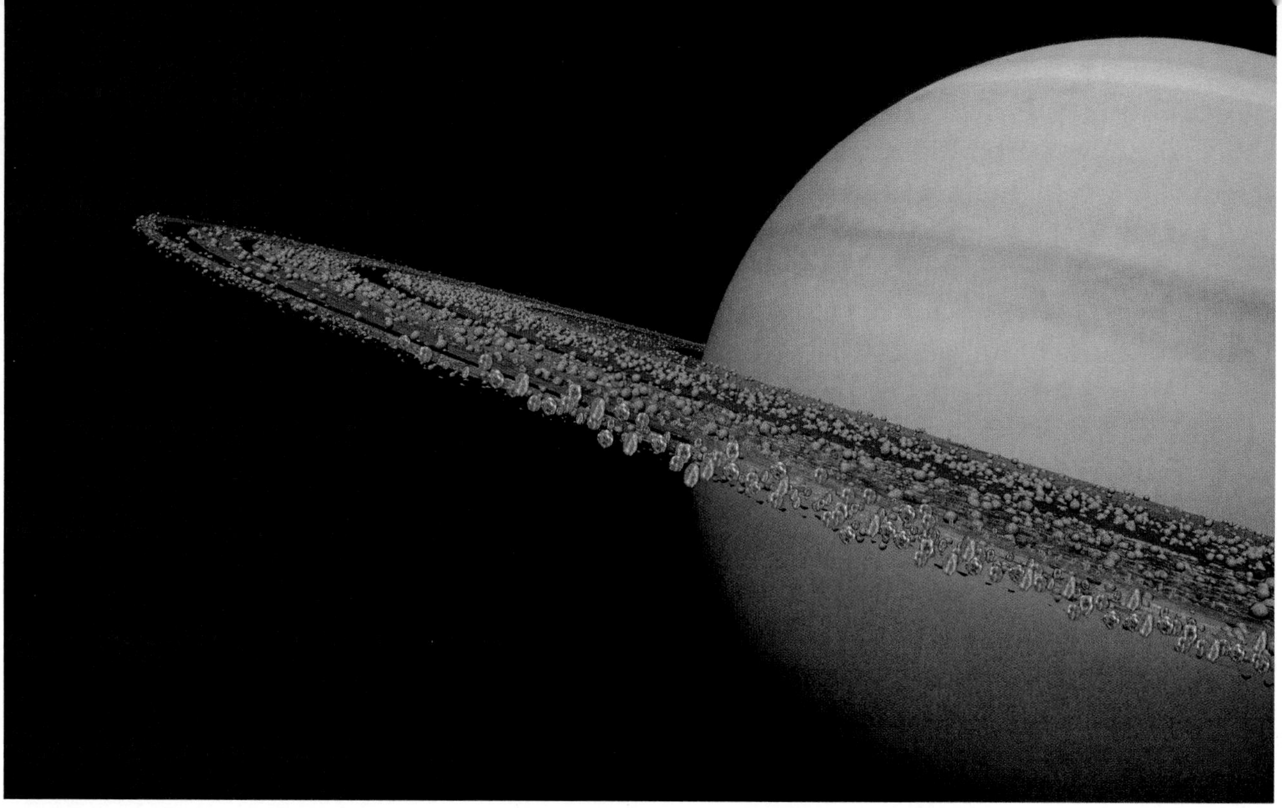

Figure 19-12 Saturn's rings are composed of pieces of rock and ice.

Similar to Jupiter, Saturn is a large, gaseous planet with a thick outer atmosphere composed mostly of hydrogen and helium. Saturn's atmosphere also contains ammonia, methane, and water vapor. As you go deeper into Saturn's atmosphere, the gases gradually change to liquid hydrogen and helium. Below its atmosphere and liquid ocean, Saturn may have a small rocky core.

The *Voyager* probes gathered new information about Saturn's ring system and its moons. The *Voyager* probes showed that Saturn has several broad rings, each of which is composed of thousands of thin ringlets. Each ring is composed of countless ice and rock particles ranging in size from a speck of dust to tens of meters across, as shown in **Figure 19-12.** This makes Saturn's ring system the most complex of all the outer gaseous planets.

At least 20 moons orbit Saturn. That's more than any other planet in our solar system. The largest of these, Titan, is larger than Mercury. It has an atmosphere of nitrogen, argon, and methane. Thick clouds prevent us from seeing the surface of Titan.

Try at Home

MiniLab

Modeling Planets

Procedure

1. Research the planets to determine how the sizes of the planets in the solar system compare with each other.
2. Select a scale for the diameter of Earth based on the size of your paper.
3. Make a model by drawing a circle with this diameter on paper.
4. Using Earth's diameter as 1.0, draw each of the other planets to scale.

Analysis

1. At this scale, how far would your model Earth need to be located from the sun?
2. What would 1 AU be equal to in this model?
3. Using a scale of 1 AU = 2 m, how large would the sun and Earth models have to be to remain in scale?

Uranus

After touring Saturn, *Voyager 2* flew by Uranus in 1986. **Uranus,** shown in **Figure 19-13,** is the seventh planet from the sun and wasn't discovered until 1781. It is a large, gaseous planet with 17 satellites and a system of thin, dark rings.

Voyager revealed numerous thin rings and ten moons that had not been seen earlier. *Voyager* also detected that the planet's magnetic field is tilted 55 degrees from its rotational poles.

The atmosphere of Uranus is composed of hydrogen, helium, and some methane. The methane gives the planet its blue-green color. Methane absorbs the red and yellow light, and the clouds reflect the green and blue. No cloud bands and few storm systems are seen on Uranus. Evidence suggests that under its atmosphere, Uranus has a mantle of liquid water, methane, and ammonia surrounding a rocky core.

One of the most unique features of Uranus is that its axis of rotation is tilted on its side compared with the other planets. The axes of rotation of the other planets, except Pluto, are nearly perpendicular to the planes of their orbits. Uranus, however, has a rotational axis nearly parallel to the plane of its orbit, as shown in **Figure 19-14.** Some scientists believe a collision with another object turned Uranus on its side.

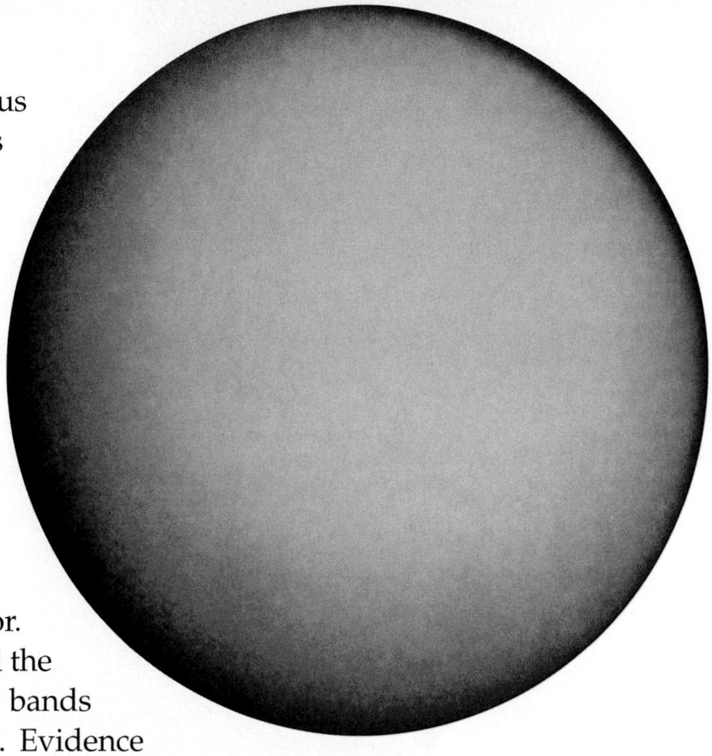

Figure 19-13 The atmosphere of Uranus gives the planet its distinct blue-green color.

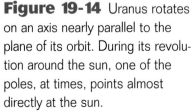

interNET CONNECTION

Visit the Glencoe Science Web Site at **www.glencoe.com/sec/science/ca** for more information about the *Voyager* space probes.

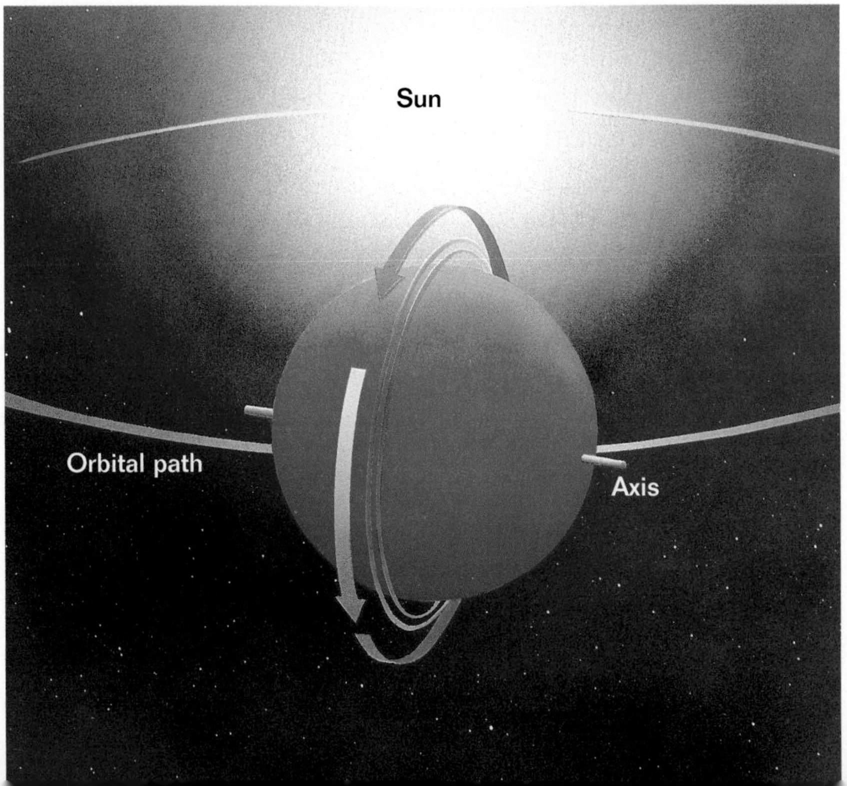

Figure 19-14 Uranus rotates on an axis nearly parallel to the plane of its orbit. During its revolution around the sun, one of the poles, at times, points almost directly at the sun.

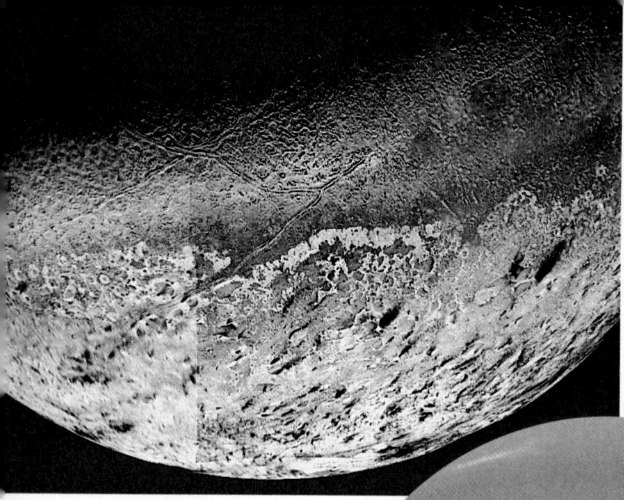

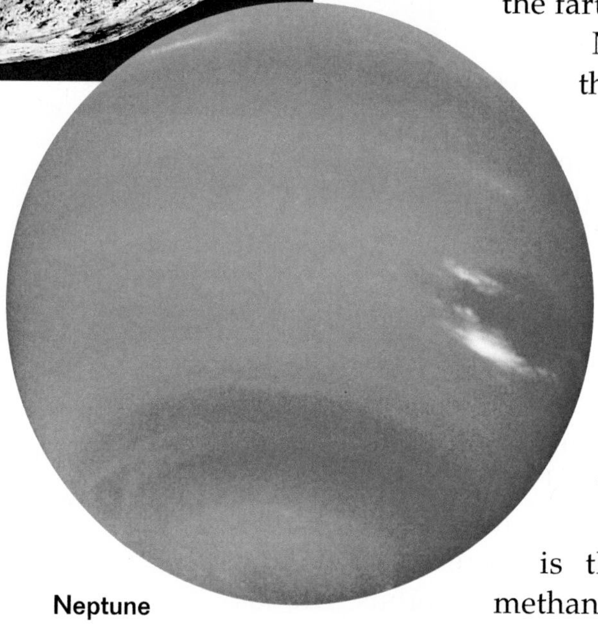

Figure 19-15
Triton, above, is Neptune's largest moon.

Neptune

Neptune

From Uranus, *Voyager 2* traveled on to Neptune, a large, gaseous planet. Discovered in 1846, **Neptune** is usually the eighth planet from the sun. However, Pluto's orbit crosses inside Neptune's during part of its voyage around the sun. Between 1979 and 1998, Pluto was closer to the sun than Neptune. In 1999, Pluto once again became the farthest planet from the sun.

Neptune's atmosphere is similar to that of Uranus. The methane content gives Neptune, shown in **Figure 19-15,** its distinctive blue-green color, just as it does for Uranus.

Neptune has dark-colored, stormlike features in its atmosphere that are similar to the Great Red Spot on Jupiter. One discovered by *Voyager* is called the Great Dark Spot.

Under its atmosphere, Neptune is thought to have liquid water, methane, and ammonia. Neptune probably has a rocky core.

Voyager 2 detected six new moons, so the total number of Neptune's known moons is now eight. Of these, Triton is the largest. Triton, shown in **Figure 19-15,** has a diameter of 2700 km and a thin atmosphere composed mostly of nitrogen. *Voyager* detected methane geysers erupting on Triton. *Voyager* also detected that Neptune has rings that are thin in some places and thick in other places. Neptune's magnetic field is tilted 47 degrees from its rotational axis. In comparison, Earth's magnetic field is tilted only 11.5 degrees from its rotational axis.

Voyager ended its tour of the solar system with Neptune. Both *Voyager* probes are now beyond the orbits of Pluto and Neptune. They will continue into space, studying how far the sun's power reaches into the outer limits of our solar system.

Reading Check

Voyager's tour ended with what planet?

Pluto

The smallest planet in our solar system, and the one we know the least about, is Pluto. Because **Pluto** is farther from the sun than Neptune during most of its orbit around the sun, it is considered the ninth planet from the sun. Pluto is not like the other outer planets. It's surrounded by only a thin atmosphere, and it's the only outer planet with a solid, icy-rock surface.

Pluto's only moon, Charon, has a diameter about half the size of Pluto's. Charon orbits close to Pluto. Pluto and Charon are shown in **Figure 19-16.** Because of their close size and orbit, they are sometimes considered to be a double planet.

Recent data from the *Hubble Space Telescope* indicate the presence of a vast disk of icy comets near Neptune's orbit, called the Kuiper belt. Some of the ice comets are hundreds of kilometers in diameter. Are Pluto and Charon members of this belt? Are they escaped moons of one of the larger gaseous giants, or did they simply form at the distance they are? Maybe planets at that distance from the sun should be small and composed of icy rock. We may not find out until we send a probe to Pluto.

With the *Voyager* probes, we entered a new age of knowledge about the solar system. The space probe *Galileo*, which arrived at Jupiter in 1995, and the *Cassini* probe, which will arrive at Saturn in 2004, will continue to extend our understanding of the solar system.

Figure 19-16 The *Hubble Space Telescope* gave astronomers their first clear view of Pluto and Charon as distinct objects.

Section Assessment

1. What are the differences between the outer planets and the inner planets?
2. Are any moons in the solar system larger than planets? If so, which ones?
3. How does Pluto differ from the other outer planets?
4. **Think Critically:** Why is Neptune sometimes the farthest planet from the sun?
5. **Skill Builder**
   Recognizing Cause and Effect
   Answer the following questions about Jupiter. If you need help, refer to Recognizing Cause and Effect in the **Skill Handbook** on page 673.
   a. What causes Jupiter's surface color?
   b. How is the Great Red Spot affected by Jupiter's atmosphere?
   c. How does Jupiter's mass affect its gravitational force?

Using Computers

Spreadsheet Design a table using spreadsheet software of the nine planets. Compare their characteristics, such as size, distance from the sun, orbital speed, and number of satellites. If you need help, refer to page 690.

Design Your Own Experiment

Activity 19.2

Solar System Distance Model

Possible Materials

- Meterstick
- Scissors
- Pencil
- String (several meters)
- Paper (several sheets of notebook paper)

Distances between the planets of the solar system are large. Can you design a model that will demonstrate the large distances between and among the sun and planets in the solar system?

Recognize the Problem

How can a model be designed that will show the relative distances between and among the sun and planets of the solar system?

Form a Hypothesis

State a hypothesis about how a model with scale dimensions of the solar system can be constructed.

Goals

- **Make a table** of scale distances that will represent planetary distances to be used in a model of the solar system.
- **Research** planetary distances.
- **Make a model** of the distances between the sun and planets of the solar system.

Safety Precautions

Take care when handling scissors.

Planetary Distances

Planet	Distance to Sun (km)	Distance to Sun (AU)	Scale Distance (1 AU = 10 cm)	Scale Distance (1 AU = 2 m)
Mercury	5.8×10^7			
Venus	1.08×10^8			
Earth	1.50×10^8			
Mars	2.28×10^8			
Jupiter	7.80×10^8			
Saturn	1.43×10^9			
Uranus	2.88×10^9			
Neptune	4.51×10^9			
Pluto	5.92×10^9			

Test Your Hypothesis

Plan

1. As a group, **agree** upon and write out your hypothesis statement.
2. **List** the steps that you need to take in making your model to **test** your hypothesis. Be specific, describing exactly what you will do at each step.
3. **Make** a list of the materials that you will need to complete your model.
4. **Make a table** of scale distances you will use in your model.
5. **Write** a description of how you will **build** your model, **explaining** how it will demonstrate relative distances between and among the sun and planets of the solar system.

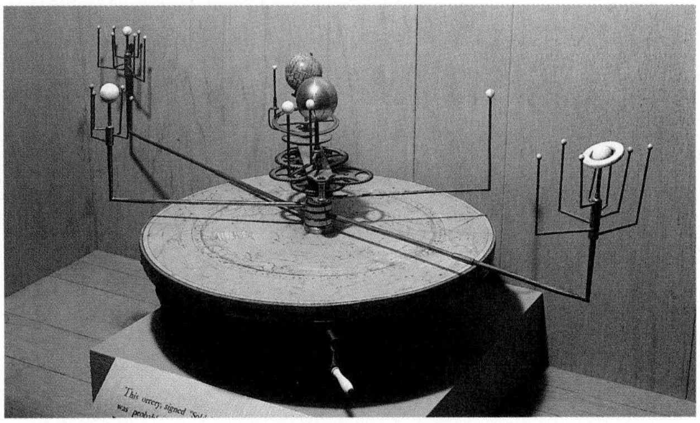

Do

1. Make sure your teacher approves your plan before you proceed.
2. **Construct the model** as planned using your scale distances.
3. While constructing the model, **write** down any observations that you or other members of your group make and complete the data table in your Science Journal.
4. **Calculate** the scale distance that would be used in your model if 1 AU = 2 m.

Analyze Your Data

1. **Explain** how a scale distance is determined.
2. How much string would be required to construct a model with a scale distance 1 AU = 2 m?

Draw Conclusions

1. Was it possible to work with your scale? **Explain** why or why not.
2. Proxima Centauri, the closest star to our sun, is about 270 000 AU from the sun. Based on your scale, how much string would you need to place this star on your model?

19·4 Other Objects in the Solar System

What You'll Learn

- Where a comet comes from and how a comet develops as it approaches the sun
- Comets, meteoroids, and asteroids

Vocabulary

comet **Oort Cloud** **meteor** **meteorite** **asteroid**

Why It's Important

- Comets, meteoroids, and asteroids may be composed of material that formed early in the history of the solar system.

Comets

Although the planets and their moons are the most noticeable members of the sun's family, many other objects orbit the sun. Comets, meteoroids, and asteroids are other objects in the solar system.

You've probably heard of Halley's comet. A **comet** is composed of dust and rock particles mixed in with frozen water, methane, and ammonia. Halley's comet was last seen from Earth in 1986. English astronomer Edmund Halley realized that comet sightings that had taken place about every 76 years were really sightings of the same comet. This comet, which takes about 76 years to orbit the sun, was named after him. Halley's comet is just one example of the many other objects in the solar system besides the planets. The Dutch astronomer Jan Oort proposed the idea that a large collection of comets lies in a cloud that completely surrounds the solar

Figure 19-17 Comet Hale-Bopp was visible in March and April 1997.

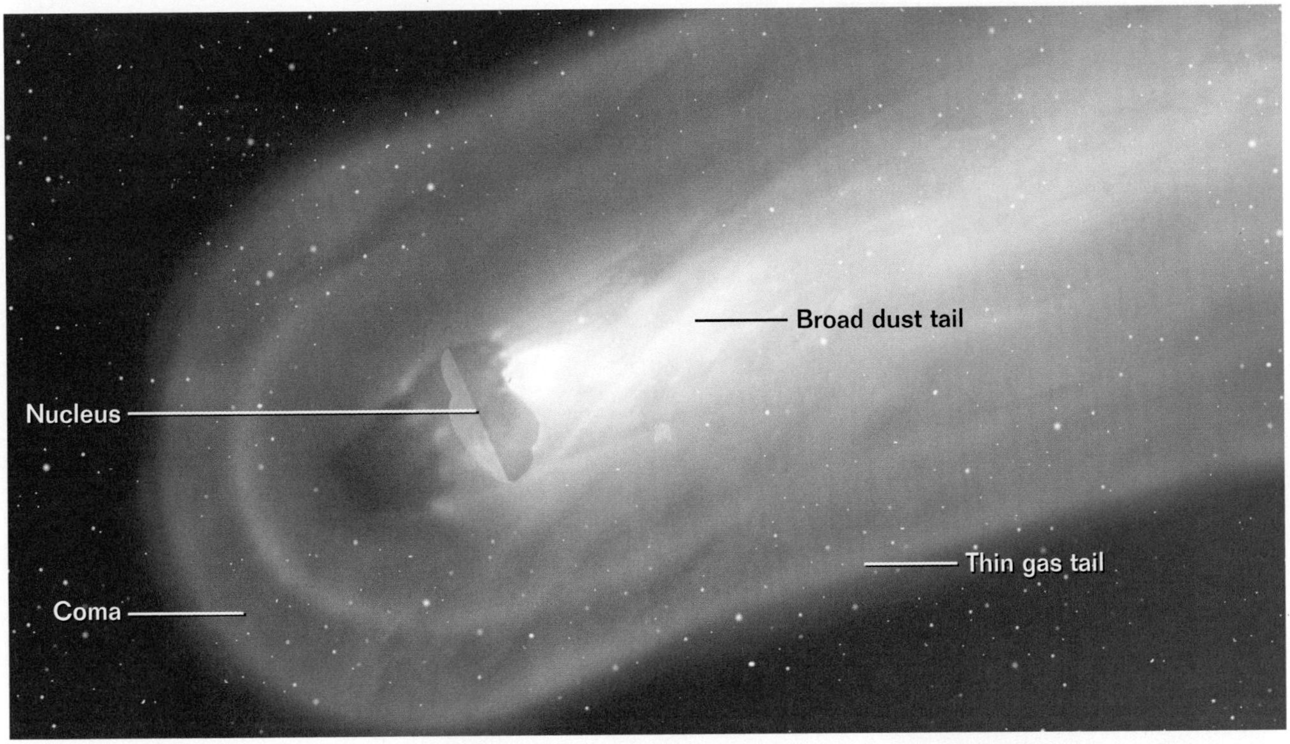

Figure 19-18 A comet consists of a nucleus, a coma, and a tail.

system. This cloud is located beyond the orbit of Pluto and is called the **Oort Cloud.** Evidence suggests that the gravity of the sun and nearby stars interacts with comets in the Oort Cloud. Comets either escape from the solar system or get captured into much smaller orbits. As mentioned earlier, another belt of comets, called the Kuiper belt, may exist near the orbit of Neptune.

On July 23, 1995, two backyard astronomers made an exciting discovery—a new comet was headed toward the sun. This comet, Comet Hale-Bopp, is larger than most that approach the sun and was the brightest comet visible from Earth in 20 years. Shown in **Figure 19-17,** it was at its brightest in March and April 1997.

Structure of Comets

The structure of a comet, shown in **Figure 19-18,** is like a large, dirty snowball or a mass of frozen ice and rock. But as the comet approaches the sun, it develops a distinctive structure. Ices of water, methane, and ammonia begin to vaporize because of the heat from the sun. Dust and bits of rock are released. The vaporized gases and released dust form a bright cloud called a coma around the nucleus, or solid part, of the comet. The solar wind pushes on the gases and released dust in the coma. These particles form a tail that always points away from the sun.

After many trips around the sun, most of the frozen ice in a comet has vaporized. All that is left are small particles that spread throughout the orbit of the original comet.

*inter***NET**
CONNECTION

Visit the Glencoe Science Web Site at **www.glencoe.com/sec/science/ca** for more information about comets.

VISUALIZING
Meteorites

Figure 19-19 Meteorites strike the surface of a moon or planet.

A A large meteorite struck Arizona 50 000 years ago.

interNET CONNECTION

Visit the Glencoe Science Web Site at **www.glencoe.com/sec/science/ca** for more information about meteor craters.

Meteoroids, Meteors, and Meteorites

You learned that comets tend to break up after they have passed close to the sun several times. The small pieces of the comet nucleus spread out into a loose group within the original orbit of the broken comet. These small pieces of rock moving through space are then called meteoroids.

When the path of a meteoroid crosses the position of Earth, it enters our atmosphere at between 15 and 70 km/s. Most meteoroids are so small that they are completely vaporized in Earth's atmosphere. A meteoroid that burns up in Earth's atmosphere is called a **meteor.** People often see these and call them shooting stars.

Each time Earth passes through the loose group of particles within the old orbit of a comet, many small particles of rock and dust enter the atmosphere. Because more meteors than usual are seen, this is called a meteor shower.

If the meteoroid is large enough, it may not completely burn up in Earth's atmosphere. When it strikes Earth, it is called a **meteorite.** Meteor Crater in Arizona, shown in **Figure 19-19A,** was formed when a large meteorite struck Earth about 50 000 years ago. Most meteorites are probably debris from asteroid collisions or broken-up comets, but some are from the moon and Mars.

Reading Check

What is a meteorite?

B This crater made by a meteorite is on the moon.

C A meteoroid that burns up in Earth's atmosphere is called a meteor.

Asteroids

An **asteroid** is a piece of rock similar to the material that formed into the planets. Most asteroids are located in an area between the orbits of Mars and Jupiter called the asteroid belt, shown in **Figure 19-20.** Why are they located there? The gravity of Jupiter may have kept a planet from forming in the area where the asteroid belt is now located.

Other asteroids are scattered throughout the solar system—they may have been thrown out of the belt by gravity. Some may have since been captured as moons around other planets.

Figure 19-20 The asteroid belt lies between the orbits of Mars and Jupiter.

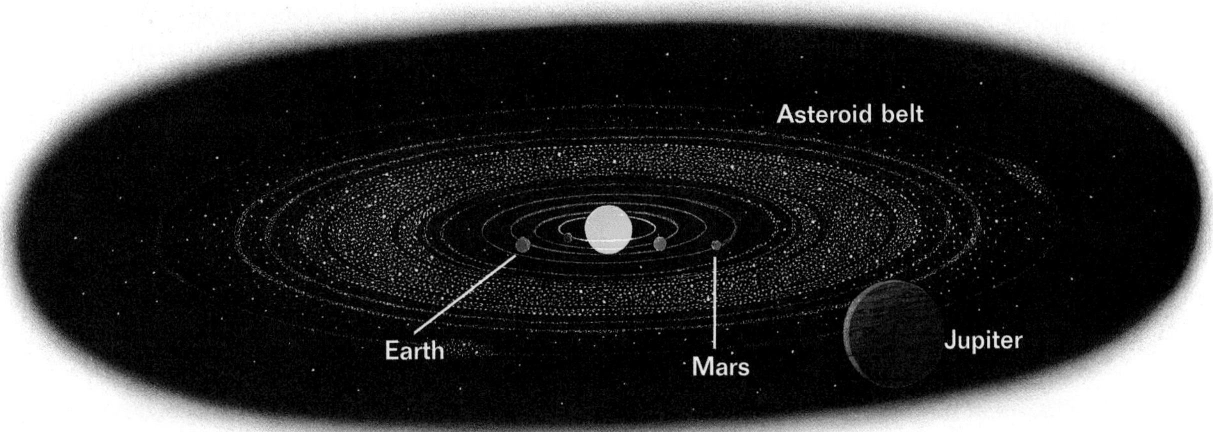

Asteroid Size

The sizes of the asteroids in the asteroid belt range from tiny particles to 940 km. Ceres is the largest and the first one discovered. The next three in size are Pallas (523 km), Vesta (501 km), and Juno (244 km). Two asteroids, Gaspra and Ida, were photographed by *Galileo* on its way to Jupiter, as shown in **Figure 19-21.**

Comets, meteoroids, and asteroids are probably composed of material that formed early in the history of the solar system. Scientists study the structure and composition of these space objects in order to better understand what the solar system may have been like long ago. Understanding what the early solar system was like could help scientists to better understand the formation of Earth and its relationship to other objects in the solar system.

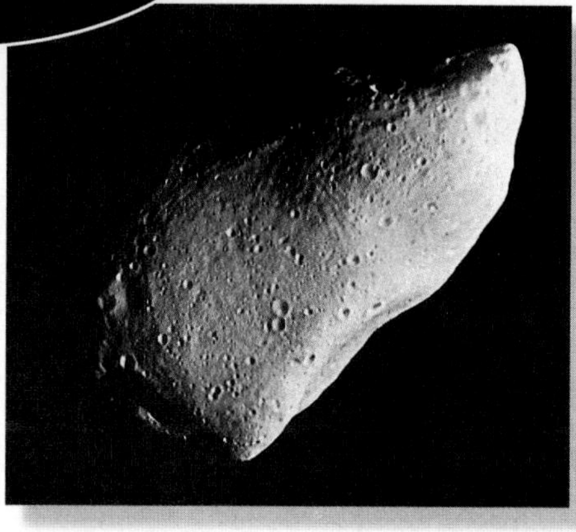

Figure 19-21 The asteroid Ida (A) is about 56 km long. Gaspra (B) is about 20 km long.

Section Assessment

1. How does a comet's tail form as it approaches the sun?
2. What type of feature might be formed on Earth if a large meteorite reached its surface?
3. Describe differences among comets, meteoroids, and asteroids.
4. **Think Critically:** What is the chemical composition of comets? Are comets more similar to the inner or the outer planets?
5. **Skill Builder**
   Inferring Scientists can learn a lot about a planet's history by studying its impact craters. Do the **Chapter 19 Skill Activity** on page 712 to infer how scientific illustrations can be used to determine the ages of impact craters.

Science Journal

The asteroid belt contains many objects—from tiny particles to objects 940 km in diameter. In your Science Journal, describe how mining the asteroids for valuable minerals might be accomplished.

Mission to Mars

Scientists are currently developing plans for further exploration of Mars. But even at its closest, Mars is 55 million km away from Earth, a distance that would take astronauts three years to travel round-trip. Given the long flight, not to mention conditions astronauts would face living on Mars, a journey to the Red Planet would be full of risks. This raises a question: Should humans or robots be sent to explore Mars?

Risks to Humans

Getting to and from Mars would take a toll on the human body. In the near-zero gravity of outer space, bones lose calcium and gradually become weaker. Muscles lose their strength as well, because they don't have to work against gravity to support and move body parts. Furthermore, in a weightless environment, body fluids don't flow downward as they do on Earth. Unusual circulation of body fluids can interfere with kidney function and lead to dehydration.

Assuming humans survived the long flight to Mars in good health, they would face other challenges upon arrival. To explore Mars properly, a team of astronauts would probably have to live on the planet for months, even years. The NASA painting, left, shows a module that could house explorers. Such a structure would have to withstand the Martian environment and protect astronauts from high levels of solar radiation.

The Case for Robots

Because of the many risks a Mars mission would pose for humans, some scientists suggest sending specialized robots that could operate equipment and carry out scientific experiments. These robots would be equipped with artificial senses that would allow researchers on Earth to experience the planet's surface in a way second only to being there in person. However, radio signals sent back and forth between robots on Mars and operators on Earth would take up to 20 minutes to travel each way. Scientists are working to solve this problem in the hope that extensive exploration of Mars will soon be a reality—by people or by machines.

Science JOURNAL

How do you think Mars should be further explored? Write a proposal to your class explaining how you would explore Mars.

Chapter 19 Reviewing Main Ideas

For a **preview** of this chapter, study this Reviewing Main Ideas before you read the chapter. After you have studied this chapter, you can use the Reviewing Main Ideas to **review** the chapter.

The Glencoe MindJogger, Audiocassettes, and CD-ROM provide additional opportunities for review.

Section

19-1 THE SOLAR SYSTEM

Early astronomers thought that the planets, the moon, the sun, and the stars were embedded in separate spheres that rotated around Earth. The sun-centered model of the **solar system** states that the sun is the center of the solar system. Using a telescope, Galileo discovered evidence that supported the sun-centered model. Later, Kepler discovered that the planets orbit the sun in elliptical orbits, not circles. ***What type of evidence did Galileo discover that indicated the sun-centered model was correct?***

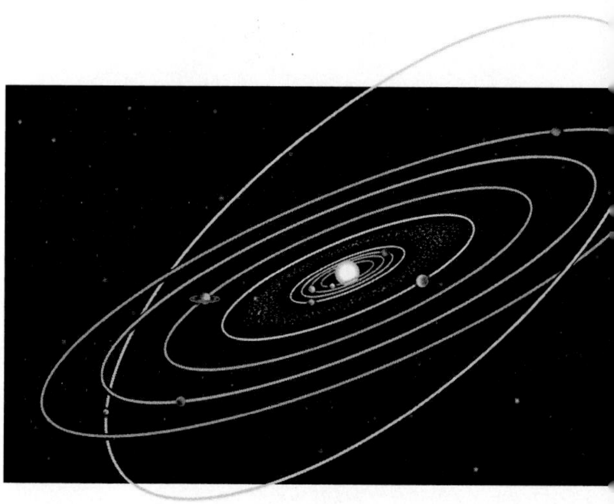

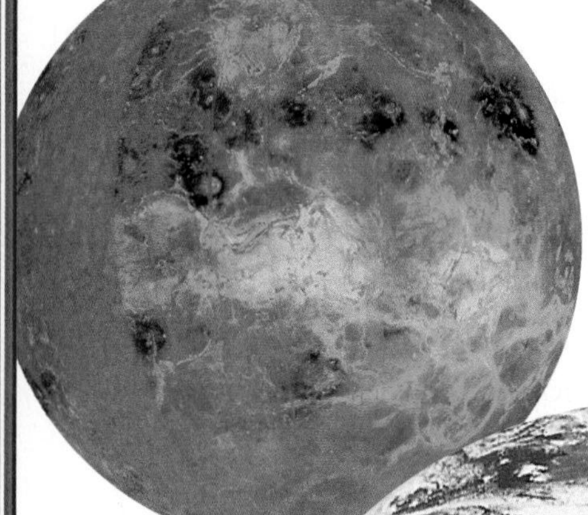

Section

19-2 THE INNER PLANETS

The **inner planets,** in increasing distance from the sun are Mercury, Venus, Earth, and Mars. The moonlike **Mercury** has craters and cliffs on its surface. **Venus** has a dense atmosphere of carbon dioxide and sulfuric acid. On **Earth,** water exists in three states. **Mars** appears red due to the iron oxide content of its weathered rocks. Recent studies by *Pathfinder* indicate that Mars's surface once had large amounts of water flowing over it. ***Venus and Earth are similar in size and mass. Why, then, are their surface characteristics so different?***

Reading Check

Locate a legend, myth, or folktale from another culture that explains the origin of all or part of the solar system. Share it with the class.

Section

19-3 THE OUTER PLANETS

Faint rings and 16 moons orbit the gaseous **Jupiter.** Jupiter's Great Red Spot is a high-pressure storm generated by huge thunderstorms in Jupiter's atmosphere. **Saturn** is made mostly of gas and has pronounced rings. **Uranus** is a large, gaseous planet with many moons and several rings. **Neptune** is similar to Uranus in size, composition, and stormlike features. **Pluto** has a thin, changing atmosphere, and its surface is icy rock. ***Why would the average densities of the four large, outer planets be so low when compared with the average densities of the inner planets?***

Section

19-4 OTHER OBJECTS IN THE SOLAR SYSTEM

As a **comet** approaches the sun, vaporized gases form a bright coma around the comet's nucleus and solar wind forms a tail that points away from the sun. Meteoroids form when asteroids collide, when comets break up, or when **meteorites** collide with the moon or other planets. An **asteroid** is a piece of rock usually found in the asteroid belt. ***Why does the tail of a comet always point away from the sun?***

Chapter 19 Assessment

Using Vocabulary

a. asteroid
b. astronomical unit
c. comet
d. Earth
e. Great Red Spot
f. inner planet
g. Jupiter
h. Mars
i. Mercury
j. meteor
k. meteorite
l. Neptune
m. Oort Cloud
n. outer planet
o. Pluto
p. Saturn
q. solar system
r. Uranus
s. Venus

Distinguish between the terms in each of the following pairs.

1. asteroid, comet
2. inner planet, outer planet
3. meteor, meteorite
4. Great Red Spot, Oort Cloud
5. Neptune, Uranus

Checking Concepts

Choose the word or phrase that best answers the question.

6. Who proposed a sun-centered solar system?
   A) Ptolemy
   B) Copernicus
   C) Galileo
   D) Oort
7. How does the sun produce energy?
   A) magnetism
   B) nuclear fission
   C) nuclear fusion
   D) the greenhouse effect
8. What is the shape of planetary orbits?
   A) circles
   B) ellipses
   C) squares
   D) rectangles
9. Which planet has extreme temperatures because it has essentially no atmosphere?
   A) Earth
   B) Jupiter
   C) Mars
   D) Mercury
10. Water is a solid, liquid, and gas on which planet?
    A) Pluto
    B) Uranus
    C) Saturn
    D) Earth
11. Where is the largest known volcano in the solar system?
    A) Earth
    B) Jupiter
    C) Mars
    D) Uranus
12. What do scientists call a rock that strikes Earth's surface?
    A) asteroid
    B) comet
    C) meteorite
    D) meteoroid
13. Which planet has a complex ring system made of hundreds of ringlets?
    A) Pluto
    B) Saturn
    C) Uranus
    D) Mars
14. Which planet has a magnetic pole tilted 60 degrees?
    A) Uranus
    B) Earth
    C) Jupiter
    D) Pluto
15. How does the tail of a comet always point?
    A) toward the sun
    B) away from the sun
    C) toward Earth
    D) away from the Oort Cloud

Thinking Critically

16. Why is the surface temperature on Venus so much higher than that on Earth?
17. Describe the relationship between the mass of a planet and the number of satellites it has.
18. Why are probe landings on Jupiter or Saturn unlikely events?
19. What evidence suggests that water is or once was present on Mars?
20. An observer on Earth can watch Venus go through phases much like Earth's moon does. Explain why this is so.

Developing Skills

If you need help, refer to the Skill Handbook.

21. **Concept Mapping:** Complete the concept map on this page to show how a comet changes as it travels through space.

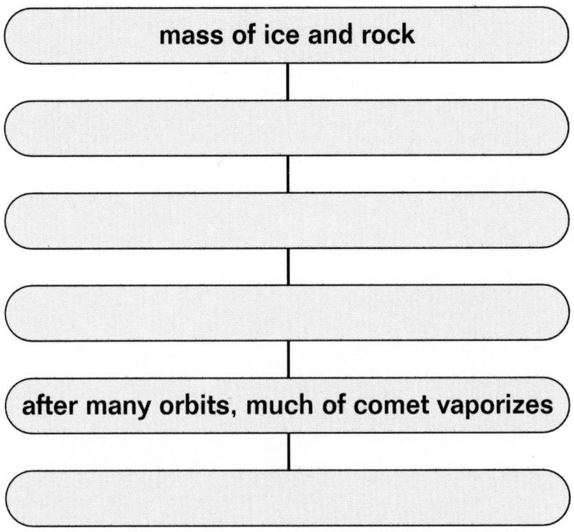

22. **Hypothesizing:** Mercury is the closest planet to the sun, yet it does not reflect much of the sun's light. What can you say about Mercury's color?
23. **Sequencing:** Arrange the following planets in order from the planet with the most natural satellites to the one with the fewest: Earth, Jupiter, Saturn, Neptune, Uranus, and Mars.
24. **Making and Using Tables:** Make a table that summarizes the main characteristics of each planet in the solar system.
25. **Measuring in SI:** The Great Red Spot of Jupiter is about 40 000 km long and about 12 000 km wide. What is its approximate area in km^2?

THE PRINCETON REVIEW

Test-Taking Tip

Get to the Root of Things If you don't know a word's meaning, you can still get an idea of its meaning if you focus on its roots, prefixes, and suffixes. For instance, words that start with *non-*, *un-*, *a-*, *dis-*, and *in-* generally reverse what the rest of the word means.

Test Practice

Use these questions to test your Science Proficiency.

1. Earth is probably the only planet in our solar system on which life exists. Which of the following statements **BEST** explains why this is true?
   A) Earth is the only planet on which water exists in all three states.
   B) Earth has frozen ice caps at its poles.
   C) Earth has carbon dioxide in its atmosphere.
   D) Earth has an atmosphere.
2. Both Copernicus and Kepler proposed a model of the solar system. What was the major difference between the two models?
   A) Copernicus's model had the sun in the center. Kepler's model had Earth in the center.
   B) Copernicus's model included Saturn. Kepler's model did not.
   C) Copernicus's model included circular orbits for the planets. Kepler's model included elliptical orbits for the planets.
   D) Copernicus's model showed the moon as a planet. Kepler's model showed the moon as a satellite of Earth.

CHAPTER 20

Stars and Galaxies

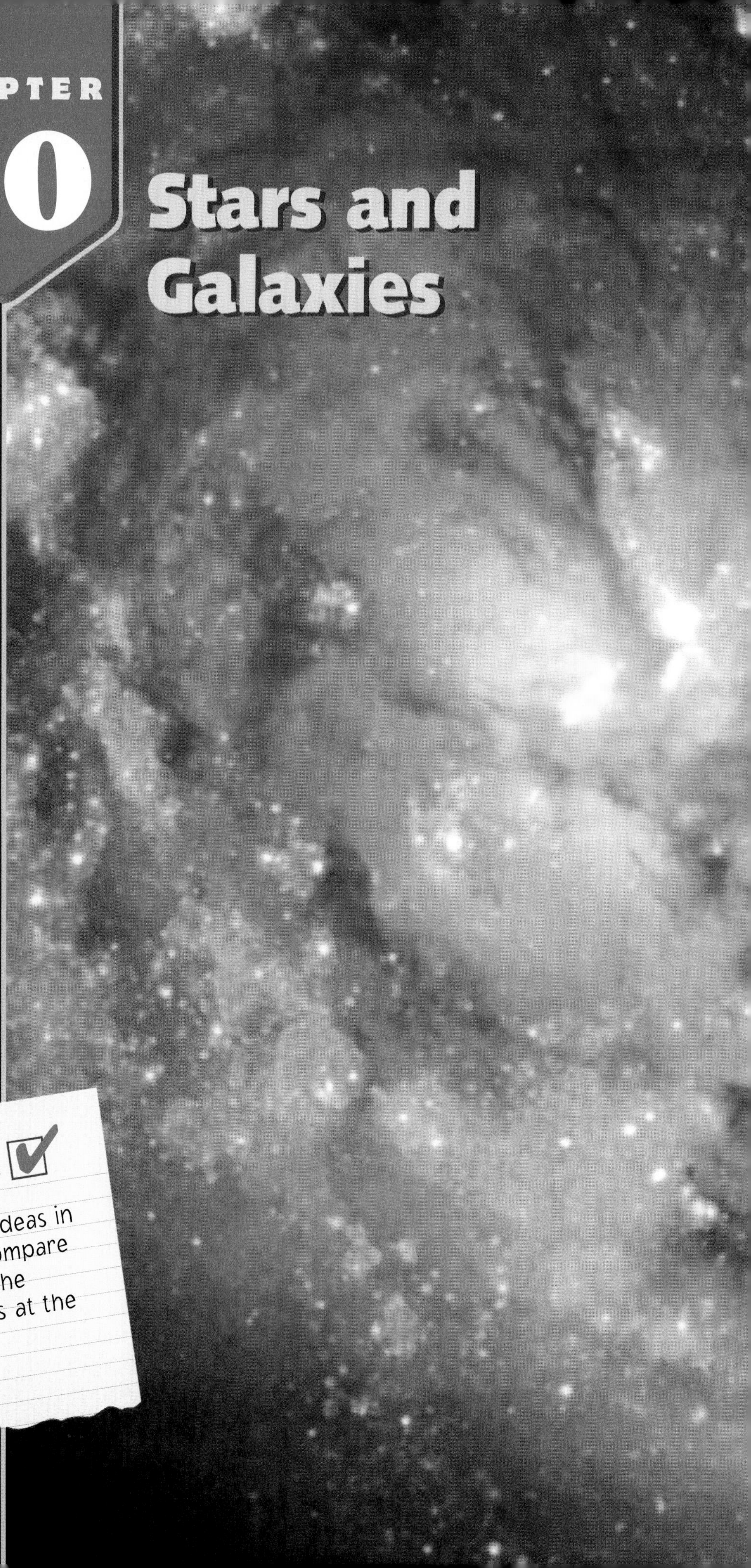

Chapter Preview

Skills Preview

Skill Builders
- Predict

Activities
- Measure in SI

MiniLabs
- Make a Model

Reading Check

Summarize the main ideas in Section 20-1. Then, compare your summary with the Reviewing Main Ideas at the end of the chapter.

Explore Activity

This photo may look like science fiction, but it shows a real event. It is a photo of two galaxies colliding. Other galaxies are moving away from each other. The universe is full of billions of galaxies, each containing billions of stars. By studying deep space, astronomers have observed that the universe is expanding in all directions. In the following activity, you can model how the universe might be expanding.

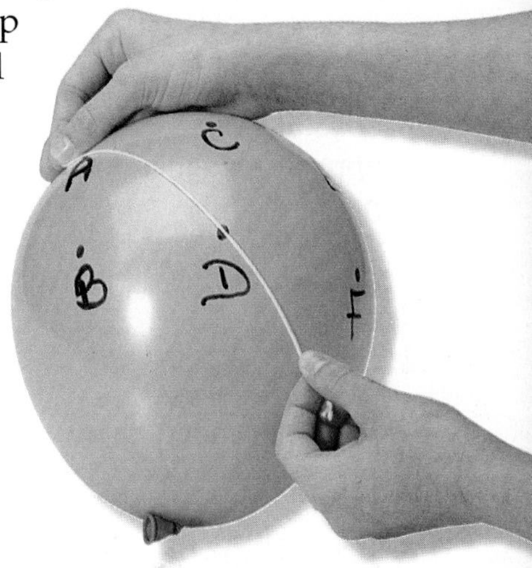

Model the Universe

1. Partially inflate a balloon. Clip the neck shut with a clothespin.
2. Draw six evenly spaced dots on the balloon with a felt-tip marker. Label the dots A through F.
3. Use a string and ruler to measure the distance, in millimeters, from dot A to each of the other dots.
4. Remove the clothespin and inflate the balloon some more.
5. Measure the distance of each dot from A again.
6. Inflate the balloon again, tie the neck shut, and take new measurements.

Science Journal

If each dot represents a galaxy and the balloon represents the universe, describe the motion of the galaxies relative to one another. Is the universe expanding? Explain.

20•1 Stars

Constellations

What **You'll Learn**

- Why the positions of the constellations change throughout the year
- Absolute magnitude and apparent magnitude
- How parallax is used to determine distance

Vocabulary
constellation
absolute magnitude
apparent magnitude
parallax
light-year

Why **It's Important**

- You'll learn to recognize groups of stars found in the night sky.

Have you ever watched clouds drift by on a summer day? It's fun to look at the clouds and imagine they have shapes familiar to you. One may look like a face. Another might resemble a rabbit or a bear. People long ago did much the same thing with patterns of stars in the sky. They named certain groups of stars, called **constellations,** after animals, characters in mythology, or familiar objects.

From Earth, a constellation looks like a group of stars that are relatively close to one another. In most cases, the stars in a constellation have no relationship to each other in space.

The position of a star in the sky can be given as a specific location within a constellation. For example, you can say that the star Betelgeuse (BEE tul jooz) is in the shoulder of the mighty hunter Orion. Orion's faithful companion is his dog, Canis Major. The brightest star in the sky, Sirius, is in the constellation Canis Major. Orion and Canis Major are shown in **Figure 20-1.**

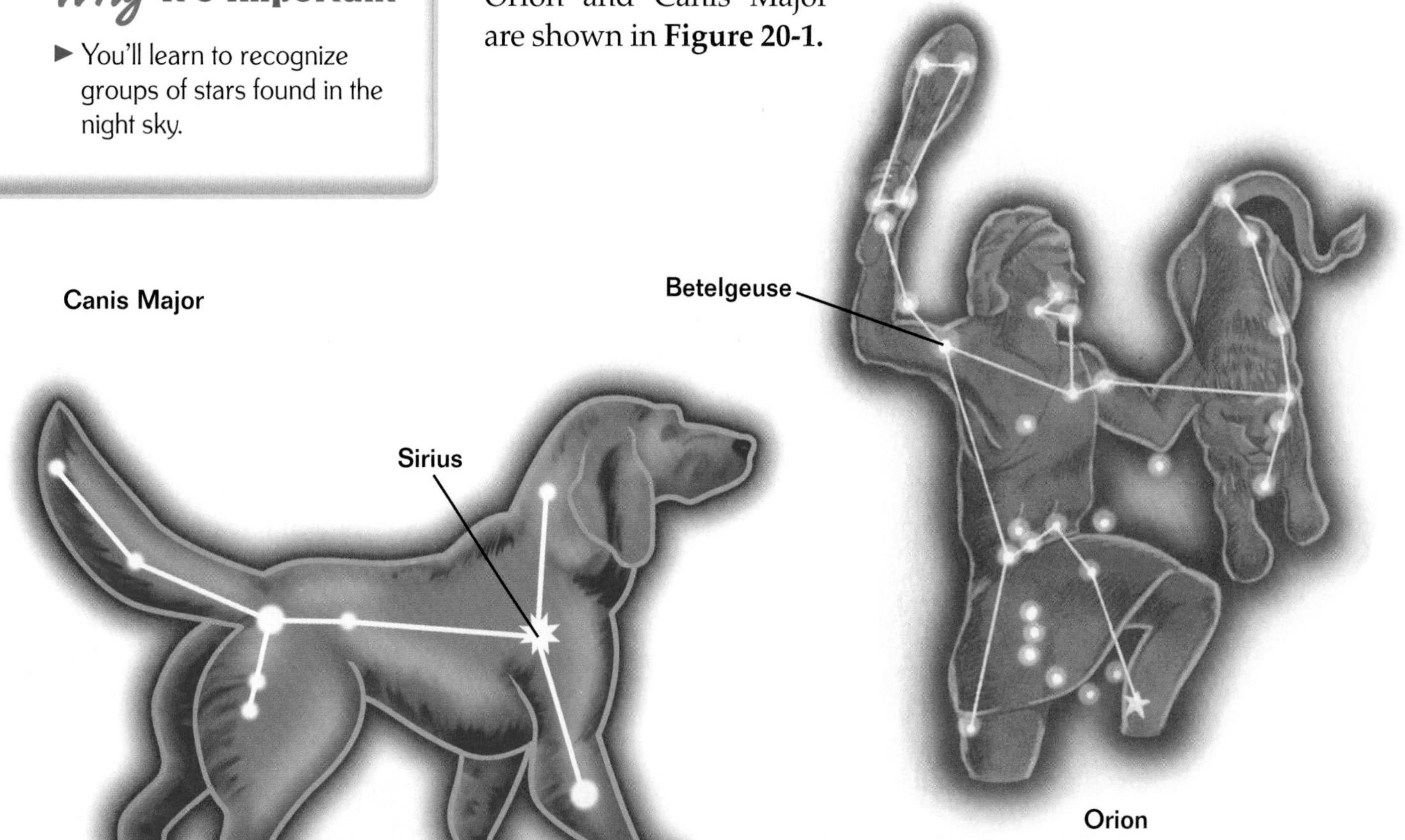

Figure 20-1 Groups of stars can form patterns that look like familiar objects or characters.

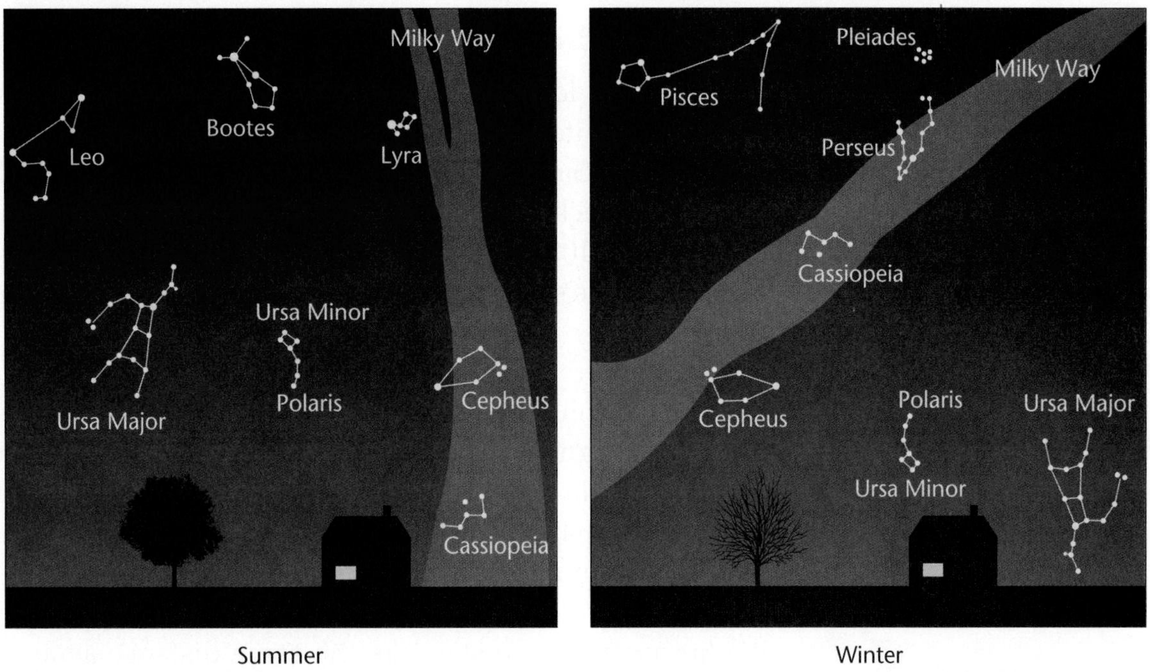

Figure 20-2 Some constellations are visible only during certain seasons of the year. Others, such as those close to Polaris, are visible year-round.

Early Greek astronomers named many constellations. Modern astronomers used many of these names to divide the sky into 88 constellations. You may already know some of them. Have you ever tried to find the Big Dipper? It's part of the constellation Ursa Major, shown in **Figure 20-2.** Notice how the front two stars of the Big Dipper point directly at the star Polaris. Polaris, also known as the North Star, is located at the end of the Little Dipper in the constellation Ursa Minor. Polaris is almost directly over Earth's north pole. You'll learn how to locate Polaris and constellations in the **Field Guide to Backyard Astronomy** at the end of this chapter.

Circumpolar Constellations

As Earth rotates, you can watch Ursa Major, Ursa Minor, and other constellations in the northern sky circle around Polaris. Because these constellations circle Polaris, they are called circumpolar constellations.

All of the constellations appear to move because Earth is moving. Look at **Figure 20-3.** The stars appear to complete one full circle in the sky in just under 24 hours as Earth rotates on its axis. The stars also appear to change positions in the sky throughout the year as Earth revolves around the sun.

Figure 20-3 This photograph shows the path of circumpolar stars over several hours. Polaris is almost directly over the north pole. **Does Polaris appear to move as Earth rotates? Explain.**

Circumpolar constellations are visible all year long, but other constellations are not. As Earth orbits the sun, different constellations come into view while others disappear. Orion, which is visible in the winter in the northern hemisphere, can't be seen in the summer because the daytime side of Earth is facing it.

Absolute and Apparent Magnitudes

When you look at constellations, you'll notice that some stars are brighter than others. Sirius looks much brighter than Rigel. But is Sirius actually a brighter star, or is it just closer to Earth, which makes it appear to be brighter? As it turns out, Sirius is 100 times closer to Earth than Rigel. If Sirius and Rigel were the same distance from Earth, Rigel would appear much brighter in the night sky than would Sirius.

When you refer to the brightness of a star, you can refer to either its absolute magnitude or its apparent magnitude. The **absolute magnitude** of a star is a measure of the amount of light it actually gives off. A measure of the amount of light received on Earth is called the **apparent magnitude.** A star that's actually rather dim can appear bright in the sky if it's close to Earth. A star that's actually bright can appear dim if it's far away. If two stars are the same distance away, what factors might cause one of them to be brighter than the other? ☑

Reading Check ☑

What is absolute magnitude?

You can experience the effect of distance on apparent magnitude when driving in a car at night. Observe the other cars' headlights as they approach. Which cars' headlights are brighter—those that are closer to you or those that are farther away?

Problem Solving

Star Light, Star Bright

Mary conducted an experiment to determine the relationship between distance and the brightness of stars. She used a meterstick, a light meter, and a lightbulb. The bulb was mounted at the zero end of the meterstick. Mary placed the light meter at the 20-cm mark on the meterstick and recorded the distance and the light-meter reading in the data table below. Readings are in luxes, which are units for measuring light intensity. Mary doubled and tripled the distance and took more readings.

Think Critically: What happened to the amount of light recorded when the distance was increased from 20 cm to 40 cm? From 20 cm to 60 cm? What does this indicate about the relationship between light intensity and distance? What would the light intensity be at 100 cm?

Effect of Distance on Light

Distance (cm)	Meter Reading (luxes)
20	4150.0
40	1037.5
60	461.1
80	259.4

How far are stars?

How do we know when a star is close to our solar system? One way is to measure its parallax. **Parallax** is the apparent shift in the position of an object when viewed from two different positions. You are already familiar with parallax. Hold your hand at arm's length and look at one finger first with your left eye closed and then with your right eye closed. Your finger appears to change position with respect to the background. Now, try the same experiment with your finger closer to your face. What do you observe? The nearer an object is to the observer, the greater its parallax.

We can measure the parallax of relatively close stars to determine their distances from Earth, as shown in **Figure 20-4.** When astronomers first realized how far away stars actually are, it became apparent that a new unit of measure would be needed to record their distances. Measuring star distances in kilometers would be like measuring the distance between cities in millimeters.

Distances in space are measured in light-years. A **light-year** is the distance that light travels in one year. Light travels at 300 000 km/s, or about 9.5 trillion km in one year. The nearest star to Earth, other than the sun, is Proxima Centauri. Proxima Centauri is 4.2 light-years away, or about 40 trillion km.

B

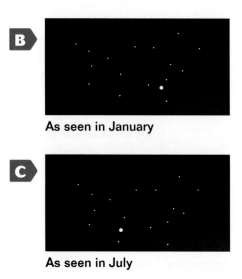

As seen in January

C

As seen in July

Try at Home

MiniLab

Observing Star Patterns

Procedure

1. On a clear night, go outside after dark and study the stars. Take an adult with you and see if you can help each other find constellations.
2. Let your imagination go to work and try to see any patterns of stars in the sky that look like something with which you are familiar.
3. Draw the stars you see, where they are in the sky, and include a drawing of what you think the star pattern resembles.

Analysis

1. How do your constellations compare with those observed by your classmates?
2. How do you think recognizing star patterns could be useful?

Figure 20-4 Parallax can be seen if you observe the same star while Earth is at two different points during its orbit around the sun (A). The star's position relative to more-distant background stars will appear to change (B and C).

A

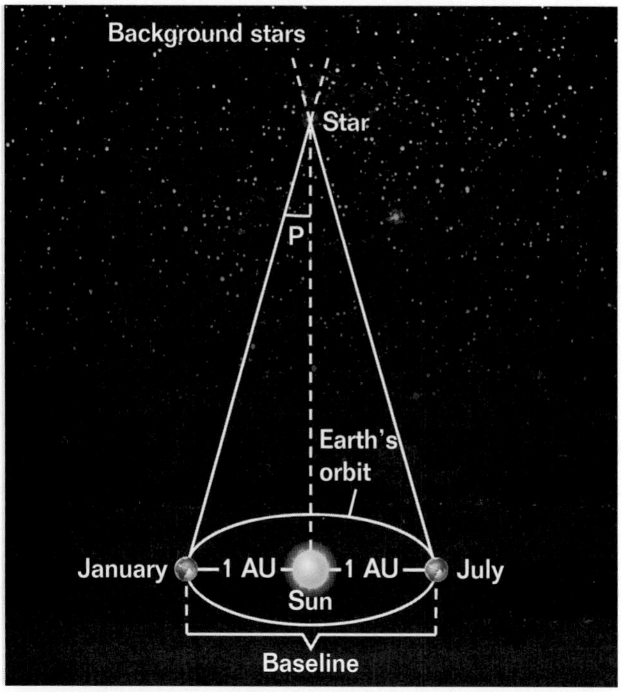

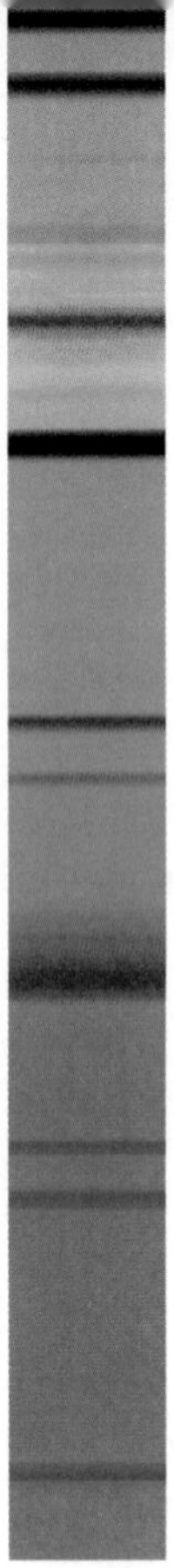

Figure 20-5
These star spectra were made by placing a prism over a telescope's objective lens. **What causes the lines in spectra?**

How hot are stars?

The color of a star indicates its temperature. For example, hot stars are a blue-white color. A relatively cool star looks orange or red. Stars the temperature of our sun have a yellow color.

Astronomers learn about other properties of stars by studying their spectra. They use spectrographs to break visible light from a star into its component colors. If you look closely at the spectrum of a star, such as the ones shown in **Figure 20-5,** you will see dark lines in it. The lines are caused by elements in the star's atmosphere.

As light radiated from a star passes through the star's atmosphere, some of it is absorbed by elements in the atmosphere. The wavelengths of visible light that are absorbed appear as dark lines in the spectrum. Each element absorbs certain wavelengths, producing a certain pattern of dark lines. The patterns of lines can be used to identify which elements are in a star's atmosphere.

Section Assessment

1. Explain how Earth's revolution affects constellations that are visible throughout the year.
2. If two stars give off the same amount of light, what might cause one to look brighter than the other?
3. If the spectrum of another star shows the same absorption lines as the sun, what can be said about its composition?
4. **Think Critically:** Only about 700 stars can be studied using parallax. Most stars are invisible to the naked eye. What does this indicate about their apparent magnitudes?
5. **Skill Builder**
Recognizing Cause and Effect
Suppose you viewed Proxima Centauri through a telescope. How old were you when the light that you see left Proxima Centauri? Why might Proxima Centauri look dimmer than the star Betelgeuse, a large star 310 light-years away? If you need help, refer to Recognizing Cause and Effect in the **Skill Handbook** on page 673.

Using Computers

Graphics Use drawing software on a computer to make a star chart of major constellations visible from your home during the current season. Include reference points to help others find the charted constellations. If you need help, refer to page 686.

The Sun

20•2

Layers of the Sun

More than 99 percent of all of the matter in our solar system is in the sun. The sun is the center of our solar system, and it makes life possible on Earth. But in the grand scheme of the universe, our sun is just another star in the sky.

The sun is an average, middle-aged star. Its absolute magnitude is about average and it shines with a yellow light. Like other stars, the sun is an enormous ball of gas, producing energy by fusing hydrogen into helium in its core. **Figure 20-6** is a model of the sun's interior and atmosphere.

The Sun's Atmosphere

The lowest layer of the sun's atmosphere and the layer from which light is given off is the **photosphere.** The photosphere is often called the surface of the sun. Temperatures there are around 6000 K. Above the photosphere is the **chromosphere.** This layer extends upward about 2000 km above the photosphere. A transition zone occurs between 2000 and 10 000 km above the photosphere. Above the transition zone is the **corona.** This is the largest layer of the sun's atmosphere and extends millions of kilometers into space. Temperatures in the corona are as high as 2 millionK. Charged particles continually escape from the corona and move through space as solar wind.

What You'll Learn

- How energy is produced in the sun
- That sunspots, prominences, and solar flares are related
- Why our sun is considered an average star and how it differs from stars in binary systems

Vocabulary
photosphere
chromosphere
corona
sunspot
binary system

Why It's Important

- The sun is the source of most energy on Earth.

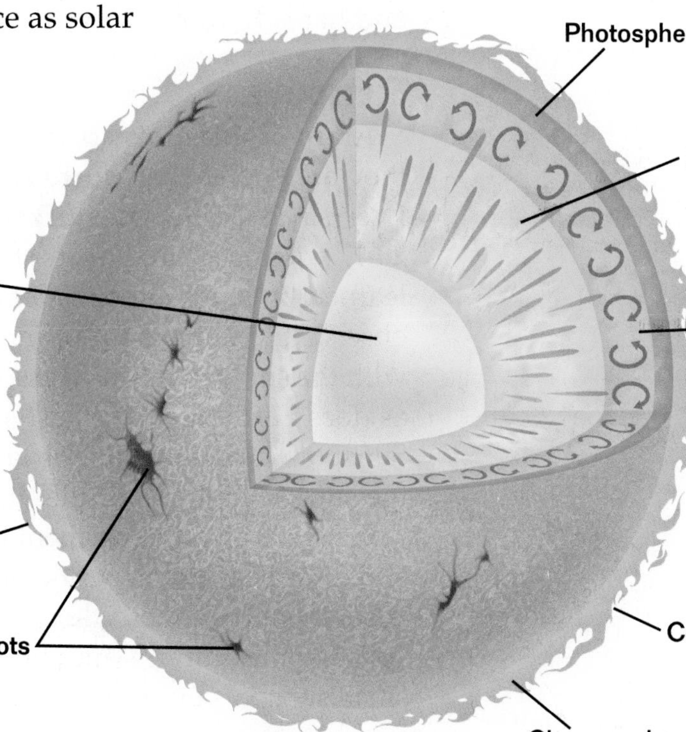

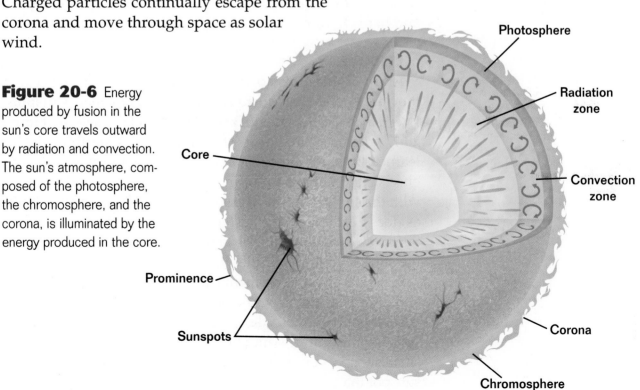

Figure 20-6 Energy produced by fusion in the sun's core travels outward by radiation and convection. The sun's atmosphere, composed of the photosphere, the chromosphere, and the corona, is illuminated by the energy produced in the core.

Figure 20-7 Sunspots are bright, but when viewed against the rest of the photosphere, they appear dark. The small photo is a close-up of a sunspot.

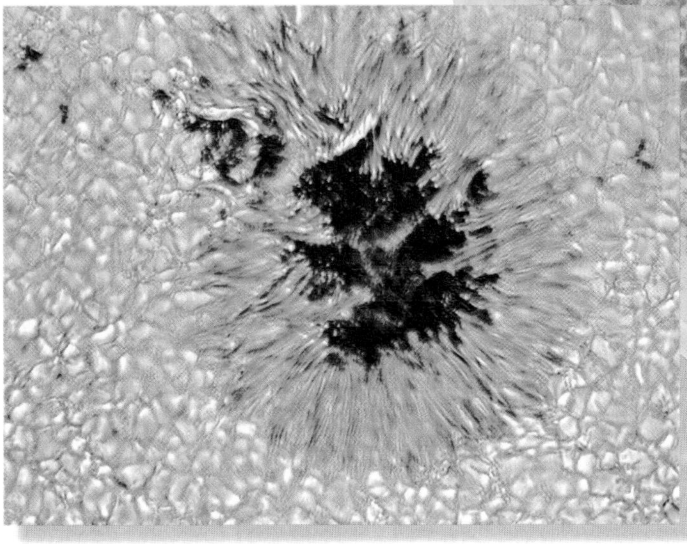

Surface Features of the Sun

Because the sun is a ball of hot gas, it's hard to imagine its surface as anything but a smooth layer. In reality, the sun's surface has many features, including sunspots, prominences, and flares.

Sunspots

Areas of the sun's surface that appear to be dark because they are cooler than surrounding areas are called **sunspots.** Ever since Galileo identified sunspots like those in **Figure 20-7,** scientists have been studying them. One thing we've learned by studying sunspots is that the sun rotates. We can observe the movement of individual sunspots as they move with the sun's rotation. The sun doesn't rotate as a solid body, as does Earth. It rotates faster at its equator than at its poles. Sunspots near the equator take about 27 days to go around the sun. At higher latitudes, they take 31 days. ☑

Reading Check ☑

What are sunspots?

Sunspots aren't permanent features on the sun. They appear and disappear over a period of several days, weeks, or months. Also, there are times when there are many large sunspots—a sunspot maximum—and times when there are only a few small sunspots or none at all—a sunspot minimum. Periods of sunspot maximum occur about every 11 years.

Prominences and Flares

Sunspots are related to several features on the sun's surface. The intense magnetic field associated with sunspots may cause prominences, which are huge arching columns of gas. Some prominences blast material from the sun into space at speeds ranging from 600 km/s to more than 1000 km/s.

Gases near a sunspot sometimes brighten up suddenly, shooting gas outward at high speed. These violent eruptions from the sun, shown in **Figure 20-8,** are called solar flares.

Ultraviolet light and X rays from solar flares can reach Earth and cause disruption of radio signals. Solar flares make communication by radio and telephone difficult at times. High-energy particles emitted by solar flares are captured by Earth's magnetic field, disrupting communication equipment. These particles also interact with Earth's atmosphere near the polar regions and create light. This light is called the aurora borealis, or northern lights, when it occurs in the northern hemisphere. In the southern hemisphere, it is called the aurora australis.

*inter***NET**
CONNECTION

Visit the Glencoe Science Web Site at **www.glencoe.com/sec/science/ca** for more information about sunspots, solar flares, and prominences.

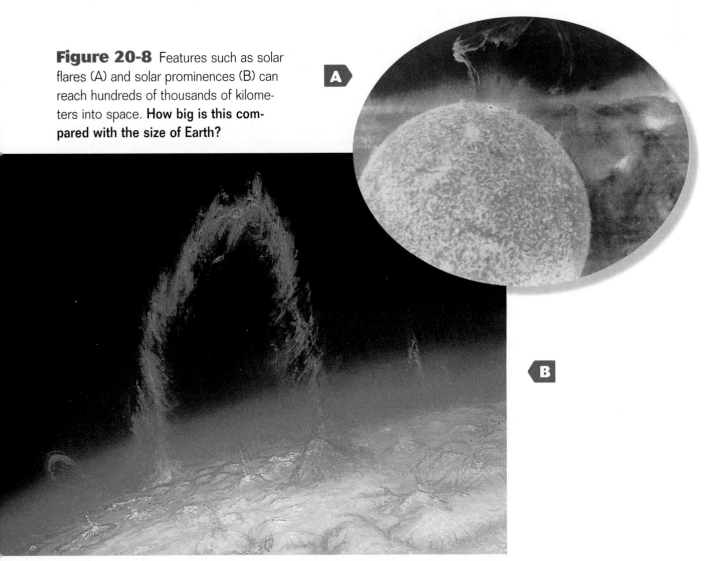

Figure 20-8 Features such as solar flares (A) and solar prominences (B) can reach hundreds of thousands of kilometers into space. **How big is this compared with the size of Earth?**

A

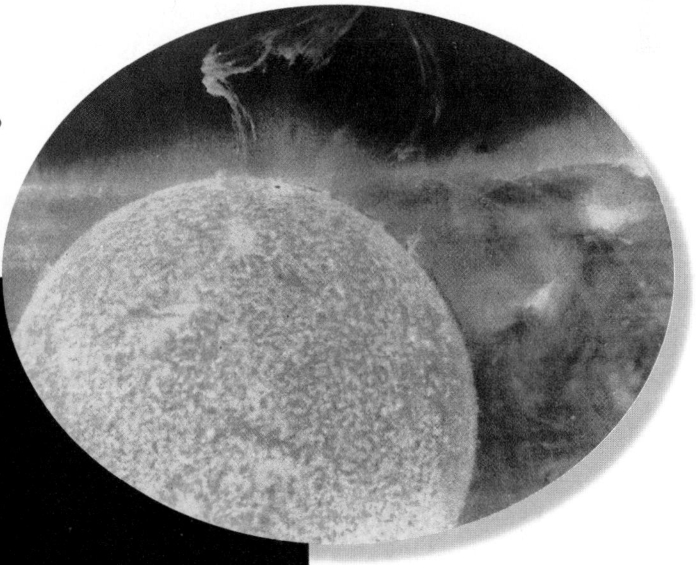

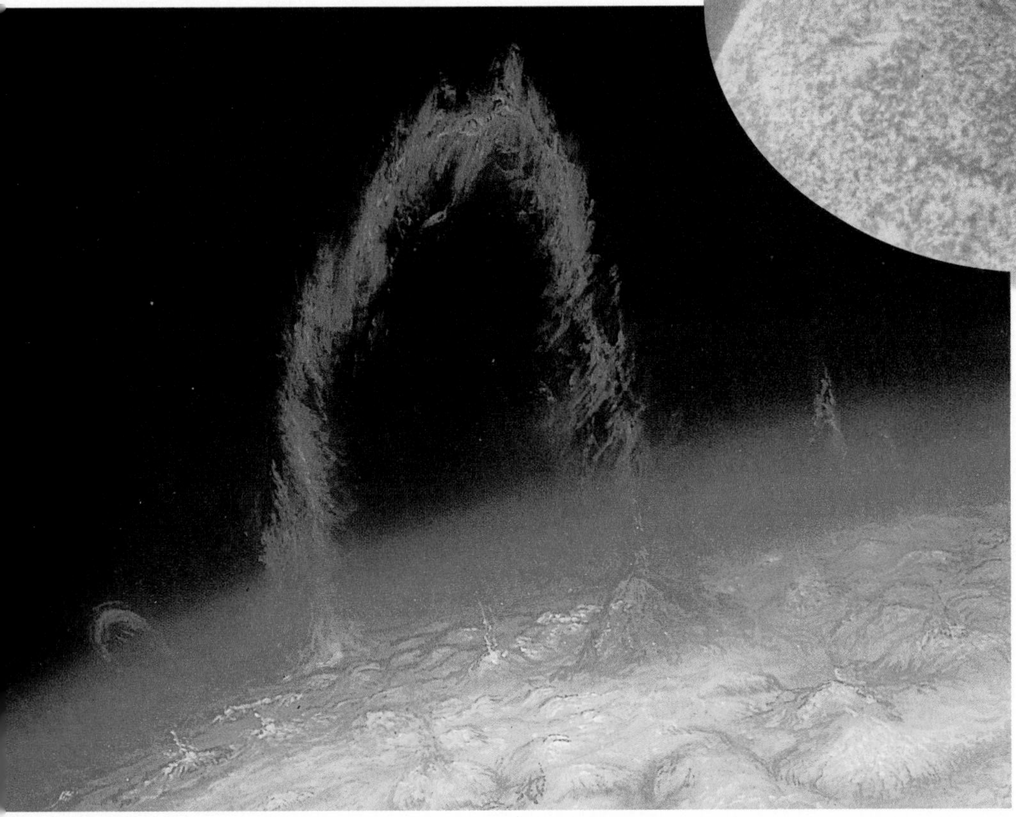

B

Our Sun—A Typical Star?

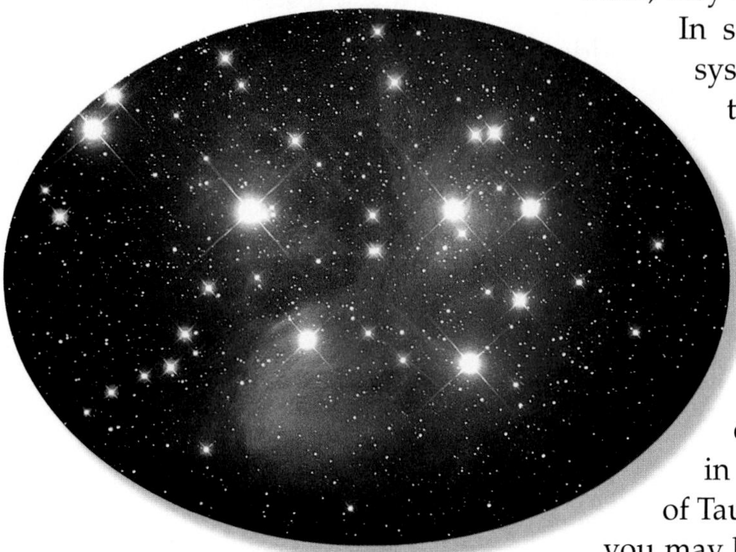

Figure 20-9 Pleiades is a cluster of stars that are gravitationally bound to each other.

Although our sun is an average star, it is somewhat unusual in one way. Most stars are in systems in which two or more stars orbit each other. When two stars orbit each other, they make up a **binary system.**

In some cases, astronomers can detect binary systems because one star occasionally eclipses the other. The total amount of light from the star system becomes dim and then bright again on a regular cycle. Algol in Perseus is an example of this.

In many cases, stars move through space together as a cluster. In a star cluster, many stars are relatively close to one another and are gravitationally attracted to each other. The Pleiades star cluster, shown in **Figure 20-9,** can be seen in the constellation of Taurus in the winter sky. On a clear, dark night, you may be able to see seven of the stars of this cluster. Most star clusters are far from our solar system and appear as a fuzzy patch in the night sky.

Section Assessment

1. How are sunspots, prominences, and solar flares related?
2. What properties does the sun have in common with other stars? What property makes it different from most other stars?
3. **Think Critically:** Because most stars are found in multiple-star systems, what might explain why the sun is a single star?
4. **Skill Builder**
   Interpreting Scientific Illustrations Use **Figure 20-6** to answer the questions below. If you need help, refer to Interpreting Scientific Illustrations in the **Skill Handbook** on page 678.
   a. Which layers make up the sun's atmosphere?
   b. What process occurs in the sun's convection zone that enables energy produced in the core to reach the surface?

Science Journal Write a brief description in your Science Journal that explains how the sun generates energy. Hypothesize what might happen to the sun when it exhausts the supply of hydrogen in its core.

Sunspots

Sunspots are dark, relatively cool areas on the surface of the sun. They can be observed moving across the face of the sun as it rotates. Do this activity to measure the movement of sunspots, and use your data to determine the sun's period of rotation.

Materials

- Several books
- Cardboard (about 8 cm × 12 cm)
- Clipboard
- Drawing paper (5 sheets)
- Small refracting telescope
- Small tripod
- Scissors

What You'll Investigate

Can sunspot motion be used to determine the sun's period of rotation?

Goals

- **Observe** sunspots.
- **Estimate** sunspot size and rate of apparent motion.

Procedure

1. **Find** a location where the sun may be viewed at the same time of day for a minimum of five days. **CAUTION:** *Do not look directly at the sun. Do not look through the telescope at the sun. You could damage your eyes.*
2. **Set up** the telescope with the eyepiece facing away from the sun, as shown below. Align the telescope so that the shadow it casts on the ground is the smallest size possible. **Cut** and **attach** the cardboard as shown in the photo.
3. **Use** books to prop the clipboard upright. Point the eyepiece at the drawing paper.
4. If the telescope has a small finder scope attached, **remove** the finder scope or keep it covered.
5. **Move** the clipboard back and forth until you have the largest possible image of the sun on the paper. Adjust the telescope to form a clear image. **Trace** the outline of the sun on the paper.
6. **Trace** any sunspots that appear as dark areas on the sun's image. Repeat this step at the same time each day for a week.
7. Using the sun's diameter (approximately 1 390 000 km), **estimate** the size of the largest sunspots that you observed.
8. **Calculate** how many kilometers any observed sunspots appear to move each day.
9. At the rate determined in step 8, **predict** how many days it will take for the same group of sunspots to return to about the same position in which you first observed them.

Conclude and Apply

1. What was the average number of sunspots observed each day?
2. What was the estimated size and rate of apparent motion of the largest sunspots?
3. **Infer** how sunspots can be used to determine that the sun's surface is not solid like Earth's.

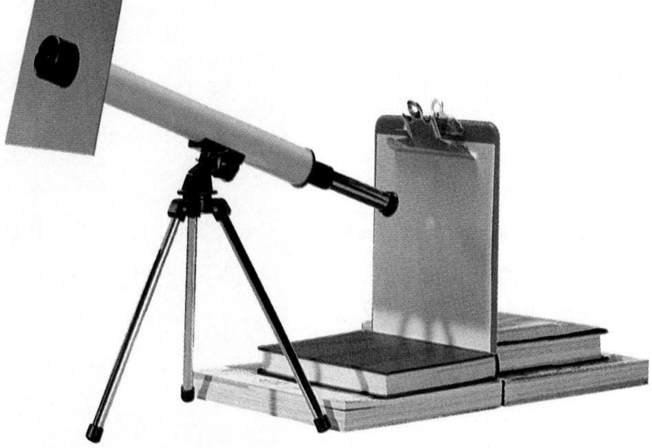

20•3 Evolution of Stars

What You'll Learn

- How stars are classified
- How the temperature of a star relates to its color
- How a star evolves

Vocabulary

main sequence, nebula, giant, white dwarf, supergiant, neutron star, black hole

Why It's Important

- The evolution of stars helps explain the theory for the evolution of the universe.

The H-R Diagram

In the early 1900s, Ejnar Hertzsprung and Henry Russell noticed that for most stars, the higher their temperatures, the brighter their absolute magnitudes. They developed a graph to show this relationship.

Hertzsprung and Russell placed the temperatures of stars across the bottom of the graph and the absolute magnitudes of stars up one side. A graph that shows the relationship of a star's temperature to its absolute magnitude is called a Hertzsprung-Russell (H-R) diagram. **Figure 20-10** shows a variation of an H-R diagram.

The Main Sequence

As you can see, stars seem to fit into specific areas of the chart. Most stars fit into a diagonal band that runs from the upper left to the lower right of the chart. This band, called the **main sequence,** contains hot, blue, bright stars in the upper left and cool, red, dim stars in the lower right. Yellow, medium-temperature, medium-brightness stars fall in between. The sun is a yellow main sequence star.

About 90 percent of all stars are main sequence stars, most of which are small, red stars found in the lower right of the H-R diagram. Among main sequence stars, the hottest stars generate the most light and the coolest generate the least. But,

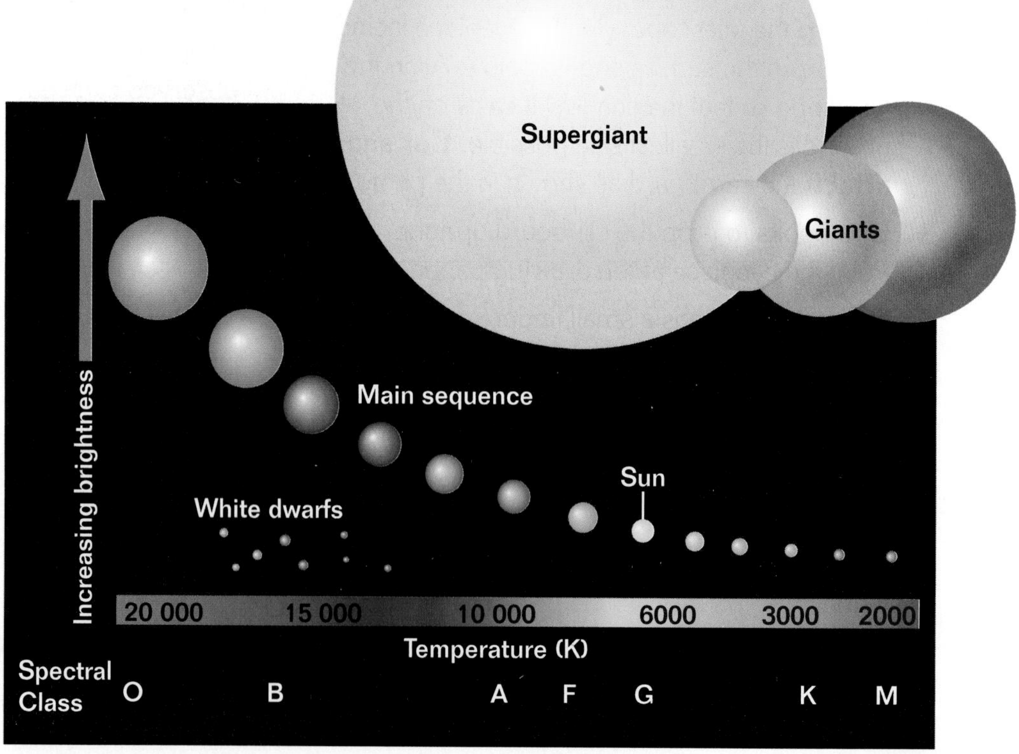

Figure 20-10 This variation of a Hertzsprung-Russell diagram shows the relationships among a star's color, temperature, and brightness. Stars in the main sequence run from hot, bright stars in the upper-left corner of the diagram to cool, faint stars in the lower-right corner. **What type of star shown in the diagram is the coolest, brightest star?**

what about the remaining ten percent? Some of these stars are hot but not bright. These small stars are located on the lower left of the H-R diagram and are called white dwarfs. Other stars are extremely bright but not hot. These large stars on the upper right of the H-R diagram are called giants, or red giants because they are usually red in color. The largest giants are called supergiants. The relative sizes of stars are shown in **Figure 20-11.**

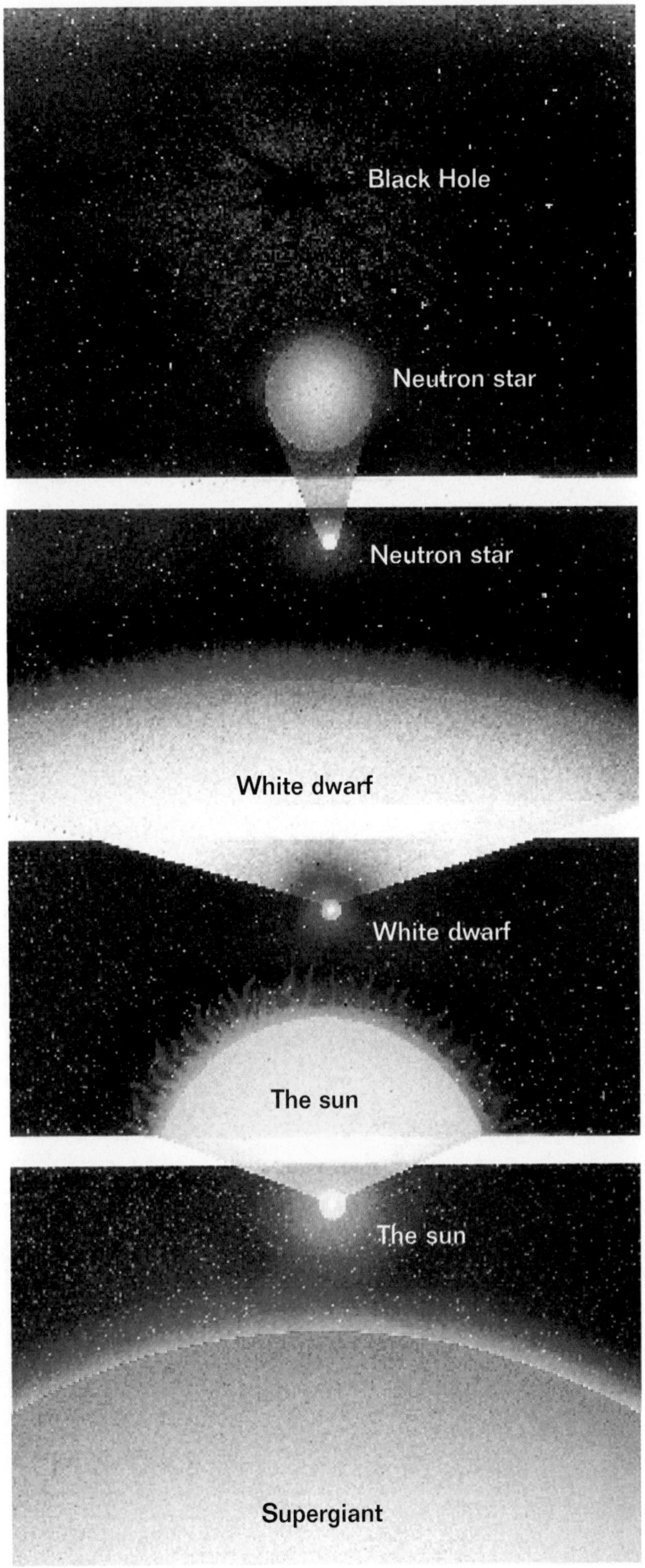

Figure 20-11 The relative sizes of stars range from supergiants as much as 800 times larger than the sun to neutron stars and black holes possibly 30 km or less across. The relative sizes of a supergiant, the sun, a white dwarf, a neutron star, and a black hole are shown.

Fusion

When the H-R diagram was developed, scientists didn't know what caused stars to shine. Hertzsprung and Russell developed their diagram without knowing what produced the light and heat of stars.

For centuries, people had been puzzled by the question of what stars were and what made them shine. It wasn't until the early part of the twentieth century that scientists began to understand how a star could shine for billions of years. Until that time, many had estimated that Earth was only a few thousand years old. The sun could have been made of coal and shined for that long. But what material could possibly burn for billions of years?

Generating Energy

In 1920, one scientist hypothesized that temperatures in the center of the sun must be high. Another scientist then suggested that with these high temperatures, hydrogen could fuse to make helium in a reaction that would release tremendous amounts of energy. **Figure 20-12** on the next page illustrates how four hydrogen nuclei could combine to create one helium nucleus. The mass of one helium nucleus is less than the mass of four hydrogen nuclei, so some mass is lost in the reaction. In the 1930s, scientists hypothesized that carbon could be used as a catalyst in fusion reactions. This explained the energy production in hotter stars.

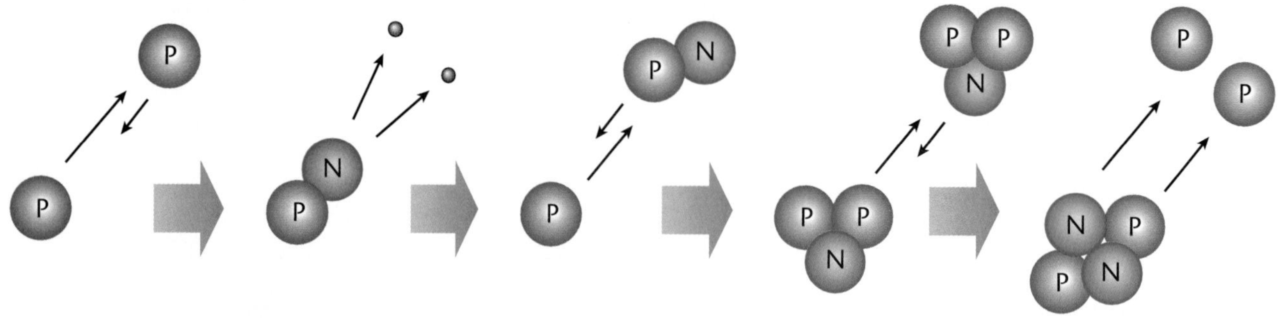

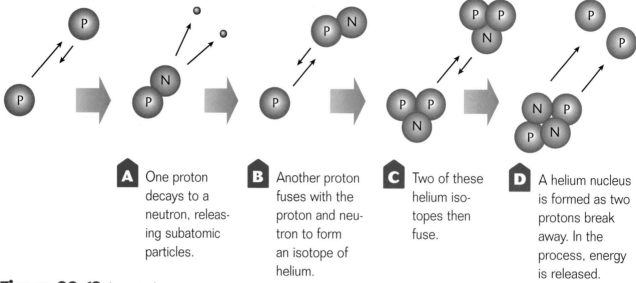

A One proton decays to a neutron, releasing subatomic particles.

B Another proton fuses with the proton and neutron to form an isotope of helium.

C Two of these helium isotopes then fuse.

D A helium nucleus is formed as two protons break away. In the process, energy is released.

Figure 20-12 In a star's core, fusion begins as two hydrogen nuclei (protons) are forced together. **What happens to the "lost" mass during this process?**

Years earlier, in 1905, Albert Einstein had proposed a theory stating that mass can be converted into energy. This was stated as the famous equation $E = mc^2$, where E is the energy produced, m is the mass, and c is the speed of light. The small amount of mass "lost" when hydrogen atoms fuse to form a helium atom is converted to a large amount of energy.

Fusion occurs in the cores of stars. Only in the core are temperatures and pressures high enough to cause atoms to fuse. Normally, they would repel each other, but in the core of a star, atoms are forced close enough together that their nuclei fuse together.

PHYSICS INTEGRATION

The Evolution of Stars

The H-R diagram and other theories explained a lot about stars. But they also led to more questions. Many wondered why some stars didn't fit in the main sequence group and what happened when a star exhausted its supply of hydrogen fuel. Today, we have a theory of how stars evolve, what makes them different from one another, and what happens when they die. **Figure 20-13** illustrates the lives of different types of stars.

Nebula

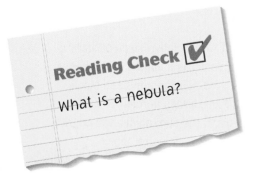

Reading Check

What is a nebula?

Stars begin as a large cloud of gas and dust called a **nebula.** The particles of gas and dust exert a gravitational force on each other, and the nebula begins to contract. Gravitational forces cause instability within the nebula. The nebula can fragment into smaller pieces. Each will eventually collapse to form a star.

As the particles in the smaller clouds move closer together, the temperatures in each nebula increase. When temperatures inside each nebula reach 10 millionK, fusion begins. The energy released radiates outward through the condensing ball of gas. As the energy radiates into space, stars are born.

Main Sequence to Giant Stars

In the newly formed star, the heat from fusion causes pressure that balances the attraction due to gravity, and the star becomes a main sequence star. It continues to use up its hydrogen fuel.

When hydrogen in the core of the star is exhausted, there is no longer a balance between pressure and gravity. The core contracts, and temperatures inside the star increase. This causes the outer layers of the star to expand. In this late stage of its life cycle, a star is called a **giant.**

Once the core temperature reaches 100 millionK, helium nuclei fuse to form carbon in the giant's core. By this time, the star has expanded to an enormous size, and its outer layers are much cooler than they were when it was a main sequence star. In about 5 billion years, our sun will become a giant.

CHEMISTRY INTEGRATION

Star Spectrum
The spectrum of a star shows absorption lines of helium and hydrogen and is bright in the blue end. Describe as much as you can about the star's composition and surface temperature.

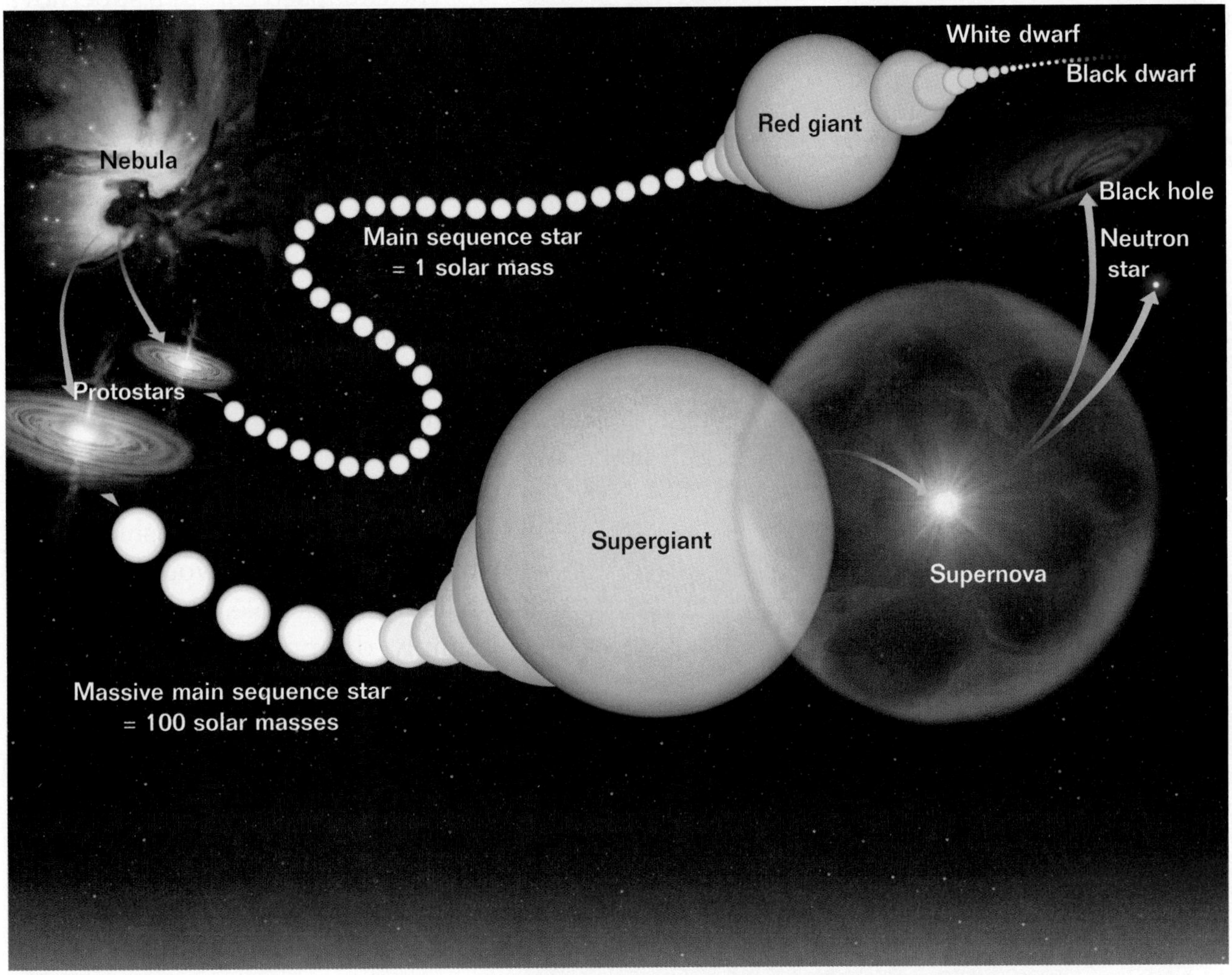

Figure 20-13 The life of a star depends greatly on its mass. Massive stars eventually become neutron stars, or possibly black holes. **What happens to stars the size of our sun?**

White Dwarfs

After the star's core uses up its supply of helium, it contracts even more. As the core of a star like the sun runs out of fuel, its outer layers escape into space. This leaves behind the hot, dense core. The core contracts under the force of gravity. At this stage in a star's evolution, it is a **white dwarf.** A white dwarf is about the size of Earth.

Supergiants and Supernovas

In stars that are over ten times more massive than our sun, the stages of evolution occur more quickly and more violently. The core heats up to much higher temperatures. Heavier and heavier elements form by fusion. The star expands into a **supergiant.** Eventually, iron forms in the core. Fusion can no longer occur once iron forms. The core collapses violently, sending a shock wave outward through the star. The outer portion of the star explodes, producing a supernova like the one shown in **Figure 20-14.** A supernova can be billions of times brighter than the original star.

Figure 20-14 This photo shows a supernova, the explosion of a star. **Explain why a supernova occurs.**

Neutron Stars

The collapsed core of a supernova shrinks to about 10 km to 15 km in diameter. Only neutrons can exist in the dense core, and the supernova becomes a **neutron star.**

If the remaining dense core is more than two times more massive than the sun, probably nothing can stop the core's collapse. It quickly evolves into a **black hole**—an object so dense that nothing can escape its gravity field.

Black Holes

If you could shine a flashlight on a black hole, the light wouldn't illuminate the black hole. The light would simply disappear into it. So, how do scientists locate black holes? Matter being pulled into a black hole can collide with other material, generating X rays. Astronomers have located X-ray sources around possible black holes. Extremely massive black holes probably exist in the centers of galaxies.

What are nebulas?

A star begins its life as a nebula, shown in **Figure 20-15.** But where does the matter in a nebula come from? Nebulas form partly from the matter that was once in other stars. A star ejects enormous amounts of matter during its lifetime. This matter can be incorporated into other nebulas, which can evolve into new stars. The matter in stars is recycled many times.

What about the matter created in the cores of stars? Are elements such as carbon and iron recycled also? Some of these elements do become parts of new stars. In fact, spectrographs have shown that our sun contains some carbon, iron, and other such elements. Because the sun is a main sequence star, it is too young to have created these elements itself. Our sun condensed from material that was created in stars that died many billions of years ago.

Figure 20-15 Stars are forming in the Crescent Nebula.

Some elements condense to form planets and other bodies rather than stars. In fact, your body contains many atoms that were fused in the cores of ancient stars. Evidence suggests that the first stars formed from hydrogen and helium and that all the other elements have formed in the cores of stars.

Section Assessment

1. Explain why giants are not in the main sequence on the H-R diagram. How do their temperatures and absolute magnitudes compare with those of main sequence stars?
2. What can be said about the absolute magnitudes of two equal-sized stars whose colors are blue and yellow?
3. Outline the history and probable future of our sun.
4. **Think Critically:** Why doesn't the helium currently in the sun's core undergo fusion?
5. **Skill Builder**
   Sequencing Sequence the following in order of most evolved to least evolved: *main sequence star, supergiant, neutron star,* and *nebula.* If you need help, refer to Sequencing in the **Skill Handbook** on page 666.

Using Math

Assume that a star's core has shrunk to a diameter of 12 km. What would be the circumference of the shrunken stellar core? Use the equation $C = \pi d$. How does this compare with the circumference of Earth with a diameter of 12 756 km?

Dreamtime Down Under

The Aborigines of Australia believe that the world began long ago—before anyone can remember—when Dreamtime began. At first, Earth was cold and dark, and the spirit Ancestors slept underground.

When the Ancestors awoke, they moved to Earth's surface and created the sun for warmth and light. Some Ancestors became people. Others became plants, animals, clouds, or stars. As the Ancestors moved over Earth, they sang, and their singing created hills, rivers, and other features.

Leaving a Path

The movement of the Ancestors left Dreaming Tracks that the Aborigines still treasure. When the Ancestors tired, they returned underground. The bodies of some Ancestors remain on Earth's surface as rock outcroppings, trees, islands, and other natural features, such as the formation in the inset, below right.

Ancient Aborigines drew maps to show where the Ancestors came out, walked, and returned underground. Drawings with traditional dot patterns (see bark painting, far right) form the basis of Aboriginal art.

Dreaming the Big Bang

Some compare the Dreamtime forces that shaped Earth to the big bang theory—huge fields of energy interacting and forming planets. Later, more energy—more Dreaming—created today's continents, including Australia.

Today, Aborigines are struggling to maintain ancient traditions while living in modern Australia. They believe that the Ancestors still live in the land and that Dreamtime continues with no foreseeable end.

Science JOURNAL

In your Science Journal, write a poem that expresses your own view of our relationship to nature and to the land.

Galaxies and the Universe

20-4

Galaxies

One reason to study astronomy is to learn about your place in the universe. Long ago, people thought they were at the center of the universe and everything revolved around Earth. Today, you know this isn't the case. But, do you know where you are in the universe?

You are on Earth, and Earth orbits the sun. But does the sun orbit anything? How does it interact with other objects in the universe? The sun is one star among many in a galaxy. A **galaxy** is a large group of stars, gas, and dust held together by gravity. Our galaxy, called the Milky Way, is shown in **Figure 20-16.** It contains about 200 billion stars, including the sun. Galaxies are separated by huge distances—often millions of light-years.

Just as stars are grouped together within galaxies, galaxies are grouped into clusters. The cluster the Milky Way belongs to is called the Local Group. It contains about 30 galaxies of various types and sizes.

What You'll Learn

- The three main types of galaxies
- Several characteristics of the Milky Way Galaxy
- How the big bang theory explains the observed Doppler shifts of galaxies

Vocabulary
galaxy
big bang theory

Why It's Important

- You'll explore theories about how the universe may have formed.

Figure 20-16 The Milky Way Galaxy is usually classified as a normal spiral galaxy. Its spiral arms, composed of stars and gas, radiate out from an area of densely packed stars called the nucleus.

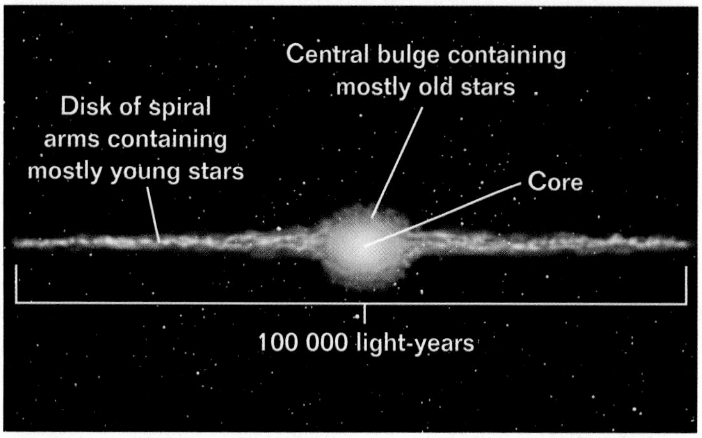

Figure 20-17 These illustrations show a side view and an overhead view of the Milky Way. **The Milky Way is part of what group of galaxies?**

Spiral Galaxies

The three major types of galaxies are elliptical, spiral, and irregular. Spiral galaxies have spiral arms that wind outward from inner regions. The Milky Way is a spiral galaxy, as shown in **Figure 20-17.** Its spiral arms are made up of bright stars and dust. The fuzzy patch you can see in the constellation of Andromeda is actually a spiral galaxy. It's so far away that you can't see its individual stars. Instead, it appears as a hazy spot in our sky. The Andromeda Galaxy is a member of the Local Group. It is about 2.2 million light-years away.

Arms in a normal spiral start close to the center of the galaxy. Barred spirals have spiral arms extending from a large bar of stars and gas that passes through the center of the galaxy.

Elliptical Galaxies

Probably the most common type of galaxy is the elliptical galaxy, shown in **Figure 20-18.** These galaxies are shaped like large, three-dimensional ellipses. Many are football-shaped, but others are round. Some elliptical galaxies are small, while some are so large that the entire Local Group of galaxies would fit inside one of them. **Figure 20-19** shows the Local Group and its relation to the solar system, the Milky Way, and large galaxy clusters. ☑

Reading Check ☑

Describe an elliptical galaxy.

Figure 20-18 This photo shows an example of an elliptical galaxy. **What are the two other types of galaxies?**

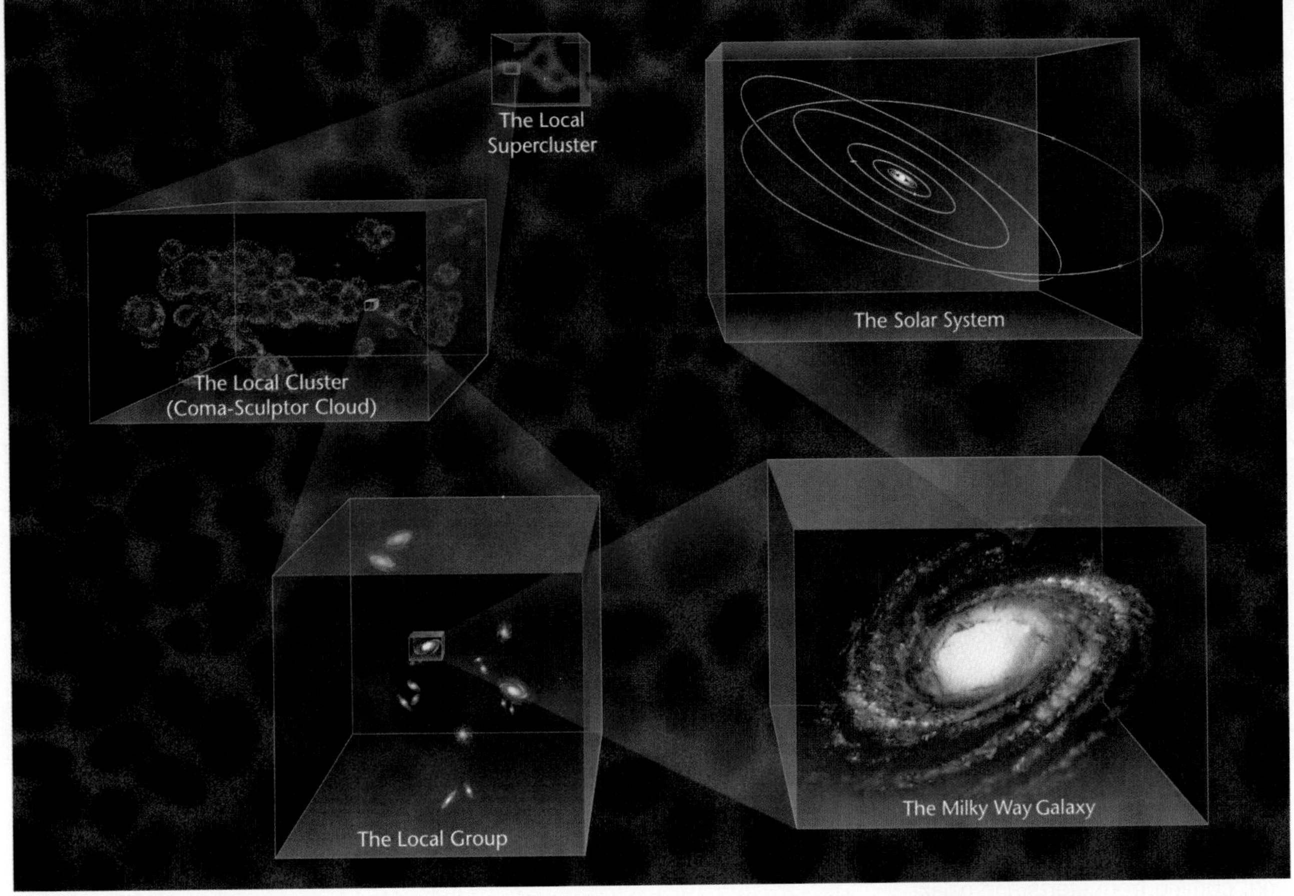

Figure 20-19 There may be more than 100 billion galaxies in the universe, and nearly all of them seem to be organized into clusters.

Irregular Galaxies

The third type of galaxy, irregular, includes most of those galaxies that don't fit into the other classifications. Irregular galaxies have many different shapes and are smaller and less common than the other types. Two irregular galaxies called the Clouds of Magellan orbit the Milky Way. The Large Magellanic Cloud is shown in **Figure 20-20.**

Figure 20-20 The Large Magellanic Cloud is an irregular galaxy. It's a member of the Local Group, and it orbits our own galaxy.

The Milky Way Galaxy

The Milky Way contains more than 200 billion stars. The visible disk of stars is about 100 000 light-years across, and the sun is located about 30 000 light-years out from its center. In our galaxy, all stars orbit around a central region. Based on a distance of 30 000 light-years and a speed of 235 km/s, the sun orbits around the center of the Milky Way once every 240 million years.

The Milky Way is usually classified as a normal spiral galaxy. However, recent evidence suggests that it might be a barred spiral. It is difficult to know for sure because we can never see our galaxy from the outside.

You can't see the normal spiral or barred shape of the Milky Way because you are

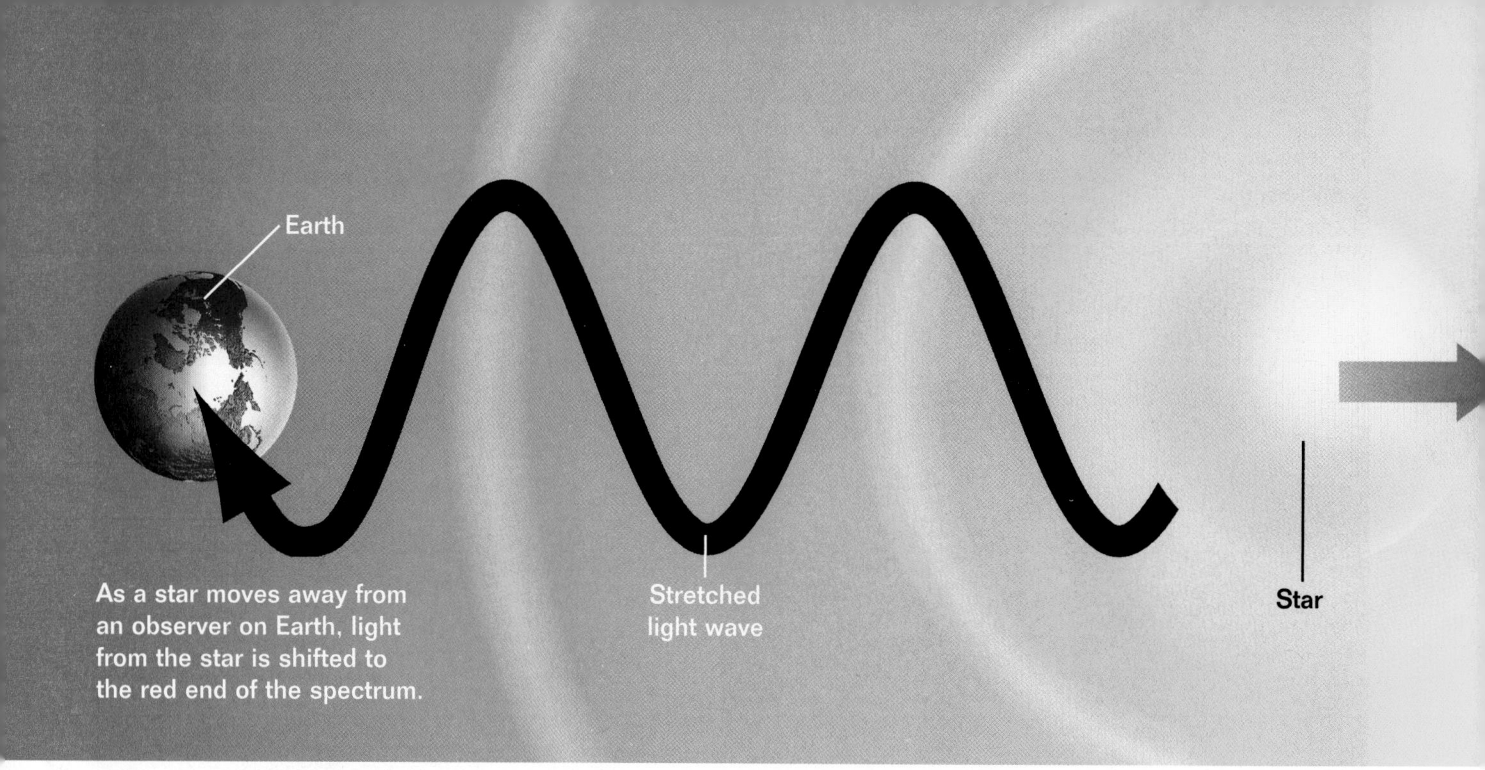
Earth
Stretched light wave
Star
As a star moves away from an observer on Earth, light from the star is shifted to the red end of the spectrum.

Figure 20-21 The Doppler shift causes the wavelengths of light coming from starts and galaxies to be compressed or stretched.

located within one of its spiral arms. You can see the Milky Way stretching across the sky as a faint band of light. All of the stars you can see in the night sky belong to the Milky Way Galaxy.

Mini Lab

Measuring Distance in Space

Procedure

1. On a large sheet of paper, draw an overhead view of the Milky Way Galaxy. If necessary, refer to **Figure 20-17.** Choose a scale to show distance in light-years.
2. Mark the approximate location of our solar system, about two-thirds of the way out on one of the spiral arms.
3. Draw a circle around the sun indicating the 4.2 light-year distance of the next closest star to the sun, Proxima Centauri.

Analysis

1. What scale did you use to represent distance on your model?
2. At this scale, interpret how far away the next closest spiral galaxy—the Andromeda Galaxy—would be located.

Expansion of the Universe

What does it sound like when a car is blowing its horn while it drives past you? The horn has a high pitch as the car approaches you, then the horn seems to drop in pitch as the car drives away. This effect is called the Doppler shift. The Doppler shift occurs with light as well as with sound. **Figure 20-21** shows how the Doppler shift causes changes in the light coming from distant stars and galaxies. If a star is moving toward us, its wavelengths of light are pushed together. If a star is moving away from us, its wavelengths of light are stretched.

The Doppler Shift

Look at the spectrum of a star in **Figure 20-22A.** Note the position of the dark lines. How do they compare with the lines in **Figures 20-22B** and **C?** They have shifted in position. What caused this shift? As you just learned, when a star is moving toward Earth, its wavelengths of light are

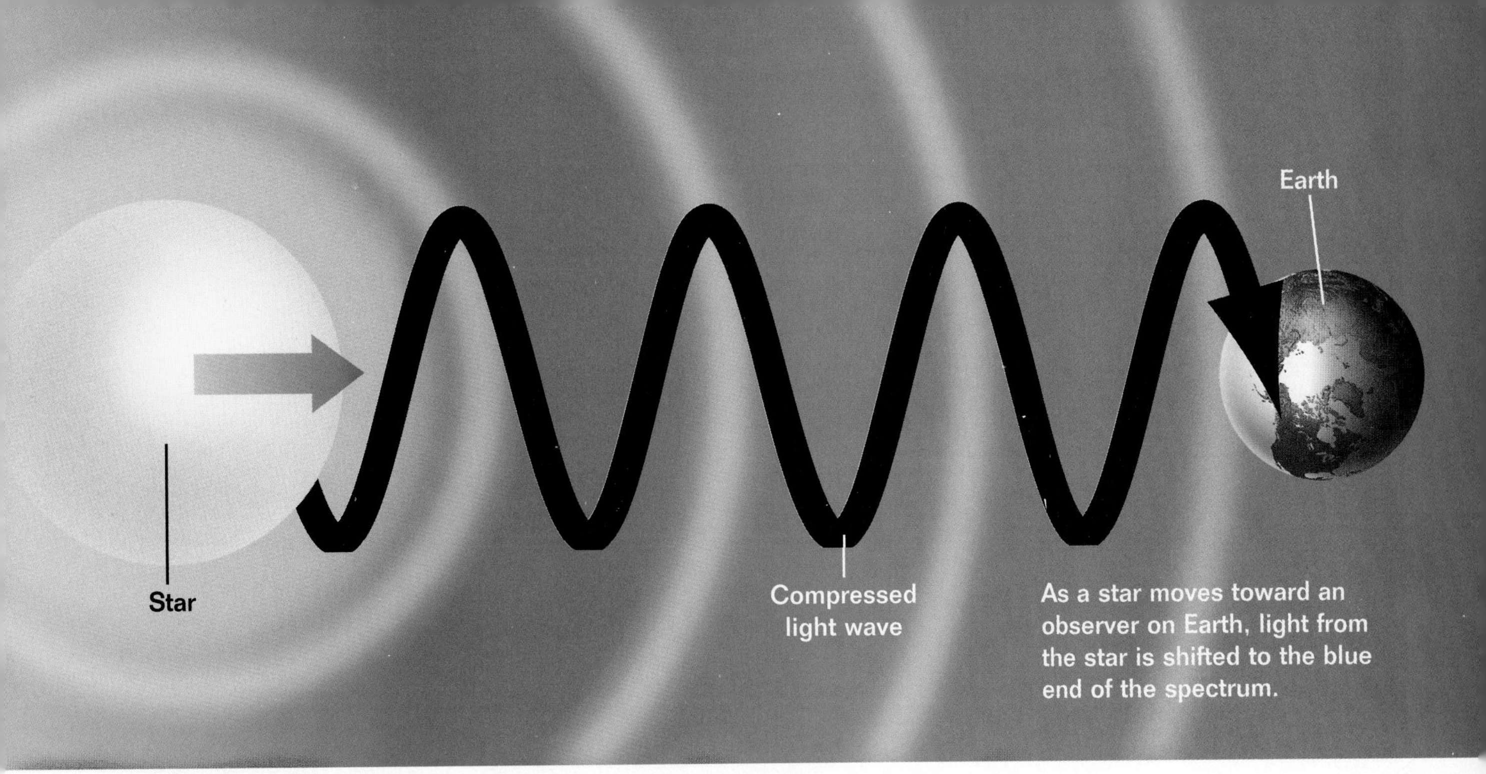

pushed together, just as the sound waves from the car's horn are. This causes the dark lines in the spectrum to shift toward the blue-violet end of the spectrum. A red shift in the spectrum occurs when a star is moving away from Earth. In a red shift, the dark lines shift toward the red end of the spectrum.

In the early twentieth century, scientists noticed an interesting fact about the light coming from most galaxies. When a spectrograph is used to study light from galaxies beyond the Local Group, there is a red shift in the light. What does this red shift tell you about the universe?

Because all galaxies beyond the Local Group show a red shift in their spectra, they must be moving away from Earth. If all galaxies outside the Local Group are moving away from Earth, this indicates that the entire universe must be expanding. Think of the Explore Activity at the beginning of the chapter. The dots on the balloon moved apart as the model universe expanded. Regardless of which dot you picked, all the other dots moved away from it. Galaxies beyond the Local Group move away from us just as the dots moved apart on the balloon.

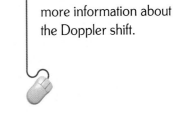

*inter***NET**
CONNECTION

Visit the Glencoe Science Web Site at **www.glencoe.com/sec/science/ca** for more information about the Doppler shift.

Figure 20-22 The dark lines in the spectra (A) are shifted toward the blue-violet end when a star is moving toward Earth (B). A red shift (C) indicates that a star is moving away from Earth.

VISUALIZING The Big Bang Theory

Figure 20-23 The universe probably began billions of years ago with a fiery explosion.

A Within fractions of a second, the uni-verse grew from the size of a pin to 2000 times the size of the sun.

B By the time the universe was one second old, it was a dense, opaque, swirling mass of elementary particles.

C Matter began collecting in clumps and eventually formed into galaxies. As matter cooled, hydrogen and helium gas formed.

D More than 1 billion years after the initial explosion, the first stars were born.

The Big Bang Theory

The big bang theory states that approximately 15 billion years ago, the universe began expanding from an enormous explosion. Recent evidence suggests a much younger age for the universe of 8 billion to 10 billion years. This creates a problem because some star clusters in the Milky Way Galaxy may have ages of 12 billion to 15 billion years. However, recent star position data from the *Hipparcos* space probe may resolve this issue. Astronomers continue to study and debate this problem in hopes of learning a more exact age of the universe.

The Big Bang Theory

When scientists determined that the universe was expanding, they realized that galaxy clusters must have been closer together in the past. The leading theory about the formation of the universe, called the big bang theory, is based on this explanation. **Figure 20-23** illustrates the **big bang theory,** which states that approximately 15 billion years ago, the universe began with an enormous explosion.

The time-lapse photograph shown in **Figure 20-24** was taken in December 1995 by the *Hubble Space Telescope*. It shows more than 1500 galaxies at a distance of more than 10 billion light-years. These galaxies may date back to when the universe was no more than 1 billion years old. The galaxies are in various stages of development. One astronomer indicates that we may be looking back to a time when our own galaxy was forming. Studies of this nature will eventually enable astronomers to determine the approximate age of the universe.

Whether the universe expands forever or stops depends on how much matter is in the universe. All matter exerts a gravitational force. If there's enough matter, gravity will halt the expansion, and the universe will contract until everything comes to one point.

Figure 20-24 The light from these galaxies in this photo mosaic took billions of years to reach Earth.

Section Assessment

1. List the three major classifications of galaxies. What do they have in common?
2. What is the name of the galaxy that you live in? What motion do the stars in this galaxy exhibit?
3. **Think Critically:** All galaxies outside the Local Group show a red shift in their spectra. Within the Local Group, some galaxies show a red shift and some show a blue shift. What does this tell you about the galaxies in the Local Group and outside the Local Group?
4. **Skill Builder**
   Predicting Astronomical distances are measured in light-years, the distance light travels in one year. It takes light from the star Betelgeuse 310 light-years to reach Earth. Do the **Chapter 20 Skill Activity** on page 713 to predict what was happening on Earth when light from distant stars began traveling toward our solar system.

Science Journal

Research and write a report in your Science Journal about the most recent evidence supporting or disputing the big bang theory. Describe how the big bang theory explains observations of galaxies made with spectrometers.

Design Your Own Experiment

Activity 20·2

Possible Materials

- Meterstick
- Metric ruler
- Masking tape
- Pencil

Measuring Parallax

Parallax is the apparent shift in the position of an object when viewed from two locations. The nearer an object is to the observer, the greater its parallax. Do this activity to design a model and use it in an experiment that will show how distance affects the amount of observed parallax.

Recognize the Problem

How can you build a model to show the relationship between distance and parallax?

Form a Hypothesis

State a hypothesis about how a model must be built in order for it to be used in an experiment to show how distance affects the amount of observed parallax.

Goals

- **Design a model** to show how the distance from an observer to an object affects the object's parallax shift.
- **Design an experiment** that shows how distance affects the amount of observed parallax.

Safety Precautions

CAUTION: *Be sure to wear goggles to protect your eyes.*

Test Your Hypothesis

Plan

1. As a group, agree upon and write out your hypothesis statement.
2. List the steps that you need to take to build your model. Be specific, describing exactly what you will do at each step.
3. Devise a method to test how distance from an observer to an object, such as a pencil, affects the relative position of the object.
4. List the steps you will take to test your hypothesis. Be specific, describing exactly what you will do at each step.
5. Read over your plan for the model to be used in this experiment.
6. How will you determine changes in observed parallax? Remember, these changes should occur when the distance from the observer to the object is changed.
7. You should measure shifts in parallax from several different positions. How will these positions differ?
8. How will you measure distances accurately and compare relative position shift?

Do

1. Make sure your teacher approves your plan before you proceed.
2. Construct the model your team has planned.
3. Carry out the experiment as planned.
4. While conducting the experiment, write down any observations that you or other members of your group make in your Science Journal.

Analyze Your Data

1. **Compare** what happened to the object when it was viewed with one eye closed, then the other.
2. At what distance from the observer did the object appear to shift the most?

Draw Conclusions

1. **Infer** what happened to the apparent shift of the object's location as the distance from the observer was increased or decreased.
2. How might astronomers use parallax to study stars?

FIELD GUIDE to Backyard Astronomy

FIELD ACTIVITY

Study the star maps included in this field guide. Each night for a week, about one hour after sundown, observe the stars and identify at least three constellations. Draw and label the constellations in your Science Journal. Then, using the key of constellations visible in the northern hemisphere, make drawings of the objects, animals, or characters your constellations represent.

To help them study the night sky, early astronomers developed ways to organize stars into recognizable patterns. We call these patterns constellations. Think of constellations as drawings in the sky. They represent objects, animals, or characters in stories—things that were familiar to ancient stargazers. Using this field guide, you can observe the stars year-round.

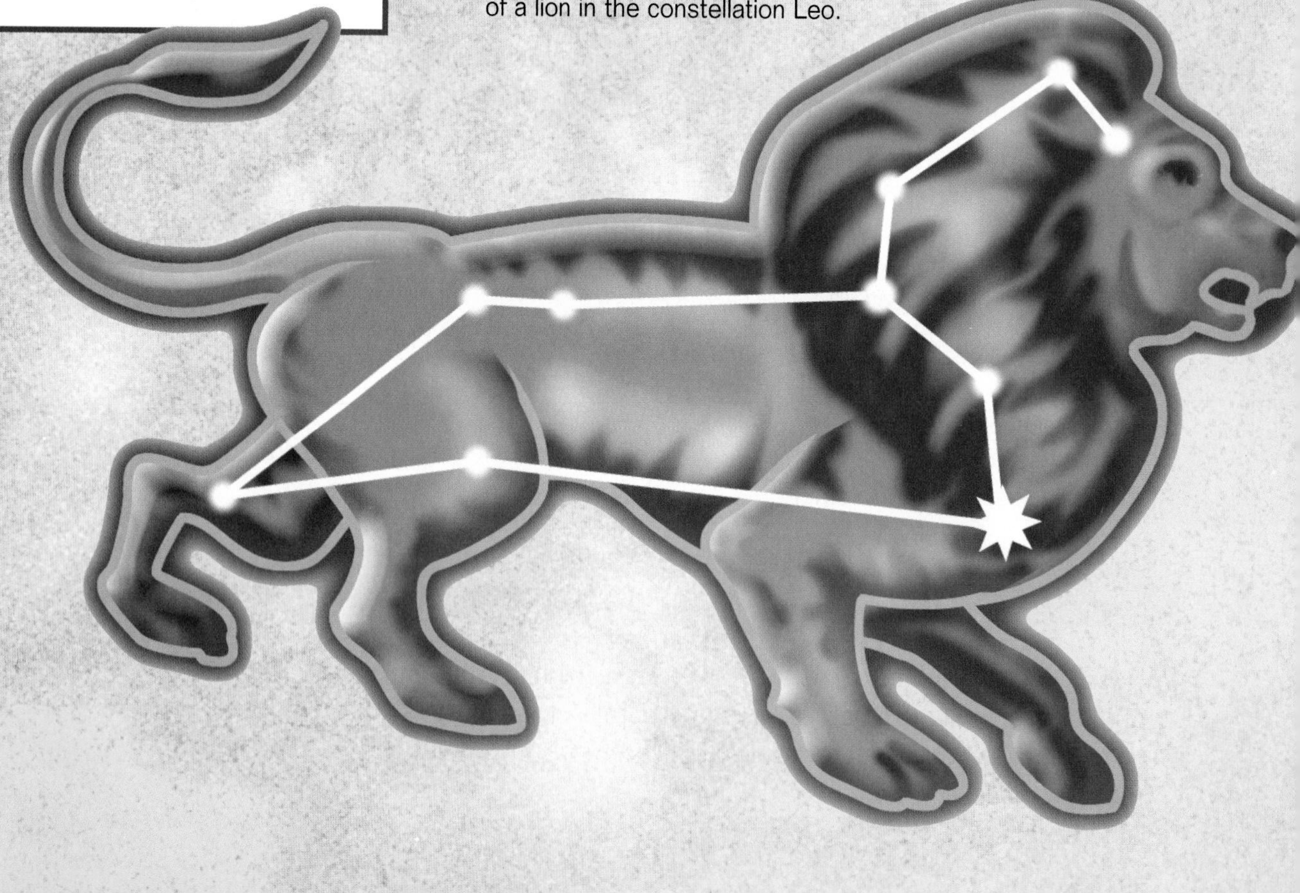

Early astronomers saw the shape of a lion in the constellation Leo.

Major Constellations Visible in the Northern Hemisphere

Name	Represents	Name	Represents
Andromeda	Princess	Lyra	Harp
Aquila	Eagle	Orion	Hunter
Bootes	Herdsman	Pegasus	Winged Horse
Canis Major	Big Dog	Sagittarius	Archer
Canis Minor	Little Dog	Scorpius	Scorpion
Cygnus	Swan (Northern Cross)	Taurus	Bull
Gemini	Twins	Ursa Major	Great Bear (Big Dipper)
Hercules	Hercules	Ursa Minor	Little Bear (Little Dipper)
Leo	Lion	Virgo	Virgin (Maiden)

This map shows the constellations that appear to circle the North Star, also known as Polaris. Because these constellations appear to circle Polaris, which is located almost directly over the north pole, they are called circumpolar constellations. Look toward the north to locate these constellations. To orient yourself, first locate Polaris, which is found by looking directly north, then up at an angle of roughly 35° to 45°.

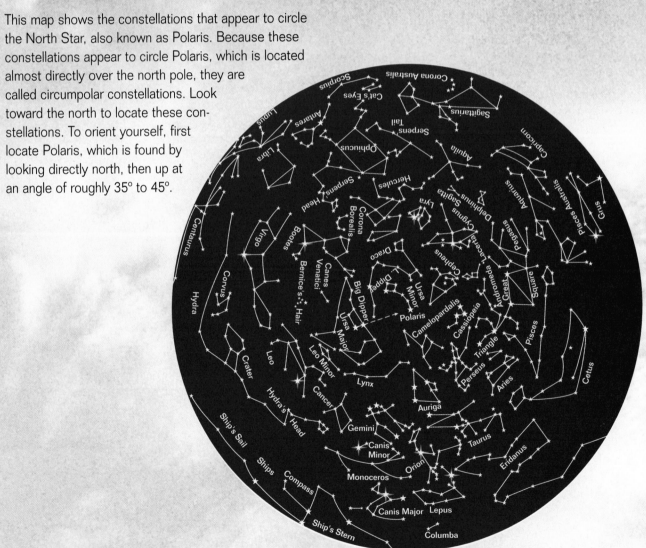

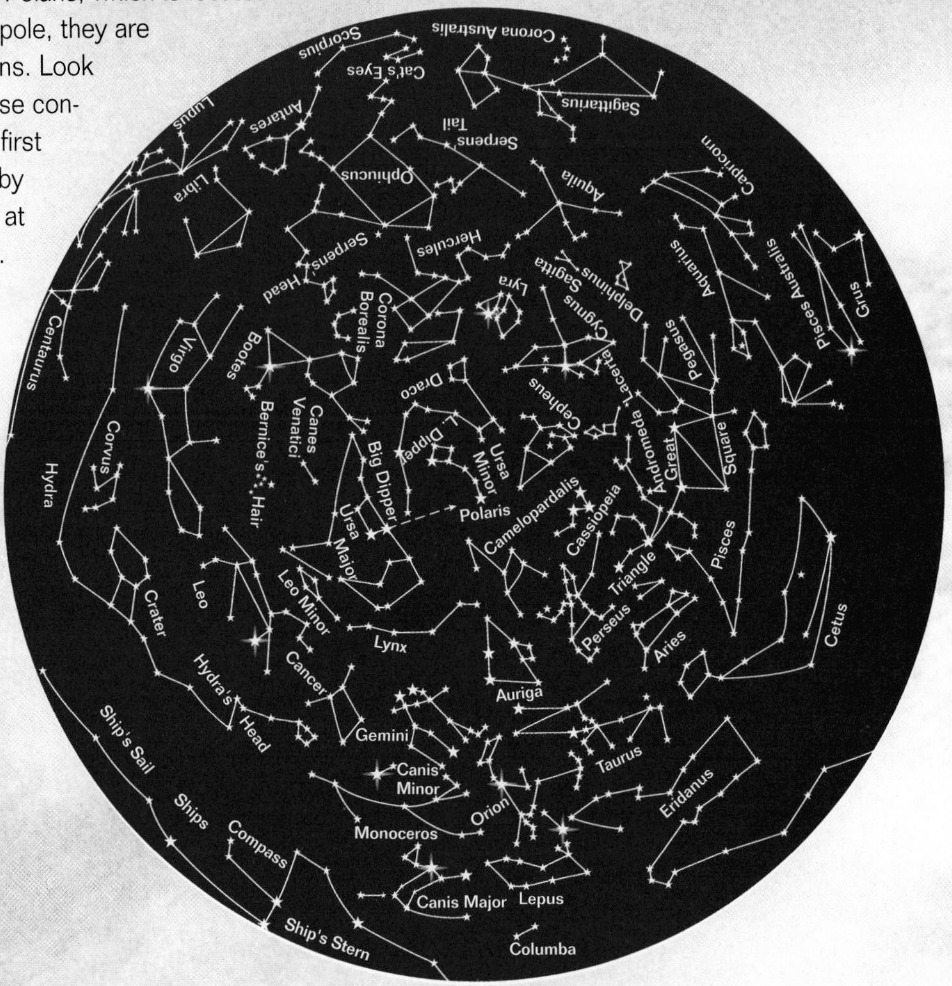

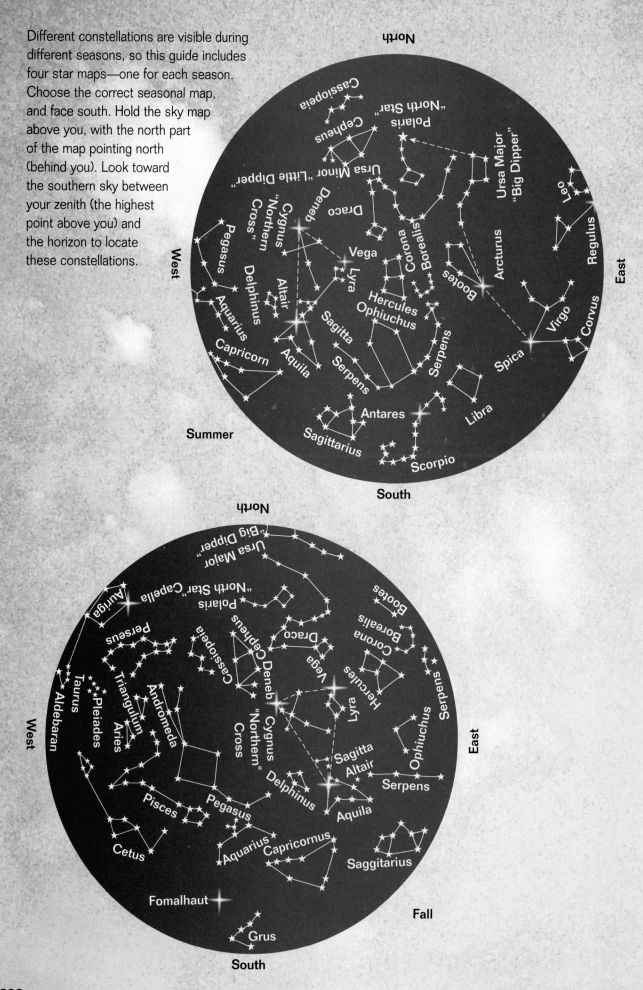

Different constellations are visible during different seasons, so this guide includes four star maps—one for each season. Choose the correct seasonal map, and face south. Hold the sky map above you, with the north part of the map pointing north (behind you). Look toward the southern sky between your zenith (the highest point above you) and the horizon to locate these constellations.

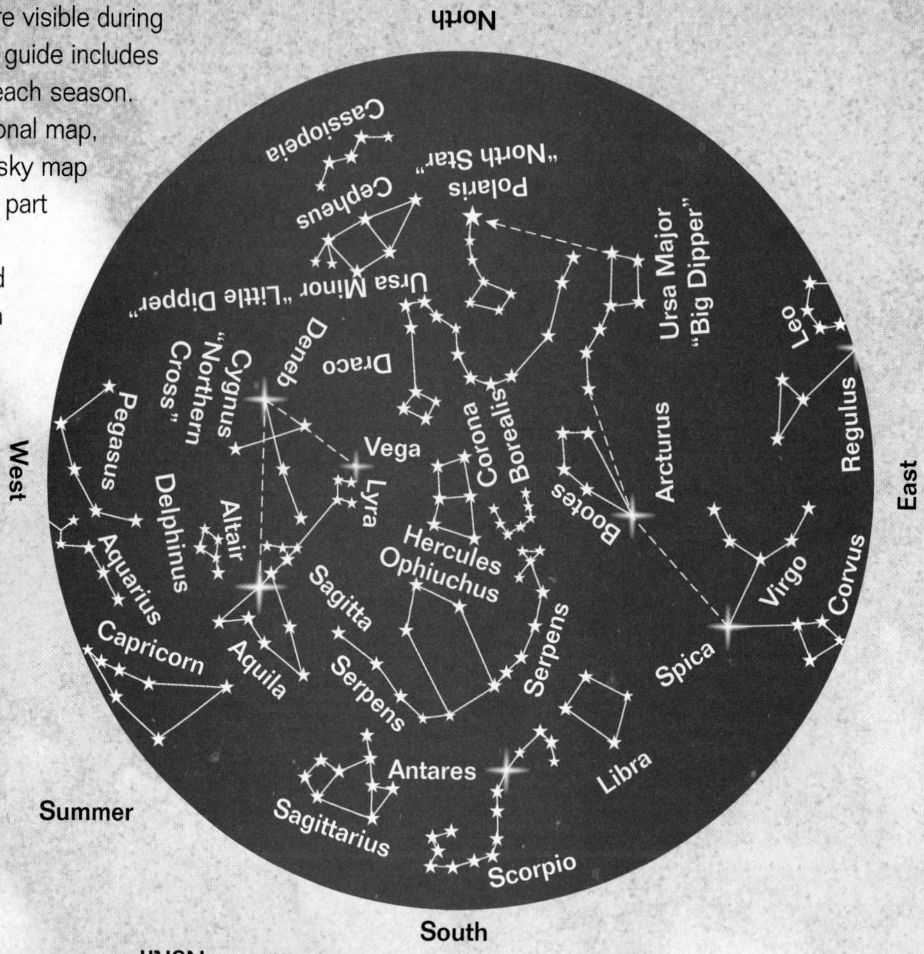

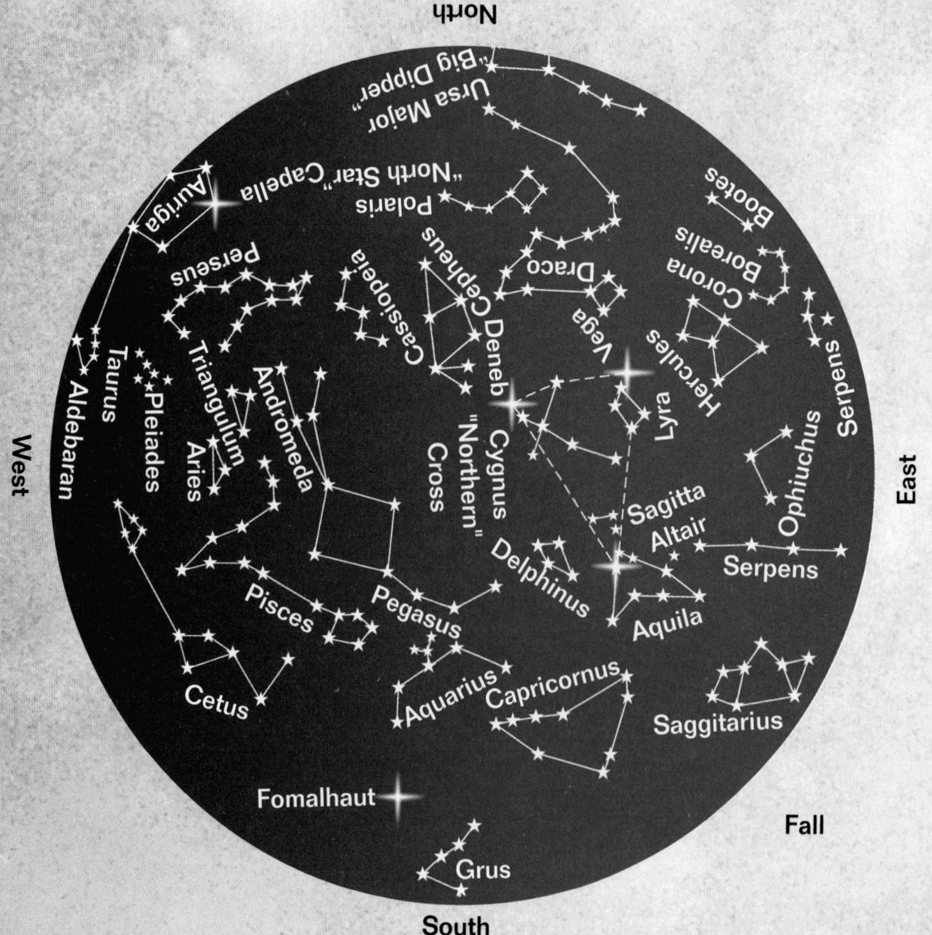

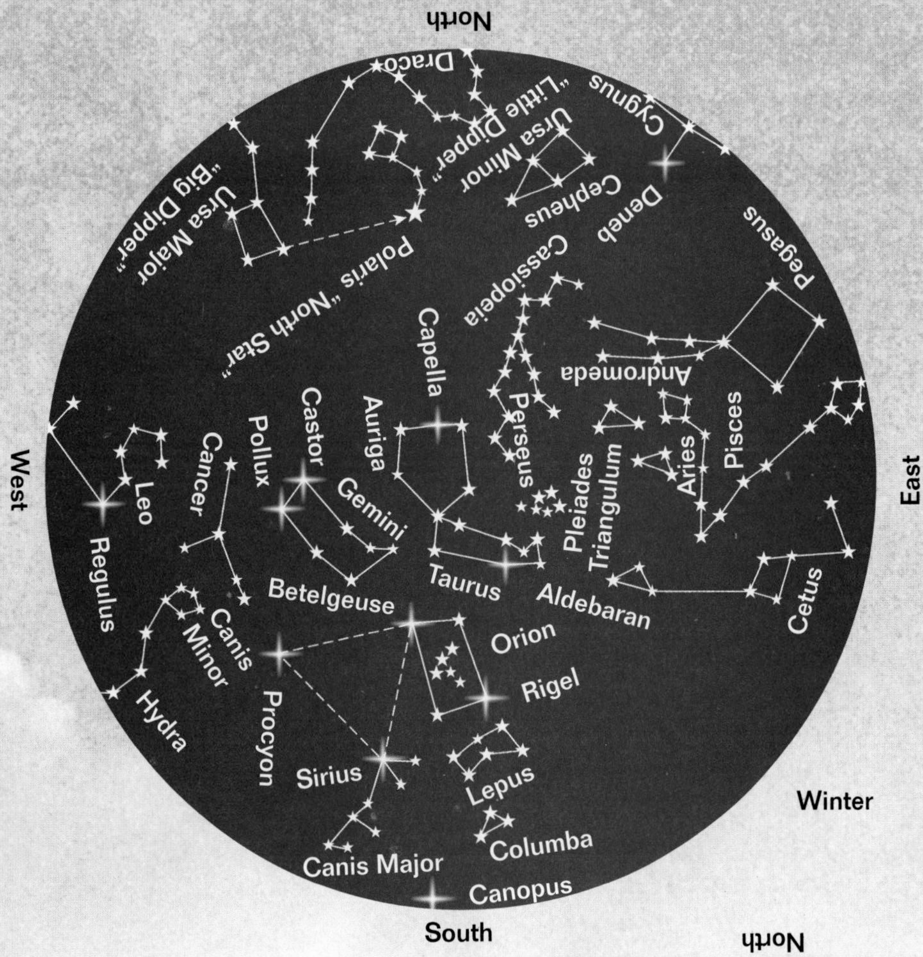
North
West
East
South
Winter
Draco
Cygnus
"Little Dipper"
Ursa Minor
Ursa Major
"Big Dipper"
Cepheus
Deneb
Polaris "North Star"
Cassiopeia
Pegasus
Capella
Andromeda
Auriga
Castor
Pollux
Perseus
Cancer
Leo
Gemini
Pleiades
Triangulum
Aries
Pisces
Regulus
Taurus
Betelgeuse
Aldebaran
Cetus
Canis Minor
Orion
Rigel
Hydra
Procyon
Sirius
Lepus
Columba
Canis Major
Canopus

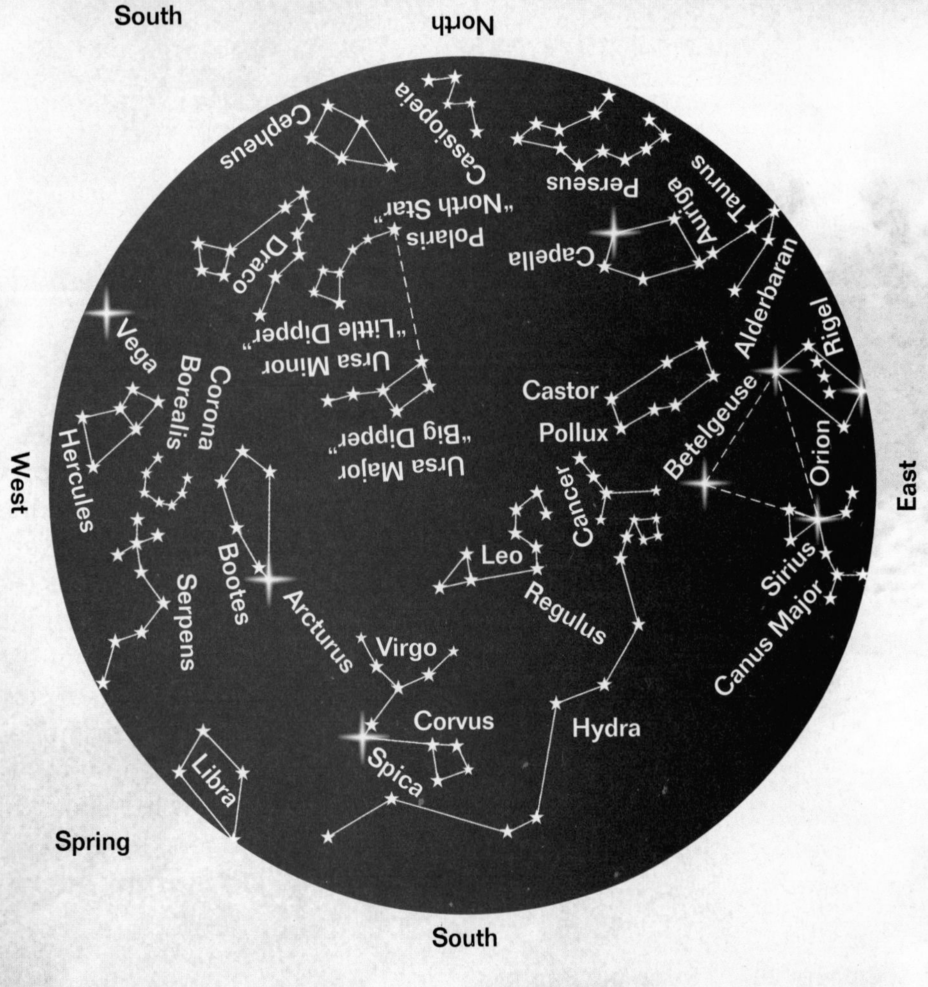
North
West
East
South
Spring
Cepheus
Cassiopeia
Perseus
Taurus
"North Star"
Polaris
Draco
Capella
Auriga
Vega
"Little Dipper"
Ursa Minor
Alderbaran
Rigel
Corona Borealis
Castor
Hercules
"Big Dipper"
Ursa Major
Pollux
Betelgeuse
Orion
Cancer
Leo
Bootes
Serpens
Regulus
Sirius
Arcturus
Canus Major
Virgo
Corvus
Hydra
Spica
Libra

Chapter 20 Reviewing Main Ideas

For a **preview** of this chapter, study this Reviewing Main Ideas before you read the chapter. After you have studied this chapter, you can use the Reviewing Main Ideas to **review** the chapter.

The Glencoe MindJogger, Audiocassettes, and CD-ROM provide additional opportunities for review.

Section
20-1 STARS

The magnitude of a star is a measure of the star's brightness. **Absolute magnitude** is a measure of the light emitted. **Apparent magnitude** is a measure of the amount of light received on Earth. **Parallax** is the apparent shift in the position of an object when viewed from two different positions. The closer to Earth a star is, the greater its shift in parallax. A star's temperature and composition can be determined from the star's spectrum. ***What term describes how bright a star looks from Earth?***

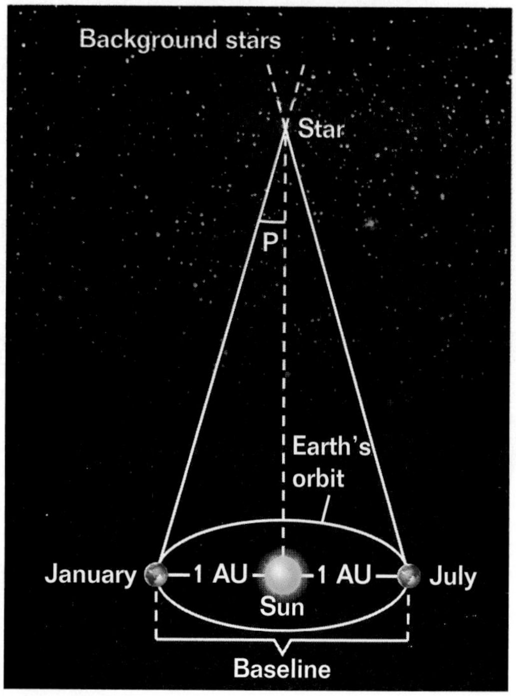

Section
20-2 THE SUN

The sun produces energy by fusing hydrogen into helium in its core. Light is given off from the photosphere, which is the lowest layer of the sun's atmosphere. **Sunspots** are areas of the sun that are cooler and less bright than surrounding areas. Sunspots, prominences, and flares are caused by the intense magnetic field of the sun, which is a main sequence star. ***Why is the sun considered an average star?***

Reading Check ✓

The big bang theory is still controversial. What part of this theory is supported by evidence? What part is opinion?

Section

20-3 EVOLUTION OF STARS

When hydrogen is used up in a **main sequence** star, the star's core collapses and its temperature increases. The star becomes a **giant** or a **supergiant,** which uses helium as fuel. As the star evolves, its outer layers escape into space and the star becomes a **white dwarf.** Stars containing high amounts of mass can explode. During a supernova explosion, the outer layers of a star are blown away and the remaining core evolves into a **neutron star** or **black hole.** ***At what temperature does fusion begin inside a nebula?***

Section

20-4 GALAXIES AND THE UNIVERSE

A **galaxy** is a large group of stars, gas, and dust held together by gravity. Galaxies can be elliptical, spiral, or irregular in shape. The galaxy that our sun belongs to, the Milky Way, contains about 200 billion stars. There may be more than 100 billion galaxies in the universe. The most accepted theory about the origin of the universe is the **big bang theory.** ***What is the Local Group of galaxies?***

Chapter 20 Assessment

Using Vocabulary

a. absolute magnitude
b. apparent magnitude
c. big bang theory
d. binary system
e. black hole
f. chromosphere
g. constellation
h. corona
i. galaxy
j. giant
k. light-year
l. main sequence
m. nebula
n. neutron star
o. parallax
p. photosphere
q. sunspot
r. supergiant
s. white dwarf

Explain the differences in the terms given below. Then explain how the terms are related.

1. absolute magnitude, apparent magnitude
2. black hole, neutron star
3. chromosphere, photosphere
4. binary system, constellation
5. light-year, parallax

Checking Concepts

Choose the word or phrase that best answers the question.

6. What do constellations form?
   A) clusters C) black holes
   B) giants D) patterns
7. What is a measure of the amount of a star's light received on Earth?
   A) absolute magnitude
   B) apparent magnitude
   C) fusion
   D) parallax
8. What increases as an object comes closer to an observer?
   A) absolute magnitude C) parallax
   B) red shift D) size
9. What begins once a nebula contracts and temperatures increase to 10 millionK?
   A) main sequencing C) fusion
   B) a supernova D) a white dwarf
10. What is about 10 km in size?
    A) giant C) black hole
    B) white dwarf D) neutron star
11. Our sun fuses hydrogen into what?
    A) carbon C) iron
    B) oxygen D) helium
12. What are loops of matter flowing from the sun?
    A) sunspots C) coronas
    B) auroras D) prominences
13. What are groups of galaxies called?
    A) clusters C) giants
    B) supergiants D) binary systems
14. Which galaxies are sometimes shaped like footballs?
    A) spiral C) barred
    B) elliptical D) irregular
15. What do scientists study to determine shifts in wavelengths of light?
    A) spectrum C) corona
    B) surface D) chromosphere

Thinking Critically

16. What is significant about the 1995 discovery by the *Hubble Space Telescope* of more than 1500 galaxies at a distance of more than 10 billion light-years?
17. How do scientists know that black holes exist if these objects don't emit any visible light?
18. Use the autumn star chart in Appendix K to determine which constellation is directly overhead at 8 P.M. on November 23 for an observer in North America.
19. How are radio waves used to detect objects in space?
20. What kinds of reactions produce the energy emitted by stars?

Developing Skills

If you need help, refer to the Skill Handbook.

21. Concept Mapping: Complete the concept map on this page that shows the evolution of a main sequence star with a mass similar to that of the sun.

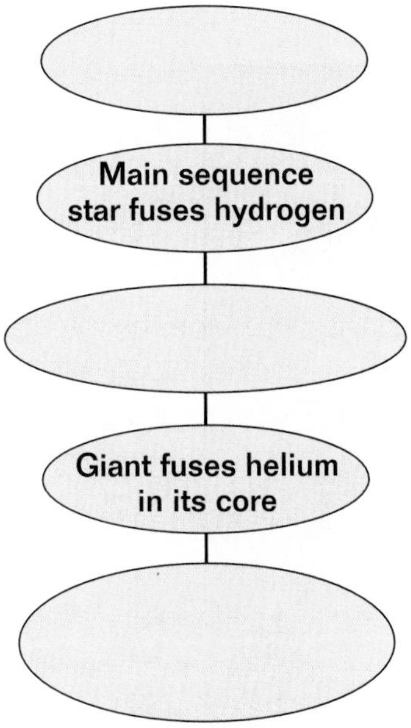

22. Comparing and Contrasting: Compare and contrast the sun with other stars on the H-R diagram.

23. Measuring in SI: The Milky Way Galaxy is 100 000 light-years in diameter. What scale would you use if you were to construct a model of the Milky Way with a diameter of 20 cm?

24. Designing an Experiment: Design and carry out an experiment that uses sunspot locations to compare rotational periods of different latitudes of the sun.

25. Making a Model: Design and construct scale models of a spiral and a barred spiral Milky Way Galaxy. Show the approximate position of the sun in each.

THE PRINCETON REVIEW

Test-Taking Tip

Read the Label No matter how many times you've taken a particular test or practiced for an exam, it's always a good idea to skim through the instructions provided at the beginning of each section.

Test Practice

Use these questions to test your Science Proficiency.

1. A white dwarf star is located in the lower-left-hand corner of an H-R diagram. Which of the following statements **BEST** explains why it is positioned there?

A) White dwarf stars have low absolute magnitudes and high surface temperatures.

B) White dwarf stars have low absolute magnitudes and low surface temperatures.

C) White dwarf stars have high absolute magnitudes and high surface temperatures.

D) White dwarf stars have high absolute magnitudes and low surface temperatures.

2. Sunspots are dark areas of the sun's surface. Which of the following statements **BEST** explains why this is true?

A) Sunspots are areas of the sun's surface that do not give off light.

B) Sunspots appear dark because they give off more energy than surrounding areas of the sun's surface.

C) Sunspots are hotter than surrounding areas of the sun's surface.

D) Sunspots are cooler than surrounding areas of the sun's surface.

California Science Standards and Case Studies

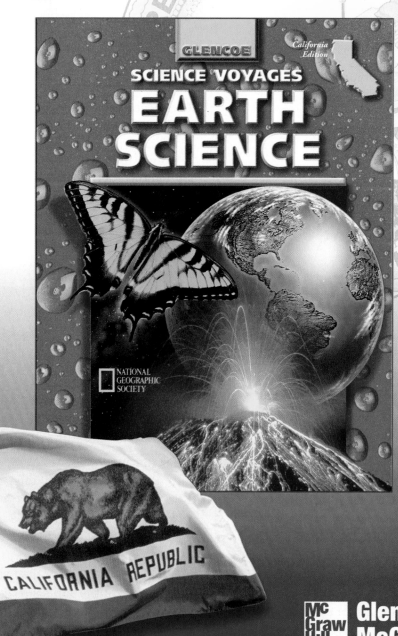

Glencoe McGraw-Hill

Level Red

California
The Golden State

State Tree: The California Red Wood

State Bird: The California Quail

State Flower: The Golden Poppy

PHOTO AND ART CREDITS: CA2 (t)Corbis Media, (b)Gerald L. French/Photo File; **CA5** David Matherly/Visuals Unlimited; **CA6** Dean Conger/Corbis Media; **CA7** Christian Michaels/FPG International; **CA8** Travelpix/FPG International; **CA9** Corbis Media; **CA10** Vic Cox/Peter Arnold Inc.; **CA11** Alison Wright/Photo Researchers; **CA12** file photo; **CA13** Raymond F. Newell Jr.; **CA14** D.C. Lowe/FPG International; **CA15** ©Jerry Lodriguss/Photo Researchers; **CA16** ©Jerry Schad/Photo Researchers; **CA17** Corbis Media; **CA18** Tony Freeman/PhotoEdit; **CA19** Richard Megna/Fundamental Photographs; **CA21** AC/GM/Peter Arnold Inc.; **CA22** Catherine Ursillo/Photo Researchers; **CA23** Kenneth Eward/BioGrafx-Science Source/Photo Researchers; **CA24** Manfred Kage/Peter Arnold Inc.; **CA25** Mark E. Gibson; **CA26** Lawrence Berkeley National Laboratory/Science Photo Library/Photo Researchers; **CA27** Tom McHugh/Photo Researchers; **CA28** James Blank/The Stock Market; **CA29** Matt Meadows; **CA30** Jim Corwin/Tony Stone Images; **CA31** John Lund/Tony Stone Images.

P/N G86731.11

California CONTENT STANDARD 1

Plate Tectonics and Earth's Structure

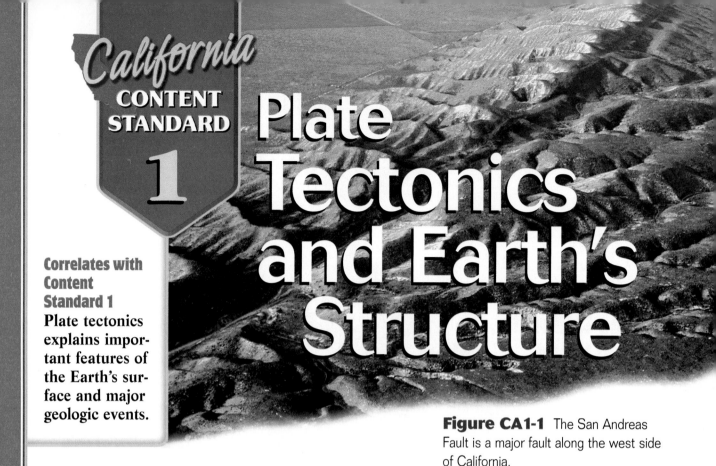

Correlates with Content Standard 1
Plate tectonics explains important features of the Earth's surface and major geologic events.

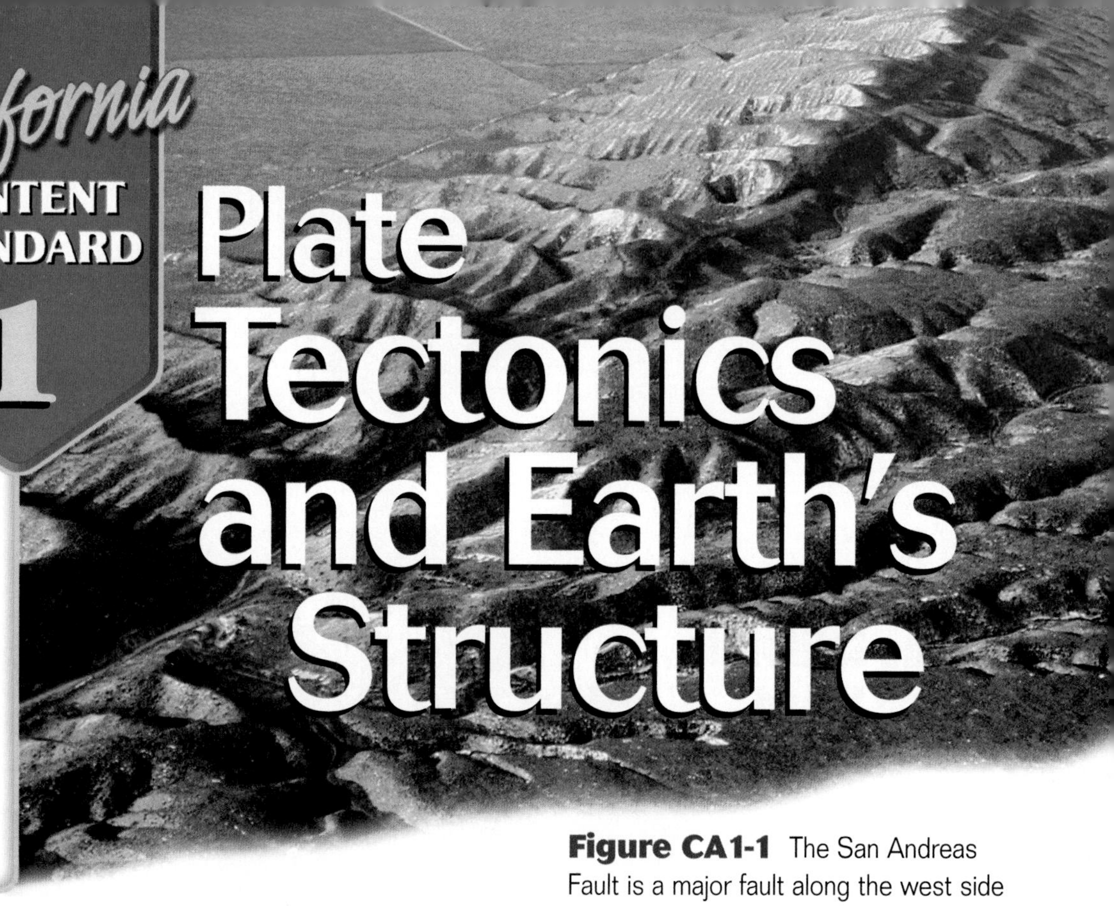

Figure CA1-1 The San Andreas Fault is a major fault along the west side of California.

1a. Evidence for Plate Tectonics

Has Earth always looked like the globes and maps you have seen? Have the continents and oceans always been in the positions they are in today? A lot of evidence suggests that Earth looked different millions of years ago.

One piece of evidence is that the shapes of the continents on opposite shores of the Atlantic Ocean look like they could fit together like pieces of a jigsaw puzzle.

Geologists have concluded that the surface of Earth, including land and the ocean floors, is made up of about a dozen large plates. Each plate moves as a single unit over a layer of Earth that is less rigid, which means that the layer is somewhat like plastic or putty. The movement of the plates is like a raft floating on water. This idea about Earth's surface is called plate tectonics.

Other evidence for plate tectonics comes from the locations of earthquakes, volcanoes, and ridges along the ocean floor. These geological features are located in areas where different plates meet. For example, the Pacific plate, the North American plate, and Juan de Fuca plate meet near the coast of California. This is why California is prone to earthquakes and why California has several volcanoes, including Mount Lassen and Mount Shasta, although no California volcanoes have erupted recently.

A third type of evidence for plate tectonics is the pattern of fossils, types of rock, and ancient climates on different continents. Fossils of land animals are found across the Atlantic Ocean from one another in areas that would have been next to each other when the continents were one large landmass. The types of rocks and the ages of those rocks match up in a way that indicates that the continents were once together. There is also evidence that continents now in the northern hemisphere once had tropical climates, while those now in the southern hemisphere were once covered with glaciers. This indicates that the continents have moved over time.

1b. Layers of Earth

When you walk along a trail in the Sierra Nevada or along a cliff near the Pacific Ocean, it feels like Earth is completely solid. Is Earth one solid mass of rock? No, Earth is made up of several layers. The ground you walk on is called the crust. The outer section including the crust and the rigid, upper mantle is called the lithosphere. The lithosphere is made up of relatively low-density rock. The next layer is called the mantle. The mantle is made up of denser rock. It is hot and in the outer part of the mantle is the plasticlike layer. The innermost layer of Earth is called the core and is separated into two sections. The outer part is liquid, while the inner core is solid. The core is made up mostly of iron, with some other metals included. It is even hotter than the mantle.

1c. Plate Movement

In standard 1a, you learned that Earth's surface is made up of large, moving plates. Are the plates still moving? Yes, they are. How fast are they moving? Scientists have measured the movement and it is a few centimeters per year. This is about as fast as fingernails grow! If the plates move small amounts each year for millions of years, they end up far from their starting points.

Why do the plates move? Part of the mantle is plasticlike and flows slowly. These movements below the plates, which are part of the lithosphere, cause the plates to move like a raft moves on the surface of water.

1d. Sudden Earth Events

If you live in California, you have probably felt the movement of Earth called an earthquake. What is an earthquake? An earthquake is the shaking of Earth caused by a sudden release of energy. Usually, an earthquake involves motion along a fault, such as the San Andreas Fault. What is a fault? A fault is a break in Earth's crust along which movement has occurred.

Another dramatic natural event is a volcanic eruption. A volcano, or other opening in the crust called a fissure, is the location where magma reaches the surface. Magma is molten rock. Once magma leaves the ground, it is called lava.

Investigation & Experimentation

Standards 7d, 7h
Find a picture or pictures that show changes in an area of land as a result of either an earthquake or a volcano. Describe the changes to your classmates.

Figure CA1-2 This photo shows Sonora Pass in the Sierra Nevada. The Sierra Nevada formed along a plate boundary.

1e. Major Geologic Events

Now that you know what earthquakes and volcanic eruptions are, why do they happen? These geologic events are caused by the motion of tectonic plates. An earthquake occurs when different plates that are next to one another shift relative to each other. Sometimes, the plates stick as they try to slide past one another. Eventually, there is a sort of sudden snap that removes the sticking point and allows the plates to move. It is this sudden movement that people experience as an earthquake.

Volcanic eruptions occur when magma is forced upward and flows through openings to Earth's surface. Mountain ranges are created when plates collide. In one case, where one plate is forced beneath another, the plate underneath pushes up on the top plate. Also, the descending plate may melt, forming magma that is forced upward, sometimes forming mountains.

1f. California Geology

Now that you have learned how plates affect geology in general, this knowledge can be applied to features in California specifically. The coast of California south of San Francisco lies near the boundary between the North American plate and the Pacific plate. North of San Francisco, the Juan de Fuca plate meets the North American plate. The movements of these plates affect the geology of California. For example, the Sierra Nevada formed millions of years ago when they were forced upward from below an ancient sea. At the same time, magma from beneath Earth's surface was forced upward and cooled to form granite that is found in the Sierra Nevada today. California also has volcanoes, such as Mount Shasta and Mount Lassen. They are part of a large number of volcanoes that formed around the boundary of the Pacific plate and Juan de Fuca plate.

Figure CA1-3 Mount Lassen in northern California is one of the volcanoes that formed along the plate boundary.

Investigation & Experimentation

Standards 7b, 7f

Using a topographic map of the area around Mount Whitney, the highest mountain in California, answer the following questions. What is the elevation of the top of Mount Whitney? What is the elevation of Whitney Portal, the place where many hikers begin to climb the mountain? What is the elevation of Lone Pine, the town closest to the road to Whitney Portal? Assuming a hiker drives from Lone Pine to Whitney Portal and then hikes up to the summit of Mount Whitney, how much elevation does the hiker gain while driving? How much while hiking?

1g. Earthquakes

How do earthquakes get their names? The name comes from the location of the epicenter of the earthquake. The epicenter is the point on Earth's surface above the location where the energy of the earthquake is released. How do you determine where the epicenter of an earthquake is?

When an earthquake occurs, the shaking is caused by seismic waves that travel outward from the area near the epicenter. These waves are recorded on an instrument called a seismograph. There are different types of seismic waves that travel at different known speeds. By comparing when the faster and slower waves reach the seismograph, you can calculate how far away the epicenter is from the location of the seismograph. If the distance from the epicenter to at least three different seismograph locations is known, the exact epicenter can be determined.

If you have ever lived through an earthquake or heard news reports about one, you know that the effects of an earthquake vary depending on how big the earthquake is; how far you are from the epicenter; how well structures such as roads, buildings, and bridges were built; and the type of land you are on. In strong earthquakes, much more damage occurs to areas near the epicenter. Structures designed to withstand earthquakes are less likely to collapse in an earthquake. Also, damage is less likely to occur in areas above a layer of solid rock than in areas over looser ground such as landfill.

Investigation & Experimentation

Standard 7h
Develop a hypothesis for why buildings with wooden or steel frames might withstand an earthquake better than buildings with a concrete frame.

Figure CA1-4 This parking garage was destroyed in the 1994 Northridge earthquake.

Going Further

To find out more about plate tectonics, see:

1a. Chapter 9, Section 1, Continental Drift
Chapter 9, Section 2, Seafloor Spreading
Chapter 9, Section 3, Theory of Plate Tectonics

1b. Chapter 10, Section 1, Forces Inside Earth
Chapter 10, Section 2, Earthquake Information

1c. Chapter 9, Section 1, Continental Drift
Chapter 9, Section 2, Seafloor Spreading
Chapter 9, Section 3, Plate Tectonics

1d. Chapter 10, Section 1, Forces Inside Earth
Chapter 10, Section 2, Earthquake Information
Chapter 11, Section 1, What causes volcanoes?
Chapter 11, Section 2, Types of Volcanoes

1e. Chapter 10, Section 1, Forces Inside Earth
Chapter 11, Section 1, What causes volcanoes?
Chapter 9, Section 3, Plate Tectonics

1f. Chapter 5, Section 1, Landforms

1g. Chapter 10, Section 1, Forces Inside Earth
Chapter 10, Section 2, Earthquake Information
Chapter 10, Section 3, Destruction by Earthquakes

California CASE STUDY

The Shifting Earth

SCIENCE FOCUS

Read this case study to learn how scientists track the movements of Earth's surface in order to predict earthquakes.

Correlates with Content Standard 1

Plate Boundaries

Much of the state of California falls at the boundaries of two large plates on Earth. The Pacific plate and the North American plate meet along the San Andreas Fault. The two plates are slowly grinding past each other. This plate movement has important effects on California. Los Angeles, located on the Pacific plate, is moving north. And San Francisco, on the North American plate, is basically stationary, or moving slightly to the south. How do scientists know this? How can they watch Earth move?

Monitoring Earth

Scientists from the United States Geological Survey (USGS) and many other scientists continually take the pulse of Earth. They gather information on the ground and from space. The Global Positioning System (GPS) includes 24 satellites, orbiting 20 000 km above Earth's surface. The GPS system uses signals between the satellites and receivers on the ground. The system can tell the exact position of the receiver on Earth.

Scientists also monitor the movement and the amount of bending in Earth's crust. To do this they use instruments called seismographs, tiltmeters, and strainmeters. Seismographs detect vibrations within Earth's surface. Tiltmeters detect tilting of the ground. Strainmeters are used to detect bending rock. Strainmeters and tiltmeters often are placed in deep holes in the ground so that scientists can monitor the positions of Earth's plates.

Figure CA1-5 Shown here is a base station used to receive the GPS satellite signal. By placing several receivers along the edge of a moving plate, scientists can see how much the plates move over time.

Seismographs, tiltmeters, and strainmeters are located in many parts of California. Their information is transmitted to a USGS computer. In a laboratory in Menlo Park, scientists analyze these data to determine how much Earth's crust has moved.

Predicting Earthquakes

Many scientists hypothesize that earthquakes come at certain intervals and that they are on a schedule. How can this be? Think of the rock that lies under the soil as a pencil. When you grip a pencil with both hands and slowly, gently bend it, you can watch it bend. It is under what is called stress. At some point, however—snap—the stress is too much, and your pencil breaks. Rock, too, is a bit flexible, although it might not seem so. Like the pencil, it will bend just a little, but the stress on the rock greatly increases and then—snap—the rock breaks, relieving the stress. That snap of the rock is an earthquake. So, earthquakes occur when the stress on rocks becomes too great. And, another earthquake won't occur until the stress on the rocks builds up again. Scientists look at the timing of past earthquakes. Then, they can estimate how long it takes for stress to build up in the rocks.

Preparing for Earthquakes?

During an earthquake, unstable buildings create much of the danger to people. Scientists and engineers work to design buildings and roads that can withstand earthquakes. They also help determine where industrial plants and utilities such as gas lines can be placed safely.

Scientists are working to learn what early signals an earthquake sends. They monitor strain, or the bending and change of shape in rock, caused by stress and look for the appearance of small cracks in the rock. They also record and analyze thousands of small ground movements that are tiny earthquakes. By doing these things, they try to determine the areas of California where stress is increasing.

California scientists also communicate with scientists from other areas where earthquakes often happen, such as Japan. They share information about predicting earthquakes.

Investigation & Experimentation

Activity 7d

Visit the library or the Glencoe Science Web Site at **www.glencoe.com/sec/science/ca** to research plate tectonics. Write a short report explaining how plate tectonics affects the mountains, volcanoes, or faults in California. Present your report to the class.

Figure CA1-6 At a laboratory in Menlo Park, a scientist studies a seismograph.

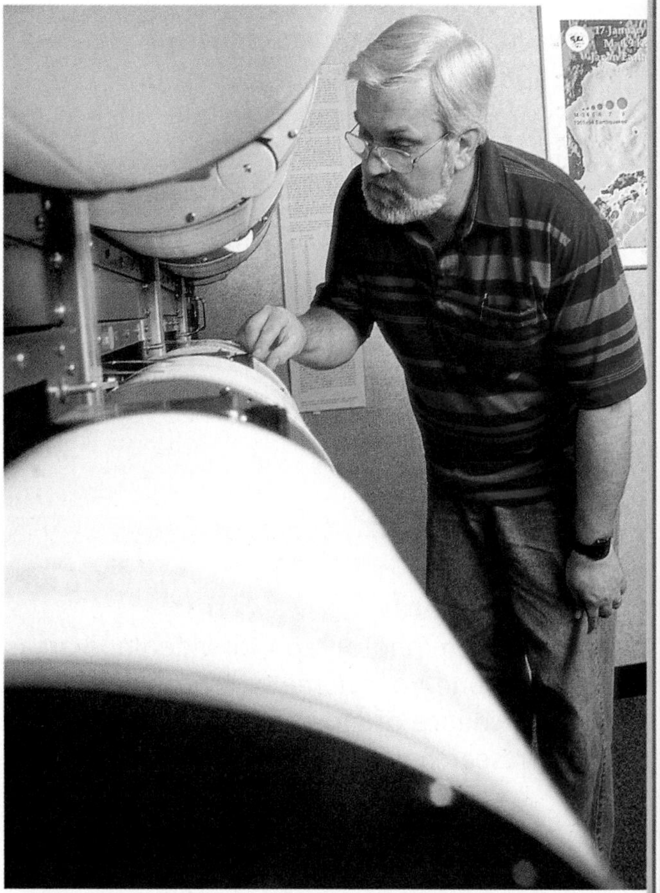

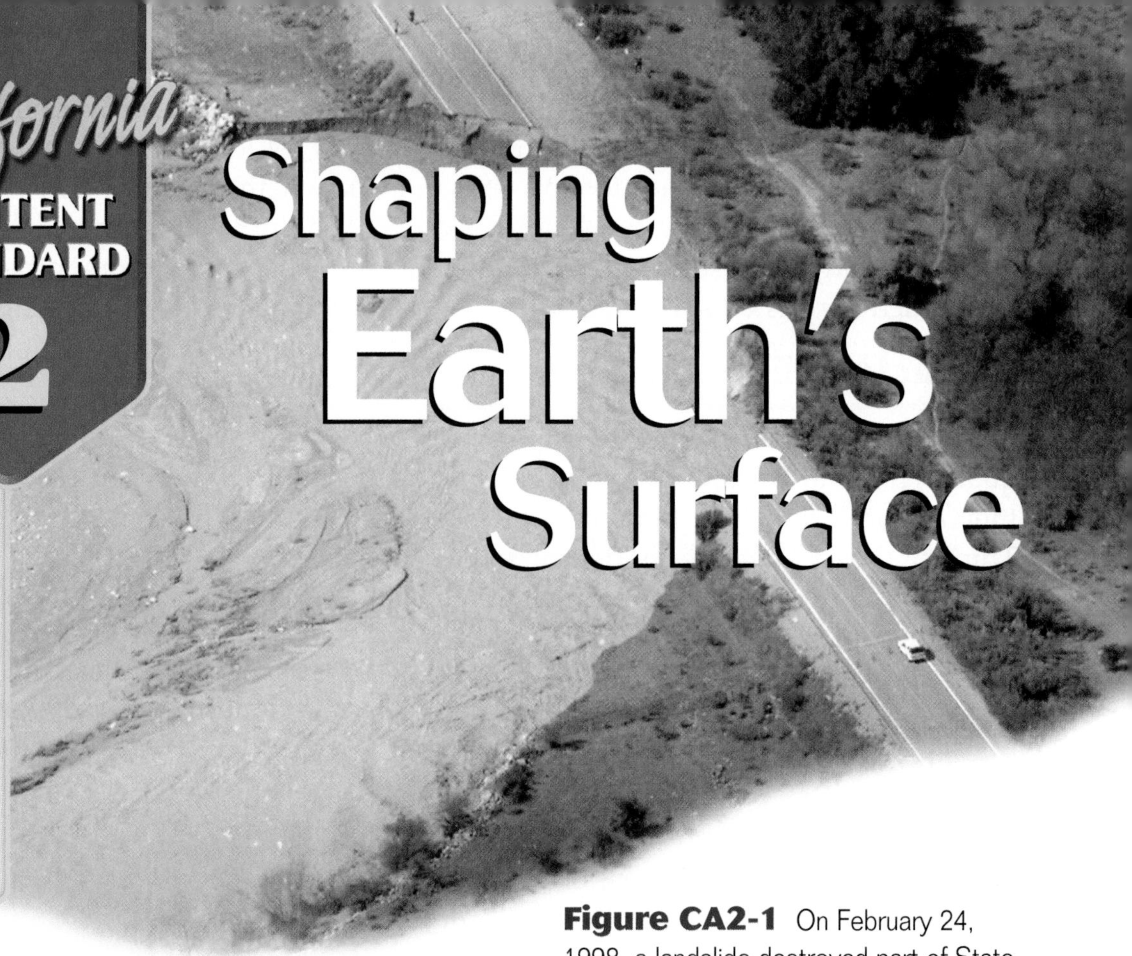

California CONTENT STANDARD 2

Shaping Earth's Surface

Content Standard 2
Topography is reshaped by weathering of rock and soil and by the transportation and deposition of sediment.

Figure CA2-1 On February 24, 1998, a landslide destroyed part of State Route 166 in Santa Barbara County.

2a. Agents of Erosion

Rugged mountains, rolling plains, sandy beaches—these things make up the topography, or physical features, of a region. Some physical features are big, such as the Sierra Nevada. Others are much smaller, such as coastal dunes. All are constantly changing as water, wind, ice, and gravity—the agents of erosion—work to reshape Earth's surface. Erosion is the wearing away and movement of surface materials, such as sand and soil, from one place to another.

Investigation & Experimentation

Standards 7e, 7g, 7h
Sketch, photograph, or videotape areas around your home or school that show evidence of erosion. Compare your research with that of other students. As a class, try to determine what caused the erosion.

The Power of Water

Water is the dominant agent of change in California, constantly shaping and reshaping the land. Many of the canyons found in the state's mountain ranges were carved mainly by running water. Millions of years ago, fast-flowing mountain streams cut through rock and began forming what is now Yosemite Valley. Slow-moving glaciers later moved down the valleys created by these streams.

In urban areas, fast-moving water flowing down steep slopes causes the rapid erosion of surface materials. This increases the chances for landslides that may damage property and cause loss of life. Grasses and other plants slow the process of water erosion. For this reason, many areas in California have adopted erosion programs aimed at vegetating steep slopes.

2b. Rivers and Streams

Rivers and streams are in constant motion. As they flow, they erode and carry tons of sediment from one place to another. When the flowing water slows down, the sediment drops out.

Why does the water slow down? Sometimes, it reaches a slower-moving body of water such as a lake or sea. Sometimes, it reaches a flatter slope. Mountain streams slow down abruptly when they reach the flat floor of a valley. They drop their sediment, which spreads out like a fan over the valley floor.

Floods may change the course of a river. During times of heavy rainfall, rivers and streams may overflow their banks and form new channels. Unlike geologic events that occur slowly, floods may drastically alter a river and the land that surrounds it overnight. Northern California had destructive flooding during the rainy winter of 1996. Thousands of homes were damaged or destroyed, hundreds of farm animals were drowned, and at least 29 people were killed.

Figure CA2-2 The raging Feather River near Ar'boga, California, where floods wiped out roads, bridges, and power lines.

Figure CA2-3 These California poppies are beautiful and help reduce erosion.

Investigation & Experimentation

Standard 7a
The river's speed and volume may change with the seasons and other enviromental factors. As a result, the course of the river may change. Hypothesize how geologic processes can alter a river's channel or the speed at which it flows.

2c. Beaches

When rivers meet with oceans, the rivers drop their load of sediment. Eventually, some of this sediment becomes the sand we see on beaches. More sediment is created as waves break over or against rocks and erode their surfaces. The sediment is constantly moved back and forth along the shoreline by the wave action. When the waves reach quieter waters, the sediment drops out. This is how sandy beaches are formed.

Figure CA2-4
Waves pound the Pacific coast in Mendocino County, California. Evidence of wave erosion can be seen all along California's rugged coast. In some places, this erosion is quite rapid. The cliffs near Santa Barbara, for instance, are receding at a rate of 15 m per century.

2d. Natural Hazards

Few states can rival California's abundance of natural wonders or its record of natural hazards.

The 1990s in particular were a tough decade for California. Table 1 shows a partial list of the earthquakes, wildfires, and floods that have hit the state since 1991.

Table 1
(Some figures are estimated.)

Hazard	Date	Losses
El Niño Storms	1998	$500 million (estimate)
Winter Floods	1995	$2 billion (estimate)
Northridge Earthquake	1994	$20 billion
Southern California Wildfires	1993	$1 billion
East Bay Wildfires	1991	$1.5 billion

Going Further

To learn more about the forces that shape Earth's surface, see:

2a. Chapter 7, Section 1, Gravity
Chapter 7, Section 2, Glaciers
Chapter 7, Section 3, Wind
Chapter 8, Section 1, Surface Water
Chapter 8, Section 2, Groundwater

2b. Chapter 8, Section 1, Surface Water
Chapter 8, Section 2, Groundwater
Chapter 8, Section 3, Ocean Shoreline

2c. Chapter 8, Section 1, Surface Water
Chapter 8, Section 3, Ocean Shoreline

2d. Chapter 10, Section 1, Forces Inside Earth
Chapter 10, Section 2, Earthquake Information
Chapter 10, Section 3, Destruction by Earthquakes
Chapter 11, Section 1, What causes volcanoes?
Chapter 11, Section 3, Igneous Rock Features

Taming Landslides

SCIENCE FOCUS

Read this case study to learn about the impact that landslides have on California.

Correlates with Content Standard 2

Gravity Exerts a Force

Earthquakes, wildfires, and floods can trigger another type of natural hazard common to California—landslides. Landslides are mass movements of soil and rock triggered by gravity. Gravity exerts a constant force on the surface of a slope. On a stable slope, the strength of the rock or soil balances the force of gravity pulling on the slope's surface. But, when rock or soil is weakened by earthquakes or saturated by water, gravity overcomes the slope's resistance. Rocks may tumble down a cliff or mud may flow quickly down a hill. Slopes that have beendamaged by wildfires are particularly vulnerable to landslides because their protective vegetation has been burned off.

During times of heavy rainfall, water mixes with the loose material, and a type of landslide known as a mud slide may occur. In 1998, El Niño driven storms in California triggered mud slides that caused many millions of dollars in property damage. Most of the damage was done to highways and roads. The California Department of Transportation estimated that road repair will cost the state 90 million dollars. The estimate for 1998 mud slide damage from El Niño is 475 million to 500 million dollars.

Like all natural hazards, landslides can damage property and wildlife habitats, and cause loss of life.

Figure CA2-5

Coastal Crash

A In 1993 near Dana Point, California, more than 44 000 tons of soil and debris crashed onto a highway and railroad tracks. Several hillside homes were destroyed.

Putting the Plan into Action

B To avoid future landslides, a plan was developed to construct a new, artificial cliff. The new cliff was anchored into the hillside with 165 stainless steel cables called tiebacks. The cables were secured with concrete.

Restoring Nature

C Latex molds of nearby cliffs were used to create a natural-looking, artificial cliff face. It was even painted to look like local rocks. Soil and native plants were added to make it appear as though it had been there forever.

Community Concerns

The city of Dana Point worked extensively with local, state, and federal agencies to finance the 3.5-million-dollar project. Using newsletters, the city kept local residents updated on the project's progress. Open-house meetings were held to encourage citizen input. These actions helped foster a spirit of community involvement and cooperation throughout the two-year project. Other cities have taken similar measures to reduce landslides. But, few have combined so many different measures into one coherent plan. That's why Dana Point is a national model for landslide control.

Investigation & Experimentation

Standard 7d

In the library or using the Glencoe Science Web Site at **www.glencoe.com/sec/science/ca,** research different methods of flood control. Then, contact local government officials to find out what measures are being taken in your area to prevent floods. Working as a group, evaluate your area's flood-control plan. Present your findings to the class.

Heat

California CONTENT STANDARD 3

Figure CA3-1 Surfers use the energy from waves at this beach in Huntington, California, to move across the water.

Content Standard 3
Heat moves in a predictable flow from warmer objects to cooler objects until all objects are at the same temperature.

3a. Flow of Energy

The refrigerator, lights, and oven in your home require energy to work. For most people, that energy is produced somewhere else and then transported to their homes. How can energy move from one place, or one object, to another? There are several ways that energy is carried from place to place, including heat, electrical conduction, water waves, light and sound, and moving objects.

Heat is the transfer of an amount of energy from one object to another because of a difference in temperature. You may notice that if you are warm and you hold something cold like a glass with ice water in it, after a little while the glass will feel warmer and your hand will feel cooler. That is because some of the thermal energy in your hand will have flowed to the glass. In general, heat transfers from warmer objects to cooler objects.

Surfers at beaches along the Pacific coast of California get energy to move toward the beach from the waves of water in the ocean. During a thunderstorm, you may see lightning and hear thunder even when the storm is far away. Light and sound also carry energy. Another way that energy is carried from one place to another is through collisions of moving objects. Have you ever stood a bunch of dominoes up in a line and then knocked the end one over? Your push to knock over the first domino takes a small amount of energy. The energy then transfers down the line of dominoes to wherever the last domino falls.

Investigation & Experimentation

Standard 7e
When you go outside and stand in a sunny spot, you probably feel warm. If you stand in a shady spot, you probably feel cooler. Knowing that the sun itself is hot, can you describe why you feel hotter or cooler depending on where you stand outside? Is heat the only type of energy that the sun provides? Can you think of another?

Figure CA3-2 A campfire gives off energy in the form of heat. In this case, the fuel is wood.

3b. Fuel

Suppose you go camping in the Sierra Nevada and it gets cool at night. What do you do to stay warm? One thing you might do is have a campfire. When wood burns, it gives off heat. Wood is one type of fuel. When fuel is consumed, most of the energy is released as heat. This is also true for other types of fuel, such as oil, gasoline, coal, or dynamite (TNT). The energy released from consuming fuel can be directed toward other purposes, such as gasoline powering a car, but there is also heat produced. The car gets warmer as it runs.

3c. Conduction and Convection

Suppose you are camping and you want to roast marshmallows over your campfire. Usually, people put the marshmallows on a stick. What would happen if you put the marshmallow on the end of a metal bar, such as a skewer? You would be able to hold the skewer for a little while, but at some point the end that you are holding would get too hot to hold. This is because the heat from the end in the fire flows through the skewer to the end in your hand. Heat also flows through wood, but not as fast as it flows through metals. Why is it safer to use a wooden stick to toast marshmallows?

In solid objects, like a spoon, heat flows by conduction. As one part of the spoon gets hot, the energy in that part is increased. Some of that energy is passed along to the handle of the spoon. In conduction, there is no flow of matter—in other words, none of the metal moves to a different place—there is only flow of energy.

Suppose you are drinking something hot, such as tea, but it has gotten cooler than you like it. One way that you could warm the tea is to add a little more hot water to it. The energy from the hot water will transfer to the cooler tea to make it a bit warmer. This is an example of heat conduction by a fluid.

Figure CA3-3 This heater uses electricity to produce heat. The energy moves through the room by convection and radiation.

Most fluids do not conduct heat well, which means that heat does not flow fast by conduction. The way that heat usually flows through fluids is called convection. In convection, matter moves from one place to another, bringing energy with it.

Investigation & Experimentation

Standard 7b

Put hot tap water in one bowl and ice water in another. Place a metal spoon in the hot water and another in the cold water. Does the spoon in the hot water feel hot? How does the spoon in the cold water feel? Explain.

3d. Radiation

You learned about conduction and convection in Section 3c, but there is another way that heat moves between places and objects, called radiation. Heat travels from one hot object to another cooler object. For example, the sun radiates energy into space. Earth is in the path of this energy, so energy is transferred from the sun to Earth through radiation. One important difference between radiation and the other two types of heat flow is that radiation does not require matter in order to happen.

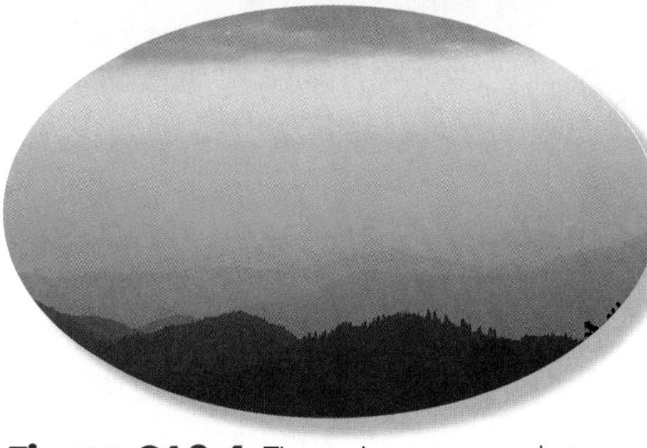

Figure CA3-4 The sun's energy travels to Earth by radiation. This photo shows a sunset over Sequoia National Park, California.

Conduction and convection require that there is a material, such as a metal or a fluid, to transfer the heat. Radiation can travel through space even though space is mostly empty of matter.

Is the sun the only object that radiates heat? Actually, no. All objects, including people, emit energy by radiation and absorb energy radiated by other objects.

Investigation & Experimentation

Standard 7a

Wrap a small, empty, frozen juice can with black construction paper. Fill it with water. Set it in a sunny window. Observe what happens to the temperature of the water inside.

Going Further

To learn more about heat, see:

3a. Chapter 26, Section 1, Energy Changes
Chapter 26, Section 2, Temperature and Thermal Energy
Chapter 26, Section 3, Chemical Energy
Chapter 25, Section 3, Compounds and Mixtures

3b. Chapter 25, Section 3, Compounds and Mixtures
Chapter 4, Section 1, Energy Resources
Chapter 4, Section 2, Alternative Energy Resources
Chapter 4, Section 4, Land

3c. Chapter 26, Section 1, Energy Changes
Chapter 26, Section 2, Temperature and Thermal Energy
Chapter 26, Section 3, Chemical Energy

3d. Chapter 26, Section 2, Temperature and Thermal Energy

California CASE STUDY

Harnessing the Dragon

SCIENCE FOCUS

Read this case study to learn how scientists are converting Earth's heat into a usable energy source.

Correlates with Content Standard 3

The Smoking Canyon

In the mid 1800s, a California explorer and surveyor stumbled into a canyon like none he had seen before. He gazed on an unearthly landscape. Clouds of billowing steam rose from cracks in the ground. Located north of San Francisco, the area was a geothermal field, which came to be called The Geysers.

Geothermal fields are formed by a special set of conditions in Earth. They generally exist along a volcanic belt, at the edge of one of Earth's plates. Here, pockets of magma or partially melted rock from Earth's interior provide the heat. A reservoir of water lies over the magma. And, as in a cooking pot on a stove, the water is heated to the boiling point or above.

Geysers and Dry Steam

You may be familiar with the spectacular eruptions of geysers such as Old Faithful in Yellowstone National Park in Wyoming. Much like a pot without a lid, geysers result if the reservoir has an opening on top. Water continually fills the heated reservoir, then boils. Pressure is released by an outflow of boiling water and steam.

So-called dry-steam fields, such as The Geysers in California, are similar to a pot with a lid. A cap of watertight rock covers

Figure CA3-5 The Geysers is the world's largest geothermal energy field.

Figure CA3-6 Old Faithful in Yellowstone National Park, Wyoming, is a natural geyser.

the boiling reservoir. This keeps most of the water in the ground. Steam vents through narrow cracks in the rock, showing the location of the geothermal field.

Power from Earth's Heat

How is electricity produced from steam? Think about a whistling teakettle and a child's toy pinwheel. If you hold the pinwheel in the plume of steam from the teakettle, the pinwheel will spin furiously. In the same way, turbines are turned by the steam escaping from Earth. The spinning turbines run generators, producing electricity. To speed up this process, wells are drilled into the boiling reservoir. This allows more steam to escape and more generators to be powered by the field. In 1960, The Geysers became the first commercial geothermal field in the United States. A system of wells, turbines, and generators was installed. The electricity that is produced travels to San Francisco through power lines strung through the Mayacmas Mountains. The Geysers now supports six separate generating plants.

A Renewable Resource?

The heat that comes from Earth's interior will continue for millions of years. It is produced by continuous physical processes deep in Earth. But, the steam from geothermal fields can be depleted. This happens in geothermal fields where many wells are drilled to increase steam production. It is like the pot boiling dry. Can a dry geothermal field be saved? Yes; to revitalize the field, water can be pumped into the ground. The water will then be heated by the bed of hot rock. This starts the steam cycle all over again. The Geysers now receives treated wastewater from three communities in Lake County. The water travels through a pipeline to The Geysers. There, it is injected into Earth at a depth of 2400 m, more than one mile. This technique provides a use for treated wastewater. And it increases steam production, extending the life of the geothermal field. The Lake County wastewater project is expected to provide an extra 625 000 megawatt-hours of electricity each year for the residents of California.

Investigation & Experimentation

Standard 7c

The quantity of electricity produced at The Geysers has changed over the years. In the library or on the Internet, research the level of output of the electrical power plants at The Geysers. Represent these changes on a graph. In a short report, identify the causes of significant changes in power production, such as addition of new generators or depletion of the water in the geothermal field.

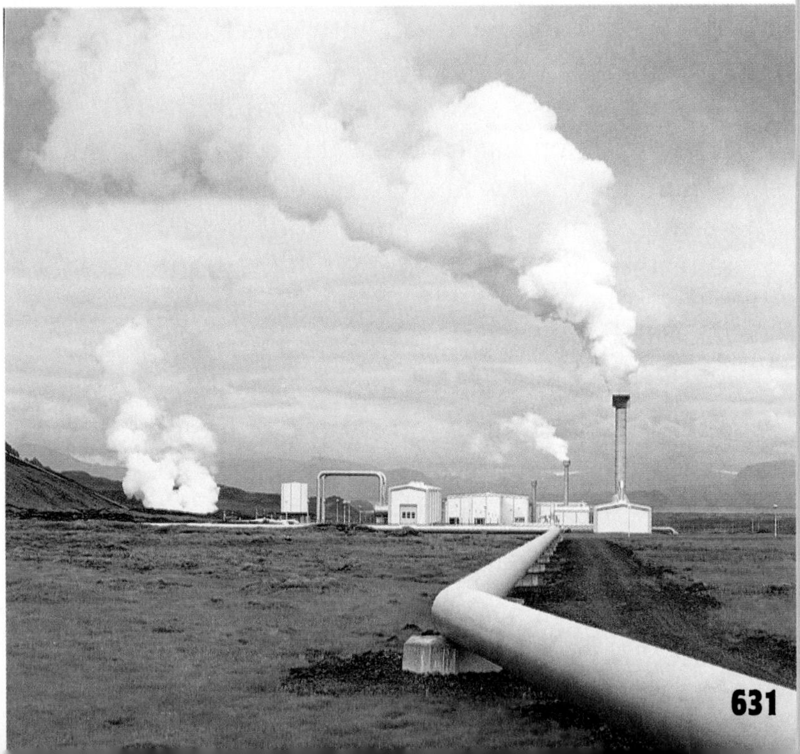

Figure CA3-7 This pipeline carries steam from a dry-steam well in Iceland.

California CONTENT STANDARD 4

Energy in the Earth System

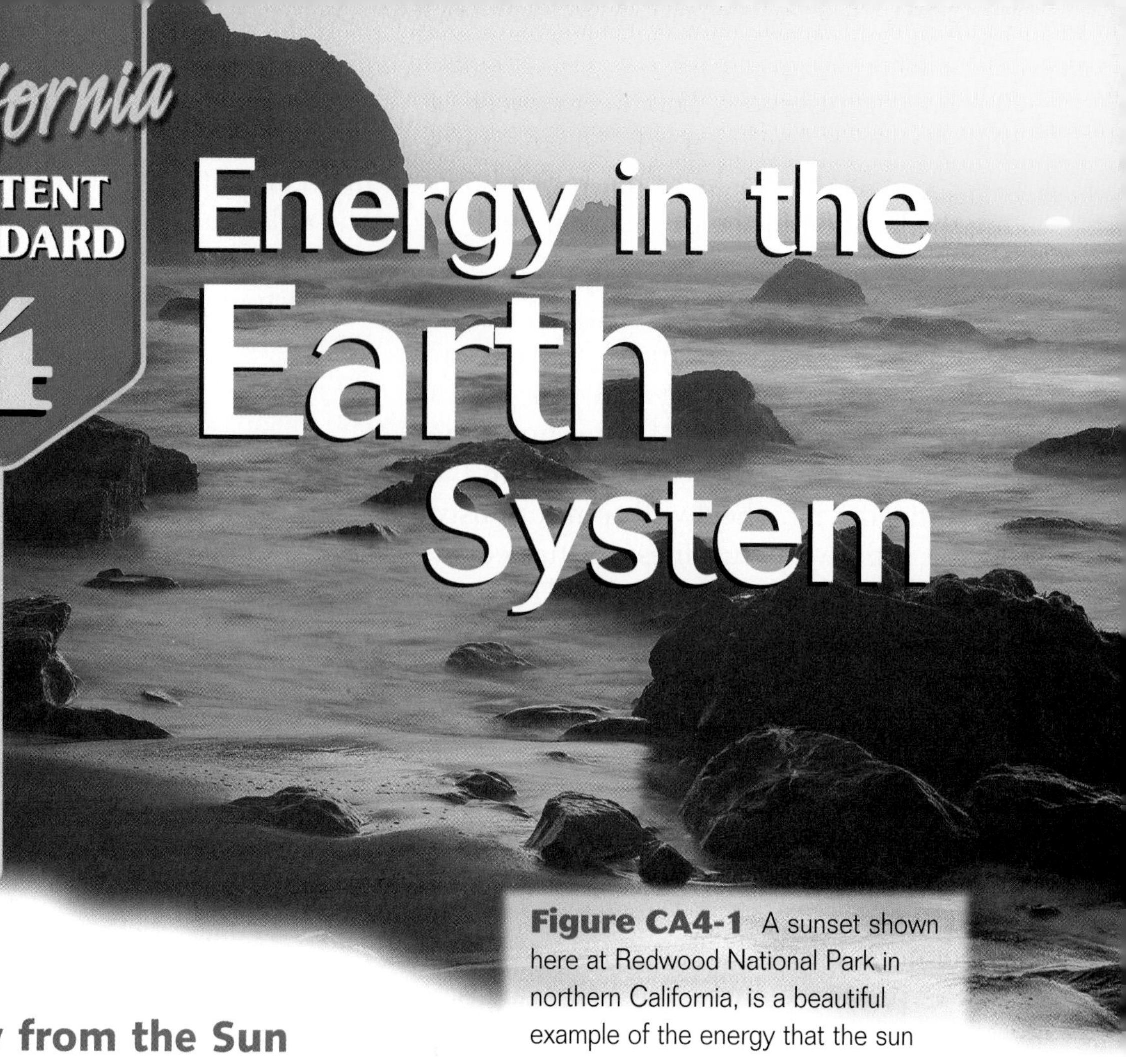

Content Standard 4
Many phenomena on Earth's surface are affected by the transfer of energy through radiation and convection currents.

Figure CA4-1 A sunset shown here at Redwood National Park in northern California, is a beautiful example of the energy that the sun provides Earth.

4a. Energy from the Sun

The sun provides light and heat to people on Earth. Did you know that the sun is also the major source of energy for things that happen on Earth's surface, such as winds and ocean currents? Energy from the sun, called solar energy, drives the winds, and the winds in turn affect currents on the ocean.

The sun also provides energy for the water cycle on Earth. The water cycle is a system in which water moves between the oceans, atmosphere, and land before returning to the oceans. Water from the oceans evaporates into the atmosphere. Winds move the air along with the moisture until clouds form. Then, the moisture returns to Earth as rain or snow. Some of that water falls directly on the oceans and the rest falls on land. The water that falls on land works its way back to the oceans—by flowing in rivers or streams—or back to the atmosphere by evaporating again.

Investigation & Experimentation

Standards 7e, 7g, 7h
Find information about the levels of lakes in California over the past ten years or so. Have the levels changed? How were lake levels affected by the drought in California in the early 1990s? How do these changes relate to the water cycle?

4b. Solar Energy

Energy from the sun causes currents in the Pacific Ocean and winds in the Sierra Nevada. However, the sun is far from Earth. How does the energy get here? Solar energy reaches Earth through radiation, which you learned about in standard 3d. Most of the energy from the sun reaches

Figure CA4-2 Renewable solar energy is produced at this solar installation near Hesperia, California.

Earth as visible light and heat, but some energy is in the form of radio waves, ultraviolet light, and other types of radiation.

Investigation & Experimentation

Standard 7d

Find out where solar energy is used to provide electricity to Californians.

4c. Heat Inside Earth

Is the sun the only source of heat that reaches Earth's surface? The inside of Earth is hot and some of that heat reaches the surface. For example, lava from volcanic eruptions is hot material from inside Earth. In standard 1b, you learned that the mantle is a layer of Earth that can flow because it is somewhat like putty or plastic and is not rigid. Heat from the mantle reaches the surface mainly through convection. In other words, hotter parts of the plastic-like material in the mantle move closer to the surface of Earth and that leads to some heating of the surface.

Investigation & Experimentation

Standards 7b, 7c

Put some cold water in a sink and measure the temperature. Put some hot water into a small bowl and measure its temperature. Carefully, place the bowl with hot water into the sink, so that the bowl is fully underwater. You know that the hot water starts in the bowl. Does it stay there? Wait a minute and measure the temperature of the water in the bowl and in an area away from the bowl. Has the cold water become warmer? Has the hot water become cooler? Measure the temperatures each minute for five minutes. Then graph the temperatures versus the time (each minute) for the water in the bowl and the water in the sink. What do the lines look like?

4d. Heat in the Atmosphere and Oceans

So far, you have read about heat coming from the sun or from the inside of Earth. Once part of the atmosphere or the ocean has been heated, the heat spreads to other parts. This is what you learned in standard 3—heat flows from warmer objects to cooler ones. In these cases, matter—air in the atmosphere and water in the ocean—spreads out from the warmer area to make other sections of the atmosphere or the ocean warmer. Again, this happens through convection.

Investigation & Experimentation

Standard 7d

You may have heard about El Niño in 1997 and 1998. El Niño is a warming of ocean waters. Find out where El Niño started and what areas of the oceans were affected. How did the heat travel to other areas to make the water warmer?

4e. Weather Changes

The movement of energy through Earth's atmosphere and oceans affects people. This energy movement controls the weather. The uneven heating of Earth causes differences in temperatures, which causes differences in atmospheric pressure. This causes wind. Wind is the movement of air from an area of high pressure to an area of low pressure. The amount of water vapor the air can hold also depends on the temperature. The amount of water vapor held in air is called humidity.

Weather is the current state of the atmosphere. Important things that determine the weather are air pressure, wind, temperature, and humidity.

Figure CA4-3 Energy from deep inside Earth melted the rock that formed this lava flow. The flow is from an 1851 eruption of a cinder cone in Lassen Volcanic National Park, California.

Going Further

To learn more about energy in the Earth System, see:

4a. Chapter 14, Section 2, Energy from the Sun
Chapter 4, Section 2, Alternative Energy Resources

4b. Chapter 14, Section 2, Energy from the Sun
Chapter 4, Section 2, Alternative Energy Resources

4c. Chapter 11, Section 1, What causes volcanoes?
Chapter 11, Section 2, Types of Volcanoes

4d. Chapter 14, Section 1, Earth's Atmosphere
Chapter 14, Section 2, Energy from the Sun
Chapter 15, Section 1, What is weather?
Chapter 15, Section 2, Weather Patterns
Chapter 16 Section 3, Climatic Changes
Chapter 17, Section 1, Ocean Water
Chapter 17, Section 2, Ocean Currents
Chapter 17, Section 3, Ocean Waves and Tides

Mount Shasta

SCIENCE FOCUS

Read this case study to learn how volcanoes, such as Mount Shasta in the Cascade Mountains in California, act as vents for thermal energy that comes from deep within Earth's interior.

Correlates with Content Standard 4

The Ingredients of a Volcano

Did you know that volcanoes don't start out as mountains? An enormous and powerful volcano starts as a crack in the ground. This crack is called a vent. Inside the vent is magma that contains melted rock, unmelted mineral crystals, and gases. Magma is found in Earth's crust and the upper parts of Earth's mantle. Because magma is a fluid, heat travels within it by the process of convection. Blobs of more fluid magma are forced through areas of cooler, denser rock materials. If there is a vent in Earth's crust, magma can be forced through it to the surface. When magma appears on Earth's surface, it is called lava.

Eruption

Have you ever heated a bowl of chili uncovered in a microwave oven? If so, you probably created your own little volcano without meaning to. Magma (now lava) contains gases. If the lava is fluid, the gases can escape easily and the lava flows quickly and quietly through the vent. If the lava is thick, gas bubbles are trapped and the pressure in the lava builds. As this thick lava exits the vent, the gas bubbles explode violently, taking lava, ash, and rocks with them through the vent and blowing them up and out.

Mountain Building

When you think of a volcano, you probably think of a cone-shaped mountain. The mountain was formed by the lava, cinders, and ash that poured out through the volcanic vent. The lava then cooled and became solid rock. Repeated lava flows gradually build a cone. In some kinds of volcanoes, the cone is mostly hardened

Figure CA4-4 Mount Shasta is a composite volcano in the Cascade Mountains in California.

Figure CA4-5 This smaller cone is Shastina, a major vent of Mount Shasta.

lava that flowed quietly out of the vent. These are called shield volcanoes. Other kinds of volcanoes called cinder cones have cones made mostly of cinders, which include ash and solid pieces of lava. The third kind of volcano is a composite volcano.

A Composite Giant

Mount Shasta in northern California is an example of a large composite volcano. Composite volcanoes are usually tall cones with steep sides, built by many eruptions, some of which are quiet and some are violent. These eruptions may have happened hundreds of years apart. Mount Shasta is probably at least 100 000 years old. Scientists estimate that it erupts about every 600 years. The last known eruption of Mount Shasta was in 1786. It was observed by a French explorer from the deck of a ship off the Pacific coast.

Mount Shasta is a complex volcano. At the top of the mountain are four separate cones, each with its own vent. There are also many other vents on the sides of the mountain. In many eruptions that have occurred during the last 10 000 years, lava and cinders formed small cones on the sides of the mountain. During that time, the forces of erosion were also at work. Thus, the volcano that we see today is not the volcano of 500 years ago. Active volcanoes can change a great deal in a short period of time.

Volcano Watching

The United States Geological Survey (USGS) warns people of potential volcanic eruptions in the United States. In 1980, Mount St. Helens, one of the Cascades volcanoes in Washington state, erupted violently. Warnings were given well in advance, and most people left the area unharmed. After that eruption, the Cascades Volcano Observatory was established. The Cascades volcanoes are monitored for any underground movement. If any activity is detected, sensitive monitoring equipment is set up near and on the volcano. If Mount Shasta shows any unusual activity, the scientists of the Cascades Volcano Observatory will know immediately. They monitor the mountain and will warn people of a coming eruption.

Investigation & Experimentation

Standard 7f

In the library or on the Internet, find the names of at least five California volcanoes. Using a topographic map of California, find the locations of the volcanoes. Trace or draw the outline of a map of California, and plot the volcano locations on the map. A geological map shows different types of volcanoes present at Earth's surface in different areas. Use a geological map of California to identify the rock formations in the area of each volcano, and label the map you have drawn.

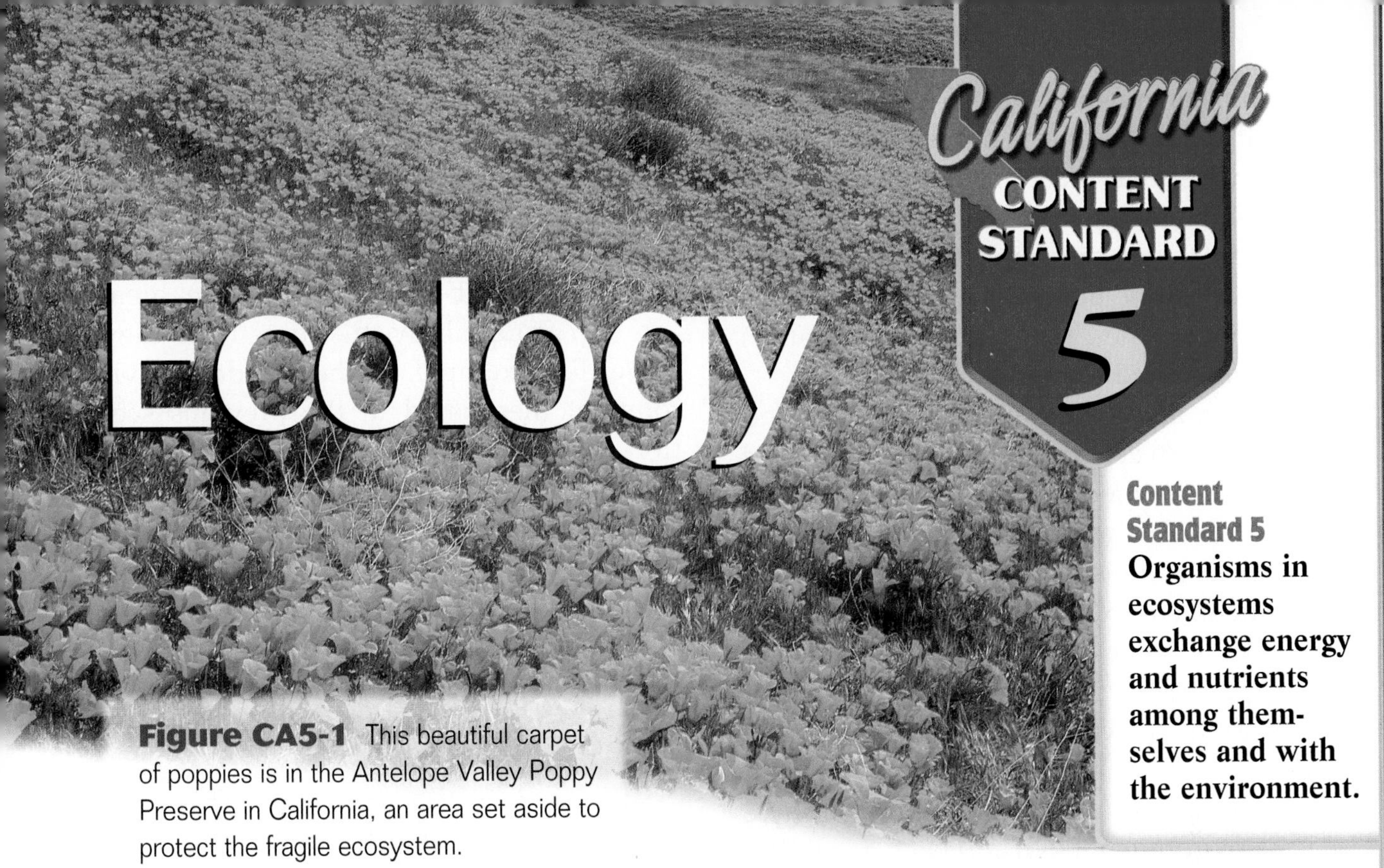

California Content Standard 5

Ecology

Figure CA5-1 This beautiful carpet of poppies is in the Antelope Valley Poppy Preserve in California, an area set aside to protect the fragile ecosystem.

Content Standard 5
Organisms in ecosystems exchange energy and nutrients among themselves and with the environment.

5a. Energy in Ecosystems

All organisms—plants, animals, and people—need energy to live and grow. Where does this energy come from? It comes from the sun. Sunlight itself is not a form of energy that all organisms can use—animals and people need food, for example. However, green plants take the energy from the sun and change it into a different type of energy (chemical energy) through photosynthesis. These plants are called producers because they basically make their own food.

The energy in the producers is passed from producers to other organisms when the plants are eaten by animals. If the animals that eat the plants are then eaten by other animals, the energy is passed along again. The transfer of energy through an ecosystem, which includes living things and the environment they live in, travels through food webs. Food webs are models of the transfer of energy that indicate which organisms eat which other organisms. On a model of a food web, there are different arrows showing that some animals might eat several different plants or other animals and they might be eaten by different types of predators. Food webs can be complex.

Investigation & Experimentation

Standard 7d

Research and draw a simple food chain (including four to eight organisms) that might exist in some environment in California (mountains, deserts, forests, etc.) Describe to your classmates the type of environment that the organisms on your food chain live in and where in California that environment might be found (e.g., Sierra Nevada, Death Valley, coastal redwood groves, etc.).

5b. Matter in Ecosystems

Is energy the only thing that is transferred between organisms in a food web? Over time, matter also moves between organisms in a food web. For example, if a small animal such as a mouse eats a plant, the matter that made up the plant is now passed to the mouse. The matter includes nutrients that are important to life and growth for the mouse. If a hawk then eats the mouse, these same nutrients (matter) are transferred to the hawk.

So far, all of the transfer of energy and matter in an ecosystem has been discussed through the food web. However, it is also possible for matter to be transferred between organisms and the physical environment. For example, after a plant or animal dies, some of its matter decomposes and provides nutrients for soil. The nutrients in the soil can then help new plants to grow. In this case, the matter moved from an organism (plant or animal) to the physical environment (soil) and back to a living organism (plant).

Investigation & Experimentation

Standard 7f

Choose a small environment in your neighborhood. Construct a simple scale map of the environment. This means that you must make your map so that the distances between things—such as trees or a stream—should be drawn on your map in relation to their actual distances. Which things on your map are biotic components? Which are abiotic components?

5c. Ecosystems

Different organisms play different roles in maintaining their ecosystems. Populations of organisms, which means all of a particular plant or animal in the area, can be grouped by the functions they serve. For example, in the meadow environment mentioned in the previous section, grasses and flowers function as producers, making food out of nonfood sources. These plants provide food and energy to plant-eating animals (herbivores) such as rabbits and deer. These animals might then be prey to meat-eating animals (carnivores) such as hawks, snakes, or coyotes. Another group in the meadow is made up of scavengers such as

Figure CA5-2 A desert tortoise is adapted to a hot, dry ecosystem.

Figure CA5-3 The desert ecosystem shown here is in Death Valley National Park, California.

earthworms or vultures that eat dead organisms. One other important group is the decomposers. Decomposers are bacteria and fungi that break down dead organisms so that the nutrients can be returned to the soil and used once again by plants.

5d. Functions of Organisms

There are several different roles for organisms to play in any ecosystem. Are the organisms that play the same roles in similar environments similar to each other? In other words, are the herbivores always small animals, while carnivores are larger ones? No, different kinds of organisms may play similar roles in similar environments.

Suppose there are two meadows or fields in two different places. It is possible that one meadow has mostly grasses as producers, while the other has more flowers or shrubs. Also, herbivores in the two meadows could include very different organisms such as deer or cattle in one meadow and crickets and rabbits in the other. The main carnivores may also be different: one meadow might have many coyotes, while the other has snakes and hawks. Scavengers in one meadow may be earthworms and insects, while the other may have vultures as the most common scavenger. As you can see, even though the meadow environments may seem fairly similar, there can be different organisms playing each role.

5e. Types of Organisms

Why might there be different organisms playing similar roles in similar ecosystems? What determines the number and types of organisms that live in an ecosystem? This depends on the resources (energy, nutrients, etc.) available in the environment as well as on abiotic factors, such as quantity of light and water, range of temperatures, and soil composition.

An ecosystem with more resources and favorable abiotic conditions will tend to have more organisms and probably more variety of organisms. Ecosystems with less favorable conditions, such as cold arctic tundra or dry desert areas, may be able to support only a small number of organisms and only those that have adapted to the fairly severe conditions. In areas where there are many opportunities for animals to find food, water and shelter, and where there are comfortable temperatures and amounts of light, there are likely to be many animals. In other areas, there may be only a few types of animals (or plants) that have adapted to the particular conditions present there.

Going Further

To learn more about ecology, see:

5a. Chapter 14, Section 2, Energy from the Sun
Chapter 23, Section 1, The Living Environment and the Nonliving Environment
Chapter 23, Section 2, Interactions Among Living Organisims
Chapter 25, Section 3, Compounds and Mixtures

5b. Chapter 25, Section 3, Compounds and Mixtures

5c. Chapter 22, Section 1, Diversity of Life
Chapter 22, Section 2, Unity of Life
Chapter 23, Section 1, The Living Environment and the Nonliving Environment

5d. Chapter 22, Section 1, Diversity of Life
Chapter 22, Section 2, Unity of Life
Chapter 23, Section 1, The Living Environment and the Nonliving Environment

5e. Chapter 23, Section 1, The Living Environment and the Nonliving Environment

California CASE STUDY

The Bloom of the Century

SCIENCE FOCUS

Read this case study to learn about wildflowers in the deserts of California.

Correlates with Content Standard 5

Desert Life

Blooming deserts are a trademark of California. But, as you look out over a Califor-nia desert, you may see nothing but soil, sand, and sunshine. It's easy to think that the desert is empty. But, California deserts are teeming with life.

Look closely at the desert soil, and you will find lizards, tortoises, insects, and thousands of seeds. In fact, you can find between 5000 and 10 000 seeds per square meter in the Sonoran Desert.

All of these seeds don't sprout and bloom at the same time or every year. Depending on the heat, light, temperature, and moisture, different seeds will germinate. In some years, the conditions are right for more seeds to develop than other years. Scientists predicted that 1998 would be a good year for many wildflowers to grow. Why? El Niño—the weather pattern that brought storms and disasters to California—also brought rain.

Desert Plants

The life cycles of desert plants vary. They have to compete for survival. Like many cultivated plants, wildflowers are classified as annuals. Perennials live for many years but may be dormant when the desert is dry. An ocotillo (oh koh TEE yoh) is an example of a California perennial. The ocotillo may grow leaves, then flowers and seeds within weeks of rain. Then, it loses its leaves and becomes dormant until conditions are favorable for it to grow again.

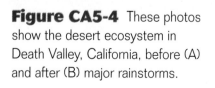

A

B

Figure CA5-4 These photos show the desert ecosystem in Death Valley, California, before (A) and after (B) major rainstorms.

Figure CA5-5 The ocotillo is a perennial desert plant.

Hundreds of wildflowers are annuals. Desert sand verbena, desert paintbrush, and mojave aster are annuals. Annuals complete their life cycle in a year or less. In fact, many desert annuals complete their entire life cycle in just a few weeks. These plants respond quickly to the right conditions. They grow, flower, make seeds, and die in a short time. The new seeds are able to withstand dry and hot weather for several years until the conditions for growth are favorable again. Then, they repeat their life cycle.

Where do the seeds come from?

Seeds are the result of the joining of sperm and eggs during sexual reproduction. The male genetic information is carried by sperm in pollen. The female genetic information is contained in eggs in the flowers. In the desert, as in a suburban or urban garden, wind, insects, and bats carry pollen from flower to flower. New combinations of genetic information are contained in seeds, which are produced in flowers.

A Big Bloom

Although it looked like El Niño might bring about a big bloom in 1998, no one knew for sure. For the seeds to grow, the rain must soak into the ground and it must come at a time when other conditions, such as temperature and the amount of light, are favorable for the seeds to germinate and develop into new plants.

The rains that came with El Niño were abundant. Some desert areas received five or six times more rain than usual. And, the rain came at key times. The winter weather was not too harsh and the spring became warm early. In short, the weather in 1998 was ideal for wildflowers.

And then, the spring wildflower season was spectacular! The prediction was correct. Not only did the flowers put on a show in the spring, some bloomed through the summer.

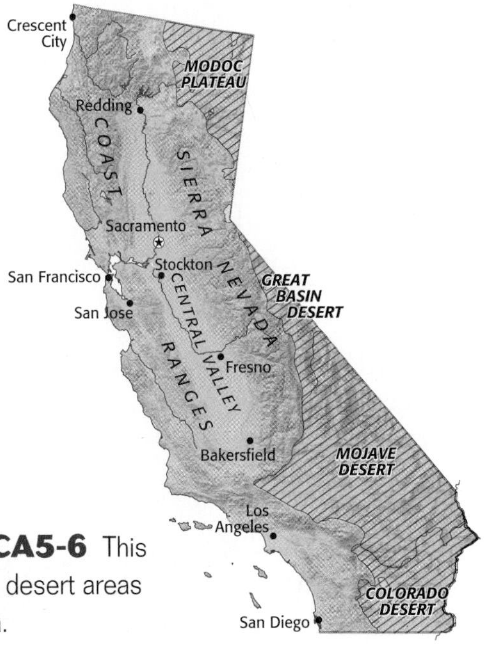

Figure CA5-6 This map shows desert areas in California.

Investigation & Experimentation

Standard 7c

Using field guides, seed catalogs, or other sources, identify native perennials and annuals growing in your community. Keep a log of the plants you find, their stage of growth, and the growing conditions. Track the plants to see how they change over several weeks and record your observations in your log. Then, try to explain your observations (whether the plants were sprouting, blooming, etc.) based on the conditions they experienced (weather conditions, whether someone watered them, etc.).

California CONTENT STANDARD 6

Resources

Content Standard 6
Sources of energy and materials differ in amounts, distribution, usefulness, and the time required for their formation.

Figure CA6-1 This windmill farm in the Tehachapi Mountains provides energy to homes and businesses.

6a. Energy Sources

Energy is necessary to have lights on, heat buildings, and run machines in factories. Where does that energy come from? There are many different sources of energy. Some energy sources such as solar power, wind power, and the power of flowing water are considered renewable. This means that more of the energy source will be available in a short time after some is used.

Not all energy sources are renewable, however. Nonrenewable resources are things which would take more than 100 years to be created again. Examples of nonrenewable energy sources are oil, natural gas, and coal. These are three of the most common fuels used throughout the world. The fact that these resources are nonrenewable is an important reason not to waste energy.

Useful Energy Sources

If renewable energy sources will never run out, why is it that people in California and around the world depend so much on nonrenewable energy sources? Wouldn't it make sense to use the renewable sources rather than the nonrenewable ones? Of course, it makes sense to use renewable energy sources whenever possible, but it is not always possible or practical to use those resources.

The usefulness of any energy source depends on how easy or difficult it is to convert to useful forms and the side effects of converting the energy source to a useful form. Wind power is a renewable resource that is available in most places. Wind can be used fairly directly for power in some cases, such as to move sailboats, or it can be converted by using windmills that are turned by wind and are attached to an

Figure CA6-2 Oil fields off the coast of California produce large amounts of petroleum.

electric generator. However, wind power is only useful in areas where there is wind much of the time. Another issue is that converting some resources into a useful form might cause other problems or pollution. For example, coal is a commonly used energy source. One problem with using coal to provide electricity is that burning coal leads to air pollution.

Investigation & Experimentation

Standard 7a
Develop a hypothesis for why solar power might not be useful for powering a car. Could the car be driven anytime? Could it be driven anywhere?

6b. Natural Resources

The last two sections have talked about energy resources. Are all the resources on Earth used for energy? No, natural resources are used for many purposes. People need clean water to drink and clean air to breathe. Clothing, appliances, paper, and other items are created from resources. Plants and animals are used for food. Energy sources are only one type of natural resource that you use every day.

Natural resources include air, freshwater, soil, rocks, minerals, petroleum, and forests. Like energy sources, some natural resources can be considered renewable, such as air, water, soil, and trees. These resources are not available immediately after being used (or polluted), but they can be replaced in a fairly short amount of time up to several years. Other natural resources such as rocks, minerals (including metals), and petroleum are nonrenewable. These resources are created so slowly that it could take millions of years to replace what is used up.

Investigation & Experimentation

Standard 7f
Look at a geologic map of California that shows the location of different natural resources. Where is there gold? Where is there oil? What other minerals or rocks are there?

6c. Origin of Items

Trees in forests all over California are pretty to look at and fun to hike past. But, trees are also used to make many things. The wood from trees is used to build houses and furniture, boats and docks, and many other things. Paper is also made from trees.

Lots of common objects are made from metals. Jewelry is often made from gold or silver. Cans for soda are made from aluminum and cans for many foods are made from steel, which contains iron.

Bottles, windows, and mirrors are made from glass which is made from sand. Gasoline is made from natural gas and petroleum and is used to power cars and trucks as well as some machines. Clothing, blankets, and other items are made from cotton, which grows in fertile soil under certain weather conditions. These are just a few examples of the natural resources used to make common items.

Figure CA6-3 Forests provide many useful things such as wood, paper, habitat for animals and plants, and recreation for humans. This forest is in King's Canyon National Park, California.

Investigation & Experimentation

Standard 7d

Choose a few common objects and find out what they are made of. Where are those resources found? Share your findings with your classmates. Are you surprised about what something is made of?

Going Further

To learn more about resources, see:

6a. Chapter 14, Section 2, Energy from the Sun
Chapter 25, Section 3, Compounds and Mixtures
Chapter 4, Section 1, Energy Resources
Chapter 4, Section 2, Alternative Energy Resources
Chapter 4, Section 4, Land

6b. Chapter 14, Section 2, Energy from the Sun
Chapter 4, Section 1, Energy Resources
Chapter 4, Section 2, Alternative Energy Resources
Chapter 4, Section 3, Water
Chapter 4, Section 4, Land

6c. Chapter 25, Section 1, Structure of Matter
Chapter 25, Section 2, Elements
Chapter 25, Section 3, Compounds and Mixtures

"Green" Energy

SCIENCE FOCUS

Read this case study to learn about one way electricity is generated in California and what you can do to decrease California's dependence on nonrenewable resources.

Correlates with Content Standard 6

Electric Power

Flip a switch, and the light comes on. Where did that electricity come from? If the light is in California, the answer may be more complicated than you think.

California is a large consumer of electricity. In fact, California consumes more electricity than many other countries in the world. California imports some of the electrical energy it consumes. With this enormous demand, it shouldn't surprise you that California's electricity has several different sources. What are sources of electric power?

In California, most electricity is generated from natural gas plants, large hydroelectric plants (such as those in dams), nuclear power plants, and coal-burning plants. They provide large amounts of electricity at low cost for consumers. However, there are problems with depending upon only these sources for power. Natural gas and coal are fossil fuels. Thus, they are nonrenewable resources. A nonrenewable resource is one that exists in a limited amount and cannot be replaced in a period of 100 years or less. In addition, the burning of fossil fuels in electrical power plants pollutes the air.

Large-scale hydroelectric plants use the movement of water to generate electricity. Hydroelectric power is nonpolluting, and is a renewable resource. However, the damming of many of California's rivers has resulted in flooding problems, particularly in California's Central Valley. Electricity is also produced in nuclear power plants, which are basically nonpolluting. Many people, however, are concerned about the safety of nuclear power plants. An accident at a nuclear power plant has the potential to seriously harm a widespread area.

Figure CA6-4 This is a hydroelectic plant at Shasta Dam, northern California.

Alternative Sources

California's electricity is produced by other sources as well, though on a smaller scale. Most alternative sources are nonpolluting and use renewable resources.

Figure CA6-5 The Solar Two plant is located near Barstow, California.

These so-called "green" energy sources include the sun, the wind, and heat from Earth. Electricity produced from solar energy has been relatively expensive in the past, but this is no longer true. Improved technology has produced more efficient methods. In one, solar energy heats a substance (such as water or even salt) to a high temperature. This heat then is used to produce steam to run generators.

The second method of solar conversion uses photovoltaic cells. In a photovoltaic cell, light is converted to electricity when it interacts with sheets of a crystalline material, such as silica. These cells have no moving parts and produce no pollution, but they also produce no electricity in the dark. Thus, some cells are attached to batteries, which can store electricity for use later.

Electricity can also be produced from the wind, using a familiar and simple machine—the windmill. Efficient windmills are placed, sometimes by the hundreds, in windy areas such as mountain passes. The turning of the windmills powers electric generators. Again, this is use of a nonpolluting, renewable energy source, but with a drawback. Some fields of windmills lay in the normal flight paths of some types of birds. Birds may fly into the windmills and be killed. This problem might be alleviated by carefully studying potential locations, and ruling out those where wildlife would be at risk.

A third type of alternative source for electricity is geothermal energy. In some areas, heat from Earth's interior warms groundwater that overlies it, producing steam. Steam from Earth can be harnessed to power electrical generators. Geothermal energy is renewable—heat will continue to be produced by Earth, but sometimes the water is depleted and must be pumped back into the ground.

Investigation & Experimentation

Standards 7a, 7d

There are several "green" mixes of electricity sources offered by California energy companies. Different companies rely on different sources and may offer different pricing. Develop a hypothesis stating which type of the alternative sources discussed is the most cost efficient. Using the library or the Internet, obtain pricing information and energy sources for several California energy companies. Use these data to support or reject your hypothesis.

Photo Credits

CA2 Craig Aurness/Corbis Los Angeles; **CA3** Chuck Place; **CA4** Jim Corwin/Photo Researchers; **CA5** Spencer Grant/Photo Researchers; **CA6** David Matherly/Visuals Unlimited; **CA7** Russell D. Curtis/Photo Researchers; **CA8** Jayson Mellom/AP/Wide World Photos; **CA9** (l)Bill Morson/Liaison International, (r)Craig Aurness/Corbis Los Angeles; **CA10** Tom Bean/DRK Photos; **CA11 CA12** Tom Southern/Sky Shots Aerial Photography; **CA13** Mark E. Gibson; **CA14** (t)Mark E. Gibson, (b)Aaron Haupt; **CA15** Chuck Place; **CA16** (l)Lowell Georgia/Photo Researchers, (r)Porterfield/Chickering/ Science Source/Photo Researchers; **CA17** Simon Fraser/Science Photo Library/Photo Researchers; **CA18** Chuck Place; **CA19** Peter Menzel/Stock Boston; **CA20** Ed Cooper/PhotoFile; **CA21** Bill Ross/Corbis Los Angeles; **CA22** Audrey Gibson; **CA23** Chuck Place; **CA24** (t)Dan Suzio/Photo Researchers, (b)Chuck Place; **CA26** (l)John Elk/Stock Boston, (r)Roy Bishop/Stock Boston; **CA27** Chuck Place; **CA28** Chuck Place; **CA29** Peter Skinner/Photo Researchers; **CA30** Greg Probst/Stock Boston; **CA31** Gerald L. French/PhotoFile; **CA32** Peter Menzel/Stock Boston.

P/N G86332.11

Appendices

Appendix A

Safety in the Science Classroom

1. Always obtain your teacher's permission to begin an investigation.
2. Study the procedure. If you have questions, ask your teacher. Be sure you understand any safety symbols shown on the page.
3. Use the safety equipment provided for you. Goggles and a safety apron should be worn during an investigation.
4. Always slant test tubes away from yourself and others when heating them.
5. Never eat or drink in the lab, and never use lab glassware as food or drink containers. Never inhale chemicals. Do not taste any substances or draw any material into a tube with your mouth.
6. If you spill any chemical, wash it off immediately with water. Report the spill immediately to your teacher.
7. Know the location and proper use of the fire extinguisher, safety shower, fire blanket, first aid kit, and fire alarm.
8. Keep all materials away from open flames. Tie back long hair and loose clothing.
9. If a fire should break out in the classroom, or if your clothing should catch fire, smother it with the fire blanket or a coat, or get under a safety shower. NEVER RUN.
10. Report any accident or injury, no matter how small, to your teacher.

Follow these procedures as you clean up your work area.

1. Turn off the water and gas. Disconnect electrical devices.
2. Return all materials to their proper places.
3. Dispose of chemicals and other materials as directed by your teacher. Place broken glass and solid substances in the proper containers. Never discard materials in the sink.
4. Clean your work area.
5. Wash your hands thoroughly after working in the laboratory.

Table A-1

First Aid	
Injury	**Safe Response**
Burns	Apply cold water. Call your teacher immediately.
Cuts and bruises	Stop any bleeding by applying direct pressure. Cover cuts with a clean dressing. Apply cold compresses to bruises. Call your teacher immediately.
Fainting	Leave the person lying down. Loosen any tight clothing and keep crowds away. Call your teacher immediately.
Foreign matter in eye	Flush with plenty of water. Use eyewash bottle or fountain.
Poisoning	Note the suspected poisoning agent and call your teacher immediately.
Any spills on skin	Flush with large amounts of water or use safety shower. Call your teacher immediately.

Appendix B

SI/Metric to English Conversions

	When you want to convert:	To:	Multiply by:
Length	inches	centimeters	2.54
	centimeters	inches	0.39
	feet	meters	0.30
	meters	feet	3.28
	yards	meters	0.91
	meters	yards	1.09
	miles	kilometers	1.61
	kilometers	miles	0.62
Mass and Weight*	ounces	grams	28.35
	grams	ounces	0.04
	pounds	kilograms	0.45
	kilograms	pounds	2.2
	tons (short)	tonnes (metric tons)	0.91
	tonnes (metric tons)	tons (short)	1.10
	pounds	newtons	4.45
	newtons	pounds	0.23
Volume	cubic inches	cubic centimeters	16.39
	cubic centimeters	cubic inches	0.06
	cubic feet	cubic meters	0.03
	cubic meters	cubic feet	35.30
	liters	quarts	1.06
	liters	gallons	0.26
	gallons	liters	3.78
Area	square inches	square centimeters	6.45
	square centimeters	square inches	0.16
	square feet	square meters	0.09
	square meters	square feet	10.76
	square miles	square kilometers	2.59
	square kilometers	square miles	0.39
	hectares	acres	2.47
	acres	hectares	0.40
Temperature	Fahrenheit	5/9 (°F − 32) =	Celsius
	Celsius	9/5 (°C) + 32 =	Fahrenheit

*Weight as measured in standard Earth gravity

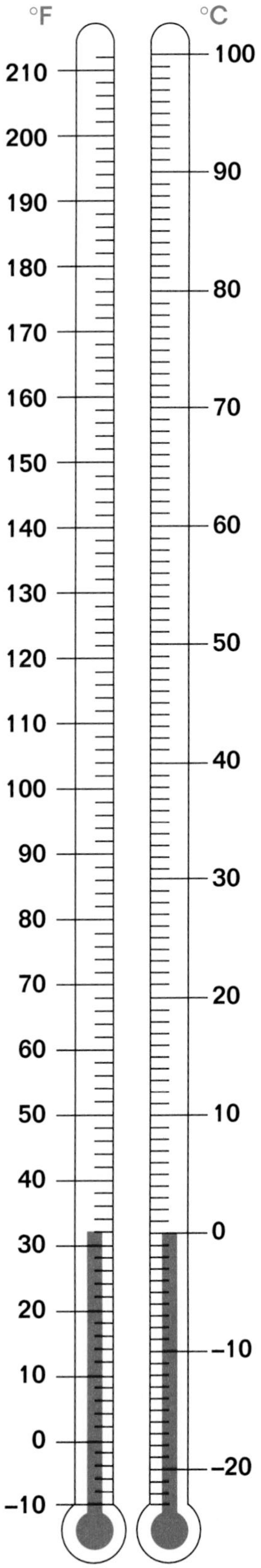

Appendix C

SI Units of Measurement

Table C-1

SI Base Units					
Measurement	**Unit**	**Symbol**	**Measurement**	**Unit**	**Symbol**
length	meter	m	temperature	kelvin	K
mass	kilogram	kg	amount of substance	mole	mol
time	second	s			

Table C-2

Units Derived from SI Base Units		
Measurement	**Unit**	**Symbol**
energy	joule	J
force	newton	N
frequency	hertz	Hz
potential difference	volt	V
power	watt	W
pressure	pascal	Pa

Table C-3

Common SI Prefixes					
Prefix	**Symbol**	**Multiplier**	**Prefix**	**Symbol**	**Multiplier**
	Greater than 1			Less than 1	
mega-	M	1 000 000	*deci-*	d	0.1
kilo-	k	1 000	*centi-*	c	0.01
hecto-	h	100	*milli-*	m	0.001
deca-	da	10	*micro-*	*μ*	0.000 001

Appendix D

Care and Use of a Microscope

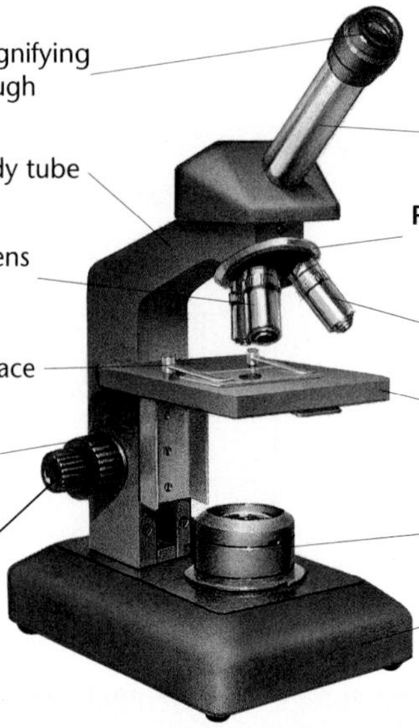
Eyepiece Contains a magnifying lens you look through
Arm Supports the body tube
Low-power objective Contains the lens with low-power magnification
Stage clips Hold the microscope slide in place
Coarse adjustment Focuses the image under low power
Fine adjustment Sharpens the image under high and low magnification
Body tube Connects the eyepiece to the revolving nosepiece
Revolving nosepiece Holds and turns the objectives into viewing position
High-power objective Contains the lens with the highest magnification
Stage Supports the microscope slide
Light source Allows light to reflect upward through the diaphragm, the specimen, and the lenses
Base Provides support for the microscope

Care of a Microscope

1. Always carry the microscope holding the arm with one hand and supporting the base with the other hand.
2. Don't touch the lenses with your fingers.
3. Never lower the coarse adjustment knob when looking through the eyepiece lens.
4. Always focus first with the low-power objective.
5. Don't use the coarse adjustment knob when the high-power objective is in place.
6. Store the microscope covered.

Using a Microscope

1. Place the microscope on a flat surface that is clear of objects. The arm should be toward you.
2. Look through the eyepiece. Adjust the diaphragm so that light comes through the opening in the stage.
3. Place a slide on the stage so that the specimen is in the field of view. Hold it firmly in place by using the stage clips.
4. Always focus first with the coarse adjustment and the low-power objective lens. Once the object is in focus on low power, turn the nosepiece until the high-power objective is in place. Use ONLY the fine adjustment to focus with the high-power objective lens.

Making a Wet-Mount Slide

1. Carefully place the item you want to look at in the center of a clean, glass slide. Make sure the sample is thin enough for light to pass through.
2. Use a dropper to place one or two drops of water on the sample.
3. Hold a clean coverslip by the edges and place it at one edge of the drop of water. Slowly lower the coverslip onto the drop of water until it lies flat.
4. If you have too much water or a lot of air bubbles, touch the edge of a paper towel to the edge of the coverslip to draw off extra water and force out air.

Appendix E

Diversity of Life: Classification of Living Organisms

Scientists use a six-kingdom system of classification of organisms. In this system, there are two kingdoms of organisms, Kingdoms Archaebacteria and Eubacteria, which contain organisms that do not have a nucleus and lack membrane-bound structures in the cytoplasm of their cells. The members of the other four kingdoms have cells which contain a nucleus and structures in the cytoplasm that are surrounded by membranes. These kingdoms are Kingdom Protista, Kingdom Fungi, the Kingdom Plantae, and the Kingdom Animalia.

Kingdom Archaebacteria

One-celled prokaryotes; absorb food from surroundings or make their own food by chemosynthesis; found in extremely harsh environments including salt ponds, hot springs, swamps, and deep-sea hydrothermal vents.

Kingdom Eubacteria

Cyanobacteria one-celled prokaryotes; make their own food; contain chlorophyll; some species form colonies; most are blue-green

Bacteria one-celled prokaryotes; most absorb food from their surroundings; some are photosynthetic; many are parasites; round, spiral, or rod-shaped

Kingdom Protista

Phylum Euglenophyta one-celled; can photosynthesize or take in food; most have one flagellum; euglenoids

Phylum Bacillariophyta one-celled; make their own food through photosynthesis; have unique double shells made of silica; diatoms

Phylum Dinoflagellata one-celled; make their own food through photosynthesis; contain red pigments; have two flagella; dinoflagellates

Phylum Chlorophyta one-celled, many-celled, or colonies; contain chlorophyll; make their own food; live on land, in fresh water, or salt water; green algae

Phylum Rhodophyta most are many-celled; photosynthetic; contain red pigments; most live in deep saltwater environments; red algae

Phylum Phaeophyta most are many-celled; photosynthetic; contain brown pigments; most live in saltwater environments; brown algae

Phylum Foraminifera many-celled; take in food; primarily marine; shells constructed of calcium carbonate, or made from grains of sand; forams

Phylum Myxomycota
Slime Mold
Magnification: 5×

Phylum Chlorophyta
Desmids Magnification: 50×

Appendix E

Phylum Rhizopoda one-celled; take in food; move by means of pseudopods; free-living or parasitic; amoebas

Phylum Zoomastigina one-celled; take in food; have one or more flagella; free-living or parasitic; zoomastigotes

Phylum Ciliophora one-celled; take in food; have large numbers of cilia; ciliates

Phylum Sporozoa one-celled; take in food; no means of movement; parasites in animals; sporozoans

Phylum Myxomycota and Acrasiomycota: one- or many-celled; absorb food; change form during life cycle; cellular and plasmodial slime molds

Phylum Oomycota many-celled; live in fresh or salt water; are either parasites or decomposers; water molds, rusts and downy mildews

Kingdom Fungi

Phylum Zygomycota many-celled; absorb food; spores are produced in sporangia; zygote fungi; bread mold

Phylum Ascomycota one- and many-celled; absorb food; spores produced in asci; sac fungi; yeast

Phylum Basidiomycota many-celled; absorb food; spores produced in basidia; club fungi; mushrooms

Phylum Deuteromycota: members with unknown reproductive structures; imperfect fungi; penicillin

Lichens organisms formed by symbiotic relationship between an ascomycote or a basidiomycote and green alga or cyanobacterium

Kingdom Plantae

Non-seed Plants

Division Bryophyta nonvascular plants; reproduce by spores produced in capsules; many-celled; green; grow in moist land environments; mosses and liverworts

Division Lycophyta many-celled vascular plants; spores produced in conelike structures; live on land; are photosynthetic; club mosses

Division Sphenophyta vascular plants; ribbed and jointed stems; scalelike leaves; spores produced in conelike structures; horsetails

Division Pterophyta vascular plants; leaves called fronds; spores produced in clusters of sporangia called sori; live on land or in water; ferns

Division Bryophyta
Liverwort

Lichens
British soldier lichen × 3

Appendix E

Seed Plants

Division Ginkgophyta: deciduous gymnosperms; only one living species; fan-shaped leaves with branching veins; reproduces with seeds; ginkgos

Division Cycadophyta: palmlike gymnosperms; large featherlike leaves; produce seeds in cones; cycads

Division Coniferophyta: deciduous or evergreen gymnosperms; trees or shrubs; needlelike or scalelike leaves; seeds produced in cones; conifers

Division Gnetophyta: shrubs or woody vines; seeds produced in cones; division contains only three genera; gnetum

Division Anthophyta: dominant group of plants; ovules protected in an ovary; sperm carried to ovules by pollen tube; produce flowers and seeds in fruits; flowering plants

Kingdom Animalia

Phylum Porifera: aquatic organisms that lack true tissues and organs; they are asymmetrical and sessile; sponges

Phylum Cnidaria: radially symmetrical organisms; have a digestive cavity with one opening; most have tentacles armed with stinging cells; live in aquatic environments singly or in colonies; includes jellyfish, corals, hydra, and sea anemones

Phylum Platyhelminthes: bilaterally symmetrical worms; have flattened bodies; digestive system has one opening; parasitic and free-living species; flatworms

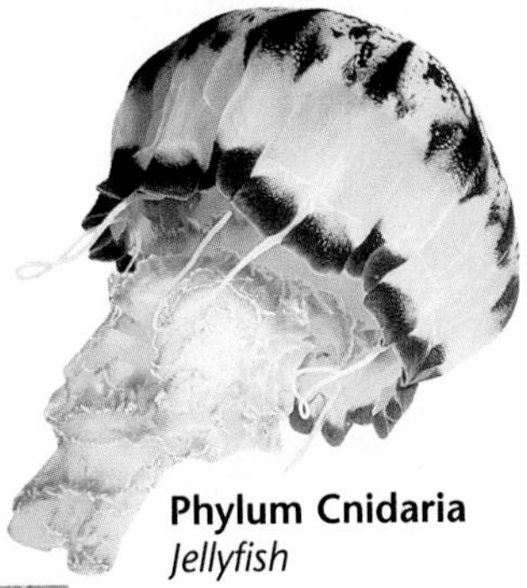

Phylum Cnidaria
Jellyfish

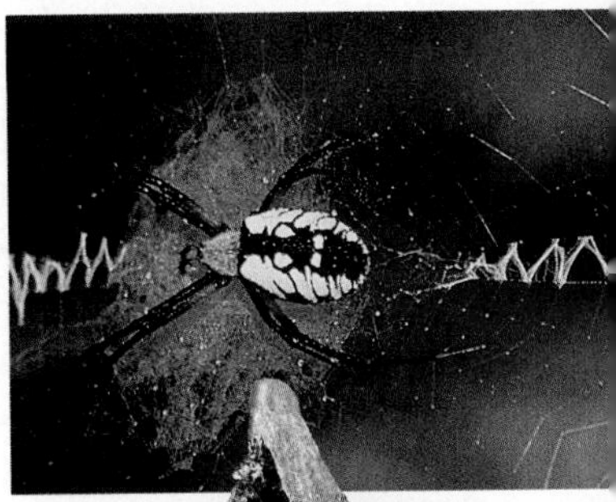

Phylum Arthopoda
Orb Weaver Spider

Division Coniferophyta
Pine cone

Division Anthophyta
Strawberry Blossoms

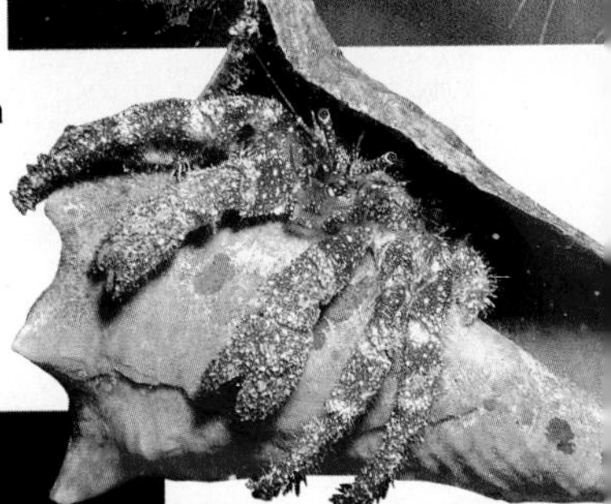

Phylum Arthropoda
Hermit Crab

Phylum Mollusca
Florida Fighting Conch

Phylum Annelida
Sabellid Worms Feather Duster

Division Anthophyta
Strawberries

Appendix E

Phylum Nematoda: round, bilaterally symmetrical body; digestive system with two openings; many parasitic forms but mostly free-living roundworms

Phylum Mollusca: soft-bodied animals, many with a hard shell; a mantle covers the soft body; aquatic and terrestrial species; includes clams, snails, squid, and octopuses

Phylum Annelida: bilaterally symmetrical worms; have round, segmented bodies; terrestrial and aquatic species; includes earthworms, leeches, and marine polychaetes

Phylum Arthropoda: largest phylum of organisms; have segmented bodies; pairs of jointed appendages; have hard exoskeletons; terrestrial and aquatic species; includes insects, crustaceans, spiders, and horseshoe crabs

Phylum Echinodermata: marine organisms; have spiny or leathery skin; water-vascular system with tube feet; radial symmetry; includes sea stars, sand dollars, and sea urchins

Phylum Chordata: organisms with internal skeletons; specialized body systems; paired appendages; all at some time have a notochord, dorsal nerve cord, gill slits, and a tail; include fish, amphibians, reptiles, birds, and mammals

Phylum Arthropoda
Giant Swallowtail Butterfly

Phylum Echinodermata
Blood Sea Star and Red Sea Urchin

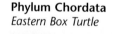

Phylum Chordata
Eastern Box Turtle

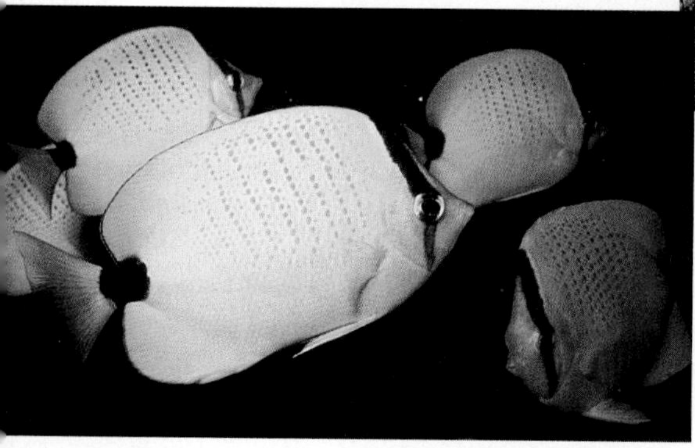

Phylum Chordata
Lemon Butterfly fish

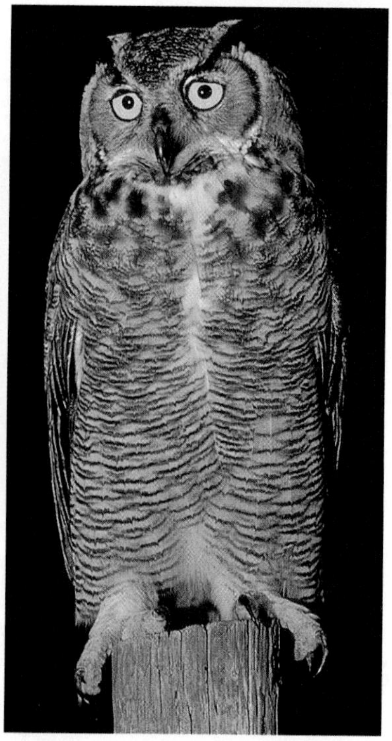

Phylum Chordata
Great Horned Owl

Appendix F

Minerals

Mineral (formula)	Color	Streak	Hardness	Breakage pattern	Uses and other properties
graphite (C)	black to gray	black to gray	1–1.5	basal cleavage (scales)	pencil lead, lubricants for locks, rods to control some small nuclear reactions, battery poles
galena (PbS)	gray	gray to black	2.5	cubic cleavage perfect	source of lead, used in pipes, shields for X rays, fishing equipment sinkers
hematite (Fe_2O_3)	black or reddish brown	reddish brown	5.5–6.5	irregular fracture	source of iron; converted to "pig" iron, made into steel
magnetite (Fe_3O_4)	black	black	6	conchoidal fracture	source of iron, naturally magnetic, called lodestone
pyrite (FeS_2)	light, brassy, yellow	greenish black	5–6.5	uneven fracture	source of iron, "fool's gold"
talc ($Mg_3Si_4O_{10}(OH)_2$)	white greenish	white	1	cleavage in one direction	used for talcum powder, sculptures, paper, and tabletops
gypsum ($CaSO_4 \cdot 2H_2O$)	colorless, gray, white brown	white	2	basal cleavage	used in plaster of paris and dry wall for building construction
sphalerite (ZnS)	brown, reddish brown, greenish	light to dark brown	3.5–4	cleavage in six directions	main ore of zinc; used in paints, dyes and medicine
muscovite ($KAl_3Si_3O_{10}(OH)_2$)	white, light gray, yellow, rose, green	colorless	2–2.5	basal cleavage	occurs in large flexible plates; used as an insulator in electrical equipment, lubricant
biotite ($K(Mg, Fe)_3(AlSi_3O_{10})(OH)_2$)	black to dark brown	colorless	2.5–3	basal cleavage	occurs in large flexible plates
halite (NaCl)	colorless, red, white, blue	colorless	2.5	cubic cleavage	salt; soluble in water; a preservative

Appendix F

Minerals

Mineral (formula)	Color	Streak	Hardness	Breakage pattern	Uses and other properties
calcite ($CaCO_3$)	colorless, white, pale blue	colorless, white	3	cleavage in three directions	fizzes when HCl is added; used in cements and other building materials
dolomite ($CaMg(CO_3)_2$)	colorless, white, pink green, gray black	white	3.5–4	cleavage in three directions	concrete and cement; used as an ornamental building stone
fluorite (CaF_2)	colorless, white, blue green, red yellow, purple	colorless	4	cleavage in four directions	used in the manufacture of optical equipment; glows under ultraviolet light
hornblende ($(CaNa)_{2\text{-}3}(Mg,Al,Fe)_5(Al,Si)_2Si_6O_{22}(OH)_2$)	green to black	gray to white	5–6	cleavage in two directions	will transmit light on thin edges; 6-sided cross section
feldspar ($KAlSi_3O_8$) ($NaAlSi_3O_8$) ($CaAl_2Si_2O_8$)	colorless, white to gray, green	colorless	6	two cleavage planes meet at ~90° angle	used in the manufacture of ceramics
augite ($(Ca, Na)(Mg, Fe, Al)(Al, Si)_2O_6$)	black	colorless	6	cleavage in two directions	square or 8-sided cross section
olivine ($(Mg, Fe)_2SiO_4$)	olive, green	none	6.5–7	conchoidal fracture	gemstones, refractory sand
quartz (SiO_2)	colorless, various colors	none	7	conchoidal fracture	used in glass manufacture, electronic equipment, radios, computers, watches, gemstones

Appendix G

Rocks

Rock Type	Rock Name	Characteristics
Igneous (intrusive)	Granite	Large mineral grains of quartz, feldspar, hornblende, and mica. Usually light in color.
	Diorite	Large mineral grains of feldspar, hornblende, mica. Less quartz than granite. Intermediate in color.
	Gabbro	Large mineral grains of feldspar, hornblende, augite, olivine, and mica. No quartz. Dark in color.
Igneous (extrusive)	Rhyolite	Small mineral grains of quartz, feldspar, hornblende, and mica or no visible grains. Light in color.
	Andesite	Small mineral grains of feldspar, hornblende, mica or no visible grains. Less quartz than rhyolite. Intermediate in color.
	Basalt	Small mineral grains of feldspar, hornblende, augite, olivine, mica or no visible grains. No quartz. Dark in color.
	Obsidian	Glassy texture. No visible grains. Volcanic glass. Fracture looks like broken glass.
	Pumice	Frothy texture. Floats. Usually light in color.
Sedimentary (detrital)	Conglomerate	Coarse-grained. Gravel or pebble-sized grains.
	Sandstone	Sand-sized grains 1/16 to 2 mm in size.
	Siltstone	Grains are smaller than sand but larger than clay.
	Shale	Smallest grains. Usually dark in color.
Sedimentary (chemical or biochemical)	Limestone	Major mineral is calcite. Usually forms in oceans, lakes, rivers, and caves. Often contains fossils.
	Coal	Occurs in swampy, low-lying areas. Compacted layers of organic material, mainly plant remains.
Sedimentary (chemical)	Rock Salt	Commonly forms by the evaporation of seawater.
Metamorphic (foliated)	Gneiss	Well-developed banding because of alternating layers of different minerals, usually of different colors. Common parent rock is granite.
	Schist	Well-defined parallel arrangement of flat, sheet-like minerals, mainly micas. Common parent rocks are shale, phyllite.
	Phyllite	Shiny or silky appearance. May look wrinkled. Common parent rocks are shale, slate.
	Slate	Harder, denser, and shinier than shale. Common parent rock is shale.
Metamorphic (non-foliated)	Marble	Interlocking calcite or dolomite crystals. Common parent rock is limestone.
	Soapstone	Composed mainly of the mineral talc. Soft with a greasy feel.
	Quartzite	Hard and well cemented with interlocking quartz crystals. Common parent rock is sandstone.

Appendix H

Topographic Map Symbols

- Primary highway, hard surface
- Secondary highway, hard surface
- Light-duty road, hard or Improved surface
- Unimproved road
- Railroad: single track and multiple track
- Railroads in juxtaposition

- Buildings
- Schools, church, and cemetery — cem
- Buildings (barn, warehouse, etc)
- Wells other than water (labeled as to type) — oil, gas
- Tanks: oil, water, etc. (labeled only if water) — water
- Located or landmark object; windmill
- Open pit, mine, or quarry; prospect

- Marsh (swamp)
- Wooded marsh
- Woods or brushwood
- Vineyard
- Land subject to controlled inundation
- Submerged marsh
- Mangrove
- Orchard
- Scrub
- Urban area

- Spot elevation — ×7369
- Water elevation — 670

- Index contour
- Supplementary contour
- Intermediate contour
- Depression contours

- Boundaries: National
  - State
  - County, parish, municipal
  - Civil township, precinct, town, barrio
  - Incorporated city, village, town, hamlet
  - Reservation, National or State
  - Small park, cemetery, airport, etc.
  - Land grant
- Township or range line, United States land survey
- Township or range line, approximate location

- Perennial streams
- Elevated aqueduct
- Water well and spring
- Small rapids
- Large rapids
- Intermittent lake
- Intermittent streams
- Aqueduct tunnel
- Glacier
- Small falls
- Large falls
- Dry lake bed

Appendix I

Weather Map Symbols

Sample Plotted Report at Each Station

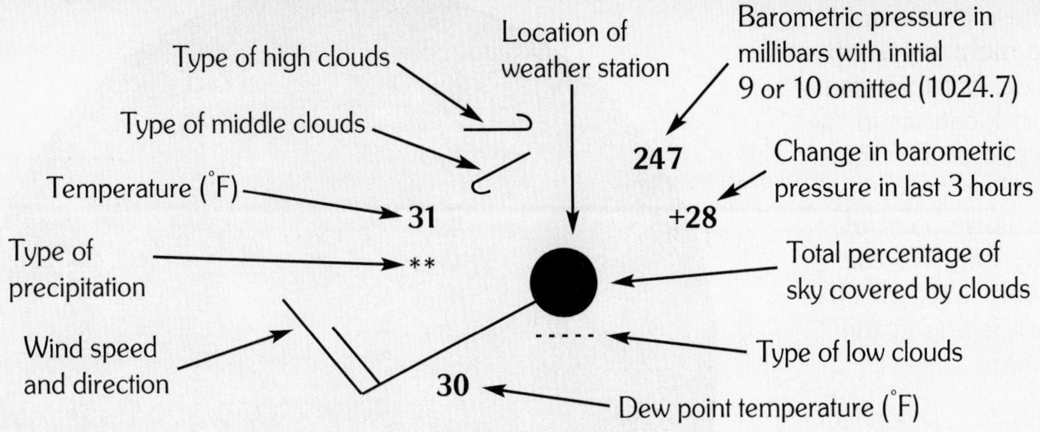

Type of high clouds
Type of middle clouds
Temperature (°F)
Type of precipitation
Wind speed and direction
Location of weather station
Barometric pressure in millibars with initial 9 or 10 omitted (1024.7)
247
Change in barometric pressure in last 3 hours
+28
31
**
Total percentage of sky covered by clouds

Type of low clouds
30
Dew point temperature (°F)

Sample Plotted Report at Each Station

Precipitation	
≡	Fog
★	Snow
●	Rain
⌈↘	Thunder-storm
,	Drizzle
▽	Showers

Wind Speed and direction	
○	0 knots; calm
╱	1-2 knots
╱˅	3-7 knots
╲╱	7-12 knots
╲╲╱	14-17 knots
╲╲╲╱	18-22 knots
╲╲╲╲╱	23-27 knots
◣╱	48-52 knots
1 knot = 1.852 km/h	

Sky coverage	
○	No cover
⦶	1/10 or less
◔	2/10 to 3/10
◔	4/10
◑	1/2
⊕	6/10
◕	7/10
⦸	Overcast with openings
●	Complete overcast

Some types of high clouds	
—⊃	Scattered cirrus
—⊃⊃	Dense cirrus in patches
⊃—⊂	Veil of cirrus covering entire sky
—⊂	Cirrus not covering entire sky

Some types of middle clouds	
∠	Thin altostratus layer
∠∠	Thick altostratus layer
⊂╱	Thin altostratus in patches
⊂⊂╱	Thin altostratus in bands

Some types of low clouds	
⌓	Cumulus of fair weather
◡	Stratocumulus
-----	Fractocumulus of bad weather
—	Stratus of fair weather

Fronts and pressure systems	
(H) or High	Center of high-or
(L) or Low	low-pressure system
▲▲▲▲	Cold front
◠◠◠◠	Warm Front
▲◠▲◠	Occluded front
◠▼◠▼	Stationary front

Appendix J

Star Charts

Shown here are star charts for viewing stars in the northern hemisphere during the four different seasons. These charts are drawn from the night sky at about 35° north latitude, but they can be used for most locations in the northern hemisphere. The lines on the charts outline major constellations. The dense band of stars is the Milky Way. To use, hold the chart vertically, with the direction you are facing at the bottom of the map.

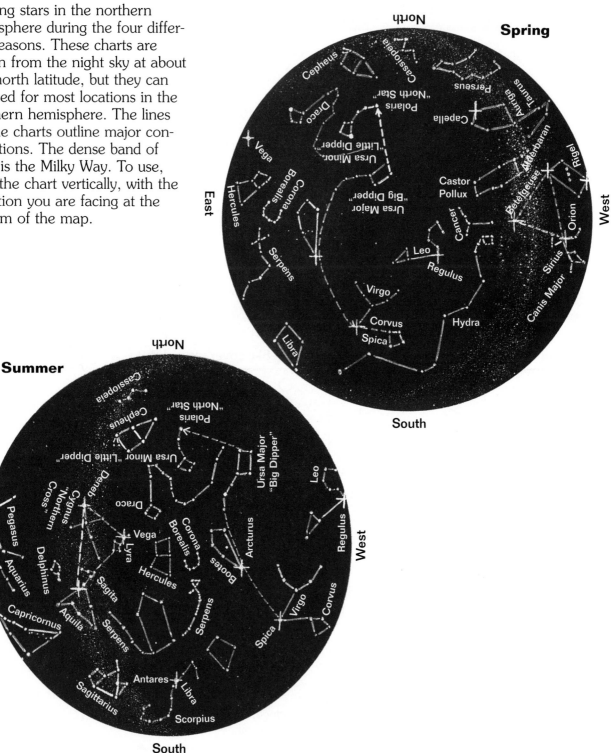

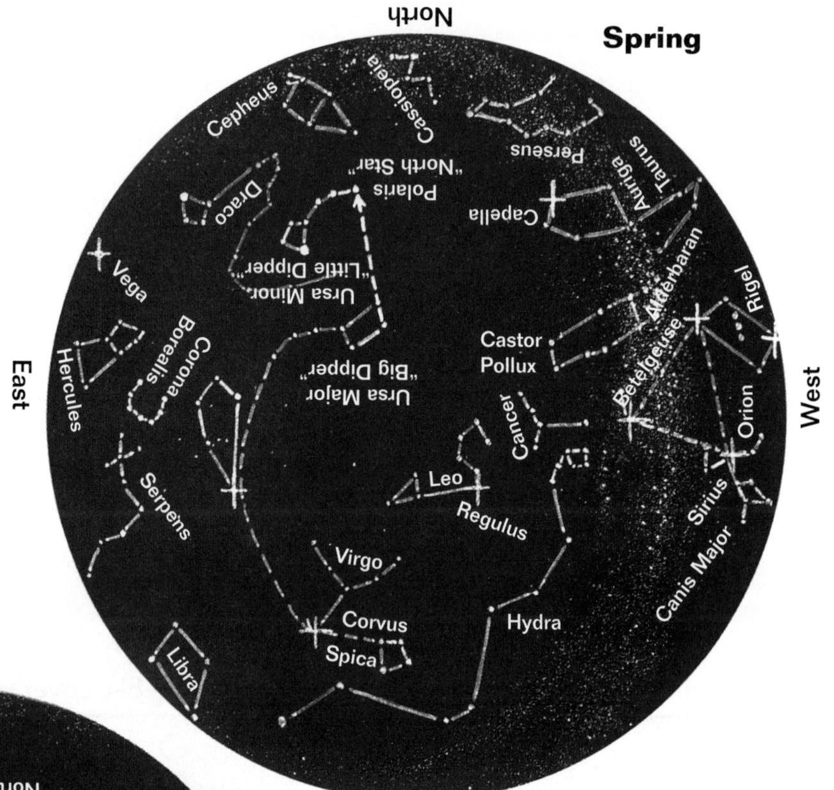

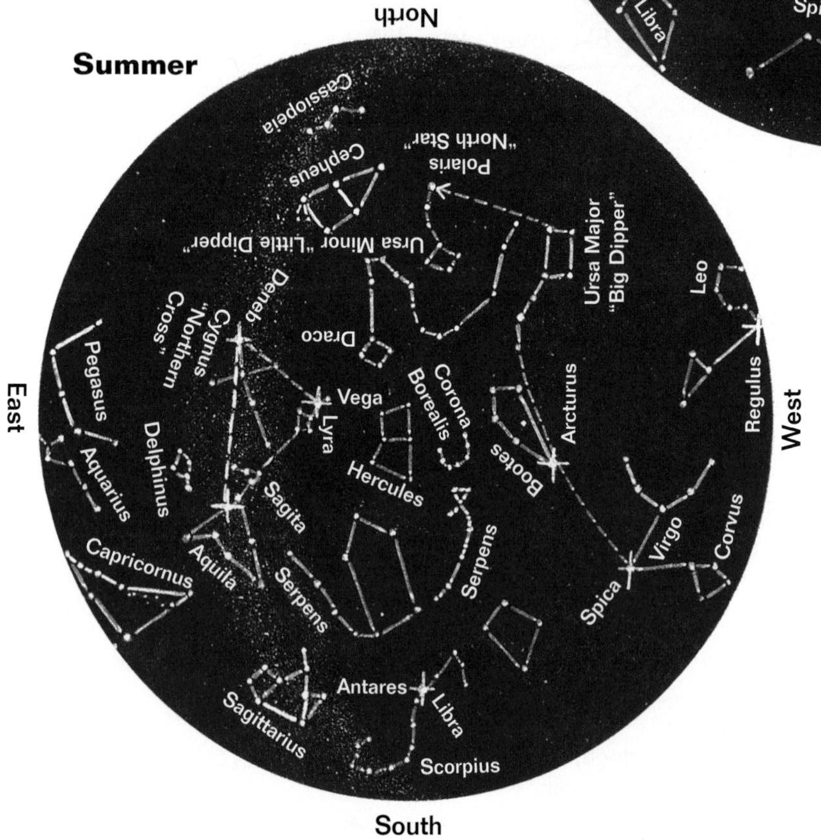

Autumn

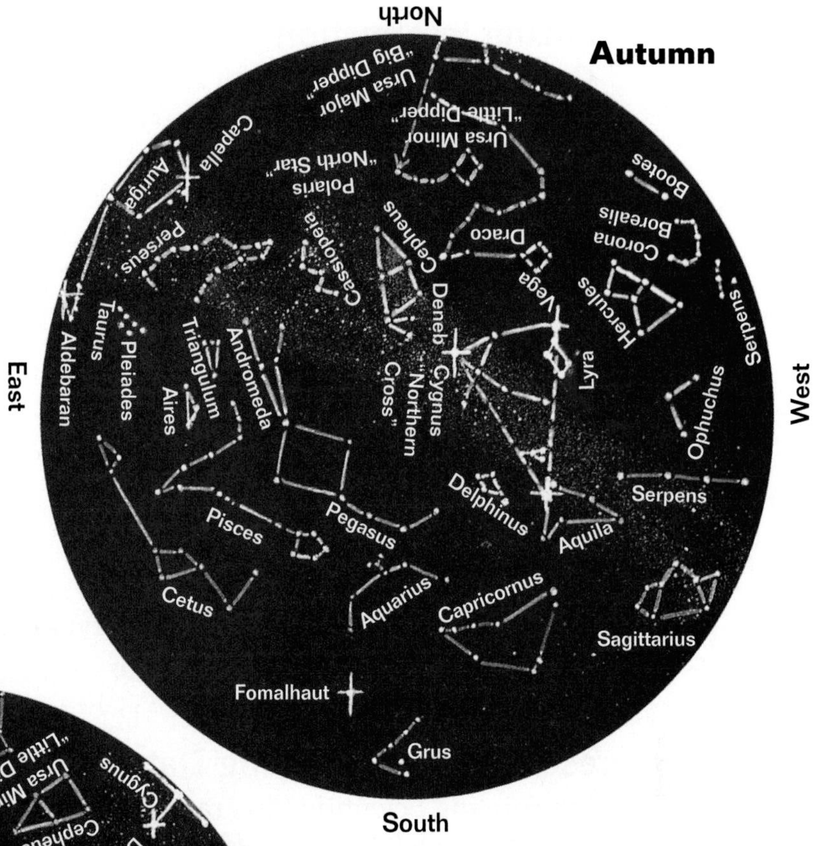

Winter

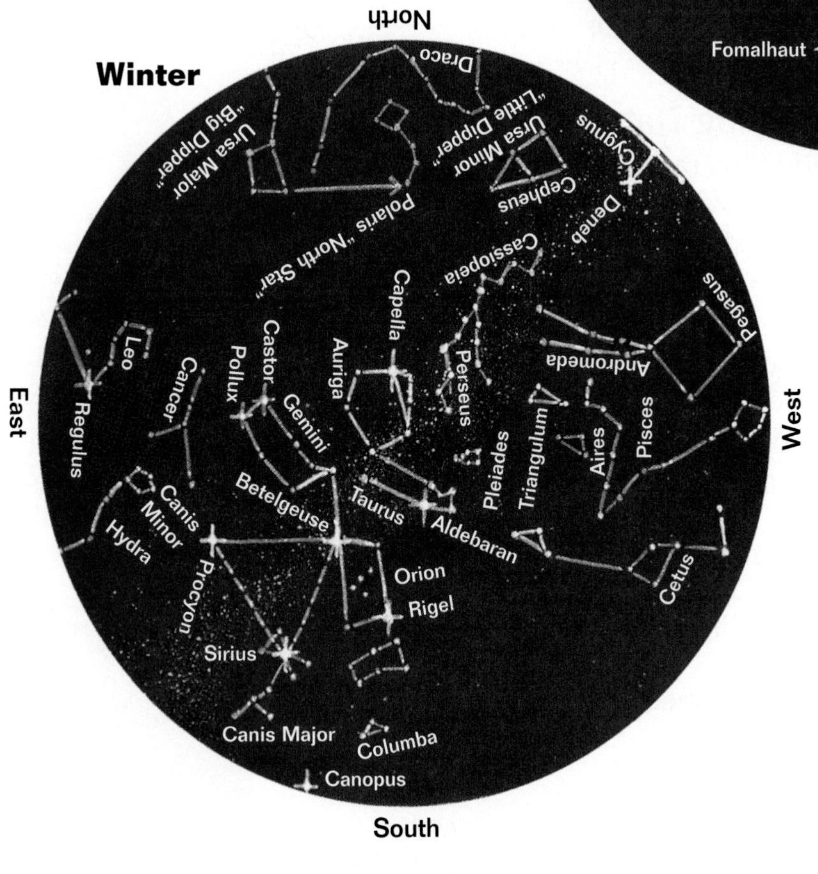

Skill Handbook

Table of Contents

Organizing Information

Communicating

The communication of ideas is an important part of our everyday lives. Whether reading a book, writing a letter, or watching a television program, people everywhere are expressing opinions and sharing information with one another. Writing in your Science Journal allows you to express your opinions and demonstrate your knowledge of the information presented on a subject. When writing, keep in mind the purpose of the assignment and the audience with which you are communicating.

Examples Science Journal assignments vary greatly. They may ask you to take a viewpoint other than your own; perhaps you will be a scientist, a TV reporter, or a committee member of a local environmental group. Maybe you will be expressing your opinions to a member of Congress, a doctor, or to the editor of your local newspaper, as shown in **Figure 1.** Sometimes, Science Journal writing may allow you to summarize information in the form of an outline, a letter, or in a paragraph.

Figure 1 A Science Journal entry

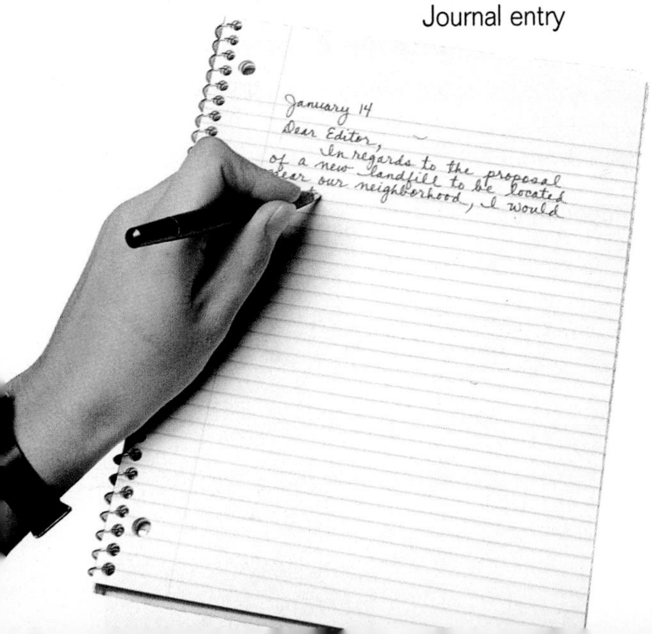

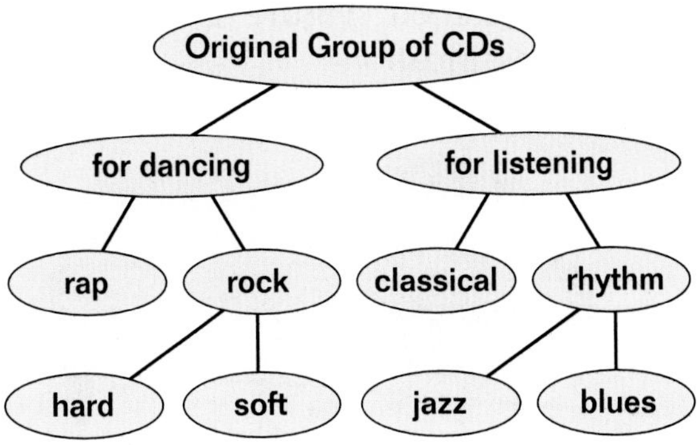

Figure 2 Classifying CDs

Classifying

You may not realize it, but you make things orderly in the world around you. If you hang your shirts together in the closet or if your favorite CDs are stacked together, you have used the skill of classifying.

Classifying is the process of sorting objects or events into groups based on common features. When classifying, first observe the objects or events to be classified. Then, select one feature that is shared by some members in the group, but not by all. Place those members that share that feature into a subgroup. You can classify members into smaller and smaller subgroups based on characteristics.

Remember, when you classify, you are grouping objects or events for a purpose. Keep your purpose in mind as you select the features to form groups and subgroups.

Example How would you classify a collection of CDs? As shown in **Figure 2,** you might classify those you like to dance to in one subgroup and CDs you like to listen to in the next subgroup. The CDs you like to dance to could be subdivided into a rap subgroup and a rock subgroup. Note that for each feature selected, each CD fits into only one subgroup. You would keep selecting features until all the CDs are classified. **Figure 2** shows one possible classification.

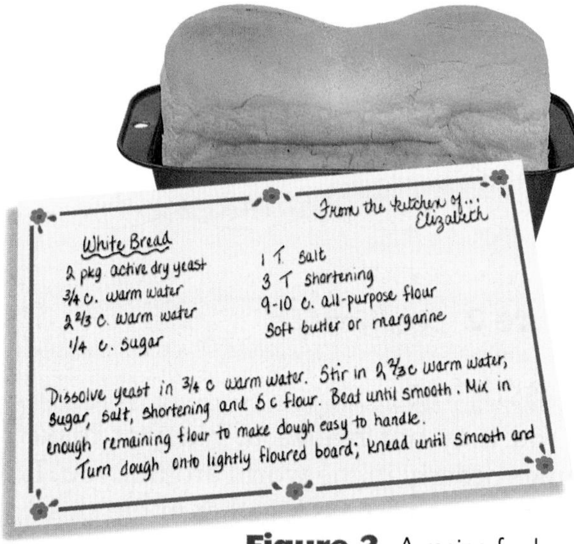

Figure 3 A recipe for bread contains sequenced instructions

Sequencing

A sequence is an arrangement of things or events in a particular order. When you are asked to sequence objects or events within a group, figure out what comes first, then think about what should come second. Continue to choose objects or events until all of the objects you started out with are in order. Then, go back over the sequence to make sure each thing or event in your sequence logically leads to the next.

Example A sequence with which you are most familiar is the use of alphabetical order. Another example of sequence would be the steps in a recipe, as shown in **Figure 3.** Think about baking bread. Steps in the recipe have to be followed in order for the bread to turn out right.

Concept Mapping

If you were taking an automobile trip, you would probably take along a road map. The road map shows your location, your destination, and other places along the way. By looking at the map and finding where you are, you can begin to understand where you are in relation to other locations on the map.

A concept map is similar to a road map. But, a concept map shows relationships among ideas (or concepts) rather than places. A concept map is a diagram that visually shows how concepts are related. Because the concept map shows relationships among ideas, it can make the meanings of ideas and terms clear, and help you understand better what you are studying.

There is usually not one correct way to create a concept map. As you construct one type of map, you may discover other ways to construct the map that show the

Figure 4 Network tree describing U.S. currency

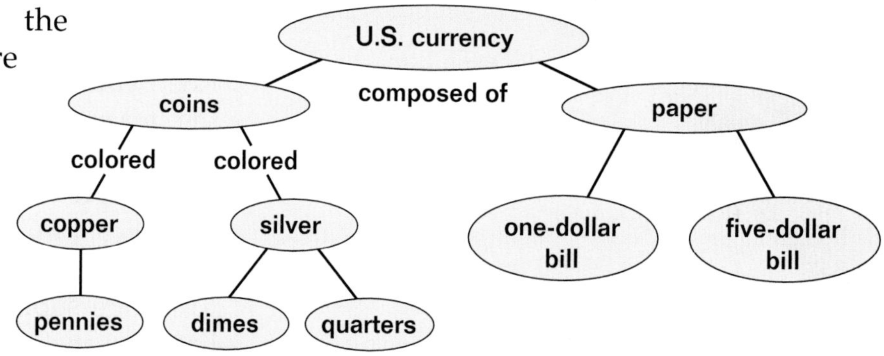

relationships between concepts in a better way. If you do discover what you think is a better way to create a concept map, go ahead and use the new one. Overall, concept maps are useful for breaking a big concept down into smaller parts, making learning easier.

Examples

Network Tree Look at the concept map about U.S. currency in **Figure 4.** This is called a network tree. Notice how some words are in ovals while others are written across connecting lines. The words inside the ovals are science concepts. The lines in the map show related concepts. The words written on the lines describe the relationships between concepts.

When you are asked to construct a network tree, write down the topic and list the major concepts related to that topic on a piece of paper. Then look at your list and begin to put them in order from general to specific. Branch the related concepts from the major concept and describe the relationships on the lines. Continue to write the more specific concepts. Write the relationships between the concepts on the lines until all concepts are mapped. Examine the concept map for relationships that cross branches, and add them to the concept map.

Events Chain An events chain is another type of concept map. An events chain map, such as the one describing a typical morning routine in **Figure 5,** is used to describe ideas in order. In science, an events chain can be used to describe a sequence of events, the steps in a procedure, or the stages of a process.

When making an events chain, first find the one event that starts the chain. This event is called the initiating event. Then, find the next event in the chain and continue until you reach an outcome. Suppose you are asked to describe what happens when your alarm rings. An events chain map describing the steps might look like **Figure 5.** Notice that connecting words are not necessary in an events chain.

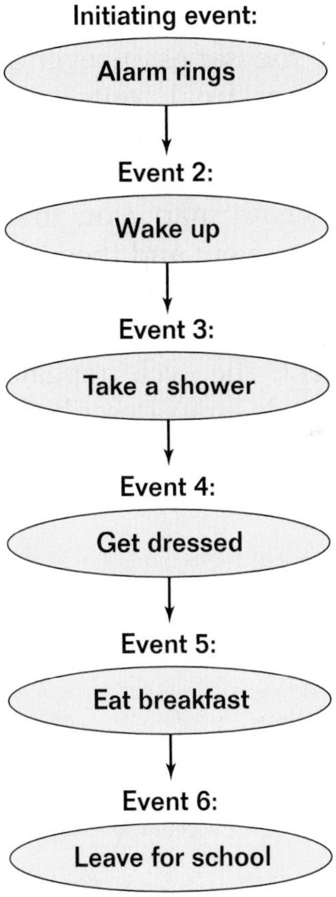

Figure 5 Events chain of a typical morning routine

Cycle Map A cycle concept map is a special type of events chain map. In a cycle concept map, the series of events does not produce a final outcome. Instead, the last event in the chain relates back to the initiating event.

As in the events chain map, you first decide on an initiating event and then list each event in order. Because there is no outcome and the last event relates back to the initiating event, the cycle repeats itself. Look at the cycle map describing the relationship between day and night in **Figure 6.**

Figure 6 Cycle map of day and night.

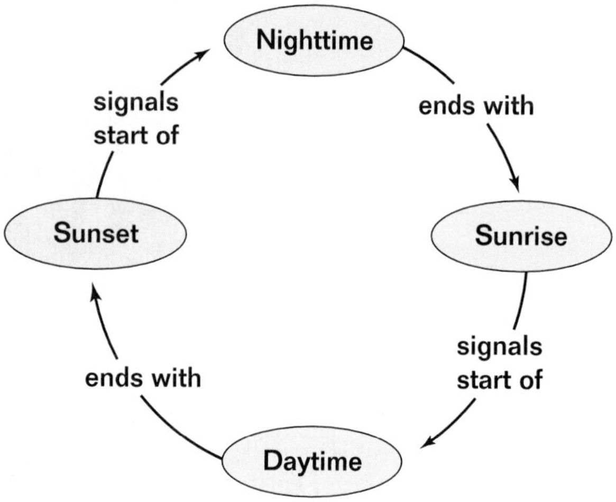

Spider Map A fourth type of concept map is the spider map. This is a map that you can use for brainstorming. Once you have a central idea, you may find you have a jumble of ideas that relate to it, but are not necessarily clearly related to each other. As illustrated by the homework spider map in **Figure 7,** by writing these ideas outside the main concept, you may begin to separate and group unrelated terms so that they become more useful.

Figure 7 Spider map about homework.

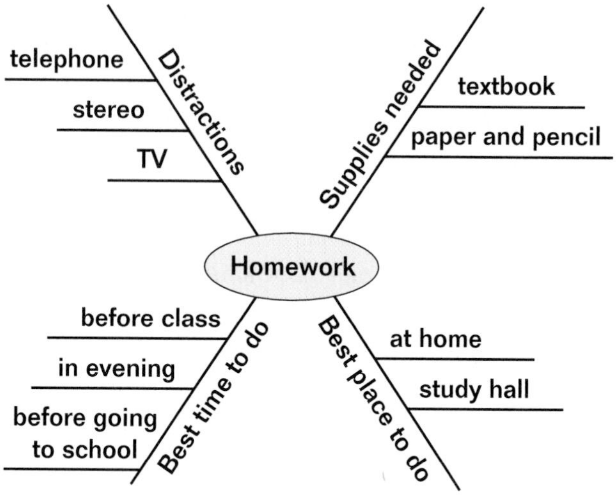

Making and Using Tables

Browse through your textbook and you will notice tables in the text and in the activities. In a table, data or information is arranged in a way that makes it easier for you to understand. Activity tables help organize the data you collect during an activity so that results can be interpreted.

Examples Most tables have a title. At a glance, the title tells you what the table is about. A table is divided into columns and rows. The first column lists items to be compared. In **Figure 8,** the collection of recyclable materials is being compared in a table. The row across the top lists the specific characteristics being compared. Within the grid of the table, the collected data are recorded.

What is the title of the table in **Figure 8?** The title is "Recycled Materials." What is being compared? The different materials being recycled and on which days they are recycled.

Making Tables To make a table, list the items to be compared down in columns and the characteristics to be compared across in rows. The table in

Figure 8 Table of recycled materials

Recycled Materials			
Day of Week	Paper (kg)	Aluminum (kg)	Plastic (kg)
Mon.	4.0	2.0	0.5
Wed.	3.5	1.5	0.5
Fri.	3.0	1.0	1.5

Figure 8 compares the mass of recycled materials collected by a class. On Monday, students turned in 4.0 kg of paper, 2.0 kg of aluminum, and 0.5 kg of plastic. On Wednesday, they turned in 3.5 kg of paper, 1.5 kg of aluminum, and 0.5 kg of plastic. On Friday, the totals were 3.0 kg of paper, 1.0 kg of aluminum, and 1.5 kg of plastic.

Using Tables How much plastic, in kilograms, is being recycled on Wednesday? Locate the column labeled "Plastic (kg)" and the row "Wed." The data in the box where the column and row intersect is the answer. Did you answer "0.5"? How much aluminum, in kilograms, is being recycled on Friday? If you answered "1.0," you understand how to use the parts of the table.

Making and Using Graphs

After scientists organize data in tables, they may display the data in a graph. A graph is a diagram that shows the relationship of one variable to another. A graph makes interpretation and analysis of data easier. There are three basic types of graphs used in science—the line graph, the bar graph, and the circle graph.

Examples

Line Graphs A line graph is used to show the relationship between two variables. The variables being compared go on two axes of the graph. The independent variable always goes on the horizontal axis, called the x-axis. The dependent variable always goes on the vertical axis, called the y-axis.

Suppose your class started to record the amount of materials they collected in one week for their school to recycle. The collected information is shown in **Figure 9.**

You could make a graph of the materials collected over the three days of the school week. The three weekdays are the independent variables and are placed on the x-axis of your graph. The amount of materials collected is the dependent variable and would go on the y-axis.

After drawing your axes, label each with a scale. The x-axis lists the three weekdays. To make a scale of the amount of materials collected on the y-axis, look at the data values. Because the lowest amount collected was 1.0 and the highest was 5.0, you will have to start numbering at least at 1.0 and go through 5.0. You decide to start numbering at 0 and number by ones through 6.0, as shown in **Figure 10.**

Next, plot the data points for collected paper. The first pair of data you want to plot is Monday and 5.0 kg of paper.

Figure 9 Amount of recyclable materials collected during one week

Materials Collected During Week		
Day of Week	Paper (kg)	Aluminum (kg)
Mon.	5.0	4.0
Wed.	4.0	1.0
Fri.	2.5	2.0

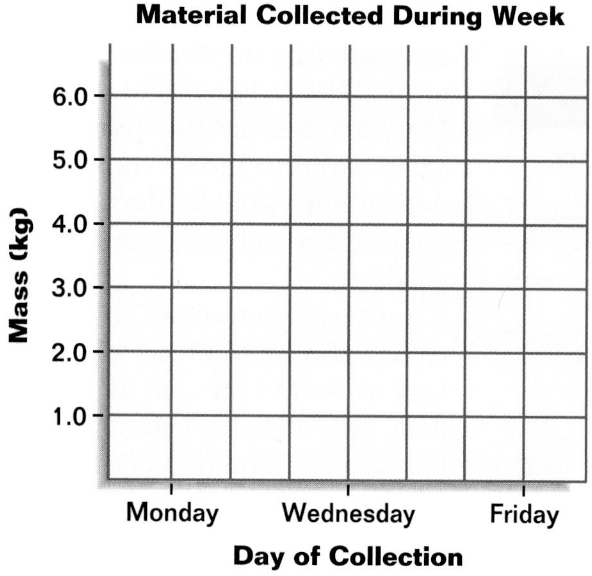

Figure 10 Graph outline for material collected during week

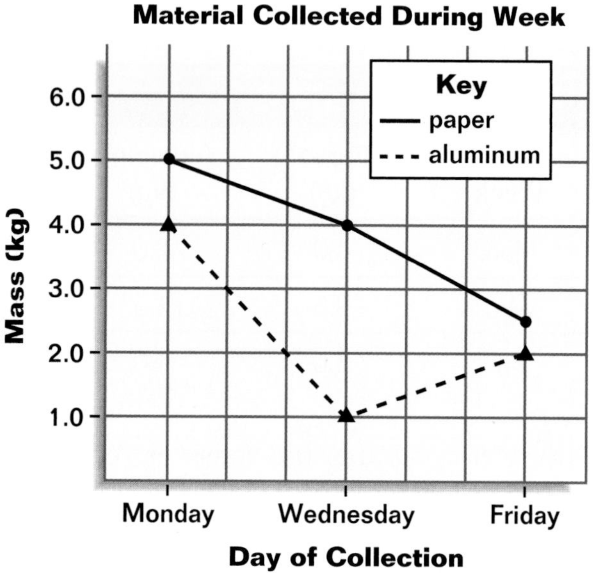

Figure 11 Line graph of materials collected during week

Locate "Monday" on the *x*-axis and locate "5.0" on the *y*-axis. Where an imaginary vertical line from the *x*-axis and an imaginary horizontal line from the *y*-axis would meet, place the first data point. Place the other data points the same way. After all the points are plotted, connect them with the best smooth curve. Repeat this procedure for the data points for aluminum. Use continuous and dashed lines to distinguish the two line graphs. The resulting graph should look like **Figure 11.**

Bar Graphs Bar graphs are similar to line graphs. They compare data that do not continuously change. In a bar graph, vertical bars show the relationships among data.

To make a bar graph, set up the *x*-axis and *y*-axis as you did for the line graph. The data is plotted by drawing vertical bars from the *x*-axis up to a point where the *y*-axis would meet the bar if it were extended.

Look at the bar graph in **Figure 12** comparing the mass of aluminum collected over three weekdays. The *x*-axis is the days on which the aluminum was collected. The *y*-axis is the mass of aluminum collected, in kilograms.

Circle Graphs A circle graph uses a circle divided into sections to display data. Each section represents part of the whole. All the sections together equal 100 percent.

Suppose you wanted to make a circle graph to show the number of seeds that germinated in a package. You would count the total number of seeds. You find that there are 143 seeds in the package. This represents 100 percent, the whole circle.

You plant the seeds, and 129 seeds germinate. The seeds that germinated will make up one section of the circle graph, and the seeds that did not germinate will make up the remaining section.

To find out how much of the circle each section should take, divide the number of seeds in each section by the total number of seeds. Then, multiply your answer by 360, the number of degrees in a circle, and round to the nearest whole number. The

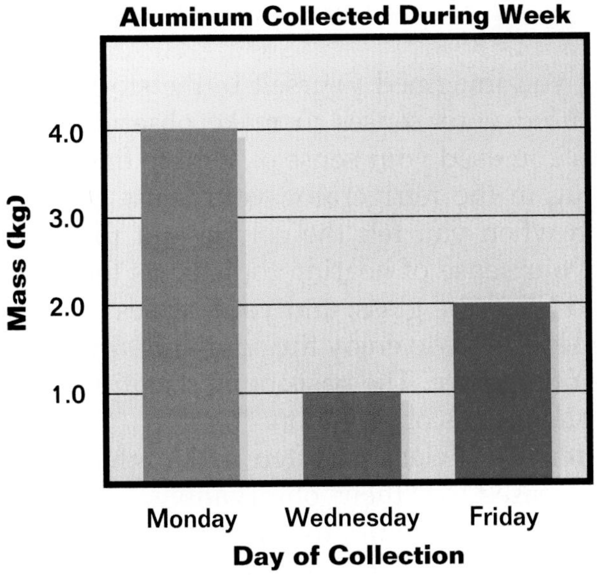

Figure 12 Bar graph of aluminum collected during week

section of the circle graph in degrees that represents the seeds germinated is figured below.

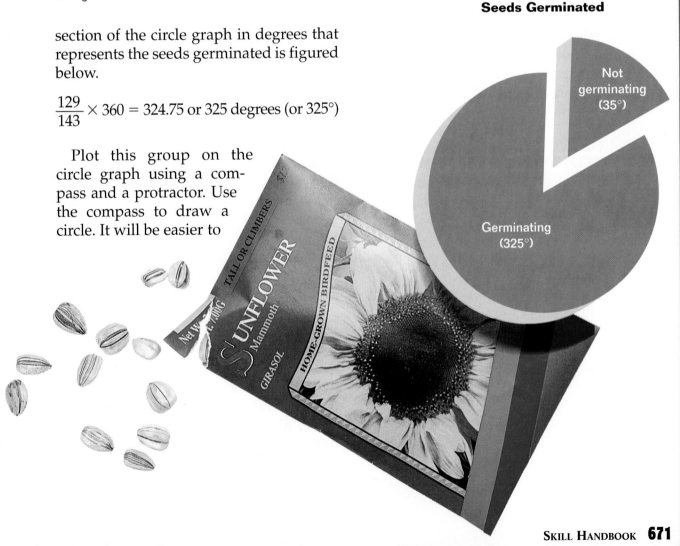

$$\frac{129}{143} \times 360 = 324.75 \text{ or } 325 \text{ degrees (or } 325°)$$

Plot this group on the circle graph using a compass and a protractor. Use the compass to draw a circle. It will be easier to measure the part of the circle representing the non-germinating seeds, so subtract 325° from 360° to get 35°. Draw a straight line from the center to the edge of the circle. Place your protractor on this line and use it to mark a point at 325°. Use this point to draw a straight line from the center of the circle to the edge. This is the section for the group of seeds that did not germinate. The other section represents the group of 129 seeds that did germinate. Label the sections of your graph and title the graph as shown in **Figure 13.**

Figure 13 Circle graph of germinated seeds

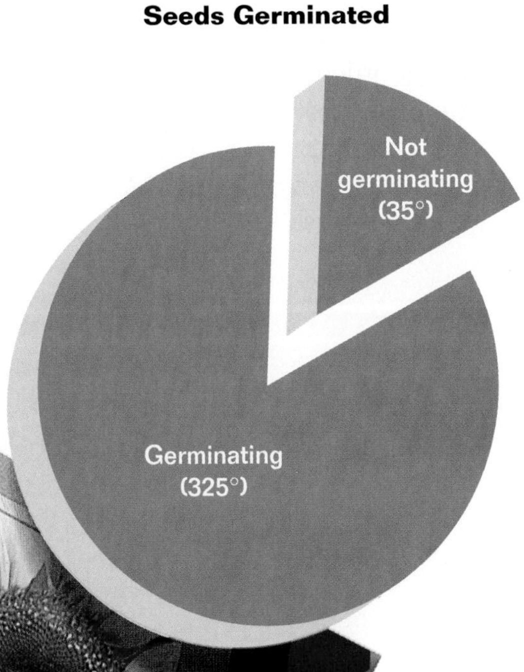

Thinking Critically

Observing and Inferring

Observing Scientists try to make careful and accurate observations. When possible, they use instruments such as microscopes, thermometers, and balances to make observations. Measurements with a balance or thermometer provide numerical data that can be checked and repeated.

When you make observations in science, you'll find it helpful to examine the entire object or situation first. Then, look carefully for details. Write down everything you observe.

Example Imagine that you have just finished a volleyball game. At home, you open the refrigerator and see a jug of orange juice on the back of the top shelf. The jug, shown in **Figure 14,** feels cold as you grasp it. Then, you drink the juice, smell the oranges, and enjoy the tart taste in your mouth.

Figure 14 Why is this jug of orange juice cold?

As you imagined yourself in the story, you used your senses to make observations. You used your sense of sight to find the jug in the refrigerator, your sense of touch when you felt the coldness of the jug, your sense of hearing to listen as the liquid filled the glass, and your senses of smell and taste to enjoy the odor and tartness of the juice. The basis of all scientific investigation is observation.

Inferring Scientists often make inferences based on their observations. An inference is an attempt to explain or interpret observations or to say what caused what you observed.

When making an inference, be certain to use accurate data and observations. Analyze all of the data that you've collected. Then, based on everything you know, explain or interpret what you've observed.

Example When you drank a glass of orange juice after the volleyball game, you observed that the orange juice was cold as well as refreshing. You might infer that the juice was cold because it had been made much earlier in the day and had been kept in the refrigerator, or you might infer that it had just been made, using both cold water and ice. The only way to be sure which inference is correct is to investigate further.

Comparing and Contrasting

Observations can be analyzed by noting the similarities and differences between two or more objects or events that you observe. When you look at objects or events to see how they are similar, you are comparing them. Contrasting is looking for differences in similar objects or events.

Figure 15 Table comparing the nutritional value of *Cereal A* and *Cereal B*

Nutritional Value		
	Cereal A	Cereal B
Serving size	103 g	105 g
Calories	220	160
Total Fat	10 g	10 g
Protein	2.5 g	2.6 g
Total Carbohydrate	30 g	15 g

Example Suppose you were asked to compare and contrast the nutritional value of two kinds of cereal, *Cereal A* and *Cereal B.* You would start by looking at what is known about these cereals. Arrange this information in a table, like the one in **Figure 15.**

Similarities you might point out are that both cereals have similar serving sizes, amounts of total fat, and protein. Differences include *Cereal A* having a higher calorie value and containing more total carbohydrates than *Cereal B.*

Recognizing Cause and Effect

Have you ever watched something happen and then made suggestions about why it happened? If so, you have observed an effect and inferred a cause. The event is an effect, and the reason for the event is the cause.

Example Suppose that every time your teacher fed the fish in a classroom aquarium, she or he tapped the food container on the edge of the aquarium. Then, one day your teacher just happened to tap the edge of the aquarium with a pencil while making a point. You observed the fish swim to the surface of the aquarium to feed, as shown in **Figure 16.** What is the effect, and what would you infer to be the cause? The effect is the fish swimming to the surface of the aquarium. You might infer the cause to be the teacher tapping on the edge of the aquarium. In determining cause and effect, you have made a logical inference based on your observations.

Perhaps the fish swam to the surface because they reacted to the teacher's waving hand or for some other reason. When scientists are unsure of the cause of a certain event, they design controlled experiments to determine what causes the event. Although you have made a logical conclusion about the behavior of the fish, you would have to perform an experiment to be certain that it was the tapping that caused the effect you observed.

Figure 16 What cause-and-effect situations are occurring in this aquarium?

Practicing Scientific Processes

You might say that the work of a scientist is to solve problems. But when you decide how to dress on a particular day, you are doing problem solving, too. You may observe what the weather looks like through a window. You may go outside and see whether what you are wearing is heavy or light enough.

Scientists use an orderly approach to learn new information and to solve problems. The methods scientists may use include observing to form a hypothesis, designing an experiment to test a hypothesis, separating and controlling variables, and interpreting data.

Forming Operational Definitions

Operational definitions define an object by showing how it functions, works, or behaves. Such definitions are written in terms of how an object works or how it can be used; that is, what is its job or purpose?

Example Some operational definitions explain how an object can be used.

- A ruler is a tool that measures the size of an object.
- An automobile can move things from one place to another.

Or such a definition may explain how an object works.

- A ruler contains a series of marks that can be used as a standard when measuring.
- An automobile is a vehicle that can move from place to place.

Forming a Hypothesis

Observations You observe all the time. Scientists try to observe as much as possible about the things and events they study so they know that what they say about their observations is reliable.

Some observations describe something using only words. These observations are called qualitative observations. Other observations describe how much of something there is. These are quantitative observations and use numbers, as well as words, in the description. Tools or equipment are used to measure the characteristic being described.

Example If you were making qualitative observations of the dog in **Figure 17,** you might use words such as *furry, yellow,* and *short-haired.* Quantitative observations of this dog might include a mass of 14 kg, a height of 46 cm, ear length of 10 cm, and an age of 150 days.

Figure 17 What observations can be made about this dog?

Hypotheses Hypotheses are tested to help explain observations that have been made. They are often stated as *if* and *then* statements.

Examples Suppose you want to make a perfect score on a spelling test. Begin by thinking of several ways to accomplish this. Base these possibilities on past observations. If you put each of these possibilities into sentence form, using the words *if* and *then,* you can form a hypothesis. All of the following are hypotheses you might consider to explain how you could score 100 percent on your test:

If the test is easy, then I will get a perfect score.

If I am intelligent, then I will get a perfect score.

If I study hard, then I will get a perfect score.

Perhaps a scientist has observed that plants that receive fertilizer grow taller than plants that do not. A scientist may form a hypothesis that says: If plants are fertilized, then their growth will increase.

Designing an Experiment to Test a Hypothesis

In order to test a hypothesis, it's best to write out a procedure. A procedure is the plan that you follow in your experiment. A procedure tells you what materials to use and how to use them. After following the procedure, data are generated. From this generated data, you can then draw a conclusion and make a statement about your results.

If the conclusion you draw from the data supports your hypothesis, then you can say that your hypothesis is reliable. *Reliable* means that you can trust your conclusion. If it did not support your hypothesis, then you would have to make new observations and state a new hypothesis—just make sure that it is one that you can test.

Example Super premium gasoline costs more than regular gasoline. Does super premium gasoline increase the efficiency or fuel mileage of your family car? Let's figure out how to conduct an experiment to test the hypothesis, "*if* premium gas is more efficient, *then* it should increase the fuel mileage of our family car." Then a procedure similar to **Figure 18** must be written to generate data presented in **Figure 19** on the next page.

These data show that premium gasoline is less efficient than regular gasoline. It took more gasoline to travel one mile (0.064) using premium gasoline than it does to travel one mile using regular gasoline (0.059). This conclusion does not support the original hypothesis made.

PROCEDURE

1. Use regular gasoline for two weeks.
2. Record the number of miles between fill-ups and the amount of gasoline used.
3. Switch to premium gasoline for two weeks.
4. Record the number of miles between fill-ups and the amount of gasoline used.

Figure 18 Possible procedural steps

Figure 19 Data generated from procedure steps

Gasoline Data			
	Miles traveled	Gallons used	Gallons per mile
Regular gasoline	762	45.34	0.059
Premium gasoline	661	42.30	0.064

Separating and Controlling Variables

In any experiment, it is important to keep everything the same except for the item you are testing. The one factor that you change is called the *independent variable.* The factor that changes as a result of the independent variable is called the *dependent variable.* Always make sure that there is only one independent variable. If you allow more than one, you will not know what causes the changes you observe in the independent variable. Many experiments have *controls*—a treatment or an experiment that you can compare with the results of your test groups.

Example In the experiment with the gasoline, you made everything the same except the type of gasoline being used. The driver, the type of automobile, and the weather conditions should remain the same throughout. The gasoline should also be purchased from the same service station. By doing so, you made sure that at the end of the experiment, any differences were the result of the type of fuel being used—regular or premium. The type of gasoline was the *independent factor* and the gas mileage achieved was the *dependent factor.* The use of regular gasoline was the *control.*

Interpreting Data

The word *interpret* means "to explain the meaning of something." Look at the problem originally being explored in the gasoline experiment and find out what the data show. Identify the control group and the test group so you can see whether or not the variable has had an effect. Then, you need to check differences between the control and test groups.

Figure 20 Which gasoline type is most efficient?

These differences may be qualitative or quantitative. A qualitative difference would be a difference that you could observe and describe, while a quantitative difference would be a difference you can measure using numbers. If there are differences, the variable being tested may have had an effect. If there is no difference between the control and the test groups, the variable being tested apparently has had no effect.

Example Perhaps you are looking at a table from an experiment designed to test the hypothesis: If premium gas is more efficient, then it should increase the fuel mileage of our family car. Look back at **Figure 19** showing the results of this experiment. In this example, the use of regular gasoline in the family car was the control, while the car being fueled by premium gasoline was the test group.

Data showed a quantitative difference in efficiency for gasoline consumption. It took 0.059 gallons of regular gasoline to travel one mile, while it took 0.064 gallons of the premium gasoline to travel the same distance. The regular gasoline was more efficient; it increased the fuel mileage of the family car.

What are data? In the experiment described on these pages, measurements were taken so that at the end of the experiment, you had something concrete to interpret. You had numbers to work with. Not every experiment that you do will give you data in the form of numbers. Sometimes, data will be in the form of a description. At the end of a chemistry experiment, you might have noted that one solution turned yellow when treated with a particular chemical, and another remained colorless, as water, when treated with the same chemical. Data, therefore, are stated in different forms for different types of scientific experiments.

Figure 21

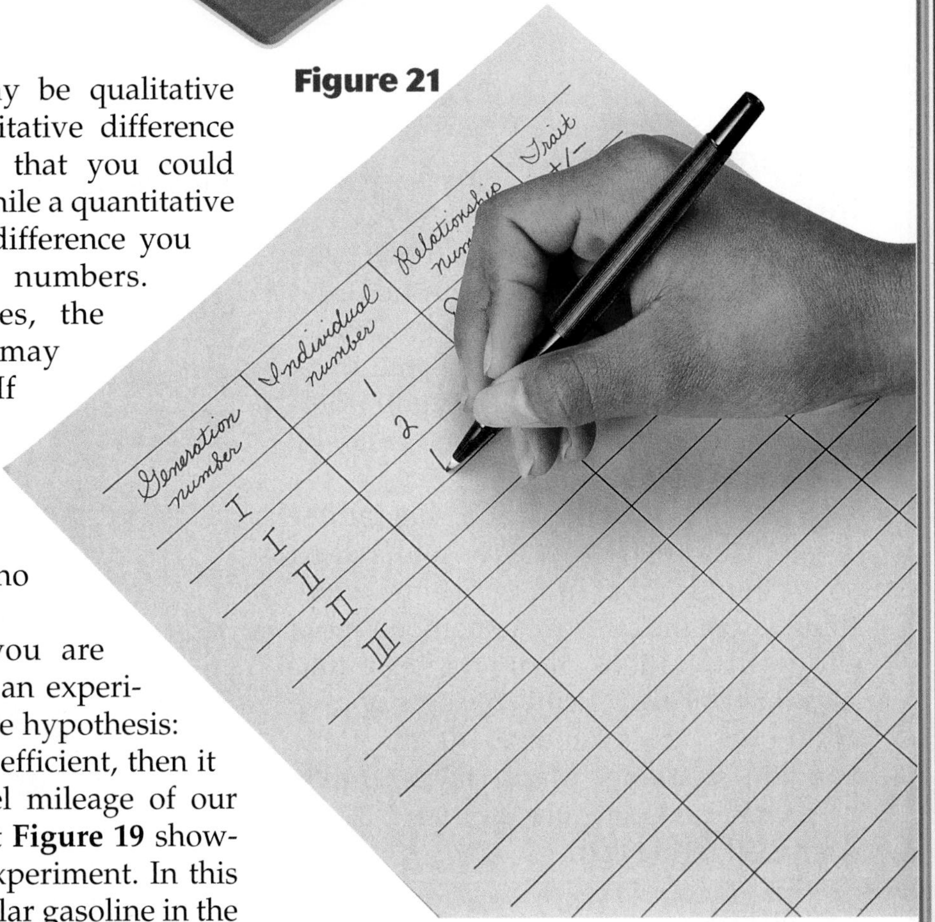

Are all experiments alike? Keep in mind as you perform experiments in science that not every experiment makes use of all of the parts that have been described on these pages. For some, it may be difficult to design an experiment that will always have a control. Other experiments are complex enough that it may be hard to have only one dependent variable. Real scientists encounter many variations in the methods that they use when they perform experiments. The skills in this handbook are here for you to use and practice. In real situations, their uses will vary.

Representing and Applying Data

Interpreting Scientific Illustrations

As you read a science textbook, you will see many drawings, diagrams, and photographs. Illustrations help you to understand what you read. Some illustrations are included to help you understand an idea that you can't see easily by yourself. For instance, we can't see atoms, but we can look at a diagram of an atom and that helps us to understand some things about atoms. Seeing something often helps you remember more easily. Illustrations also provide examples that clarify difficult concepts or give additional information about the topic you are studying. Maps, for example, help you to locate places that may be described in the text.

Examples

Captions and Labels Most illustrations have captions. A caption is a comment that identifies or explains the illustration. Diagrams, such as **Figure 22,** often have labels that identify parts of the organism or the order of steps in a process.

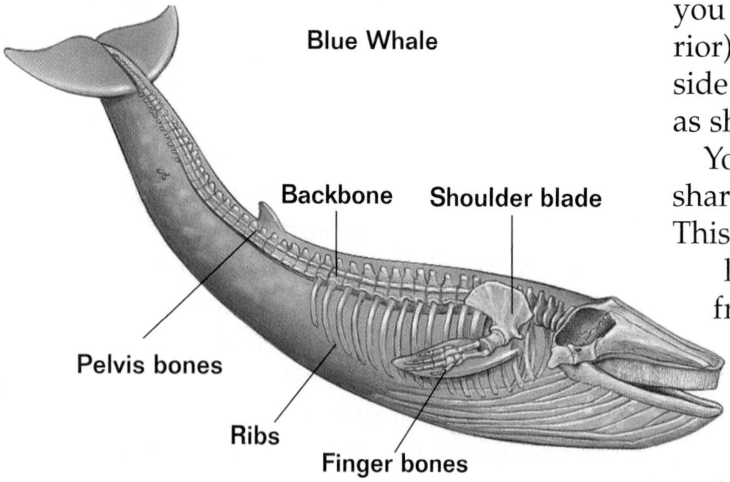

Figure 22 A labeled diagram of a blue whale

Figure 23 The orientation of a dog is shown here.

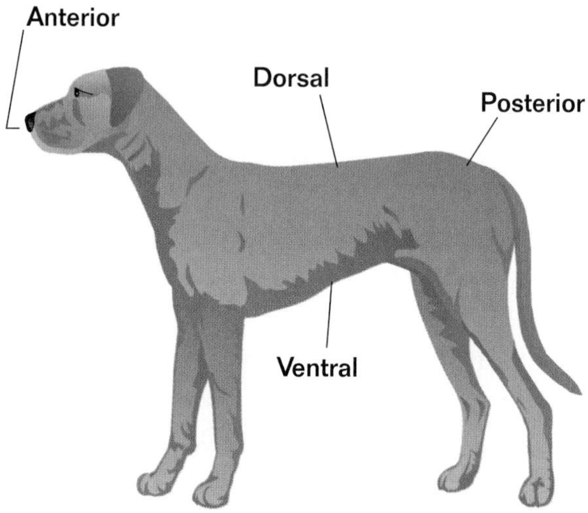

Learning with Illustrations An illustration of an organism shows that organism from a particular view or orientation. In order to understand the illustration, you may need to identify the front (anterior) end, tail (posterior) end, the underside (ventral), and the back (dorsal) side, as shown in **Figure 23.**

You might also check for symmetry. A shark in **Figure 24** has bilateral symmetry. This means that drawing an imaginary line through the center of the animal from the anterior to posterior end forms two mirror images.

Radial symmetry is the arrangement of similar parts around a central point. An object or organism, such as a hydra, can be divided anywhere through the center into similar parts.

Some organisms and objects cannot be divided into two similar parts. If an

Figure 24 A shark (A) illustrating bilateral symmetry and a pear (B) illustrating a longitudinal section and a cross section

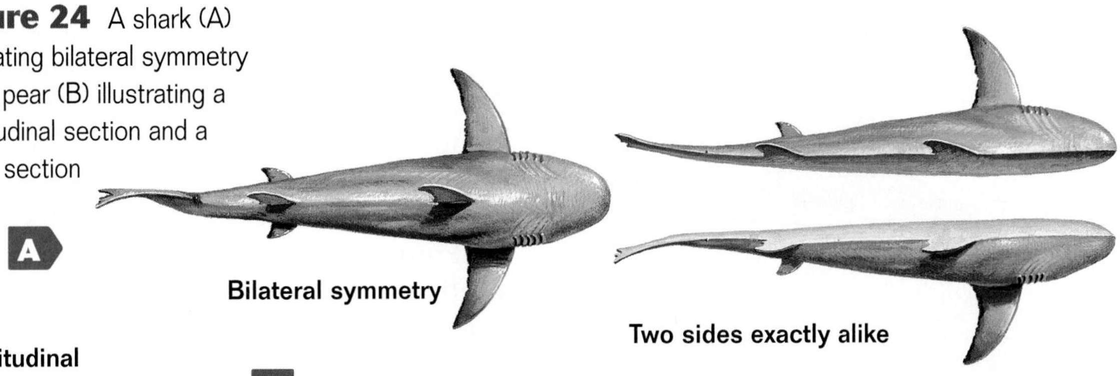

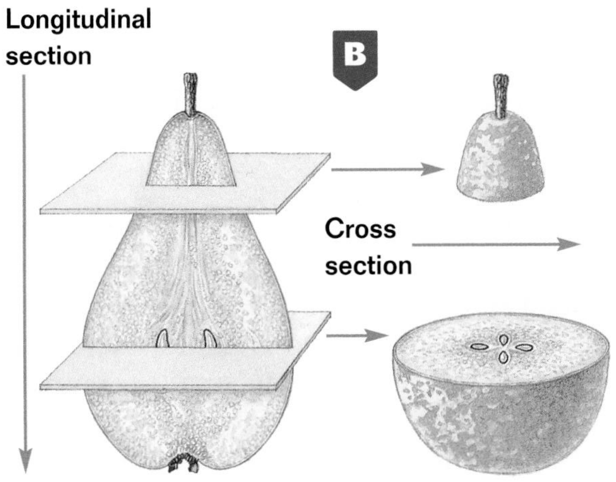

organism or object cannot be divided, it is asymmetrical. Regardless of how you try to divide a natural sponge, you cannot divide it into two parts that look alike.

Some illustrations enable you to see the inside of an organism or object. These illustrations are called sections. **Figure 24** also illustrates some common sections.

Look at all illustrations carefully. Read captions and labels so that you understand exactly what the illustration is showing you.

Making Models

Have you ever worked on a model car, plane, or rocket? These models look, and sometimes work, much like the real thing, but they are often on a different scale than the real thing. In science, models are used to help simplify large or small processes or structures that otherwise would be difficult to see and understand. Your understanding of a structure or process is enhanced when you work with materials to make a model that shows the basic features of the structure or process.

Example In order to make a model, you first have to get a basic idea about the structure or process involved. You decide to make a model to show the differences in size of arteries, veins, and capillaries. First, read about these structures. All three are hollow tubes. Arteries are round and thick. Veins are flat and have thinner walls than arteries. Capillaries are small.

Now, decide what you can use for your model. Common materials are often most useful and cheapest to work with when making models. As illustrated in **Figure 25** on the next page, different kinds and sizes of pasta might work for these models. Different sizes of rubber tubing might do just as well. Cut and glue the different noodles or tubing onto thick paper so the openings can be seen. Then label each. Now you have a simple, easy-to-understand model showing the differences in size of arteries, veins, and capillaries.

What other scientific ideas might a model help you to understand? A model of a molecule can be made from balls of modeling clay (using different colors for the different elements present) and toothpicks (to show different chemical bonds).

Figure 25 Different types of pasta may be used to model blood vessels

A working model of a volcano can be made from clay, a small amount of baking soda, vinegar, and a bottle cap. Other models can be devised on a computer. Some models are mathematical and are represented by equations.

Measuring in SI

The metric system is a system of measurement developed by a group of scientists in 1795. It helps scientists avoid problems by providing standard measurements that all scientists around the world can understand. A modern form of the metric system, called the International System, or SI, was adopted for worldwide use in 1960.

The metric system is convenient because unit sizes vary by multiples of 10. When changing from smaller units to larger units, divide by 10. When changing from larger units to smaller, multiply by 10. For example, to convert millimeters to centimeters, divide the millimeters by 10. To convert 30 millimeters to centimeters, divide 30 by 10 (30 millimeters equal 3 centimeters).

Prefixes are used to name units. Look at **Figure 26** for some common metric prefixes and their meanings. Do you see how the prefix *kilo-* attached to the unit *gram* is *kilogram,* or 1000 grams? The prefix *deci-* attached to the unit *meter* is *decimeter,* or one-tenth (0.1) of a meter.

Examples

Length You have probably measured lengths or distances many times. The meter is the SI unit used to measure length. A baseball bat is about one meter long. When measuring smaller lengths, the meter is divided into smaller units called centimeters and millimeters. A centimeter is one-hundredth (0.01) of a meter, which is about the size of the width of the fingernail on your ring finger. A millimeter is one-thousandth of a meter (0.001), about the thickness of a dime.

Most metric rulers have lines indicating centimeters and millimeters, as shown in

Figure 26 Common metric prefixes

Metric Prefixes			
Prefix	Symbol	Meaning	
kilo-	k	1000	thousand
hecto-	h	200	hundred
deca-	da	10	ten
deci-	d	0.1	tenth
centi-	c	0.01	hundredth
milli-	m	0.001	thousandth

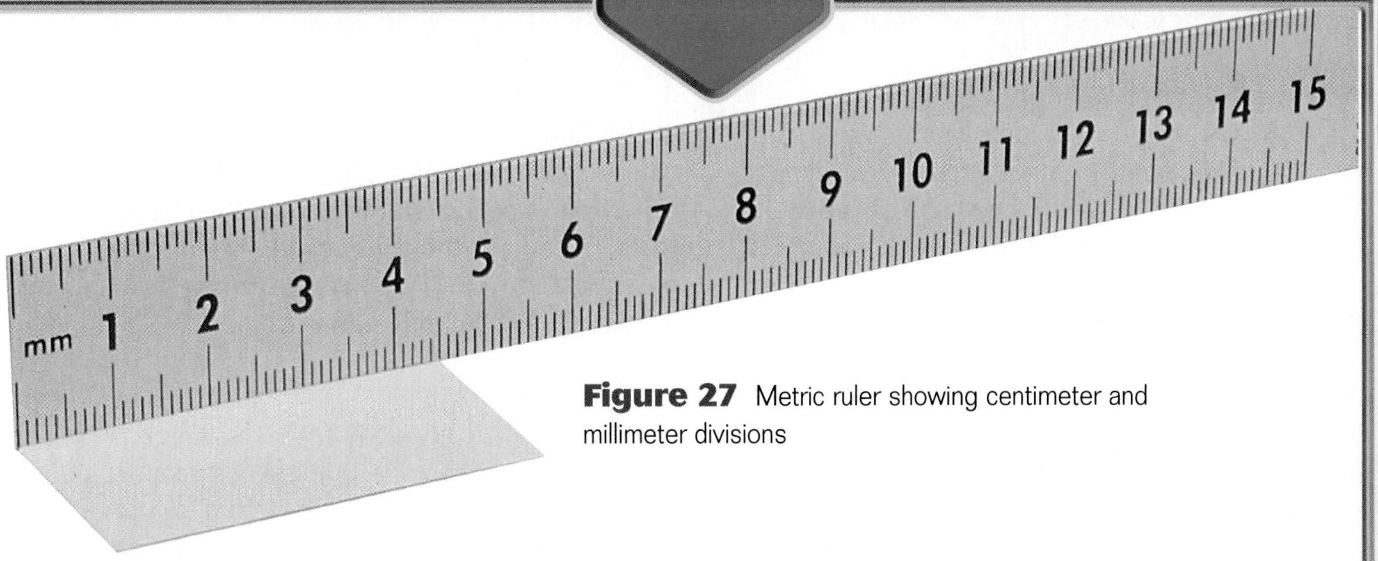

Figure 27 Metric ruler showing centimeter and millimeter divisions

Figure 27. The centimeter lines are the longer, numbered lines; the shorter lines are millimeter lines. When using a metric ruler, line up the 0-centimeter mark with the end of the object being measured, and read the number of the unit where the object ends, in this instance 4.5 cm.

Surface Area Units of length are also used to measure surface area. The standard unit of area is the square meter (m^2). A square that's one meter long on each side has a surface area of one square meter. Similarly, a square centimeter, (cm^2), shown in **Figure 28,** is one centimeter long on each side. The surface area of an object is determined by multiplying the length times the width.

Volume The volume of a rectangular solid is also calculated using units of length. The cubic meter (m^3) is the standard SI unit of volume. A cubic meter is a cube one meter on each side. You can determine the volume of rectangular solids by multiplying length times width times height.

Liquid Volume During science activities, you will measure liquids using beakers and graduated cylinders marked in milliliters, as illustrated in **Figure 29.** A graduated cylinder is a cylindrical container marked with lines from bottom to top.

Liquid volume is measured using a unit called a liter. A liter has the volume of 1000 cubic centimeters. Because the prefix *milli-* means thousandth (0.001), a milliliter equals one cubic centimeter. One milliliter of liquid would completely fill a cube measuring one centimeter on each side.

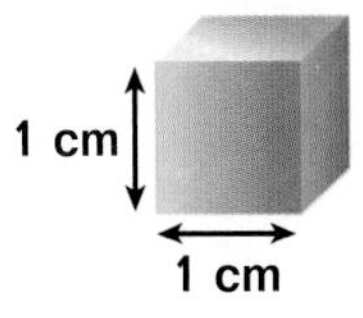

Figure 28 A square centimeter

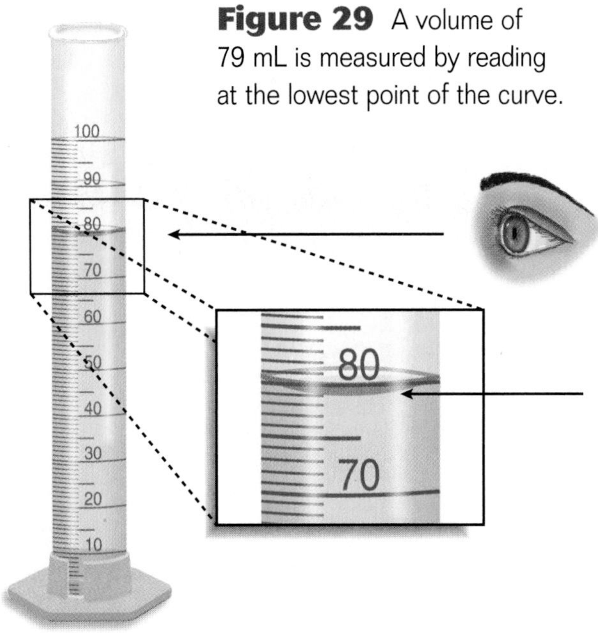

Figure 29 A volume of 79 mL is measured by reading at the lowest point of the curve.

Mass Scientists use balances to find the mass of objects in grams. You might use a beam balance similar to **Figure 30.** Notice that on one side of the balance is a pan and on the other side is a set of beams. Each beam has an object of a known mass called a *rider* that slides on the beam.

Before you find the mass of an object, set the balance to zero by sliding all the riders back to the zero point. Check the pointer on the right to make sure it swings an equal distance above and below the zero point on the scale. If the swing is unequal, find and turn the adjusting screw until you have an equal swing.

Place an object on the pan. Slide the rider with the largest mass along its beam until the pointer drops below zero. Then move it back one notch. Repeat the process on each beam until the pointer swings an equal distance above and below the zero point. Add the masses on each beam to find the mass of the object.

You should never place a hot object or pour chemicals directly onto the pan. Instead, find the mass of a clean beaker or a glass jar. Place the dry or liquid chemicals in the container. Then find the combined mass of the container and the chemicals. Calculate the mass of the chemicals by subtracting the mass of the empty container from the combined mass.

Predicting

When you apply a hypothesis, or general explanation, to a specific situation, you predict something about that situation. First, you must identify which hypothesis fits the situation you are considering.

Examples People use prediction to make everyday decisions. Based on previous observations and experiences, you may form a hypothesis that if it is wintertime, then temperatures will be lower. From past experience in your area, temperatures are lowest in February. You may then use this hypothesis to predict specific temperatures and weather for the month of February in advance. Someone could use these predictions to plan to set aside more money for heating bills during that month.

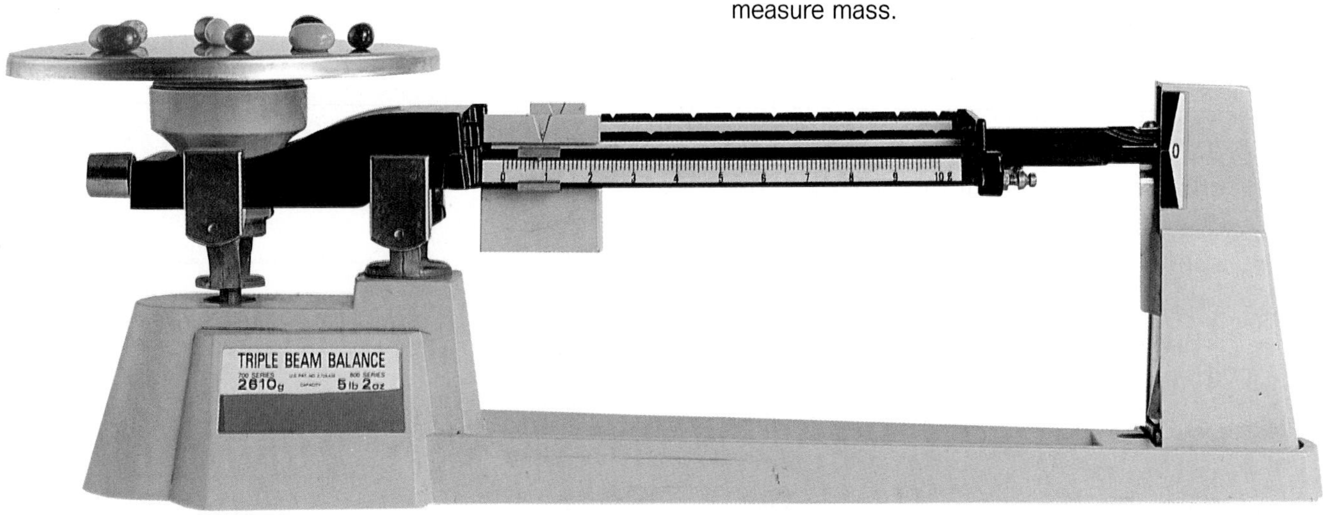

Figure 30 A beam balance is used to measure mass.

Using Numbers

When working with large populations of organisms, scientists usually cannot observe or study every organism in the population. Instead, they use a sample or a portion of the population. To sample is to take a small representative portion of organisms of a population for research. By making careful observations or manipulating variables within a portion of a group, information is discovered and conclusions are drawn that might then be applied to the whole population.

Scientific work also involves estimating. To estimate is to make a judgment about the size of something or the number of something without actually measuring or counting every member of a population.

Examples Suppose you are trying to determine the effect of a specific nutrient on the growth of black-eyed Susans. It would be impossible to test the entire population of black-eyed Susans, so you would select part of the population for your experiment. Through careful experimentation and observation on a sample of the population, you could generalize the effect of the chemical on the entire population.

Here is a more familiar example. Have you ever tried to guess how many beans were in a sealed jar? If you did, you were estimating. What if you knew the jar of beans held one liter (1000 mL)? If you knew that 30 beans would fit in a 100-milliliter jar, how many beans would you estimate to be in the one-liter jar? If you said about 300 beans, your estimate would be close to the actual number of beans. Can you estimate how many jelly beans are on the cookie sheet in **Figure 31?**

Scientists use a similar process to estimate populations of organisms from bacteria to buffalo. Scientists count the actual number of organisms in a small sample and then estimate the number of organisms in a larger area. For example, if a scientist wanted to count the number of bacterial colonies in a petri dish, a microscope could be used to count the number of organisms in a one-square-centimeter sample. To determine the total population of the culture, the number of organisms in the square-centimeter sample is multiplied by the total number of square centimeters in the culture.

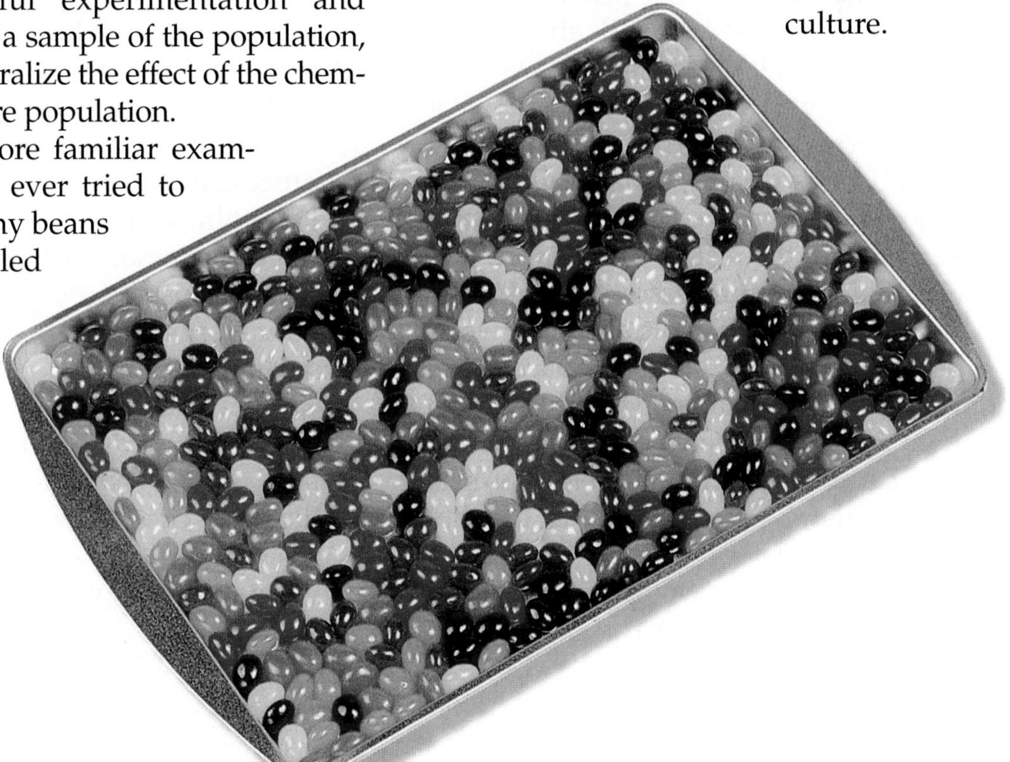

Figure 31
Sampling a group of jelly beans allows for an estimation of the total number of jelly beans in the group.

Using a Word Processor

Suppose your teacher has assigned you to write a report. After you've done your research and decided how you want to write the information, you need to put all that information on paper. The easiest way to do this is with a word processor.

A word processor is a computer program in which you can write your information, change it as many times as you need to, and then print it out so that it looks neat and clean. You can also use a word processor to create tables and columns, add bullets or cartoon art, include page numbers, and even check your spelling.

Example Last week in Science class, your teacher assigned a report on the history of the atom. It has to be double spaced and include at least one table. You've collected all the facts, and you're ready to write your report. Sitting down at your computer, you decide you want to begin by explaining early scientific ideas about the atom and then talk about what scientists think about the atom now.

After you've written the two parts of your report, you decide to put a heading or subtitle above each part and add a title to the paper. To make each of these look different from the rest of your report, you can use a word processor to make the words bigger and bolder. The word processor also can double space your entire report, so that you don't have to add an extra space between each line.

You decide to include a table that lists each scientist that contributed to the theory of the atom along with his or her contribution. Using your word processor, you can create a table with as many rows and columns as you need. And, if you forget to include a scientist in the middle, you can go back and insert a row in the middle of your table without redoing the entire table.

When you've finished with your report, you can tell the word processor to check your spelling. If it finds misspelled words, it often will suggest a word you can use to replace the misspelled word. But, remember that the word processor may not know how to spell all the words in your report. Scan your report and double check your spelling with a dictionary if you're not sure if a word is spelled correctly.

After you've made sure that your report looks just the way you want it on the screen, the word processor will print your report on a printer. With a word processor, your report can look like it was written by a real scientist.

Helpful Hints

- If you aren't sure how to do something using your word processor, look under the help menu. You can look up how to do something, and the word processor will tell you how to do it. Just follow the instructions that the word processor puts on your screen.
- Just because you've spelled checked your report doesn't mean that the spelling is perfect. The spell check can't catch misspelled words that look like other words. So, if you've accidentally typed *mind* instead of *mine,* the spell checker won't know the difference. Always reread your report to make sure you didn't miss any mistakes.

Using a Database

Imagine you're in the middle of research project. You are busily gathering facts and information. But, soon you realize that its becoming harder and harder to organize and keep track of all the information. The tool to solve "information overload" is a database. A database is exactly what it sounds like—a base on which to organize data. Similar to how a file cabinet organizes records, a database also organizes records. However, a database is more powerful than a simple file cabinet because at the click of a mouse, the entire contents can be reshuffled and reorganized. At computer-quick speeds, databases can sort information by any characteristic and filter data into multiple categories. Once you use a database, you will be amazed at how quickly all those facts and bits of information become manageable.

Example For the past few weeks, you have been gathering information on living and extinct primates. A database would be ideal to organize your information. An entry for gorillas might contain fields (categories) for fossil locations, brain size, average height, earliest fossil, and so on. Later on, if you wanted to know which primates have been found in Asia, you could quickly filter all entries using Asia in the field that listed locations. The database will scan all the entries and select the entries containing Asia. If you wanted to rank all the primates by arm length, you would sort all the entries by arm length. By using different combinations of sorting and filtering, you can discover relationships between the data that otherwise might remain hidden.

Helpful Hints

- Before setting up your own database, it's easier to learn the features of your database software by practicing with an established database.
- Entering the data into a database can be time consuming. Learn shortcuts such as tabbing between entry fields and automatic formatting of data that your software may provide.
- Get in the habit of periodically saving your database as you are entering data. That way, if something happens and your computer locks up or the power goes out, you won't lose all of your work.

Most databases have specific words you can use to narrow your search.

- AND: If you place an AND between two words in your search, the database will look for any entries that have both the words. For example, "blood AND cell" would give you information about both blood and cells.
- OR: If you place an OR between two words, the database will show entries that have at least one of the words. For example, "bird OR fish" would show you information on either birds or fish.
- NOT: If you place a NOT between two words, the database will look for entries that have the first word but do not have the second word. For example, "reproduction NOT plant" would show you information about reproduction but not about plant reproduction.

Using Graphics Software

Having trouble finding that exact piece of art you're looking for? Do you have a picture in your mind of what you want but can't seem to find the right graphic to represent your ideas? To solve these problems, you can use graphics software. Graphics software allows you to change and create images and diagrams in almost unlimited ways. Typical uses for graphics software include arranging clip-art, changing scanned images, and constructing pictures from scratch. Most graphics-software applications work in similar ways. They use the same basic tools and functions. Once you master one graphics application, you can use any other graphics application relatively easily.

Example For your report on bird adaptations, you want to make a poster displaying a variety of beak and foot types. You have acquired many photos of birds, scanned from magazines and downloaded off the Internet. Using graphics software, you separate the beaks and feet from the birds and enlarge them. Then, you use arrows and text to diagram the particular features that you want to highlight. You also highlight the key features in color, keeping the rest of the graphic in black and white. With graphics software, the possibilities are endless. For the final layout, you place the picture of the bird next to enlarged graphics of the feet and beak. Graphics software allows you to integrate text into your diagrams, which makes your bird poster look clean and professional.

Helpful Hints

- As with any method of drawing, the more you practice using the graphic software, the better your results.
- Start by using the software to manipulate existing drawings. Once you master this, making your own illustrations will be easier.
- Clip art is available on CD-ROMs, and on the Internet. With these resources, finding a piece of clip art to suit your purposes is simple.
- As you work on a drawing, save it often.
- Often you can learn a lot from studying other people's art. Look at other computer illustrations and try to figure out how the artist created it.

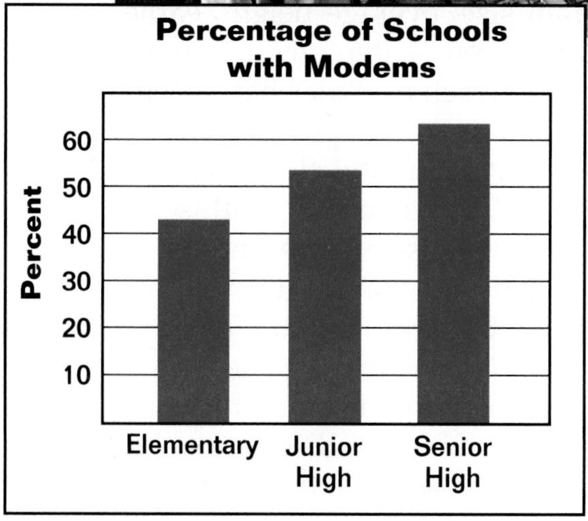

Using a Computerized Card Catalog

When you have a report or paper to research, you go to the library. To find the information, skill is needed in using a computerized card catalog. You use the computerized card catalog by typing in a subject, the title of a book, or an author's name. The computer will list on the screen all the holdings the library has on the subject, title, or author requested.

A library's holdings include books, magazines, databases, videos, and audio materials. When you have chosen something from this list, the computer will show whether an item is available and where in the library to find it.

Example You have a report due on dinosaurs, and you need to find three books on the subject. In the library, follow the instructions on the computer screen to select the "Subject" heading. You could start by typing in the word *dinosaurs.* This will give you a list of books on that subject. Now you need to narrow your search to the kind of dinosaur you are interested in, for example, *Tyrannosaurus rex.* You can type in *Tyrannosaurus rex* or just look through the list to find titles that you think would have information you need. Once you have selected a short list of books, click on each selection to find out if the library has the books. Then, check on where they are located in the library.

Helpful Hints

- Remember that you can use the computer to search by subject, author, or title. If you know a book's author, but not the title, you can search for all the books the library has by that author.
- When searching by subject, it's often most helpful to narrow your search by using specific search terms. If you don't find enough, you can then broaden your search.
- Pay attention to the type of materials found in your search. If you need a book, you can eliminate any videos or other resources that come up in your search.
- Knowing how your library is arranged can save a lot of time. The librarian will show you where certain types of material are kept and how to find something.

Technology Skill Handbook

Developing Multimedia Presentations

It's your turn—you have to present your science report to the entire class. How do you do it? You can use many different sources of information to get the class excited about your presentation. Posters, videos, photographs, sound, computers, and the Internet can help show our ideas. First, decide the most important points you want your presentation to make. Then, sketch out what materials and types of media would be best to illustrate those points. Maybe you could start with an outline on an overhead projector, then show a video, followed by something from the Internet or a slide show accompanied by music or recorded voices. Make sure you don't make the presentation too complicated, or you will confuse yourself and the class. Practice your presentation a few times for your parents or brothers and sisters before you present it to the class.

Example Your assignment is to give a presentation on bird-watching. You could have a poster that shows what features you use to identify birds, with a sketch of your favorite bird. A tape of the calls of your favorite bird or a video of birds in your area would work well with the poster. If possible, include an Internet site with illustrations of birds that the class can look at.

Helpful Hints

- Carefully consider what media will best communicate the point you are trying to make.
- Keep your topic and your presentation simple.
- Make sure you learn how to use any equipment you will be using in your presentation.
- Practice the presentation several times.
- If possible, set up all of the equipment ahead of time. Make sure everything is working correctly.

Using E-Mail

It's science fair time and you want to ask a scientist a question about your project, but he or she lives far away. You could write a letter or make a phone call. But you can also use the computer to communicate. You can do this using electronic mail (E-mail). You will need a computer that is connected to an E-mail network. The computer is usually hooked up to the network by a device called a *modem.* A modem works through the telephone lines. Finally, you need an address for the person you want to talk with. The E-mail address works just like a street address to send mail to that person.

Example There are just a few steps needed to send a message to a friend on an E-mail network. First, select Message from the E-mail software menu. Then, enter the E-mail address of your friend. Next, type your message. Make sure you check it for spelling and other errors. Finally, click the Send button to mail your message and off it goes! You will get a reply back in your electronic mailbox. To read your reply, just click on the message and the reply will appear on the screen.

Helpful Hints

- Make sure that you have entered the correct address of the person you're sending the message to.
- Reread your message to make sure it says what you want to say, and check for spelling and grammar.
- If you receive an E-mail message, respond to it as soon as possible.
- If you receive frequent email messages, keep them organized by either deleting them, or saving them in folders according to the subject or sender.

Using an Electronic Spreadsheet

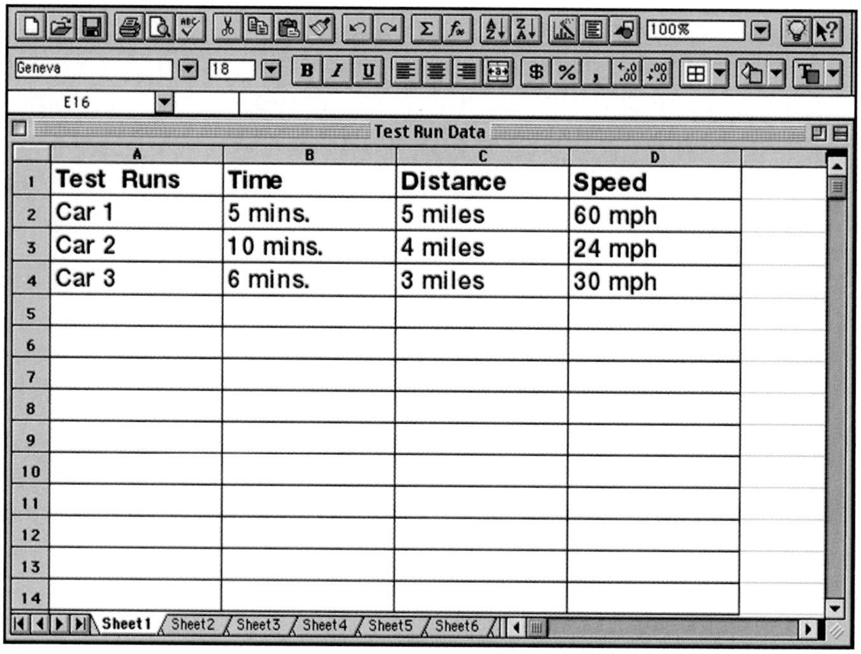

Your science fair experiment has produced lots of numbers. How do you keep track of all the data, and how can you easily work out all the calculations needed? You can use a computer program called a *spreadsheet* to keep track of data that involve numbers. A spreadsheet is an electronic worksheet. Type in your data in rows and columns, just as in a data table on a sheet of paper. A spreadsheet uses some simple math to do calculations on the data. For example, you could add, subtract, divide, or multiply any of the values in the spreadsheet by another number. Or you can set up a series of math steps you want to apply to the data. If you want to add 12 to all the numbers and then multiply all the numbers by 10, the computer does all the calculations for you in the spreadsheet. Below is an example of a spreadsheet that is a schedule.

Example Let's say that to complete your project, you need to calculate the speed of the model cars in your experiment. Enter the distance traveled by each car in the rows of the spreadsheet. Then enter the time you recorded for each car to travel the measured distance in the column across from each car. To make the formula, just type in the equation you want the computer to calculate; in this case, *speed* = *distance* ÷ *time*. You must make sure the computer knows what data are in the rows and what data are in the columns so the calculation will be correct. Once all the distance and time data and the formula have been entered into the spreadsheet program, the computer will calculate the speed for all the trials you ran. You can even make graphs of the results.

Helpful Hints

- Before you set up the spreadsheet, sketch out how you want to organize the data. Include any formulas you will need to use.
- Make sure you have entered the correct data into the correct rows and columns.
- As you experiment with your particular spreadsheet program you will learn more of its features.
- You can also display your results in a graph. Pick the style of graph that best represents the data you are working with.

Using a CD-ROM

What's your favorite music? You probably listen to your favorite music on compact discs (CDs). But, there is another use for compact discs, called CD-ROM. CD-ROM means Compact Disc-Read Only Memory. CD-ROMs hold information. Whole encyclopedias and dictionaries can be stored on CD-ROM discs. This kind of CD-ROM and others are used to research information for reports and papers. The information is accessed by putting the disc in your computer's CD-ROM drive and following the computer's installation instructions. The CD-ROM will have words, pictures, photographs, and maybe even sound and video on a range of topics.

Example Load the CD-ROM into the computer. Find the topic you are interested in by clicking on the Search button. If there is no Search button, try the Help button. Most CD-ROMs are easy to use, but refer to the Help instructions if you have problems. Use the arrow keys to move down through the list of titles on your topic. When you double-click on a title, the article will appear on the screen. You can print the article by clicking on the Print button. Each CD-ROM is different. Click the Help menu to see how to find what you want.

Helpful Hints

- Always open and close the CD-ROM drive on your computer by pushing the button next to the drive. Pushing on the tray to close it will stress the opening mechanism over time.
- Place the disc in the tray so the side with no printing is facing down.
- Read through the installation instructions that come with the CD-ROM.
- Remember to remove the CD-ROM before you shut your computer down.

Using Probeware

Data collecting in an experiment sometimes requires that you take the same measurement over and over again. With probeware, you can hook a probe directly to a computer and have the computer collect the data about temperature, pressure, motion, or pH. Probeware is a combination sensor and software that makes the process of collecting data easier. With probes hooked to computers, you can make many measurements quickly, and you can collect data over a long period of time without needing to be present. Not only will the software record the data, most software will graph the data.

Example Suppose you want to monitor the health of an enclosed ecosystem. You might use an oxygen and a carbon dioxide sensor to monitor the gas concentrations or humidity or temperature. If the gas concentrations remain stable, you could predict that the ecosystem is healthy. After all the data is collected, you can use the software to graph the data and analyze it. With probeware, experimenting is made efficient and precise.

Helpful Hints

- Find out how to properly use each probe before using it.
- Make sure all cables are solidly connected. A loose cable can interrupt the data collection and give you inaccurate results.
- Because probeware makes data collection so easy, do as many trials as possible to strengthen your data.

Using a Graphing Calculator

Science can be thought of as a means to predict the future and explain the past. In other language, if *x* happens, can we predict *y*? Can we explain the reason *y* happened? Simply, is there a relationship between *x* and *y*? In nature, a relationship between two events or two quantities, *x* and *y*, often occurs. However, the relationship is often complicated and can only be readily seen by making a graph. To analyze a graph, there is no quicker tool than a graphing calculator. The graphing calculator shows the mathematical relationship between two quantities.

Example If you have collected data on the position and time for a migrating whale, you can use the calculator to graph the data. Using the linear regression function on the calculator, you can determine the average migration speed of the whale. The more you use the graphing calculator to solve problems, the more you will discover its power and efficiency.

Graphing calculators have some keys that other calculators do not have. The keys on the bottom half of the calculator are those found on all scientific calculators. The keys located just below the screen are the graphing keys. You will also notice the up, down, left, and right arrow keys. These allow you to move the cursor around on the screen, to "trace" graphs that have been plotted, and to choose items from the menus. The other keys located on the top of the calculator access the special features such as statistical computations and programming features.

A few of the keystrokes that can save you time when using the graphing calculator are listed below.

- The commands above the calculator keys are accessed with the 2nd or ALPHA key. The 2nd key and its commands are yellow and the ALPHA and its commands are green.
- 2nd [ENTRY] copies the previous calculation so you can edit and use it again.
- Pressing ON while the calculator is graphing stops the calculator from completing the graph.
- 2nd [QUIT] will return you to the home (or text) screen.
- 2nd [A-LOCK] locks the ALPHA key, which is like pressing "shift lock" or "caps lock" on a typewriter or computer. The result is that all letters will be typed and you do not have to repeatedly press the ALPHA key. (This is handy for programming.) Stop typing letters by pressing ALPHA again.
- 2nd [OFF] turns the calculator off.

Helpful Hints

- Mastering the graphing calculator takes practice. Don't expect to learn it all in an afternoon.
- Programming a graphing calculator takes a plan. Write out all of the steps before entering them.
- It's easiest to learn how to program the calculator by first using programs that have already been written. As you enter them, figure out what each step is telling the calculator to do.

Skill Activities

Table of Contents

Separating and Controlling Variables

Background

Scientists often will conduct experiments to answer questions, test hypotheses, or solve problems. In any experiment, it is important to keep all factors the same except for the one you are testing. The factor you change is called the independent variable. If you change more than one variable in an experiment, you will not know which factor caused the effects you observe in the experiment.

Can you identify the independent variable in the following experiment?

Suppose a scientist has the job of studying the factors that affect the growth rate of marigolds. She sets up three plants to test her experiment. Descriptions of the plants are listed below.

Procedure

Study the experiment descriptions and identify the independent variable. You may wish to make a table to organize the information.

Plant 1—soil mix A, 12 hours of light per day, no fertilizer, 22°C, water every other day.

Plant 2—soil mix A, 12 hours of light per day, no fertilizer, 22°C, water once a week.

Plant 3—soil mix A, 12 hours of light per day, no fertilizer, 22°C, water every day.

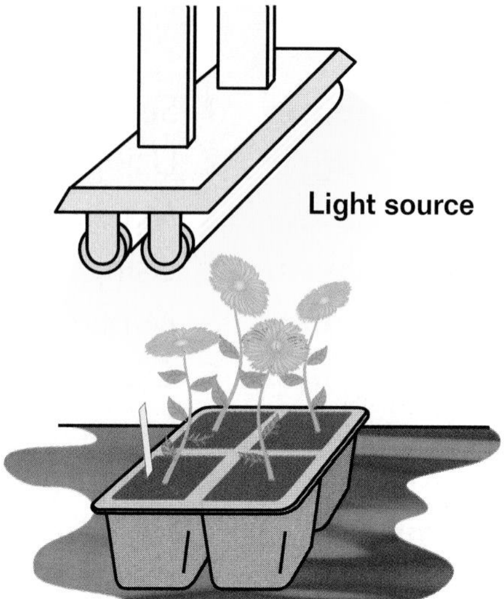

Practicing the SKILL

1. What variable is being tested in this experiment?
2. Name three other variables in this experiment.
3. Plant 2 grew taller than Plant 3. Infer what caused this effect.
4. Write a hypothesis that would be appropriate for this experimental design.
5. How might the experiment change if the scientist wanted to study the effect of sunlight on the growth rate of marigolds? Write a hypothesis for this experiment.

For more skill practice, do the Chapter 1 Interactive Exploration on the **Science Voyages Level Red CD-ROM.**

Using Numbers

Background

Data can be reported in a variety of ways. Sometimes, data presented as percentages are more useful than data presented as round numbers. For example, if you learned that your city experienced 91 days that had a high temperature of over 20°C last year, you might think that the weather was quite warm for most of the year. But, what if you learned that the temperature rose above 20°C only 25 percent of the year? Would you interpret those results differently than the first results? The data presented as a percentage can provide a meaningful description.

However, you need to make sure you know exactly what the percentage represents. Sometimes, data results can be misleading. If 70 percent of the people polled before an election said they planned to vote for candidate A and 30 percent said they planned to vote for candidate B, would you think that candidate A would be the winner? Before you make a decision based on data, you should find out if the research method is biased, or slanted toward one particular view.

Percentages provide a useful means of summarizing and reporting data. How would you go about presenting information as a percentage?

Procedure

1. Results of a class survey show the different types of transportation that 35 students use to get to school every day. Look at the data in the table.
2. To calculate the percentage of the class that walks to school, use the following formula:

$$\frac{\text{number of students who walk}}{\text{total number of students surveyed}} \times 100$$

$$\frac{10}{35} \times 100 = 29\%$$

About 29 percent of the class walks to school.

Transportation to School

Method of Transportation	Number of Students
Walk	10
Ride a bus	14
Ride a bike	4
Ride in a car	7

Practicing the SKILL

1. Use the data in the table to calculate the percentage of students who use each method of transportation.
2. There are 30 students in a class. If 65 percent of the class reports that cheese pizza is their favorite lunch, how many students is that?

For more skill practice, do the Chapter 2 Interactive Exploration on the **Science Voyages Level Red CD-ROM.**

Chapter 3

Skill Activity

Use After Section 3-4

Making Tables

Background

Tables are a way of organizing information. Sometimes information is presented in a way that is hard to understand. A well designed table can help you compare and understand data that might be confusing or mixed up. A data table is usually designed so that each row contains information about a specific item and each column contains a single characteristic that is being compared. For example, information in the Student Characteristics table compares the heights and ages of students. Each row corresponds to a particular student and one column is for height and another column is for age.

Student Characteristics

Student	Height (cm)	Age (years)
Paul	170	14
Chris	156	13
Erin	167	14
Jean	182	14

Consider this problem: a geologist has written descriptions of different rocks that were collected on a field trip.

How can you organize information about rocks?

Procedure

1. Read the paragraph labelled "Rock Descriptions," which contains six rock descriptions.
2. Construct a data table to organize the information in the paragraph that follows. Each sample should have its own row in the table and each column should contain a single rock characteristic.

Rock Descriptions

Sample 1 is a pink-gray granite. It is an igneous rock with coarse grains of quartz, biotite, and feldspar. Sample 2 is a brownish black shale. It is a fine-grained sedimentary rock containing clay minerals, quartz, and feldspar. Fossil plant leaves are found in the shale. Sample 3 is a light brown, fine-grained limestone. It is composed of the mineral calcite and has assorted shell fossils. Sample 4 is a black, fine-grained basalt. This igneous rock is composed primarily of augite, olivine, and plagioclase. Sample 5 is a beautiful, fine-grained marble that is white with faint red streaks. It is composed of metamorphosed calcite. Sample 6 is a white sandstone. This sedimentary rock contains medium-sized grains that are mostly quartz.

Practicing the SKILL

1. How many rock characteristics are compared in your data table?
2. Which mineral is found most frequently in the rock samples?
3. Which two rock samples contained fossils?
4. Do you find it easier to find the rock information in the paragraph or in the table? Explain your answer.

For more skill practice, do the Chapter 3 Interactive Exploration on the **Science Voyages Level Red CD-ROM.**

Chapter 4

Skill Activity

Use After Section 4-2

Using Numbers

Background

Wind farms and photovoltaics use renewable energy sources. In a wind farm, wind energy is produced using large wind turbines that turn generators and create electricity. Most wind farms have hundreds or thousands of wind turbines. A typical wind turbine has rotors 43 m in diameter and produces 600 kW (kilowatt). Each turbine is generally placed 5 rotor diameters apart.

Photovoltaics (PVs) are flat panels that are able to convert sunlight into electricity. A typical PV panel produces 125 W (watts) per m^2.

Both PVs and wind farms use nonpolluting, renewable energy sources—sunlight and wind. PVs have no moving parts—this is an advantage over wind turbines. However, PVs work only when the sun is shining, while wind turbines work day and night if the wind is blowing. One drawback to both of these systems is that they require large amounts of land to be able to produce electricity for many homes and businesses.

WIND FARM INFORMATION
THIS WIND FARM OF 300 ELECTRIC WIND TURBINES
IS BEING CONSTRUCTED ON THE JESS RANCH,
ALTAMONT PASS, CALIFORNIA. ELECTRICITY GENERATED
BY THE WIND TURBINES WILL BE PURCHASED AND
DISTRIBUTED BY PACIFIC GAS AND ELECTRIC COMPANY.
THE PROJECT WILL CONSERVE APPROXIMATELY 50,000
TO 60,000 BARRELS OF OIL EACH YEAR BY CONVERTING
WIND POWER TO ELECTRICITY.

Procedure

1. Study the information about wind turbines, photovoltaic panels, and electricity consumption.
2. Average domestic power demand is 0.7 kW per person. Therefore, on average, 500 000 people would require:

$$\frac{0.7 \text{ kW}}{\text{person}} \times 500\ 000 \text{ people}$$

$$= 350\ 000 \text{ kW}.$$

Practicing the SKILL

1. How many wind turbines would it take to meet the electrical needs of a city of 500 000 people?
2. How many m^2 of PV panels would it take to produce the electricity required by a city of 500 000 people?
3. Evaluate wind power and PVs. Which do you think is a better alternative energy source? Explain your answer.

For more skill practice, do the Chapter 4 Interactive Exploration on the **Science Voyages Level Red CD-ROM.**

Making Models

Background

Architects, builders, and designers often use detailed drawings as they plan their work. These are known as floorplans and represent a type of scale drawing. A scale drawing is a 2-dimensional model where an object's size and location are kept in the same proportions as in the actual object. For example, suppose a floorplan has a scale of 1 cm = 1 m. A room shown on this plan measures 10 cm × 15 cm. The actual room is 10 m × 15 m. A 1 m × 2 m desk in that room would be drawn as a rectangle 1 cm × 2 cm. The procedure below will help you make a scale drawing of your classroom.

Procedure

1. Measure the length and width of your classroom and decide on a scale to use that will allow your plan to cover most of your piece of paper. For example, if your paper is 25 cm × 36 cm and your room is 12 m × 15 m you could use a scale of 1 cm = 0.5 m. This would create a drawing of the classroom that measures 24 cm × 30 cm, which would fit on the paper.
2. Convert the dimensions of the room to your floorplan scale. Use a pencil and ruler to neatly draw the outline of the room on your paper.
3. Measure the width of the doorway and where it is located. Convert these measurements to your floorplan scale and draw the doorway on your plan.
4. Measure your teacher's desk and how far it is located from the walls. Use these measurements to accurately draw the desk in its proper position on your floorplan.
5. Repeat the procedure for any windows and other furniture in the classroom.
6. Title your classroom map and be sure to include your scale in the map key.

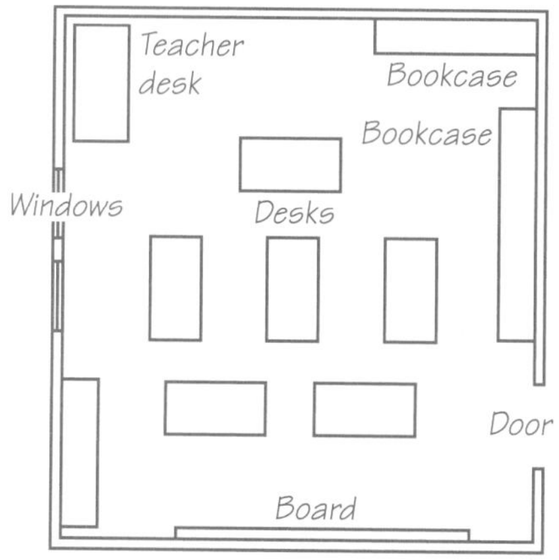

Classroom floor plan (scale: 1 cm = 2 m)

Practicing the SKILL

Imagine that your teacher has received two new computer work-stations. Each station has a desk that measures 1 m × 2 m. Use your scale drawing to determine where these work-stations might fit in the classroom. You may need to "move" some furniture on your map. Draw the workstations on your classroom floorplan.

For more skill practice, do the Chapter 5 Interactive Exploration on the **Science Voyages Level Red CD-ROM.**

Observing and Inferring

Background

You have learned that mechanical weathering occurs when rocks break apart without changing their chemical composition. Two common mechanisms of mechanical weathering are ice wedging and growing plants.

Mechanical weathering from plants can cause problems with human-made structures such as sidewalks, driveways, walls, and house foundations. These structures usually are made of concrete, a rocklike material made of sand, crushed rock, and cement. People often plant trees near sidewalks, driveways, and houses, or there may be preexisting trees in the area. Tree roots will grow beneath the concrete slabs, seeking the moisture that collects there. As the roots grow in diameter, they generate a force that is often great enough to lift and crack the concrete. A broken sidewalk is a relatively minor problem to replace, but if tree roots lift and break a house foundation, it can lead to expensive repairs.

Procedure

1. Carefully observe the outside environment where you live. Look for evidence of mechanical weathering caused by plant roots. Some good places to look might be sidewalks, driveways, and walls near large trees. In addition, you might also look for areas where plant roots have cracked large rocks.
2. Once you have found a good example, write a description and draw a sketch of the mechanical weathering you observe.
3. Use a ruler to measure in centimeters how wide a crack is, or how much the structure has been lifted by the plant. This is called displacement. Note this distance in your written description.
4. Do some research to find out when the sidewalk, driveway, or wall was built or when the tree was planted. Use this information to determine the age of the crack.

Practicing the SKILL

1. Share your observations with the class. How many different examples of mechanical weathering were observed?
2. What was the greatest amount of displacement that was observed?
3. If you were able to determine how old your structure is, divide the displacement by the age to calculate how many centimeters per year the crack moves.

For more skill practice, do the Chapter 6 Interactive Exploration on the **Science Voyages Level Red CD-ROM.**

Concept Mapping

Background

You have learned that erosion is the process by which surface materials are transported between locations by the agents of gravity, wind, water, and glaciers. Erosional agents can be divided into two main groups: erosion caused by moving or flowing water, such as rivers and ocean waves; and erosion caused by other agents like glaciers, gravity, and wind. All of these erosional forces have similarities and differences. A concept map of erosional forces can help you understand these relationships.

Procedure

A list of terms related to erosion by glaciers, gravity, and wind is written above. Study the list and create separate tree concept maps for these three agents of erosion. Select terms for each specific tree from the list. Some of the terms may not be used. Wind has been done for you.

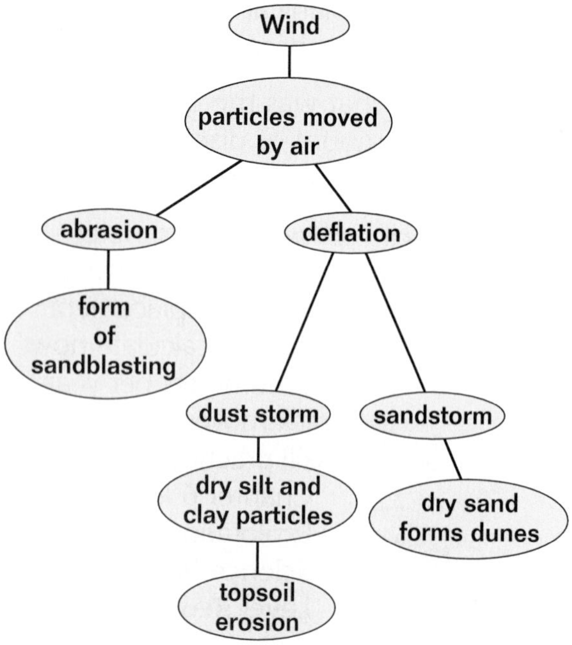

Erosion Terms	
gravity	glacial deposits
glaciers	slow movement
mass movement	glacial erosion features
till	fast movement
moraine	creep
outwash plains	rock slide
leaning trees and telephone poles	material moved by ice
mudflow	piles of broken rock
curved scars	thick mix of sediment and water
cirque	slump
arête	U-shaped valleys

Practicing the SKILL

1. Describe two characteristics that glaciers, gravity, and wind, as erosional agents, have in common.
2. For each erosional agent, describe one characteristic that is not shared by the other two agents.
3. How do concept maps help you learn about erosional forces?

For more skill practice, do the Chapter 7 Interactive Exploration on the **Science Voyages Level Red CD-ROM.**

Interpreting Scientific Illustrations

Background

A drainage basin is the land area from which a stream or river gets its water. A drainage basin can be as small as a backyard or cover thousands of square miles. The size of drainage basins can be interpreted from a topographic map.

Procedure

1. Use a sheet of tracing paper and a pencil to trace the streams on the map at right or from another topographic map your teacher has provided.
2. Use the map scale to determine the approximate size of 4 km^2 on this map. Study your stream tracings and use a colored pencil to outline the drainage basins that are larger than 4 km^2.

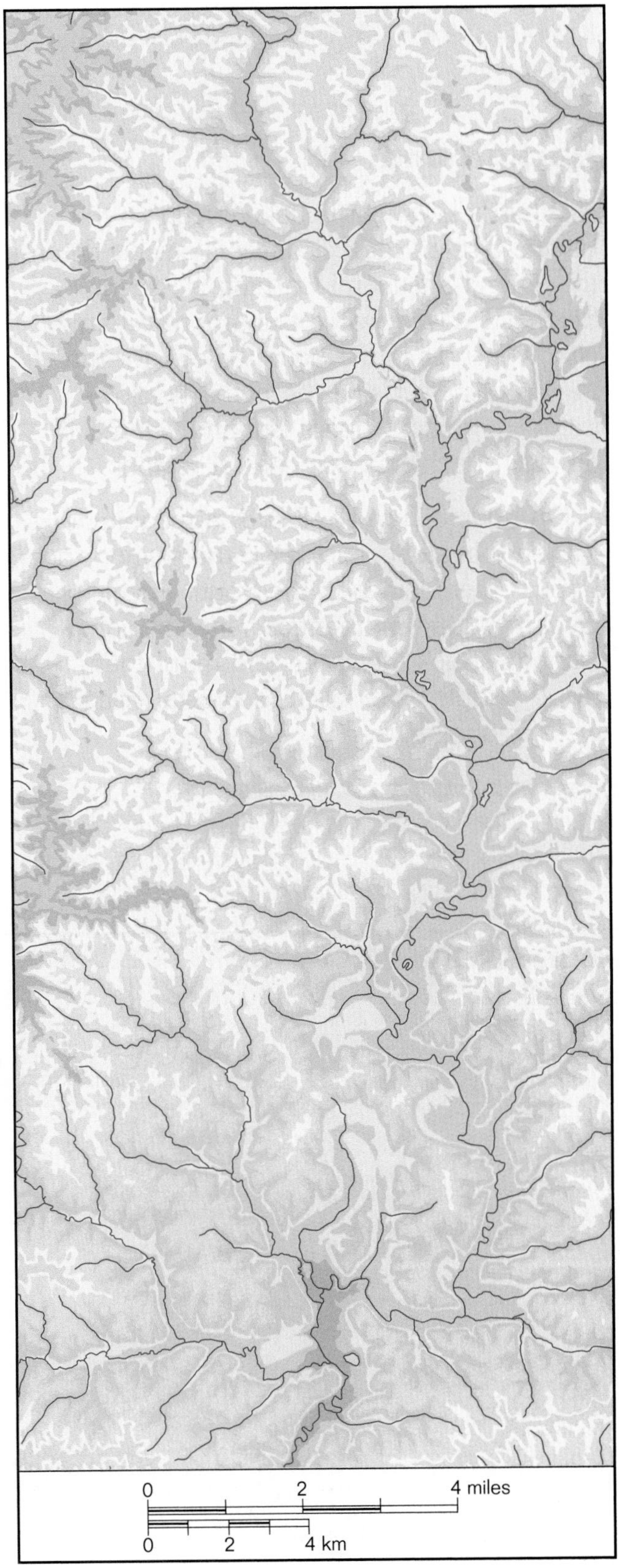

Practicing the SKILL

1. How many different drainage basins can you identify?
2. Can a stream belong to more than one drainage basin? Explain your answer.

For more skill practice, do the Chapter 8 Interactive Exploration on the **Science Voyages Level Red CD-ROM.**

Chapter 9 Skill Activity

Use After Section 9-2

Interpreting Scientific Diagrams

Background

When a large earthquake occurs in the Pacific Ocean, the epicenter is quickly determined and a tsunami warning is issued. Scientists have created tsunami travel-time charts such as in the figure below, for the Pacific Ocean. Using these charts allows them to predict when a tsunami will reach different Pacific Ocean coastal regions.

On Friday, July 17, 1998, a magnitude 7.0 earthquake occurred on the seafloor near Papua New Guinea in the South Pacific Ocean. Within moments a 7-meter-high tsunami struck the shore and more than 3000 people were killed as coastal villages were washed away.

Procedure

Study the figure below. If you know the epicenter of an earthquake you can determine when a tsunami might reach land. For example, a tsunami caused by an earthquake in Guam would take about 8 hours to reach Hilo, Hawaii.

Practicing the SKILL

1. A large earthquake off the coast of Peru has generated a tsunami. If you live in Hilo, Hawaii, how long do you have before the tsunami reaches your beach house?
2. An underwater volcanic eruption near Midway Island has caused a tsunami. How long before this wave reaches Tokyo, Japan?
3. Why was a tsunami warning of no use to the villagers in Papua New Guinea?

For more skill practice, do the Chapter 9 Interactive Exploration on the **Science Voyages Level Red CD-ROM.**

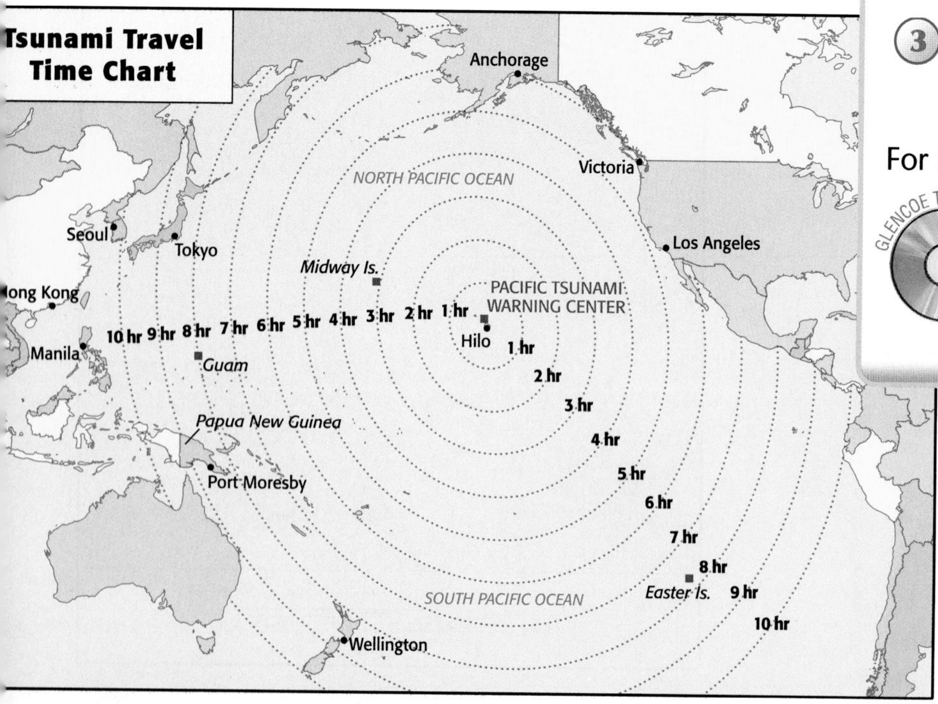

Using Numbers

Background

What do people need to survive? What is the difference between a necessity and a luxury? An earthquake can make the answers to these questions clear to people. During a damaging earthquake, basic services such as water, power, communication, and roads may be unavailable. Disaster relief experts advise that you should be prepared to be self-sufficient for 72 hours. An earthquake survival pack is a good way to be prepared.

Procedure

1. Study the list of items in the Survival Kit Items table. Decide which items are necessities and which are luxuries.
2. Using prices in your area, calculate the total cost of items you have chosen for your survival pack.

Survival Kit Items

Item	Cost ($)	Item	Cost ($)	Item	Cost ($)
aspirin or acetaminophen	1.49	prescription medicines (insulin, etc.)	varies	water-purification tablets	2.69
ipecac*	2.69	latex gloves	1.39	crackers	3.19
adhesive bandages	1.59	gauze pads 4" × 4"	2.89	canned beans	0.69
tweezers	0.99	flashlight	5.79	dried fruit	4.79
thermometer	4.29	batteries	8.49	blankets	7.99
rubbing alcohol	0.49	radio	9.99	plastic tarp	6.49
tissues	0.89	bottled water 4 liters/person	2.16	first aid handbook	4.99
pocketknife	12.99	canned tuna	2.79	matches	0.39
adhesive tape	2.19	canned juice	1.19	candles	1.99
scissors	3.19	pet food	3.00	can opener	2.39
canned heat	1.89	paper and pencil	2.00	ax	15.89
disposable dishes	2.39	antibiotic ointment	2.59	disposable utensils	2.19
bucket	3.99	chlorine bleach	0.25	eye dropper	1.99
clothing	varies	cotton swabs	0.89	signal flare	6.19
towel	5.49	books	7.50	toilet paper	0.49
elastic bandage	2.49	peanut butter	1.19	shovel	12.98

*drug used to induce vomiting in case of accidental poisoning

Practicing the SKILL

1. Which items do you consider to be the most important? Why?
2. Are there any items not on the list that you think should be included? What are they and why do you want to include them?
3. Which items would you buy if you were restricted to a 50 dollar budget?

For more skill practice, do the Chapter 10 Interactive Exploration on the **Science Voyages Level Red CD-ROM.**

Chapter 11

Skill Activity

Use After Section 11-2

Making and Using Bar Graphs

Background

You have learned that composite volcanoes can sometimes erupt violently, throwing large volumes of material into the atmosphere. Volcanologists have used various methods to rank these explosive eruptions. One of the most commonly used is to compare the volumes of erupted material. Because the amount of material is huge, scientists use cubic kilometers (km^3). A cubic kilometer is the amount of material in a cube that measures one kilometer on each side. That's a lot of rock!

Procedure

The Volcano Information table contains information about violent volcanic eruptions from around the world. Use these data to make a bar graph that compares the volume of material that was ejected by these volcanoes. Put the eruption date on the *x*-axis and the volume of material on the *y*-axis.

Practicing the SKILL

1. When was the largest eruption of Mount St. Helens? How many km^3 of material were ejected?
2. How are the data organized in the Volcano Information table?
3. What was the largest eruption of the 20th century? When did it occur?

For more skill practice, do the Chapter 11 Interactive Exploration on the **Science Voyages Level Red CD-ROM.**

Volcano Information

Volcano Name and Location	Eruption Date	Volume (km^3)
Mount Pinatubo, Philippines	1991	5.0
El Chichón, Mexico	1982	0.85
Mount St. Helens, Washington	1980	1.3
Mount Katmai, Alaska	1912	12.8
Mount Pelée, Martinique	1902	0.85
Krakatau, Indonesia	1883	19.0
Mount St. Helens, Washington	1842–1857	1.5
Tambora, Indonesia	1815	32.0
Mount Fuji, Japan	1707	2.1
Mount St. Helens, Washington	1480–1482	2.6
Vesuvius, Italy (Pompeii)	A.D. 79	3.0
Mount St. Helens, Washington	1900 B.C.	3.4
Mount Mazama, Oregon (Crater Lake)	5000 B.C.	43.0

Observing and Inferring

Background

Throughout Earth's history, many changes have taken place. Unfortunately, there is no written record from prehistoric time. There are clues to Earths past imbedded in rock though. fossils are the remains of once living organisms that have been preserved in rock.

Scientists study fossils in order to gain knowledge about the organism. They also learn what the environment was like when the organism was alive.Scientists look at (observe) the fossil and estimate (infer) what the environment was like during the lifetime of the organism. In this skill activity, you will make observations of certain fossils and infer the type of environment that existed when the organism was alive.

Organism	Location
	•Found in California •1 million years old
	•Found in Kansas •1.5 million years old
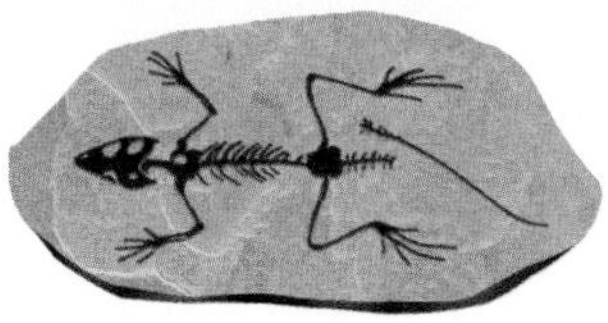	•Found in Wyoming •5 million years old

Procedure

1. Look at the table above. What type of organism is fossilized in each rock in this table? Research the conditions necessary for each of these organisms to survive.
2. Read the information given about each fossil next to the picture.

Practicing the SKILL

1. What can you infer abut the environment of the fossil found in California?
2. What does finding a reptile fossil tell you about the climate in Wyoming 5 million years ago?
3. What can you infer about the fossil found in Kansas?

For more skill practice, do the Chapter 12 Interactive Exploration on the **Science Voyages Level Red CD-Rom.**

Chapter 13 Skill Activity

Use after Section 13-2

Interpreting Data

Background

Dinosaurs were a successful group of animals. They lived on Earth for about 160 million years and became extinct about 66 million years ago. Several species of dinosaur, such as *Tyrannosaurus rex* and Stegosaurus, are well known. Many people have the misconception that these well known dinosaurs lived at the same time. During the Jurassic and Cretaceous periods, species of dinosaurs died out while new species developed. In other words, not all the dinosaurs lived at the same time. The approximate time periods for several well-known dinosaurs are listed in the Life Spans table.

Interpret the age relationships between different dinosaurs.

Life Spans

Dinosaur Species	Approximate time that species lived (million yrs ago)
Allosaurus	180-144
Ankylosaurus	90-66
Apatosaurus	185-144
Brachiosaurus	165-140
Diplodocus	180-125
Iguanodon	144-110
Megalosaurus	208-170
Stegosaurus	170-150
Tyrannosaurus rex	100-66
Triceratops	90-66
Velociraptor	95-66

Procedure

Use the information in the Life Spans table and a geologic time scale in Chapter 13 to answer the following questions.

a. Which dinosaur species were present at the end of the Cretaceous Period?

b. Which dinosaur species lived during the Upper Jurassic Period and survived into the Lower Cretaceous?

c. Which dinosaur species lived during the Jurassic Period?

Practicing the SKILL

Read each of the following statements and decide if it could be true or must be false. Explain your answer.

1. A Tyrannosaurus skeleton has been found with Ankylosaurus bones in the stomach region.
2. The bones of Megalosaurus, Brachiosaurus, and Iguanodon are found mixed together in a fossil bed.
3. Triceratops were frequent prey for groups of Velociraptors.

For more skill practice, do the Chapter 13 Interactive Exploration on the **Science Voyages Level Red CD-Rom.**

Predicting

Background

In the early 1600s Galileo began to observe the sun with a telescope and noticed dark spots on the surface of the sun. Scientists now know that sunspots are cooler regions on the sun's surface. The lower temperature causes these areas to appear as dark spots against the hotter, lighter colored background. Astronomers noticed that sunspots were temporary features lasting a few days or months. They began to keep track of the numbers of sunspots.

When does the sun display large numbers of sunspots? Solar maximums are times when there are large numbers of sunspots. Conversely, solar minimums are times of relatively few sunspots. It can be important to predict solar maximums because solar flares are associated with sunspots. The intense radiation from solar flares affects Earth's atmosphere and can disrupt radio, telephone, and television signals. In addition, this radiation can disable satellites and pose a hazard to astronauts in orbit.

Procedure

The sunspot table lists the average number of sunspots per month each year from 1954–1997. Use these data to construct a line graph of sunspot activity for these years.

Practicing the SKILL

1. Describe the pattern you observe in sunspot activity over the last 44 years.
2. Predict when the next solar maximum will occur.
3. Predict the average number of sunspots per month during the next solar maximum.

For more skill practice, do the Chapter 14 Interactive Exploration on the **Science Voyages Level Red CD-ROM.**

Sunspots

Year	Avg. # sunspots/mo.	Year	Avg. # sunspots/mo.	Year	Avg. # sunspots/mo.	Year	Avg. # sunspots/mo.
1954	5	1965	15	1976	12	1987	29
1955	38	1966	46	1977	27	1988	99
1956	141	1967	93	1978	93	1989	157
1957	189	1968	105	1979	155	1990	142
1958	194	1969	105	1980	154	1991	145
1959	158	1970	104	1981	140	1992	94
1960	112	1971	66	1982	116	1993	55
1961	54	1972	68	1983	66	1994	30
1962	38	1973	38	1984	45	1995	17
1963	28	1974	34	1985	18	1996	9
1964	10	1975	15	1986	13	1997	21

Interpreting Scientific Illustrations

Background

Weather changes are caused by the movements of air masses. Meteorologists keep track of where air masses are moving in order to predict or forecast future weather. The area where two air masses come together is called a front. One type of front, a cold front, is formed when cold air pushes up warm air, causing a narrow band of violent storms. Tornados, hail, heavy rain, and strong winds can all occur along cold fronts. Strong cold fronts that move south from Canada are carefully monitored so that severe weather warnings can be issued to people living in the path of the storms. In this activity, you will predict the movement of a cold front.

Procedure

1. Examine the map below. It is a weather map showing the location of a cold front moving from Canada. This front is moving south at an average speed of 30 km/h.

   How many kilometers will the front travel in 24 hours? Use the formula:

   distance = rate × time ($d = rt$)

2. You can also calculate how much time it will take for the front to reach a specific city by using this formula:

   time = distance ÷ rate ($t = d/r$)

   How long will it take for the front to reach the cities of Bismarck, North Dakota; Lincoln, Nebraska; and Des Moines, Iowa?

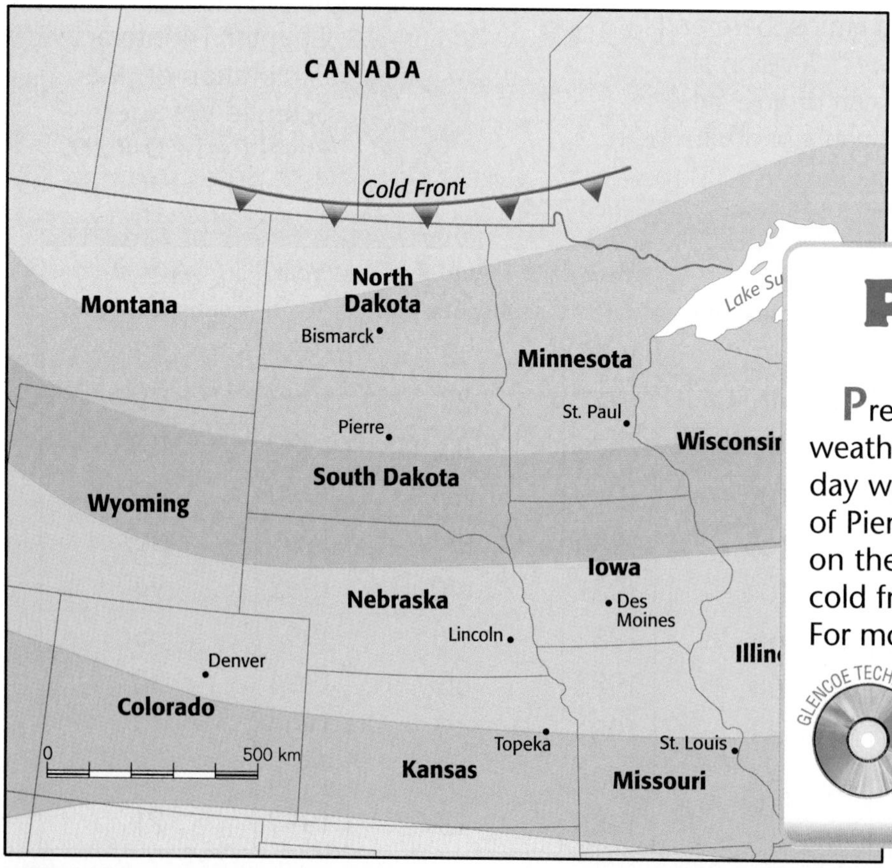

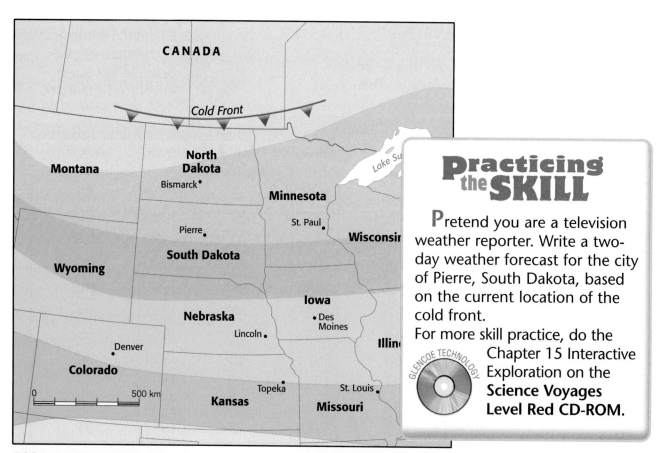

Practicing the SKILL

Pretend you are a television weather reporter. Write a two-day weather forecast for the city of Pierre, South Dakota, based on the current location of the cold front.

For more skill practice, do the Chapter 15 Interactive Exploration on the **Science Voyages Level Red CD-ROM.**

Interpreting Data

Background

Scientists use air bubbles trapped in glacial ice to study Earth's past climate. They drill a sample of ice out of the glacier. Air bubbles trapped in this ice contain atmospheric gases. The composition of these gases can be analyzed to give an indication of past average global temperatures.

How have average global temperatures changed over the past 160 000 years? The figure below is a graph of Vostok Ice core data so named because it was drilled in east Antarctica at the Soviet Research Station Vostok. The values plotted are the difference between past global temperatures and the present. For example, –2°C means that the average temperature was 2°C colder than presently. Scientists have determined that an ice age occurs when the average temperature is only 5°C colder than today.

Procedure

Study the figure below. Use this graph to infer past climate conditions on Earth.

Practicing the SKILL

1. How long ago did the last ice age end?
2. What percent of the last 160 000 years was spent in ice ages?
3. How often in the last 160 000 years has the average temperature been about the same or warmer than the present average temperature?
4. If Earth was currently experiencing an ice age, what climatic conditions do you think would exist at your location? How would they differ from present conditions?

For more skill practice, do the Chapter 16 Interactive Exploration on the **Science Voyages Level Red CD-ROM.**

Average Global Temperature Compared to Present

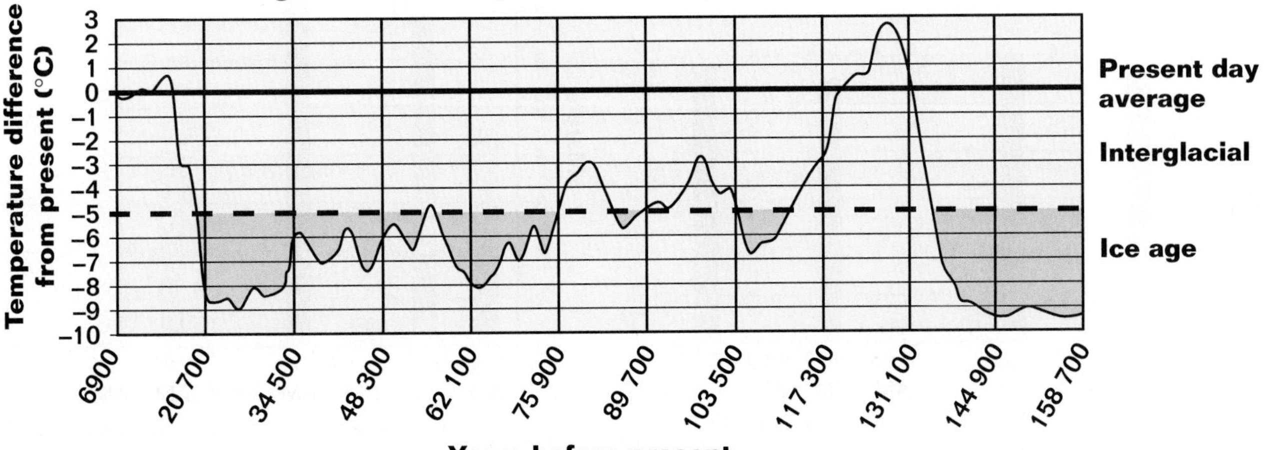

Comparing and Contrasting

Background

You have learned that ocean tides are caused by the gravitational interactions of the sun, moon, and Earth. Most coastal locations experience two high and two low tides each day. However, the amplitude, or overall height, of these tides varies a great deal from place to place. The size of the ocean basin, the shape of the coastline, and the depth of the water are local factors affecting tides.

Procedure

1. Study the tide graphs for Charleston, South Carolina, and Bellingham, Washington. Compare and contrast their patterns.
2. Use a United States map to find these two coastal cities that are represented by the tide graphs.

Practicing the SKILL

1. What are the similarities between the locations of Charleston and Bellingham? What are the differences?
2. Describe the similarities and differences between the two tide graphs.
3. What is the maximum tidal range for each city and when did it occur?
4. When did neap tide conditions occur? Draw a diagram showing the positions of the sun, moon, and Earth during this time period.

For more skill practice, do the

Chapter 17 Interactive Exploration on the **Science Voyages Level Red CD-ROM.**

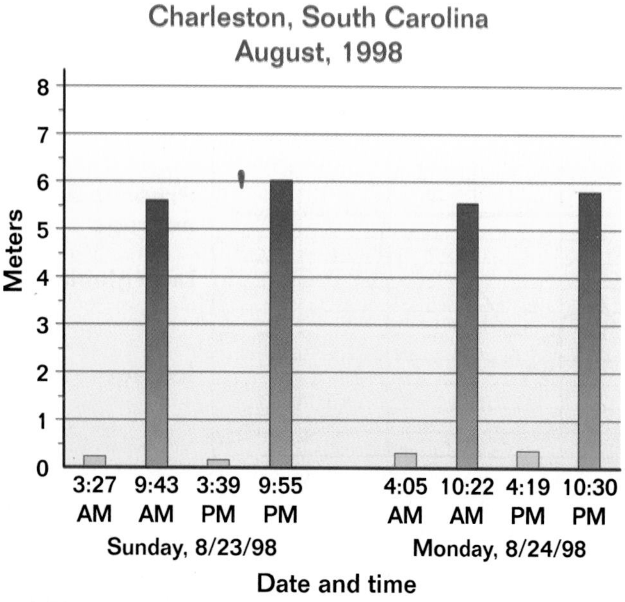

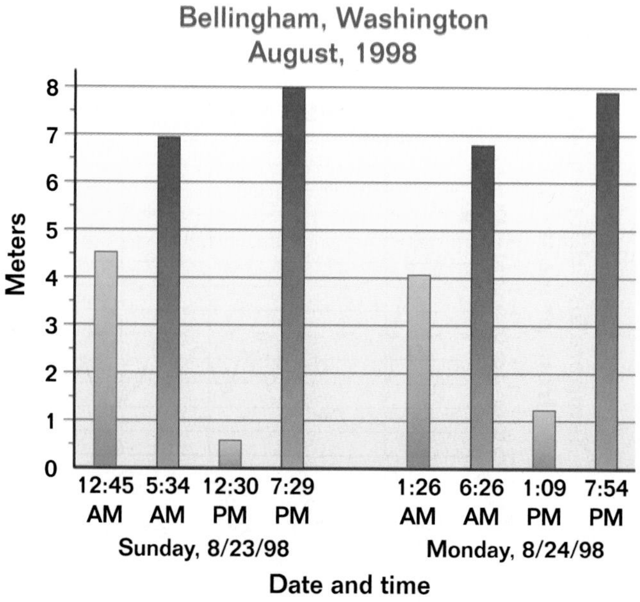

Chapter 18

Skill Activity

Use After Section 18-2

Interpreting Scientific Illustrations

Background

During a total solar eclipse, the moon's shadow falls on Earth. The darkest part of the shadow, the umbra, traces a narrow, curved path across Earth's surface. By plotting the moon's orbit and phases, scientists are able to predict the umbra's path for future total solar eclipses. The world map below shows the times and locations of all total solar eclipses until the year 2020.

When and where will future total solar eclipses occur?

Procedure

1. Study the map of future eclipses.
2. Answer the questions in the Practicing the Skill box.

Practicing the SKILL

1. When will the next total solar eclipse occur in the United States? How old will you be at this time?
2. Which eclipse path will be located mostly over the ocean?
3. How many total solar eclipses will occur between the years 1999 and 2020?

For more skill practice, do the Chapter 18 Interactive Exploration on the **Science Voyages Level Red CD-ROM.**

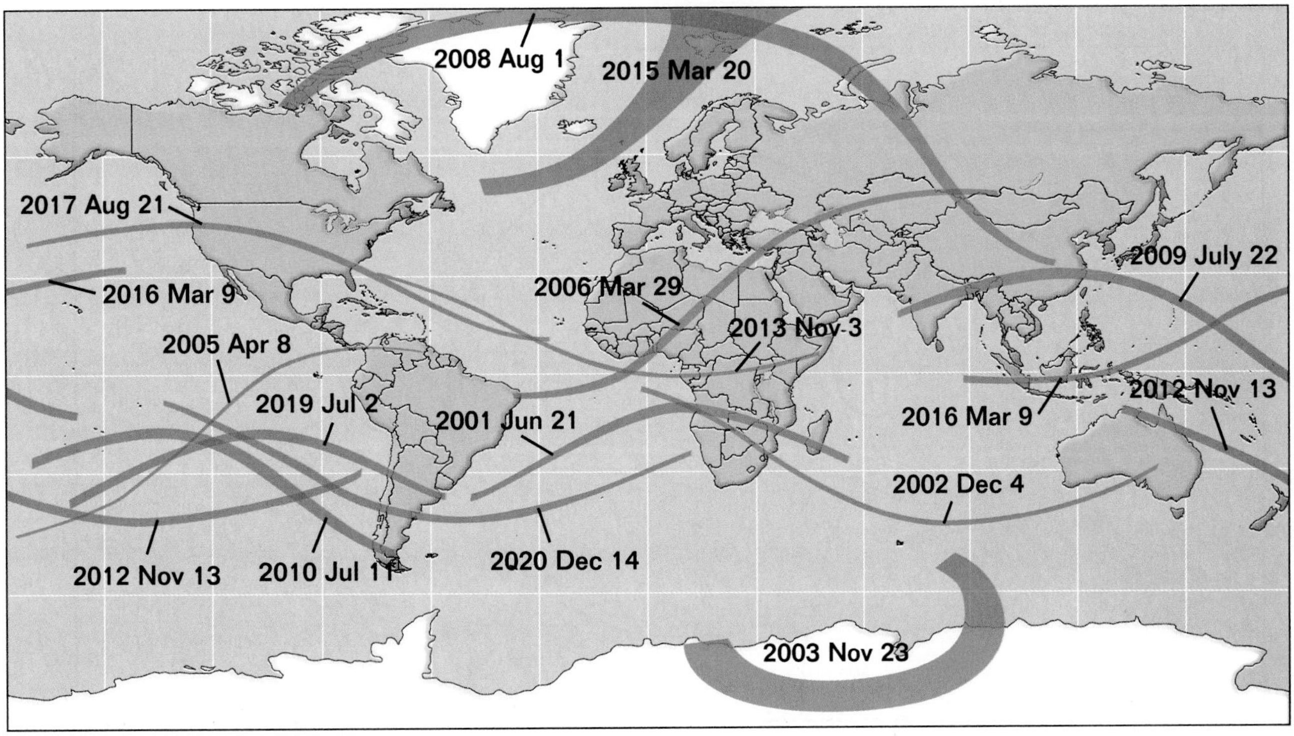

Inferring

Background

The surfaces of Earth's moon, Mercury, and other planetary bodies often are covered with craters. Scientists usually are unable to determine the exact age of the craters because they do not have actual rock samples. However, photographs taken by satellites help scientists determine the rough ages of the craters. For example, if two craters overlap, the crater that appears to be underneath is the older of the two.

Procedure

1. The diagram below shows an area containing several craters. Each crater is labeled by a letter in its center. Study the relationships between the craters and determine their relative ages.

Practicing the SKILL

1. Which crater occurred first, crater A or crater C?
2. Can the rough age of crater J be determined? Why or why not?
3. What is the estimated diameter of crater D?
4. List craters A through I in order of increasing age (youngest crater first).

For more skill practice, do the Chapter 19 Interactive Exploration on the **Science Voyages Level Red CD-ROM.**

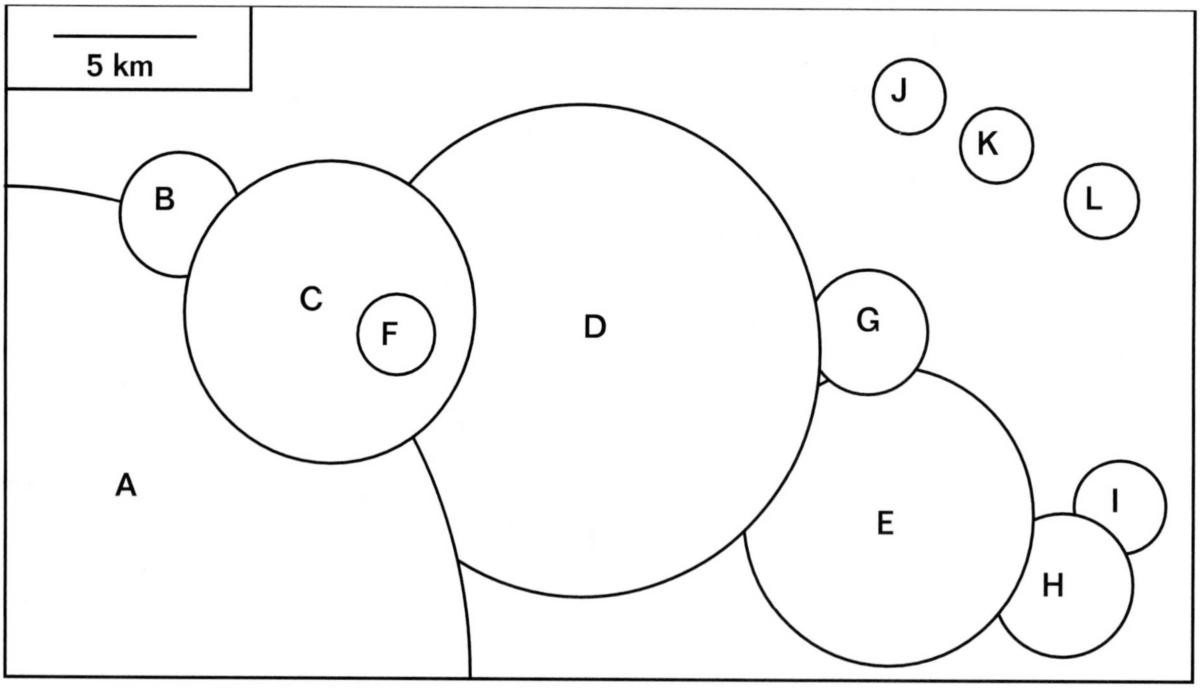

Skill Activity

Predicting

Background

Astronomical distances are measured in light-years. A light-year is the distance that light can travel in one year. Proxima Centauri is a star that is 4.2 light-years away from Earth. When astronomers observe Proxima Centauri, they are seeing what occurred 4.2 years ago. In other words, when you look at the stars, you are looking back in time. The light astronomers observe for Proxima Centauri left the star 4.2 years ago.

What was happening on Earth when a star's light began its journey?

Star Distances

Star	Distance from Earth in light-years	Star	Distance from Earth in light-years
Sirius	8.8	Deneb	1800
Arcturus	36	Barnard's Star	5.9
Rigel	920	Wolf 359	7.6
Betelgeuse	310	Procyon	11
Antares	330	Altair	17
Vega	26	Regulus	85

Procedure

1. The Star Distances table lists the distances to several different stars. Study these distances to determine how long the light has been traveling toward Earth.
2. Using your history references, find a significant event that occurred when light from a particular star began its journey to Earth.
3. Make a data table that lists the significant historical events that occurred when light from the stars began the journey to Earth. Include the historical event, date, and the star in your table. Use at least six of the stars listed.

Practicing the SKILL

1. On July 20, 1969, astronauts landed on the moon. If a television signal showing this landing had been broadcast out to space, which stars would it have reached by the year 2000? by 2005? (Television signals travel at the speed of light, which is 300 000 km/s in a vacuum.)
2. Describe a historic event that took place when light from Rigel began traveling toward Earth.
3. How many times farther is Arcturus from Earth than Barnard's Star is?

For more skill practice, do the Chapter 20 Interactive Exploration on the **Science Voyages Level Red CD-ROM.**

English Glossary

This glossary defines each key term that appears in bold type in the text. It also shows the chapter and page number where you can find the word used.

Pronunciation Key

a...**ba**ck (bak)	oh...g**o** (goh)	sh...**sh**elf (shelf)
ay...d**ay** (day)	aw...s**o**ft (sawft)	ch...na**t**ure (nay chur)
ah...f**a**ther (fahth ur)	or...**or**bit (or but)	g...**g**ift (gihft)
ow...fl**ow**er (flow ur)	oy...c**oi**n (coyn)	j...**g**em (jem)
ar...**car** (car)	oo...f**oo**t (foot)	ing...**sing** (sing)
e...**le**ss (les)	ew...f**oo**d (fewd)	zh...vi**s**ion (vihzh un)
ee...**lea**f (leef)	yoo...p**u**re (pyoor)	k...ca**k**e (kayk)
ih...tr**i**p (trihp)	yew...**few** (fyew)	s...**s**eed, **c**ent (seed, sent)
i (i + con + e)...**i**dea (i dee uh), l**i**fe (life)	uh...comm**a** (cahm uh)	z...**z**one, rai**s**e (zohn, rayz)
	u (+ con)...flow**er** (flo ur)	

A

absolute dating: process that uses the properties of atoms in rocks and other objects to determine their exact ages, in years. (ch. 20, p. 573)

acceleration: rate at which speed or direction changes; can be found by dividing the change in speed by the given time. (ch. 8, p. 213)

acid rain: rain or snow with a pH below 5.6; results from the mixture of water vapor and air pollutants in the atmosphere. (ch. 19, p. 542)

active immunity: long-lasting immunity that occurs when the body makes its own antibodies to inactivate an antigen. (ch. 17, p. 470)

active transport: energy-requiring movement of substances through a cell membrane. (ch. 3, p. 80)

adolescence: stage of development when a person becomes physically able to reproduce, beginning around ages 12 to 13. (ch. 16, p. 450)

adulthood: final stage in a person's development, extending from the end of adolescence to old age. (ch. 16, p. 452)

alleles (uh LEELZ): different forms a gene may have for a trait. (ch. 6, p. 152)

allergen: substance that causes an allergic reaction. (ch. 17, p. 479)

allergy: overly strong reaction of the immune system to a foreign substance (an allergen). (ch. 17, p. 478)

alternation of generations: occurs when a plant's life cycle alternates between a sex-cell–producing stage and a spore-producing stage. (ch. 5, p. 125)

alveoli (al VE uh li): in the lungs, the tiny, thin-walled sacs arranged in grapelike clusters at the end of each bronchiole; oxygen and carbon dioxide exchange takes place between the alveoli and capillaries. (ch. 14, p. 386)

amino acid: building block of protein. (ch. 12, p. 328)

amniotic (am nee AH tihk) **sac:** thin membrane that begins to form around the embryo during the third week of pregnancy; helps cushion and protect the unborn baby and can store nutrients and wastes. (ch. 16, p. 445)

amphibians: animals that live on land and breathe air but return to water to reproduce. (ch. 22, p. 628)

antibody: protein made by the body in response to a specific antigen and that reacts with the antigen to make it harmless. (ch. 17, p. 470)

antigens: proteins and chemicals that are foreign to the body. (ch. 17, p. 470)

antiseptic: agent that is applied to the skin to kill pathogens and prevent their regrowth. (ch. 17, p. 464)

artery: blood vessel with a thick elastic wall made of smooth muscle that moves blood away from the heart. (ch. 13, p. 358)

asexual reproduction: process by which a new organism is produced that has DNA identical to the DNA of the parent organism. (ch. 4, p. 101)

asthma (AZ muh): lung disorder in which there may be shortness of breath, wheezing, or coughing and that may occur as an allergic reaction. (ch. 14, p. 391)

atherosclerosis (ah thur oh skluh ROH sus): cardiovascular condition resulting from fatty deposits on arterial walls, which can clog blood vessels and interfere with blood flow. (ch. 13, p. 362)

atria (AY tree uh): two upper chambers of the heart. (ch. 13, p. 355)

average speed: distance traveled divided by the time it takes to travel this distance. (ch. 8, p. 212)

axon (AK sahn): branch of neuron that carries messages, or impulses, away from the cell body. (ch. 15, p. 409)

B

balanced forces: describes forces acting on an object that cancel each other. (ch. 8, p. 220)

basaltic: dense, heavy, dark-colored igneous rock that is rich in magnesium and iron. (ch. 18, p. 501)

bladder: muscular, elastic organ that holds urine until it leaves the body. (ch. 14, p. 397)

blood pressure: force exerted on vessel walls by blood when the heart pumps it through the cardiovascular system; normally 120 over 80 for a young adult. (ch. 13, p. 359)

brain stem: part of the brain that controls heartbeat, breathing, and blood pressure by coordinating the involuntary movements of these functions; extends from the cerebrum and connects the brain to the spinal cord. (ch. 15, p. 411)

bronchi: two short branches at the lower end of the trachea that carry air into the lungs. (ch. 14, p. 386)

C

cancer: chronic, noncommunicable disease that results from uncontrolled cell division. (ch. 17, p. 478)

capillary: microscopic blood vessel that connects arteries and veins; nutrients, oxygen, waste materials, and carbon dioxide diffuse through its walls. (ch. 13, p. 359)

carbohydrates (kar boh HI drayts): class of organic nutrients that supplies the body with its major energy sources—sugar, starch, and cellulose; contain carbon, hydrogen, and oxygen atoms. (ch. 12, p. 327)

carbonaceous (kar boh NAY shus) **film:** fossil formed when the remains of a once-living organism are subjected to heat and pressure, leaving only a thin film of carbon behind. (ch. 20, p. 559)

cardiac muscle: striated, involuntary muscle that is found only in the heart. (ch. 11, p. 313)

cartilage: thick, slippery tissue layer covering the ends of bones; absorbs shock and helps make joint movements easier by reducing friction. (ch. 11, p. 304)

cast: fossil formed when sediments fill a mold and harden into rock. (ch. 20, p. 559)

cell membrane: structure that allows only certain things to pass in and out of the cell and forms the outer boundary of the cell. (ch. 2, p. 50)

cell theory: major theory based on observations and conclusions by many scientists; states that the cell is the basic unit of life, organisms are composed of one or more cells, and all cells come from other cells. (ch. 2, p. 44)

cell wall: rigid structure that supports and protects the plant cell and is made mostly of bundles of cellulose fibers. (ch. 2, p. 55)

cementation: process of sedimentary rock formation in which large sediments are held together by natural cements produced when water soaks through rock and soil. (ch. 18, p. 509)

Cenozoic (sen uh ZOH ihk) **era:** geologic era in which we live; began with the extinction of dinosaurs and many other life-forms. (ch. 22, p. 638)

central nervous system: division of the nervous system, containing the brain and spinal cord, which sorts and interprets information from stimuli. (ch. 15, p. 410)

cerebellum (ser uh BEL um): part of the brain that coordinates voluntary muscle movements and maintains balance and muscle tone; located behind and under the cerebrum. (ch. 15, p. 411)

cerebrum (suh REE brum): largest part of the brain; is divided into two hemispheres; controls the work of voluntary muscles, interprets impulses from the senses, and stores memory. (ch. 15, p. 411)

chemical digestion: process that breaks down large molecules of food into different, smaller molecules that can be absorbed by the body's cells; takes place in the mouth, stomach, and small intestine. (ch. 12, p. 340)

chemotherapy: use of chemicals to destroy cancer cells. (ch. 17, p. 478)

childhood: period from the end of infancy to age 12 that is marked by development of muscular coordination and mental abilities. (ch. 16, p. 450)

chloroplast: green, chlorophyll-containing organelle in the cytoplasm of many plant cells, where plants make their own food. (ch. 2, p. 55)

chromatin: long strands of hereditary material within the cell nucleus that are made up of proteins and DNA. (ch. 2, p. 51)

chromosomes: structures in the cell nucleus that contain hereditary material. (ch. 4, p. 99)

chronic bronchitis: long-lasting respiratory disease in which the bronchial tubes are irritated and too much mucus is produced. (ch. 14, p. 389)

chyme (KIME): thin, watery product that is the result of digestion. (ch. 12, p. 342)

circuit: closed, unbroken path through which an electric current can flow. (ch. 10, p. 277)

cochlea (KOH klee uh): structure of the inner ear that is shaped like a snail's shell and contains fluids that vibrate, sending impulses to the brain by the auditory nerve. (ch. 15, p. 417)

communicable disease: disease that spreads from an infected organism or the environment through agents such as viruses, fungi, protists, and some bacteria. (ch. 17, p. 465)

compaction: formation of solid sedimentary rock in which layers of small sediments build up and are squeezed together by the weight of the overlying sediment layers. (ch. 18, p. 509)

compound light microscope: magnifies by allowing light to pass through an object and then through two or more lenses. (ch. 2, p. 41)

compound machine: combination of two or more simple machines. (ch. 9, p. 248)

concave lens: lens whose edges are thicker than its middle; causes light waves to diverge. (ch. 7, p. 197)

conductor: material, such as copper, silver, and iron, through which electrons can move easily. (ch. 10, p. 273)

constant: variable that stays the same in an experiment. (ch. 1, p. 19)

consumer: organism that can't make its own food. (ch. 3, p. 83)

control: sample that is treated like other experimental groups except that the variable is not applied. (ch. 1, p. 19)

convex lens: lens whose center is thicker than its edges; causes light waves to converge. (ch. 7, p. 196)

coronary (KOR uh ner ee) **circulation:** flow of blood to the tissues of the heart. (ch. 13, p. 357)

cyanobacteria: one of the earliest life-forms on Earth; evolved during Precambrian time. (ch. 22, p. 625)

cytoplasm: constantly moving, gelatin-like mixture inside the cell membrane; contains structures that carry out life processes of the cell. (ch. 2, p. 52)

D

dendrite: branch of neuron that receives messages and sends them to the cell body. (ch. 15, p. 409)

dependent variable: factor that is being measured in an experiment. (ch. 1, p. 19)

dermis: layer of tissue beneath the dermis; contains blood vessels, nerves, and oil and sweat glands. (ch. 11, p. 318)

diaphragm (DI uh fram): muscle beneath the lungs that contracts and relaxes with breathing and that helps move air in and out of the body. (ch. 14, p. 387)

diffusion: movement of molecules from areas where there are more of them to areas where there are fewer of them. (ch. 3, p. 77)

digestion: mechanical and chemical process that breaks down food into small molecules so they can be used by the body's cells. (ch. 12, p. 338)

disinfectant: agent that is used to kill disease-causing organisms on objects such as surgical instruments. (ch. 17, p. 464)

DNA (deoxyribonucleic [dee AHK sih ri boh noo klay ihk] acid): chemical that contains an organism's information code and is found in the cell nucleus; is made up of two twisted strands of sugar-phosphate molecules and nitrogen bases. (ch. 4, p. 110)

dominant (DAHM uh nunt): describes a trait that covers up, or dominates, another form of the trait. (ch. 6, p. 154)

E

efficiency: ability of a machine to convert work input to work output; always less than 100 percent in real machines due to some loss to friction or heat. (ch. 9, p. 256)

effort force (F_e): force applied to a machine. (ch. 9, p. 248)

egg: sex cell that is formed in the reproductive organs of a female and has only half the number of chromosomes of a body cell. (ch. 4, p. 104)

electric current: continuous flow of electrons through a conductor; measured in units of amperes (A). (ch. 10, p. 277)

electric discharge: rapid movement of excess electrons from one place to another. (ch. 10, p. 274)

electrical power: rate at which an appliance converts electrical energy to another form of energy; unit is the watt (W). (ch. 10, p. 288)

electromagnetic wave: type of wave, such as a light wave or a radio wave, that can travel in a vacuum as well as in various materials. (ch. 7, p. 180)

electron microscope: bends beams of electrons in a magnetic field and can magnify images up to one million times or more. (ch. 2, p. 42)

embryo: unborn child during the first two months of pregnancy. (ch. 16, p. 444)

embryology (em bree AHL uh jee): study of development in organisms. (ch. 21, p. 602)

emphysema (em fuh SEE muh): respiratory disease in which the alveoli in the lungs lose their ability to expand and contract. (ch. 14, p. 390)

endangered species: species that is in danger of becoming extinct unless action is taken to protect it. (ch. 19, p. 533)

endocytosis: process in which substances too large to cross the cell membrane enter the cell; occurs when the cell membrane folds in on itself and encloses the large particles in a sphere, which pinches off, allowing the vacuole to enter the cytoplasm. (ch. 3, p. 81)

endoplasmic reticulum (ER): complex series of folded membranes in the cell cytoplasm that is involved in moving cellular products. (ch. 2, p. 52)

enzymes: specific proteins that regulate almost all chemical reactions in cells without being changed themselves (ch. 3, p. 75); molecules that speed up the rate of chemical reactions in the body. (ch. 12, p. 339)

epidermis: outer layer of the skin; constantly produces new cells to replace those that are rubbed off. (ch. 11, p. 317)

epoch: division of geologic time smaller than a period. (ch. 22, p. 617)

equilibrium: state in which the molecules of a substance are evenly distributed throughout another substance. (ch. 3, p. 78)

era: major subdivision of the geologic time scale based on differences in life-forms. (ch. 22, p. 617)

erosion: wearing away of soil by wind and water. (ch. 19, p. 532)

evolution: changes in the inherited features of a species over time; can occur slowly (gradualism) or rapidly (punctuated equilibrium). (ch. 21, p. 586)

exocytosis: process in which large particles leave the cell; occurs when vesicles and vacuoles fuse with the cell membrane and release their contents outside the cell. (ch. 3, p. 81)

extinction: dying out of an entire species either naturally or through the actions of humans. (ch. 19, p. 532)

extrusive: type of igneous rock with fine-grained texture that is formed as lava cools quickly at or near Earth's surface. (ch. 18, p. 500)

F

fats: class of organic nutrients that provides energy and helps the body absorb some vitamins; may be saturated or unsaturated. (ch. 12, p. 330)

fermentation: form of respiration without oxygen; releases only part of the energy in food. (ch. 3, p. 84)

fertilization: joining of an egg and a sperm, generally from two different organisms. (ch. 4, p. 104)

fetus: developing baby after the first two months of pregnancy until birth. (ch. 16, p. 446)

focal length: distance of the focal point from the center of the mirror or lens. (ch. 7, p. 190)

focal point: single point on the optical axis of a mirror or lens. (ch. 7, p. 190)

foliated: type of metamorphic rock, such as slate, whose mineral grains line up in parallel layers when exposed to heat and pressure. (ch. 18, p. 505)

food group: foods that contain the same nutrients; for example, the milk, yogurt, and cheese group. (ch. 12, p. 335)

force: a push or a pull; can be measured by the amount of acceleration it can give a mass. (ch. 8, p. 219)

fossil: remains or traces of a once-living organism preserved in rock. (ch. 20, p. 556)

fossil fuel: nonrenewable energy source, such as natural gas, that formed from the bodies of organisms that died hundreds of millions of years ago. (ch. 19, p. 526)

frequency: number of wavelengths that pass a point in one second. (ch. 7, p. 183)

friction: force that resists motion between two objects in contact and that always acts opposite to the direction of motion. (ch. 8, p. 225)

frond: leaf of a fern that grows from a rhizome. (ch. 5, p. 126)

fulcrum: point about which a lever pivots. (ch. 9, p. 252)

G

gametophyte (guh MEET uh fite) **stage:** plant life cycle stage in which all plant structures are made of cells with a haploid number (n) of chromosomes. (ch. 5, p. 124)

gastroliths: stones swallowed by dinosaurs and by modern birds to help with digestion. (ch. 22, p. 637)

gene: section of DNA on a chromosome that directs the making of a specific protein. (ch. 4, p. 112)

genetic engineering: changing of a gene's DNA sequence by biological and chemical methods. (ch. 6, p. 170)

genetics (juh NET ihks): study of how traits are inherited through the actions of alleles. (ch. 6, p. 153)

genotype (JEE nuh tipe): genetic makeup of an organism. (ch. 6, p. 156)

geologic time scale: record of events in Earth's history based on major evolutionary changes and geologic events; major subdivisions are eras, periods, and epochs. (ch. 22, p. 617)

geothermal energy: heat energy from below the surface of Earth. (ch. 19, p. 528)

global warming: increase in the average yearly temperature of Earth. (ch. 19, p. 543)

Golgi bodies: stacks of membrane-covered sacs that package materials and move them to the outside of the cell. (ch. 2, p. 53)

gradualism: model of evolution that shows a slow change of one species to another, new species through continued mutations and variations over time. (ch. 21, p. 592)

granitic: light-colored, silica-rich igneous rock of a lower density than basaltic rock. (ch. 18, p. 501)

gravity: attraction between all matter; a force that pulls on all objects that have mass. (ch. 8, p. 219)

greenhouse effect: warming of Earth due to a blanket of gases in the atmosphere that prevents heat from radiating back into space. (ch. 19, p. 543)

groundwater: water contained in the soil or trapped in underground pockets formed by nonporous rock; comes from rainfall and runoff that soaks through the soil. (ch. 19, p. 545)

H

half-life: time it takes for half the atoms in a radioactive isotope to decay. (ch. 20, p. 574)

hazardous waste: waste materials, such as pesticides and nuclear waste, that are harmful to human health or poisonous to living organisms and that must be properly disposed of. (ch. 19, p. 544)

helper T cell: type of white blood cell that helps other types of white blood cells produce antibodies. (ch. 17, p. 472)

hemoglobin: chemical in red blood cells that can carry oxygen and carbon dioxide. (ch. 13, p. 365)

heredity (huh RED ut ee): passing of traits from parent to offspring. (ch. 6, p. 152)

heterozygous (het uh roh ZI gus): organism that has two different alleles for a single trait. (ch. 6, p. 156)

hominids: humanlike primates that walked upright on two feet and ate both meat and vegetables. (ch. 21, p. 607)

Homo sapiens: human species thought to have evolved about 400 000 years ago. (ch. 21, p. 608)

homologous (huh MAHL uh gus): body structures that are similar in origin and show that two or more species may share common ancestors. (ch. 21, p. 601)

homozygous (hoh muh ZI gus): organism that has two identical alleles for a single trait. (ch. 6, p. 156)

hormones: endocrine chemicals that are produced from glands directly into the bloodstream and that affect target tissues. (ch. 15, p. 424)

host cell: cell in which a virus reproduces. (ch. 2, p. 60)

hydroelectric power: electricity produced by the energy of flowing water. (ch. 19, p. 528)

hypertension: cardiovascular disorder, also called high blood pressure, that can be caused by atherosclerosis. (ch. 13, p. 362)

hypothesis: prediction or statement that can be tested; may be formed by using prior knowledge, new information, and previous observations. (ch. 1, p. 18)

I

igneous rock: rock formed from fast-cooling lava at or near Earth's surface (extrusive igneous rock) and from slow-cooling magma deep inside Earth (intrusive igneous rock). (ch. 18, p. 498)

immovable joint: type of joint that allows little or no movement. (ch. 11, p. 306)

immune system: complex group of defenses that work to fight disease in the body. (ch. 17, p. 469)

inclined plane: simple machine that is a sloped surface, or ramp; allows heavy loads to be lifted by using less force over a greater distance. (ch. 9, p. 250)

incomplete dominance: production of a phenotype that is intermediate to those of the two homozygous parents. (ch. 6, p. 160)

independent variable: factor that is changed in an experiment. (ch. 1, p. 19)

index fossils: fossils of species that existed on Earth for only a short time, were abundant, and were widespread geographically; used by scientists to determine the age of rock layers. (ch. 20, p. 562)

inertia (ih NUR shah): measure of an object's ability to remain at rest or to keep moving. (ch. 8, p. 221)

infancy: period of rapid growth and development of both mental and physical skills that extends from the neonatal period to one year. (ch. 16, p. 450)

inorganic compounds: most compounds made from elements other than carbon; for example, water, which makes up a large part of living matter. (ch. 3, p. 76)

insulator: material, such as rubber or glass, through which electrons cannot move easily. (ch. 10, p. 273)

intrusive: type of igneous rock with large mineral grains that is formed from slow-cooling magma beneath Earth's surface. (ch. 18, p. 500)

involuntary muscles: muscles, such as cardiac muscles, that can't be consciously controlled. (ch. 11, p. 310)

J

joint: place where two or more bones meet; may be immovable, such as in the skull, or movable, such as in the hip. (ch. 11, p. 305)

K

kidney: bean-shaped organ of the urinary system that is made up of about one million nephrons and that filters blood to produce waste liquid (urine). (ch. 14, p. 396)

L

larynx: airway to which the vocal chords are attached. (ch. 14, p. 385)

lava: name given to the thick, gooey, molten material known as magma when it reaches

Earth's surface and flows from volcanoes. (ch. 18, p. 499)

law of reflection: states that the angle of incidence is equal to the angle of reflection. (ch. 7, p. 187)

lens: transparent object that has at least one curved side that causes light to bend. (ch. 7, p. 195)

lever: simple machine made from a rod or plank that pivots about a point. (ch. 9, p. 252)

ligament: tough band of tissue that holds bones together at joints. (ch. 11, p. 305)

light ray: narrow beam of light traveling in a straight line. (ch. 7, p. 180)

lymph: tissue fluid that has moved from around cells and into lymph vessels; consists mostly of water, dissolved substances, and lymphocytes. (ch. 13, p. 374)

lymph nodes: bean-shaped structures found throughout the body that filter out microorganisms and foreign materials engulfed by lymphocytes. (ch. 13, p. 374)

lymphatic (lihm FAT ihk) **system:** collects fluid from body tissue spaces and returns it to the blood through lymph capillaries and lymph vessels; plays a vital role in protecting against infection. (ch. 13, p. 373)

lymphocyte (LIHM fuh site): type of white blood cell produced by the lymphatic system that fights infections and foreign materials that enter the body. (ch. 13, p. 374)

lysosome: eukaryotic cell organelle that contains digestive chemicals that break down food molecules, cell wastes, and worn-out cell parts. (ch. 2, p. 54)

M

marrow: fatty, soft tissue in the center of long bones and the spaces of spongy bones; produces red blood cells and white blood cells. (ch. 11, p. 302)

mass: amount of matter in an object. (ch. 8, p. 221)

mechanical advantage (*M.A.*): comparison of the effort force to the resistance force for a machine. (ch. 9, p. 250)

mechanical digestion: process that occurs when food is chewed and mixed in the mouth and churned in the stomach. (ch. 12, p. 340)

medium: material in which a light wave travels. (ch. 7, p. 180)

meiosis (my OH sus): process by which sex cells are created in the reproductive organs, producing four haploid sex cells from one diploid cell. (ch. 4, p. 104)

melanin (MEL uh nun): pigment that gives skin its color. (ch. 11, p. 317)

menopause: occurs for most women between the ages of 45 and 60 when the menstrual cycle becomes irregular and eventually stops. (ch. 16, p. 439)

menstrual cycle: monthly cycle of changes in the female reproductive system. (ch. 16, p. 437)

menstruation: monthly discharge of blood and tissue cells from the thickened lining of the uterus that begins when a girl reaches puberty and her reproductive organs have matured. (ch. 16, p. 438)

Mesozoic (mez uh ZOH ihk) **era:** geologic era in which Pangeae broke up, the present-day continents were formed, and whose dominant land life-forms were reptiles and gymnosperms. (ch. 22, p. 633)

metabolism: total of all chemical reactions in a living thing. (ch. 3, p. 83)

metamorphic rock: rock that forms because of changes in temperature and pressure, or the presence of hot, watery fluids in igneous, sedimentary, or other metamorphic rock. (ch. 18, p. 503)

minerals: inorganic nutrients that regulate many chemical reactions in the body. (ch. 12, p. 332)

mitochondria: eukaryotic cell organelles where food molecules are broken down and energy is released. (ch. 2, p. 53)

mitosis (mi TOH sus): series of continuous steps (prophase, metaphase, anaphase, and telophase) in which the cell nucleus divides to form two identical nuclei. (ch. 4, p. 98)

mixture: combination of substances in which each substance retains its own properties. (ch. 3, p. 73)

model: mathematical equation or object that saves time and money by testing ideas that may be too large or too small, take too long to build, happen too quickly, or are too dangerous to observe directly. (ch. 1, p. 16)

mold: fossil formed when an organism is buried, decays, and leaves behind a hollow place in the rock. (ch. 20, p. 559)

movable joint: type of joint (pivot, ball-and-socket, hinge, gliding) that allows a wide range of movements. (ch. 11, p. 306)

multiple alleles: term used when a trait is controlled by more than two alleles. (ch. 6, p. 160)

muscle: organ that relaxes and contracts to allow movement of bones and body parts. (ch. 11, p. 309)

mutation: any permanent change in a gene or chromosome of a cell. (ch. 4, p. 114)

N

natural resource: material found in nature that is useful or necessary for living organisms. (ch. 19, p. 524)

natural selection: Darwin's theory of evolution, which says that organisms with traits best suited to their environments are more likely to survive and reproduce. (ch. 21, p. 589)

nephron: tiny filtering unit of the kidney. (ch. 14, p. 396)

neuron (NOO rahn): working unit of the nervous system, made up of a cell body and branches called dendrites and axons. (ch. 15, p. 409)

Newton's laws of motion: three rules describing how things move—an object will move with constant motion if no net force is acting on it; an object that has an unbalanced force acting on it will accelerate in the direction of the force; forces occur in equal but opposite pairs. (ch. 8, p. 224)

noncommunicable disease: disease that is not spread from one person to another but may result from factors such as poor diet or uncontrolled cell growth. (ch. 17, p. 476)

nonfoliated: type of metamorphic rock, such as marble, whose mineral grains grow and rearrange when exposed to heat and pressure but do not form layers. (ch. 18, p. 505)

nonrenewable resource: natural resource, such as petroleum, that is available in limited amounts and cannot be replaced or is only replaced slowly. (ch. 19, p. 525)

normal force: upward force of the ground, perpendicular to the surface. (ch. 8, p. 220)

nuclear energy: energy produced when the nuclei of uranium atoms split apart in a nuclear fission reaction. (ch. 19, p. 529)

nucleus: eukaryotic organelle that directs all the activities of the cell and is surrounded by a double membrane. (ch. 2, p. 51)

nutrients (NEW tree unts): substances in foods that provide energy and materials for cell development, growth, and repair; carbohydrates, proteins, fats, vitamins, minerals, and water. (ch. 12, p. 326)

O

Ohm's law: relationship between voltage, current, and resistance in an electric circuit; $V = IR$, where V represents the voltage, I represents the electrical current, and R the resistance. (ch. 10, p. 285)

olfactory cells: nerve cells in the nasal passages that respond to gas molecules in the air and send impulses to the brain for the interpretation of odors. (ch. 15, p. 420)

organ: structure made up of different types of tissues that work together to do a certain job. (ch. 2, p. 56)

organelle: structure within the cytoplasm of a eukaryotic cell having a specific function or functions. (ch. 2, p. 52)

organic compounds: most compounds that contain carbon; four groups make up living things: carbohydrates, lipids, proteins, and nucleic acids. (ch. 3, p. 74)

osmosis: diffusion of water through a cell membrane. (ch. 3, p. 79)

ovary: in angiosperms, the swollen base of the pistil where ovules are formed (ch. 5, p. 133); in humans, the female reproductive organ that produces eggs. (ch. 16, p. 436)

ovulation (AHV yuh LAY shun): process in which an egg is released about once a month from an ovary. (ch. 16, p. 437)

ovule: in a seed plant, the structure that contains an egg cell, food-storage tissue, and a sticky fluid. (ch. 5, p. 130)

ozone depletion: thinning of Earth's protective ozone layer, primarily from chlorofluorocarbons reacting with and destroying ozone molecules. (ch. 19, p. 543)

P

Paleozoic (pay lee uh ZOH ihk) **era:** geologic era marked by the first appearance of life-forms with hard parts. (ch. 22, p. 626)

parallel circuit: circuit that has more than one path for the electric current to follow. (ch. 10, p. 286)

passive immunity: shorter-term immunity that occurs when antibodies produced in another animal are transferred into the body. (ch. 17, p. 470)

passive transport: movement of substances through a cell membrane without the use of cellular energy. (ch. 3, p. 80)

pasteurization: process of heating food to a temperature that kills most bacteria. (ch. 17, p. 462)

pedigree: tool that shows the occurrence of a trait in a family. (ch. 6, p. 169)

period: next-smaller division of the geologic time scale after the era. (ch. 22, p. 617)

periosteum (per ee AHS tee um): tough, tight-fitting membrane that covers the surface of bones. (ch. 11, p. 303)

peripheral (puh RIHF rul) **nervous system:** division of the nervous system, made up of all the nerves outside the central nervous system; connects the brain and spinal cord to other parts of the body. (ch. 15, p. 410)

peristalsis (per uh STAHL sus): wavelike, muscular contractions that move food through the digestive system. (ch. 12, p. 341)

petrified (PEH truh fide) **remains:** fossils that form when some or all of the original materials that made up the organisms are replaced with minerals. (ch. 20, p. 558)

pharynx: tubelike passageway for both food and air through which inhaled air passes after it is warmed and moistened in the nasal cavity. (ch. 14, p. 385)

phenotype (FEE nuh tipe): physical expression of a particular genotype. (ch. 6, p. 156)

photovoltaic (PV) cell: device made of silicon that turns sunlight directly into electric current. (ch. 19, p. 527)

pistil: female reproductive organ inside the flower of an angiosperm; consists of a sticky stigma, a style, and an ovary. (ch. 5, p. 133)

plasma: liquid part of blood, consisting mostly of water plus dissolved nutrients, minerals, and oxygen; makes up more than half the volume of blood. (ch. 13, p. 365)

platelet: irregularly shaped cell fragment that circulates with red and white blood cells and helps to clot blood. (ch. 13, p. 366)

pollen grains: produced by the male reproductive organs of seed plants; two sperm develop in each pollen grain. (ch. 5, p. 130)

pollination: transfer of pollen grains from the stamen to the stigma. (ch. 5, p. 134)

pollutant: any substance that contaminates the environment and causes pollution. (ch. 19, p. 541)

polygenic (pahl ih JEHN ihk) **inheritance:** occurs when a group of gene pairs acts together to produce a single trait. (ch. 6, p. 161)

power: measures the rate at which work is done in a certain period of time; unit is the watt (W). (ch. 9, p. 245)

Precambrian (pree KAM bree un) **time:** longest geologic time unit in Earth's history; has a poor fossil record. (ch. 22, p. 624)

pregnancy: nine-month period of development during which the fertilized egg grows into a baby within the uterus. (ch. 16, p. 444)

primates: group of mammals that includes monkeys, apes, and humans and that shares several characteristics, such as opposable thumbs and binocular vision. (ch. 21, p. 606)

principle of superposition: states that for undisturbed layers of rocks, older rocks lie underneath younger and younger rocks. (ch. 20, p. 564)

producer: organism, such as a green plant, that makes its own food. (ch. 3, p. 83)

proteins: large, organic molecules that are made up of amino acids and that are needed for growth and repair of body cells. (ch. 12, p. 328)

prothallus: fern gametophyte, which can make its own food, absorb water and nutrients, and has both male and female reproductive structures. (ch. 5, p. 126)

pulley: surface, such as a wheel, that redirects force using a rope; a simple machine that allows you to pull down to lift a weight. (ch. 9, p. 255)

pulmonary (PUL muh ner ee) **circulation:** flow of blood through the heart, to the lungs, and back to the heart. (ch. 13, p. 356)

punctuated equilibrium: model of evolution that shows the rapid change of a species caused by the mutation of just a few genes, resulting in the appearance of a new species. (ch. 21, p. 592)

Punnett square: tool used to predict results in Mendelian genetics; shows all the ways in which alleles can combine. (ch. 6, p. 156)

R

radioactive decay: process in which the decay of an atom of an isotope results in a change in the number of protons and the formation of a new element. (ch. 20, p. 573)

radioactive element: element that gives off radiation due to an unstable nucleus. (ch. 21, p. 598)

radiometric dating: process to determine the absolute ages of rocks by measuring the amounts of parent and daughter materials in a rock and by knowing the half-life of the parent. (ch. 20, p. 575)

rate: fraction in which the numerator and denominator have different units. (ch. 8, p. 212)

recessive (rih SES ihv): describes a trait that is covered up, or dominated, by another form of the trait. (ch. 6, p. 154)

recycling: process that reduces the use of natural resources by reusing an item after it has been changed or reprocessed. (ch. 19, p. 535)

reflection: process of light striking an object and bouncing off. (ch. 7, p. 181)

reflex: involuntary and automatic response to a stimulus that allows the body to respond without having to think about what action to take. (ch. 15, p. 413)

refraction: bending of a light wave when it changes speed in moving from one material to another. (ch. 7, p. 195)

relative dating: method to determine the order of events and relative age of the rocks by examining the position of rocks in a sequence. (ch. 20, p. 565)

renewable resource: natural resource, such as water, that is recycled or replaced by ongoing natural processes. (ch. 19, p. 524)

reptiles: egg-laying, scaly skinned animals that do not need to return to water to reproduce and probably evolved from the same ancestor as amphibians. (ch. 22, p. 628)

reproduction: the process through which organisms produce more individuals. (ch. 16, p. 434)

resistance: measure of how difficult it is for electrons to flow through a material; unit is the ohm. (ch. 10, p. 280)

resistance force (F_r): force a machine must overcome. (ch. 9, p. 248)

retina: light-sensitive tissue at the back of the eye; contains rods and cones; impulses stimulated here pass to the optic nerve, which carries them to the brain. (ch. 15, p. 418)

rhizome: underground stem of a fern, from which fronds and roots grow. (ch. 5, p. 126)

ribosomes: small, two-part organelles on which cells make their own proteins. (ch. 2, p. 53)

RNA (ribonucleic acid): nucleic acid that carries codes for making proteins from the nucleus to the ribosomes. (ch. 4, p. 113)

rock: dynamic mixture of one or more minerals, mineraloids, glass, or organic matter. (ch. 18, p. 492)

rock cycle: continuous, dynamic process by which sedimentary, igneous, and metamorphic rocks are changed from one form to another by means such as weathering, erosion, compaction, melting, and cooling. (ch. 18, p. 493)

S

saliva (suh LI vuh): watery, enzyme-containing fluid in the mouth that is mixed with food during digestion. (ch. 12, p. 341)

science: process used to solve problems or answer questions about what is happening in the world; can provide information that people use to make decisions. (ch. 1, p. 6)

scientific methods: approaches taken to solve a problem in science; steps can include recognize the problem, form a hypothesis, test the hypothesis, do the experiment, analyze the data, and draw conclusions. (ch. 1, p. 14)

screw: inclined plane wrapped around a shaft. (ch. 9, p. 251)

sedimentary rock: rock formed by compaction and cementation of sediments or when minerals precipitate out of solution or are left behind when a solution evaporates (ch. 18, p. 507); rock type formed from particles of preexisting rocks contains the most fossils. (ch. 21, p. 597)

sediments: loose materials, such as rock fragments, minerals dissolved in water, and the remains of once-living plants and animals, that have been moved by wind, water, gravity, or ice. (ch. 18, p. 507)

semen: mixture of sperm and fluid that leaves the body through the urethra. (ch. 16, p. 436)

series circuit: circuit that has only one path for the electric current to follow. (ch. 10, p. 286)

sex-linked gene: allele inherited on a sex chromosome. (ch. 6, p. 168)

sexual reproduction: process by which a new, unique organism is created when two sex cells, an egg and a sperm, come together. (ch. 4, p. 104)

sexually transmitted diseases (STDs): diseases that are transmitted from one person to another during sexual contact and that are caused by both viruses and bacteria. (ch. 17, p. 466)

simple machine: machine that works with only one motion—an inclined plane, lever, wheel and axle, and pulley. (ch. 9, p. 248)

skeletal muscles: striated, voluntary muscles that move bones. (ch. 11, p. 312)

skeletal system: all the bones in the body; gives the body shape and support, protects internal organs, forms blood cells, stores minerals for later use, and provides for muscle attachment. (ch. 11, p. 302)

smog: air pollution that forms when sunlight reacts with pollutant chemicals produced by burning fossil fuels. (ch. 19, p. 541)

smooth muscles: nonstriated, involuntary muscles that move many internal organs. (ch. 11, p. 312)

soil depletion: removal of soil nutrients from land used for agriculture due to the replacement of native plants with crops that do not decay and replenish the soil. (ch. 19, p. 531)

soil management: use of plowing methods to prevent or reduce soil depletion and erosion. (ch. 19, p. 532)

sori: spore-producing structures on the undersides of fern fronds. (ch. 5, p. 126)

species: group of similar organisms that can successfully reproduce among themselves in their natural environment. (ch. 21, p. 586)

sperm: sex cell produced in the reproductive organs of a male and that has only half the number of chromosomes of a body cell; has a whiplike tail that provides motion and a head that contains genetic information. (ch. 4, p. 104; ch. 16, p. 435)

sporophyte (SPOR uh fite) **stage:** plant life-cycle stage in which all plant structures are made of cells with a diploid number ($2n$) of chromosomes. (ch. 5, p. 124)

stamen: male reproductive organ inside the flower of an angiosperm; consists of a filament and an anther. (ch. 5, p. 133)

static charge: buildup of electric charges in one place. (ch. 10, p. 271)

synapse (SIHN aps): small space between neurons, across which an impulse moves by means of a chemical released by the axon. (ch. 15, p. 410)

systemic circulation: most extensive part of the circulatory system in which blood moves to and from all body organs and tissues except the heart and lungs. (ch. 13, p. 357)

T

target tissue: specific tissue affected by hormones; often is located in a part of the body distant from the gland that affects it. (ch. 15, p. 424)

taste buds: major sensory receptors for taste that are located on the tongue and respond to chemical stimuli. (ch. 15, p. 420)

technology: application of science to make products or tools. (ch. 1, p. 10)

tendon: thick band of tissue that attaches muscle to bone. (ch. 11, p. 312)

testes: male reproductive organs that produce sperm and the male sex hormone, testosterone. (ch. 16, p. 435)

tissue: group of similar cells that work together to do one job. (ch. 2, p. 56)

trachea: cartilage-reinforced tube that remains open and connects with the bronchi; is lined with mucous membranes and cilia to trap dust, bacteria, and pollen. (ch. 14, p. 385)

trilobite (TRI luh bite): organism that lived hundreds of millions of years ago and is considered an index fossil of the Paleozoic era. (ch. 22, p. 619)

U

unconformities (un kun FOR mihteez): gaps in the rock layers due to erosion, nondeposition, or both. (ch. 20, p. 567)

uniformitarianism (yew nih for mih TAHR ee ah nizm): states that Earth processes happening today are similar to those that happened in the past. (ch. 20, p. 577)

ureter: tube that leads from the kidney to the bladder. (ch. 14, p. 397)

urethra (yoo REE thruh): tube that carries urine from the bladder to the outside of the body. (ch. 14, p. 397)

urinary system: system of excretory organs that rids the blood of wastes produced by the metabolism of nutrients, controls blood volume by removing excess water produced by body cells, and balances concentrations of certain salts and water. (ch. 14, p. 395)

urine: waste liquid of the urinary system, containing excess water, salts, and other wastes. (ch. 14, p. 396)

uterus: hollow, pear-shaped, thick-walled muscular organ where a fertilized egg develops into a baby. (ch. 16, p. 437)

V

vaccination: process of giving a vaccine either orally or by injection. (ch. 17, p. 470)

vaccine: preparation made from damaged virus particles that are no longer able to cause disease and that can prevent some viral disease such as polio and measles. (ch. 2, p. 62)

vagina: female muscular tube connecting the lower end of the uterus with the outside of the body; also called the birth canal. (ch. 16, p. 437)

variation: an inherited trait that makes an individual different from other members of the same species; can be beneficial, harmful, or neutral in a population. (ch. 21, p. 590)

vein: blood vessel that moves blood to the heart and has valves to prevent backward movement of the blood. (ch. 13, p. 358)

ventricles (VEN trih kulz): two lower chambers of the heart. (ch. 13, p. 355)

vestigial (veh STIHJ ee ul) **structure:** body structure with no obvious use, which may once have functioned in an ancestor. (ch. 21, p. 602)

villi: fingerlike projections in the small intestine where nutrients are absorbed into the bloodstream. (ch. 12, p. 344)

virus: nonliving structure that consists of a core of hereditary material surrounded by a protein coat. (ch. 2, p. 58)

vitamins: water-soluble or fat-soluble essential, organic nutrients that are needed in small quantities to help regulate body functions. (ch. 12, p. 331)

voltage: measure of electric potential energy; measured in units of volts (V). (ch. 10, p. 279)

voluntary muscles: muscles, such as face muscles, that can be consciously controlled. (ch. 11, p. 310)

W

wavelength: distance between the tops of two adjacent ripples. (ch. 7, p. 183)

wedge: moving inclined plane with one or two sloping sides. (ch. 9, p. 251)

weight: downward pull of gravity on an object. (ch. 8, p. 219)

wheel and axle: simple machine made from two rigidly attached wheels that rotate together. (ch. 9, p. 254)

work: occurs when a force produces movement parallel to the direction in which the force is applied; unit is the joule (J). (ch. 9, p. 242)

Z

zygote: new diploid cell that is formed when a sperm fertilizes an egg. (ch. 4, p. 105)

Glossary/Glosario

Este glossario define cada término clave que aparece en **negrillas** en el texto. También muestra el número de página donde se usa dicho término.

A

absolute dating/datación absoluta: Método utilizado para determinar la edad, en años, de una roca u otro objeto. (Cap. 20, pág. 573)

acceleration/aceleración: Razón a la cual cambia la rapidez o la dirección. (Cap. 8, pág. 213)

acid rain/lluvia ácida: Lluvia o nieve con un pH menor de 5.6; resulta de la mezcla de vapor de agua y contaminantes del aire en la atmósfera. (Cap. 19, pág. 542)

active immunity/inmunidad activa: Ocurre cuando el cuerpo, por sí solo, produce anticuerpos en respuesta a un patógeno. (Cap. 17, pág. 470)

active transport/transporte activo: Movimiento de sustancias a través de la membrana celular que requiere energía. (Cap. 3, pág. 80)

adolescence/adolescencia: Etapa de desarrollo que comienza alrededor de los 12 a 13 años, cuando una persona es capaz de producir progenie. (Cap. 16, pág. 450)

adulthood/edad adulta: Etapa final de desarrollo; comienza al terminar la adolescencia y se extiende hasta la vejez. (Cap. 16, pág. 452)

alleles/alelos: Diferentes formas que puede tener un gene para cierto rasgo. (Cap. 6, pág. 152)

allergen/alérgeno: Sustancia que causa una respuesta alérgica. (Cap. 17, pág. 479)

allergy/alergia: Reacción potente del sistema inmunológico a una sustancia extraña. (Cap. 17, pág. 478)

alternation of generations/alternación de generaciones: Ciclo vital de las plantas en la cual se alternan las etapas de producción de esporas y de producción de células sexuales. (Cap. 5, pág. 125)

alveoli/alvéolos: Manojos de sacos pequeños de paredes delgadas ubicados en el extremo de cada bronquiolo; el intercambio de oxígeno y dióxido de carbono se lleva a cabo entre los alvéolos y los capilares. (Cap. 14, pág. 386)

amino acid/aminoácido: Subunidad de la cual están compuestas las proteínas. (Cap. 12, pág. 328)

amniotic sac/bolsa amniótica: Bolsa pegada a la placenta que contiene el fluido amniótico; ayuda a proteger al embrión contra golpes y puede almacenar nutrientes y desperdicios. (Cap. 16, pág. 445)

amphibians/anfibios: Animales que viven en tierra y respiran aire, pero que deben regresar al agua con el fin de reproducirse. (Cap. 22, pág. 628)

antibody/anticuerpo: Proteína que fabrica un animal en respuesta a un antígeno específico. (Cap. 17, pág. 470)

antigens/antígenos: Proteínas y químicos extraños para el cuerpo. (Cap. 17, pág. 470)

antiseptic/antiséptico: Sustancia química que destruye los patógenos sobre la piel y previene su crecimiento. (Cap. 17, pág. 464)

artery/arteria: Vaso sanguíneo de paredes gruesas y elásticas, hechas de músculo liso, que transporta sangre fuera del corazón. (Cap. 13, pág. 358)

asexual reproduction/reproducción asexual: Tipo de reproducción en que se produce un nuevo organismo con DNA idéntico al del organismo progenitor. (Cap. 4, pág. 101)

asthma/asma: Trastorno pulmonar en que la persona puede sentirse corta de aliento, sufrir resollos asmáticos o tos; puede ocurrir como una reacción alérgica. (Cap. 14, pág. 391)

atherosclerosis/aterosclerosis: Acumulación de depósitos grasos en las paredes arteriales, la cual puede obstruir vasos sanguíneos e interferir con el flujo de sangre. (Cap. 13, pág. 362)

atria/aurículas: Las dos cavidades superiores del corazón. (Cap. 13, pág. 355)

average speed/rapidez promedio: La distancia viajada entre el tiempo que llevó viajar dicha distancia. (Cap. 8, pág. 212)

axon/axón: Parte de la neurona que transmite mensajes, llamados impulsos, desde el cuerpo celular. (Cap. 15, pág. 409)

B

balanced forces/fuerzas equilibradas: Ocurren cuando las fuerzas que actúan sobre un objeto se cancelan entre sí. (Cap. 8, pág. 220)

basaltic/basáltica: Roca ígnea densa, pesada y oscura que es rica en hierro y magnesio. (Cap. 18, pág. 501)

bladder/vejiga: Órgano muscular elástico que almacena la orina hasta que sale del cuerpo. (Cap. 14, pág. 397)

blood pressure/presión sanguínea: Fuerza que ejerce la sangre sobre las paredes de los vasos sanguíneos a medida que el corazón la bombea a través del sistema cardiovascular. (Cap. 13, pág. 359)

brain stem/bulbo raquídeo: Parte del encéfalo que se extiende desde el cerebro y conecta el encéfalo con la médula espinal; controla los latidos del corazón, la respiración y la presión sanguínea, al coordinar los movimientos involuntarios de estas funciones. (Cap. 15, pág. 411)

bronchi/bronquios: Dos ramificaciones cortas en el extremo bajo de la tráquea que llevan aire a los pulmones. (Cap. 14, pág. 386)

C

cancer/cáncer: Enfermedad crónica grave que resulta del crecimiento celular descontrolado. (Cap. 17, pág. 478)

capillary/capilar: Vaso sanguíneo microscópico, con paredes de una sola célula, que conecta las arterias y las venas. (Cap. 13, pág. 359)

carbohydrates/carbohidratos: Nutrientes orgánicos que le proveen al cuerpo sus principales fuentes de energía: azúcares, almidones y celulosa; contienen átomos de carbono, hidrógeno y oxígeno. (Cap. 12, pág. 327)

carbonaceous film/película carbonácea: Fósil producido por una película fina de residuo carbonoso, la cual forma un bosquejo del organismo original. (Cap. 20, pág. 559)

cardiac muscle/músculo cardíaco: Músculo involuntario estriado que solo se encuentra en el corazón. (Cap. 11, pág. 313)

cartilage/cartílago: Capa gruesa de tejido suave y resbaloso que cubre los extremos de los huesos; absorbe choques y facilita el movimiento al reducir la fricción. (Cap. 11, pág. 304)

cast/impresión fósil: Fósil que se forma cuando los sedimentos llenan un molde, se endurecen y forman una roca. (Cap. 20, pág. 559)

cell membrane/membrana celular: Estructura que forma el límite exterior de la célula y permite que solo ciertos materiales se muevan dentro y fuera de la célula. (Cap. 2, pág. 50)

cell theory/teoría celular: Teoría principal basada en las observaciones y conclusiones de muchos científicos; enuncia que la célula es la unidad constitutiva de la vida, que los organismos están compuestos de una o más células y que todas las células provienen de otras células. (Cap. 2, pág. 44)

cell wall/pared celular: Estructura rígida que brinda apoyo y protección a la célula vegetal. Está formada por manojos de fibras celulosas fuertes. (Cap. 2, pág. 55)

cementation/cementación: Proceso en que los cementos naturales, producidos cuando el agua se cuela entre el suelo y las rocas, cementan los sedimentos grandes formando rocas sedimentarias. (Cap. 18, pág. 509)

Cenozoic era/era Cenozoica: Era geológica en que vivimos; comenzó con la extinción de los dinosaurios y muchas otras formas de vida. (Cap. 22, pág. 638)

central nervous system/sistema nervioso central: Uno de los dos sistemas principales en que se divide el sistema nervioso. Está compuesto por el encéfalo y la médula espinal. (Cap. 15, pág. 410)

cerebellum/cerebelo: Parte del encéfalo ubicada detrás y debajo del cerebro que coordina los movimientos de los músculos voluntarios y mantiene el equilibrio y el tono muscular. (Cap. 15, pág. 411)

cerebrum/cerebro: La parte más grande del encéfalo; está dividida en dos hemisferios; controla el trabajo de los músculos voluntarios, interpreta los impulsos provenientes de

batholiths / batolitos: Las masas más grandes de rocas ígneas intrusivas, las cuales pueden extenderse por cientos de kilómetros y tener varios kilómetros de profundidad. (Cap. 11, pág. 327)

beaches / playas: Depósitos de sedimentos que corren paralelos a la costa. (Cap. 8, pág. 236)

big bang theory / teoría de la gran explosión: Teoría que enuncia que hace unos 15 billones de años, el universo comenzó con una enorme explosión. (Cap. 20, pág. 603)

binary system / sistema binario: Sistema en el cual dos estrellas giran una alrededor de la otra. (Cap. 20, pág. 588)

black hole / agujero negro: Núcleo restante de una estrella de neutrones, el cual es tan denso y masivo que nada puede escapar de su campo de gravedad, ni siquiera la luz. (Cap. 20, pág. 594)

breaker / cachón: Ola de mar que rompe en la playa debido a que su parte superior viaja más rápido que su parte inferior. (Cap. 17, pág. 506)

C

caldera / caldera: Gran abertura que resulta cuando la cima de un volcán se hunde. (Cap. 11, pág. 329)

carbonaceous film/película carbonácea: Fósil producido por una película fina de residuo carbonoso, la cual forma un bosquejo del organismo original. (Cap. 12, pág. 345)

cast/impresión fósil: Fósil que se forma cuando los sedimentos llenan un molde, se endurecen y forman una roca. (Cap. 12, pág. 345)

cave / caverna: Abertura subterránea que se forma cuando el agua subterránea ácida corre por las resquebrajaduras naturales de la piedra caliza y la disuelve. (Cap. 8, pág. 232)

cementation/cementación: Proceso en que los cementos naturales, producidos cuando el agua se cuela entre el suelo y las rocas, cementan los sedimentos grandes formando rocas sedimentarias. (Cap. 3, pág. 77)

Cenozoic era/era Cenozoica: Era geológica en que vivimos; comenzó con la extinción de los dinosaurios y muchas otras formas de vida. (Cap. 13, pág. 394)

chemical weathering / meteorización química: Meteorización que ocurre cuando el agua, el aire y otras sustancias reaccionan con los minerales presentes en las rocas. (Cap. 6, pág. 159)

chlorofluorocarbons / clorofluorocarburos: Grupo de compuestos químicos que se usan en refrigeradores, atomizadores en aerosol y empaques de espuma, los cuales destruyen el ozono al entrar en la atmósfera,. (Cap. 14, pág. 413)

chromosphere / cromosfera: Capa que se encuentra encima de la fotosfera y que se extiende por encima de esta unos 2000 km. (Cap. 20, pág. 585)

cinder cone / cono de carbonilla: Volcán de lados empinados y ligeramente empacado que se forma cuando la tefrita llega al suelo. (Cap. 11, pág. 324)

circle graph / gráfica circular: Gráfica que muestra las partes de un todo mediante un círculo. (Cap. 2, pág. 46)

climate / clima: Patrón de tiempo que ocurre en una región en particular, a lo largo de muchos años. (Cap. 6, pág. 160; Cap. 16, pág. 468)

comet / cometa: Objeto compuesto de polvo y partículas rocosas mezclados con agua congelada, metano y amoníaco. (Cap. 19, pág. 568)

compaction/compactación: Proceso mediante el cual los sedimentos pequeños se unen y forman roca sólida. (Cap. 3, pág. 77)

composite volcano / volcán compuesto: Volcán que se forma del continuo y alternado ciclo de erupciones de lava y tefrita. (Cap. 11, pág. 324)

conduction / conducción: Transferencia de energía que ocurre cuando las moléculas chocan unas con otras. (Cap. 14, pág. 419)

conic projection / proyección cónica: Se usa para producir mapas de áreas pequeñas proyectando puntos y líneas desde un globo a un cono. (Cap. 5, pág. 137)

conservation / conservación: Uso cuidadoso de los recursos, cuya meta es disminuir el daño al ambiente. (Cap. 4, pág. 113)

constant / constante: Factor que permanece igual en un experimento. (Cap. 1, pág. 19)

constellation / constelación: Grupo de estrellas en el firmamento. Las constelaciones recibieron nombres de animales, figuras mitológicas u objetos cotidianos. (Cap. 20, pág. 580)

continental drift / deriva continental: Hipótesis propuesta por Alfred Wegener que dice que los continentes se han movido lentamente a sus posiciones actuales. (Cap. 9, pág. 248)

contour interval / intervalo entre curvas de nivel: Diferencia en elevación entre dos curvas de nivel consecutivas. (Cap. 5, pág. 139)

contour line / curva de nivel: Línea en un mapa que conecta puntos de igual elevación. (Cap. 5, pág. 139)

control / control: Un estándar que se usa para comparar. (Cap. 1, pág. 19)

convection / convección: Transferencia de energía térmica que ocurre cuando las partículas se mueven de un lugar a otro donde existe una diferencia de temperaturas (Cap. 14, pág. 419)

convection current / corriente de convección: Ciclo completo de calentamiento, ascenso, enfriamiento y hundimiento. (Cap. 9, pág. 262)

Coriolis effect / efecto de Coriolis: Efecto que cambia la dirección de todos los objetos que se mueven libremente, tales como el aire y el agua, hacia la derecha en las regiones al norte del ecuador y hacia la izquierda en las regiones al sur del ecuador. (Cap. 14, pág. 425)

corona / corona: La capa más grande de la atmósfera solar, la cual se extiende millones de kilómetros en el espacio. (Cap. 20, pág. 585)

crater / cráter: Depresión de paredes empinadas alrededor de la chimenea de un volcán. (Cap. 11, pág. 314)

creep / corrimiento: Movimiento que recibe su nombre por la manera en que los sedimentos lentamente se deslizan cuesta abajo, pulgada a pulgada. Es común en áreas que se congelan y descongelan. (Cap. 7, pág. 185)

crest / cresta: El punto más alto de una ola. (Cap. 17, pág. 505)

crust / corteza: La capa más externa de la Tierra y separada del manto por la discontinuidad de Moho. (Cap. 10, pág. 292)

cyanobacteria/cianobacterias: Una de las formas de vida más tempranas sobre la Tierra; evolucionaron durante la Era Precámbrica. (Cap. 13, pág. 381)

D

deflation / deflacción: Erosión causada cuando el viento sopla los sedimentos sueltos, extrayendo pequeñas partículas tales como la arcilla, el cieno y la arena, y dejando atrás materiales más gruesos. (Cap. 7, pág. 199)

deforestation / deforestación: Tala y destrucción de árboles, la cual afecta la cantidad de dióxido de carbono en la atmósfera. (Cap. 16, pág. 484)

delta / delta: Depósito, en forma de abanico o triángulo, formado por los sedimentos arrastrados por un río, cuando este desemboca en un océano, golfo o lago. (Cap. 8, pág. 225)

density current / corriente de densidad: Corriente que se forma cuando el agua marina más densa se hunde bajo el agua marina menos densa, empujando el agua oceánica de la superficie hacia las profundidades del océano. (Cap. 17, pág. 502)

dependent variable / variable dependiente: Es el factor que se mide en un experimento. (Cap. 1, pág. 19)

deposition / depositación: Etapa final del proceso de erosión. Ocurre cuando los agentes erosivos disminuyen su energía erosiva y depositan los sedimentos y las rocas que transportaban. (Cap. 7, pág. 183)

dew point / punto de rocío: Temperatura a la cual el aire está saturado y se condensa. (Cap. 15, pág. 438)

dike / dique: Magma que ha sido apretujado en una resquebrajadura, generalmente, vertical y el cual atraviesa capas rocosas y se endurece. (Cap. 11, pág. 329)

Doppler radar / radar Doppler: Dispositivo que envía señales radiales repetitivas para inspeccionar las ondas reflejadas de las tormentas distantes y detectar la dirección en que se mueve una tormenta. (Cap. 15, pág. 449)

drainage basin / cuenca hidrográfica: Extensión territorial de donde obtiene agua una corriente de agua. (Cap. 8, pág. 219)

E

Earth / la Tierra: El tercer planeta a partir del sol; tiene temperaturas superficiales que permiten que el agua exista como sólido, líquido y gas y una atmósfera que protege la vida de la radiación solar. (Cap. 19, pág. 556)

earthquakes / terremotos: Vibraciones producidas por las rocas que se rompen a lo largo de las fallas; la mayoría resulta del movimiento de las placas. (Cap. 10, pág. 283)

El Niño / El Niño: Evento climático que comienza en el Océano Pacífico tropical y que inicia cambios en la atmósfera. (Cap. 16, pág. 479)

ellipse / elipse: Curva cerrada y alargada. La órbita de la Tierra forma un elipse. (Cap. 18, pág. 523)

epicenter / epicentro: Punto en la superficie terrestre directamente encima del foco de un terremoto. (Cap. 10, pág. 289)

epoch/época: División del tiempo geológico más pequeña que un período. (Cap. 13, pág. 373)

equator / ecuador: Línea imaginaria que circunda la Tierra exactamente equidistante entre los polos norte y sur. Divide la Tierra en dos mitades iguales. (Cap. 5, pág. 132)

equinox / equinoccio: Época del año cuando el sol está directamente encima del ecuador terrestre y las horas de luz solar son iguales a las horas de oscuridad. (Cap. 18, pág. 525)

era/era: Subdivisión importante de la escala del tiempo geológico que se basa en las diferencias en las formas de vida. (Cap. 13, pág. 373)

erosion / erosión: Proceso que desgasta los materiales de la superficie y los transporta de un lugar a otro. Los principales agentes de la erosión son la gravedad, los glaciares, el viento y el agua. (Cap. 7, pág. 182)

estimation / estimación: Valoración bruta de la medida de un objeto, haciendo una conjetura basada en la experiencia. (Cap. 2, pág. 31)

extrusive/extrusiva: Roca ígnea que se forma de la lava que se enfría sobre la superficie terrestre y que posee granos minerales pequeños. (Cap. 3, pág. 68)

F

fault / falla: Superficie a lo largo de la cual se mueven y rompen las rocas, al exceder su límite de elasticidad. (Cap. 10, pág. 282)

fault-block mountains / montañas de bloques de falla: Montañas formadas por inmensos bloques rocosos inclinados y separados de rocas circundantes por fallas. (Cap. 5, pág. 130)

first quarter / cuarto creciente: Fase de la luna cuando, desde la Tierra, se puede observar la mitad de su faz iluminada o un cuarto de la superficie lunar. (Cap. 18, pág. 531)

floodplain / llanura aluvial: Piso de un valle ancho y llano tallado por una corriente de agua serpenteante. (Cap. 8, pág. 222)

focus / foco: Punto en el interior de la Tierra donde ocurre la liberación de energía de un terremoto. (Cap. 10, pág. 287)

fog / neblina: Nube estrato que se forma cuando el aire se enfría a su punto de rocío y se condensa cerca del suelo. (Cap. 15, pág. 440)

folded mountains / montañas plegadas: Tipo de montañas que se forman cuando las capas rocosas son apretadas desde lados opuestos, haciendo que se doblen y plieguen. (Cap. 5, pág. 128)

foliated/foliada: Roca metamórfica que posee una textura de granos alineados en capas paralelas. (Cap. 3, pág. 73)

fossil/fósil: Resto, impresión o huella de organismos que una vez estuvieron vivos, conservado en las rocas. (Cap. 12, pág. 342)

fossil fuel / combustible fósil: Recurso energético formado de los restos de plantas y animales antiguos, en proceso de descomposición. (Cap. 4, pág. 92)

front / frente: Límite entre masas de aire caliente y frío, donde ocurren las tormentas y la precipitación. (Cap. 15, pág. 445)

full moon / luna llena o plenilunio: Fase lunar durante la cual toda la superficie lunar que da a la Tierra está totalmente iluminada. (Cap. 18, pág. 531)

G

galaxy / galaxia: Grupo inmenso de estrellas, gas y polvo que se mantiene unido gracias a la gravedad. Nuestra galaxia, la Vía Láctea contiene unos 200 billones de estrellas. (Cap. 20, pág. 597)

gastroliths/gastrolitos: Piedras ingeridas por ciertos animales para facilitar la digestión. (Cap. 13, pág. 393)

geologic time scale/escala del tiempo geológico: Récord de los eventos en la historia de la Tierra, el cual se basa en cambios evolutivos y en eventos geológicos; las subdivisiones principales son las eras, períodos y épocas. (Cap. 13, pág. 372)

geothermal energy / energía geotérmica: Energía térmica proveniente de las rocas calientes que rodean el magma y la cual se puede usar para generar electricidad. (Cap. 4, pág. 101)

geyser / géiser: Fuente termal que hace erupción periódicamente disparando agua y vapor en el aire. (Cap. 8, pág. 232)

giant / gigante: Etapa en el ciclo de vida de una estrella en que se agota el hidrógeno del núcleo, el núcleo estelar se contrae y las temperaturas dentro de la estrella aumentan, haciendo que las capas externas de la estrella se expandan. (Cap. 20, pág. 593)

glaciers / glaciares: Masas móviles de hielo y nieve. (Cap. 7, pág. 190)

global warming / calentamiento global: Aumento de las temperaturas globales. (Cap. 16, pág. 483)

granitic/granítica: Roca ígnea de color claro y rica en sílice que es menos densa que la roca basáltica. (Cap. 3, pág. 69)

graph / gráfica: Representación gráfica que se usa para recoger, organizar y resumir datos de manera visual. (Cap. 2, pág. 45)

Great Red Spot / la Gran Mancha Roja: Espectacular tormenta de gas turbulento y de alta presión que se puede observar continuamente en Júpiter. (Cap. 19, pág. 560)

greenhouse effect / efecto de invernadero: Calentamiento natural que ocurre cuando los gases en la atmósfera atrapan el calor. (Cap. 16, pág. 482)

groundwater / agua subterránea: Agua que se filtra en el suelo y que se junta en los pequeños espacios entre pedacitos de roca y suelo. (Cap. 4, pág. 105; Cap. 8, pág. 228)

gully erosion / erosión en barrancos: Surco o zanja que se ensancha y profundiza formando un barranco. (Cap. 8, pág. 217)

H

half-life/media vida: El tiempo que se demora la mitad de los átomos de un isótopo para desintegrarse. (Cap. 12, pág. 360)

hibernation / hibernación: Período de inactividad durante el invierno, en que las temperaturas y procesos corporales de ciertos animales disminuyen a un nivel mínimo. (Cap. 16, pág. 476)

horizon / horizonte: Nombre que recibe cada capa del perfil del suelo. (Cap. 6, pág. 166)

hot spot / punto cálido: Área del manto que según algunos geólogos es más caliente que otras áreas y en donde se derriten las rocas que luego brotan en forma de magma hacia la corteza terrestre. (Cap. 11, pág. 316)

humidity / humedad: Cantidad de vapor de agua que sostiene el aire. (Cap. 15, pág. 437)

humus / humus: Materia de color oscuro que se forma de la descomposición de la materia orgánica, como las plantas. (Cap. 6, pág. 165)

hurricane / huracán: Sistema de baja presión, de gran alcance y turbulento, que se forma sobre los océanos tropicales. Es la tormenta más poderosa sobre la Tierra. (Cap. 15, pág. 450)

hydroelectric power / potencia hidroeléctrica: Producción de electricidad mediante la utilización del agua. (Cap. 4, pág. 100)

hydrosphere / hidrosfera: Toda el agua que se encuentra en la superficie de la Tierra. (Cap. 14, pág. 420)

hypothesis / hipótesis: Enunciado que se puede probar y el cual está basado en observación, investigación y conocimiento previo del problema bajo estudio. (Cap. 1, pág. 18)

I

ice wedging / grietas debido al hielo: Proceso de meteorización mecánica que ocurre cuando el agua se congela en las grietas de las rocas y se expande, rompiendo la roca en pedazos. (Cap. 6, pág. 158)

igneous rock/roca ígnea: Se forma de lava que se enfría rápidamente sobre la superficie terrestre (roca ígnea extrusiva) y de magma que se enfría lentamente dentro de la Tierra. (roca ígnea intrusiva). (Cap. 3, pág. 66)

impermeable / impermeable: Material que no se deja atravesar por el agua. (Cap. 8, pág. 229)

independent variable / variable independiente: Es el factor que puedes cambiar en un experimento. (Cap. 1, pág. 19)

index fossil/fósil guía: Proviene de especies que existieron abundantemente en la Tierra durante cortos períodos de tiempo y que se encontraban muy extendidas geográficamente; los científicos los usan para determinar la edad de las rocas. (Cap. 12, pág. 348)

inference / inferencia: Conclusión basada en una observación. (Cap. 1, pág. 18)

inner core / núcleo interno: Núcleo sólido, muy denso en el mismo centro de la Tierra, compuesto principalmente de hierro y pequeñas cantidades de oxígeno, sílice, azufre o níquel. (Cap. 10, pág. 291)

inner planets / planetas interiores: Planetas sólidos rocosos situados más cerca del sol: Mercurio, Venus, la Tierra y Marte. (Cap. 19, pág. 551)

International Date Line / Línea Internacional de cambio de fecha: Es la línea de transición para los días del calendario. (Cap. 5, pág. 134)

intrusive/intrusiva: Tipo de roca ígnea que presenta granos minerales grandes y que se forma cuando el magma se enfría lentamente dentro de la corteza terrestre. (Cap. 3, pág. 68)

ionosphere / ionosfera: Capa importante de la termosfera, la cual es una capa de partículas cargadas eléctricamente. (Cap. 14, pág. 409)

isobar / isobara: Línea que se dibuja para conectar puntos de igual presión atmosférica. (Cap. 15, pág. 454)

isotherm / isoterma: Línea que conecta puntos de igual temperatura. (Cap. 15, pág. 454)

J

jet stream / corriente de chorro: Banda estrecha de viento fuerte que sopla cerca de la parte superior de la troposfera. (Cap. 14, pág. 427)

Jupiter / Júpiter: El planeta más grande del sistema solar y está ubicado en quinto lugar a partir del sol. (Cap. 19, pág. 560)

K

Kelvin / Kelvin: Escala para medir la temperatura en el SI; comienza en cero Kelvin, la temperatura más fría posible en la naturaleza. (Cap. 2, pág. 41)

kilogram / kilogramo: Unidad de masa del SI. (Cap. 2, pág. 40)

L

land breezes / brisas terrestres: Movimientos del aire hacia el agua, producidos por corrientes de convección durante la noche, al enfriarse la tierra más rápidamente que el agua oceánica. (Cap. 14, pág. 428)

latitude / latitud: Distancia, en grados, ya sea al norte o al sur del ecuador. (Cap. 5, pág. 132)

lava/lava: Magma que fluye de volcanes y que llega a la superficie terrestre. (Cap. 3, pág. 67)

leaching / lixiviación: Extracción de materiales, al ser disueltos en agua. (Cap. 6, pág. 167)

light-year / año luz: Distancia que viaja la luz en un año. Es también la unidad que se usa para medir distancias en el espacio. (Cap. 20, pág. 583)

line graph / gráfica lineal: Representación gráfica que muestra la relación entre dos variables y en la cual ambas variables deben ser numéricas. (Cap. 2, pág. 45)

lithosphere / litosfera: Nombre que reciben la corteza y una parte del manto superior terrestres. (Cap. 9, pág. 257)

litter / lecho superficial: Capa compuesta de hojas, ramas y otros materiales orgánicos, la cual se convierte en humus. (Cap. 6, pág. 167)

loess / loes: Depósitos de grano fino arrastrados por el viento. (Cap. 7, pág. 203)

longitude / longitud: Se refiere a la distancia, en grados, al este o al oeste del primer meridiano. (Cap. 5, pág. 133)

longshore current / corriente costera: Corriente que corre a lo largo de la costa. (Cap. 8, pág. 235)

lunar eclipse / eclipse lunar: Ocurre cuando la sombra de la Tierra cae sobre la luna. (Cap. 18, pág. 534)

M

magnitude / magnitud: Medida de la energía liberada en un terremoto. (Cap. 10, pág. 298)

main sequence / secuencia principal: En el diagrama H-R, la banda diagonal de estrellas que corre desde las estrellas calientes y brillantes, en la parte superior izquierda del diagrama, hasta las estrellas frías y tenues, en la parte inferior derecha. (Cap. 20, pág. 590)

mantle / manto: Capa más extensa de la Tierra ubicada directamente encima del núcleo externo y compuesta principalmente de sílice, oxígeno, magnesio y hierro. (Cap. 10, pág. 291)

map legend / leyenda de un mapa: Explica el significado de los símbolos que se usan en un mapa. (Cap. 5, pág. 140)

map scale / escala de un mapa: Relación entre las distancias en el mapa y las distancias verdaderas en la superficie terrestre. (Cap. 5, pág. 140)

maria / maria: Regiones oscuras y relativamente planas de la superficie lunar. (Cap. 18, pág. 535)

Mars / Marte: Denominado el planeta rojo, Marte es el cuarto planeta a partir del sol. (Cap. 19, pág. 556)

mascon / concentración de masa: Concentración de masa ubicada debajo de las cuencas de impacto en la Luna. (Cap. 18, pág. 539)

mass / masa: Mide la cantidad de materia en un objeto. (Cap. 2, pág. 40)

mass movement / movimiento de masa: Movimiento de materiales cuesta abajo debido solo a la gravedad. Algunos movimientos de masa pueden ocurrir lentamente, pero otros sin embargo ocurren rápidamente. (Cap. 7, pág. 184)

meander / meandro: Curva que se forma en una corriente de agua cuando el agua que se mueve rápidamente erosiona el costado de la corriente donde el agua es más fuerte. (Cap. 8, pág. 222)

measurement / medida: Una manera de describir el mundo haciendo uso de los números. (Cap. 2, pág. 30)

mechanical weathering / meteorización mecánica: Proceso que parte las rocas, pero sin cambiar su composición química. (Cap. 6, pág. 157)

Mercator projection / proyección de Mercator: Tipo de mapa que muestra las formas correctas de los continentes, pero sus áreas están distorsionadas. (Cap. 5, pág. 137)

Mercury / Mercurio: El planeta más cercano al sol y es también el segundo planeta más pequeño. (Cap. 19, pág. 554)

Mesozoic era/era Mesozoica: Era geológica en que se separó Pangaea, se formaron los continentes actuales y cuyas formas de vida terrestres dominantes fueron los reptiles y las gimnospermas; comenzó hace unos 245 millones de años; también denominada era de vida media. (Cap. 13, pág. 389)

metamorphic rock/roca metamórfica: Roca que ha cambiado debido a la temperatura y la presión, o la presencia de fluidos acuosos calientes. (Cap. 3, pág. 71)

meteor / meteoro: Meteoroide que se quema en la atmósfera terrestre. (Cap. 19, pág. 570)

meteorite / meteorito: Meteoroide lo suficientemente grande como para caer sobre la superficie terrestre. (Cap. 19, pág. 570)

meteorologist / meteorólogo: Especialista que estudia el tiempo. (Cap. 15, pág. 453)

meter (m) / metro (m): Unidad de longitud del SI. (Cap. 2, pág. 38)

mold/molde: Fósil que se forma cuando un organismo es enterrado y se descompone dejando solo un espacio vacío en la roca. (Cap. 12, pág. 345)

moon phase / fase lunar: Apariencia cambiante de la luna vista desde la Tierra. La fase que vemos depende de las posiciones relativas de la luna, la Tierra y el sol. (Cap. 18, pág. 531)

moraine / morena frontal o terminal: Tipo de depósito parecido a un cerro que se forma de tierra y piedras arrastradas por un glaciar. Este tipo de depósito no cubre un área muy amplia de terreno. (Cap. 7, pág. 194)

N

nebula / nebulosa: Nube extensa de gas y polvo que corresponde a la etapa inicial de formación de una estrella. (Cap. 20, pág. 592)

Neptune / Neptuno: Planeta grande y gaseoso descubierto en 1846; por lo general es el octavo planeta a partir del sol. (Cap. 19, pág. 564)

neutron star / estrella de neutrones: La etapa de una supernova cuando el núcleo denso y colapsado de la estrella se encoge hasta unos 10 a 15 km en diámetro y solo pueden existir neutrones en él. (Cap. 20, pág. 594)

new moon / luna nueva: Ocurre cuando la cara iluminada de la luna mira hacia el Sol y la cara oscura mira hacia la Tierra. La luna se encuentra en el firmamento, pero no podemos verla desde la Tierra. (Cap. 18, pág. 531)

nonfoliated/no foliada: Roca metamórfica en que los granos minerales cambian, se combinan o se ordenan de manera diferente pero no forman bandas visibles. (Cap. 3, pág. 73)

nonpoint source / emisión no puntual: Contaminación proveniente de muchas fuentes diferentes, tales como las industrias, los hogares y las fincas. (Cap. 4, pág. 107)

nonrenewable / no renovable: Recurso que no puede ser reemplazado mediante procesos naturales en menos de 100 años, como por ejemplo el petróleo, el carbón y el gas natural. (Cap. 4, pág. 96)

normal fault / falla normal: Falla que se forma cuando las rocas, bajo tensión sobre la superficie de la falla, se mueven hacia abajo en relación con las rocas debajo de la superficie. (Cap. 10, pág. 284)

nuclear energy / energía nuclear: La que se produce del rompimiento de los núcleos de ciertos elementos. (Cap. 4, pág. 102)

O

observations / observaciones: Información que recoges usando tus sentidos, principalmente los sentidos de la visión y la audición, pero también el tacto, el gusto y el olfato. (Cap. 1, pág. 18)

Oort Cloud / Nube de Oort: Nube que, según el astrónomo holandés Jan Oort, está ubicada más allá de la órbita de Plutón y la cual rodea completamente el sistema solar. (Cap. 19, pág. 569)

ore / mena: Recurso mineral que puede minarse para obtener una ganancia. (Cap. 4, pág. 114)

outer core / núcleo externo: Núcleo líquido ubicado directamente encima del núcleo interno sólido; también compuesto principalmente de hierro. (Cap. 10, pág. 291)

outer planets / planetas exteriores: Planetas más alejados del sol: Júpiter, Neptuno, Saturno, Urano y Plutón. (Cap. 19, pág. 551)

oxidation / oxidación: Ocurre cuando un material, como el hierro, se expone al oxígeno y al agua. La oxidación causa la herrumbre. (Cap. 6, pág. 160)

ozone layer / capa de ozono: Capa atmosférica con una alta concentración de ozono, ubicada en la estratosfera. (Cap. 14, pág. 412)

P

Paleozoic era/era Paleozoica: Era geológica cuyo comienzo lo marca la presencia de los primeros organismos con partes duras, lo cual facilitó la formación de fósiles. (Cap. 13, pág. 382)

Pangaea / Pangaea: Inmensa extensión territorial que, según Wegener, una vez conectó a todos los continentes y que se separó hace unos 200 millones de años. (Cap. 4, pág. 248)

parallax / paralaje: Cambio aparente en la posición de un objeto cuando uno lo observa desde dos posiciones diferentes. (Cap. 20, pág. 583)

period/período: Unidad de tiempo en que se subdividen las eras de la escala del tiempo geológico. (Cap. 13, pág. 373)

permeable / permeable: Cuando los espacios entre poros de suelo y roca están conectados de manera que el agua pueda pasar a través de ellos. (Cap. 8, pág. 229)

petrified remains/restos petrificados: Restos duros y de consistencia parecida a la roca, en los cuales algunos o todos los materiales originales han sido reemplazados por minerales. (Cap. 12, pág. 344)

photosphere / fotosfera: Capa más baja de la atmósfera del sol y desde la cual se emite la luz solar. A menudo llamada superficie solar. (Cap. 20, pág. 585)

plain / llanura: Extensa superficie de terreno relativamente llano. (Cap. 5, pág. 124)

plate tectonics / tectónica de placas: Teoría que afirma que la corteza y el manto superior de la Tierra están separados en secciones que se mueven sobre una capa del manto que parece plástico. (Cap. 9, pág. 257)

plateau / meseta: Área llana situada en partes elevadas de terreno. (Cap. 5, pág. 126)

plates / placas: Secciones de la litosfera terrestre compuestas de corteza oceánica, corteza continental y el manto superior rígido, que se mueven sobre una capa del manto que parece plástico. (Cap. 9, pág. 257)

plucking / ablación: Proceso en que un glaciar rompe las rocas mediante la acción del agrietamiento debido al hielo; resulta en piedras grandes, grava y arena. (Cap. 7, pág. 192)

Pluto / Plutón: El planeta más pequeño del sistema solar y del cual tenemos menos información. Se le considera el noveno planeta a partir del sol. (Cap. 19, pág. 564)

point source / punto de emisión: Fuente identificable y única que causa algún tipo de contaminación. (Cap. 4, pág. 107)

polar zones / zonas polares: Regiones que se extienden desde las latitudes 66.5° norte y sur, hasta los polos. (Cap. 16, pág. 468)

pollution / contaminación: Introducción de productos residuales, químicos y sustancias dañinas en el ambiente. (Cap. 4, pág. 94)

Precambrian time/Era Precámbrica: Representa la unidad de tiempo geológico más larga de la historia de la Tierra, la cual duró desde hace 4.6 billones de años hasta hace 544 millones de años. (Cap. 13, pág. 380)

precipitation / precipitación: Agua que cae de las nubes; incluye la lluvia, la nieve, la cellisca o el granizo. (Cap. 15, pág. 441)

primary waves / ondas primarias: Ondas que hacen que las partículas en las rocas se muevan oscilatoriamente, en la misma dirección de la onda. (Cap. 10, pág. 288)

prime meridian / primer meridiano: Punto de referencia para distancias de este a oeste, el cual representa longitud 0°. (Cap. 5, pág. 133)

principle of superposition/principio de sobreposición: Principio que dice que en las capas rocosas inalteradas, las rocas más antiguas se encuentran en las capas inferiores y que las rocas son más y más recientes hacia la parte superior. (Cap. 12, pág. 350)

R

radiation / radiación: Transferencia de energía en forma de ondas electromagnéticas. (Cap. 14, pág. 417)

radioactive decay/desintegración radiactiva: Proceso en que la descomposición de un átomo de algunos isótopos resulta en un cambio en el número de protones y en la formación de un nuevo elemento. (Cap. 12, pág. 359)

radiometric dating/datación radiométrica: Proceso que se usa para calcular la edad absoluta de las rocas al medir las cantidades de material original y de los productos de desintegración que hay en la roca, conociendo el período de media vida del material original. (Cap. 12, pág. 361)

rate / tasa: Una razón de dos medidas que usan diferentes unidades. (Cap. 2, pág. 41)

relative dating/datación relativa: Se usa para determinar el orden de los sucesos y la edad relativa de las rocas al examinar sus posiciones en una secuencia. (Cap. 12, pág. 351)

relative humidity / humedad relativa: Medida de la cantidad de vapor de agua que contiene el aire, comparada con la cantidad que puede contener, a una temperatura específica. (Cap. 15, pág. 438)

remote sensing / teledetección remota: Manera de recopilar información, desde el espacio, acerca de la Tierra, mediante el uso de satélites y sonar, por ejemplo. (Cap. 5, pág. 142)

renewable / renovable: Recurso energético que puede ser reciclado o reemplazado, mediante procesos naturales, en menos de 100 años. (Cap. 4, pág. 98)

reptiles/reptiles: Animales con piel escamosa que ponen huevos y que no necesitan regresar al agua para reproducirse; probablemente evolucionaron de los mismos antepasados que los anfibios. (Cap. 13, pág. 384)

reverse fault / falla invertida: Falla en que las rocas sobre la superficie son forzadas hacia arriba y sobre las rocas debajo de la superficie de la falla. (Cap. 10, pág. 284)

revolution / revolución: Órbita anual de la Tierra alrededor del sol. (Cap. 18, pág. 523)

rill erosion / erosión en regueras: Tipo de erosión que comienza cuando se forma una corriente de agua durante una lluvia intensa. Al correr, esta corriente posee suficiente energía como para arrastrar consigo plantas y tierra, dejando una cicatriz sobre el terreno erosionado. (Cap. 8, pág. 217)

Robinson projection / proyección de Robinson: Mapa que muestra las formas correctas de los continentes y extensiones territoriales precisas. (Cap. 5, pág. 137)

rock/roca: Sustancia compuesta de minerales, mineraloides, vidrio o materia orgánica. (Cap. 3, pág. 60)

rock cycle/ciclo de las rocas: Transformación de un tipo de roca a otro mediante procesos tales como meteorización, erosión, compactación, cementación, derretimiento y enfriamiento. (Cap. 3, pág. 61)

rotation / rotación: Movimiento de la Tierra alrededor de su eje, el cual causa el día y la noche. (Cap. 18, pág. 521)

runoff / agua de desagüe: Agua que no se filtra en el suelo o que no se evapora y, por consiguiente, corre sobre la superficie de la Tierra. (Cap. 8, pág. 214)

S

salinity / salinidad: Una medida de la cantidad de sales disueltas en agua marina. Generalmente se mide en gramos de sal por kilogramo de agua. (Cap. 17, pág. 496)

Saturn / Saturno: Conocido como el planeta anular, es el sexto planeta a partir del sol. (Cap. 19, pág. 561)

science / ciencia: Es el proceso de tratar de entender el mundo. (Cap. 1, pág. 7)

scientific methods / métodos científicos: Procedimientos paso a paso que se usan para resolver problemas científicos y que involucran varios pasos. (Cap. 1, pág. 14)

sea breezes / brisas marinas: Movimientos de aire producidos por corrientes de convección durante el día, porque la radiación solar calienta más la tierra que el agua. (Cap. 14, pág. 428)

seafloor spreading / expansión del suelo marino: Teoría que dice que el magma proveniente de debajo de la superficie terrestre es forzado a ascender a la superficie a través de la dorsal mediooceánica, en donde fluye de las grietas a medida que el suelo marino se esparce, y se solidifica al enfriarse, formando nuevo suelo marino. (Cap. 9, pág. 253)

season / estación: Período climático de corto plazo causado por una diferencia regular en la luz del día, la temperatura y los patrones climáticos. (Cap. 16, pág. 478)

secondary waves / ondas secundarias: Ondas que se mueven a través de la Tierra haciendo que las partículas en las rocas vibren formando un ángulo recto a la dirección de la onda. (Cap. 10, pág. 288)

sedimentary rock / roca sedimentaria: La que se forma cuando los sedimentos se acumulan o se cementan o cuando los minerales se precipitan de soluciones acuosas, a bajas temperaturas. (Cap. 3, pág. 75)

sediments/sedimentos: Materiales sueltos, tales como pedazos de rocas, granos minerales y restos de plantas y animales que son arrastrados por el viento, el agua, el hielo o la gravedad. (Cap. 3, pág. 75)

seismic waves / ondas sísmicas: Ondas generadas por un terremoto. (Cap. 10, pág. 287)

seismograph / sismógrafo: Instrumento que registra las ondas primarias, secundarias y de superficie que producen los terremotos por todo el mundo. (Cap. 10, pág. 298)

seismologist / sismólogo: Científico que estudia los terremotos y las ondas sísmicas. (Cap. 10, pág. 298)

sheet erosion / erosión laminar o en capas: Tipo de erosión que ocurre cuando el agua de lluvia fluye hacia elevaciones más bajas arrastrando consigo sedimentos. (Cap. 8, pág. 217)

shield volcano / volcán de escudo: Volcán amplio con suaves pendientes formado por la acumulación de capas llanas de lava basáltica. (Cap. 11, pág. 323)

SI / SI: Sistema Internacional de medidas establecido en 1960 y diseñado para proveer un estándar mundial de medidas físicas para la ciencia, la industria y el comercio. (Cap. 2, pág. 37)

sill / intrusión: Magma que después de ser apretujado formando una resquebrajadura horizontal entre capas rocosas se endurece. (Cap. 11, pág. 329)

slump / derrumbe: Movimiento de masa que ocurre cuando materiales sueltos o capas rocosas se deslizan cuesta abajo. (Cap. 7, pág. 184)

soil / suelo: Mezcla de roca meteorizada, materia orgánica, fragmentos minerales, agua y aire. (Cap. 6, pág. 164)

soil profile / perfil del suelo: Capas diferentes de suelo. (Cap. 6, pág. 166)

solar eclipse / eclipse solar: Ocurre cuando la luna se mueve directamente entre el sol y la Tierra y proyecta una sombra sobre parte de la Tierra. (Cap. 18, pág. 532)

solar energy / energía solar: Energía renovable proveniente del sol, la cual no causa contaminación. (Cap. 4, pág. 99)

solstice / solsticio: Punto en que el sol alcanza su mayor distancia al norte o al sur del ecuador. (Cap. 18, pág. 525)

sphere / esfera: Objeto redondo tridimensional cuya superficie en cualquiera de sus puntos está a la misma distancia de su centro. (Cap. 18, pág. 520)

spring / manantial: Agua que fluye en lugares donde la superficie terrestre se junta con la capa freática. (Cap. 8, pág. 231)

station model / código meteorológico: Muestra las condiciones del tiempo en una localidad específica usando símbolos en un mapa. (Cap. 15, pág. 454)

strike-slip fault / falla transformante: Falla en la cual las rocas en cualquiera de los dos lados de la falla se alejan unas de otras sin mucho movimiento ascendente o descendente. (Cap. 10, pág. 285)

sunspot / mancha solar: Área de la superficie solar que parece oscura porque es más fría que las áreas que la rodean. (Cap. 20, pág. 586)

supergiant / supergigante: Etapa en la formación de una estrella en la cual se forman elementos cada vez más pesados por medio de la fusión, haciendo que a la larga, se forme hierro en su núcleo. (Cap. 20, pág. 594)

surface currents / corrientes de superficie: Corrientes que mueven el agua horizontalmente–paralela a la superficie terrestre. Estas corrientes son accionadas por el viento. (Cap. 17, pág. 499)

surface waves / ondas de superficie: Ondas que viajan hacia afuera del epicentro y mueven las partículas de arriba hacia abajo y de un lado a otro, en un movimiento oscilatorio. Estas ondas causan la mayor parte de la destrucción durante un terremoto. (Cap. 10, pág. 289)

T

table / tabla: Representación gráfica de información en hileras y columnas para facilitar la lectura y entendimiento de los datos representados. (Cap. 2, pág. 45)

technology / tecnología: Aplicación del conocimiento adquirido a través de la ciencia para elaborar productos o herramientas que la gente pueda usar. (Cap. 1, pág. 9)

temperate zones / zonas templadas: Regiones ubicadas entre los trópicos y las zonas polares. (Cap. 16, pág. 468)

tephra / tefrita: Pedazos de roca o lava solidificada que cae del aire después de ser expulsados en una erupción explosiva. (Cap. 11, pág. 323)

third quarter / cuarto menguante: Cuando se ve solo la mitad de la faz iluminada de la luna. (Cap. 18, pág. 532)

tidal range / alcance de la marea: La diferencia entre el nivel del océano durante la marea alta y la marea baja. (Cap. 17, pág. 508)

tide / marea: Ascenso y descenso del nivel del mar. (Cap. 17, pág. 508)

till / morena: Mezcla de sedimentos de diferentes tamaños: piedras grandes, arena, arcilla y cieno que deposita la base un glaciar, cuando este disminuye su velocidad. Este tipo de depósito puede cubrir grandes extensiones de terreno. (Cap. 7, pág. 194)

topographic map / mapa topográfico: Mapa que muestra los cambios en elevación del relieve terrestre. (Cap. 5, pág. 138)

tornado / tornado: Viento violento y arremolinado que se mueve sobre una estrecha trayectoria sobre la tierra, por lo general, del suroeste al noreste. (Cap. 15, pág. 448)

trilobite/trilobites: Organismos que vivieron hace cientos de millones de años. (Cap. 13, pág. 375)

tropics / trópico: La región entre las latitudes 23.5° norte y 23.5° sur. (Cap. 16, pág. 468)

troposphere / troposfera: La capa de la atmósfera terrestre que se encuentra más cerca del suelo; contiene el 75 por ciento de los gases atmosféricos como también polvo, hielo y agua líquida. (Cap. 14, pág. 408)

trough / valle: El punto más bajo de una ola. (Cap. 17, pág. 505)

tsunami / tsunami: Onda oceánica sísmica causada por un terremoto. (Cap. 10, pág. 299)

U

ultraviolet radiation / radiación ultravioleta: Es una de las muchas formas de energía que llega a la Tierra desde el sol. Una excesiva exposición a la radiación ultravioleta puede causar daños a la piel, cáncer y otros problemas de salud. (Cap. 14, pág. 412)

unconformities/discordancias: Brechas entre las capas rocosas. (Cap. 12, pág. 353)

uniformitarianism/uniformitarianismo: Dice que los procesos terrestres que tienen lugar actualmente son similares a los del pasado. (Cap. 12, pág. 363)

upwarped mountains / montañas plegadas anticlinales: Montañas que se forman cuando la corteza terrestre es empujada hacia arriba por fuerzas del interior de la Tierra. (Cap. 5, pág. 129)

upwelling / corriente de aguas resurgentes: Circulación en el océano que lleva agua profunda y fría hacia la superficie. (Cap. 17, pág. 502)

Uranus / Urano: El séptimo planeta a partir del sol, descubierto en 1781. Es un planeta grande y gaseoso, con 17 satélites y un sistema de anillos oscuros y delgados. (Cap. 19, pág. 563)

V

vent / chimenea: Abertura por la cual fluye el magma que llega a la superficie terrestre. (Cap. 11, pág. 314)

Venus / Venus: A veces llamado el gemelo de la Tierra, Venus es el segundo planeta a partir del sol; tiene una atmósfera densa de dióxido de carbono y ácido sulfúrico. (Cap. 19, pág. 555)

volcanic mountains / montañas volcánicas: Montañas que comienzan a formarse cuando el material derretido llega hasta la superficie terrestre a través de un área debilitada de la corteza y forma una estructura en forma de cono. (Cap. 5, pág. 130)

volcanic neck / cuello volcánico: Núcleo ígneo sólido que queda después de que el cono de un volcán se erosiona, después de que el volcán deja de hacer erupción. (Cap. 11, pág. 329)

volcano / volcán: Abertura en la superficie terrestre que a menudo forma una montaña, cuando se arrojan y acumulan capas de lava y cenizas volcánicas. (Cap. 11, pág. 312)

W

waning / octante menguante: Cuando la cantidad de la faz iluminada de la luna, que se puede ver desde la Tierra, comienza a disminuir. (Cap. 18, pág. 532)

water cycle / ciclo del agua: Viaje continuo del agua entre la atmósfera y la Tierra; involucra los procesos de evaporación, condensación y precipitación. (Cap. 14, pág. 420)

water table / nivel hidrostático o capa freática: Superficie superior de la zona de saturación o zona donde todos los poros rocosos están llenos de agua. (Cap. 8, pág. 229)

waves / ondas: Perturbaciones regulares que transportan energía a través de la materia o del espacio, sin transportar materia; pueden tener diferentes amplitudes, frecuencias, longitudes de onda y velocidades (Cap. 17, pág. 505)

waxing / octante creciente: Cuando se hace cada vez más visible la cara iluminada de la luna. (Cap. 18, pág. 531)

weather / tiempo: Término que se refiere al estado actual de la atmósfera. (Cap. 15, pág. 436)

weathering / meteorización: Proceso que parte las rocas en fragmentos más y más pequeños. (Cap. 6, pág. 156)

white dwarf / enana blanca: Etapa tardía en el ciclo de vida de una estrella, en que su núcleo agota su abastecimiento de helio, se contrae y sus capas externas se escapan hacia el espacio, dejando un núcleo denso y caliente. (Cap. 20, pág. 594)

Index

The index for *Science Voyages* will help you locate major topics in the book quickly and easily. Each entry in the index is followed by the numbers of the pages on which the entry is discussed. A page number given in **boldface type** indicates the page on which that entry is defined. A page number given in *italic type* indicates a page on which the entry is used in an illustration or photograph. The abbreviation *act.* indicates a page on which the entry is used in an activity.

A

D

E

F

G

H

M

O

P

Q

R

S

T

U

V

W

X

Y

Art Credits

Front Matter - **00 00** Ortelius Design

TABLE OF CONTENTS

xiv Rolin Graphics; **xv** (t)Morgan-Cain & Associates.

UNIT 1

Chapter 1 - **8 9** James Edwards/Sheryl Beranbaum; **14** PP/FA, Inc.; **17** Preface, Inc.; **20** John Edwards & Associates; **22** Luke Crumley/PP/FA, Inc.; **27** Glencoe.

Chapter 2 - **33** Kathie Kelleher/Publisher's Graphics; **39 41** Dartmouth Publ., Inc.; **44** Kathie Kelleher/Publisher's Graphics; **45 46 47** Glencoe; **53** Chris Higgins/PP/FA, Inc.; **53** Dartmouth Publ., Inc.; **54** Kathie Kelleher/Publisher's Graphics; **55** Dartmouth Publ., Inc.; **55 57** Glencoe.

Chapter 3 - **61** Morgan-Cain & Associates; **66-7** John Edwards; **71** Morgan-Cain & Associates; **77** (t)John Edwards, (b)Morgan-Cain & Associates; **89** Glencoe/McGraw-Hill.

Chapter 4 - **92-3** Kathie Kelleher/Publisher's Graphics; **94** John Edwards; **95** Dartmouth Publ., Inc.; **95 96** Glencoe; **97** National Geographic Society; **100** John Edwards; **102** George Bucktell; **104** Dartmouth Publ., Inc.; **105 108** John Edwards and Associates; **109** Ortelius Design; **118** Dartmouth Publ., Inc.; **121** John Edwards.

Chapter 5 - **124** John Edwards; **125** Ortelius Design; **128 129 130 131** John Edwards; **132 133** Precision Graphics; **135** Ortelius Design; **136 137 140** Dartmouth Publ., Inc.; **141** USGS; **142** John Edwards; **143** Edwin Huff; **144** USGS; **148** Precision Graphics; **151** Glencoe.

UNIT 2

Chapter 6 - **157** John Edwards; **158** Rolin Graphics; **164 165 166 170** John Edwards; **171** Dartmouth Publ., Inc.; **176** John Edwards; **179** Glencoe.

Chapter 7 - **184** John Edwards; **184** Dartmouth Publ., Inc.; **190** Tom Kennedy; **192-3 195** John Edwards; **199** Preface, Inc.; **201** Glencoe; **204 205 208** Dartmouth Publ., Inc.; **211** Glencoe.

Chapter 8 - **218** Edwin Huff; **219** Ortelius Design; **220-1** John Edwards; **223** Glencoe; **228** Dartmouth Publ., Inc.; **229** Leon Bishop; **231** Thomas Gagliano; **232** Leon Bishop; **234** Chris Forsey/Morgan-Cain & Assoc.; **238** Rolin Graphics; **238** Preface, Inc.; **243** Glencoe.

UNIT 3

Chapter 9 - **248-9** Chris Forsey/Morgan-Cain & Assoc.; **249 251** Ortelius Design; **252** John Edwards; **255** Ortelius Design; **256** Glencoe; **257** Leon Bishop; **258** Ortelius Design; **260-1** Gary Hinks/Publisher's Graphics; **263** Edwin Huff; **264** John Edwards; **270 271 272** Chris Higgins/PP/FA, Inc.; **277** Edwin Huff; **279** Glencoe.

Chapter 10 - **283** Tom Kennedy; **284 285 288-9** Chris Forsey/Morgan-Cain & Assoc.; **290** Dartmouth Publ., Inc.; **291** Ortelius Design; **291** Chris Higgins/PP/FA, Inc.; **292-3** Gary Hinks/Publisher's Graphics; **295** Ortelius Design; **302** Tom Kennedy; **303** National Geographic Society; **304** Glencoe; **306** Chris Higgins/PP/FA, Inc.; **306** Chris Forsey/Morgan-Cain & Assoc.; **307** Ortelius Design; **308** Preface, Inc.; **309** Glencoe.

Chapter 11 - **314** Tom Kennedy; **315** Dartmouth Publ., Inc.; **316** Gary Hinks/Publisher's Graphics; **316** John Edwards; **317** Terry Duennebier/SOEST/University of Hawaii; **322 323 327 330** Gary Hinks/Publisher's Graphics; **334** John Edwards; **337** Glencoe.

UNIT 4

Chapter 12 - **342** John Edwards; **345** (t)Glencoe/McGraw-Hi (b)Rolin Graphics; **347** Jim Shough; **348** Leon Bishop; **351** Joh Edwards; **352 353 354** Morgan-Cain & Associates; **355 35** Dartmouth Publishing; **357 360** Tom Kennedy; **361** Dartmou Publishing; **362** Morgan-Cain & Associates; **365** Glencoe/McGraw Hill; **367** (t)Morgan-Cain & Associates, (b)Tom Kennedy; **3** Glencoe/McGraw-Hill.

Chapter 13 - **374** Morgan-Cain & Associates; **375** Pond & Giles; **37** Morgan-Cain & Associates; **378** Pond & Giles; **379** Rolin Graphic **381** Laurie O'Keefe; **382** Pond & Giles; **385** Laurie O'Keefe; **38** Precision Graphics; **390 391 392 394** Sarah Woodward; **398** Morga Cain & Associates; **399** Precision Graphics; **401** Glencoe/McGraw Hill.

UNIT 5

Chapter 14 - **406** Felipe Passalacqua; **408** Tom Kennedy; **409** Chr Higgins/PP/FA, Inc.; **410** Glencoe; **412** Tom Kennedy; **416-7 41** **419** John Edwards; **420** Leon Bishop; **424** Dartmouth Publ., Inc.; **42** Edwin Huff; **425 426** Chris Higgins/PP/FA, Inc.; **428 429 430** Joh Edwards; **431** Leon Bishop; **433** Glencoe.

Chapter 15 - **437** Dartmouth Publ., Inc.; **439** Tom Kennedy; **44** Glencoe; **444** Tom Kennedy; **446** Dartmouth Publ., Inc.; **448** Barbar Hoopes; **450** John Edwards; **454** Dartmouth Publ., Inc.; **455** Orteliu Design; **458** Sandra McMahon; **465** Glencoe.

Chapter 16 - **468** Leon Bishop; **469** Tom Kennedy; **470** Kathi Kelleher/Publisher's Graphics; **470** Glencoe; **471** Ortelius Desigr **475** Dartmouth Publ., Inc.; **478 481 483** John Edwards; **488** Orteliu Design; **491** Glencoe.

Chapter 17 - **495** John Edwards; **496** Dartmouth Publ., Inc.; **49** Precision Graphics; **502** John Edwards; **505** Glencoe; **506 507 50** John Edwards; **512** Dartmouth Publ., Inc.; **513** Precision Graphics **515** Glencoe.

UNIT 6

Chapter 18 - **521** John Edwards; **522** Rolin Graphics; **523** Bruc Sanders; **524 525** John Edwards; **530** John Edwards/Morgan-Cai & Associates; **531** Morgan-Cain & Associates; **532** Joh Edwards/Morgan-Cain & Associates; **533 534 536-7** Roli Graphics; **542** John Edwards; **545** Glencoe/McGraw-Hill.

Chapter 19 - **548-9** Morgan-Cain & Associates; **550 551** Dav Fischer/John Edwards; **553** Dartmouth Publishing; **562** Morgan Cain & Associates; **563 569** John Edwards; **570-1** (t)Morgan-Cain & Associates, **571** (b)John Edwards; **574** Dave Fischer/John Edwards **575** Morgan-Cain & Associates; **577** Glencoe/McGraw-Hill.

Chapter 20 - **580** (l)Morgan-Cain & Associates, (r)Precisior Graphics; **581 583** John Edwards; **585 590** Morgan-Cain & Associates; **591 592 593** John Edwards; **598** Morgan-Cain & Associates; **599** John Edwards; **600-1** Morgan-Cain & Associates **601** (b)Jim Shough; **602** John Edwards; **606 607 608 609** Morgan Cain & Associates; **610** John Edwards; **613** Glencoe/McGraw-Hill

Chapter Skill Activities - **673 675 676 677 678 679 680** Glencoe; **68** Ortelius Design; **683** Glencoe; **684 686** Ortelius Design; **687** Glencoe; **689 690** Kathie Kelleher/Publisher's Graphics.

Photo Credits

ABLE OF CONTENTS
ii (t)Biophoto Assoc./Photo Researchers, (b)Wendell etzen/Bruce Coleman Inc.; **ix** (l)David R. Frazier, (c)Richard P. cobs/JLM Visuals, (r)Ted Rice; **x** Holt Studios/Photo esearchers; **xi** (l)Paul Chesley/Tony Stone Images, (r)Gregory G. imijian/Photo Researchers; **xii** (t)StudiOhio, (bl)James L. mos/Photo Researchers, (br)Doug Martin; **xiii** Charles 'Rear/Corbis Los Angeles; **xiv** (r)Vince Covataio/Pacific Stock; v (b)Bill and Sally Fletcher/Tom Stack & Associates; **xvii** (l)Coco IcCoy/Rainbow, (r)Mark McDermott/Tony Stone Images; **xviii** latt Meadows; **xix** Geoff Butler; **xx** (t)Brent Turner/BLT roductions, (b)Morrison Photography; **xxi** (l)Peter French/DRK hoto, (r)StudiOhio; **xxii** KS Studio; **xxiii** Matt Meadows; **xxiv** oy Johnson/Tom Stack & Assoc.

NIT 1

pener - **2-3** NASA/TSADO/Tom Stack & Assoc.; **3** Jim ichardson.

hapter 1 - **4-5** Jim Richardson/Corbis Los Angeles; **5** Matt leadows; **6** Wendell Metzen/Bruce Coleman Inc.; **7** (t)Coco IcCoy/Rainbow, (b)Mark Burnett/Photo Researchers; **9** (l)KS tudio, (r)Ted Horowitz/The Stock Market; **10** (l)Latent Image,)Morton & White; **11** Bob Daemmrich/Stock Boston; **12** KS tudio; **13** StudiOhio; **15** Geoff Butler; **16** (t)Matthew orkoski/Stock Boston, (b)Matt Meadows; **19** Morrison hotography; **21** Brent Turner/BLT Productions; **23** (t)Lynn Veinstein/Woodfin Camp & Assoc., (b)Hank Morgan/Rainbow; 4 (t)Coco McCoy/Rainbow, (b)Wendell Metzen/Bruce Coleman nc.; **24-5** courtesy Amanda Shaw and Focus One.

hapter 2 - **28-9** Al Bello/Allsport; **29** Matt Meadows; **30** David M. ennis; **31** (t)Duomo/William R. Sallaz, (b)Scott Cunningham; **32** l)Doug Martin, (r)StudiOhio; **34** Timothy Fuller; **36**)Rockwell/TSADO/Tom Stack & Assoc., (r)courtesy Magellan orporation; **37** Nicholas DeVore/Tony Stone Images; **38** Biophoto ssoc./Photo Researchers; **39** Fred Bavendam/Tony Stone Images; 0 (tl)Matt Meadows, (bl)NASA/FPG, (r)file photo; **42** Doug lartin; **43** (r)Duomo/Chris Cole, (others)Paul McCormick/The mage Bank; **44** Doug Martin; **45** (t)F. D'Elbee/The Image Bank, b)Bill Ross/Corbis Los Angeles; **46** (t)Oliver Benn/Tony Stone mages, (b)Lynn M. Stone; **47** Duomo/William Sallaz; **48** KS tudio; **50 51 52** Matt Meadows; **53** (t)Matt Meadows, (b)Doug lartin; **54** David M. Dennis.

hapter 3 - **58-9** Pete Saloutos/The Stock **59** Geoff Butler; **60** tl)Ted Rice, (tc)Richard P. Jacobs/JLM Visuals, (tr)Chas Krider, bl)Doug Martin, (br)E.R. Degginger/Color-Pic; **61** (t)Brent Turner, bl)E.R. Degginger/Color-Pic, (br)Doug Martin; **62** Charles reitner/Visuals Unlimited; **63** (l)Geco UK/Science Photo ibrary/Photo Researchers, (r)Ken M. Johns/Photo Researchers; 4 Geoff Butler; **65** (l)Doug Martin, (c)University of Houston, r)Tim Courlas; **66, 67** E.R. Degginger/Color-Pic; **68** (tl)Doug Martin, (tr)Douglas Peebles/Westlight, (c)John R. Foster/Photo Researchers, (b)A.J. Copley/Visuals Unlimited; **69** Simon raser/Science Photo Library/Photo Researchers; **70** Frank ournier/Contact Press Images; **71** Doug Martin; **72** (tl)Ray imons/Photo Researchers, (tr, br)A.J. Copley/Visuals Unlimited, bl)E.R. Degginger/Color-Pic; **73** (t)E.R. Degginger/Color-Pic, b)William E. Ferguson; **74** Ben Simmons/The Stock Market; **75** Mark Burnett; **76** (tl)Aaron Haupt, (tr)Brent Turner/BLT roductions, (bl)Doug Martin, (br)Richard P. Jacobs/JLM Visuals; 78 (l)Cliff Leight, (r)Lawrence Migdale/Photo Researchers; **79** Jack Dykinga; **80** Mitchell Bleier/Peter Arnold Inc.; **81** Beth Davidow/Visuals Unlimited; **82** (l)Lynn McLaren/Photo Researchers, (r)E.R. Degginger/Color-Pic; **83** (l)courtesy Inter-Power/AhlCon Partners, (r)Simon Fraser/Science Photo Library/Photo Researchers; **84** Geoff Butler; **85** (tl)E.R. Degginger/Color-Pic, (tr)University of Houston, (bl)Glenn M. Oliver/Visuals Unlimited, (br)E.R. Degginger/Color-Pic; **86** (t)Ken M. Johns/Photo Researchers, (b)Simon Fraser/Science Photo Library/Photo Researchers; **87** (t)Ben Simmons/The Stock Market, (b)Mark Burnett.

Chapter 4 - **90-1** Rafael Macia/Photo Researchers; **91** Doug Martin; **97** (l)NASA, (r)National Geographic Society/Art by Michelle Brinson; **98** Tony Craddock/Photo Researchers; **99** (t)Frank Balthis, (b)Morton & White; **100** David R. Frazier; **101** Simon Fraser/Science Photo Library/Photo Researchers; **103** E.R. Degginger/Color-Pic; **104** Tom Van Sant, The Geosphere Project/Planetary Visions/Science Photo Library/Photo Researchers; **106** *The News & Observer,* Raleigh, NC; **107** (l)Simon Fraser/Science Photo Library/Photo Researchers, (r)Telegraph Colour Library/FPG; **111** Kent Knudson/Stock Boston; **112** (t)Lynn M. Stone, (bl)Lily Solmssen/Photo Researchers, (br)Larry Miller/Photo Researchers; **113** (l)J.P. Jackson/Photo Researchers, (r)Christiana Dittman/Rainbow; **114** (t)Geoff Butler, (c)Ron Whitby/FPG, (b)Michael Simpson/FPG; **115** C.G. Randall/FPG; **116 117** Morrison Photography; **118** (l)Frank Balthis, (r)Morton & White; **119** (l)Lynn M. Stone, (t)Tom Van Sant, The Geosphere Project/Planetary Visions/Science Photo Library/Photo Researchers.

Chapter 5 - **122-3** NASA; **123** StudiOhio; **127** Stephen J. Krasemann/DRK Photo; **128** Peter French/DRK Photo; **129** Phil Lauro/Profiles West; **130** Daniel D. Lamoreux/Visuals Unlimited; **131** Paul Chesley/Tony Stone Images; **134** Doug Martin; **138** Jeff Gnass; **141** Geographix, Inc.; **145** Matt Meadows; **146** Bob Sacha with Chip Calvin; **147** Matt Meadows; **148** Peter French/DRK Photo; **149** (t)Jeff Gnass, (b)Geographix, Inc.

UNIT 2

Opener - **152-3** A. & L. Sinibaldi/Tony Stone Images; **153** Larry Ulrich/Tony Stone Images.

Chapter 6 - **154-5** Henry Georgi/Comstock; **155** Matt Meadows; **156** (l)Larry Roberts, (r)William Silliker/Earth Scenes; **157** StudiOhio; **158** Chuck Wise/Earth Scenes; **159** Tom Bean/DRK Photo; **160** Carr Clifton/Minden Pictures; **161** (l)Henley & Savage/The Stock Market, (r)Tom Stack & Assoc.; **162** Matt Meadows; **166** Rich Buzzelli/Tom Stack & Assoc.; **167** William E. Ferguson; **168** H.R. Bramaz/Peter Arnold Inc.; **169** USDA; **172**(t)Lee Battaglia/Colorific!, (bl)Dr. Morely Read/Science Photo Library/Photo Researchers, (br) S. Michael Bisceglie/Earth Scenes; **173** Larry Lefever from Grant Heilman; **174** Matt Meadows; **175** (l)Bianca Lavies, (r)Paintings by William H. Bond, National Geographic Art Division; **176** Tom Bean/DRK Photo; **177** (t)William E. Ferguson, (b)courtesy Susan Colclazer.

Chapter 7 - **180-1** Henry Georgi/Comstock; **181** Matt Meadows; **182** Rod Plank/Photo Researchers; **183** Jack Stein Grove/Profiles West; **184** (t)Thomas G. Rampton from Grant Heilman, (b)E.R. Degginger/Color-Pic; **185** Chris Cox; **186** Stephan C. Porter; **187** Tim Crosby/Liaison International; **188** Nigel J.H. Smith/Earth Scenes; **189** A. Ramey/Stock Boston; **191** (t)Wolfgang Kaehler, (b)Cliff Leight; **192** (l)Phil Schermeister/National Geographic Image Collection, (r)Mark Burnett; **193** Cliff Leight; **194** E.R. Degginger/Color-Pic; **195** Grant Heilman Photography; **196** (l)Tom Till, (r)Tom Bean/DRK Photo; **197** Matt Meadows; **198** (l)Science VU/Visuals Unlimited, (r)courtesy the National Archives/Photo-Assist, Inc.; **199** Debbie Dean; **200** (t)Floyd Holdman/The Stock Market, (b)Runk/Schoenberger from Grant Heilman; **202** Mark Boulton/Photo Researchers; **203** Grant Heilman Photography; **204** Jeff Gnass; **206 207** Matt Meadows; **208** A. Ramey/Stock Boston; **209** (t)Cliff Leight, (b)M.J. Cole/Earth Scenes.

Chapter 8 - **212-3** Galen Rowell/Peter Arnold Inc.; **213** Geoff Butler; **214** (l)E.R. Degginger/Color-Pic, (r)Tom Bean/DRK Photo; **215** Jim Richardson/Corbis Los Angeles; **216** Holt Studios/Photo Researchers; **217** Grant Heilman Photography; **219** Mark A.

Schneider/Visuals Unlimited; **220** (t)Elaine Shay, (b)Tom Bean/DRK Photo; **221** Ray Fairbanks/Photo Researchers; **222** (l)C. Davidson/Comstock, (r)Ed Lallo/Liaison International; **224** (l)Nigel Press/Tony Stone Images, (r)Martin G. Miller/Visuals Unlimited; **225** NASA/TSADO/Tom Stack & Assoc.; **226** Geoff Butler; **228** Matt Meadows; **230** file photo; **231** Albert Copley/Visuals Unlimited; **232** Jeff & Alexa Henry/Peter Arnold Inc.; **233** Dave Harris/Tom Stack & Assoc.; **234** Darrell Gulin/DRK Photo; **235** Charles Kreb/The Stock Market; **236** (t)Matt Meadows, (b)USDA-ASCS; **237** Lynn M. Stone; **239** (l)Peter Essick, (r)John Elk/Tony Stone Images; **240** Holt Studios/Photo Researchers; **241** (tl)Ray Fairbanks/Photo Researchers, (tr)Jeff & Alexa Henry/Peter Arnold Inc., (b)Lynn M. Stone.

UNIT 3

Opener - **244-5** Alberto Garcia/Saba Press Photos; **245** Patrick Robert/Sygma.

Chapter 9 - **246-7** Tom Van Sant, The Geosphere Project/Science Photo Library/Photo Researchers; **247** Doug Martin; **250** David M. Dennis; **253** Scripps Institution of Oceanography; **254** (l)Woods Hole Oceanographic Institution, (r)Emory Kristof/National Geographic Image Collection; **259** file photo; **262** Craig Aurness/Corbis Los Angeles; **264** Altitude/Peter Arnold Inc.; **265** CNES/Photo Researchers; **266** NASA; **267** James Balog/Tony Stone Images; **270** Martin G. Miller/Visuals Unlimited; **270-5** (bkgd)A.J. Copely/Visuals Unlimited; **271** E.R. Degginger/Color-Pic; **272** (t)E.R. Degginger/Color-Pic, (b)Bill Beatty/Visuals Unlimited; **273** (t)J. Wengle/DRK Photo, (b)Phil Degginger/Color-Pic; **274** (t)David Matherly/Visuals Unlimited, (b)Martin G. Miller/Visuals Unlimited; **275** (t)Mark Epstein/Visuals Unlimited, (b)Doug Sokell/Visuals Unlimited; **276** (t)file photo, (b)Emory Kristof/National Geographic Image Collection; **277** Bob Kalmbach/University of Michigan.

Chapter 10 - **280-1** Kurita/Liaison International; **281** StudiOhio; **282** Doug Martin; **284** (t)Cliff Leight, (b)Cosmo Condina/Tony Stone Images; **285** David Parker/Photo Researchers; **286** Gregory G. Dimijian/Photo Researchers; **287** Ron Haviv/Saba Press Photos; **294** David Parker/Science Photo Library/Photo Researchers; **294** Tom McHugh/Science Source/Photo Researchers; **297** Les Stone/Sygma; **300** AP Photo/Rick Rycroft; **301** James L. Stanfield/National Geographic Image Collection; **303** National Geographic Society, Art by Lina Chesak; **307** Les Stone/Sygma.

Chapter 11 - **310-1** Kevin West/Liaison International; **311** Doug Martin; **312** Francois Gohier/Photo Researchers; **313** Emory Kristof/National Geographic Image Collection; **316** *The Floor of the Oceans* by Bruce C. Heezen and Marie Tharp, © 1980 by Marie Tharp. Reproduced by permission of Marie Tharp.; **318** Matt Meadows; **320 321** Gary Rosenquist; **322** (l)Steve Lissau, (r)Tom Bean/DRK Photo; **323** (t)Greg Vaughn/Tony Stone Images, (b)Thomas Del Brase/Tony Stone Images; **325** Patrick Aventurier/Liaison International; **328** (l)Gregg Hade/Tony Stone Images, (r)David Muench; **329** (l)David Hosking/Photo Researchers, (r)Ken M. Johns/Photo Researchers; **331** Greg Vaughn; **332** Doug Martin; **333** Paul Chesley/Tony Stone Images; **334** Tom Bean/DRK Photo; **335** (t)David Muench, (b)Woods Hole Oceanographic Institution.

UNIT 4

Opener - **338-9** Sisse Brimber/National Geographic Image Collection; **339** Michael Snively/Alaska Stock.

Chapter 12 - **340-1** Ken Lucas/Visuals Unlimited; **341** StudiOhio; **342** Louis Psihoyos/Matrix; **343** Phil Degginger/Color-Pic; **344** (tl)Charlie Ott/Photo Researchers, (tr)Francois Gohier/Photo Researchers, (b)Jane Burton/Bruce Coleman Inc.; **345** Dr. E.R. Degginger/Color-Pic.; **346** (t)Vaughan Fleming/Photo Researchers, (bl)Louis Psihoyos/Matrix, (br)Louis Psihoyos/Matrix; **349** (l)Doug Martin, (r)Fred Bavendam/Peter Arnold, Inc.; **350** Aaron Haupt; **351** John Shelton; **354** Jim Hughes/PhotoVenture/Visuals Unlimited; **355** StudiOhio; **358** Kevin Schafer/Allstock/PNI; **359** Aaron Haupt; **362** Jan-Peter Lahall/Peter Arnold, Inc.; **364** Geoff Butler; **366** (t)Dr. E.R. Degginger/Color-Pic., (bl,br)Louis Psihoyos/Matrix, **367** StudiOhio.

Chapter 13 - **370-1** Louis Psihoyos/Matrix; **371** Peter Vadnai; **372** (l)James L. Amos/Photo Researchers, (r)Gary Retherford/Photo Researchers; **373** (l)Ken Lucas/Visuals Unlimited, (r)David M. Dennis; **376** (l)Breck P. Kent, (c)Sinclair Stammers/Science Photo Library, (r)David M. Dennis; **377** (tl)John Cancalosi/Tom Stack & Assoc., (tr)David M. Dennis, (bl)Sinclair Stammers/Science Photo Library/Photo Researchers, (br)TA Wiewandt/DRK Photo; **378** Ken Lucas/Visuals Unlimited; **379** Larry Lipsky/DRK Photo; **380** Fred Bavendam/Peter Arnold,Inc.; **381** Sinclair Stammers/Science Photo Library/Photo Researchers; **382** James W. Collinson, Department of Geology, Ohio State University; **383** Doug Martin; **384** (tl)O. Louis Mazzatenta/National Geographic Image Collection, (tr)O. Louis Mazzatenta/National Geographic Image Collection, (bl)Glenn Oliver/Visuals Unlimited, (br)E.R. Degginger/Photo Researchers; **385** (t)Animals Animals, (b)David J. Books/Visuals Unlimited; **387** Matt Meadows; **388** David Harvey/Woodfin Camp & Assoc.; **392** (t)O. Louis Mazzatenta/National Geographic Image Collection, (bl)O. Louis Mazzatenta/National Geographic Image Collection, (br)Michael Collier; **393** Patti Murray/Animals Animals; **395** Dave Watts/Tom Stack & Assoc.; **396** (t)David M. Dennis, (b)Mark Burnett; **397** David M. Dennis; **398** Fred Bavendam/Peter Arnold, Inc.; **399** (t)Michael Collier, (b)Animals Animals/Patti Murray.

UNIT 5

Opener - **402-3** GOES-8/NASA; **403** Paul Chesley/Photographers Aspen.

Chapter 14 - **404-5** Warren Bolster/Tony Stone Images; **405** Mark Burnett; **406** David S. Addison/Visuals Unlimited; **407** A.J. Copley/Visuals Unlimited; **409** David Lawrence/The Stock Market; **411** Galen Rowell/Peter Arnold Inc.; **413** NASA; **414** Aaron Haupt; **415** Michael Busselle/Tony Stone Images; **421** E.R. Degginger/Color-Pic; **422** Geoff Butler; **427** Michael Melford/The Image Bank; **430** David Lawrence/The Stock Market; **431** Michael Melford/The Image Bank.

Chapter 15 - **434-5** Richard Kaylin/Tony Stone Images; **435** Mary Lou Uttermohlen; **436** Howard B. Bluestein/Photo Researchers; **438** Mary Lou Uttermohlen; **440** (t)Roy Morsch/The Stock Market, (c)Jose L. Pelaez, (bl)Mark McDermott/Tony Stone Images, (br)EPI/Nancy Adams/Tom Stack & Assoc.; **441** Charles O'Rear/Corbis Los Angeles; **442** NCAR/Tom Stack & Assoc.; **443** Bruce Dale; **447** Roy Johnson/Tom Stack & Assoc.; **448** Merrilee Thomas/Tom Stack & Assoc.; **449** (t)Warren Faidley/Weatherstock; (b)A. & J. Verkiak/The Stock Market; **450** NOAA/NESDIS/Science Source/Photo Researchers; **451** Gary Williams/Liaison International; **452** KS Studio; **453** Greg Stumpf; **458-61** (bkgd)Kevin Schafer/Peter Arnold Inc.; **459** (l)Ruth Dixon, (r)Bryan Pickering/Eye Ubiquitous/Corbis; **460** (t)Rod Currie/Tony Stone Images, (cl)Warren Faidley/Weatherstock, (cr)James Westwater, (b)Steve Austin; Papilio/Corbis; **461** (t)Mark Burnett, (cl)Chinch Gryniewicz; Ecoscene/Corbis, (cr)James Westwater, (b)Annie Griffiths Belt/Corbis; **462** Mary Lou Uttermohlen; **463** (l)A. & J. Verkiak/The Stock Market, (r)Roy Johnson/Tom Stack & Assoc.

Chapter 16 - **466-7** Art Wolf/Tony Stone Images; **467** Matt Meadows; **474** (l)Jeff Gnass, (r)David Muench; **476** (tl)E.R. Degginger/Color-Pic, (bl)Fritz Polking/Visuals Unlimited, (r)Jeff

Photo Credits

Lepore/Photo Researchers; **477** (l)Michio Hoshino/Minden Pictures, (r)David Young Wolff/Tony Stone Images; **479** (l)AP/Wide World Photos, (r)Frank Balthis; **480** (t)E.R. Degginger/Color-Pic, (b)Galen Rowell/Mountain Light; **482** Rhonda Klevansky/Tony Stone Images; **484** Chip & Jill Isenhart/Tom Stack & Assoc.; **485** Thomas Del Broise/The Stock Market; **486** Matt Meadows; **487** (l)Michael Sewell/Peter Arnold, Inc., (r)Albert Copely/Visuals Unlimited; **488** E.R. Degginger/Color-Pic; **489** (t)Rhonda Klevansky/Tony Stone Images, (b)Chip & Jill Isenhart/Tony Stone Images.

Chapter 17 - **492-3** Warren Bolster/Tony Stone Images; **493** Matt Meadows; **494** (l)Mark A. Lennan/Tony Stone Images; (r)Zoltan Gaal/Photo Researchers; **497** Huramaty Mula/Phototake NYC; **498** Matt Meadows; **501** NOAA; **503** Matt Meadows; **504** John Nordquist; **506** Matt Meadows; **507** Vince Covataio/Pacific Stock; **508** (t)C. Del/Photo Researchers, (b)Adam G. Sylvester/Photo Researchers; **511** James P. Blair; **513** Vince Covataio/Pacific Stock.

UNIT 6

Opener - **516-7** NASA; **517** NASA/Corbis Media.

Chapter 18 - **518-9** NASA/TSADO/Tom Stack & Associates; **519** Matt Meadows; **520** Jerry Schad/Photo Researchers; **523** Skip Comer; **524** (t)Rafael Macia/Photo Researchers, (b)Richard Price/FPG International; **526** NASA/GSFC/Tom Stack & Associates; **527** Tom Croke/Liaison International; **528 529** Matt Meadows; **531** Dr. Fred Espenak/Science Photo Library/Photo Researchers; **533** Bruce Herman/Tony Stone Images; **535** Kazuaki Iwasaki/The Stock Market; **538** NASA; **539** Zuber et al/Johns Hopkins University/NASA/Photo Researchers; **540** BMDO/NRL/LLNL/Science Photo Library/Photo Researchers; **542** (t)Rafael Macia/Photo Researchers, (b)Kazuaki Iwasaki/The Stock Market; **543** (t)NASA, (b)courtesy Gibor Basri.

Chapter 19 - **546-7** Telegraph Colour Library/FPG International; **547** Matt Meadows; **552** Scala/Art Resource, NY; **554** (l)US Geological Survey/Science Photo Library/Photo Researchers, (r)JPL/TSADO/Tom Stack & Associates; **555** JPL/TSADO/Tom Stack & Associates; **556** NASA; **557** (l)USGS/NASA/TASDO/Tom Stack & Associates, (r)NASA/TSADO/Tom Stack & Associates; **558** (l)Science Photo Library/Photo Researchers, (r)TSADO/JPL/NASA/Tom Stack & Associates; **559** USGS/TSADO/Tom Stack & Associates; **560** (t)NASA/Mark Marten/Photo Researchers, (b)NASA/Tom Stack & Associates; **561** (right-1)USGS/TSADO/Tom Stack & Associates, (right-2)TSADO/NASA/Tom Stack & Associates, (right-3)TSADO/NASA/Tom Stack & Associates, (right-4)JPL, (b)Space Telescope Science Institute/NASA/Science Photo Library/Photo Researchers; **563** NASA/JPL/Tom Stack & Associates; **564** (t)NASA, (b)NASA/Photo Researchers; **565** NASA/ESA/Tom Stack & Associates; **567** Tom McHugh/Photo Researchers; **570** David Parker/Science Photo Library/Photo Researchers; **571** Planet Earth Pictures/FPG International; **572** JPL/TSADO/Tom Stack & Associates; **573** NASA; **574** (t)JPL/TSADO/Tom Stack & Associates, (b)NASA; **575** NASA/Mark Marten/Photo Researchers.

Chapter 20 - **578-9** Space Telescope Science Institute/NASA/Science Photo Library/Photo Researchers; **579** Matt Meadows; **581** Bill & Sally Fletcher/Tom Stack & Associates; **582** Tim Courlas; **584** David Parker/Science Photo Library/Photo Researchers; **586** (l)NOAO/TSADO/Tom Stack & Associates, (r)ESA/TSADO/Tom Stack & Associates; **587** (l)Chris Butler/SPL/Photo Researchers, (r)NASA; **588** Bill & Sally Fletcher/Tom Stack & Associates; **589** Tim Courlas; **594** Celestial Image Co./Science Photo Library/Photo Researchers; **595** Bill & Sally Fletcher/Tom Stack & Associates; **596** (l)National Geographic Photographer Sam Abell, (r)David Robert Austen; **597** ©Jerry Lodriguss/Photo Researchers; **598** Telegraph Colour Library; **599** Celestial Image Co./Science Photo Library/Photo Researchers; **603** NASA/Science Source/Photo Researchers; **604** Matt Meadows; **606-9** David S. Addison/Visuals Unlimited; **610** NASA; **611** (t)Celestial Image Co./Science Photo Library/Photo Researchers, (b)©Jerry Lodriguss/Photo Researchers.